Health & Wellness
Features and Benefits

		Example Pages
Dynamic Instruction	**...presents a clear and comprehensive coverage of health.**	
	■ Content and activities are correlated to the National Health Education Standards.	iii
	■ Nationally renowned in the field of health education, authors Linda Meeks and Phil Heit have co-authored over 300 health publications for preschool to college.	59, 321, 398
	■ Student-centered features help teens understand the importance of health education.	441, 511
A Strong Reading Strand	**...encourages active reading and learning for students of all reading levels.**	
	■ Mid-lesson Reading Reviews and 5-Minute Checks assess students' comprehension of content.	114, 152
	■ Project CRISS study skills help students process and organize what they have read.	16T-17T, 242
	■ Standardized Test Practice in each unit assesses reading and writing skills in a health context.	131, 481
Differentiated Instruction	**...makes health content accessible to students of all ability levels.**	
	■ Specially designated activities meet the needs of students with learning disabilities, physical challenges, hearing impairment, visual impairment, behavioral disorders, and students who are gifted and talented.	48, 267, 508, 13, 345, 743
	■ Offers engaging and appropriate content for all learners.	
Teacher Resources	**...provide convenient strategies to help new and experienced teachers.**	
	■ Easy-to-use Lesson Resource Manager at the beginning of each lesson in the Teacher Wraparound Edition directs you to relevant support materials.	295, 425
	■ FAST FILE™ Unit Resources contain important reproducible masters.	
Online Resources	**...enrich the learning experience with the click of a mouse.**	
	■ Link to glencoe.com for prescreened Web links, career links, and additional tools for students.	3, 73
	■ Access the complete interactive Student Edition and textbook updates.	
	■ Web Quests extend student learning by allowing students to engage in health projects.	
Technology	**...provides time-saving software products to help you creatively engage your students.**	
	■ Easy-to-edit Interactive Chalkboard Microsoft® PowerPoint® presentations include step-by-step lessons, an image bank, and transparencies.	227, 411
	■ **Exam**View® Assessment Suite CD-ROM in English and Spanish allows you to create, edit, and customize tests and quizzes.	
	■ TeacherWorks Plus™ CD-ROM all-in-one resource center helps you organize lessons.	206B

Healthy People 2010

Healthy People 2010 is a U.S. government program consisting of a set of national health goals and detailed plans to achieve by 2010. It sets forth two primary health goals for the nation and describes ten leading health indicators that are currently major health concerns for the United States. For more information on Healthy People 2010, see pages 58–59 in the text.

Goal 1: Increase quality and years of healthy life for individuals of all ages

Goal 2: Eliminate health disparities among segments of the population

Healthy People 2010 Top Ten National Health Concerns

Leading Health Indicators	Objectives
Physical activity is important for maintaining a healthy body, enhancing psychological well-being, and preventing premature death.	Increase the number of adolescents and adults who engage in regular physical activity.
Overweight and obesity are major contributors to many preventable causes of death.	Reduce the number of overweight and obese individuals.
Tobacco use is the most preventable cause of disease and death in the United States.	Reduce cigarette smoking.
Substance abuse is associated with many serious problems, including violence, injury, and HIV infection.	Reduce the proportion of individuals using illicit drugs or engaging in binge drinking.
Responsible sexual behavior can prevent unplanned pregnancies and sexually transmitted diseases.	Increase the number of adolescents who abstain from sexual intercourse, and increase condom use among sexually active persons.
Mental health disorders affect approximately 20% of the U.S. population in a given year. Depression is the most common disorder and a leading cause of disability and suicide.	Increase the proportion of adults diagnosed with depression who receive treatment.
Injury and violence cause more than 400 deaths each day in the United States.	Reduce homicides and motor vehicle deaths.
Environmental quality can be linked to an estimated 25% of preventable illnesses worldwide.	Reduce the proportion of nonsmokers exposed to tobacco smoke.
Immunization can prevent disability and death from infectious diseases and control the spread of infections.	Increase the proportion of children and adults over the age of 65 who receive recommended vaccinations.
Access to health care can be hindered by financial constraints or lack of health insurance.	Increase the proportion of people with health insurance coverage and a source of ongoing care.

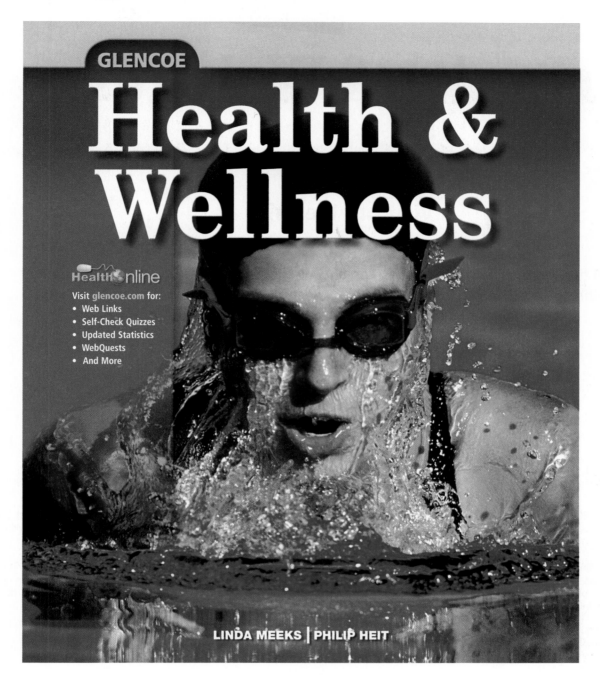

GLENCOE

Health & Wellness

Health Online

Visit glencoe.com for:
- Web Links
- Self-Check Quizzes
- Updated Statistics
- WebQuests
- And More

LINDA MEEKS | PHILIP HEIT

AUTHORS

Linda Meeks
The Ohio State University

Philip Heit
The Ohio State University

Randy Page
Brigham Young University

 Glencoe

New York, New York   Columbus, Ohio   Chicago, Illinois   Woodland Hills, California

Health&Wellness

Health Online

Visit our Web site at
www.glencoe.com

You'll find Interactive Tutor, Podcasts, Lesson Self-Check Quizzes, Unit Tests, Online Student Edition, Web Links, Vocabulary Puzzlemaker, WebQuest projects, Career links, textbook updates, Teacher Bulletin Board, Teaching Today—Professional Development

and much more!

 Glencoe

The McGraw·Hill Companies

Unit 11 outlines emergency care procedures that reflect the standard of knowledge and accepted practices in the United States at the time this book was published. Updates are available at www.glencoe.com. It is the teacher's responsibility to stay informed of changes in emergency care procedures in order to teach current accepted practices. The teacher also may recommend that students gain complete, comprehensive training from courses offered by the American Red Cross.

Send all inquiries to:
Glencoe/McGraw-Hill
21600 Oxnard Street, Suite 500
Woodland Hills, CA 91367

ISBN: 978-0-07-876026-6   (Student Edition)
MHID: 0-07-876026-7   (Student Edition)

ISBN: 978-0-07-876027-3   (Teacher Wraparound Edition)
MHID: 0-07-876027-5   (Teacher Wraparound Edition)

Printed in the United States of America

1 2 3 4 5 6 7 8 9   079/043   12 11 10 09 08 07

ABOUT THE AUTHORS

Linda Meeks, M.S.
The Ohio State University

Philip Heit, Ed.D.
The Ohio State University

Randy Page, Ph.D.
Brigham Young University

Linda Meeks and **Philip Heit** are emeritus professors at The Ohio State University. As faculty members, they held joint appointments in Health Education in the College of Education and Human Ecology and Allied Medicine in the College of Medicine. Both Linda and Philip are Fellows in the Association for the Advancement of Health Education. They are the coauthors of *Health & Wellness K–6* (available from Macmillan McGraw-Hill in New York) as well as *Health & Wellness 6-8*, and this textbook (for students in grades 9–12). This gives them the distinction of being America's only coauthors to have produced an organized, sequential K–12 health education program. To date, Linda and Philip have coauthored more than 300 different health education textbooks and materials, such as CD-ROMs, videos, and multimedia programs that are used by millions of students, preschool through college. They have helped state departments of education write curricula and implement the National Health Education Standards. Linda and Philip have trained teachers throughout the United States, as well as in Egypt, Jordan, Greece, Saudi Arabia, Japan, England, Germany, Spain, Bermuda, Canada, Puerto Rico, and the Virgin Islands.

Randy Page is a Professor of Health Sciences at Brigham Young University. He is the author or coauthor of more than 90 journal articles most of which focus on adolescent health issues. Randy has been a guest lecturer and has conducted research in Taiwan, the Philippines, Thailand, Eastern Europe, and Ireland. He currently is involved in an international humanitarian project and study abroad program in the Dominican Republic. Randy also has served as a consultant to the Office of Smoking and Health in the Centers for Disease Control and Prevention.

Linda, Philip, and Randy have collaborated since 1990. They are the coauthors of *Comprehensive School Health Education: Totally Awesome® Strategies for Teaching Health*, the most widely used professional preparation textbook for colleges and universities and teacher resource book for elementary, middle, and secondary school teachers. They also are coauthors of *Drugs, Alcohol, and Tobacco: Totally Awesome® Teaching Strategies* and *Violence Prevention: Totally Awesome® Teaching Strategies*, used as professional preparation textbooks and teacher resource books.

Linda, Philip, and Randy are committed to healthful lifestyles. Linda has served as a member of the Board of Directors for the International Women Presidents' Organization and is an avid cyclist and golfer. Philip has run many marathons and organizes walking races. Randy enjoys jogging and walking to stay fit.

GLENCOE

Health & Wellness

LINDA MEEKS | PHILIP HEIT

TEACHER ADVISORY BOARD

The health educators on the Teacher Advisory Board met with Glencoe/McGraw-Hill staff periodically throughout the production of *Health & Wellness*. They gave advice on scope and sequence, design, content, ancillaries, and technology. The authors and editor wish to thank these teachers for lending their experience and expertise to this program.

CONSULTANTS

Each consultant reviewed one or more units in the Student Edition and gave suggestions for improving the effectiveness of the health instruction.

Dr. Donna Bacchi, M.D., M.Ph.
Associate Professor of Pediatrics
Texas Tech University Health Sciences
    Center
Lubbock, TX

Jane A. Beogher, Ph.D.
Professor Emeritus of Health and Sports
    Sciences
Capital University
Bexley, OH

Brenda Garza
Health Communications Specialist
Centers for Disease Control and
    Prevention
Atlanta, GA

Linda Harrill-Rudisill, M.A.
Health Educator
Gaston County Schools
Gastonia, NC

Dianne Hensley
Envision Training
Hewitt, TX

Debra A. Ogden, M.A.
Coordinator for Health and Physical
    Education
District School Board of Collier County
Naples, FL

Dr. Deitra Wengert, Ph.D., CHES
Professor and School Health Coordinator
Towson University
Towson, MD

Susan Wooley, Ph.D., CHES
Executive Director
Kent, OH

Linda Wright, M.A.
Program Director
HIV/AIDS Education Program
D.C. Public Schools
Washington, D.C.

REVIEWERS

Each reviewer reviewed one unit of the Student Edition, giving feedback and suggestions for improving the effectiveness of the health instruction.

Shawn Alderman, M.Ed.
Health Teacher
Tigard High School
Tigard, OR

Jacqua Ballas, M.S.,
    Specialist in Science
    Education, Educational
    Leadership Certification
Teacher on assignment for
    Science
Marion County Public School
    System
Ocala, FL

Denise Baumbusch, M.A.
Health and Physical
    Education Designer
Grove City High School
Grove City, OH

Scott Beery
Health Educator
Newark High School
Newark, OH

Barbara Jean Bennett, M.S.
Supervisor of Practical Arts
    and Business Education
Evansville-Vanderburgh
    School Corporation
Evansville, IN

John Bucey, M.A.
Consultant
Corpus Christi ISD
Corpus Christi, TX

Jeff Clayton
Health Educator
Pearce High School
Richardson, TX

Tracy A. Diggs, M.Ed.
Coordinator of Student
    Health Services
Austin ISD
Austin, TX

Linda Cool Fadel
Health Educator
Waterville Central School
    District
Waterville, NY

Heather Favale, M.Ed.
Health Educator
Carbondale Community High
    School
Carbondale, IL

Debra C. Harris, Ph.D.
Department Chair/Teacher
Health/Physical Education
West Linn High School
West Linn, OR

Lori Hewlett, M.A.
Chairperson, Health
    Education
Sachem School District
Holbrook, NY

Margo Jacobs, Ph.D.
Health Teacher
Logan High School
La Crosse, WI

Alan R. Johnson, M.S.
Co-Coordinator of Health
    and Physical Education
CIVA Charter High School
Colorado Springs, CO

Brian D. Kopp, M.S.
Health Educator
Bowling Green High School
Bowling Green, OH

Linda Moskowitz, M.Ed.,
    RN, NCSN
School Nurse
Pinnacle High School
Phoenix, AZ

Kevin Murphy, M.Ed.
Health Instructor
North Salem High School
Salem, OR

Greg Prince, M.A.
Health Educator
Elkhorn High School
Elkhorn, WI

Michael J. Schaffer, M.A.
Supervisor of Health
    Education and Wellness
Prince George's County
    Public Schools
Upper Marlboro, MD

Paula A. Terry, M.S., M.Ed.
Health Educator
Northern York County School
    District
Dillsburg, PA

Joseph Varga
Health Instructor
Burlington County Alternative
    High School
Pemberton, NJ

Kely Walk
Health Teacher
Lewisville High School
Lewisville, TX

TEACHER HANDBOOK

Total Health Program...
Developed under the guidance of teachers like you

- **Designed for the way health teachers teach health**
  Our Teacher Advisory Board led the way in shaping content, design, scope, and sequence.

- **Magazine Format** is engaging, relevant, and up-to-date.

- **Comprehensive!** *Health & Wellness* is accompanied by a full package of print and technology resources. This Teacher Wraparound Edition contains a wealth of teaching strategies to assist learners who have a wide variety of abilities.

Teacher Advisory Board:
Jill B. Ponzi, Gerard Iquina,
James Schwarz, Peter L. Walter,
Dawn M. Ayres, and Valerie
Cummings (clockwise from left)
Not pictured: Martha N. Buko,
Jim Gaul, Tamara Moushey, and
Michael Flusche.

Contents

Active Learning. . .

The active learning strategy of the text emphasizes linking health topics to students' lives. Students are asked to consider how the lessons relate to their lives, their families, and their communities. They will learn to apply their knowledge of health topics in real life.

Lesson Opener

What You'll Learn at the beginning of each lesson introduces the lesson objectives.

Why It's Important provides a convincing answer to the question "Why do we have to learn this?"

Key Terms lists new vocabulary at the beginning of each lesson for easy reference.

Life Skills and Health Goals show students what goals they should work toward in each lesson.

Write About It! offers students a scenario in which to apply what they will learn from each lesson.

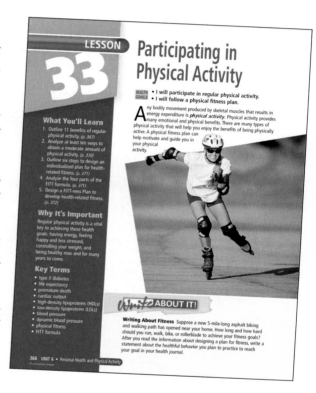

Lesson Features

Magazine format is easy to read.

Illustrated tables provide organized summaries of important facts, supported by photos and/or artwork. (Table 40.1 is an example.)

Make the Connection directs students to related material in other lessons.

Through Real-Life Health Issues

Up-to-date features engage students by tying lessons to current events, popular culture, and real-life situations to which the students can relate.

TEST YOUR DRUG IQ

Test Your IQ uses true/false questions and answers to evaluate student knowledge and/or misconceptions.

In the News at the beginning of each unit, uses a quote from a well-known person to start a class discussion.

EVALUATING MEDIA MESSAGES

Evaluating Media Messages prompts students to decipher advertisements and evaluate health messages delivered through media and technology.

Did You Know? gives surprising facts about the subject matter to catch students' attention.

Just the FACTS:

Just the Facts debunks common misconceptions by presenting frequently asked questions and factual answers.

SPEAKING OUT

Speaking Out presents testimonials from real teens about how they addressed health-related issues in their schools and communities.

FACTSABOUT

Facts About provides students with additional information on a topic that is especially interesting or relevant to teens.

Health News draws on recent research or current headlines to present newspaper-style articles about health topics.

Using Life Skills

Using Life Skills offers strategies or activities to help students implement the skills emphasized in the National Health Education Standards.

The Teacher Wraparound Edition

The Teacher Wraparound Edition is your key to all of the teaching resources in *Health & Wellness.* In addition to teaching strategies and suggestions, the Teacher Wraparound Edition provides a guide for all of the print and software materials available for each lesson.

Unit Openers

Unit Organizer on the interleaf pages provides correlations to National and/or State Health Education Standards, pacing for each lesson, activities and features by lesson, and quick reference to **FAST FILE™ Unit Resources.**

Two-Minute Unit Launcher is a short demonstration or discussion that gets students immediately interested in the topic of the unit.

Health Online directs students to www.glencoe.com for updated statistics and additional tools to further their understanding of lesson and unit content such as:
• prescreened Web links
• WebQuest projects
• career links
• textbook updates
• Interactive Tutor

Teaching Outline

1 Focus

Focus elements at the beginning of each lesson include the following:
• **Out of Time?** lists three or four lesson activities that provide an overview of the lesson if time does not permit in-depth study of the topic.
• **Health Goals** or **Life Skills** engage students in an activity or discussion related to the health goals or life skills for the lesson.
• **Write About It?** has students respond to the real-life scenario in the Student Edition.

2 Teach

Teach elements provide a variety of teaching tools, such as:
• Class Activity
• Class Discussion
• Transparencies
• Teacher FYI
• Extension
• Quick Demo
• Using the Table
• Explain the Concept
• Reading Review
• 5-Minute Check

3 Assess

Assess elements at the end of each lesson include:
• Vocabulary Practice
• Lesson and Unit Study Guide answers
• Standardized Test Practice answers

Teaching Strategies

 Achieving Health Literacy offers an activity, related to the Student Edition page, that helps students meet the National Health Education Standards. Goals include Critical Thinker, Problem Solver, Responsible Citizen, Self-Directed Learner, and Effective Communicator.

 Teacher to Teacher shares teaching tips, teaching strategies, or activities that other teachers have used in their classrooms.

 Cross-Curricular Connections relate health to other disciplines, such as art, literature, history, language arts, math, social studies, music, geography, and science, through creative activities.

 Healthy People 2010 is the prevention agenda for the nation. It has established national goals to reduce the most significant, preventable threats to health. These activities get students involved in trying to fulfill the identified national health objectives.

 Community Involvement and Family Involvement activities encourage students to work with their families and communities to learn about health issues and health resources, and to promote positive health behaviors for themselves and others.

 Legal Issues are activities or information that connect health topics to the law and/or government agencies. These activities or information help students understand how health is affected by laws and policies.

 Health Projects are long-term activities, often involving groups of students or the whole class, although they also could be individual activities.

 Differentiated Instruction activities present various teaching strategies designed to help you meet the special needs of students who are gifted and talented, or have learning disabilities, physical challenges, visual impairment, hearing impairment, or behavioral disorders.

Time-Saving Teacher Resources

Health & Wellness provides an extensive list of support materials and resources designed to help you customize your health course quickly and easily.

Lesson Resource Manager, at the beginning of each lesson, directs you to relevant pages in the FAST FILE™ Unit Resources and other support materials.

FAST FILE™ Unit Resources contain key reproducible masters, additional teaching strategies, teacher support, and answer keys for each of the 11 units.

FAST FILE™ includes:
- Parent/Family Letters in English and Spanish
- Health Behavior Contract
- 81 Transparency Masters and Worksheets
- Reading Strategies
- Vocabulary Practice
- Real-Life Health Activities
- 5-Minute Checks
- Lesson Quizzes
- Family Involvement Activities
- Community Involvement Activities
- Health Labs
- Activity: Strengthening Health Skills
- Health in the News
- Health Career Research Activities
- Two Complete Unit Tests

Interactive Chalkboard
This CD-ROM brings editable Microsoft® PowerPoint® presentations right to your classroom. Use this tool to teach key concepts from each lesson or customize your own presentations.

Includes:
- Lesson Presentations
- Interactive graphics
- 5-Minute Checks
- Image Bank
- All transparencies
- Audio and video

TeacherWorks™

TeacherWorks Plus™ is your all-in-one teacher resource center. Personalize lesson plans, access resources from the Teacher Wraparound Edition, connect to the Internet, or make a to-do list.

Other Features:
- Point and click access to teaching resources
- Launch *ExamView*® Assessment Suite with one click
- Access updated correlations and teaching resources from the TeacherWorks™ Web site
- Customize the calendar to create unique lesson plans for your class
- Select and insert teaching strategies into your lesson plans
- View and print your calendar by day, week, or month

Tools for All Ability Levels

Following each suggested activity in the Teacher Wraparound Edition, ability levels are supplied to help you accommodate all students.

L1 **Level 1 activities** should be appropriate for students with learning difficulties.

L2 **Level 2 activities** should be within the ability range of all students.

L3 **Level 3 activities** are designed for above-average students.

ELL **ELL activities** should be within the ability range of English language learners or students who speak English as a second language (ESL).

Glossary/Glosario offers side-by-side English and Spanish definitions to help English language learners better understand and learn health vocabulary.

 Differentiated Instruction

Differentiated Instruction activities present various teaching strategies designed to help you meet the special needs of students who are gifted and talented, or have learning disabilities, physical challenges, visual impairment, hearing impairment, or behavioral disorders.

Sensitive Issues

Sensitive Issues such as race, religion, gender, disabilities, past trauma, privacy issues, family status, and mental-health issues may arise in the course of classroom discussion. This feature will help you address these issues while keeping your students' feelings and best interests in mind.

Effective Tools to Measure Success

Health & Wellness gives you all the tools you need to prepare your students for success in any testing situation. You will find assessment questions and activities located throughout each lesson.

FAST FILE™ Unit Resources contain vocabulary practice, a quiz for every lesson, and two complete tests for each unit.

Reading Reviews offer quick, two- or three-question assessments at point of use in the Student Edition. Answers are provided in the Teacher Wraparound Edition.

5-Minute Checks included in the FAST FILE™ Unit Resources and referenced in the Teacher Wraparound Edition provide blackline masters with questions covering lesson content.

Lesson Study Guides at the end of each lesson include the following tools:
- **Key Terms Review**
- **Recalling the Facts** prompts students to remember specific details from the lesson.
- **Critical Thinking** asks open-ended questions that require students to further analyze the lesson content.
- **Activities** assess thinking and behavioral skills, including decision making and problem solving.

Unit Study Guides provided at the end of each unit include these tools:
- **Recalling the Facts**
- **Critical Thinking**
- **Health Literacy Activities** that address National Health Education Standards
- **Standardized Test Practice** that applies health concepts in testing reading and writing skills

Exam*View*® Assessment Suite Use this convenient test platform to:
- Use QuickTest Wizard to create a test or build your own
- Incorporate standards-based questions into your tests
- Create a test in English and, with one click, convert it to Spanish

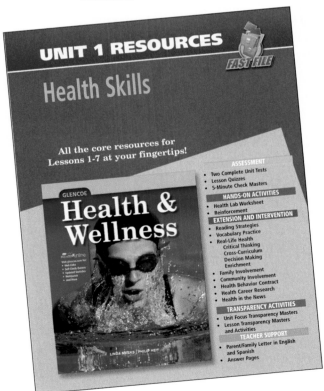

Meeting Standards

The assessment features in *Health & Wellness* have been written to cover National Health Education Standards (NHES) and the State Collaborative on Assessment and Student Standards (SCASS). In addition, the text is designed to help prepare students for standardized tests in reading and writing.

The State Collaborative on Assessment and Student Standards has designated four types of activities, which are appropriate assessment tools for use in health education. *Health & Wellness* includes many activities of each type throughout the lessons. SCASS assessment tools are:

• Performance Tasks (long-term)
• Performance Events (short-term)
• Constructed Response (short answer)
• Selected Response (multiple choice)

Standardized Test Practice at the end of every unit tests students on vocabulary, reading comprehension, and written expression in a format that mimics standardized tests on reading and writing in a health context.

Health Literacy is defined in the National Health Education Standards as "the capacity of individuals to obtain, interpret, and understand basic health information and services and the competence to use such information and services in ways which enhance health." Every unit in *Health & Wellness* includes activities that assess students on each of the four characteristics essential to health literacy as defined by the NHES:

• Being a critical thinker and problem solver
• Being a responsible, productive citizen
• Being a self-directed learner
• Being an effective communicator

Standardized Test Practice

Read the following selection and answer the questions that follow.

Can you train your mind to control body responses? With biofeedback, a technique in which a person gets feedback on body responses by viewing measurements on monitors or other devices, or hearing specific sounds, this may be possible. Biofeedback training has been used to help people deal with stress. Biofeedback works by closely monitoring body functions and displaying the measurements taken in different ways. The subject becomes familiar with the kinds of external forces that cause the stress. For example, blood pressure can be displayed on a chart or meter, while an elevated heart rate can set off a bell or alarm.

Multiple Choice

1 In this paragraph, the word *elevated* means:

 A lower than normal

 B higher than normal

 C dangerous

 D changeable

2 Biofeedback training has been used to help people deal with:

 A Weight issues

 B Peer pressure

 C Stress

 D Conflict resolution

Course Planning Guide

Health & Wellness provides a complete selection of core concepts that are presented in a way that meets the needs of all students. The following course planning guide offers suggestions for pacing your students through the book. A full-year schedule, block schedule, and semester schedule are provided to assist you in designing a health course that meets the needs of your individual students and classes.

Lesson	Full-Year Schedule (160 days)	Block Schedule (80 days)	Semester Schedule (80 days)
1	1	1	1
2	2	1	1
3	1	1	1
4	1	1	1
5	2	1	1
6	2	1	1
7	1	1	1
8	2	1	1
9	2	1	1
10	2	1	1
11	3	1	1
12	3	1	1
13	3	1	1
14	2	1	1
15	2	1	1
16	4	2	2
17	2	1	1
18	4	1	1
19	4	1	1
20	3	1	1
21	2	1	1
22	1	1	1
23	1	1	1
24	2	1	1
25	5	2	2
26	4	1	1
27	3	1	1
28	4	2	2
29	3	1	1
30	2	1	1
31	2	1	1
32	1	1	1
33	3	1	1
34	2	1	1
35	2	1	1

Lesson	Full-Year Schedule (160 days)	Block Schedule (80 days)	Semester Schedule (80 days)
36	3	1	1
37	4	2	2
38	4	2	2
39	4	2	2
40	3	2	2
41	2	1	1
42	2	1	1
43	1	1	1
44	1	1	1
45	1	1	1
46	4	2	2
47	3	1	1
48	2	1	1
49	3	1	1
50	1	1	1
51	1	1	1
52	2	1	1
53	1	1	1
54	1	1	1
55	1	1	1
56	2	1	1
57	2	1	1
58	1	1	1
59	2	1	1
60	1	1	1
61	2	1	1
62	1	1	1
63	2	1	1
64	1	1	1
65	3	1	1
66	4	2	2
67	2	1	1
68	1	1	1
69	5	2	2
70	4	1	1

Correlations

The tables below will help you review the health content required for the Health Education Standards for grades 9–11. For each Health Education Standard, the tables show the pages in *Health & Wellness* where the content can be found.

Health Education Standard 1

Students will comprehend concepts related to health promotion and disease prevention to enhance health.

Performance Indicators	Introduce	Master	Review
As a result of health instruction in grades 9–11, students will:			
1. Predict how healthy behaviors can impact health status.	2, 26, 74, 82, 158, 166, 174, 206, 280, 310, 324, 332, 340, 342, 352, 360, 362, 366, 374, 401, 402, 410, 444, 468, 487, 490, 498, 514, 530, 636	7, 14, 27–31, 36, 48, 67, 68, 73, 75–78, 83–88, 95–97, 103, 109, 111, 112, 114, 116, 118–120, 125, 128, 160, 167–169, 172–175, 179–184, 207, 248–249, 271, 272, 274, 281, 283–289, 295–300, 303–307, 311–314, 316–322, 328–331, 333–335, 340, 341, 345–347, 350, 353–355, 357, 360, 362–364, 367–369, 379, 380, 382–386, 389, 390, 393, 396, 422, 432, 434, 450, 456–457, 464, 465, 466, 470–472, 488, 491, 492, 499–503, 506–509, 515, 516, 518, 519, 523, 524, 526–528, 531, 533–535, 552, 561, 562, 568, 614, 639, 659–662, 671–674, 677, 679, 680, 682, 684, 705, 711	15, 26, 31, 33, 39, 69, 76, 81, 93, 121, 129, 130, 147, 175, 177, 183–185, 202–204, 253, 277, 278, 289, 293, 296, 298, 300–301, 309, 310, 323, 324, 337, 338, 342, 351, 355, 359, 365, 369, 373, 374, 381, 383, 399–401, 404, 407, 409, 423, 435, 452, 461, 462, 466, 467, 473, 489, 497, 509, 521, 529, 530, 537–539, 561, 563, 573, 617, 634, 663, 673, 685, 721
2. Describe the interrelationships of emotional, intellectual, physical, and social health.	5, 72, 74, 79, 82, 94, 136, 166, 332, 336, 352, 362, 366, 401, 410, 444, 452, 551, 552	5, 73, 78–80, 85, 89–91, 95–97, 100–103, 110–116, 119, 120, 124, 125, 135–143, 151–156, 160, 161, 164, 168, 169, 183, 187, 188, 190–192, 196, 197, 271, 273, 274, 311, 313, 329, 332–336, 363, 364, 367, 380, 384, 386, 412, 413, 417–420, 425, 437–442, 444–449, 453, 551, 552, 561, 562, 596, 615, 657, 695, 710	9, 15, 81, 107, 112, 115, 121, 129, 130, 139, 141, 147, 157, 163–165, 169, 177, 185, 189, 197, 203, 204, 277, 324, 337, 338, 365, 373, 381, 387, 391, 400, 421, 435, 438, 447, 451, 555, 561, 563
3. Analyze how environment and personal health are interrelated.	592, 594, 595, 602, 612, 613, 622, 624, 626, 636	9, 91, 103, 116, 354, 356, 396, 397, 426, 428, 454, 494, 496, 535, 592, 593, 595–598, 603–605, 607, 608, 613–615, 621, 624, 627, 630, 637, 659, 744	12, 91, 351, 399, 594, 598, 601, 602, 605, 610, 611, 615, 617, 625, 633, 634
4. Analyze how genetics and family history can impact personal health.		6, 22, 23, 24, 83, 84, 111, 243, 244, 420, 455, 518	22, 25, 245, 421, 535
5. Propose ways to reduce or prevent injuries and health problems.	4, 16, 26, 32, 34, 40, 82, 94, 108, 122, 134, 148, 166, 178, 208, 226, 282, 294, 302, 310, 352, 360, 366, 374, 392, 404, 410, 424, 436, 452, 462, 468, 484, 490, 498, 514, 522, 530, 602, 638, 650, 656, 664, 670, 686, 698, 704, 708, 722	5, 6–9, 10, 13, 17, 18, 23–24, 27, 28–31, 35–36, 41–43, 44, 45–46, 47, 49, 51, 61, 87, 92, 95, 96, 97, 98–99, 100–102, 103, 104–105, 106, 109, 113, 115, 117, 118–119, 120, 126–127, 128, 144, 146, 151, 152, 153, 154, 155, 156, 167, 170, 171, 172–173, 174–175, 184, 192, 196–197, 200, 210, 213, 215, 217, 219, 221, 223, 224, 232, 233, 239, 240, 247–248, 256–257, 258–259, 274, 275, 291, 292, 296–300, 303, 304–305, 307, 312–313, 317, 318, 320–321, 322, 324, 325–326, 327, 328, 329, 333, 334, 335, 342, 343, 346, 350, 353–355, 362–363, 364, 369, 370, 372, 383, 394–395, 407, 408, 414–415, 420, 422, 431, 432–433, 434, 450, 456–457, 464–465, 466, 469, 470, 488, 495, 508–509, 512, 517, 520, 524, 534–535, 538, 599, 606, 639, 642, 647, 648, 660, 661, 662, 665, 672, 673, 674, 689, 692, 702, 706, 712, 717, 725–732, 734–737, 738, 739, 742, 743, 744–747, 748	9, 15, 25, 31, 33, 55, 93, 107, 115, 121, 129, 130, 157, 175, 177, 185, 203, 204, 225, 241, 253, 261, 277, 278, 293, 301, 309, 323, 337, 338, 351, 359, 365, 373, 391, 399, 400, 409, 423, 435, 451, 461, 467, 473, 489, 497, 513, 521, 529, 537, 538, 611, 649, 655, 663, 669, 685, 697, 703, 707, 721, 749, 750
6. Analyze the relationship between access to health care and health status.	564, 582	249, 566, 568, 569, 570, 583–584, 568, 587–588	573, 589
7. Compare and contrast the benefits of and barriers to practicing a variety of healthy behaviors.	360, 484	233, 291, 307, 308, 316, 317, 322, 329, 330–331, 332–333, 334, 335, 362, 389, 403, 413, 415, 421, 430–431, 454–455, 456–457, 508–509	338, 365, 537, 538
8. Analyze personal susceptibility to injury, illness, or death if engaging in unhealthy behaviors.	7, 10, 174, 186, 452, 498, 664, 698	84, 114, 115, 119, 125, 140–143, 150–151, 160, 162, 163, 174, 199, 330–331, 412–413, 416–419, 437–442, 444–449, 453, 499, 505, 677, 698, 705	15, 141, 147, 165, 359, 418, 423, 441, 482, 509, 529, 667, 703, 704, 707
9. Analyze the potential severity of injury or illness if engaging in unhealthy behaviors.	452, 498, 664	150–151, 160, 162, 163, 174, 330–331, 248, 416–419, 437–442, 444–449, 453, 499–505, 677, 698, 705	141, 147, 165, 253, 359, 423, 441, 482, 509, 529, 669, 703, 707

Health Education Standard 2

Students will analyze the influence of family, peers, culture, media, technology, and other factors on health behaviors.

Performance Indicators	Introduce	Master	Review
As a result of health instruction in grades 9–11, students will:			
1. Analyze how family influences the health of individuals.	2, 4, 45, 74, 79, 132, 134, 136, 148, 178, 410, 422, 452, 462, 636	5, 35, 36, 45, 46, 75–77, 79, 80, 88, 113, 118, 119, 123, 124, 128, 135–143, 150–156, 161, 162, 164, 169–172, 174, 179–183, 192–202, 304, 315, 333–335, 390, 416, 419, 420, 428, 432, 454–457, 459, 460, 463–466, 491, 540, 562, 659, 665, 675, 700, 701	47, 55, 81, 89, 93, 121, 124, 130, 139, 141, 147, 157, 164, 165, 175, 177, 183–185, 193, 197, 203–205, 279, 391, 461, 462, 466, 467, 480, 666, 669, 751
2. Analyze how culture supports and challenges health beliefs, practices, and behaviors.	34, 205, 310, 493, 582	7, 35, 238, 315, 317, 319, 358, 587, 588	9, 39, 131, 205, 359, 401, 481, 588–591, 601
3. Analyze how peers influence healthy and unhealthy behaviors.	2, 4, 45, 74, 79, 148, 158, 166, 178, 410, 422, 452, 462, 490	35, 36, 45, 46, 75–77, 79, 80, 88, 113, 117, 118, 119, 123, 124, 128, 150–151, 159, 161, 162–163, 164, 167, 169–173, 174–175, 179–183, 333–335, 390, 416, 428, 432, 454–457, 459, 460, 463–466, 491, 540, 562, 659–660, 665, 666, 674, 675, 676–677, 682, 700, 701	15, 47, 55, 81, 89, 93, 121, 124, 130, 139, 141, 147, 164, 165, 175, 177, 183–185, 193, 197, 203–205, 279, 391, 461, 462, 466, 467, 480, 666, 669, 703, 751
4. Evaluate how the school and community can impact personal health practice and behaviors.	595	58, 59, 72, 123, 124, 491, 543, 547, 595, 599, 632	60, 63, 124, 129, 601
5. Evaluate the effect of media on personal and family health.	34, 154, 410, 424, 540, 556, 557, 591, 599, 656	3, 7, 35–38, 73, 78, 133, 173, 207, 280, 281, 314, 332, 335, 341, 403, 417, 421, 422, 430, 431, 434, 450, 541, 545, 557–562, 593, 630, 637, 651	15, 34, 37, 39, 81, 185, 193, 204, 337, 359, 365, 373, 421, 423, 435, 451, 473, 483, 489, 539, 548, 549, 556, 561, 563, 590, 591, 601, 633, 655, 751
6. Evaluate the impact of technology on personal, family, and community health.	3, 34, 73, 133, 207, 281, 341, 403, 424, 541, 556, 557, 591, 593, 599, 637	7, 21, 35, 116, 402, 417, 421, 422, 430, 431, 434, 557–562	39, 193, 497, 513, 548, 556, 561, 563, 590, 591, 601, 633, 635
7. Analyze how the perceptions of norms influence healthy and unhealthy behaviors.		90, 332–333, 334, 335, 421, 427, 443, 454, 456–457	
8. Analyze the influence of personal values and beliefs on individual health practices and behaviors.	74	75, 76–77, 137, 169, 265	76, 81, 139
9. Analyze how some health risk behaviors can influence the likelihood of engaging in unhealthy behaviors.		406, 413, 416–417, 418, 425, 426–427, 437, 439, 440, 442, 444, 446–447, 448, 449, 469, 470, 472	418, 423, 435, 441, 451, 473
10. Analyze how public health policies and government regulations can influence health promotion and disease prevention.	290, 404, 424, 540, 582, 602, 609	19, 21, 58, 193, 248, 288, 290–292, 295–298, 377, 389, 406–408, 415, 418, 428, 430, 431, 543, 544, 547, 559, 560, 583–586, 593, 599, 600, 603, 609, 636, 642, 643, 646, 651, 654, 658, 675, 678, 681, 691, 693, 705	60, 203, 293, 296, 301, 309, 339, 409, 423, 435, 549, 563, 589, 590, 600, 601, 606, 634, 646, 649, 655, 697, 705, 707, 750

Health Education Standard 3

Students will demonstrate the ability to access valid information and products and services to enhance health.

Performance Indicators	Introduce	Master	Review
As a result of health instruction in grades 9–11, students will:			
1. Evaluate the validity of health information, products, and services.	2, 16, 17, 310, 495, 540, 542, 564, 591	3, 6, 12–14, 17–19, 73, 87, 92, 120, 133, 207, 275, 281, 292, 314, 315, 341, 350, 355, 403, 477, 541, 544–546, 566, 568, 593, 637	15, 16, 20, 25, 34, 282, 293, 310, 323, 338, 365, 549, 564, 567, 569, 573, 574, 590, 591
2. Utilize resources from home, school and community that provide valid health information.	16, 17, 20, 82, 474, 564	12–14, 17, 19–21, 92, 116, 120, 478, 565, 566, 575, 694, 730	15, 16, 25, 93, 146, 152, 193, 279, 323, 423, 467, 479, 481, 482, 497, 521, 646, 549, 575, 649, 751
3. Determine the accessibility of products and services that enhance health.	16, 564	17–18, 19, 20–21, 249, 565–566, 567, 568, 569, 570, 571–572	573, 581
4. Determine when professional health services may be required.	108	19, 87, 92, 113, 114, 116, 125, 144, 146, 149, 251, 300, 307, 308, 325, 328–331, 334–336, 343–349, 353–356, 395, 406, 407, 420, 429, 433, 475, 492, 496, 499–503, 510–512, 517, 524, 531, 536, 683, 684, 692, 694, 695, 712, 714–720, 723, 725–727, 729–731, 733, 734, 736, 738, 739, 741–748	25, 309, 337, 351, 359, 409, 476, 479, 686, 721, 750
5. Access valid and reliable health products and services.	474, 564, 574	7, 11, 17–19, 114, 116, 120, 255, 275, 276, 343–350, 432, 478, 571, 572, 575–579, 695, 702, 734	15, 25, 261, 277, 479, 573, 579, 581, 590, 591, 611, 686

Health Education Standard 4

Students will demonstrate the ability to use interpersonal communication skills to enhance health and avoid or reduce health risks.

Performance Indicators	Introduce	Master	Review
As a result of health instruction in grades 9–11, students will:			
1. Utilize skills for communicating effectively with family, peers, and others to enhance health.	40, 158	14, 41–44, 54, 96, 116, 137, 146, 151, 159, 162, 163, 255, 256, 258–260, 273, 450, 548, 689, 690, 692, 694, 696, 710, 713, 739	4, 40, 55, 64, 74, 82, 108, 131, 134, 147, 148, 157, 165, 254, 261, 262, 269, 270, 277–279, 309, 339, 351, 399, 436, 451, 481, 482, 490, 498, 521, 522, 539, 542, 549, 550, 555, 581, 638, 649, 650, 655, 656, 663, 664, 669, 670, 685, 686, 698, 703, 704, 707, 708, 722, 751
2. Demonstrate refusal, negotiation, and collaboration skills to enhance health and avoid or reduce health risks.	40, 166, 410	7, 8, 41, 47, 162, 171–173, 422, 434, 450, 464, 465, 548, 687, 689	15, 47, 55, 81, 165, 175, 177, 204, 309, 351, 410, 451, 461, 467, 490, 549, 550, 556, 638, 669, 685, 698, 707
3. Demonstrate strategies to prevent, manage, or resolve interpersonal conflicts without harming self or others.	40, 158	2, 8, 14, 50–53, 62, 138, 145, 146, 149, 184, 475, 692	40, 53, 55, 63, 69, 74, 81, 134, 147, 165, 185, 277, 351, 365, 410, 468, 542, 555, 556, 656, 693, 697, 707
4. Demonstrate how to ask for and offer assistance to enhance the health of self and others.	72, 122, 128, 166	5, 7, 14, 42, 43, 44, 52, 54, 62, 75–78, 96, 114, 119, 124, 126–128, 137, 151, 159, 162, 163, 167, 169–173, 174, 175, 187–189, 258, 259, 273, 333, 390, 431, 450, 476, 548, 614, 694, 696, 739, 748	39, 40, 55, 63, 74, 76, 81, 96, 107, 108, 124, 129, 130, 131, 157, 165, 166, 177, 203, 204, 254, 261, 269, 277, 309, 391, 476, 479, 490, 542, 549, 550, 685, 686, 703, 749

Health Education Standard 5

Students will demonstrate the ability to use decision-making skills to enhance health.

Performance Indicators	Introduce	Master	Review
As a result of health instruction in grades 9–11, students will:			
1. Examine barriers that can hinder healthy decision making.	27, 34, 45, 178	35–36, 46, 84, 88, 143, 179–181, 332–333, 413, 416–417, 430, 454–455	39, 55, 93, 338, 423, 435, 461
2. Determine the value of applying a thoughtful decision-making process in health-related situations.	8, 14, 56	60, 61, 62, 416–417, 470	63, 70, 473
3. Justify when individual or collaborative decision making is appropriate.		116, 475	122, 147, 270, 309, 591, 686, 708
4. Generate alternatives to health-related issues or problems.	8, 64	32, 44, 46, 47, 48, 54, 57, 60, 65	33, 55, 57
5. Predict the potential short- and long-term impact of each alternative on self and others.		61, 116, 191, 192, 194, 195, 198, 199, 470	122, 147, 186, 197, 203–205, 270, 278, 436, 461, 473, 482, 529, 537, 591, 686, 721
6. Defend the healthy choice when making decisions.	64	47, 48, 60, 62, 68, 106, 176, 315, 443, 623, 713	63
7. Evaluate the effectiveness of health-related decisions.	10, 174, 186, 452, 498, 664	7, 10, 84, 114, 115, 119, 125, 136–143, 150, 151, 160, 162, 163, 174, 188, 191, 199, 200, 330, 413, 416–419, 437–442, 444–449, 453, 471, 472, 499–505, 553, 667, 668, 677, 705	4, 15, 141, 147, 163, 165, 186, 359, 418, 423, 440, 441, 482, 509, 529, 667, 704, 707

Health Education Standard 6

Students will demonstrate the ability to use goal-setting skills to enhance health.

Performance Indicators	Introduce	Master	Review
As a result of health instruction in grades 9–11, students will:			
1. Assess personal health practices and overall health status.	11, 94, 342, 360, 366	22, 23–24, 27, 28–31, 83, 96, 97, 115, 232–233, 266, 292, 311, 325, 327, 343, 344, 346, 348, 350, 362, 367, 372, 383, 394, 426–427, 455, 496, 518–519, 534–535, 558, 561, 603, 606, 613	25, 33, 101, 293, 337, 338, 351, 365, 373, 400, 521, 563, 611
2. Develop a plan to attain a personal health goal that addresses strengths, needs, and risks.	56	32, 57, 59, 103, 200, 267, 317, 327, 364, 371, 372, 383, 517, 552, 554, 648	33, 56, 63, 366, 391
3. Implement strategies and monitor progress in achieving a personal health goal.	56, 168, 722	8, 14, 32, 48, 57, 59, 60, 61, 103, 104, 116, 138, 200, 267, 288, 292, 317, 327, 364, 372, 383, 431, 470, 475, 517, 552, 554, 648, 662, 710, 712, 713, 723, 724, 726, 727, 731–738, 742, 745	15, 25, 26, 33, 56, 63, 69, 81, 82, 93, 96, 107, 121, 147, 157, 165, 177, 185, 203, 261, 262, 278, 282, 293, 294, 301, 302, 309, 323, 337, 351, 359, 365, 373, 391, 399, 404, 409, 410, 423, 424, 435, 451, 461, 473, 479, 480, 537, 563, 573, 581, 589, 601, 611, 617, 625, 635, 649, 650, 663, 664, 669, 685, 686, 708, 721, 722, 749–751
4. Formulate an effective long-term personal health plan.	270	10, 364, 372, 432, 488, 517, 524	269, 270

Health Education Standard 7

Students will demonstrate the ability to practice health-enhancing behaviors and avoid or reduce risks.

Performance Indicators	Introduce	Master	Review
As a result of health instruction in grades 9–11, students will:			
1. Analyze the role of individual responsibility for enhancing health.	4, 74, 166, 310, 342, 352, 374, 490, 498, 626	11–14, 23, 24, 75–78, 80, 98, 99, 105, 109, 144, 150, 161, 167, 168, 170, 175, 255–259, 264–266, 271–274, 283–287, 289, 312–314, 316–319, 322, 328, 329, 345, 347, 350, 353–355, 357, 360, 363, 407, 432, 433, 450, 457, 464–466, 508, 509, 526, 553, 606, 632, 639–642, 644, 645, 647, 651–654, 660, 671–675, 677, 682, 689, 690, 692, 696, 706, 711	15, 25, 26, 33, 76, 81, 166, 261, 279, 310, 323, 342, 351, 359, 452, 467, 482, 489, 497, 646, 649, 654, 655, 670, 673, 685, 693, 707
2. Demonstrate a variety of healthy practices and behaviors that will maintain or improve the health of self and others.	108, 134, 270, 310, 324, 342, 366, 374, 424, 468, 556, 602, 612, 618, 626, 708, 722	5, 13, 31, 47, 48, 98, 99, 113–115, 117–120, 125, 128, 163, 167, 173, 175, 181, 184, 190, 191, 255–259, 263–266, 273, 289, 300, 304–307, 312–322, 328, 329, 353–355, 357, 360, 362, 363, 370–372, 379–381, 384, 385, 393, 407, 422, 428, 429, 432–434, 450, 484, 488, 495, 496, 508, 509, 598, 605, 606, 609, 610, 614, 616, 620–622, 628–630, 632, 682, 702, 711–720, 723–739, 741–748	15, 47, 55, 56, 63, 121, 130, 177, 178, 185, 204, 261, 270, 300, 309, 310, 323, 339, 342, 352, 359, 365, 366, 373, 374, 401, 409, 423, 497, 563, 601, 602, 605, 606, 610, 611, 615, 617, 621, 625, 632–635, 663, 708, 722, 749–751
3. Demonstrate a variety of behaviors to avoid or reduce health risks to self and others.	392, 468, 638, 650, 656, 670, 686, 698, 704, 708, 722	114, 117, 256, 257, 259, 385–389, 394–397, 465, 469, 527, 639–642, 644, 645, 647, 651–654, 660, 671–675, 677, 687–690, 692, 696, 699, 702, 706, 712–720, 723–739, 741–748	121, 261, 392, 399, 400, 467, 473, 638, 646, 649, 650, 654, 655, 673, 685, 693, 703, 707, 708, 721, 722, 749–751

Health Education Standard 8

Students will demonstrate the ability to advocate for personal, family, and community health.

Performance Indicators	Introduce	Master	Review
As a result of health instruction in grades 9–11, students will:			
1. Utilize accurate peer and societal norms to formulate a health-enhancing message.	4, 40, 64, 65, 66, 74, 158, 166, 167, 410, 424, 436, 452, 462	32, 38, 44, 45, 47, 48, 51, 54, 75, 76, 77, 78, 105, 117, 118–119, 120, 126–127, 159, 162–163, 164, 167, 168–169, 170, 171, 172–173, 248–249, 416, 417, 422, 434, 450, 464, 466, 470	39, 55, 81, 121, 129, 130, 165, 177, 423, 435, 451
2. Demonstrate how to influence and support others to make positive health choices.	64, 65, 626, 631	9, 13, 14, 65, 66, 170, 171, 173, 176, 422, 431, 434, 443, 450, 629, 631, 632, 689, 696	15, 33, 34, 39, 64, 65, 69, 82, 93, 107, 108, 121, 165, 177, 185, 203, 205, 261, 270, 277, 278, 294, 301, 323, 337, 373, 423, 436, 441, 451, 462, 467, 474, 479, 513, 522, 529, 537, 539, 549, 564, 574, 581, 582, 589, 594, 601, 611, 612, 617, 618, 626, 632–634, 655, 670, 685, 686, 703, 707, 749, 751
3. Work cooperatively as an advocate for improving personal, family, and community health.	631	9, 65, 66, 575, 580, 597, 610, 616, 631, 632	15, 65, 69, 131, 205, 279, 481, 539, 575, 581, 589, 590, 626, 632–634, 703, 749, 751
4. Adapt health messages and communication techniques to a specific target audience.	631	65, 67, 629	65, 69, 121, 131, 157, 165, 205, 373, 399, 441, 467, 473, 482, 498, 521, 582, 589, 703, 707

National Health Education Standards

Project CRISS Strategies

To improve students' study skills, **Health & Wellness** Teacher Wraparound Edition includes proven study strategies from Project CRISS (CReating Independence through Student-owned Strategies). Use the descriptions on this page and the next to implement the strategy suggestions located at point of use in the margins of each lesson. For more information about Project CRISS, please visit **www.glencoe.com**.

Note-Taking Strategies

Selective Underlining/Highlighting
Have students underline or highlight the key ideas in an article or in a photocopied section of the text. This strategy will help them organize their thoughts and the information they are trying to process.

Two-Column Notes: Main Idea-Detail
Encourage students to organize their notes into two columns. On the left, they should list a main idea from the reading. On the right, they should list the details that support it.

Two-Column Notes: Conclusion-Support
Have students write a conclusion they derive in the left-hand column of their notes and then use the right-hand column to write supporting evidence for their conclusion.

Vocabulary Strategies

Mapping Complete Definitions
Use a definition map to describe and define vocabulary words and their related ideas. Each map should include branches that answer questions about the vocabulary word, such as, "What is it?", "What is it like?", and "What are some examples?"

Word Combining
After an in-class discussion, have the class summarize the main ideas in 1–2 sentences that incorporate 3–5 key vocabulary words from the appropriate content.

Summarizing Strategy

Read–Recall–Check–Summarize
Use the following strategy to reinforce particularly difficult topics. Have the entire class *read* a section.

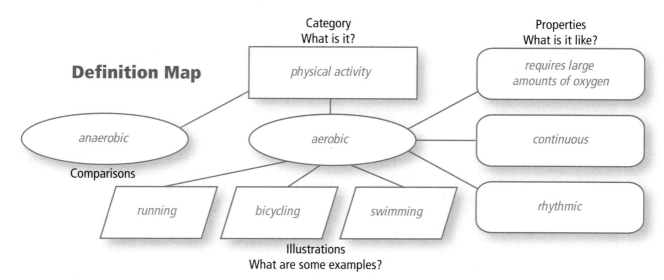

Definition Map

Category
What is it?

Properties
What is it like?

physical activity

requires large amounts of oxygen

anaerobic

aerobic

continuous

Comparisons

running

bicycling

swimming

rhythmic

Illustrations
What are some examples?

Then have them *recall* the main ideas of that section as a group. Ask them to re-read the section to *check* the details they brainstormed to ensure accuracy. Then have them use the brainstorming notes to *summarize* what they have read.

Journaling Strategies

Teacher-Student Journals Use journals as a way to maintain a dialogue with students. This is especially helpful when a topic is sensitive or when students have concerns about what they are studying.

Pre- and Postreading Responses In their journals, have students write about a topic before you begin discussing it and then again after the topic has been covered. Use these entries to evaluate what students have learned in class.

Discussion Strategies

Authentic Questions Let students know that all readers have questions about what they read. These questions are personally meaningful to the individual student and are, therefore, more likely to be investigated. Have them write down their questions in order to monitor their comprehension or their interest in a topic.

Know—Want to Know—Learned (KWL) or Know—Expect to Learn—Learned (KEL) Charts Have students brainstorm what they know about a topic, what they want to know or expect to learn, and, once the topic has been covered, what they learned. This strategy helps teachers to tailor lessons to what students have missed or to target misconceptions.

Read-and-Say-Something Have students use this study strategy in pairs or small groups to understand difficult passages. Students read a paragraph to themselves. They then take turns saying something about what they have read. This could be either a question or comment. Other students in the group then continue the discussion until that topic has been thoroughly covered. Each person in the group must say something during the discussion.

Seed Discussions To involve students in leading their own discussions, ask them to write down one important thing about what they are reading. These "seeds" can be used for small group discussions.

Sticky-Note Discussions Provide students with sticky-notes and allow them to mark pages in the textbook that they find interesting or that they have a question about. Or ask students to pick one fact that they found to be surprising, and discuss why.

Think-Pair-Share Getting students involved as active participants is key to helping them learn. The Think-Pair-Share strategy works by providing time for students to think about a topic and record what they know about it, pair up to discuss what they know, and finally, get involved in a whole-class share session.

Note Taking Refer to the Two-Column Notes: Main Idea-Detail Strategy on page 16T and ask students to list the body systems in the left-hand column and list the components of each system in the right-hand column.

CONTENTS IN BRIEF

CONTENTS

CONTENTS

p. 4

p. 118

p. 380

UNIT 6

Personal Health and Physical Activity 340

UNIT 7

Alcohol, Tobacco, and Other Drugs ... 402

p. 465

UNIT 9

Consumer and Community Health. . . . 540

p. 602

p. 654

p. 709

FEATURE CONTENTS

Activity: Using Life Skills

p. 662

SPEAKING OUT

FACTSABOUT

HEALTH NEWS

Just the FACTS:

Health Skills

STANDARDS AND FEATURES

Lesson	National Standards	State/Local Standards	Activities and Features
Lesson 1 *(1 session, 1 block)* Taking Responsibility for Health	1.5, 3.1, 3.2, 7.1		**Using Life Skills:** Comprehending Health Concepts: Comprehending Skin Cancer Facts, p. 13
Lesson 2 *(2 sessions, 1 block)* Accessing Valid Health Information, Products, and Services	1.5, 3.1, 3.2, 3.3, 6.1		**Using Life Skills:** Accessing Health Services: Making an Emergency Telephone Call, p. 19 **Health News:** The CDC, p. 21 **Facts About:** Family Health Histories, p. 22
Lesson 3 *(1 session, 1 block)* Practicing Healthful Behaviors	1.1, 1.5, 6.1		
Lesson 4 *(1 session, 1 block)* Analyzing Influences on Health	1.5, 2.5, 5.1		**Using Life Skills:** Analyze Influences: Evaluating Ads, p. 38
Lesson 5 *(2 sessions, 1 block)* Using Communication Skills	1.5, 4.1, 4.2, 4.3, 8.1		**Using Life Skills:** Using Communication Skills: Sharpening Your Listening Skills, p. 44 **Just the Facts:** Conflicts, p. 52
Lesson 6 *(2 sessions, 1 block)* Setting Health Goals and Making Responsible Decisions	5.4, 6.2		**Using Life Skills:** Using Goal-Setting and Decision-Making Skills: Setting a Health Goal, p. 59
Lesson 7 *(1 session, 1 block)* Being a Health Advocate	8.2, 8.3, 8.4		**Using Life Skills:** Advocating for Health: Being a Volunteer, p. 67 **Speaking Out:** Volunteering, p. 68

Key to Differentiated Instruction

L1 Level 1 activities should be appropriate for students with learning difficulties.

L2 Level 2 activities should be within the ability range of all students.

L3 Level 3 activities are designed for above-average students.

ELL ELL activities should be within the ability range of English language learners.

FAST FILE RESOURCES

INTRODUCING THE UNIT

Parent and Family Letter	p. 1	Health Behavior Contract	p. 3
Spanish Parent and Family Letter	p. 2	Unit Focus Transparency Master and Worksheet	p. 4

TEACHING THE UNIT LESSONS

Reproducible Student Pages	Lesson 1	Lesson 2	Lesson 3	Lesson 4	Lesson 5	Lesson 6	Lesson 7
Reading Strategy	p. 7	p. 21	p. 33	p. 45	p. 57	p. 71	p. 83
Vocabulary Practice	p. 8	p. 22	p. 34	p. 46	p. 58	p. 72	p. 84
Transparency Master and Worksheet	p. 9	p. 23	p. 35	p. 47	p. 59	p. 73	p. 85
Real-Life Health	p. 11	p. 25	p. 37	p. 49	p. 61	p. 75	p. 87
5-Minute Check	p. 15	p. 29	p. 41	p. 53	p. 65	p. 79	p. 91
Lesson Quiz	p. 17	p. 30	p. 42	p. 54	p. 67	p. 80	p. 92

CLOSING THE UNIT

Family Involvement Activity	p. 95	Health in the News	p. 105
Community Involvement Activity	p. 97	Health Career Research Activity	p. 107
Health Lab	p. 99	Unit Test A	p. 109
Activity: Strengthening Health Skills	p. 103	Unit Test B	p. 113

Technology

- **Interactive Chalkboard CD-ROM**
- **TeacherWorks™ CD-ROM**
- **StudentWorks™ CD-ROM**
- **Reading Essentials CD-ROM**
- **Exam*View*® Assessment Suite**

Glencoe Exclusive!

TeacherWorks™
All-In-One Planner and Resource Center

www.glencoe.com
- **Vocabulary Puzzlemaker**
- **Interactive Tutor**
- **Your Health Checklist**
- **Web Links**
- **Student Web Activities**

UNIT 1 — Health Skills

TEST YOUR HEALTH IQ

Use the three statements on the student page to initiate a class discussion about general health myths. *Additional True/False statements are:*

4. **I do not have any control over the decisions made about my health.**
   FALSE: You are the person most responsible for your health. You control many of the decisions you make about your health every day.

5. **To get what you want and to stand up for yourself, you have to be disrespectful to others.**
   FALSE: To stand up for yourself, you need to be assertive. Assertive behavior is the honest expression of ideas, feelings, and decisions in a respectful manner.

6. **An estimated 4.1 million adolescents, age 12–17, smoke tobacco products.**
   TRUE: According to the American Heart Association, an estimated 3000 young people become smokers every day. Risks to health due to tobacco use include increased frequency of respiratory infections and the development of lung cancer later in life.

in the news — Conflict Resolution

Role Models Ask students if they agree with the statement about conflict resolution made by Martin Luther King, Jr. Ask students to think of methods of resolving conflict that might be more successful than revenge, aggression, and retaliation. **L2**

TEST YOUR HEALTH IQ
True or False?

1. **The Internet is the best way to get health information.**
   FALSE: Because anyone can post information on the Internet—not just medical and health professionals—it is not necessarily a reliable source.

2. **Peer pressure always causes people to do bad things.**
   FALSE: Peer pressure often can be a good thing, such as when it encourages others to follow rules or volunteer in the community. When pressure is used to convince a peer to do a negative act, peer pressure then becomes problematic.

3. **Fifteen percent of the teen population in the United States is overweight.**
   TRUE: An overweight teen population is on the rise. The problem has been linked with increasingly sedentary lifestyles.

> "Man must evolve for all human conflict a method which rejects revenge, aggression, and retaliation. The foundation of such a method is love."
>
> —Martin Luther King, Jr.,
> Civil Rights activist and proponent of nonviolent conflict resolution as a basic communication skill

in the news — Conflict Resolution

Research There are many ways to resolve differences—some are more successful than others. As a class, research an event where people are currently in conflict. Divide the class into two groups representing the two sides of the conflict. Select one person as a mediator to work with both of the groups to select appropriate conflict-resolution skills. Role-play a scene where the two parties attempt to resolve their differences using the agreed upon conflict-resolution skills.

LESSON 1 Taking Responsibility for Health	**LESSON 2** Accessing Valid Health Information, Products, and Services	**LESSON 3** Practicing Healthful Behaviors	**LESSON 4** Analyzing Influences on Health

⏳ Two-Minute Unit Launcher

Activity Anyone searching for health information on the Internet needs to make sure the Web site is offering reliable information and not trying to sell a product. Ask students to think of a health concern and create two fictitious Web sites for it. (Students can do this project on paper or on the computer.) The first Web site should use elements that indicate the site is trustworthy, such as being full of unbiased facts or being part of a government or nonprofit health organization Web site. The second Web site should use elements that indicate the site is unreliable, such as making claims that are too good to be true or being part of a personal Web site. Students can use www.glencoe.com to find examples of reliable health-related Web sites. This site is updated regularly. **L2**

EVALUATING MEDIA MESSAGES

HealthyCheckup

ANSWERS
Your Health
Questions

With only one click,
HealthyCheckup
is there when you are
concerned about your
health and need answers
NOW. You can access
information from medical
professionals on any
health-related topic.

HealthyCheckup
WHEN YOU NEED TO KNOW

 WHAT'S YOUR VERDICT?
To evaluate this advertisement, use the criteria for analyzing and evaluating health messages delivered through media and technology that you will learn in this unit.

 Health Online

Visit www.glencoe.com to find regularly updated statistics on teens and media messages. Using the information provided, determine the answer to this question: How many teens find health information on the Internet?

Visit www.glencoe.com to use *Your Health Checklist* ✔, an interactive tool that helps you determine your health status.

| **LESSON 5** | **LESSON 6** | **LESSON 7** |
| Using Communication Skills | Setting Health Goals and Making Responsible Decisions | Being a Health Advocate |

UNIT 1 • Health Skills **3**

Health Online

Answers According to the Kaiser Family Foundation, 76 percent of people age 15–17 have obtained health information online; so it is important for teens to learn how to evaluate online sources. Reliable sources of information are based on scientific study and empirical evidence, rather than speculation or personal testimonials. The National Institutes of Health offers the following advice for evaluating medical resources on the Internet: consider the source of the information, look for evidence of medical research to back up claims made on a Web site, check for currency of information, find out who pays for the Web site, beware of claims of miracle cures, check out the "about us" page.

3

1 Focus

LIFE SKILL Promoting Health Have students respond to the Life Skill for this lesson by giving examples of behaviors that promote health and prevent disease. Write the examples on the chalkboard. Have students compare their examples to the in-depth table of contents at the front of this book. Ask students: What topics did they leave out? Did they suggest topics not included in the text? *Possible answers: eating a balanced diet, getting enough sleep, exercising, not using alcohol.* **L2**

Write ABOUT IT!

Journaling Ask students to write in their health journals about a time that they took a calculated risk. Have them include the answers to these questions: Did the risk they took pay off? Why or why not? **L2**

LESSON 1

Taking Responsibility for Health

LIFE SKILLS • **I will comprehend health concepts related to health promotion and disease prevention.**

Who is responsible for your health? Certainly your parents or guardian and other family members contribute to your health as you grow and develop. However, you control many factors that influence your health. This lesson describes the health triangle and identifies factors that can affect your health status.

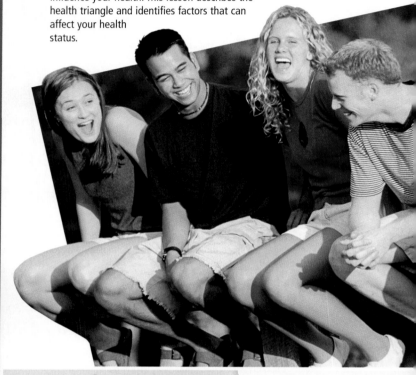

What You'll Learn

1. Draw and label the health triangle. *(p. 5)*
2. Discuss ten factors that affect health status. *(p. 6)*
3. Identify seven life skills to practice. *(p. 10)*
4. Discuss the steps to follow to help you comprehend health concepts related to health promotion and disease prevention. *(p. 12)*
5. Discuss four kinds of skills needed to be a health-literate person. *(p. 14)*

Why It's Important

Good health is a product of many factors. Many factors that affect health can be controlled so that good health status is maintained. Practicing life skills enables you to take responsibility for your health.

Key Terms

- health
- mental-emotional health
- family-social health
- health status
- health knowledge
- risk
- random event
- wellness
- health concept
- health-literate person

Write ABOUT IT!

Writing About Healthful Risks Suppose that summer vacation is almost over, and you are talking with some friends about the upcoming school year. One of your friends wants to try out for the school play, but he is worried he won't be chosen. Read the information about calculated and unnecessary risks on page 10 and write a paragraph in your health journal about what you might say to your friend about his dilemma.

National Health Education Standards—Guide for Lesson 1		
1.5	Propose ways to reduce or prevent injuries and health problems.	pp. 4, 5, 6–9, 15
3.1	Evaluate the validity of health information, products, and services.	pp. 6, 12–14, 15
3.2	Utilize resources from home, school and community.	pp. 12–14, 15
7.1	Analyze the role of individual responsibility for enhancing health.	pp. 4, 11–14, 15

Your Health

Physical, mental-emotional, and family-social health are included in the quality of life known collectively as *health.* A person who pays attention to each of the three kinds of health can achieve balanced healthful living. Sometimes, things in your life get out of balance, but you can learn skills to use when that balance becomes upset.

What to Know About the Health Triangle

The Health Triangle The Health Triangle on this page shows relationships among the three kinds of health: physical health, mental-emotional health, and family-social health. Each of these relationships forms a point on the triangle and each side supports the other.

Physical health is the condition of a person's body. Eating healthful meals and getting exercise and sleep are examples of ways to keep the body in good physical health.

Mental-emotional health is the condition of a person's mind and the ways that a person expresses feelings. Reading, having challenging conversations, and expressing feelings in healthful ways are ways to maintain mental-emotional health. Taking the time to understand one's feelings, express them in healthful ways, and meet one's own needs without interfering with the rights of others are ways to stay emotionally healthy.

Family-social health is the condition of a person's relationships with family members and with others. Expressing yourself clearly and listening when others speak are two examples of ways to maintain family-social health.

When your health triangle is unbalanced What happens if one of the points of the Health Triangle is missing? Expressing feelings is a skill that helps maintain mental and emotional health. If this skill is lacking, the Health Triangle can begin to lose its balance and the other two parts of the Health Triangle are affected. Physical health could be affected because you might feel stress. Your family-social health also might be affected because you might have difficulty expressing your feelings. These factors diminish your health status.

Did You Know?

Attitude Your mind can have powerful effects on your health. Some scientists have run studies in which people claim to feel better even though they're taking only a placebo—an inactive substance—instead of actual medicine.

The Health Triangle

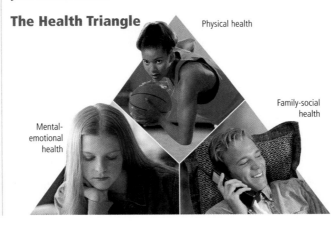

Physical health

Family-social health

Mental-emotional health

---

2 Teach

Class Activity

Health Triangle Have students make a three-dimensional health triangle. Cut three pieces of poster board into three triangles of equal size. Students can work in groups of three or four to design a collage for each side: physical, mental-emotional, and family-social. Attach the three pieces together in the shape of a pyramid. Display the pyramids in the classroom. **L2** **ELL**

INTERACTIVE CHALKBOARD with Image Bank

PowerPoint® Presentations

This CD-ROM is an editable Microsoft® PowerPoint® presentation that includes:
- Lesson presentations
- Lesson checks
- Interactive graphics
- 5-Minute Checks
- Image Bank
- All transparencies

CRISS Project

Note-Taking Refer to the Selective Underlining/ Highlighting Strategy on page 16T to help students organize and comprehend basic terms and information in Lesson 1 that will be used throughout the book.

Lesson Resource Manager

- **Unit 1 Fast File Resources**
  Reading Strategy, p. 7
  Vocabulary Practice, p. 8
  Transparency Master and Worksheet, p. 9
  Real-Life Health, p. 11
  Real-Life Health, p. 13
  5-Minute Check, p. 15
  Lesson 1 Quiz, p. 17
- **Unit 1 Transparency**
- **Lesson 1 Transparency**

- **Reading Essentials**
- **Technology**
  TeacherWorks™ CD-ROM
  StudentWorks™ CD-ROM
  Reading Essentials CD-ROM
  Exam*View*® Assessment Suite
  Vocabulary Puzzlemaker

National Health Education Standards
Pages 4–5: 1.2, 1.5, 2.1, 2.3, 7.1, 7.2

Health Status

The sum of the positive and negative influences on a person's health and well-being is a person's ***health status.*** Ten factors that affect your health status are described in this section and the next. The extent to which a person practices, makes use of, or reacts to each of these factors affects the person's health status. Health status can be improved as you develop familiarity and skill in using each of these factors for good health.

Factors That Affect Health Status

> **Make the Connection**
>
> **Healthy Skin** For more information on keeping your skin healthy, see page 353 in Lesson 31.

Ten factors that can affect a person's health status are:

(1) health knowledge; **(2)** the access a person has to health information, products, and services; **(3)** the behaviors that a person practices; **(4)** the way a person responds to influences on health, such as culture, media, and technology; **(5)** communication skills, including resistance skills and conflict-resolution skills; **(6)** the decisions a person makes; **(7)** a person's advocacy skills; **(8)** a person's heredity; **(9)** the quality of the environment in which a person lives; and **(10)** random events that occur in a person's life and how that person deals with risks.

Health knowledge The information and understanding a person has about health is that person's ***health knowledge.*** When you understand information about a health product and use it correctly, you promote your own good health and prevent disease. For example, suppose you are going to be outside for several hours. You have been told that it is wise to wear sunscreen to protect yourself from the sun's ultraviolet (UV) rays because UV light has been associated with causing skin cancer. You select a product from a company with a safe reputation and read the information on the label and the directions before applying the sunscreen. By doing so, you have made use of information and added to your health knowledge.

Accessing health information, products, and services To access something means to obtain, get, or find what you are looking for. When you access useful health information, you help yourself make decisions about products or services and choose behaviors that will keep you healthy. If you cannot access this information, your health status can be impacted negatively. A health service is help that is provided by a health-care facility or a health-care provider. Paramedics who provide services at the scene of an accident and then rush you to a hospital are providing health services.

Cross-Curricular Connections

Social Studies Have students research the availability of health services in the United States, such as ambulances and emergency medical care or the availability of prescription medicines. Then have students research the same topic in another industrialized nation as well as in a developing country that has limited resources. When they've completed their research, students can compare health services in the three countries in a written report. In addition to writing about statistical information, students should address what each country can learn from the other two. Students also should include any alternative ways the developing country has of dealing with health issues. **L3**

Because you have been able to access this health service quickly, your chances of recovery are improved.

A health product is something that is used to restore or maintain health. Examples of health products are toothbrushes, sunscreens, and prescription drugs. Suppose you need a prescription drug, but are unable to obtain it because you don't have a prescription drug plan and can't afford to buy the drug. If you cannot access the prescription drug, your health status might be affected.

Behaviors The way a person chooses to act or respond to a situation is that person's behavior. Two types of behavior can affect health—healthful behaviors and risk behaviors. How healthful behaviors and risk behaviors can affect health status are described at the bottom of the page.

Influences such as culture, media, and technology Many people and circumstances affect your health each day. Examples of these are culture, the media, and technology. *Culture* is the arts, beliefs, and customs that make up a way of life for a group of people at a certain time. What beliefs does your family have about eating breakfast, drinking alcohol, and smoking cigarettes? *Media* are the various forms of mass communications. If you watch a television commercial for pizza and then order one from that pizza shop, it is safe to say that your behavior (buying the advertised pizza) was influenced by the advertisement that you saw. *Technology* is the practical application or use of knowledge. Suppose that you log on to the Internet and read an article on ways to protect yourself from violence. As a result, you decide to start locking the doors of your home or car. By doing so, you can conclude that your health status has been influenced (positively) by technology.

Communication skills The ways in which a person chooses to share feelings, thoughts, and information with others tells you something about that person's *communication skills.* Your ability to speak clearly and listen carefully affects your relationships. This, in turn, may affect your health status or the health status of others. For example, suppose you keep angry feelings bottled up inside you. Eventually, this choice of behaviors can have a negative effect on your health status because you still feel angry. Often, talking things out will help reduce your anger.

Other communication skills can affect your health status, including resistance skills and conflict-resolution skills. *Resistance skills* are methods a person can use to say no to an action or situation that could damage health status.

Behavior Choices and Health Status

Before you make a choice, think about how your behavior will affect your health status.

Healthful Behavior	Risk Behavior
• Promotes health	• Threatens health
• Prevents injury, illness, and premature death	• Can cause injury, illness, and premature death
• Improves the quality of the environment	• Damages or destroys the environment
• Examples: wearing a seat belt, exercising regularly, and eating healthful foods	• Examples: playing sports without safety equipment, smoking, and drinking alcohol

LESSON 1 • Taking Responsibility for Health   **7**

Class Activity

Making Decisions Have students work in small groups and list situations in which they might need to make a decision. Situations could range from whether or not to exercise or eat breakfast to more serious decisions, such as whether or not to ride in a car with a driver under the influence or how to handle pressure from friends to cheat in school or shoplift. Ask each group to role-play a situation from its list using the Responsible Decision-Making Model on page 61. **L2**

NHES Assessment/SCASS

Performance Task Have students research the factors that influence a person's style of conflict resolution. Factors such as parents, school, media, society, and cultural values may all play a part in the development of a person's conflict-response style. Ask students to use their research to analyze their own conflict-response style. Have them write a short paper on how they might improve their conflict-resolution skills. **L2**

Using the Table

Behavior Choices Have students list examples of responsible and irresponsible decisions, based on what they see in Table 1.1. Have them explain how each example is related to personal health status or the health status of the environment. *Possible answers: Responsible decisions include getting regular checkups by your doctor and dentist, following directions when using a health-care product or medication, and knowing first aid. Irresponsible decisions include playing with weapons, listening to music with headphones at a high volume, and using and disposing of strong chemicals improperly.* **L2**

Suppose someone pressures you to smoke a cigarette. You know that smoking harms health, but you just can't say no. Your inability to say no leads to an action—accepting and smoking the cigarette—that is a threat to your health status. However, if you use resistance skills and say no when someone pressures you to smoke, you protect your health status, stay healthy, and probably feel good about yourself.

When you use conflict-resolution skills to solve a disagreement, you're likely to remain ▼ friends afterward.

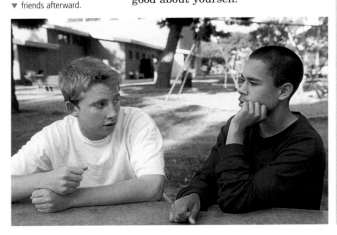

Conflict-resolution skills are steps that you can take to settle a disagreement in a responsible way. Suppose you have a disagreement with a friend and decide to settle it by using conflict-resolution skills. In making that choice, you protect your friendship and the health status of you and your friend. What if you choose to fight instead? Then you risk damaging a friendship, and both of you might become injured.

Decisions involve choices Many decisions, such as what to wear, are made almost automatically, or are of little consequence to your health. But many decisions have long-term consequences. What you choose to eat, whether you choose to smoke cigarettes or use drugs, and who you choose to spend time with are decisions that can affect your health now and later.

Decisions you make may cause you to take actions that affect health status. **Table 1.1** compares two types of decisions that you face, responsible decisions and wrong—or irresponsible—decisions.

TABLE 1.1 Decisions and Health Status	
Responsible Decisions	**Irresponsible Decisions**
Promote health	Can harm health
Keep safety in mind	Result in unsafe behaviors
Follow laws	May be illegal
Show respect for self and others	Show disrespect for self and others
Follow guidelines of parents and adults	Show disregard for guidelines of parents and others
Demonstrate good character	Are part of normal character development

8   UNIT 1 • Health Skills

 Community Involvement

Health Advocacy Have students research a specific health problem in their community. They could read the local newspaper or watch a TV news program for ideas. Students should find out what steps are being taken to address the problem, what factors are thwarting the resolution of the problem, what they can do to help address the problem, and where someone who has this health problem can get help. Have students present the results of their research to the class in a report or in a graphic-enhanced computer presentation. **L2**

Health advocacy skills Skills used to influence the health behavior and decisions of others and to advance health-related beliefs and concerns are health advocacy skills. A *health advocate* is a person who influences the health behavior and decisions of others and advances certain health-related beliefs and concerns. What other people do in your community, nation, and world affects your health status.

Think about the health status of the community or country where you live. Illegal drug use is linked to violence, accidents, and crime. If you become a health advocate for teens to be drug-free, and more teens actually do turn away from drugs as a result of your actions, then you have helped improve the health status of people in your country.

An individual can even help to improve world health. Maybe you're working with a group that informs people about the spread of human immunodeficiency virus (HIV) or the increase in death from acquired immunodeficiency syndrome (AIDS) at home and in other countries. Whenever you work to improve the health of others, you act as a health advocate. At the same time, you improve your own health status.

Heredity The passing of characteristics or traits from biological parents to their children is heredity. Characteristics passed to you from your biological parents either promote your health status or do not promote your health status. Inherited characteristics may therefore be protective factors or risk factors. A **protective factor** is something that increases the odds of a positive outcome, such as healthful traits. Of course, a

protective factor may be little help to your health status if you engage in harmful habits, such as smoking cigarettes and living on a high-fat diet.

Inherited characteristics can be a for **risk factor** some diseases. A risk factor is something that increases the odds of a negative outcome. Knowing the risk factors you have inherited is valuable. If you are at risk for heart disease because of your heredity, you can make choices that may offset this factor. You could make sure that you eat a healthful diet, exercise regularly, and learn how to manage stress.

Your environment Everything around a person is the environment. Your environment includes the air you breathe, the water you drink, and the place in which you live. Many people have living conditions that include access to clean water, healthful food, and health services they can call upon for help when needed. Because they have access to these things, their environment is a protective factor and promotes their health status. Other people live in environments that lack these basic needs and do not promote a positive health status. Their environment is a risk factor and compromises their health status.

Random Events A discussion of how random events can affect health status is included on page 10.

> **Make the Connection**
> **Environment** For more information about the environment, see page 595 in Lesson 56.

Reading Review

1. List the three parts of the Health Triangle.
2. What factors can affect your Health status?
3. How can culture affect your health?

A healthful environment can be a positive
▼ influence on your health.

LESSON 1 • Taking Responsibility for Health **9**

Risks and Random Events

Risks and Random Events

A chance that has an unknown outcome is a *risk*. A person has little or no control over a random event. Risks and random events can have positive or negative effects on health status, so take calculated risks and avoid unnecessary risks.

How Risks Differ From Random Events

Risks A *calculated risk* is a chance that a person takes after carefully considering all possible outcomes. For example, you list the possible outcomes of trying out for an athletic team. If you make the team, you will benefit from regular physical activity and competition. If you do not make the team, you risk feeling disappointed. You decide that the risk is worth taking. You try out for the team.

An *unnecessary risk* is a chance that, after weighing all the possible outcomes, you decide is not worth it.

▲ Thinking about the possible results of your actions before you act helps you make better decisions. For instance, you know that if you drive recklessly, you may get into an accident, so you should make sure that you drive safely.

For example, if you take a shorter route to school, you can sleep later, but the route takes you through gang turf. If you take the shorter route, you're also taking an unnecessary risk.

Random events A *random event* is an incident over which a person has little or no control. For example, a person may be in a hotel during a fire and suffer the effects of smoke inhalation. This person had little or no control over the random event that changed his or her health status.

Health Skills to Practice for Life

As you learn and practice the health skills listed below, you take increased responsibility for your health status. You promote the health of others and the quality of the environment when you:

- comprehend health concepts related to health promotion and disease prevention;
- access information about health products and services;
- analyze influences on health, such as culture, media, technology, and other factors;
- practice healthful behaviors;
- use communication skills, resistance skills, and conflict-resolution skills;
- set goals and make responsible decisions;
- advocate for personal, family, and community health.

10   UNIT 1 • Health Skills

Responsibility for Health

Quality of life is the degree to which a person lives life to the fullest capacity. **Wellness** is the quality of life that results from a person's health status. *The Wellness Scale* is a scale that shows the range in quality of life. Quality of life can range from optimal wellness to premature death. Optimal wellness means that a person is living at a very high level of health status with few, if any, risk factors.

How to Use the Wellness Scale

The Wellness Scale Ten factors can affect your health status and wellness. A factor that has a positive effect, such as using conflict-resolution skills, promotes optimal wellness. A factor that has a negative effect, such as fighting, increases your risk of illness, injury, and premature death.

Examine the ten factors that affect health status on page 6. Then rate your wellness by considering where you might be on the Wellness Scale. Do you have optimal wellness in each category? If not, can you think of ways that will move you closer to optimal wellness on the scale? Which factors can you control?

For example, take the factor "accessing health information, products, and services." Do you have a health-care provider you can see if you are ill? Do you ask your health-care provider questions if you don't understand something he or she says? When you need to take medicine, do you read the label before you

take it? Do you research your condition on reputable Web sites? If you answer "yes" to these questions, you are on the road to optimal wellness.

Even though you cannot control some factors of your health and wellness, such as heredity, you can control other factors that will have long-term effects on your health status. Optimal wellness is something you can work toward using the factors that affect health status because you are ultimately responsible for your health and wellness.

Wellness is the quality of life that results from your ▼ health status.

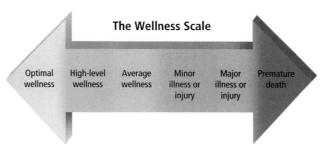

The Wellness Scale

Optimal wellness | High-level wellness | Average wellness | Minor illness or injury | Major illness or injury | Premature death

Comprehending Health Concepts

Class Activity

Testing Health Knowledge Have students work in small groups to create a health survey to test their classmates' health knowledge. They can use true/false, multiple choice, or fill-ins as a format for the survey. They can focus on the health misconceptions students may have, such as the belief that tanning booths are safer than tanning in the sun or that a person cannot become addicted to a drug after using it only one time. Have students exchange and complete the surveys. Based on their results, ask students how thorough their health knowledge is. **L2**

Using the Table

Questions About Health Concepts Have students write down a question they have about a health concept or issue. They should research the answer using reliable sources. After they understand the concept, have them write in their health journals how they will apply their new knowledge to future situations and how they will use the concept to promote health and prevent disease. **L2**

Class Activity

Reliable versus Unreliable Sources Collect and bring in pamphlets and other health information from reliable health sources. Also find and bring in information from questionable sources. Have students analyze the materials and classify each source as either reliable or unreliable. Have them explain their reasoning for each. **L2**

Comprehending Health Concepts

A general idea formed from an understanding of health knowledge is a ***health concept.*** Health concepts help you apply general ideas to real-life situations. They also help you know what to do with information related to health promotion and disease prevention. Developing comprehension of health concepts is a lifelong process. You will have many opportunities to practice this life skill.

How to Comprehend Health Concepts

Where do I begin? Are you concerned that you might not know how to become better at understanding what health is all about? There are skills that you can learn and practice that will help you become better at recognizing reliable health information.

Table 1.2 shows an example of basic skills you can practice to help you develop health knowledge. This example concerns heart disease. A first step may involve something as simple as reading a pamphlet provided by your physician about how nutrition affects the health of your heart. This can be followed by asking questions about any of the information that you don't understand.

TABLE 1.2	Steps to Comprehend Health Concepts Related to Health Promotion and Disease Prevention
The Plan	**Developing the Life Skill**
Step 1 Study health information about heart disease.	Use valid sources, such as health textbooks and the American Heart Association website. You learn that eating broiled foods is more healthful for the heart than eating fried foods.
Step 2 Ask questions about heart disease information you don't understand.	Ask your health teacher, physician, or other health expert why eating broiled foods is more healthful for the heart than eating fried foods. They tell you fried foods may contain more saturated fats. A diet high in saturated fats increases the risk of heart disease.
Step 3 Use health knowledge to form health concepts to prevent heart disease.	The health knowledge you have learned helped you form this concept: I can reduce my risk of heart disease by eating fewer fried foods.
Step 4 Use this health concept to reduce your risk of heart disease.	When you dine out, you order broiled food instead of fried food.

♥ Health Project

Gender Differences Although many basic health issues and guidelines are not gender specific, males and females do have different health risks. As a project, have students investigate gender-related risk factors for both teens and adults. They may want to narrow the topic to something specific, such as cardiovascular and heart disease, mental health, cancer, drug misuse or abuse, or unintentional injury. Students can share the results of their research with the class in the form of a multimedia presentation. **L3**

Activity: Using Life Skills

Comprehending Health Concepts: Comprehending Skin Cancer Facts

Malignant melanoma is a form of skin cancer that can be fatal. By studying the latest facts about skin cancer, you can set a health goal to reduce your risk of skin cancer, including malignant melanoma.

1 Study health knowledge. Visit the library and find a book or reputable journal that lists facts about skin cancer. Study health knowledge by reading the list of facts about skin cancer.

2 Ask questions about health knowledge that you don't understand. Make certain you get an answer you can understand. For instance, you could ask, "How does protecting the body from UV radiation reduce the risk of developing skin cancer?" Teachers, physicians, or librarians might be able to answer your questions.

3 Use health knowledge to form health concepts. Write three health concepts that you have derived from your knowledge of skin cancer. For example, these are health concepts:

- A person can reduce the risk of developing skin cancer by enjoying outdoor activities before 10 a.m. and after 4 p.m.
- A person can reduce the risk of developing skin cancer by protecting the body from UV radiation.

4 Use health concepts to promote health and prevent disease. Form a group with five classmates. Identify health goals that help you reduce the risk of developing skin cancer. For example, one classmate might say, "I will avoid skin cancer by always completing my tennis workout before 10 a.m."

Researching your condition on a reputable Web site also can help you develop health knowledge. Developing an understanding of health concepts is a lifelong process. You will have many opportunities to practice these skills.

The steps shown in **Table 1.2** use heart disease as one example of how you can understand health concepts. You can use these steps to understand more about any side of the health triangle—physical, mental-emotional, and family-social. Suppose that you want to know more about conflict-resolution skills. You could read a book or watch a film about conflict-resolution skills, then ask your parents or guardian your questions. Staying informed and asking questions about all aspects of your health will point you in the direction of health literacy.

▲ Your doctor can tell you the facts about UV radiation and skin cancer.

LESSON 1 • Taking Responsibility for Health **13**

Using Life Skills

Comprehending Health Concepts
Have students consider their risk factors for developing skin cancer (genetic predisposition, length of time in the sun, etc.). Then ask them how their knowledge of risk factors will influence their lifestyles. Have them list ways to reduce their risk of developing skin cancer. *Answers can include wearing sunscreen with an SPF of at least 15, wearing protective clothing, and avoiding the sun during peak hours.* For more information about skin cancer, see Lesson 49. **L2**

INTERACTIVE CHALKBOARD with Image Bank

5-Minute Check

Page 16, **Unit 1 Fast File Resources**

1. What is wellness? *the quality of life that results from a person's health status*
2. What is the Wellness Scale? *a scale that shows the range in quality of life*
3. How can a person move closer to optimal wellness? *make lifestyle changes and choose to practice more positive health behaviors*
4. Why is it important that you understand health concepts? *The more you know about health, the more you will be skilled in making choices that promote health.*
5. Give an example of how you can use health knowledge to promote health and prevent disease. *Answers may vary, but could include choosing not to use alcohol and other drugs after learning how they can negatively affect health.*

(D I) Differentiated Instruction

Physical Challenges To ensure that a physically challenged student feels that he or she is a true contributor to class activities, pair the student with an artistically talented classmate. Ask them to create a comic strip together, which encourages teens to set health goals. Have the artistic student draw the comic strip and the physically challenged student provide the dialogue. Ask their permission to display their work. **L3**

National Health Education Standards

Pages 12–13: 1.5, 3.1, 3.2, 7.1, 7.2, 8.2

Health Literacy

Class Activity

Creative Presentation Have students pick a health topic that interests them. Students should research the topic, then write, design art, or use technology to express their health knowledge. Display the artwork or have students make a presentation of their results.
L2

Health Literacy

A person who demonstrates the skills of effective communication, self-directed learning, critical thinking (and problem solving), and responsible citizenship is a *health-literate person.* Being health literate will keep you more informed about your health, and it will help you make smart decisions that will have positive effects on your health.

How to Attain Health Literacy

Health literacy Everyone can learn to be a health-literate person. Read the skills listed below and how you can develop the characteristics of each skill. The benefits of using these skills include enhanced health status for you and others.

Effective communication Expressing your health knowledge, beliefs, and ideas is effective communication. To be an effective communicator, practice expressing yourself in different ways. Have conversations with others about health. You can share tips with your friends on your favorite work-out routine. Teaching someone how to play a sport is another way to express your health knowledge. A third way can occur when you and a friend disagree on a health topic—look up the answer together so you both know. Write, design, create graphics, and use technology to express your health knowledge, beliefs, and ideas.

Self-directed learning Taking personal responsibility for gathering and using health-related information is self-directed learning. To become a self-directed learner, set aside time to stay informed about health-related matters. Read magazines and books, watch videos, access health-related

information on a reputable Web site, watch up-to-date health programs on television, and attend talks. Start with subjects that interest you, such as getting rid of acne or eating properly, then branch out from there. Once you start studying health topics, you will quickly discover that many health issues are related to each other.

Critical thinking Evaluating the facts and examining possible outcomes before making decisions is critical thinking. To become a critical thinker, you can use the Responsible Decision-Making Model outlined in Lesson 6. This model includes six questions you can use to evaluate the possible consequences of a decision. When you make a decision using the Responsible Decision-Making Model, you are likely to make a good decision.

Responsible citizenship Behaving in ways that improve your home, school, community, nation, and world is responsible citizenship. This can include keeping your neighborhood free of litter, volunteering, or staying informed about health issues in your community. Remember that your actions can influence others. To be a responsible citizen, always choose responsible behavior. Practice being a health advocate.

14   UNIT 1 • Health Skills

🔥 Achieving Health Literacy

Critical Thinker Present students with the following scenario: You know that your family has a history of heart disease, including high blood pressure and high cholesterol. The American Heart Association states that daily physical activity throughout life reduces the risk of heart disease. Less physically fit people have a 30 to 50 percent greater risk of developing high blood pressure. Ask students how knowing these facts will affect their decision to be physically active. Have students write their answers in their health journals. **L2**

family-social health
health
health concept
health knowledge
health status
health-literate
  person
mental-emotional
  health
protective factor
random event
risk
risk factor
wellness

Key Terms Review

Complete these fill-in-the-blank statements with the lesson Key Terms on the left. Do not write in this book.

1. A _____ is a person who demonstrates effective communication, self-directed learning, critical thinking, and responsible citizenship.

2. _____ includes physical, mental-emotional, and family-social health.

3. A _____ is a chance that has an unknown outcome.

4. A _____ is an event over which a person has little or no control.

5. A general idea formed from an understanding of health knowledge is a _____.

6. The condition of a person's mind and the ways he or she expresses feelings is _____.

7. _____ is the quality of life that results from a person's health status.

8. _____ is the sum total of the positive and negative influences on a person's health.

9. _____ is the information and understanding a person has about health.

10. The condition of a person's relationships with family members and with others is _____.

Recalling the Facts

11. List the three parts of the health triangle.

12. Name factors that affect health status.

13. Identify health skills you can practice.

14. What are four steps you can follow to help you comprehend health concepts related to health promotion and disease prevention?

15. List skills of a health-literate person.

16. What are three ways that risk behaviors can affect health status?

17. What six characteristics do making responsible decisions demonstrate?

18. On what levels can a health advocate work?

Critical Thinking

19. Comment on the following: a calculated risk is always better than an unnecessary risk.

20. What is a person communicating when he or she uses resistance skills to turn down participating in an irresponsible activity?

21. Explain and give examples of how media can affect health status.

22. How might a health-literate, self-directed learner respond to news that a parent or sibling has a rare form of cancer?

Real-Life Applications

23. Develop a list of resistance strategies to use if offered a chance to drink underage.

24. Write a strategy to evaluate the effect of video games on health.

25. How can you make people aware of health issues in your community?

26. How would you describe your health status if you determine that you are at the optimal wellness end of the Wellness scale?

Activities

Responsible Decision Making

27. **Discuss** Suppose a classmate invites you to a party with no adult supervision. Would attending the party be a responsible decision? Why? Refer to the Responsible Decision-Making Model on page 61 for help.

Sharpen Your Life Skills

28. **Comprehend Health Concepts** Research periodontal disease. Why is it important to keep plaque from forming around the gums? Use health concepts to plan how you will prevent periodontal disease.

Key Terms Review

1. health-literate person
2. Health
3. risk
4. random event
5. health concept
6. mental-emotional health
7. Wellness
8. Health status
9. Health knowledge
10. family-social health

Recalling the Facts

11. mental-emotional health, physical health, and family-social health
12. See list on page 6.
13. See list on page 10.
14. See steps on page 13.
15. effective communication; self-directed learning; critical thinking; responsible citizenship
16. threaten health; cause injury, illness or premature death; damage or destroy the environment
17. See Table 1.1 on page 8.
18. community, nation, and world

Critical Thinking

19. Students should provide logical reasons for their conclusions.
20. healthful choices that respect self, the law, and others
21. Answers can include providing information to promote health awareness or causing a person stress if they watch intense news programming.
22. The person would probably try to gather information from responsible, reliable resources.

Real-Life Applications

23. Answers may include stating reasons why underage drinking does not promote wellness.
24. Scenarios will vary, but might reflect information about the influence of technology. Students could assess whether a particular video game encourages irresponsible behaviors that show disrespect for others.

25. Plans will vary, but students can outline how a health advocate would act responsibly to address a particular health problem.
26. You are living at a very high level of health status with few, if any, risk factors.

Activities

Responsible Decision Making

27. Answers should reflect Table 1.1 on page 8.

Sharpen Your Life Skills

28. Hardened dental plaque becomes calculus, which makes gums red and swollen. Tissues around teeth become damaged, making it easier for teeth to decay or fall out. Brushing, flossing, and having teeth cleaned prevents disease.

LESSON 2

Accessing Valid Health Information, Products, and Services

Out of Time?

If time does not permit an in-depth study of this topic, use the following activities in this Teacher Wraparound Edition:
- Write About It! p. 16
- Class Activity, p. 20
- Health Project, p. 22

1 Focus

LIFE SKILL **Being Informed** Ask students to respond to the Life Skill for this lesson by discussing why they should be informed about health issues, even if they see a physician regularly. *Being informed about health issues allows you to communicate more effectively with a doctor and to ask important questions about your health.* **L2**

Write ABOUT IT!

Evaluating Sources Encourage students to pick a product that they use, are interested in using, or have heard about in the media. Ask students what they should consider when they choose their information sources and how different sources may present different views or biases on the product. **L2**

LESSON 2

Accessing Valid Health Information, Products, and Services

What You'll Learn

1. Discuss the steps needed to access valid health information, products, and services. *(p. 17)*
2. Describe what should be included in a family health history. *(p. 22)*
3. Explain how to keep a personal health record. *(p. 24)*

Why It's Important

Part of staying healthy is being able to find reliable health information, products, and services when you need them. Having reliable sources increases your chances of making responsible decisions about your health.

Key Terms

- health-care provider
- health service
- health product
- health-care facility
- emergency
- governmental health resources
- health professionals groups
- health advocate group
- pedigree
- personal health record

LIFE SKILLS • **I will access valid health information and health-related products and services.**

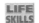

This lesson will teach you how to identify, locate, and evaluate valid health information, products, and services as well as take action when the information is misleading or the product or service is defective or substandard.

Writing About Health Products Suppose that your health assignment this week is to write a one-page report on a health product. You need to use three reliable sources of information. After reading the information on accessing resources on pages 20–21, write an entry in your health journal about the health product you will choose and where to find the sources of information that you need.

National Health Education Standards—Guide for Lesson 2		
1.5	Propose ways to reduce or prevent injuries and health problems.	pp. 17, 18, 23–24, 25
3.1	Evaluate the validity of health information, products, and services.	pp. 16, 17–19, 20, 25
3.2	Utilize resources from home, school and community.	pp. 16, 17, 19–21, 25
3.3	Determine the accessibility of products and services that enhance health.	pp. 16, 17–18, 19, 20–21
6.1	Assess personal health practices and overall health status.	pp. 22, 23–24, 25

Accessing Resources

F inding valid sources of reliable health information, products, and services is a health skill that could save your life. Take time to identify specific information, products, or services that you need. Once you find these items, evaluate them to make sure you have found the most reliable, healthful sources available. Follow the steps below to master this health skill.

How to Access Health Information, Products, and Services

1 Identify health information, products, and services you need. Where do you look for reliable information about a health question? For example, where do you go if you need advice about keeping your teeth and gums healthy? You would probably look for a practicing dentist who could provide information about how to brush and floss teeth correctly. A dentist is a health-care provider. A *health-care provider* is a trained, licensed professional who performs services that help people maintain or restore their health status. Examples of health-care providers are dentists, doctors, pharmacists, and nurses. A *health service* is the work performed by a health-care provider. Examples of health services are cleaning teeth, filling a prescription, performing an operation, or administering a vaccine.

Health-care providers might also recommend products for health. A *health product* is something that is made specifically to maintain or restore health. Some health products you need to keep teeth and gums healthy are a toothbrush, toothpaste, and floss. Other health-related products are crutches, wheelchairs, bandages, glucose test kits, and syringes.

Health services are usually performed in a health-care facility. A *health-care facility* is a place where people receive health care. Hospitals, emergency-care facilities, and clinics are examples of health-care facilities. Dentists' and doctors' offices are also health-care facilities.

2 Find health information, products, and services. The next step is to find what you need. You usually can find information about health topics in a doctor's or dentist's office, at a pharmacy, and at the grocery store. Suppose you need information for a report about acne. You can begin by using one or more of the resources listed on page 21. Practice looking in these places for free printed health information.

You can get health products from a health-care provider, a pharmacy, or a grocery store. In most instances, a parent or guardian will help you access health products, such as prescription and over-the-counter drugs.

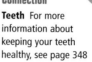

Make the Connection

Teeth For more information about keeping your teeth healthy, see page 348 in Lesson 30.

2 Teach

Class Activity

Identifying Give students a local telephone book and have them find various examples to be listed under the following categories: health-care providers, health services, and health-care facilities. **L2** **ELL**

INTERACTIVE CHALKBOARD with Image Bank

PowerPoint® Presentations

This CD-ROM is an editable Microsoft® PowerPoint® presentation that includes:
- Lesson presentations
- Lesson checks
- Interactive graphics
- 5-Minute Checks
- Image Bank
- All transparencies

CRISS Project

Vocabulary Refer to the Sentence Synthesis Strategy on page 16T and, after discussion of Lesson 2, have students brainstorm one or two sentences using the Key Terms to make certain they understand the terms.

Lesson Resource Manager

- **Unit 1 Fast File Resources**
  Reading Strategy, p. 21
  Vocabulary Practice, p. 22
  Transparency Master and Worksheet, p. 23
  Real-Life Health, p. 25
  Real-Life Health, p. 27
  5-Minute Check, p. 29
  Lesson 2 Quiz, p. 30
- **Unit 1 Transparency**
- **Lesson 2 Transparency**

- **Reading Essentials**
- **Technology**
  TeacherWorks™ CD-ROM
  StudentWorks™ CD-ROM
  Reading Essentials CD-ROM
  ExamView® Assessment Suite
  Vocabulary Puzzlemaker

National Health Education Standards
Pages 16–17: 1.5, 3.1, 3.2, 3.3, 3.5

Different Agencies Ask students which agency listed in Table 2.1 would be most helpful with untruthful advertising. *Federal Trade Commission* With phony mail-order health products? *United States Postal Service* With unsafe toys? *Consumer Product Safety Commission* With an unsafe herbal supplement? *Food and Drug Administration* **L2**

INTERACTIVE CHALKBOARD with Image Bank

5-Minute Check

Page 29, **Unit 1 Fast File Resources**

1. What is a health service? *the work performed by a health-care provider*
2. What is a health product? *something that is made specifically to maintain or restore health*
3. What are some reliable sources of health information? *health-care professionals, government agencies, community agencies*
4. What can consumers do if they are not satisfied with health products or health services? *contact one of the government agencies that enforces laws and monitors health products and services*
5. Why is it important to have reliable sources of health-related information? *It increases your chances of making responsible decisions about your health and safety.*

TABLE 2.1 Federal Agencies That Can Help With a Health Complaint

Agency	Empowered to
FDA Food and Drug Administration (FDA)	• enforce laws governing the safety of food, drugs, medical devices, and cosmetics • recall food, drug, medical devices, and cosmetic products for safety concerns • maintain the FDA Consumer Affairs Information Line
Federal Trade Commission (FTC)	• check advertising practices • stop or force changes in wording of ads
Consumer Product Safety Commission (CPSC)	• establish and enforce product safety standards • recall products
U.S. MAIL United States Postal Service (USPS)	• protect the public when products or services are sold through the mail • maintain the U.S. Postal Service Inspector General's Hotline 1-800-654-8896

3 **Evaluate health information, products, and services.** The next time you read a brochure on a health topic, analyze the information in it by using the questions listed below. These questions will help you check the reliability of the information.

What is the source of the information? The information should come from reliable sources, such as health-care professionals, government agencies, and community agencies.

If you have questions about medicine you need to take, ask a pharmacist for help.

What are the qualifications of the person or group providing the information? Is the brochure produced by a recognized medical group, such as the American Heart Association?

Is the information up-to-date? Outdated information can be harmful to your health.

Have reputable health-care professionals evaluated the information? The health information should agree with accepted medical knowledge.

What is the purpose of the information? The purpose of reliable health information is to inform, not to sell something or make money.

Does the information educate or merely appeal to your emotions? The information should educate without arousing fear or anxiety.

How can you obtain additional information? Think of other reliable sources of additional information.

Does the information make realistic claims? Be cautious about claims to cure diseases that scientists do not know how to cure.

👥 Healthy People 2010

Objective 7.7 *Increase the proportion of health-care organizations that provide patient and family education.*

Hold a class discussion on the types of health information needed by teenagers. Have students identify the health issues that most affect them. Identify health-care organizations that might be able to provide this information (keeping in mind issues such as privacy and sensitive information), as well as locations and organizations that teenagers are likely to frequent that could provide the information. Have the students write letters to the organizations, asking them to provide patient and family education if they do not do so already. **L2**

Activity: Using Life Skills

Accessing Health Services: Making an Emergency Telephone Call

An emergency situation is one in which there is a threat to life or property that calls for an *immediate* response from the police, fire department, or emergency medical team. Knowing how to get help during an emergency could save someone's life. The fastest way to get help in many communities is to dial 911. A trained emergency dispatcher will answer the call and decide who to contact for help. Here are some things to be prepared with if you ever have to call 911 for emergency assistance.

1 **Identify health information, products, and services you need.** Before you dial, ask yourself, Is this an emergency? Only use 911 to report a crime in progress, a car accident, a fire, or a serious injury or illness. A 911 call is free, even from a pay phone.

2 **Find health information, products, and services.** Be prepared with the location, the phone number you are calling from, your name, what happened, and the number and condition of any injured people. Do not hang up unless told to do so.

3 If you are calling from a cellular telephone, the dispatcher will not be able to pinpoint your location unless you tell him or her where you are.

4 **Evaluate health information, products, and services.** Listen carefully if you are told how to care for the victim. Stay on the phone and stay with the victim until help arrives.

5 **Take action.** With some classmates, brainstorm situations that would require a call to 911. Then, without actually dialing 911, practice giving information about the emergency. Remain calm and speak clearly.

Evaluate Before you buy a health product or pay for a health service, ask yourself these questions: Do I need this product or service? Do I understand what the product or service does and how to use it? Is the product or service safe to use for my current need? Is the product or service worth the price? Is the product or service of high quality? What can I do about the product or service if I am not satisfied? What do consumer agencies have to say about the product or service?

4 **Take action when health information is misleading.** Suppose you hear, read, or see health information that is misleading, inaccurate, or unsafe. What can you do if you are not satisfied with health products or services as they are described? There are laws that protect the public from false advertising. Discuss your findings with your parents or guardian. You might write a letter of complaint or contact one of the federal agencies with your concerns. **Table 2.1** lists various government agencies and their responsibilities. Taking action helps protect your health and the health of others.

Community emergency care There may be times when you need health services immediately. An *emergency* is a serious situation that occurs without warning and calls for quick action. In an emergency, you must be able to access health care right away. In many communities, you can dial 911 to get immediate help from the fire department, police, or emergency medical services. Use the activity on this page to learn how to use 911 service in the event of an emergency.

Reading Review

1. What is a health-care provider?

2. Where can you purchase health products?

3. List five tips for evaluating health information, products, and services.

LESSON 2 • Accessing Valid Health Information, Products, and Services   **19**

19

Health Resources

Health Resources

There are many kinds of health problems that occur in a person's life. A detailed Directory of Health Resources with a description of the work of specific agencies and organizations begins on page 752. When you need valid health information, a health resource can help with your specific need. Health resources can direct you to agencies in your immediate geographic area. Valid health resources also can answer questions for you about health products and support services in their area of expertise.

Types of Health Resources

Health-related groups in the United States can be found within governmental agencies, such as the National Institutes of Health and the Centers for Disease Control and Prevention (CDC). Other health resource groups, such as the American Medical Association, are health professional groups. Still other groups advocate for groups of people with specific health problems. Some of these groups are the American Cancer Society and the American Diabetes Association.

Governmental health resources Agencies that are established by the federal government that oversee the health of the nation are *governmental health resources.* Many of these agencies, such as the National Institutes of Health, carry out their own research and also provide funding for health research at universities and other research facilities. Because disease and illness do not respect geographic borders, agencies like the Centers for Disease Control and Prevention work with other agencies, such as the World Health Organization, to address health conditions worldwide.

Health professionals groups Groups called *health professionals groups* monitor the training and ethics of health professionals so that you know the doctor or other health professional you see at a medical facility has completed a program with the good of your health as their focus. These groups also advocate for health professionals.

There are numerous health advocate groups. A *health advocate*

Categories of Health Resources

Health resources can be grouped according to the types of health conditions they deal with.

- Mental-emotional health
- Family and social health
- Growth and development
- Personal health and physical activity
- Alcohol, tobacco, and other drugs
- Consumer and community health
- Environmental health
- Injury prevention and safety
- Communicable and chronic diseases
- Nutrition

📖 Family Involvement

Product Recalls Sometimes defects in products are not discovered until after the product is on the market. Companies announce a product recall, and consumers can return the defective merchandise. One way to integrate this lesson into the lives of students and their families is to have the students organize a periodic review of recalls issued on the Web site of the Consumer Product Safety Commission. The students could periodically print a list of recent recalls and share it with their families to ensure recalled products are eliminated from their households. **L3**

group educates the public about a specific health condition. Health advocate groups also raise funds for research and some provide assistance to people with specific health conditions. There are cancer, heart, diabetes, and lung associations, as well as groups that work for the interests of children, adoption, people who suffer burns, alcoholism and other drug addictions, food safety, the aged, mental health, sports injuries, and many others. These groups usually have a national headquarters and local or state level groups mostly staffed by volunteers.

Many health services will be found through a referral to a specialist from a family health-care provider. In some cases, you might call a local hospital or the American Medical Association's Doctor Finder to find a specific health service in your area.

Sources of reliable health information include:

- Health-care professionals, such as a physician or a dentist
- The Centers for Disease Control and Prevention
- Professional health-related organizations, such as the American Heart Association, the American Cancer Society, the American Medical Association, and the American Association for Health Education
- Medical journals
- A school counselor
- Videos and television programs produced by recognized professional health organizations
- The local public library

www.glencoe.com

The CDC

Do you have to do a report about smallpox? Has a family member been diagnosed with an illness you've never heard of? Where can you find reliable information about these topics? One place to start is on the Internet at the CDC Web site. The CDC is an agency of the United States federal government, located in Atlanta, GA. It has an excellent reputation for providing reliable, up-to-date information about factors that affect the health and safety of people worldwide.

The CDC Web site includes the latest news reports, statistics, and fact sheets on epidemics and infectious diseases, such as severe acute respiratory syndrome (SARS), smallpox, anthrax, and the West Nile virus. You can search the Web site for information on health and safety topics ranging from AIDS and air pollution to violence.

If you, or someone you know, is traveling out of the United States, the CDC website contains travel information pages with current health information about the area you will be visiting. There also are safety tips on how to avoid illness from food or water while traveling. Links to other Web sites, such as The National Institutes of Health and the American Heart Association, can be found as well.

Visit www.glencoe.com for more information about the history and work of the Centers for Disease Control and Prevention.

West Nile Virus in the United States*, 2003

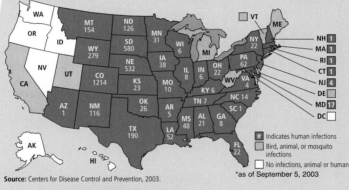

Source: Centers for Disease Control and Prevention, 2003.

Analyzing Graphs

Study the figure above and answer these questions.

1. Which states reported no cases of West Nile virus?

2. Which state reported the most human cases of West Nile virus?

Analyzing Graphs

1. Washington, Oregon, Idaho, Nevada, Alaska, Hawaii, and Washington, D.C.
2. Colorado

Project

CDC Information Have students find an article in a newspaper or magazine about an infectious disease that is currently making news. The students should read the article and then summarize the facts it gives about the disease in a paragraph. Then have the students access the CDC Web site for information on the same disease. Have the students write a second paragraph using information from the CDC site. Ask students what kinds of information were found on the CDC Web site that were not present in the media piece. **L3**

Explain the Concept

Health Advocacy Groups Although students may be familiar with many health advocacy groups, such as the American Cancer Society, they may not be clear on what these groups do. Explain that advocacy groups fill many roles, including:

- serving as information sources for people affected or concerned with specific health issues
- collecting and distributing valid, up-to-date information
- driving large, nationwide campaigns to raise money for research
- reviewing promising research programs and distributing funds, and
- lobbying the government for funding and legislation to benefit and protect health-issue causes.

Community Involvement

Health Advocacy Groups Have students select a health advocacy group they are interested in learning more about, such as the American Heart Association or the American Cancer Society. Have students research the organization. Ask students to answer these questions: What publications does the organization release? What type of research does the organization support? How is the organization involved in fund-raising? Have students write a paper on their research and encourage them to find out how they can become actively involved in the organization. **L3**

National Health Education Standards
Pages 20–21: 2.6, 2.10, 3.1, 3.2, 3.3

Extension

Family Health Issues With their parents' or guardian's permission, have students create a family health history and pedigree. Encourage the students to discuss with their families any health issues that run in their families' histories. If a student is adopted or is not living with his or her biological family, the student can talk to his or her parents or guardian to find out what is known about the student's family health history. Students should research what corrective measures or precautions might be taken to proactively treat these family health issues and, with their parents' or guardian's permission, write a paper about the results of their research and family discussions. This paper is for family reference only; it is not to be shown in class. **L2**

Investigating the Issue

- *Student answers will vary but may include hemophilia and sickle-cell anemia. Other conditions that are thought to have a genetic risk factor include lupus, Parkinson's disease, Alzheimer's disease, osteoporosis, and obsessive-compulsive disorder.*
- *Knowing that genetic risk factors exist for certain diseases can help shape health behaviors, such as diet, exercise, and other lifestyle decisions. A health-care professional also can monitor a patient's health for early signs of disease.*
- *Student answers will vary, but the tree should resemble the one shown in the figure.*

FACTS ABOUT
FAMILY HEALTH HISTORIES

Martin: 73
Heart attack: 73

Ellen: 90

William: 69
Heart attack: 69

Catherine C.: 73
Hodgkins disease: 72

Marion: 85
Heart attack: 85

Thomas: 44
Heart attack: 44

Catherine P.: 95

Marion: 82
Breast cancer: 82

Ellen: 62
Arrhythmia: 57

Richard: 65
Heart attack: 55

Barbara: 66
High blood pressure: 30

Key:
Male
Female
Deceased
Heart attack

▲ A pedigree can be used to track a condition through several generations.

A *family health history* is a record of any illnesses or medical conditions that have afflicted members of a person's family. It is also a record of the ages of living members of a family, as well as the age at death of deceased family members and the illnesses or conditions that precipitated their demise.

Family health histories Putting together a family health history is not difficult. You can use **Table 2.3** on page 24 to help gather information about the personal health histories of the people in your family. You will need to fill out one for each family member. You will need to find information including vital statistics (date of birth, health status at birth, etc.); family history (information pertaining to diseases or conditions that run in the family); immunizations (which immunizations your family members received, when they received them, and their reactions to them); personal health information (information from periodic checkups); health habits (whether your family members smoke, drink alcohol, exercise, etc.); dental history; medications (which prescription and OTC medications they take); health insurance information; and information about your family members' health-care professionals.

If you were a physician and knew of a condition that has been showing up periodically in a family, you might gather evidence by tracking the condition through several generations in the family. You would begin by making a diagram like the one shown above, which is called a pedigree.

Pedigrees A *pedigree* shows how family members are related and can be used to track genetic diseases or conditions through families. Each square represents a male family member and each circle represents a female family member.

For each person in the diagram, use the correct symbol for male or female. Then record the name, current age, or age at which death occurred. If the person is still living, record the age at which any significant medical condition developed and what the condition is or was. For example, in the diagram above, Catherine P. is 95. Because no medical condition is given, you can assume that she is healthy. Thomas died from a heart attack at 44. His death is indicated by a slash through the square. Be sure to include a key for the symbols or colors you use in the diagram. When the pedigree is completed, attach it to each person's health history.

Investigating the Issue

Visit www.glencoe.com for more help on how to construct your family health history diagram. Be sure to ask members of your family for help.

- What diseases, other than the ones listed in the article, have a genetic risk factor?
- How can knowing your family health history help you stay healthy?
- Use the information from the Web site listed above to make your own family health history diagram.

Use a computer graphics program to create your family health tree. When you have completed your family health tree, discuss it with your family. Talk about precautions you can take to avoid health issues that are hereditary.

www.glencoe.com

Health Project

Decreasing Risk Even though some conditions appear in family health histories, lifestyle choices, such as diet and physical fitness, can affect a family member's chances of contracting a disease. Divide students into small groups and assign each group a disease. Have students create a multimedia presentation to influence someone who has a genetic risk for a disease to make healthful lifestyle choices to reduce his or her risk for the disease. Students can show their multimedia presentations to the class. **L2**

Family and Personal Health Records

D ocumentation of a person's health, health care, and health-care providers is a *personal health record.* When you keep a personal health record (see **Table 2.3** on page 24), you have important information about your health in one place. A personal health record needs to be updated periodically, especially if you have new immunizations, suffer injuries or diseases, or develop adverse reactions to medications. Before you begin keeping your personal health record, you should compile a family health history (see page 22).

What to Know About Family Health Histories and Personal Health Records

Knowing about family health How much do you really know about your family's health? Is there anyone in the family who has sickle cell anemia or is a cancer survivor? Do you know if you are at risk for developing glaucoma or cataracts later in life? How does knowing about your family's health help you?

Tracking family health As research continues in the field of genetics, scientists are finding more links between genes and certain diseases. Some disorders, such as cystic fibrosis and Huntington's disease, are inherited conditions that usually result from the inability to make a necessary enzyme. For other disorders and diseases, genetics may be a risk factor rather than a direct cause. A *risk factor* is anything that increases a person's chance of developing a disease, such as cancer or diabetes. Many diseases develop as a result of a combination of factors including genetics, environment, nutrition, and lifestyle. Keeping a family health his-

tory can be an important part of your health practices.

Health history questionnaires can reveal risk factors. When you visited the doctor in the past, you may have filled out a questionnaire about your family health history. The survey usually consists of a list of diseases, and you indicate which relative, if any, has or had a particular disease. It is now known that genetics is a risk factor for many diseases, including cancer, heart disease, glaucoma, alcoholism, and mental illnesses such as depression.

Monitoring health Being aware of your family health history can help a health-care professional, like your family doctor, monitor your health and look for early warning signs of disease. Knowing that you may have some risk factors for certain diseases also can help shape your attitude toward diet, exercise, and other lifestyle behaviors. That's when a family health history becomes important.

Did You Know?

Reliable Sources Some companies recommend certain health-care providers because the doctor or dentist paid them for the recommendation. When looking for a health-care provider, make certain the referral comes from a respected source or organization.

Family and Personal Health Records

Quick Demo

Reviewing Health Records Create a fictional health record as a transparency or a handout that can be shared with the class. Go over the health record together, discussing any portion that students may not understand or may have questions about. **ELL**

Class Activity

Creating Health Records Have students each create a personal health record. They will need to talk with their parents, other family members, a physician, a dentist, and other health-care providers to gain the information needed to complete the personal health record. This record is for the student's personal use. It is not to be turned in or brought to class. Encourage students to keep this record at home, possibly on a home computer, and to update it regularly with the help of their family health-care providers. **L2**

⚖️ Legal Issues

Health Privacy In recent years, the government has taken steps to protect an individual's privacy regarding health issues. This protection includes restrictions on sharing information among health-care providers, insurance plans, and marketing companies. Tell students that the health records that a physician keeps are legally confidential documents. Except for special situations, other people cannot see a person's health records unless he or she signs a form to release the health records. Patients who are under 18 share these rights and privileges with their legal guardians. Ask students why they think it is important that this information is kept confidential by law. **L2**

National Health Education Standards
Pages 22–23: 1.4, 1.5, 6.1, 7.1

3 Assess

Vocabulary Practice

Page 22, **Unit 1 Fast File Resources**

A personal health record should include the following information.

TABLE 2.3   A Personal Health History

Health Factor	What to Record	
Vital Statistics Data on your birth	• Date of birth, weight, height • Name of hospital or place where born • Biological father and mother • Information such as was the birth normal, breech, or a cesarean section?	• Health status at birth — were there any complicating factors, such as jaundice? How was it treated? • Copy of birth certificate
Family History Health of close blood relatives (biological parents, siblings, grandparents, aunts, uncles, cousins)	• Record information pertaining to genetic diseases, allergies, cancer, heart disease, type II diabetes, high blood pressure, and any other diseases, such as sickle-cell anemia, or conditions that family members may have or have had. • Record the age at the time of death and the cause of death, if any.	
Immunizations	• Dates at which you were immunized or received boosters for polio, Diphtheria-tetanus-pertussis (DTP), measles-mumps-rubella (MMR), haemophilus influenza type b (Hib), hepatitis B (HBV), chickenpox (VZV) • Reactions you may have had to any of the above	
Personal Health Information Information from periodic check-ups	• Height • Weight • Blood pressure • Blood cholesterol • Vision	• Hearing • Allergies • Injuries • Major illnesses • Age associated with each of the above • Records of dates of visits to the doctor, reason for visit, outcome
Health Habits Information that will be asked by a physician	• Do you smoke? Have you ever smoked? Do you drink alcohol? How often? How much? How much do you exercise? How much sleep do you get? What is the quality of your relationships with people in your family? At school? At work? What interests do you have outside of school or work?	
Dental History	• Record history of visits to your dentist (every six months beginning at age 6). • Overall and/or specific history of dental problems — decay, gum disease, wisdom teeth, crowns, bridges, implants	
Medications prescribed and over-the-counter	• Date medication prescribed, what prescribed for, strength, by whom • Record any reaction you might have had to any medication and the date on which you notified a physician of the reaction.	
Health Insurance Information	• Name, address, telephone number of the insurance company • Policy holder's name (usually your parent or guardian) • Policy number, copy of the policy • Written record of all contacts with the insurance company, whether by phone or mail	
Your Health-Care Professionals	Name, address, phone number of: • family doctor • medical specialist (allergist, orthopedist, etc.)	• dentist • dental specialist (oral surgeon, orthodontist)

Sensitive Issues

Personal Health History For some students, making a family health history may bring up sensitive issues. A student may be adopted and not know any information about his or her birth parents. In single-parent homes, a biological parent may not be a significant part of a student's life or may be unavailable to question. Other sensitive issues, such as a history of mental illness or substance abuse in a family, may be upsetting for students if they think they will have to share information with the class. Reassure students and their parents or guardian that they will not be asked to share their family health history with other students or with you.

Key Terms Review

Complete these fill-in-the-blank statements with the lesson Key Terms on the left. Do not write in this book.

1. A(n) _____ works to raise money and awareness for a specific health condition.
2. Use 911 in the event of a(n) _____.
3. The place people receive health care is a(n) _____.
4. _____ oversee the health of the nation.
5. A(n) _____ is a trained, licensed professional who helps people maintain or restore their health status.

6. A(n) _____ helps you keep track of important health information.
7. _____ work to make sure you are treated by someone with appropriate training.
8. Doctors can use a(n) _____ to track genetic diseases.
9. An example of a(n) _____ is filling a prescription.
10. Crutches are an example of a(n) _____ .

emergency
family health history
governmental health
  resources
health advocate
  group
health product
health professionals
  group
health service
health-care facility
health-care provider
pedigree
personal health
  record

Recalling the Facts

11. Name three things that you need to find and evaluate for positive health status.
12. What are seven sources of reliable health information?
13. List eight questions you can ask to evaluate health information.
14. What should you do with health information that you think is misleading?

15. Name five health products that you might find in a medicine cabinet at home.
16. Name three situations in which you might make a 911 emergency call.
17. What is one function of the Centers for Disease Control and Prevention?
18. What pieces of information make up your personal health record?

Critical Thinking

19. Why does a person need to know his or her family health history?
20. Why is the question "Do I really need this health product or service?" important?
21. Select a specific health problem and develop a list of strategies to evaluate information about this health issue.
22. Research, describe, and evaluate the products that are available for treating acne.

Real-Life Applications

23. Where can you find listings for medical equipment or home health-care equipment?
24. How could you research available emergency services in your area?
25. How many hospitals are in your area? Which one is closest to your house?
26. Identify specific health services available for older people in your community.

Activities

Responsible Decision Making

27. **Discuss** You and a classmate are doing research on nutrition for a project at school. You click on a Web site about diets. Your classmate wants to try a liquid diet that is described. You ask your classmate to evaluate the diet before trying it. Refer to the Responsible Decision-Making Model on page 61 for help.

Sharpen Your Life Skills

28. **Access Health Products** Imagine that you are taking a two week vacation. Make a list of the health products that you will need to take with you. Next to each health product identify where it might be located or purchased. Write a paragraph about what you would do if you bought a product and it was defective.

Visit www.glencoe.com for more *Health & Wellness* quizzes.

Key Terms Review

1. health advocate group
2. emergency
3. health-care facility
4. Governmental health resources
5. health-care provider
6. personal health record
7. Health professionals groups
8. pedigree
9. health service
10. health product

Recalling the Facts

11. health information, health products, health services
12. Answers may include: government agencies; community agencies; health-care professionals; the CDC; professional, health-related organizations; medical journals; school counselors; programs by recognized professional health organizations; public libraries.
13. Students' answers should incorporate the questions listed on pages 18–19.
14. Answers can include: discuss with parents, guardian, or responsible adult; write a letter of complaint or contact a federal agency.
15. Answers can include: antiseptics, bandages, floss, toothpaste, and aspirin.
16. Responses may include a crime in progress, a car accident, a fire, or a serious injury or illness.
17. The CDC is a source of up-to-date information about health and safety worldwide.
18. Answers should include the information in Table 2.3 on page 24.

Critical Thinking

19. so hereditary conditions can be tracked
20. Sometimes people are convinced by people other than health professionals to try products or services that they might not need. In some cases, the product or service could harm health.
21. Responses could include reading brochures or online information from recognized health groups or talking with a health professional.

---

22. Descriptions might reflect research from health professionals and/or recognized professional groups or evaluated literature on available medications.

Real-Life Applications

23. phone books, the Internet
24. Answers will vary with the community.
25. Answers will vary with the community.
26. Answers will vary with the community.

Activities

Responsible Decision Making

27. Answers should reflect the Responsible Decision-Making Model on page 61.

Sharpen Your Life Skills

28. Answers will vary with the type of vacation (Will they be in a tent in the wilderness or in a hotel?) and availability of products.

Practicing Healthful Behaviors

Practicing Healthful Behaviors

 Out of Time?

If time does not permit an in-depth study of this topic, use the following activities in this Teacher Wraparound Edition:

- Write About It! p. 26
- Class Activity, p. 28
- Family Involvement, p. 32

1 Focus

LIFE SKILL **Healthful Behaviors** Have students respond to the Life Skill for this lesson as a class by brainstorming healthful behaviors or recalling them from Lesson 1. Ask students to privately consider which health behaviors they may want to modify this year. **L2**

 ABOUT IT!

NHES Assessment/SCASS

Performance Event Ask students to write a health goal about nutritious eating in their health journals. Using the information on page 32, have them create a Health Behavior Contract using the goal they wrote in their health journals. **L2**

What You'll Learn

1. Discuss the purpose of a health behavior inventory (p. 27)
2. Discuss healthful behaviors. (p. 27)
3. Give examples of risk behaviors (p. 27)
4. List the six categories of risk behaviors in teens. (p. 27)
5. List the five parts of a health behavior contract (p. 32)

Why It's Important

You can take control of your health and become aware that the choices you make affect your health status. For optimal health status, you will want to know what healthful behaviors are and make the decision to practice them.

Key Terms

- behavior
- habits
- healthful behaviors
- risk behaviors
- health behavior inventory
- health behavior contract

LIFE SKILLS • **I will practice healthful behaviors to reduce health risks.**

Becoming and staying a healthful person requires you to look at the way you live your life. In this lesson, you are going to learn what healthful behaviors you already practice and what healthful behaviors you may want to add to your routine.

 ABOUT IT!

Writing About Healthful and Risk Behaviors Suppose your parents give you enough money to buy your lunch for a week. You could choose to buy the healthful school lunch or buy tasty but unhealthy food from the fast-food restaurant near your school. After you read the information about healthful behavior on page 27, write an entry in your health journal about how you would handle this responsibility.

National Health Education Standards—Guide for Lesson 3		
1.1	Predict how healthy behaviors can impact health status.	pp. 26, 27–31, 33
1.5	Propose ways to reduce or prevent injuries and health problems.	pp. 26, 27, 28–31, 32, 33
6.1	Assess personal health practices and overall health status.	pp. 26, 27, 28–31, 33

Health Behavior Inventories

Do actions really speak louder than words? A *behavior* is the way you act or choose to act in a situation. Behaviors can be healthful, or they can put you and others at risk. Behaviors can be learned. They can become *habits,* which are fixed behaviors that you use automatically. It is more beneficial to your health status to learn and practice *healthful behaviors*—behaviors that promote health, prevent injury and premature death, and improve the quality of the environment—than to have to unlearn *risk behaviors*—behaviors that threaten health, can cause injury or premature death and harm, or destroy the environment.

The Value of a Health Behavior Inventory

You can have optimal health. Practicing healthful behaviors and avoiding risk behaviors helps you to maintain optimal health status. Where do you stand in terms of healthful behavior? You can find out by completing a health behavior inventory. A *health behavior inventory* is a tool that helps a person decide how well he or she is practicing healthful behaviors. The inventory is a list of healthful behaviors to which a person can respond positively, "I practice this healthful behavior," or to which a person can respond negatively, "I don't practice this healthful behavior at this time."

The healthful behaviors listed in the inventory are not of equal value. For example, consider these two healthful behaviors: "I avoid tobacco use and secondhand smoke" and "I investigate health careers." You will benefit from practicing both of these healthful behaviors, but your health status is protected more by choosing not to use tobacco products and avoiding secondhand smoke than by investigating health careers.

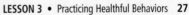

> **Make the Connection**
> **Smoking Risks** For more information on the dangers of smoking, see page 426 in Lesson 38.

Six Categories of Risk Behaviors in Teens

These behaviors threaten health, can cause injury or premature death, and/or destroy the environment:

- Behaviors that result in unintentional and intentional injuries
- Tobacco use
- Alcohol and other drug abuse
- Sexual behaviors that result in HIV infection or other sexually transmitted diseases and in unplanned pregnancies
- Diet choices that contribute to disease
- Lack of physical activity

Source: Centers for Disease Control and Prevention

LESSON 3 • Practicing Healthful Behaviors **27**

Health Behavior Inventories

2 Teach

Teacher FYI

Tobacco Use According to the Centers for Disease Control and Prevention (CDC), from 1999 to 2001 frequent smoking by teens dropped from more than 16 percent to less than 14 percent. Three factors were cited as having contributed to this decline: increased retail prices, increased school-based prevention, and increased exposure to mass media anti-smoking campaigns.

PowerPoint® Presentations

This CD-ROM is an editable Microsoft® PowerPoint® presentation that includes:
- Lesson presentations
- Lesson checks
- Interactive graphics
- 5-Minute Checks
- Image Bank
- All transparencies

Journaling Refer to the Pre-and Post-Reading Responses Strategy on page 17T and have students record in their health journals the ways they feel they practice healthful behaviors, both before and after they have read the lesson.

Lesson Resource Manager

- **Unit 1 Fast File Resources**
  Reading Strategy, p. 33
  Vocabulary Practice, p. 34
  Transparency Master and Worksheet, p. 35
  Real-Life Health, p. 37
  Real-Life Health, p. 39
  5-Minute Check, p. 41
  Lesson 3 Quiz, p. 42
- **Unit 1 Transparency**
- **Lesson 3 Transparency**

- **Reading Essentials**
- **Technology**
  TeacherWorks™ CD-ROM
  StudentWorks™ CD-ROM
  Reading Essentials CD-ROM
  ExamView® Assessment Suite
  Vocabulary Puzzlemaker

> **National Health Education Standards**
> Pages 26–27: 1.1, 5.1, 6.1

Completing a Health Behavior Inventory

NHES Assessment/SCASS

Performance Task Have students research the effects of stress on the body and stress-management techniques. You could assign each student or group of students a different body system to research. Have students share their findings with the class. **L2**

Explain the Concept

Dietary Guidelines The Dietary Guidelines were developed, in part, by the USDA. Explain that it is recommended that anyone 2 years or older eat a diet comprised of a variety of foods with plenty of fruits and vegetables. A diet low in fat with moderate use of sugar and salt also is recommended.

Class Activity

Body Systems Have students form five groups. Each group should investigate ways to keep one of the following body systems healthy: circulatory, digestive, muscular, skeletal, respiratory. Have each group report its findings to the class. **L2**

Completing a Health Behavior Inventory

You can use this inventory to become aware of healthful behaviors that you already practice and discover new habits that could improve your health status. You will also learn to think of your health in broader terms that include relationships, and the environment.

How to Complete a Health Behavior Inventory

To take the inventory, number from 1 to 100 on a separate sheet of paper. Read each behavior carefully. Write "yes" or "no" next to the same number on your paper. Each yes indicates a behavior you practice to promote your health status. Each no indicates a behavior you do not currently practice on a regular basis. Then review your responses and analyze them to identify any healthful behaviors that you do not currently practice.

Mental and Emotional Health

1. I will develop good character.
2. I will interact in ways that help create a positive social-emotional environment.
3. I will develop healthful personality characteristics.
4. I will choose behaviors that promote a healthy mind.
5. I will express emotions in healthful ways.
6. I will use stress-management skills.
7. I will seek help if I feel depressed.
8. I will use suicide prevention strategies when appropriate.
9. I will cope with loss and grief in healthful ways.
10. I will be resilient during difficult times.

Family and Social Health

11. I will develop healthful family relationships.
12. I will work to improve difficult family relationships.
13. I will make healthful adjustments to family changes.
14. I will develop healthful friendships.
15. I will develop healthful dating skills.
16. I will choose to practice abstinence from sex.

🛡 Sensitive Issues

Student Privacy The health behavior inventory on pages 28–31 may touch on issues that personally affect students, including drug misuse or abuse, eating disorders, HIV, or physical and sexual abuse. Reassure them that no one, including you, will read their health behavior inventory. Personal questions should be avoided. While some students may be comfortable talking about these subjects, the teacher should consider keeping all comments in the hypothetical sense. Let students know their privacy is respected and, if they need to speak to someone, counselors and other resources are available.

17. I will recognize harmful relationships.
18. I will develop skills to prepare for marriage.
19. I will develop skills to prepare for parenthood.
20. I will choose to practice abstinence from sex to avoid the risks of teen marriage and parenthood.

Growth and Development

21. I will keep my body systems healthy.
22. I will recognize habits that protect female reproductive health.
23. I will recognize habits that protect male reproductive health.
24. I will learn about pregnancy and childbirth.
25. I will learn about the growth and development of infants and children.
26. I will provide responsible care for infants and children.
27. I will develop my learning style.
28. I will achieve the developmental tasks of adolescence.
29. I will develop habits that promote healthful aging.
30. I will share my feelings with my family about dying and death.

Nutrition

31. I will select foods that contain nutrients.
32. I will evaluate food labels.
33. I will eat the recommended servings from the MyPyramid food guidance system.
34. I will follow the Dietary Guidelines.
35. I will follow a healthful diet that reduces the risk of disease.

36. I will develop healthful eating habits.
37. I will follow Dietary Guidelines when I go out to eat.
38. I will protect myself from foodborne illnesses.
39. I will maintain a desirable weight and body composition.
40. I will develop skills to prevent eating disorders.

Personal Health and Physical Activity

41. I will have regular physical examinations.
42. I will follow a dental health plan.
43. I will be well-groomed.
44. I will get adequate sleep and rest.
45. I will participate in regular physical activity.
46. I will follow a physical fitness plan.
47. I will develop and maintain health-related and skill-related fitness.
48. I will be a responsible spectator and participant in sports.
49. I will try to prevent physical activity-related injuries and illnesses.

Alcohol, Tobacco, and Other Drugs

50. I will follow guidelines for the safe use of prescription and OTC drugs.

▲ These teens are following the healthful behavior, "I will develop healthful eating habits."

Did You Know?

Health Goals You may have a few setbacks as you develop good health habits. If you keep your mind on your goal of good health, you will get back on track.

Explain the Concept

Fitness Explain the different aspects of physical fitness: health-related fitness and skill-related fitness. Health-related fitness includes the aspects of physical fitness that affect good health. These include flexibility, muscular strength and endurance, cardiovascular endurance, and body composition. Skill-related fitness includes aspects that affect coordination, balance, agility, speed, and power.

Teacher FYI

Sleep According to the National Institutes of Health, teens need between 8 and 9 hours of sleep each night. Less than that could result in increased behavior problems and memory lapses, as well as a decrease in the student's ability to concentrate.

Extension

Quality Health Care Assign students a health issue, such as skin cancer, heart disease, or depression. Have them find five health-care providers or facilities in the area that can help with this issue. Next, have them create a list of questions to evaluate which provider would be the best choice if someone they knew had this health concern. They could enlist the help of a health advocacy group, if applicable. They also could consider cost and location as evaluation factors. Have them report their findings to the class. **L3**

Cross-Curricular Connections

Math Divide the class into small groups, each with a pre-set budget for the month. Provide the students with newspapers so that they can research expenses, such as rent and groceries. Provide students with other estimates for expenses such as utilities and insurance. Have students consider other costs, such as transportation, entertainment, telephone service, and unexpected expenses, such as car repairs or medical bills. Students should manage their money to ensure their hypothetical household does not go over its allotted budget for the month. **L2** **ELL**

National Health Education Standards
Pages 28–29: 1.1, 1.5, 6.1

Drug-Free Lifestyle Because most drugs lower users' inhibitions and slow thought processes, people under the influence of drugs are less likely to practice abstinence. This can lead to an unplanned pregnancy or infection with STDs, including HIV. Explain to students that abusing drugs, even once, can affect the rest of their lives.

Class Discussion

Entertainment Health behavior item number 74 from the list on this page involves healthful entertainment. Ask students to list types of healthful entertainment. Record their ideas on the chalkboard. **L2**

Class Discussion

Energy Conservation Engage the class in a discussion as to how students can become more involved in recycling and conserving energy—all of which save their families money. **L2**

51. I will not drink alcohol.
52. I will avoid tobacco use and secondhand smoke.
53. I will not be involved in illegal drug use.
54. I will avoid risk factors and practice protective factors for drug misuse and abuse.
55. I will not misuse or abuse drugs.
56. I will use resistance skills if I am pressured to misuse or abuse drugs.
57. I will choose a drug-free lifestyle to reduce the risk of violence and accidents.
58. I will choose a drug-free lifestyle to reduce the risk of HIV infections and unwanted pregnancy.
59. I will be aware of resources for the treatment of drug misuse and abuse.

Communicable and Chronic Diseases

60. I will choose behaviors to reduce my risk of infection with communicable diseases.
61. I will be aware of immunizations that protect health.

These teens are following the healthful behavior, "I will protect the natural environment."

62. I will choose behaviors to reduce my risk of infection with respiratory diseases.
63. I will recognize ways to manage asthma and allergies.
64. I will choose behaviors to reduce my risk of infection with sexually transmitted diseases.
65. I will choose behaviors to reduce my risk of HIV infection.
66. I will choose behaviors to reduce my risk of cardiovascular diseases.
67. I will choose behaviors to reduce my risk of diabetes.
68. I will recognize ways to manage chronic health conditions.
69. I will choose behaviors to reduce my risk of cancer.

Consumer and Community Health

70. I will acquire knowledge of laws to protect health.
71. I will recognize my rights as a consumer.
72. I will take action if my consumer rights are violated.
73. I will make a plan to manage time and money.
74. I will choose healthful entertainment.
75. I will analyze ways that messages delivered through technology might affect health status.
76. I will make responsible choices about health-care providers and facilities.
77. I will evaluate ways to pay for health care.
78. I will investigate health careers.
79. I will investigate public and international health needs.

30 UNIT 1 • Health Skills

♥ Health Project

Health Careers Health behavior item number 78 from the list on this page is, "I will investigate health careers." Have students choose a health career that interests them. Have them research the duties that are associated with the career to answer the following questions: Which duties would they enjoy? Which duties would not be enjoyable? Students can interview someone who has this career to gain more insight. Have students write a one-page paper and present their findings to the class. Ask the students if the career is something they would still consider doing after investigating it. **L2**

National Health Education Standards

Pages 30–31: 1.1, 1.5, 6.1

Environmental Health

80. I will stay informed about environmental issues.

81. I will be aware of organizations that protect the environment.

82. I will help keep the air clean.

83. I will help keep the water safe.

84. I will help keep noise at a safe level.

85. I will help improve the visual environment.

86. I will help conserve energy and natural resources.

87. I will help reduce and dispose of waste.

88. I will protect the natural environment.

89. I will be a health advocate for the environment.

Injury Prevention and Personal Safety

90. I will follow safety guidelines to reduce the risk of unintentional injuries.

91. I will follow guidelines for motor vehicle safety.

92. I will follow safety guidelines for severe weather, natural disasters, and national alerts.

93. I will practice protective factors to reduce the risk of violence.

94. I will respect authority and obey laws.

95. I will practice strategies to help protect myself from physical violence.

96. I will practice strategies to help protect myself from sexual violence.

97. I will stay away from gangs.

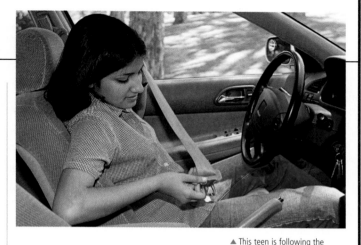

98. I will follow guidelines to help reduce the risk of weapon injuries.

99. I will be skilled in common first aid procedures.

100. I will be skilled in emergency first aid procedures.

Review Your Responses

Plan to continue each health behavior that you already practice.

Analyze Each Health Behavior

Make a list of the health behaviors that you do not yet practice. Select one that could be an important, positive change to your health status. For example, if you do not exercise often, you can choose number 45, "I will participate in regular physical activity." Perhaps you might start this health behavior by taking 30-minute walks after school four times a week. Maybe you would like to start playing a sport. Set realistic steps to achieve this goal because becoming active now will have long-term benefits to your health status. On page 32, you will learn to make a health behavior contract to develop this healthful behavior.

▲ This teen is following the healthful behavior, "I will follow guidelines for motor vehicle safety."

Reading Review

1. List the three components of a healthful behavior.

2. What are six categories of risk behaviors in teens?

3. What is a habit?

LESSON 3 • Practicing Healthful Behaviors **31**

Teaching Transparency

Page 35, **Unit 1 Fast File Resources**

5-Minute Check

Page 41, **Unit 1 Fast File Resources**

1. What is a behavior? *the way you act or choose to act in a situation*

2. Are the health behaviors listed in the health behavior inventory of equal value? *No; some are more important than others.*

3. What are three healthful behaviors that improve family and social health? *Answers should reflect the Family and Social Health list on pages 28–29.*

4. List at least three healthful behaviors that also help the environment. *Answers should reflect the Environmental Health list on page 31.*

5. Explain how a healthful behavior differs from a risk behavior. *See definitions on page 27.*

Reading Review

1. *promotes health, prevents injury and premature death, improves the quality of the environment*

2. *Answer should reflect the list on page 27.*

3. *a fixed behavior that you use automatically*

🏛 **Community Involvement**

Obey Laws Invite a police officer to speak to the class about the laws in your area that are broken most by young people. Divide the class into groups, and assign each group a law. After they research the background of their law, have the groups create a campaign to promote obeying their law. They can make advertisements, multimedia presentations, and public service announcements as part of their efforts. Ask the principal if the campaigns can be employed around the school, or ask community leaders if they would like to employ the campaigns in a public space. **L2**

Health Behavior Contracts

Quick Demo

Bicycle Safety Demonstrate the hand signals that bicyclists use to show right turn, left turn, and stop. Ask students to call out the signal if they know which one you are using. As a class, think of creative ways to remember which hand signal goes with each action. **ELL**

NHES Assessment/SCASS

Constructed Response With help from the students, fill out a health behavior contract on the chalkboard or on an overhead transparency. Ask students to write a paragraph explaining what they should do if they are not reaching a health goal as quickly as they would like. **L2**

3 Assess

Vocabulary Practice
Page 34, **Unit 1 Fast File Resources**

National Health Education Standards
Pages 32–33: 5.4, 6.2, 6.3, 8.1

Health Behavior Contracts

A written plan that a person makes in which he or she agrees to develop the habit of practicing a specific healthful behavior is a ***health behavior contract***. The healthful behavior you want to practice becomes a health goal.

How to Create a Health Behavior Contract

> **Make the Connection**
>
> **Health Behavior Contracts** For information on making a health behavior contract, see page 367 in Lesson 33.

A health behavior contract is a written plan to develop the habit of practicing a healthful behavior. These are the five steps to follow when making a health behavior contract:

1. Write your name and the date.
2. Write the healthful behavior you want to practice as a health goal.
3. Write specific statements that describe how this healthful behavior reduces health risks.
4. Make a specific plan for recording your progress.
5. Complete the evaluation of how the plan helped you accomplish the health goal.

Health Behavior Contract

Health Goal: I will eat a healthful diet that reduces the risk of disease.

Effects on Health Status: The American Cancer Society suggests eating cruciferous vegetables (broccoli, cauliflower, cabbage, brussels sprouts, turnips) to reduce the risk of colon cancer. The ACS also recommends eating a diet high in fiber (fruits, vegetables, whole grains) to reduce the risk of colon cancer.

Plan of Action: I will eat three servings of vegetables a day; one serving will be cruciferous. I will eat at least two servings of fruit each day. I will eat whole-grain cereal and whole-wheat toast for breakfast. I will keep a food diary for one week.

Food Intake Record by Day for One Week						
Day 1	**Day 2**	**Day 3**	**Day 4**	**Day 5**	**Day 6**	**Day 7**
cereal, toast, peas, spinach, radishes, orange, raspberries, strawberries	cereal, toast, corn, lima beans, orange, grapes, canned pears	bacon, egg, toast, squash, peas, broccoli, orange, grapes, plum	cereal, toast, okra, sprouts, cabbage, orange, apple, plum	cereal, toast, lettuce, tomato, broccoli, orange, grapes, watermelon	bacon, 2 eggs, cabbage, corn, lettuce, tomato, pear, pineapple, apple	sausage, pancakes (with syrup), broccoli, peppers, lettuce, tomato, apple, grapes, plum

Evaluation: I slipped up on days 3, 6, and 7 with a high-fat breakfast. I didn't always want to eat cereal. I could add another serving of whole-wheat toast to get more fiber. The vegetables made me feel stuffed, but I'm getting used to it. I like eating fruit as a snack.

32 UNIT 1 • Health Skills

📖 Family Involvement

Family Discussion Some of the healthful behaviors the students may want to begin practicing will require family involvement. For example, if a student plans to modify his or her diet, he or she will need to talk to his or her parents or guardian and accompany them to the grocery store. Have students discuss the health behavior inventory with their families. Family members may be able to offer advice and support in the students' quest to meet their health goals. Have students write about this conversation with their parents or guardian in their health journals. **L3**

behavior
habits
health behavior contract
health behavior inventory
healthful behaviors
risk behaviors

Key Terms Review

Complete these fill-in-the-blank statements with the lesson Key Terms on the left. Do not write in this book.

1. A _____ is a written plan to develop the habit of practicing a healthful behavior.
2. _____ are actions that promote health.
3. _____ are actions that threaten health.
4. A _____ is a personal assessment tool that helps a person learn if he or she is practicing healthful behaviors.
5. Automatic behaviors are _____.
6. The way you act in a situation is a _____.

Recalling the Facts

7. What is the difference between a healthful behavior and a risk behavior?
8. What is included in a health behavior contract?
9. Name three ways that risk behaviors can affect health status.
10. What are the six risk behaviors for teens as indicated by the CDC?
11. What are the ten major areas in the health-behavior inventory?
12. Name three growth and development behaviors that can affect health status.
13. Name four nutrition behaviors that promote health.
14. Give three behaviors you can use to conserve energy and natural resources.
15. What are three ways to promote good mental health?
16. Name four family and social health behaviors you should practice.
17. Name four safety issues that are part of a health inventory.
18. What are three ways to be a healthy consumer?

Critical Thinking

19. Why does putting your name on a health behavior contract indicate your commitment to the contract?
20. Why might a person complete a health-behavior inventory?
21. Why aren't all healthful behaviors of equal value in reducing health risks? Give several examples from pages 28–31.
22. How can managing time and money help your health status? Give several specific examples that relate to your life.

Real-Life Applications

23. How can completing a health behavior inventory help you protect your health?
24. Select a health-related service from your community. Describe its role in preventing disease and promoting health.
25. How could health be threatened if you develop a risk-behavior habit? Describe a specific example.
26. How does knowing specific healthful behaviors help improve health status?

Activities

Responsible Decision Making

27. **Role-Play** In health class, you have just completed the health behavior inventory. A student tells you she was surprised when she read, "I will stay away from gangs." She asks you if she made a wrong decision because she already belongs to a gang. Role-play this situation in class. Refer to the Responsible Decision-Making Model on page 61 for help.

Sharpen Your Life Skills

28. **Set Health Goals** Make a health behavior contract using the health goal: I will get adequate sleep and rest. Include the categories of: the health goal, the effects on health status, a plan of action, a plan for recording your progress, and an evaluation of how the plan worked. Then put your plan into action and evaluate whether it helped you get enough sleep.

Visit **www.glencoe.com** for more *Health & Wellness* quizzes.

Key Terms Review

1. health behavior contract
2. Healthful behaviors
3. Risk behaviors
4. health behavior inventory
5. habits
6. behavior

Recalling the Facts

7. A healthful behavior promotes health while a risk behavior threatens health.
8. See steps on page 32.
9. threaten health, can cause injury or premature death or harm, destroy the environment
10. See list on page 27.
11. mental and emotional health; family and social health; growth and development; nutrition; personal health and physical activity; alcohol, tobacco, and other drugs; communicable and chronic diseases; consumer and community health; environmental health; injury prevention and personal safety
12. Answers can be any from the list on page 29.
13. Answers can be any from the list on page 29.
14. Answers can be any from the list on page 31.
15. Answers can be any from the list on page 28.
16. Answers can be any from the list on pages 28–29.
17. Answers can be any from the list on page 31.
18. Answers can be any from the list on page 30.

Critical Thinking

19. Your name makes the contract more like a legal contract; putting your name on something means you own it.
20. because he or she wants to attain a health goal
21. Some risk factors are life-threatening, while some health behaviors have a minor impact.
22. Answers will vary. Managing time and money effectively lowers a person's stress level, and stress affects health.

Real-Life Applications

23. by helping you recognize ways to improve your health status
24. Answers will vary.
25. By definition, risk behaviors threaten health. Examples will vary.
26. Knowing a healthful behavior can influence a person to make more healthful decisions.

Activities

Responsible Decision Making

27. The role-play should include the steps from the Responsible Decision-Making Model on page 61.

Sharpen Your Life Skills

28. Answers should follow the guidelines for a health behavior contract on page 32.

If time does not permit an in-depth study of this topic, use the following activities in this Teacher Wraparound Edition:
- Class Activity, p. 35
- Class Discussion, p. 36
- Class Activity, p. 36

1 Focus

LIFE SKILL **Influences on Health** Have students respond to the Life Skill for this lesson by bringing in an advertisement or describing a commercial for a health product or issue that they think is especially entertaining or noteworthy. Ask them how these advertisements or commercials influence their health outlook or decisions. *Students will likely find ads or describe commercials that cover and influence a broad range of health issues. Some ads may promote a product in an exaggerated manner or use humor, while other ads will promote a healthy lifestyle or habit. Use the examples to start a class discussion.* **L2**

Write ABOUT IT!

Evaluating Sources Have students write in their health journals the name of a health product they would like to purchase. Ask them to use the Questions to Evaluate Ads on page 37 to evaluate whether this purchase would be responsible. **L2**

LESSON 4 | Analyzing Influences on Health

LIFE SKILL • I will analyze the influence of culture, media, technology, and other factors on health.

How aware are you of all of the things that influence your health? It can be quite a long list. Family members, friends, and peers might influence you. Ads in magazines and in the media can be strong influences on you. How strong is their influence? Do you respond to advertising by making responsible decisions and practicing healthful behaviors?

What You'll Learn

1. Discuss steps to follow to analyze influences on health. *(p. 35)*
2. Explain why it is important to be media literate. *(p. 36)*
3. Identify questions to ask when evaluating ads. *(p. 37)*
4. Identify ten appeals used in advertisements. *(p. 38)*

Why It's Important

The influence of media or technology can be very strong. Having the skill to analyze influences helps you to stay in charge, make responsible decisions, and practice healthful behaviors for optimal health.

Key Terms

- media
- advertisement (ad)
- commercial
- technology
- culture
- media literacy
- advertising

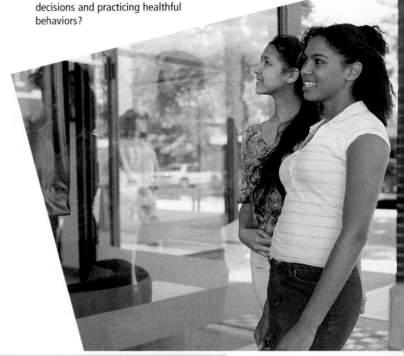

Write ABOUT IT!

Writing About Influences Suppose that you are shopping with a friend when you see an advertisement in a store window promoting a skin cleanser that will solve teens' acne problems overnight. Your friend wants to go into the store and buy the cleanser. After you read the information about advertisements on page 37, write an entry in your health journal about what you would tell your friend about the ad she saw.

National Health Education Standards—Guide for Lesson 4		
1.5	Propose ways to reduce or prevent injuries and health problems.	pp. 34, 35–36
2.5	Evaluate the effect of media on personal and family health.	pp. 34, 35–38
5.1	Examine barriers that can hinder healthy decision making.	pp. 34, 35–36, 39

Influences on Health

I nfluence is the ability to indirectly sway an opinion, a choice, or an outcome. A quick look around will tell you that you are surrounded every day by any number of things that affect what you wear, read, eat, or say. You can't easily escape their influence. But you can take charge of the amount of influence these things have on your health. There are four steps you can take to master this life skill.

How to Analyze Influences on Health

1. Identify people and things that might influence you. Make a list of the people who have the most influence on you. What family members influence you? What friends or peers have the most influence on you? Don't forget famous people, such as politicians, movie stars, and sport heroes, and people in your community, such as doctors or members of the clergy.

Now think about things that influence you. One possible influence is the media. **_Media_** are the various forms of mass communication. There are commercials and advertisements in the media. An **_advertisement (ad)_** is a paid announcement about a product or service. A **_commercial_** is an advertisement on television or radio. Ads appear online, on TV, radio, and billboards, and in magazines and newspapers. Ads are paid for by companies and people who want to influence consumers.

Technology in media takes the form of using high-tech equipment to communicate information. Think about the computer games you might have played. Some of these may have

a very strong influence on mental health and how an individual looks at other members of society. Advertisements that pop up when you log on to the Internet can affect what you purchase or how often you might want to use services. CD-ROMs, videos, or DVDs also might include behaviors that could influence you.

Culture also can have a strong influence on your life. **_Culture_** is the arts, beliefs, and customs that make up a way of life for a group of people at a certain time. Your culture influences you.

Did You Know?

Commercials The average American child may view up to 40,000 commercials on television each year.

Computer or video games can have an influence on physical and ▼ mental health.

Influences on Health

2 Teach

Class Activity

Influential People Have students take a moment to think of three people whom they do not personally know (such as a celebrity or newscaster whom they regularly watch or read about) who influence them on a regular basis. Students will use this list for the Class Activity on page 36. **L2**

INTERACTIVE CHALKBOARD
with Image Bank

PowerPoint® Presentations

This CD-ROM is an editable Microsoft® PowerPoint® presentation that includes:
• Lesson presentations
• Lesson checks
• Interactive graphics
• 5-Minute Checks
• Image Bank
• All transparencies

Discussion Use the Think-Pair-Share Strategy on page 17T to initiate a discussion on media influence.

Lesson Resource Manager

- **Unit 1 Fast File Resources**
  Reading Strategy, p. 45
  Vocabulary Practice, p. 46
  Transparency Master and Worksheet, p. 47
  Real-Life Health, p. 49
  Real-Life Health, p. 51
  5-Minute Check, p. 53
  Lesson 4 Quiz, p. 54
- **Unit 1 Transparency**
- **Lesson 4 Transparency**

- **Reading Essentials**
- **Technology**
  TeacherWorks™ CD-ROM
  StudentWorks™ CD-ROM
  Reading Essentials CD-ROM
  ExamView® Assessment Suite
  Vocabulary Puzzlemaker

National Health Education Standards
Pages 34–35: 1.5, 2.1, 2.2, 2.3, 2.5, 2.6, 5.1

Make the Connection

Media For more information on evaluating the effects different forms of entertainment have on behavior and decisions, see page 558 in Lesson 52.

2. Evaluate how the influence might affect your health behavior and decisions. How do you react to each of the influences in your life? Use the Guidelines for Analyzing Influences on Health shown below. If you answer "yes" to the questions, then a particular influence has a positive effect on you. If you answer "no" to one or more of the questions, then that particular influence has a negative influence on you.

For example, think about the person who influences you the most. Write down three behaviors this person practices and ask yourself the questions in the guidelines. Then you will know whether or not to imitate this person's behavior.

Using these guidelines to evaluate media messages can help you to develop media literacy. ***Media literacy*** is the skill of being able to recognize and evaluate the influence of messages in media.

3. Choose positive influences on health. Your goal is to be influenced only in positive ways. Suppose a

person encourages you to exercise regularly. Your answer to each question in the guidelines will be "yes." This person is making a valuable contribution to your health by influencing you in a positive way. Suppose you watch a television commercial in which a star talks about being drug free. This commercial makes a valuable contribution to your health by influencing you in a positive way.

Associating with people who influence you to make responsible decisions and practice healthful behaviors is a smart choice. It also is wise to watch television programs, play computer games, and listen to music or lyrics that encourage positive responses from you.

4. Protect yourself from negative influences on health. As you analyze different influences, you will become aware of some that are more negative than positive. Negative influences can motivate people to choose behaviors that are harmful, unsafe, illegal, disrespectful, in disagreement with family guidelines, or demonstrate bad character. Whenever possible, reduce your exposure to negative influences on health.

For example, suppose you turn on the radio and begin to hear lyrics to a song that include inappropriate language and suggest using violence. These are negative influences. What can you do to protect yourself from being influenced to curse or act in violent ways? You could choose to change to a station that plays music that doesn't promote these negative influences. Other choices include not to sing the lyrics or purchase the CD made by this group or individual.

Guidelines for Analyzing Influences on Health

Answer these questions before you allow something or someone to influence you.

- Does this influence promote healthful behavior?
- Does this influence promote safe behavior?
- Does this influence promote legal behavior?
- Does this influence promote behavior that shows respect for myself and others?

- Does this influence promote behavior that follows the guidelines of responsible adults, including my parents or my guardian?
- Does this influence promote behavior that demonstrates good character?

36 UNIT 1 • Health Skills

Achieving Health Literacy

Critical Thinker When examining health information, understanding the source is very important. Have students think of a disease or condition, such as diabetes or heart disease. Then ask them to list a private company and a nonprofit organization that work with the disease or condition they selected. Finally, students should create a table comparing and contrasting the motives of each group. Have them consider where each group gets its financial funding and who benefits from their work. **L3**

Advertisements

A form of selling products and services is **advertising**. The advertising industry is big business. Advertising agencies help companies by designing ads to influence people's choices. A lot of money, time, and effort goes into the production of ads. People who create ads carefully develop them to appeal to the wants and needs of a certain audience.

How to Evaluate Advertisements

Ads are designed to influence people. A person's feelings as to what life will be like if he or she used a certain product are influenced by ads. For example, ads for beverages or cigarettes often show people, usually young adults, having a great time with lots of friends. These ads send a strong message that people who smoke and drink alcohol will have a good time and will be popular.

Most teens want to be popular. People who create ads know this and design ads to appeal to this need. Ads usually show young, healthy, vibrant, happy, attractive people. As a result, people who see these ads get a message that the product shown will make them attractive, youthful, and happy.

Advertisers think very carefully about when and where to place their ads. They want to place them where they will have the greatest effect. For example, commercials for children's toys often are shown during Saturday morning cartoons. Commercials for beer and cars often appear during televised football, baseball, and basketball games. Advertisements for clothes for teens often are placed in teen magazines and the other places where teens will see them.

Tobacco and alcohol ads are not allowed in teen magazines, but many teens read young adult magazines

and are exposed to these products anyway. Advertisers pay athletes to wear company logos during sports and social events.

Products that actors and actresses use in movies and on television programs are intended to influence your choices. At one time, fake brands of soft drinks or household products appeared in movies. Now, companies with name brands pay to have their products appear in the media. Practice media literacy. Always evaluate ads before being motivated to purchase a product or service just because it is being used by someone who is famous. The Questions to Evaluate Ads listed here can help you make healthful choices.

Make the Connection

Smoking For more information on tobacco use (a leading cause of death), see page 426 in Lesson 38.

Reading Review

1. List five places advertisements can appear.
2. What is media literacy?

Questions to Evaluate Ads

Smart consumers ask these questions whenever they see an advertisement.

- What is being advertised?
- Where and when did the ad appear?
- Why was this particular type of media selected?
- Who appears to be the targeted audience?
- What advertising appeals (page 38) are used in the ad?

- What does the advertiser want me to believe?
- What do I know to be fact?
- Will the product or service in the ad promote health and safety? Is it legal? Will its use promote self-respect and respect for others, follow family guidelines, and demonstrate good character?

LESSON 4 • Analyzing Influences on Health   **37**

🔰 Health Project

Marketing Campaign Have students form small groups. Each group should decide on a positive, healthful behavior or product to promote. Have the groups design a complete marketing campaign. Groups should discuss strategies to use, such as their message, target audience, placement of their message, the image they want to promote, and specific influences they can use to make the message effective. Have the students design an advertisement or commercial that shows the benefits of the healthful behavior or product that they are marketing. **L2**

Advertisements

Reading Review

1. online; on TV, radio, and billboards; and in magazines and newspapers
2. the skill of being able to recognize and evaluate the influence of messages in media

NHES Assessment/SCASS

Performance Task Have students examine the images from advertisements for cigarettes, alcohol, and fast foods. Have them consider how the use of these products might lead to different results than those images portray. Students can create an advertisement for these products showing some of the downsides to using them. Encourage the students to be creative and use art, photographs, or even video to make their advertisements. **L2**

INTERACTIVE CHALKBOARD with Image Bank

5-Minute Check

Page 53, **Unit 1 Fast File Resources**

1. What does the term "media" refer to? *various forms of mass communication*
2. Why is media literacy an important tool? *It is essential for evaluating health information that comes from the media.*
3. How can identifying positive health influences help you to make good health decisions? *Positive health influences encourage you to make good decisions about your health and motivate you to do healthful activities.*
4. What kind of influences encourage behavior that is illegal, harmful, unsafe, or disrespectful? *negative influences*
5. How do advertisers decide where to place their ads? *They put them where their target audience, or type of person who is most likely to buy their product, will see them.*

Using Life Skills

Analyze Influences Provide examples of ads that obviously contain the advertising appeals listed on this page. Display the ads for the class and as a group analyze advertising appeals in each ad. **L2**

Class Activity

Analyzing Advertisements Using the advertisements that students brought in for the Life Skill at the beginning of the lesson, evaluate advertisements with the Questions to Evaluate Ads on page 37. **L2**

3 Assess

Vocabulary Practice

Page 46, **Unit 1 Fast File Resources**

Activity: Using Life Skills

Analyze Influences: Evaluating Ads

There are many subtle ways to influence people's choices. Certainly not all of these things will harm your health, but influence is a strong factor in your life. To analyze influences on health, follow these four steps: 1) Identify people and things that might influence you; 2) Evaluate how the influence might affect your behavior and decisions; 3) Choose positive influences on health; and 4) Protect yourself from negative influences on health.

1 Study the ten advertising appeals shown on this page. Find ads in magazines that demonstrate at least five of the advertising appeals. Write the name of the advertising appeal on the back of each ad.

2 Keep track of the type of magazine that the ad is in. It could be a magazine for teens, men, women, health, science, tools, cooking, news, or fishing.

3 Share the ads in class. Classmates can read the ads and label them with the type of advertising appeal used. Have your classmates explain why they think it is that type of appeal.

▲ When you are looking at the ads online or in a newspaper, magazine, or catalog, keep in mind that photographers work for hours to create the perfect photos in which all the models look attractive and happy.

Ten Advertising Appeals

Companies often use advertising appeals to influence people to choose their product. Learn to recognize the hidden message behind the appeal.

Brand loyalty appeal This technique tries to convince a person that one particular brand is better than all the others.

False image appeal This advertising technique tries to convince people that they will have a certain image by using a particular product or service.

Bandwagon appeal This advertising technique implies that everyone you know is using this brand. Teens who want to be "in" may "jump on the bandwagon" and buy the product.

Humor appeal This advertising technique contains something that sticks in the mind. It may be a catchy slogan, jingle, or cartoon. A teen may remember this "hook" and purchase the product.

Glittering generality appeal This technique contains an exaggerated appeal that gets to your emotions. Teens may believe that a product will take care of their needs and buy it.

Scientific evidence appeal This technique uses data from surveys and laboratory test results to try to convince you this product is the best. Teens may believe that because data is shown, it has to be the best choice.

Progress appeal "The latest version is the best one to buy because it is new!" People often want to be known for having purchased the "latest."

Reward appeal This advertising technique often offers a special prize, gift, or coupon. People can be tempted by this technique because they think that they will get something for nothing.

Sex appeal This technique tries to convince you that a certain brand will make you attractive and alluring beyond your wildest dreams.

Testimonial appeal This technique uses a spokesperson, who sometimes is famous, to name the benefits of the product or service.

 Legal Issues

Legal Limitations on Advertising Have students explore the legal limitations of advertising in your state. Using various resources, such as the Advertising Council and Attorney General, have students discover what advertisements can legally say or imply about their products. Encourage them to investigate and find examples of advertising or product claims that were found to be in violation of the law, and have them create a presentation about why the advertising or product claims were misleading. Discuss the presentations in class. **L3**

National Health Education Standards

Pages 38–39: 2.5, 8.1

4 STUDY GUIDE

advertisement
advertising
commercial
culture
media
media literacy
technology

Key Terms Review

Complete these fill-in-the-blank statements with the lesson Key Terms on the left. Do not write in this book.

1. A(n) _____ is a paid announcement about a product or service.

2. _____ is the arts, beliefs, and customs that make up a way of life for a group of people at a certain time.

3. _____ is skill in recognizing and evaluating the messages in media.

4. _____ is a form of selling products.

5. _____ are the various forms of mass communication.

6. A(n) _____ is an ad on TV or radio.

7. In media, _____ takes the form of using high-tech equipment to communicate information.

Recalling The Facts

8. Name four influences that can affect health behavior.

9. What is the difference between an advertisement and a commercial?

10. Name four places where commercials can appear.

11. What are the six guidelines for analyzing influences on health?

12. What six behaviors can result from negative influences?

13. What are advertisements designed to do?

14. What eight questions can you ask to evaluate an ad?

15. Name five advertising appeals and make up an example to illustrate each one.

16. Why is it important to know how to analyze the influences in your life?

17. Name two places ads are placed to influence a specific group.

18. What is the goal of an advertising agency?

Critical Thinking

19. How can teens analyze influences on their health behavior and decisions?

20. Create two strategies to show disapproval of people using inappropriate language in front of your peers.

21. Discuss the following statement: Being media-literate means disregarding all health-related ads and commercials.

22. Today, ads and commercials appear in innovative places. Describe several unexpected places you have seen ads.

Real-Life Applications

23. What strategies would you use to evaluate information in a televised news report about West Nile virus? Explain your choices.

24. Describe a situation in which you responded to a positive health influence.

25. Describe a situation in which you responded to a negative health influence.

26. What questions might you use to evaluate an ad for a fungal foot powder in which a sports figure is the spokesperson?

Activities

Responsible Decision Making

27. **Write a Response** After your friend sees a TV commercial in which a well-known athlete promotes a brand of athletic shoes, he wants to buy the shoes. How can you help your friend make a responsible decision? Refer to the Responsible Decision-Making Model on page 61 for help.

Sharpen Your Life Skills

28. **Analyze Influences on Health** Compose a television commercial for an imaginary product. Target the commercial to teens. Include one or more of the advertising appeals from this lesson. Present your commercial to your classmates. Have them tell which appeal(s) were used.

Visit **www.glencoe.com** for more *Health & Wellness* quizzes.

LESSON 4 • Study Guide **39**

LESSON 4

STUDY GUIDE

Key Terms Review

1. advertisement
2. Culture
3. Media literacy
4. Advertising
5. Media
6. commercial
7. technology

Recalling the Facts

8. Answers can include family, friends, famous people, community members, media, and culture.

9. An advertisement is a paid announcement about a product or service. A commercial is an advertisement on TV or radio.

10. online, TV, radio, during movie previews

11. See list on page 36.

12. behaviors that are harmful, unsafe, illegal, disrespectful, in disagreement with family guidelines, and/or demonstrate bad character

13. influence people to buy or use a specific product, use a specific service, or to hold a certain opinion

14. See list on page 37.

15. See list on page 38.

16. So you can take charge of how much influence they have.

17. Answers can include an athlete wearing company logos or toy commercials during Saturday morning cartoons.

18. to influence people's choices

Critical Thinking

19. Make use of the Guidelines for Analyzing Influences on Health on page 36.

20. Answers should include behaviors that are legal, safe, healthful, respectful of self and others, in agreement with family guidelines, and demonstrate good character.

21. Being media literate means people need to evaluate ads before believing them or not.

22. Answers will vary.

Real-Life Applications

23. Strategies should include those in Guidelines for Analyzing Influences on Health on page 36.

---

24. Situation should include behaviors that are legal, safe, healthful, respectful of self and others, in agreement with family guidelines, and demonstrate good character.

25. Answers will vary.

26. Answers should refer to Questions to Evaluate Ads on page 37.

Activities

Responsible Decision Making

27. Responses should caution the friend that it is true everyone needs comfortable shoes, but shoes should not be purchased just because a famous person advertises them.

Sharpen Your Life Skills

28. Individual commercials will vary with the type of appeal chosen.

LESSON 5

Using Communication Skills

 Out of Time?

If time does not permit an in-depth study of this topic, use the following activities in this Teacher Wraparound Edition:
- Class Activity, p. 46
- Using the Table, p. 48
- Class Discussion, p. 51
- Extension, p. 54

1 Focus

LIFE SKILLS **Communication Skills** Have students respond to the Life Skills for this lesson by giving examples of when they use communication skills, resistance skills, and conflict-resolution skills during the course of a day. *possible answers: talking with friends at school; participating in class; saying no to alcohol, tobacco, and other drugs; trying to avoid a physical altercation* **L2**

Write ABOUT IT!

Role-Play Divide the class into pairs. Have each pair role-play the conversations they wrote in their health journals. Make sure each person gets a chance to play the part of the person who corrects the prejudicial behavior. **L2**

Using Communication Skills

LIFE SKILLS
- I will use interpersonal communication skills to enhance health.
- I will use resistance skills when appropriate.
- I will use conflict-resolution skills to settle disagreements.

How are your communication skills? Do you speak clearly? Do you listen carefully when others speak? When you say "no," do people take you seriously? This lesson includes life skills that help you communicate effectively.

What You'll Learn

1. Identify steps to follow to develop interpersonal communication skills. *(p. 41)*
2. Discuss I-messages, you-messages, mixed messages, and active listening. *(p. 42)*
3. Outline consequences of and ways to correct wrong actions. *(p. 46)*
4. Discuss resistance skills. *(p. 47)*
5. Describe how to be self-confident and assertive. *(p. 48)*
6. Describe types of conflict, conflict response styles, conflict-resolution skills, and the mediation process. *(p. 49)*
7. Discuss ways to avoid prejudicial behavior. *(p. 54)*

Why It's Important

Communication skills help you converse with others, resist negative peer pressure, and resolve conflicts. These actions protect and promote health.

Key Terms

- communication skills
- I-message
- you-message
- active listening
- peer pressure
- resistance skills
- assertive behavior
- conflict-resolution skills
- mediation
- prejudice

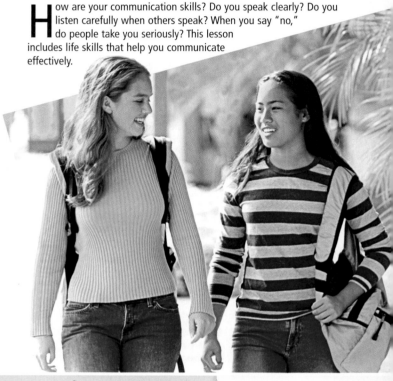

Write ABOUT IT!

Writing About Avoiding Prejudicial Behavior You are speaking with a classmate about a new student at your school. The new student is of a different ethnicity than your classmate. Your classmate makes prejudicial remarks. Read page 54 about ways to avoid prejudicial behavior. Then write an entry in your health journal discussing a conversation you might have with your friend.

National Health Education Standards

Pages 40–41: 1.5, 4.1, 4.2, 8.1

National Health Education Standards—Guide for Lesson 5		
1.5	Propose ways to reduce or prevent injuries and health problems.	pp. 40–47, 49, 51, 55
4.1	Utilize skills for communicating effectively with family, peers, and others to enhance health.	pp. 40, 41–44, 55
4.2	Demonstrate refusal, negotiation, and collaboration skills to enhance health and avoid or reduce health risks.	pp. 40, 41, 47, 55
4.3	Demonstrate strategies to prevent, manage, or resolve interpersonal conflicts without harming self or others.	pp. 40, 50–53, 55
8.1	Utilize accurate peer and societal norms to formulate a health-enhancing message.	pp. 40, 44, 45, 47, 48, 51, 54, 55

Communication Skills

S kills that help a person share feelings, thoughts, and information with others are ***communication skills.*** Some people communicate clearly and easily with everyone around them. Others struggle to make themselves understood. You can take steps to develop this skill to the benefit of your health and that of others.

How to Use Interpersonal Communication Skills

1. Choose the best way to communicate. Your choices for how you communicate with others are almost unlimited. When you need to communicate with another person, you can choose to speak to someone in person, speak to someone on the telephone, write a letter, draw a picture, use body language (including facial expressions), use sign language, leave a message on voice mail or on an answering machine, or send an e-mail.

How you communicate may depend on what you are trying to say. There is a difference between communicating directions to a restaurant and communicating your feelings about another person. If you want to give someone directions to a restaurant, you could describe it in words, or you could draw a map.

Suppose you want to share your feelings about something with someone. You might choose a private place to talk. Most likely, you would not talk about your feelings on voice mail that someone else might hear or in an e-mail that someone else might read.

What if you are in a position where you need to say "no" to someone and want to send a strong message? Then, you might use body language as well as verbal communication, and shake your head "no." ***Nonverbal communication*** is the use of actions or body language to express emotions and thoughts. Ignoring someone also is a means of nonverbal communication.

◀ A person's voice and his or her nonverbal communication both send a message. What emotions can you associate with this student?

2 Teach

Class Discussion

Nonverbal Communication Have students list examples of nonverbal communication. *possible answers: making or not making eye contact, rolling eyes, crossing arms, closing fists, facial expressions, hand gestures* Ask students why it is important to pay attention to nonverbal communication. **L2**

PowerPoint® Presentations

This CD-ROM is an editable Microsoft® PowerPoint® presentation that includes:
- Lesson presentations
- Lesson checks
- Interactive graphics
- 5-Minute Checks
- Image Bank
- Links to www.glencoe.com
- All transparencies

CRISS
Project

Discussion Refer to the KWL Strategy on page 17T to determine what students know about peer pressure and conflict resolution, what they would like to know, and what they have learned from the lesson.

Lesson Resource Manager

- **Unit 1 Fast File Resources**
  Reading Strategy, p. 57
  Vocabulary Practice, p. 58
  Transparency Master and Worksheet, p. 59
  Real-Life Health, p. 61
  Real-Life Health, p. 63
  5-Minute Check, p. 65
  Lesson 5 Quiz, p. 67
- **Unit 1 Transparency**
- **Lesson 5 Transparency**

- **Reading Essentials**
- **Technology**
  TeacherWorks™ CD-ROM
  StudentWorks™ CD-ROM
  Reading Essentials CD-ROM
  Exam*View*® Assessment Suite
  Vocabulary Puzzlemaker

I-Messages After reviewing the difference between an I-message and a you-message with students, as a class go through several examples of changing you-messages into I-messages. For example: Your friend was late meeting you. The you-message might be, "You were rude to be so late without calling." The I-message could be, "I had to wait alone in the parking lot. I was worried about you. I was upset." Another example: Your brother, who was playing computer games, refused to let you use your family's home computer. The you-message might be, "You were so inconsiderate when you would not let me use the computer." The I-message could be "When I could not get on the computer, I could not do my homework. I was angry and stressed about not getting my work done." Have the class break into groups and create their own scenarios of changing you-messages to I-messages. Have them role-play their scenarios for the class. **L2**

Quick Demo

Vocal Cues Before class, write several sentences from an imagined conversation. Ask the students to shut their eyes. Read the conversation in several styles: confidently, sarcastically, and timidly. Ask students which style sends the strongest message. Ask them which style sends a mixed message.

Teaching Transparency

Page 59, **Unit 1 Fast File Resources**

▲ No matter how angry someone is, he or she will get better results using I-messages instead of you-messages.

 Make the Connection

Express Yourself For more information about expressing emotions, see page 96 in Lesson 10.

2. Express your thoughts and feelings clearly. Take responsibility for expressing your thoughts clearly. Do not expect others to figure out what you mean—you must tell them.

You have two choices when you communicate: I-messages and you-messages. An **I-message** expresses your feelings or thoughts on a subject. It contains a specific behavior or event, the effect of the behavior or event on the person speaking, and the emotions that result. Examples of I-messages are: "I am in a difficult situation because you didn't return my book to me before class today. Now if the teacher calls on me to read, I won't be able to, and Mrs. Clark will think I'm not prepared for class."

When you use an I-message, you express your emotions without blaming or shaming another person, you avoid attacking another person or putting him or her on the defensive, and you give the other person a chance to respond.

On the other hand, a you-message will result in the opposite response. A **you-message** is a statement that blames or shames another person. A you-message puts down another person for what he or she has said or done, even if you don't have the whole story about what happened. A you-message for the situation above might be, "I can't believe you forgot my book. You are so stupid! Can't you do anything right?"

If you use a you-message, you don't share your emotions in a healthful way, and you don't give the other person a chance to share his or her emotions. You-messages put people in a defensive position, so they are more likely to respond negatively to your negative you-statement.

You should try to become skilled at using I-messages. Compare the I-message and the you-message in the situation described above. Think about which way you would prefer to be treated if someone were upset with you.

Even in situations where you are angry, using I-messages will be more effective than using you-messages. You will still share your emotions, but you will also maintain healthy relationships with others.

Avoid sending mixed messages. When you express your feelings, you will have the best response if you send one clear message. A **mixed message** is a message that gives two different meanings, such as "I want to do this" and "I don't really want to do this."

For example, the words people use and the tone of their voice when they speak can send different meanings. Suppose a friend apologizes for something that he has done to you, but the tone of his voice is sarcastic. Do you believe his apology is sincere?

Sending one message is important. If you send a mixed message, you present yourself as being confused or insincere. Sometimes, you may need to take a moment to decide how you feel about a situation. Take that moment, then voice a single message with consistent words, tone, and body language.

 Teacher to Teacher

Role Models To illustrate the need for having a strong support system, a variety of sources for help, and good communication with those sources, use a large balloon or a lightweight ball and some yarn. Have two students hold a piece of yarn between them and place the ball on the yarn. This will show that the ball is not supported by one link. Add more students and yarn to show that the more links (pieces of yarn), the better the ball is supported. Students should have at least five adults in their support system and should work to make sure they are communicating their needs clearly to them. **L2** **ELL**

Frank Pickett
Thorne Bay School, Thorne Bay, AK

3. Listen to the other person. Speaking clearly is an important communication skill. Listening carefully is just as important. When someone is speaking to you, pay attention to what he or she is saying.

Maintain eye contact with the person—this is a nonverbal way to show the speaker that you are interested in what he or she has to say. If you are preoccupied with something else, the speaker isn't sure if you are listening at all, and he or she may give up trying to hold a conversation.

You can use gestures, such as nodding your head, to encourage further conversation, as well. Pay attention to the speaker's body language and tone to see if he or she might be sending a mixed message. If so, you may want to ask more questions to find out what he or she really means. Do your best to remember everything the person is saying.

When you show a speaker respect as he or she speaks, he or she will enjoy communicating with you, and you will have more effective conversations. You are also showing the speaker the way you like to be treated when you speak.

4. Make sure you understand each other. The way you respond in a conversation to show that you hear and understand what the speaker is saying is called *active listening.* An active listener can let a speaker know that he or she is really hearing and understanding what is being said.

By clarifying, restating, summarizing, or affirming what was said, you are proving that you take interest in what the other person had to say. Using these tools also helps you

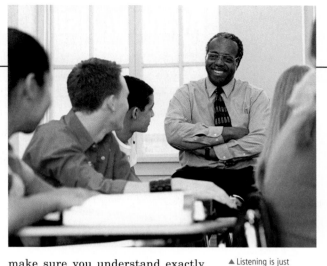

▲ Listening is just as important a communication skill as speaking is. Good listeners have more effective conversations.

make sure you understand exactly what it is the speaker intended to communicate.

Techniques for Active Listening

Have you ever misunderstood someone? Maybe you've even gotten into an argument with a friend or family member only to find out later that you both were saying the same thing—you just didn't understand each other. Active listening will help you communicate better and avoid hurt feelings and other problems that stem from misunderstanding each other.

When You Don't Listen

When you tune out someone who is speaking to you, you risk having that person feel unimportant. You risk harming your relationship with the person.

You may tune out because you:

- were thinking of something or someone else.
- could not hear the speaker.
- were tired and dozing off while the other person was talking.

- were thinking about what you were going to say next.
- heard a distracting noise in the room.
- thought you knew what the speaker was going to say next.

LESSON 5 • Using Communication Skills   **43**

Teacher FYI

Facial Expressions Charles Darwin first wrote about the universality of facial expressions across cultures in his book *The Expression of Emotions in Man and Animals,* published in 1872. Since then, several researchers, including psychologist Paul Ekman, have concluded that there are seven universally recognized facial expressions: sadness, anger, disgust, happiness, surprise, fear, and contempt.

Another area of Ekman's research explores the differences in the use of facial muscles between a genuine expression, such as a smile of happiness, and a "put on" expression in which a person tries to hide his or her true feelings. A genuine smile involves using the muscles around the eyes, whereas a fake smile does not.

Class Activity

Ideas for Active Listening In pairs, have students practice the suggestions for active listening under step 3. One student should begin by telling a story while the other student follows the suggestions in step 3. Students should then reverse roles. Have students discuss how they feel when they think someone is not listening to them. Ask them to express their feelings using I-messages.   **L2**

NHES Assessment/SCASS

Performance Task Have students review the current research regarding differences in communication between genders. Divide the research into three categories: females communicating with females, males with males, and opposite-gender communication. Assign one group of students to each category. Then have the students present a summary of the research to the class in a creative way (a skit, song, collage, etc.).   **L3**

👥 Healthy People 2010

Objective 28-11 *Increase the proportion of newborns who are screened for hearing loss by age one month, have audiologic evaluation by three months, and are enrolled in appropriate intervention services by six months.*

It is estimated that 28 million people in the United States are deaf or have some degree of hearing impairment. The most important period of language development in humans, either spoken or signed, occurs before the age of four. Early identification and intervention for deafness or hearing loss is critical to the development of language in a child. Have students investigate what types of intervention or rehabilitation are possible if a child has hearing loss. *Possible answers: hearing aids, sign language instruction, cochlear implant.*   **L2**

National Health Education Standards
Pages 42–43: 1.5, 4.4

Using Life Skills

Using Communication Skills

Have students create scenarios in which one person is not actively listening to the other. Then have students perform the scenarios for the class. The class audience should write down all of the actions the listener is taking or not taking that show he or she is not actively listening. After each scenario, ask the students to discuss how these actions can be corrected. **L2** **ELL**

INTERACTIVE CHALKBOARD
with Image Bank

5-Minute Check

Page 65, **Unit 1 Fast File Resources**

1. What is nonverbal communication? Give an example. *the use of actions or body language to express emotions and thoughts. Examples may include making eye contact or nodding.*

2. What is the difference between an I-message and a you-message? *An I-message is a statement that contains a specific behavior or event, the effect of the behavior or event on the person speaking, and the emotions that result. A you-message is a statement that blames or shames another person.*

3. Why is sending a mixed message poor communication? *It is difficult for the listener to determine what the speaker really means. The speaker may appear confused or insincere.*

4. Why is listening an important part of communication skills? *Listening shows respect for the speaker and interest in the conversation.*

5. How could you tell someone you are too distracted to actively listen to him or her? *Use I-messages: I really want to be able to talk to you about this. Right now, I have to finish this homework. Let's talk later when I can give you my full attention.*

Activity: Using Life Skills

Using Communication Skills: Sharpening Your Listening Skills

You can sharpen your listening skills by practicing active listening. When you listen actively, you show that you understand. Being a good listener helps you develop and maintain personal relationships. Here are some ways to listen actively.

1 **Choose the best way to communicate.** Give nonverbal feedback. Make eye contact with the speaker. Nod your head when you agree and use appropriate facial expressions. Give short, but sincere verbal responses such as "yes" or "I see."

2 **Express your thoughts and feelings clearly.** Ask questions to clarify what the speaker has said. Wait until the person has finished before asking questions.

3 **Listen to the other person.** Restate or summarize what you think the speaker has said. Restating shows that you have processed the speaker's message and want to understand.

4 **Make sure you understand each other.** Acknowledge the speaker's feelings. You might say, "I know what you mean." "That's terrific!" Responses like this show acceptance.

5 With a partner, take turns describing your day. When it's your turn to listen, practice the active listening techniques described here.

► It may take some practice to become an effective communicator, but the results can include effective conversations and better friendships.

Here are some ways to respond to a speaker to make sure you understand what he or she is saying.

Clarifying a response Ask the speaker for more information. The more information you have, the more likely you are to understand what that person is trying to say. "What do you mean when you say. . . ?" "Can you give me another example?"

Restating a response Repeat what you think the speaker has said. Sometimes, if a person is speaking too quietly, you literally may not be able to hear him or her. And sometimes, you may simply misunderstand the point the speaker is trying to make. "Do I understand you to say that. . . ?" "What I am hearing you say is. . ."

Summarizing a response Summarize the main idea the speaker has stated. If the speaker has gone off on conversational tangents, you may have trouble understanding what his or her point is. "You're saying that the main point, then, is. . . ."

Affirming a response State your appreciation for what the speaker has said. Showing the person that he or she has helped you understand the conversation will make the person feel good, and good feelings can lead to better conversation. "Thank you for explaining that. . ." "Oh, now I understand what you were saying. . ."

🔷 Cross-Curricular Connections

Science Other animal species use many different forms of communication. Bees have an elaborate system of dancing to communicate to the rest of the hive the location of food sources. Dogs bark, growl, and have forms of nonverbal communication, such as wagging their tails. Male birds sing in order to mark territory. Many animals use pheromones, chemical messengers used for communication between individuals of the same species, to convey messages about mating. Have students choose an animal species and research how the species communicates. They can create a multimedia presentation to share their findings with the class. **L2**

Peer Pressure

The influence that people of similar age or status place on others to behave in a certain way is called **peer pressure.** Peer pressure can be either positive or negative, and it can be exerted consciously or unconsciously. Sometimes all you need is to see that someone in your class has bought the latest athletic shoes, and you feel driven to own the same kind of shoes.

How to Recognize Types of Peer Pressure

Peer pressure can be positive. It's the night before a proficiency test that affects your graduation status. You cannot graduate with your class if you do not pass this test. You are determined to go into the test well rested to succeed. A friend calls and wants to go to a movie. He also has to pass this test to graduate. You manage to resist his pleading and convince him that it would be better for him to get to bed early to be prepared for the test. After all, the movie will still be there on the weekend.

This situation is an example of positive peer pressure. You have influenced your friend to do something that will benefit him. *Positive peer pressure* is influence from peers to behave in a responsible way.

Peer pressure can be negative. Have you ever been stuck in a situation where a classmate pesters you for answers to homework instead of figuring them out for herself? A few times, you actually have given in and let her copy the answers that you worked out. This is an example of negative peer pressure. *Negative peer pressure* is influence from peers to behave in a way that is not responsible. Negative peer pressure involves pressure to risk your health and safety, break laws, show disrespect for yourself and others, disobey your family, and show lack of character.

Wanting the best for others People who are mature, responsible, and caring want the best for others. People who exert negative peer pressure don't have your best interests in mind. They are really thinking only of themselves, even if they aren't aware of it. They want you to support their irresponsible choices, such as drinking alcohol or being sexually active before marriage. Peers who pressure you to make irresponsible decisions want support for their actions. They are not thinking about the negative outcomes you may have to experience.

> **Make the Connection**
>
> **Pressure to be Sexually Active** For more information on recognizing and resisting pressure to be sexually active, see page 170 in Lesson 16.

Ten Negative Peer Pressure Statements

The following are some "lines" you may have heard.

- No one will ever know.
- What's the big deal? It won't kill you.
- I do it all the time and have never been caught or hurt!
- We'll go down together if anything happens.
- Everybody else is doing it.
- You'll look older and more mature.
- Try it! You'll really like it.
- You only live once.
- Don't be such a wimp.
- Don't be a chicken.

LESSON 5 • Using Communication Skills **45**

Health Project

Anonymous Survey Students can conduct an anonymous survey in their school on the topic of peer pressure. They can create a survey that evaluates the impact peer pressure has on teens' behavior. Their questions should be formed in order to create a simple statistical analysis of the results, such as percentages. A question could read, "Have you ever bought something because several other students had it?" or "Have you ever done something that you didn't want to do because others were pressuring you to do it?" Students can divide the work of handing out and collecting surveys amongst themselves. Have students analyze the results of the survey, then use the survey results to start a discussion about peer pressure. **L3**

Class Discussion

Peer Pressure Statements Have students brainstorm responses for each of the ten negative peer pressure statements listed on the previous page. Ask them to give examples of what they could say the next time someone makes one of these statements to them. **L2**

Class Activity

Board Game Have students create a board game about peer pressure. They can make cards with scenarios that describe positive peer pressure and negative peer pressure. Depending on what happens in the cards, players can advance or regress on the board. For example, a card could read, "You are at a party and your friends start drinking. You don't want to drink but they are badgering you to join the 'fun.' You decide one or two drinks won't hurt you. Go back three spaces." Another card could read, "At the end of the night, an acquaintance offers to drive you and your friends home. This person has been drinking alcohol all evening. You decline and call a cab for you and your friends. Move ahead four spaces." Students can be creative with the content of the cards and the title of the game. **L2**

Drunk Driving Approximately 17,000 people are killed each year in alcohol-related vehicle crashes.

Consequences of Giving in to Negative Peer Pressure

Giving in to negative peer pressure may:

Harm health The nicotine in tobacco increases heart rate and blood pressure. If you give in and start smoking, you also increase your risk of heart disease.

Threaten your safety If you give in to pressure to ride in a motor vehicle driven by someone who has been drinking, you increase your risk of being injured or killed in a traffic accident.

Cause you to break laws It is against the law for minors to drink alcoholic beverages. By drinking underage, you risk being in trouble with the police, parents, and guardians.

Cause you to show disrespect for yourself and others If you repeat an unflattering story that you heard about someone because you think it will make you look important in someone else's eyes, you risk offending the person you talked about.

Cause you to disregard the guidelines of your parents and other responsible adults Curfew is a fixed time a person agrees to be at home. If you break curfew, you risk experiencing your parents' or guardians' loss of trust.

Cause you to feel disappointed in yourself What happens when you give in to pressure and do something? You risk long-term regret for not being able to stand up for yourself.

Cause you to feel resentment toward peers If you make a wrong decision under pressure that results in physical injury to yourself, you might resent your peers or feel left out as you deal with your injury.

Harm your self-confidence If you give in to pressure, you risk damaging your self-confidence. You would know that you were not in control of yourself or of the situation.

Cause you to feel guilty and ashamed If you give in to pressure and another person is harmed because of your action, you will feel guilty and ashamed that you were responsible for what happened.

Repairing the Damage

If you become aware that you have done something irresponsible because you have given in to negative peer pressure, use these strategies to face up to the situation.

- Be honest; do not blame others. Take responsibility for any decisions, actions, or judgments that result from giving in.
- Make things right; is restitution needed? Restitution may involve paying for damages, repairing or replacing something that was damaged or taken. Responsible adults can help you decide how to correct any harm you have done.
- Analyze your excuses for giving in. Think about the situation. Were there specific statements made by peers that influenced you to give in? Did some peers influence you more than others?
- Learn from your mistakes. Be prepared to handle similar situations again. Bolster your confidence by being ready for all kinds of pressure statements.
- Ask a parent, guardian, or other responsible adult for help. Find a responsible adult whom you trust and review the situations in which you have given in.

Achieving Health Literacy

Responsible Citizen Have students create a campaign to encourage positive peer pressure. As a class, come up with a memorable slogan for your campaign. Students can work in groups to create multimedia presentations, advertisements, pamphlets, or commercials for the campaign. The campaign can address the benefits of positive peer pressure or the consequences of negative peer pressure. Students can use humor to communicate their message. After students present their part of the campaign in class, display their work in the classroom. Ask the principal of your school if your students can launch the campaign in the school. **L2**

Resistance Skills

Skills that help a person say "no" to an action or to leave a situation that they feel or know is dangerous or illegal are called **resistance skills**. Resistance skills sometimes are called refusal skills and can be used to resist negative peer pressure. How to Use Resistance Skills below is a list of eight suggestions to use to resist negative peer pressure.

How to Use Resistance Skills

1. **Say "no" with self-confidence.** Look directly at the person or people to whom you are speaking. Say "no" clearly.

2. **Give reasons for saying "no."** Refer to the six Guidelines for Making Responsible Decisions on page 61 for reasons for saying "no."
   - "No, I want to promote my health."
   - "No, I want to protect my safety."
   - "No, I want to follow laws."
   - "No, I want to show respect for myself and others."
   - "No, I want to follow the guidelines of my parents and other responsible adults."
   - "No, I want to demonstrate good character."

3. **Repeat your "no" response several times.** You strengthen your "no" response every time you repeat it. This makes your response more convincing, especially to yourself.

4. **Use nonverbal behavior to match verbal behavior.** Nonverbal behavior is the use of actions to express emotions and thoughts. Shaking your head "no" is an example of nonverbal behavior.

5. **Avoid situations in which there will be pressure to make wrong decisions.** Think ahead. Avoid situations that might be tempting. For example, do not spend time at a peer's house when his or her parents or guardians are not home.

6. **Avoid people who make wrong decisions.** Remember that your reputation is the impression others have of you. Choose to be with people who have a reputation for making responsible decisions. Protect your good reputation.

7. **Resist pressure to engage in illegal behavior.** You have a responsibility to protect yourself and others and to obey the laws in your community.

8. **Influence others to make responsible decisions.** Physically remove yourself when a situation poses immediate risk or danger. If there is no immediate risk, try to turn a negative situation into a positive situation. Be a positive role model.

Reading Review

1. What is positive peer pressure?
2. List five actions to take if you give in to negative peer pressure.
3. What are eight ways to resist pressure?

Resistance Skills

NHES Assessment/SCASS

Performance Event Have students write in their health journals about a time when they used resistance skills to avoid risk behaviors. Have them compare this to a time when they did not use resistance skills, thereby taking an unnecessary risk. **L2**

Class Discussion

Resistance Skills Ask your students which of the tactics in the resistance skills model may be the most difficult to carry out in a real-life situation. Have them explain why they feel this way and discuss what they could do to improve their skills in this area. *Saying no with confidence and assertiveness may be difficult for some students who are shy or lacking in self-confidence. A solution could be to practice saying no at home in front of a mirror. Other students may have difficulty removing themselves from a situation if they do not have a car or other mode of transportation. A solution could be to carry the number for a taxi company or make arrangements with a parent or guardian to be able to call for a ride without fear of punishment.* **L2**

Reading Review

1. *influence from peers to behave in a responsible way*
2. *Answers should reflect the ideas in Repairing the Damage on page 46.*
3. *Answers should reflect the ideas in How to Use Resistance Skills on this page.*

Family Involvement

Practice Resistance Skills Practicing resistance skills is an important part of being able to use them effectively in a real social situation. Being able to say "no" with confidence and easily state reasons or alternative activities will help a student feel more comfortable using resistance skills. Give students a list of several scenarios in which they would need to use resistance skills, such as someone offering them a cigarette or trying to get them to skip class. Suggest that students practice their resistance skills by role-playing the scenarios with a parent or guardian. **L2**

National Health Education Standards

Pages 46–47: 1.5, 2.1, 2.3, 5.1, 5.4, 7.2, 8.1

Self-Confidence and Assertiveness

Class Activity

Role-Playing Ask students to role-play a situation in which conflict occurs. Have the students play the scene three different ways: with assertive behavior, with passive behavior, and with aggressive behavior. Ask the students to observe and think about how these different behaviors affect the appearance of the person displaying the behavior as well as others in the situation. **L2**

Using the Table

Being Self-Confident and Assertive Have students think of a recent situation in which they did not have enough self-confidence. Have them replay the situation in their minds after thinking about and applying the steps in the table. Ask students if they feel differently about the situation after visualizing it this way. Encourage them to prepare for a similar situation in the future by using this exercise. **L2**

Quick Demo

Becoming Self-Confident Demonstrate the correct use of the table by using it in a hypothetical situation in front of the class. For example: Students are trying to start a rumor that you know is untrue about another student. Encourage the class to provide input as you reason through the six questions in step one and follow steps two and three in order to make the best decision about what action to take.

Self-Confidence and Assertiveness

How do you feel when you tell others about a decision you have made? Do you feel confident, or do you begin to downplay your ideas? *Self-confidence* is belief in oneself. When you are self-confident, you believe in your ideas, feelings, and decisions.

How Can You Be Self-Confident and Assertive?

When your behavior is self-confident and assertive, you show others that you are in control of yourself. The honest expression of ideas, feelings, and decisions without worrying about what others think or without feeling threatened by the reactions of others is *assertive behavior.* You clearly state your feelings or decisions and do not back down.

Passive behavior The holding back of ideas, feelings, and decisions is called *passive behavior.* People with passive behavior do not stand up for themselves. They make excuses for their behavior. They might look away or laugh when sharing feelings or making decisions. They lack self-confidence.

Aggressive behavior The use of words or actions that are disrespectful toward others is called *aggressive behavior.* People with aggressive behavior might interrupt others or monopolize a conversation. They might call others cruel names or make loud, sarcastic remarks. They threaten others because they lack self-confidence.

TABLE 5.1 Steps to Be Self-Confident and Assertive

Steps	Things to Consider
Step 1: Always use the six questions in the Responsible Decision-Making Model.	Will this decision promote health, protect safety, follow laws, show respect for myself and others, follow parental guidelines, and demonstrate good character? A positive response to each question helps guarantee that you will make a responsible decision and become more assertive and more confident in your decisions.
Step 2: Picture a shield of protection in front of you.	Whenever someone pressures you to make wrong decisions, picture yourself as being protected. If peers make negative pressure statements, visualize the statements as bouncing off the shield.
Step 3: When you doubt yourself, talk with a parent, guardian, or other responsible adult.	Reinforce that you have support you can rely upon. Teens who are self-confident and assertive appreciate and rely on parents or guardians who can give them a morale boost and help them resist negative peer pressure.

Differentiated Instruction

Hearing Impairment Having a person who is hearing-impaired in your classroom is a unique opportunity to learn more about self-confidence. Ask this student to demonstrate the body language that accompanies self-confident and assertive behavior. Have the student contrast this behavior by demonstrating the body language the goes along with passive behavior. Finally, ask the student to display the body language that defines aggressive behavior. Hearing students will benefit from the hearing-impaired student's insight, and the hearing-impaired student will gain self-confidence by being able to help his or her classmates better understand the content of this lesson. **L2**

Conflicts

A disagreement between two or more people or between two or more choices is a *conflict*. Conflicts arise in the home, at school, in the workplace, and at sports and entertainment events. An individual person can have conflict within him or herself. In short, the potential for conflict is wherever there are people. The reasons for conflicts are about as many as there are people in the world. People have strong preferences or their emotions can run high on a particular topic. Some conflicts can erupt into violence, which is harmful. Because of this potential, there is great need for ways to resolve conflict. There are four types of conflict and three conflict response styles.

What to Know About Types of Conflict

Intrapersonal conflict Any conflict that occurs within a person is an intrapersonal conflict. For example, you may say to yourself, "I would like to watch television after dinner." You also may think, "I should study for the test I have tomorrow." You are involved in intrapersonal conflict.

Interpersonal conflict Any conflict that occurs between two or more people is an interpersonal conflict. You and your sister alternate doing the dinner dishes, but she was sick yesterday so you did the dishes two days in a row. You think she should do the dishes for the next two days, but she disagrees. You and your sister are involved in interpersonal conflict.

Intragroup conflict An intragroup conflict is a difference between people belonging to the same group. Suppose you and several friends in the Debate Club have had a prank played on you by other members of the club. Suppose a rival group of teens has made your group of friends look foolish. Some of your friends want to get even by "egging" a car belonging to one of the other teens. You and a friend are against this decision. You and your friend are involved in an intragroup conflict because you disagree with members of your own group.

Intergroup conflict An intergroup conflict is a disagreement between two or more groups of people. The conflict may involve different neighborhoods, schools, gangs, racial groups, religious groups, or nations. For example, you may be on an athletic team that is playing another school. A player on your school's team bumps into a player on the other team. The team members of the other school believe the action was intended to harm their team member. Players from your school and players from the other school are involved in an intergroup conflict.

What Is Your Conflict Response Style?

Make the Connection

Family Relationships For more on conflict resolution in families, see page 137 in Lesson 13.

Conflict response style What is your reaction at the first sign of a disagreement? Do you feel scared? Defensive? Is your first thought to try to make everyone feel better? Maybe your first reaction is to run for cover. Some reactions are probably more helpful than others. A *conflict response style* is a pattern of behavior a person uses in a conflict situation. The person may use one or a combination of the following conflict response styles.

Conflict avoidance In this conflict response style, a person chooses to avoid disagreements. If you use this style, you avoid telling others that you disagree with them. You may be so concerned that others will not like you if you disagree with them that you are unwilling to challenge their behavior, even when you don't like what they are doing. Rather than disagree with someone, you sit back and allow others to solve problems in a manner of their choosing. This is also an example of passive behavior.

Conflict is a natural part of life. Learning conflict-resolution skills will help you settle disagreements in a healthful, responsible manner. ▼

Conflict confrontation Using conflict confrontation, a person attempts to settle a disagreement in a hostile, defiant, and aggressive way. If you use conflict confrontation, you like to be aggressive and confront others. As a confronter, you want to win or be right. You view conflict as a win-lose proposition. You believe your side of the story is the only one worth considering.

Conflict resolution Conflict resolution is a response style in which a person uses conflict-resolution skills to resolve a problem. *Conflict-resolution skills* are steps that can be taken to settle a disagreement in a responsible way. If you use these skills, you remain rational and in control when you have disagreements with others. You listen to the other person's side of the story. You see the potential for a win-win solution in situations and relationships in which there is conflict. Conflict resolution is the healthful way to resolve problems.

Your conflict response style may be different in different situations. When there is a conflict between you and your sister or brother, you may act differently than if you had a conflict with a stranger or a close friend. On the other hand, you may feel like you need to agree with an adult even if you don't because the adult is in an authority position.

If you use conflict-resolution skills and show proper respect, you can work through conflict with people of any age.

Conflict-Resolution Skills

A guiding principle of conflict resolution is the concept of win-win. When all of the people in a conflict feel that they have won, it is a win-win situation. It is important to realize that there does not have to be a loser in every conflict.

How to Use Conflict-Resolution Skills

Conflict-resolution skills can be used to settle a disagreement in a responsible way. The list below identifies steps that can be used to resolve conflict in a responsible way.

1. Remain calm. Try to increase your patience and lower your personal "boiling point." This way, both parties are calm and not in danger of doing harm to themselves or others.

2. Set a positive tone. Avoid placing blame, put-downs, and threats; be sincere; and reserve judgment. Demonstrate that you want to be fair and find a mutually acceptable solution.

3. Define the conflict. Each person should describe the conflict in writing. Make it short and to the point. The focus then becomes describing the conflict, not describing the people involved in the conflict.

4. Take responsibility for personal actions. Admit what part you have played. Apologize if your actions were questionable or wrong. This step shows each person takes responsibility for his or her part of the conflict.

5. Listen to the needs and feelings of others. Listening allows the other person to share his or her feelings. Do not interrupt. Use I-messages. Listening shows that you want to resolve conflict. It shows respect for the other person.

6. List and evaluate possible solutions. Identify as many solutions as possible for the conflict. Discuss positive and negative consequences of each possible solution. This enables the parties to select the solution that is healthful, safe, legal, in accordance with family guidelines and good character, and nonviolent.

7. Agree on a solution. Select a solution. State what each party will do. Make a written agreement, if necessary. Restating and summarizing an agreement makes public what each person will do to honor the agreement.

👫 Healthy People 2010

Objective 15-38 *Reduce physical fighting among adolescents.*

According to the Healthy People 2010 study, 36 percent of adolescents in grades 9–12 engaged in physical fighting the previous year. Discuss with students how using conflict resolution can reduce physical fighting between adolescents. Let them know that their demeanor can help diffuse a situation and prevent a fight. Encourage them to use conflict resolution skills to reduce their frustration when conflicts arise.

Conflict-Resolution Skills

Explain the Concept

Successful Resolution Using a hypothetical situation, illustrate the steps of conflict resolution, making sure the solution satisfies both sides and is responsible. Ask students the following questions: What did each party gain from the solution? Did they have to compromise in order to reach a solution? Do you find the solution fair? Do you think it is realistic?

Class Discussion

Defining a Conflict Give students an example of a conflict between two people or groups. Ask half the class to write down the point of view of one side; have the other half of the class address the other side of the conflict. When they are finished writing, read several versions of the conflict from each side. Have the class discuss how a conflict can be seen differently, even when both sides feel they are being honest. L2

National Health Education Standards
Pages 50–51: 1.5, 4.3, 8.1

Just the FACTS: CONFLICTS

5-Minute Check

Page 66, **Unit 1 Fast File Resources**

1. What should you do if you doubt yourself in a situation where you are not self-confident? *Talk with a parent, guardian, or other responsible adult to give you support and a morale boost.*

2. Why might constantly exhibiting passive behavior lead to unnecessary risks? *Passive behavior prevents someone from standing up for himself or herself. As a result, he or she may take an unnecessary risk.*

3. What can you visualize as part of the steps for becoming self-confident and assertive to make you feel protected? *Visualize a shield of protection around you that wards off negative statements.*

4. You and a friend disagree about what movie to see. What kind of conflict is this? *interpersonal*

5. Why is it important to have good conflict-resolution skills? *You can remain rational and in control when you have disagreements with others.*

66Do only wimps try to settle disagreements peacefully?99

66Do real friends have conflicts?99

66During a conflict, shouldn't a real friend know how the other person feels?99

the FACTS Some people have only one way to settle disagreements—with violence or threats of violence. People who are assertive have a range of tools available to them when they become involved in a disagreement. They have enough self-control to talk things out and enough respect to listen to the other person's point of view. They are mature enough to realize that they will not get their way all the time.

the FACTS Conflict is a part of most relationships. Two or more people cannot spend time together without having different opinions and ideas from time to time. If there is no conflict in a relationship, one person might be dominating the other, or one person might be playing the role of martyr, constantly giving in to please the other person. Perhaps both people are denying there is any conflict. These are not healthful relationships. Real friends welcome the chance to explore different ideas, learn more about each other and themselves, and find resolutions that help them both feel good about the relationship.

the FACTS Reading minds is not a requirement for friendship or for family members. Sometimes during a conflict, we aren't sure how we ourselves feel, and we know even less about how the other person feels. Resolving a conflict in a peaceful, satisfying way requires everyone involved to express his or her feelings, needs, and expectations. Assuming that others know how we feel or what we want is unrealistic. Only when we take responsibility for telling others what we would like to happen in order to resolve a conflict can we begin to find a resolution.

What to Do After You Have Reached a Responsible Solution

Even if you have taken great care to resolve a conflict responsibly, it may still take time for people to feel comfortable. Your opinions going into the conflict were very strong, and the other person's opinions were probably just as strong. Agreeing to settle a conflict responsibly does not mean your personal opinions have disappeared. But, by the time you have reached a solution you should have developed an understanding of the other person's opinions. How can you make sure that you and the other person will keep the agreement that you have made?

Be respectful. Do not talk about the other individual(s) with whom you have been in conflict. Do not blame and shame others or put them on the defensive. Use I-messages and take responsibility for your feelings.

Keep your word and follow the agreement that you made. Share any difficulties you might expect to have in keeping the agreement. Be honest about the ways in which you may need help holding up your portion of the agreement. Always be sincere in your intention to keep your word. State honestly where you will need help and know whom you can trust if you need help keeping your part of the agreement.

Ask for assistance if the agreement seems to be falling apart. Admit that sometimes a conflict is hard to resolve and needs outside help to be kept. Be willing to agree on mediation—one or more individuals not involved in the conflict who can help.

52 UNIT 1 • Health Skills

 Community Involvement

Mediation Resources Have students investigate the various types of mediation services available in their community. Several types of mediation should be available from such organizations as their school, local government, etc. Often, organizations and local governments sponsor an ombudsman or community agency to try to resolve conflicts so that legal action is not necessary. Using the information that students have gathered, have students create a master list of resources for mediation. **L2**

Mediation

In most instances, two people can resolve their differences using the steps on page 51. But there are instances when people have a difficult time solving their differences and mediation has to be used. *Mediation* is a process in which an outside person, or *mediator,* helps people in conflict reach a solution.

What to Know About Mediation

Agree upon a mediator. The purpose of a mediator is to help the people involved find a responsible solution. A mediator will not ask you to compromise your values or the guidelines of your parents or guardians. The mediator should not express an opinion. The only bias the mediator should have is for the solution to be healthful, safe, legal, respectful of all people involved, and nonviolent.

Set ground rules. Appropriate ground rules include: tell the truth; commit to resolve the conflict; avoid blaming; put-downs, threats, sneering, or rolling your eyes, pushing, and hitting; reserve judgment; and listen without interruption.

Define the conflict. The people involved begin by describing the conflict. They need to agree about what has taken place and about what the conflict is really about.

Identify solutions to the conflict. The people involved brainstorm ways to resolve the conflict. The mediator also can make suggestions.

Evaluate suggested solutions. Predict the possible outcome of the solutions by using the Guidelines for Making Responsible Decisions. Will the solution result in actions that are healthful, safe, legal, respectful, in accordance with family guidelines and good character, and nonviolent?

Negotiate a solution. The mediator helps the people involved negotiate a solution. The mediator may suggest making trade-offs so all people involved feel they are in a win-win situation. Participants can meet with the mediator either together or separately.

Write and sign an agreement. The people involved should enter into the agreement in an entirely voluntary manner. After they agree to do so, an agreement should be written. Those involved should read the agreement, ask questions, then sign and date it.

Schedule a follow-up meeting. The mediator can arrange a follow-up meeting to renew the agreement.

Did You Know?

Judging A judge in a courtroom is a mediator. He or she can mediate a problem between two people or between the government and a citizen.

Reading Review

1. What is self-confidence?
2. Name four types of conflict.
3. How can you solve a conflict responsibly?
4. What does a mediator do?

Family Involvement

House Rules Using a computer or by hand, students can create a formal-looking copy of the guidelines of mediation listed on this page to discuss with their families. Afterward, students should find an article in a newspaper or magazine that contains a conflict, or you could provide several conflict scenarios for students. The family should pretend that it needs to be the mediator for this conflict, and, together, the family should set ground rules, define the conflict, and identify, evaluate, and negotiate solutions using the information found in the article. The student should take notes on each step of the mediation process and write a one-page paper about the conflict and why his or her family members chose the solution they did. **L2**

Mediation

Explain the Concept

Mediator Explain to students that a mediator is an individual who is accepted and respected by all parties in a disagreement. The mediator should not be involved in the conflict at hand and should not benefit by any possible resolutions.

Class Discussion

Ground Rules Discuss as a class why ground rules are important. Ask students how setting common ground rules makes conflict resolution possible. As a class, identify or brainstorm some ground rules involving both positive actions and negative actions, explaining the importance of each rule. **L2**

Reading Review

1. *belief in oneself*
2. *intrapersonal, interpersonal, intragroup, intergroup*
3. *use conflict-resolution skills*
4. *helps people in conflict reach a solution*

NHES Assessment/SCASS

Selected Response If you were involved in a conflict with a friend, which of these people would make the best mediator?
A. another friend
B. your parent or guardian
C. *school guidance counselor*
D. a sibling

National Health Education Standards
Pages 52–53: 4.3, 4.4

53

Prejudicial Behavior

Extension

Stereotypes Up Close Have students think about themselves and the stereotypes that people who don't know them might attach to them. Have them make a two-column list and write stereotypical observations about themselves in one column. In the other column, list accurate traits about themselves. **L2**

3 Assess

Vocabulary Practice
Page 58, **Unit 1 Fast File Resources**

Prejudicial Behavior

To distinguish between things or people by noticing or emphasizing differences between them is to **discriminate**. An adverse judgment formed without looking at the facts is **prejudice**. Prejudice can be characterized by suspicion, intolerance, or irrational hatred directed at an individual or group of people.

How to Avoid Prejudicial Behavior

Show respect for all people. When you show respect for others, you increase the likelihood that they will be at their best and respect you. Respect increases the likelihood that people will be able to live together, be productive, and behave in nonviolent ways.

Challenge stereotypes. A prejudiced attitude that assigns a specific quality or characteristic to all people who belong to a particular group is a **stereotype.** Stereotypes imply that an individual is the same as every other member in a group, which is unfair. People who belong to a specific racial, religious, ethnic, or gender group have their race, religion, ethnicity, or gender in common. However, each person in each of these groups is different from each other in any number of ways.

Create synergy through diversity. A positive outcome that occurs when people cooperate is **synergy.** Diversity is the quality of being different or varied. When there is synergy, people with different backgrounds, talents, and skills produce better and more creative solutions.

Show empathy for all people. The ability to share in another person's emotions or feelings is **empathy.** When you have empathy, you understand what a person is feeling and can express that understanding with words or actions.

Avoid prejudicial comments. Words can cause emotional wounds that are more difficult to heal than physical wounds. Always think before you speak. Avoid making jokes or snide remarks about other people. Avoid laughing or affirming others when they make jokes or snide remarks about other people.

Learn about people who are different from you. Being informed prevents adverse judgments. Learn the talents of others. Study a foreign language, read about other races and cultures, and reach out to those who are different from you.

54   **UNIT 1** • Health Skills

⚖ Sensitive Issues

Avoiding Prejudice In addition to having stereotypes attributed to religion, ethnicity, gender, and disability, students have to deal with other stereotypes, such as the assumptions that accompany athletic ability or intellect. When discussing stereotypes and prejudice in class, care needs to be taken to avoid asking students for personal experiences with any type of prejudice. Avoid listing actual stereotypes attributed to certain groups. Consider explaining the concept of prejudice by using a hypothetical situation in which you create stereotypes based on a person's eye color.

National Health Education Standards

Pages 54–55: 4.1, 4.4, 5.4, 8.1

active listening
assertive behavior
communication skills
conflict-resolution
   skills
I-message
mediation
nonverbal
   communication
peer pressure
prejudice
resistance skills
stereotype
you-message

Key Terms Review

Complete these fill-in-the-blank statements with the lesson Key Terms on the left. Do not write in this book.

1. _____ is a way of responding to show that a person hears and understands.

2. _____ are skills that help a person say "no" to an action or leave a situation.

3. _____ is influence that people place on others to behave in a certain way.

4. _____ is expressing your ideas and feelings without feeling threatened.

5. _____ are skills that help a person share thoughts and information with others.

6. _____ is a message that blames or that shames someone.

7. _____ contains a specific behavior, the effect it had, and the emotions that resulted.

8. _____ is an adverse judgment formed without looking at the facts.

9. _____ are steps that can be taken to settle a disagreement in a responsible way.

10. _____ is a process in which an outside person helps people reach a solution.

Recalling the Facts

11. What are four ways to demonstrate active listening?

12. What steps can you take to resist pressure to do something wrong?

13. List nine consequences of giving in to negative peer pressure.

14. What can you do if you have given in to negative peer pressure?

15. What steps help you settle conflict without fighting?

16. Select five statements that peers might use to get you to make a wrong choice and write a statement to counter each one.

17. How can teens demonstrate empathy toward other people?

18. What are eight steps in mediation?

Critical Thinking

19. How does active listening show respect for the person who is speaking?

20. Why is win-win a healthful goal for both individuals in a conflict?

21. How can seeing a person leave a risky situation influence others?

22. How can assertive behavior, rather than passive or aggressive behavior, help teens make responsible decisions?

Real-Life Applications

23. Write an I-message to express feelings.

24. Explain four benefits to using mediation for a conflict between you and a sibling over whose turn it is to do a chore.

25. What steps can you take to influence others to avoid prejudicial behavior?

26. Why is it important to avoid people who seem to always make wrong decisions?

Activities

Responsible Decision Making

27. **Write a Response** One of your classmates has just relocated from a different country. He has an accent when he speaks, so some students make fun of him. They want you to make a prank call to his house. What will your response be? Use the Responsible Decision-Making Model on page 61 for help.

Sharpen Your Life Skills

28. **Use Resistance Skills** Some of your classmates have stolen the master key to your school. They are going to sneak in and "trash" the principal's office over the weekend. They want you to join them. On a sheet of paper, write resistance skills that you might use to help you resist this peer pressure.

Visit **www.glencoe.com** for more *Health & Wellness* quizzes.

Key Terms Review

1. Active listening
2. Resistance skills
3. Peer pressure
4. Assertive behavior
5. Communication skills
6. You-message
7. I-message
8. Prejudice
9. Conflict-resolution skills
10. Mediation

Recalling the Facts

11. clarifying, restating, summarizing, and affirming what was said
12. Answers should reflect How to Use Resistance Skills on page 47.
13. Answers should reflect Consequences of Giving In to Negative Peer Pressure on page 46.
14. be honest, make things right, analyze excuses for giving in, learn from mistakes, ask a parent or guardian for help.
15. Answers should reflect How to Use Conflict-Resolution Skills on page 51.
16. Answers can include statements from page 45.
17. with words and actions
18. Answers should reflect What to Know About Mediation on page 53.

Critical Thinking

19. It shows you are interested and want to understand what the speaker is saying.
20. Both sides of the conflict walk away with something, so there is less resentment than if the result was win-lose.
21. It reinforces the idea that you don't have to stay in an uncomfortable or unsafe situation.
22. Being assertive means making decisions for yourself and not allowing others to influence your opinions.

Real-Life Applications

23. Answers should be an I-message.

---

24. Answers can include an outside person will help you with your decision; you will negotiate an agreement together; you will not fight; the solution becomes a win-win situation.

25. Answers should list steps from How to Avoid Prejudicial Behavior on page 54.

26. You protect your reputation and avoid situations in which you might be tempted to make a wrong decision.

Activities

Responsible Decision Making

27. Answers should reflect the Responsible Decision-Making Model on page 61.

Sharpen Your Life Skills

28. Answers should include steps from How to Use Resistance Skills on page 47.

LESSON 6

Setting Health Goals and Making Responsible Decisions

 Out of Time?

If time does not permit an in-depth study of this topic, use the following activities in this Teacher Wraparound Edition:

- Class Discussion, p. 58
- Healthy People 2010, p. 58
- Class Activity, p. 60
- Using the Table, p. 62

1 Focus

LIFE SKILLS **Setting Health Goals** Have students respond to the first Life Skill for this lesson by reviewing the leading health indicators on page 59 and writing in their health journals those goals they may wish to set for themselves. L2

Write ABOUT IT!

Evaluating Sources Have students research foods that provide more nutrition than potato chips or cookies as an after-school snack. For English language learners, provide a list of foods for them to categorize as nutritious or non-nutritious. Students can compare the information from processed snack food labels with information about less processed food, such as fruits and vegetables. Use the results of their comparisons to lead a class discussion on changing health habits. L2 ELL

LESSON 6

What You'll Learn

1. Discuss steps you can use to set and reach a health goal. *(p. 57)*
2. Discuss the two main goals of Healthy People 2010. *(p. 58)*
3. List the ten leading health indicators that will be used to measure the health of the nation over the next ten years. *(p. 59)*
4. Describe three decision-making styles. *(p. 60)*
5. Outline the six steps in The Responsible Decision-Making Model. *(p. 61)*
6. Explain four steps to take if you make a wrong decision. *(p. 62)*

Why It's Important

You will have respect for yourself and others will have respect for you when you achieve health goals and form the habit of making responsible decisions.

Key Terms

- health goal
- Healthy People 2010
- life expectancy
- leading health indicators
- inactive decision-making style
- reactive decision-making style
- proactive decision-making style
- Responsible Decision-Making Model
- wrong decision
- restitution

56 UNIT 1 • Health Skills

Setting Health Goals and Making Responsible Decisions

LIFE SKILL
- I will set health goals.
- I will make responsible decisions.

A desired achievement toward which a person works is a ***goal***. A choice that a person makes is a ***decision***. In this lesson, you will learn steps to take to make a healthful behavior into a habit.

Write ABOUT IT!

Writing About Changing a Habit Suppose that every day after school, you eat five or six cookies or a bag of potato chips. You know these foods are not nutritious, but this is a habit you've had since fifth grade. How should you go about changing this health habit? After you read the information about health goals on page 57, write in your health journal the steps you think you should take to change this habit.

National Health Education Standards—Guide for Lesson 6		
5.4	Generate alternatives to health-related issues or problems.	pp. 57, 60
6.2	Develop a plan to attain a personal health goal that addresses strengths, needs, and risks.	pp. 56, 57, 59, 63

Health Goals

A healthful behavior a person works to achieve and maintain is a *health goal*. A healthful behavior a person plans to achieve in the near future is a *short-term health goal*. A healthful behavior a person plans to achieve after a period of time is a *long-term health goal*. Setting and achieving health goals helps you form healthful habits for a lifetime.

How to Set Health Goals

1. Write your health goal. Write your health goal in a short sentence beginning with "I will." Review pages 28–31 in this book for a list of possible health goals. A long-term goal may take a month, a year, or a lifetime to accomplish. Long-term goals often can be broken down into smaller, short-term goals, which are easier to accomplish. For example, suppose your long-term health goal is "I will lose ten pounds." A short-term health goal might be "I will lose two pounds each week."

2. Make an action plan to meet your health goal. An action plan is a detailed description of the steps you will take to reach a goal. Some people use a health behavior contract for their action plan. Refer to page 32 in this book for how to make a health behavior contract. Have someone you trust review it for you to see if it is realistic.

3. Identify obstacles to your plan. Brainstorm obstacles that might interfere with carrying out your plan. Prioritize them from most to least important and think of ways to work with the most important ones.

4. Set up a timeline to accomplish your health goal. Set a date for each point along your action plan. When does your action plan begin? What is the date you expect to achieve your health goal? Have you considered all other obligations? Is your timeline realistic?

5. Keep a chart or diary in which you record progress toward your health goal. Keep track of progress. Writing down a goal helps you to stick to your plan to accomplish it.

6. Build a support system. Make a list of people who will support you or be available for advice as you work toward your health goal. Join a support group or associate with others who are working toward the same health goal. Stay away from people who might sabotage your health goal.

7. Revise your action plan or timeline, if necessary. Do not give up on a health goal. There are too many benefits that will come from reaching it. Give yourself more time or ask for the help of others if you can't make an action plan that works for you.

8. Reward yourself when you reach your health goal. Once you've succeeded in reaching your health goal, do something nice for yourself. Just make certain your reward fits with your new healthful lifestyle.

> **Make the Connection**
>
> **Health Behavior Contract** For more information about making a health behavior contract, see page 32 in Lesson 3.

Reading Review

1. What is a long-term health goal?
2. Rather than give up on a health plan, what should you do?

Lesson Resource Manager

- **Unit 1 Fast File Resources**
  Reading Strategy, p. 71
  Vocabulary Practice, p. 72
  Transparency Master and Worksheet, p. 73
  Real-Life Health, p. 75
  Real-Life Health, p. 77
  5-Minute Check, p. 79
  Lesson 6 Quiz, p. 80
- **Unit 1 Transparency**
- **Lesson 6 Transparency**

- **Reading Essentials**
- **Technology**
  TeacherWorks™ CD-ROM
  StudentWorks™ CD-ROM
  Reading Essentials CD-ROM
  Exam*View*® Assessment Suite
  Vocabulary Puzzlemaker

Health Goals

2 Teach

Quick Demo

Long-Term versus Short-Term Goals Provide students with a list of health goals either on the chalkboard or on an overhead transparency. Goals could include: I will eat five servings of fruit and vegetables each day; I will get a yearly health physical to maintain good health; and I will watch less television each evening. Students should then determine which goals are long-term and which are short-term. **L2**

Reading Review

1. *a healthful behavior a person plans to achieve after a period of time*
2. *revise your action plan or timeline or ask for others' help*

INTERACTIVE CHALKBOARD with Image Bank

PowerPoint® Presentations

This CD-ROM is an editable Microsoft® PowerPoint® presentation that includes:
- Lesson presentations
- Lesson checks
- Interactive graphics
- 5-Minute Checks
- Image Bank
- All transparencies

Discussion Use the Seed Discussions Strategy on page 17T to initiate discussion on setting goals and making responsible decisions.

> **National Health Education Standards**
> Pages 56–57: 5.4, 6.2

Healthy People 2010

During the 1990s, groups of scientists produced a set of national health goals and detailed plans to achieve them by the year 2010. The result, *Healthy People 2010,* outlines goals for disease prevention and includes twenty-eight health-promoting objectives for the nation to achieve by 2010. It also describes ten leading health indicators that are currently the major health concerns for the United States.

The Goals of Healthy People 2010

There are two main goals for Healthy People 2010.

Did You Know?

Longevity Japan ranks first in life expectancy for both men and women.

Goal 1: To increase quality and years of healthy life

Life expectancy The average number of years that people are expected to live is called *life expectancy.* At the beginning of the twentieth century, life expectancy at birth was 47.3 years. One hundred years later, the average life expectancy is nearly 77 years. Life expectancy continues to increase. People who are 65 years old today can expect to live an average of 18 more years, for a total of 83.

Although life expectancy has increased, it is not what it could be in the United States. At least 18 countries with populations of one million or more have life expectancies greater than the United States.

Quality of life Health-related quality of life includes physical and mental well-being and the ways people respond to their environment. Quality of life is more difficult to measure than life expectancy. It might be measured by having people describe their lives by rating their overall life as poor, fair, good, very good, or excellent.

A Healthy People 2010 report found that too many people reported experiencing days of less than optimal health. For many people in this nation, health-related quality of life could be better. Healthy People 2010 hopes to see an increase in life expectancy and improvement in the quality of life by helping people become more knowledgeable and more motivated about the choices they can make to improve their health.

Goal 2: To eliminate health disparities in the population

Health disparities There are measurable differences, or disparities, in opportunities for optimal health in the United States. Some factors that were found to create health disparities are gender, race and ethnicity, education and income level, disability status, sexual orientation, and whether a person lives in a rural or urban area. For instance, individuals with less education are less likely to be healthy than people with more education. Injury rates are 40 percent higher for people living in communities with fewer than 2500 residents than for people living in urban areas. Healthy People 2010 promotes reducing such disparities in health by helping people access valid health information and care.

Healthy People 2010

Objective 22-7 *Increase the proportion of adolescents who engage in vigorous physical activity that promotes cardiorespiratory fitness three or more days per week for 20 or more minutes per occasion.*

Heart disease is the number one cause of death in America; physical activity has been shown to decrease one's risk of cardiovascular disease. The American Heart Association recommends all children participate in at least 30 minutes of moderately intense physical activity per day. Have students, as a class, list ways they can exercise more. Each student should then choose ways to become more physically active and keep a log of the physical activities they perform daily. **L2**

Activity: Using Life Skills

Using Goal-Setting and Decision-Making Skills: Setting a Health Goal

Setting goals can help you focus your energies and motivate you to take action. Be realistic about your goals and the time it will take to reach them. The activity below will give you practice in setting goals that are relevant and reachable.

1 **Write your health goal.** Think of a short-term goal that you would like to achieve within the next month. Make the goal one that will improve your physical or emotional health.

2 **Make an action plan to meet your health goal.** Write down your goal. Be realistic and specific. State your goal in a positive way. Include a deadline. Stating your goal clearly also gives you a way to measure your progress toward your goal.

3 **Identify obstacles to your plan.** Post your goal statement in a place where you will see it—the refrigerator, bathroom mirror, or on a notebook. Seeing a goal helps to reinforce it and keep you on track.

4 **Set up a timeline to accomplish your health goal** and keep a chart or diary in which you can record progress toward your goal. Measure progress regularly. Keep a daily written record.

5 **Build a support system.** When you reach your goal, tell someone. Be proud of yourself. After all, you have just improved your health.

6 **Revise your action plan or timeline, if necessary, and reward yourself when you reach your health goal.** What do you do if you fall short of your goal? Revise it. Maybe a month is too long of a time for you. How about setting a goal of one week? When you accomplish this revised goal, then try two weeks.

▲ Choices that you make every day may seem trivial, but they add up to important effects on your health status.

The Nation's Top Ten Health Concerns

Scientists will know if the nation's health has improved from 2000 to 2010 by studying the *leading health indicators,* the ten national health concerns that will be evaluated during this period. What changes can you make in your health behavior that would improve the nation's health?

Ten Leading Health Indicators

Physical activity Increase the number of adolescents who engage in vigorous physical activity.

Overweight and obesity Reduce the number of overweight or obese children and adolescents.

Tobacco use Reduce cigarette smoking in adolescents.

Substance abuse Increase the proportion of adolescents not using alcohol or illicit drugs.

Responsible sexual behavior Increase the number of adolescents who abstain from sexual intercourse.

Mental health Increase the proportion of adults diagnosed with depression who receive treatment.

Injury and violence Reduce homicides and motor vehicle deaths.

Environmental quality Reduce non-smokers exposed to tobacco smoke.

Immunization Increase the proportion of young children who receive all recommended vaccines for at least five years.

Access to health care Increase the proportion of people with health insurance coverage.

Using Life Skills

Using Goal-Setting and Decision-Making Skills Have students set a health goal and write it in their health journals, starting with "I will." Next, students should create an action plan and timeline to assist them in meeting their goal. They should track their progress in their health journals daily. If, after one or two weeks, they have not made progress, they can consider revising their timelines to help meet their health goal. **L1**

Class Activity

Health Indicators Divide the class into five or more groups. Assign each group one of the health indicators listed. Students should then determine what the current trend is for their health indicator as well as what is being done by the government and organizations such as the American Heart Association to meet the Healthy People 2010 objectives for the goal. Each group should compile their research into a short multimedia report to present to the rest of the class. **L2**

Extension

Health Indicators Have students choose one of the leading health indicators to research. Students should look at a cross-curricular connection between their chosen goal and a field of study, such as art, history, science, social studies, or math. For example, students may research the science behind immunizations or the history behind tobacco in the United States. Have students present the results of their research to the class or create a visual presentation that can be displayed in the school. **L3**

⚖ Legal Issues

Tobacco Sales In 1992 Congress passed the Synar Amendment to the Alcohol, Drug Abuse, and Mental Health Administration (ADAMHA) Reorganization Act that requires states to create restrictions on tobacco sales to minors. Within this amendment, referred to as the Synar law, states must also enforce the restrictions they create. Failure of states to enforce these restrictions, if discovered via unannounced inspections, could result in states losing federal grant funding. The amendment has proven effective. In 1997, the national average of retailers selling tobacco to minors was 40 percent; in 2001, the average violation rate was 17.4 percent, with nine states reporting violation rates of 10 percent or less.

National Health Education Standards

Pages 58–59: 2.4, 2.10, 6.2, 6.3

Decision-Making Styles

Class Activity

Role-Playing Divide the class into groups. Have each group create a scenario to role-play based on one of the decision-making styles. Have one student from each group type his or her group's scenario. Collect the scenarios and make copies. Pass out the copies before the groups perform their role-plays so students can follow along. Have the class determine which decision-making style the role-playing falls into. **L1**

Teaching Transparency

Page 73, **Unit 1 Fast File Resources**

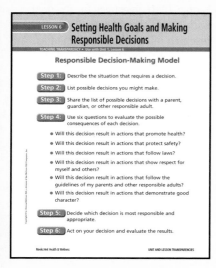

LESSON 6 **Setting Health Goals and Making Responsible Decisions**

TEACHING TRANSPARENCY • Use with Unit 1, Lesson 6

Responsible Decision-Making Model

Step 1: Describe the situation that requires a decision.

Step 2: List possible decisions you might make.

Step 3: Share the list of possible decisions with a parent, guardian, or other responsible adult.

Step 4: Use six questions to evaluate the possible consequences of each decision.

- Will this decision result in actions that promote health?
- Will this decision result in actions that protect safety?
- Will this decision result in actions that follow laws?
- Will this decision result in actions that show respect for myself and others?
- Will this decision result in actions that follow the guidelines of my parents and other responsible adults?
- Will this decision result in actions that demonstrate good character?

Step 5: Decide which decision is most responsible and appropriate.

Step 6: Act on your decision and evaluate the results.

Meeks Heit Health & Wellness

UNIT AND LESSON TRANSPARENCIES

Reading Review

1. *to increase quality and years of healthy life and to eliminate health disparities in the population*
2. *See page 59 for full list.*
3. *a habit in which a person allows others to make his or her decisions*

Decision-Making Styles

An individual can achieve a goal by learning how to make informed decisions. Do you weigh information carefully and consider the consequences before you make a decision? Do you make decisions based on what your friends are doing? Do you discuss important decisions with your parents or guardian? You can analyze your decision-making style and change it if necessary.

How to Evaluate Your Decision-Making Style

Make the Connection

Self-Confidence For more information about self-confidence and assertiveness, see page 48 in Lesson 5.

Reading Review

1. What are the goals of Healthy People 2010?
2. List the ten leading health indicators.
3. What is a reactive decision-making style?

Three possible decision-making styles are described here. Each style has its own consequences. Which of these three styles might produce healthful results and which will produce results that are not healthful?

Inactive decision-making style A person who fails to make choices has an *inactive decision-making style*. The failure to make a decision determines the outcome. Teens who use the inactive decision-making style may have the following habits. They postpone something until a future time. They take little control over the direction of their lives. They have difficulty gaining the self-confidence that would result if they took responsibility for making decisions when they should.

Reactive decision-making style A habit in which a person allows others to make his or her decisions is a *reactive decision-making style*. Teens using the reactive decision-making style are easily influenced by what others think, do, or suggest. They lack self-confidence and have a great need to be liked by others. They give control of the direction of their lives to others.

Proactive decision-making style A habit in which a person describes the situation that requires a decision, identifies and evaluates possible decisions, makes a decision, and takes responsibility for the outcome is a *proactive decision-making style*.

Teens who use the proactive decision-making style demonstrate the following characteristics in their lives. They are not driven by circumstances and conditions. They are not easily influenced by peers. They have principles, such as integrity, honesty, and dignity, which guide their decisions and behavior. They are empowered. A person who is empowered is energized because he or she has some control over his or her decisions and behavior.

Differentiated Instruction

Hearing Impairment Students who have a hearing impairment can participate in the role-playing activity above, too. Engage them by distributing typed copies of the scenarios for the role-plays so that they may follow along. If the student prefers, he or she could work alone to create a dialogue responding to a decision-making situation. He or she can act out the scenario with other students. **L1**

Responsible Decisions

You can develop a proactive decision-making style. When you have decisions to make, use the Responsible Decision-Making Model. The **Responsible Decision-Making Model** is a series of steps to follow to assure that people make good decisions.

How to Use the Responsible Decision-Making Model

Step 1: Describe the situation that requires a decision. Describe the situation in writing if no immediate decision is necessary. Describe the situation out loud or to yourself in a few sentences if an immediate decision is necessary. Being able to describe the situation in your own words helps you see it more clearly.

Step 2: List possible decisions you might make. List all the possible decisions you can think of in writing, if no immediate decision is necessary. If you must decide right away, review the possible decisions out loud or to yourself.

Step 3: Share the list of possible decisions with a parent, guardian, or other responsible adult. Share possible decisions with a responsible adult when no immediate decision is necessary. If possible, delay making a decision until you have had a chance to discuss the possible decisions with a parent, guardian, or other responsible adult. The adult may help you evaluate the possible consequences of each decision.

Step 4: Use six questions to evaluate the possible consequences of each decision.
• Will this decision result in actions that promote health?

• Will this decision result in actions that protect safety?
• Will this decision result in actions that follow laws?
• Will this decision result in actions that show respect for myself and others?
• Will this decision result in actions that follow the guidelines of my parents and of other responsible adults?
• Will this decision result in actions that demonstrate good character?

Step 5: Decide which decision is most responsible and appropriate. Rely on the six questions in Step 4 as you compare the decisions.

Step 6: Act on your decision and evaluate the results. Follow through with your decision with confidence.

◄ Share a list of possible decisions with a parent, guardian, or other responsible adult.

LESSON 6 • Setting Health Goals and Making Responsible Decisions **61**

🖋 Achieving Health Literacy

Responsible Citizen Responsible citizens make responsible decisions for themselves, their families, and the community. Have students write in their health journals about recent decisions they have made. If they are comfortable doing so, have students list on the chalkboard ways in which the decisions they made affected not only themselves but also their families and community. Ask students the following questions: If they could go back in time, would they make a different decision? If they are faced with a similar decision in the future, would they act in the same way? **L2**

Wrong Decisions

Using the Table

Restitution After students read Table 6.1, repeat the definition of "restitution" for them. Ask them to write in their health journals different ways they can think of to make restitution for harm done to others. Have students share their ideas with the class and use the ideas to start a discussion on restitution. **L2**

Explain the Concept

Promoting Health In Step 4 of the Responsible Decision-Making Model, students must ask themselves a series of questions to help make responsible decisions. Question 1 asks if the decision will promote health. Offer a review of Lesson 3, in which students learned that actions that promote health are healthful behaviors.

3 Assess

Vocabulary Practice

Page 72, **Unit 1 Fast File Resources**

National Health Education Standards
Pages 62–63: 4.3, 4.4, 5.2, 5.6

Wrong Decisions

Everyone makes a wrong decision at one time or another. A **wrong decision** is a choice that can lead to actions that harm health, are unsafe, are illegal, show disrespect for self and others, disregard the guidelines of parents and other responsible adults, or show lack of good character.

What to Do If You Make a Wrong Decision and Want to Correct It

What can you do if you suddenly realize that you intentionally made a wrong decision and now wish you hadn't? Do something to correct your wrong actions. If you do, you take steps to earn back the respect of others. This helps you keep your self-respect. In **Table 6.1** below, read the four steps you can take if you make a wrong decision.

TABLE 6.1 Four Steps to Take If You Make a Wrong Decision

	Step to Take	What This Means for You
	1. Take responsibility and admit you made a wrong decision.	Wrong is wrong. Do not make excuses if you make a wrong decision. Do not try to cover up what you have done.
	2. Do not continue actions based on wrong decisions.	The very moment you recognize that you have made a wrong decision, think about what actions you have taken based on your wrong decision.
	3. Discuss the wrong decision with a parent, guardian, or other responsible adult.	Your parents or guardian are responsible for guiding the decisions that you make. If your decisions are wrong, your parents or guardian need to know. They can help you correct what you have done.
	4. Make restitution for harm done to others.	**Restitution** is making up for any loss, damage, or harm you have caused. An apology is not always enough to correct the harm done. You might have to replace something, pay money, or volunteer time to make things right.

Family Involvement

Family Discussion Step 4 in Table 6.1 concerns making restitution for wrong decisions. Encourage students to take home their journal entries on past decisions to discuss with their families. Family members can offer advice on how best to make restitution for any wrong decisions. If the restitution involves money, the student can work with his or her family to decide the best way to come up with the money. The family also might consider asking the person who was harmed by the wrong decision what he or she feels is the best way to make restitution. **L2**

health goal
Healthy People 2010
inactive decision-
    making style
leading health
    indicators
life expectancy
long-term health
    goal
proactive decision-
    making style
reactive decision-
    making style
Responsible
    Decision-Making
    Model
restitution
short-term health
    goal
wrong decision

Key Terms Review

Match the definitions below with the lesson Key Terms on the left. Do not write in this book.

1. health objectives for the nation
2. ten major health concerns
3. failing to make choices determines outcome
4. decision that is harmful, unsafe, illegal
5. making good for loss or damage
6. allowing others to make choices for you

7. average number of years you are expected to live
8. series of steps to follow to make responsible decisions
9. empowering style of making decisions
10. healthful behavior you work to achieve

Recalling the Facts

11. What are eight steps you can take to reach a health goal?
12. List the ten leading health indicators.
13. Describe three decision-making styles.
14. What are six questions you might ask to proactively evaluate the possible consequences of a decision?

15. What are ways of making restitution for loss, damage, or harm?
16. What are the two main goals of Healthy People 2010?
17. Give an example of a health goal.
18. How has life expectancy changed from the twentieth to the twenty-first century?

Critical Thinking

19. Why is making restitution for a wrong decision important? Give several examples of ways to make restitution.
20. How does eliminating health disparities in the population promote health for all people?
21. Why might sharing a possible decision with a responsible adult help make your decision-making process easier?
22. How does following a law show respect for self and others?

Real-Life Applications

23. What can you do to help the nation reach its goals for 2010?
24. Explain why you should write down a health goal and make a plan for it.
25. Describe the difference between short-term and long-term health goals.
26. Select one of the ten areas of concern in the leading health indicators and, using a proactive decision-making style, plan how to improve that area in your own life.

Activities

Responsible Decision Making

27. **Record a Message** Imagine that you are playing softball with friends. You hit the softball, and it breaks a car windshield. Your friends convince you to leave, but you feel guilty. Record a message in which you tell the owner of the automobile about your wrong decision and offer to make restitution. Refer to the Responsible Decision-Making Model on page 61 for help.

Sharpen Your Life Skills

28. **Set a Health Goal** One of the leading health indicators for Healthy People 2010 is physical activity that promotes cardiorespiratory fitness three or more times a week for 20 or more minutes per occasion. List exercises you can do this week to meet this health goal. List things that might keep you from exercising this week. Tell what you can do to overcome these obstacles.

Visit www.glencoe.com for more *Health & Wellness* quizzes.

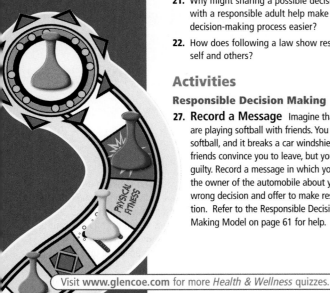

PHYSICAL FITNESS

LESSON 6

STUDY GUIDE

Key Terms Review

1. Healthy People 2010
2. leading health indicators
3. inactive decision-making style
4. wrong decision
5. restitution
6. reactive decision-making style
7. life expectancy
8. Responsible Decision-Making Model
9. proactive decision-making style
10. health goal

Recalling the Facts

11. See list on page 57.
12. See list on page 59.
13. See page 60 for descriptions of inactive, reactive, and proactive decision-making styles.
14. See Step 4 of the Responsible Decision-Making Model on page 61.
15. apologizing, replacing something, paying money, or volunteering time
16. to increase quality and years of healthy life and to eliminate health disparities in the population
17. Answers will vary.
18. It has improved from 47.3 years to nearly 77 years.

Critical Thinking

19. because an apology is not always enough to make things right and because you are responsible for any damage you have caused
20. More people will have access to health care and valid health information.
21. An adult might think of new possibilities or consequences. Also, when the student includes the adult, he or she will have support from the adult.
22. Laws are made to protect the public, so obeying the law protects self and others.

Real-Life Applications

23. lead a healthy lifestyle; encourage others to maintain a healthy lifestyle; volunteer
24. Writing down a goal makes it more "real" and increases a person's commitment to it.

25. A short-term goal can be reached in the near future. A long-term goal can be reached after a longer period of time. Examples will vary.
26. Answers should include one of the leading health indicators on page 59. Students should also include goal-setting steps from How to Set Health Goals on page 57.

Activities

Responsible Decision Making

27. Answers should reflect What to Do If You Make a Wrong Decision and Want to Correct It on page 62.

Sharpen Your Life Skills

28. Answers can include walking to school or playing sports. Obstacles can include homework and family commitments.

LESSON 7

Being a Health Advocate

Out of Time?

If time does not permit an in-depth study of this topic, use the following activities in this Teacher Wraparound Edition:
- Life Skill, p. 64
- Family Involvement, p. 66
- Health Project, p. 67

1 Focus

LIFE SKILL **Advocacy** Have students respond to the Life Skill for this lesson by taking time to write in their health journals about how they can be an advocate for their own health as well as their families' and communities' health. **L2**

Write ABOUT IT!

Discussion Ask students why they think people should volunteer. Then, ask them to discuss reasons why many people do not volunteer. **L2**

LESSON 7

Being a Health Advocate

LIFE SKILL • **I will advocate for personal, family, and community health.**

Someone once said, "People can be divided into three groups: those who make things happen, those who watch things happen, and those who wonder what happened." A health advocate is a person who "makes things happen." This lesson includes steps to follow to be a health advocate. It explains how to get involved as a volunteer and how you can benefit from advocacy.

What You'll Learn

1. Identify four steps to follow to be a health advocate. *(p. 65)*
2. Explain eight steps that can be taken to get involved as a volunteer. *(p. 66)*
3. Discuss the benefits of being a volunteer. *(p. 67)*
4. Explain the healthy-helper syndrome. *(p. 67)*
5. List at least ten volunteer opportunities for teens. *(p. 67)*

Why It's Important

Suppose everyone at your school became a health volunteer. Consider how these efforts might improve the quality of life in your community.

Key Terms

- health-advocacy skills
- health advocate
- volunteer
- volunteer center
- volunteer burnout
- beta-endorphins
- healthy-helper syndrome

Writing About Volunteering Suppose your best thinks that volunteer work and fun do not mix, but you are volunteering by helping an older adult once a week, and you and he really have a good time together. Write a paragraph in your health journal trying to convince your friend that volunteering is fun. Remember to include volunteer opportunities that include skills you already have or activities that already interest you.

National Health Education Standards—Guide for Lesson 7		
8.2	Demonstrate how to influence and support others to make a positive health-enhancing message.	pp. 64, 65, 66, 69
8.3	Work cooperatively as an advocate for improving personal, family, and community health.	pp. 65, 66, 69
8.4	Adapt health messages and communication techniques to a specific target audience.	pp. 65, 67, 69

Health Advocacy Skills

The process of supporting a cause is advocacy (AD vuh cuh see). Skills that are used to influence the health behavior and decisions of others and to advance specific health-related beliefs and concerns are known as *health-advocacy skills*. A *health advocate* is a person who uses skills to influence the health behavior and decisions of others for the advancement of health-related beliefs and concerns. There are steps you can follow to become a health advocate within your family, your school, in your community, or in the world.

How to Become a Health Advocate

1. Select a health-related concern. Teens often select advocacy interests for which they may have a strong personal connection. Here are examples of two teens' advocacy selections. A drunk driver killed Miguel's best friend in an automobile accident. Miguel selects drunk driving as his health-related concern. Tonya's grandmother recently developed colon cancer. Tonya selects colon cancer as her health-related concern.

2. Gather reliable information. Advocates often volunteer to help or provide service for the group they are interested in. A *volunteer* is a person who provides a service without pay. For example, Miguel gathers data on traffic fatalities caused by teens that drink alcohol and drive. He contacts SADD (Students Against Drunk Driving) to learn more about this organization. Tonya contacts the American Cancer Society to learn ways to reduce the risk of developing colon cancer.

3. Identify your purpose and target audience. The purpose of advocating for a health concern might be to educate people about a specific health

problem, to get laws passed, and/or to motivate others to advocate for a health-related cause. Miguel wants to influence teens not to drink and drive. This will reduce their risk of being in a fatal accident involving alcohol. Tonya wants to influence her family. She wants them to make healthful food choices to reduce their risk of colon cancer.

4. Develop a convincing and appropriate message. Focus on your purpose and target audience and prepare your message. Consider how you can have the most influence on others. Miguel joins SADD. Together with other members of SADD, he participates in a program to bring awareness to other teens. He helps make posters to display at school and writes announcements about the dangers of drinking and driving to be read on the school's public address system. Tonya learns about high fiber, low-fat diets that help reduce the risk of colon cancer and shares this information with her family. Together, they modify some of the family's favorite recipes to accomplish this. These teens are health advocates.

Did You Know?

Volunteer According to the Bureau of Labor, 65.4 million people in the United States over the age of 16 volunteered for a variety of organizations in the period from September 2004 to September 2005.

Reading Review

1. What is a health advocate?
2. List the steps to become a health advocate.

Lesson Resource Manager

- **Unit 1 Fast File Resources**
  Reading Strategy, p. 83
  Vocabulary Practice, p. 84
  Transparency Master and Worksheet, p. 85
  Real-Life Health, p. 87
  Real-Life Health, p. 89
  5-Minute Check, p. 91
  Lesson 7 Quiz, p. 92
- **Unit 1 Transparency**
- **Lesson 7 Transparency**

- **Reading Essentials**
- **Technology**
  TeacherWorks™ CD-ROM
  StudentWorks™ CD-ROM
  Reading Essentials CD-ROM
  ExamView® Assessment Suite
  Vocabulary Puzzlemaker

Health-Advocacy Skills

2 Teach

Reading Review

1. *a person who uses skills to influence the health behavior and decisions of others for the advancement of health-related beliefs or concerns*
2. *See How to Become a Health Advocate steps on this page.*

INTERACTIVE CHALKBOARD with Image Bank

PowerPoint® Presentations

This CD-ROM is an editable Microsoft® PowerPoint® presentation that includes:
- Lesson presentations
- Lesson checks
- Interactive graphics
- 5-Minute Checks
- Image Bank
- All transparencies

Note-Taking Refer to the Two-Column Notes: Main Idea-Detail Strategy on page 16T. Instruct students to use the left-hand column to list places where they would be interested in volunteering and to use the right-hand column to detail how to begin the process.

National Health Education Standards
Pages 64–65: 5.4, 8.1, 8.2, 8.3, 8.4

65

Volunteering

Class Discussion

Volunteering Engage the students in discussing health concerns for which they could volunteer. Students who already volunteer or who have family members who volunteer may want to offer additional ideas or information. Compile student responses on the chalkboard. **L2**

Class Activity

Becoming a Volunteer Have students list their interests and skills in their health journals. Students also should examine their schedule to determine how much time they could allot to volunteering. Encourage students to decide on one or two areas in which they would like to volunteer. **L2**

Extension

Motivating Volunteers Have students research who typically volunteers. For example, the U.S. Bureau of Labor Statistics offers facts about volunteers, such as their education level, their age, and whether they have children. With that information, students also can determine who does not volunteer. Then, in a one-page report, have students create a plan to motivate those who do not volunteer. **L3**

Volunteering your time and talent is a powerful way to improve the quality of life for you and others, whether you are doing something simple like boxing canned goods or something more demanding, such as planning an event to raise money. You derive many benefits when you volunteer. As a volunteer, you meet new people, develop new skills, and may add to your self-respect and health status. Are you ready to roll up your sleeves and get started? To be a successful volunteer, you need to plan and then act.

How to Be a Volunteer

Make the Connection

Time Management For more information on managing your time, see page 551 in Lesson 51.

Assess your interests, skills, talents, and resources. List your interests, skills, and talents. Identify how much time you have to spend volunteering.

Identify organizations in your community that use or need volunteers. Ask your parents or guardian, teachers, or look in the telephone directory for organizations that utilize volunteers. Call a volunteer center. A *volunteer center* is an organization that matches people with volunteer jobs.

Call or visit organizations or agencies for which you would like to volunteer. Obtain permission from a parent or guardian. Call the organization or agency for which you would like to volunteer and express your interest. Be prepared with questions. What does the organization or agency do? What tasks and responsibilities might you do as a volunteer?

Make final preparations. Obtain permission from a parent or guardian to volunteer. Discuss your schedule and the tasks you will perform, and arrange for transportation.

Set high expectations for yourself. Be on time, dress appropriately, follow rules and guidelines, and complete assigned tasks in a timely manner. If you must be late or absent, tell your supervisor in advance.

If you do not find an organization or agency where you can serve as a volunteer, create and organize your own projects. Think of ways you can help in your community. Would supplies, transportation, or equipment be needed? Who will pay for those items? Write an action plan. Get the approval and support of your parents or guardian, teacher, principal, or other official if needed. Involve others as you plan your event.

Keep a log of your volunteer experiences. Include a description of the tasks you are doing and whether you like them or not. Discuss ways your experience benefits others. Discuss ways it is benefiting you. How would you improve this experience?

Avoid volunteer burnout. Be careful not to overdo or to take on responsibilities that are too much for you. *Volunteer burnout* is a loss of enthusiasm about volunteering that results from feeling overwhelmed. Watch out for signs of burnout, such as feeling stressed, bored, or tired.

Family Involvement

Family Discussion Have students take home their volunteer ideas and discuss them with their families. Families can provide advice and other input to help students choose a way to volunteer. Students should consider whether volunteering will affect their obligations at home and whether the family can work around this. Depending on the volunteer activity chosen, students may need family support for transportation or to have a release form signed. Students also may encourage family members to volunteer with them. **L2**

Activity: Using Life Skills

Advocating for Health: Being a Volunteer

A volunteer is a person who provides a service to others without pay. Volunteering isn't just good for your community; it's good for you, too. Being a volunteer contributes to self-respect, helps you learn new skills, gives you a chance to meet new people, and contributes to your health.

1 **Select a health-related concern.** Read through the list at the bottom of this page for volunteering ideas. Select an activity from the list that appeals to you.

2 **Gather reliable information.** Research an organization in your community that offers the opportunity to volunteer in the way you have chosen.

3 **Identify your purpose and target audience.** In a small group, explain why you would be interested in advocating health in this particular way. How would this activity benefit others? How might it benefit you?

4 **Develop a convincing and appropriate message.** Based on your discussion and the ideas you have researched, create a poster that encourages others to become health advocates by volunteering.

Can Being a Volunteer Affect Your Health Status?

Effects of positive feelings There is some evidence that the positive feelings that come from doing good deeds help boost the effectiveness of the immune system. Acts of giving stimulate the brain to release beta-endorphins. **Beta-endorphins** are substances produced in the brain that create a feeling of well-being.

The **healthy-helper syndrome** is a state in which a person feels increased energy, relaxation, and improved mood as a result of giving service to others. Those volunteers who have the most face-to-face contact with those they help seem to experience the most health benefits.

▲ Because volunteering makes you feel good, it has a positive effect on your health status. Volunteers who work directly with other people get the most health benefits.

Volunteering Opportunities

There are any number of ways you can serve the needs of other people to the betterment of their mental, physical, or emotional health. Some of these are:

- Coach a sports team
- Tutor or read to children
- Teach reading
- Participate in walk-a-thons and fun-runs
- Serve food in a homeless shelter
- Perform chores for an elderly person or a person with a physical disability

- Clean up a vacant lot, roadway, or other area
- Collect food or clothing
- Form a teen coalition to counter tobacco and alcohol advertising in your community
- Help prepare and deliver meals

- Organize entertainment
- Organize drug- and alcohol-free activities
- Participate in a neighborhood or roadside cleanup
- Plant a garden or a tree

LESSON 7 • Being a Health Advocate **67**

Using Life Skills

Advocating for Health Arrange for the posters that students have made to be displayed at an elementary or a middle school. The class also can create a presentation on volunteering for younger students. Arrange for the class to share their presentation with the students at an elementary or a middle school. **L2**

5-Minute Check

Page 91, **Unit 1 Fast File Resources**

1. What is a health advocacy skill? *a skill used to influence people's health behavior and decisions while promoting specific health-related beliefs and concerns*

2. How can you become a health advocate? *select a health-related concern, gather information, identify your purpose and audience, and develop a convincing message*

3. Where can you go to be matched with volunteer jobs? *a volunteer center*

4. How can you ensure as a volunteer you will not become burned out? *Do not overdo or take on too much responsibility; watch for signs of burnout, which include stress, boredom, or fatigue.*

5. How can volunteering make you feel good as well as help others? *Volunteering stimulates the release of beta-endorphins, which produce a feeling of well-being sometimes called the "healthy-helper syndrome."*

⚡ Health Project

Volunteering As a class, have students brainstorm ideas for ways they can volunteer as a group. Ideas could include setting up a program within the school, such as encouraging healthier eating in the cafeteria. Project ideas also could involve the community, such as participating in a walk-a-thon. The students should then choose one idea that they would like to pursue. Students should form groups to work on different aspects of implementing their project, including getting administration and family approval, creating an action plan, and preventing volunteer burnout. **L2**

Analyzing the Feature

Use the following questions to help students uncover the main points in this feature.

1. **What are two ways Sarah has volunteered in her community?** *by making friendship baskets and by cleaning a ravine near school*

2. **Who are the friendship baskets for, and what do they hold?** *The baskets are for students at an elementary school; they hold candy, toys, and books.*

3. **According to Sarah, who can volunteer?** *Anyone can volunteer.*

Journaling Activity

Have students write a paragraph in their health journals about the point at which the healthy helper syndrome can turn into volunteer burnout. Have them list ways to prevent volunteer burnout. **L2**

3 Assess

Vocabulary Practice

Page 84, **Unit 1 Fast File Resources**

Name _____ Date _____ Class _____

LESSON 7 **Being a Health Advocate**

Vocabulary Practice

Read the passage below. For each underlined phrase in the passage, write the vocabulary term that can replace it. Use each vocabulary term once.

beta-endorphins	healthy helper syndrome	volunteer burnout
health advocacy skills	volunteer	volunteer center
health advocate		

How can you become a (1) person who influences the health behavior and decisions of others for the advancement of health-related beliefs and concerns? Use your (2) skills that influence the health behavior of others for the advancement of specific health-related concerns to interact with people in ways that allow you to share your health knowledge. For example, you might contact a (3) organization that matches people with volunteer jobs in order to become a (4) person who provides a service without pay. There are numerous opportunities to share your time and talent. Be sure to pick a position that suits your schedule and interests.

Volunteering benefits other people. It also benefits you! Volunteers meet new people and develop new skills. Volunteering can also help to stimulate the release of (5) substances produced in the brain that create a feeling of well-being. Maintain the (6) state in which a person feels increased energy, relaxation, and improved mood as a result of giving service to others by avoiding (7) a loss of enthusiasm about volunteering that results from feeling overwhelmed.

1. _____
2. _____
3. _____
4. _____
5. _____
6. _____
7. _____

84 LESSON 7 • Being a Health Advocate   UNIT 1

National Health Education Standards

Pages 68–69: 1.1, 5.6

SPEAKING OUT
Teens Talk About Health

Sarah Tynon
Volunteering

> **"Volunteering has opened my eyes to ways other people live."**

If Sarah Tynon is typical, it might be a good idea to put a warning label on all volunteer projects. It would say "Warning: Volunteering can be habit-forming. It also may cause feelings of satisfaction at knowing you've made a difference in other people's lives." Sarah explained why: "Doing a volunteer project is a great experience. Doing one seems to make you want to do more, just for the new experience."

For the community At Sarah's school, most of the volunteer projects are on the local level. "We have what we call Young Volunteers," she explained. "We try to do different community-oriented things. One of the most fun things we do is make friendship baskets. They're for an elementary school our school has adopted. We put candy, little toys, books, and other things in the baskets. We buy the things for the baskets by raising money throughout the year. The kids who receive the baskets always write back to us to thank us, and it's a good feeling."

Benefits all around What do people get out of a volunteer project like the friendship baskets? According to Sarah, "The big benefit of a program like this is knowing that you've made someone happy. There are a lot kids who haven't had those things that are easy to take for granted." Sarah put her finger on one of the key reasons that people volunteer. Those on the receiving end aren't the only ones who get a benefit. "I'm doing it for the kids, but I'm also doing it for myself." The payoff for volunteers like Sarah is the good feeling that comes from helping other people.

Variety: the spice of volunteering Sarah has worked on many different kinds of volunteer projects. "A few years back, we went to a little ravine near our school. There's usually a lot of trash down there, so our group goes and cleans it up." Sarah made an important point about volunteering. "Even if you don't have that much time to give, there are always small things that don't require a huge time commitment." Another plus according to Sarah is that anyone can volunteer. "The volunteer projects I work on don't require any special skills at all. All it really takes is the will to do it."

Toward the future "Volunteering has opened my eyes to ways other people live," Sarah concluded. "It's made me realize I want to work with people, so I think I might be a teacher. I think that's a good way to help people improve their lives. But I know I'll want to continue volunteering throughout my life. I'll just make the time for it."

Journaling Activity

Think about a volunteer project you've worked on. Do you agree with Sarah that volunteers can get as much out of a project as the people they are helping? Why or why not?

68 UNIT 1 • Health Skills

Cross-Curricular Connections

History Clara Barton founded the American Red Cross in 1881. By 1918, more than 20 million members belonged to 3000 Red Cross chapters. Have students choose a volunteer organization that interests them, such as the American Red Cross, American Cancer Society, or American Society for Prevention of Cruelty to Animals. Students can then research the history of the organization and create a multimedia presentation to share with the class. Have them include the date the organization was founded, by whom, and why. **L2**

beta-endorphins
health-advocacy skills
health advocate
healthy-helper syndrome
volunteer
volunteer burnout
volunteer center

Key Terms Review

Complete the fill-in-the-blank statements with the lesson Key Terms on the left. Do not write in this book.

1. You use _____ when you make a poster about avoiding secondhand smoke.

2. You are a(n) _____ when you do errands for an elderly neighbor.

3. Someone at a(n) _____ can match your skills with volunteer opportunities.

4. The increased energy you get from being a volunteer is called _____.

5. When you perform acts of kindness, such as helping a neighbor do yard work, _____ give you a feeling of well-being.

6. You are a(n) _____ when you make a "No Smoking" sign to display in your home.

7. If you take on too many volunteer responsibilities, that take up too much of your time, you might get _____.

Recalling the Facts

8. What is the meaning of "select your target audience"?

9. What are eight steps that help you get involved as a volunteer?

10. How might your health status improve if you develop the healthy-helper syndrome?

11. Why could volunteer burnout affect the health of the people you are trying to help?

12. How are beta-endorphins healthful?

13. Why might a person who delivers mail in a hospital exhibit healthy-helper syndrome?

14. List three things that you might keep track of in a volunteer log.

15. What three questions might you ask a health agency before you volunteer with them?

16. Why might active volunteers seem to have fewer infections?

17. Why is a health advocate "a person who makes things happen"?

18. Why is "show up on time" important to a group for which you volunteer?

Critical Thinking

19. Why would teens advocate for a group for which they have strong emotional ties?

20. How might reading to a child advance his or her health?

21. Explain why many high schools have volunteer service as a requirement for graduation.

22. What are the benefits of keeping a log of your volunteer activities?

Real-Life Applications

23. What steps would you follow to be a health advocate?

24. List five types of tasks you might do as a volunteer for a health organization.

25. List five organizations in your community that depend upon volunteers.

26. If your community does not have a volunteer center, write out a plan for organizing one.

Activities

Responsible Decision Making

27. **Role-Play** Suppose you volunteer a few hours each Saturday at a children's hospital. Your friend invites you to a sports game that is during the hours you volunteer. Pair up with a classmate and role-play this scenario. Refer to the Responsible Decision-Making Model on page 61 for help.

Sharpen Your Life Skills

28. **Be an Advocate** Select a health agency that helps prevent a specific disease or condition through education. Contact this agency for information about ways to reduce the risk of the disease or condition. Select a target group and prepare a convincing and appropriate message.

Visit www.glencoe.com for more Health & Wellness quizzes.

LESSON 7 • Study Guide **69**

---

22. It helps you learn what you like and don't like to do as a volunteer; it enables you to make suggestions on improving the work.

Real-Life Applications

23. Answers should reflect How to Become a Health Advocate on page 65.
24. Answers will vary.
25. Answers will vary.
26. Answers will vary.

Activities

Responsible Decision Making

27. The role-play should reflect the Responsible Decision-Making Model on page 61.

Sharpen Your Life Skills

28. You may want to contact the principal to see if the visual aids can be posted in the hallway so all students can see these messages.

Key Terms Review

1. health-advocacy skills
2. volunteer
3. volunteer center
4. healthy-helper syndrome
5. beta-endorphins
6. health advocate
7. volunteer burnout

Recalling the Facts

8. Advocacy can take different tones with different audiences. Your target audience is the group of people you most want to influence.
9. Answers should reflect How to Be a Volunteer on page 66.
10. increased energy, relaxation, and improved mood
11. If you are stressed or tired you may cause the same reaction in others.
12. They create a feeling of well-being.
13. Volunteers who have the most face-to-face contact receive the most health benefits.
14. a list of tasks; whether you like them or not; how the experience benefits self and others
15. What does the organization do? What tasks might I do as a volunteer? How much time should I commit?
16. Volunteering may boost the effectiveness of the immune system.
17. The goal of a health advocate is to influence others for the advancement of health.
18. The group depends on you to be there on time.

Critical Thinking

19. Because the topic already holds their interest; they may feel they understand the cause.
20. Reading to a child makes him or her feel cared for. It may also encourage him or her to learn to read, which can help him or her make informed health decisions later in life.
21. Volunteerism is important to society and has positive effects on both the volunteers and those who benefit from their work.

69

Key Terms Review

1. a	6. j
2. d	7. i
3. g	8. b
4. f	9. c
5. k	10. e

Recalling the Facts

11. physical health, mental-emotional health, and family-social health
12. A healthful behavior is an action a person chooses that promotes health; prevents injury, illness, and premature death; and improves the quality of the environment. A risk behavior is an action a person chooses that harms health; can cause injury, illness, and premature death; or damages or destroys the environment.
13. See page 18.
14. your name and date, a health goal, how you will reduce health risks by practicing specific healthful behaviors, a plan to record progress, and an evaluation of how the plan worked
15. See list on page 36.
16. Positive peer pressure is influence from peers to behave in a responsible way. Negative peer pressure is influence from peers to behave in a way that is not responsible.
17. Ask for more information—clarifying response; repeat in your own words what the speaker said—restating response; summarize the main idea—summarizing response; and acknowledge and show appreciation for the speaker's feelings—affirming response.
18. Remain calm, set a positive tone, define the conflict, take responsibility for personal actions, listen to the needs and feelings of others, list and evaluate possible solutions, and agree on a solution.
19. See step 4 in The Responsible Decision-Making Model on page 61.
20. See page 66.

UNIT 1
STUDY GUIDE

Key Terms Review

Match the following Key Terms with the correct definition. Do not write in this book.

a. beta-endorphins *(p. 67)*
b. habits *(p. 27)*
c. health advocate *(p. 65)*
d. health-care provider *(p. 17)*
e. health status *(p. 6)*
f. media *(p. 35)*
g. media literacy *(p. 36)*
h. peer pressure *(p. 45)*
i. random event *(p. 10)*
j. restitution *(p. 62)*
k. volunteer *(p. 65)*
l. wrong decision *(p. 62)*

1. substances produced in the brain that create a feeling of well-being
2. trained licensed professional who performs services that maintain or restore people's health
3. skills in recognizing and evaluating the messages in media
4. various forms of mass communication
5. person who provides service without pay
6. making up for any loss, damage, or harm you caused
7. an incident over which a person has little or no control
8. fixed behaviors that you use automatically
9. person who uses skills to influence health behaviors and decisions of others
10. sum total of the positive and negative influences on a person's health and well-being

Recalling the Facts

11. What are three points on the Health Behavior Triangle? *(Lesson 1)*
12. What is the difference between a risk behavior and a healthful behavior? *(Lesson 1)*
13. What questions might you ask to evaluate health-related information? *(Lesson 2)*
14. What is included in a health behavior contract? *(Lesson 3)*
15. What six questions might you ask to determine the influence of watching a particular TV program? *(Lesson 4)*
16. What is the difference between positive peer pressure and negative peer pressure? *(Lesson 5)*
17. What are four kinds of active listening? *(Lesson 5)*
18. What are conflict-resolution skills you can use to settle disagreements? *(Lesson 5)*
19. What are six questions used to evaluate the outcome of a decision you made? *(Lesson 6)*
20. What are eight steps to take to become a volunteer? *(Lesson 7)*

Critical Thinking

21. How can random events affect health status? *(Lesson 1)*
22. How might the Wellness Scale be used to evaluate health status? *(Lesson 1)*
23. What can you do if you have purchased a defective health product? *(Lesson 2)*
24. What actions might you take after using a health behavior inventory? *(Lesson 3)*
25. When would you use a health behavior contract? *(Lesson 3)*
26. Why do companies pay athletes to wear their logos when they are competing in sports events on TV? *(Lesson 4)*
27. Why is it important to develop media literacy? *(Lesson 4)*
28. When would mediation be used? *(Lesson 5)*
29. How can changes in life expectancy affect health? *(Lesson 6)*
30. How might being a volunteer improve health status? *(Lesson 7)*

Use **Interactive Tutor** at **www.glencoe.com** for additional help.

Critical Thinking

21. They might have a positive or negative effect on health status, and a person has no control over them.
22. You might place an *X* on the Wellness Scale to rate your health status and then decide what actions might move your health status closer to the "Optimal Wellness" end of the scale.

23. You might talk with your parents or guardian, return the health product, write a letter of complaint, or contact a federal agency.
24. You might begin to practice more healthful behaviors.
25. You might make a health behavior contract when you want to make a healthful behavior a health habit.

Health Literacy Activities

What Do You Know?
Critical Thinking Keep a journal for one week. List the decisions you made that week. Analyze your decision-making style for each situation. When did you use each style and why? How might you improve on your decision-making style? Set a health goal and write a plan to make this improvement.

Connection to Language Arts
Effective Communication Prepare a 3-minute story for the evening newscast about the ten factors that affect health status. Make a written or printed copy of your story. Present it to classmates.

Family Involvement
Responsible Citizenship Ask an adult in your family to share a situation in which he or she was pressured by peers and resisted that pressure. Show him or her the resistance skills on page 47 in Lesson 5 and ask which ones he or she finds most effective.

Group Project
Self-Directed Learning Suppose that you have read two articles about the same health issue in two different sources. Which is the more accurate report? Explain how you would determine accuracy. Present your analysis to the class. Give them a list of guidelines they can use.

Investigating Health Careers
Problem Solving Find a mentor who works in a health career that interests you. A mentor is a responsible person who guides another person. Ask your mentor about volunteer opportunities that you can participate in to learn more about the health career. Make an action plan that identifies tasks you will perform and the amount of time you will spend investigating and volunteering in that area. Visit www.glencoe.com for more information.

26. to influence people to buy their products
27. If you develop media literacy, you will be able to analyze the effect media has on you and make appropriate choices.
28. You might use mediation when you are unable to resolve conflict in a responsible way on your own.
29. An increase in life expectancy means that people are, on the whole, healthier than they used to be.
30. It may boost the effectiveness of the immune system, improve mood, increase energy, and make a person feel relaxed.

Health Literacy Activities

What Do You Know?
Students' decisions should reflect the Responsible Decision-Making Model on page 61. Their health goals should reflect the steps listed in How to Set Health Goals on page 57.

Connection to Language Arts
Each news story should include the factors listed on page 6.

Family Involvement
Students' interviews should incorporate How to Use Resistance Skills on page 47.

Group Project
Analysis should reflect knowledge of the Guidelines for Analyzing Influences on Health on page 36.

Investigating Health Careers
The action plan should include the guidelines in How to Be a Volunteer on page 66.

Standardized Test Practice

Reading & Writing

Read the following selection and answer the questions that follow.

For people seeking information about health issues, the Internet is like a "good news, bad news" joke. The good news is that the Internet offers a great deal of health information. The bad news is that it's hard to tell if the information is of any value. Experts suggest several rules for making sure what you find on-line is good advice, not bad medicine. Use common sense. Information that sounds too good to be true probably is. Make sure that the source of the information is trustworthy. Government agencies, universities, medical associations, and hospitals generally are reliable. Check the timeliness of the data. Lastly, get a second opinion before you act on something you see on the Internet. Your family doctor is always a good place to start.

www.glencoe.com

Multiple Choice

1 According to this paragraph, which of these statements is true?
   A All information on the Internet is 100 percent reliable.
   B All Web sites are kept up-to-date.
   C Hospitals are usually not trustworthy sources.
   D It's a good idea to apply common sense to internet claims.

2 Why is old and outdated information a problem?
   A People will avoid getting a second opinion.
   B Experts are not in agreement as to how careful people need to be about information they find on-line.
   C Actions based on outdated health information can lead to serious medical consequences.
   D Universities will become untrustworthy.

Open-Ended

3 Think of a health-related issue you would like to know more about. Write a paragraph describing the steps you would take, using the Internet, to learn more about it.

Standardized Test Practice
Reading & Writing

Multiple Choice
1. D   2. C

Open-Ended
3. Students' paragraphs should accurately describe a health issue and suggest appropriate ways to research it and ensure that the information obtained is trustworthy. For example, steps might include using a search engine to find suitable Web sites, examining the site, checking its reliability, and downloading and printing the data. Paragraphs should contain correct spelling, capitalization, punctuation, grammar, usage, and sentence structure.

Mental and Emotional Health

STANDARDS AND FEATURES

Lesson	National Standards	State/Local Standards	Activities and Features
Lesson 8 *(2 sessions, 1 block)* Developing Good Character	1.1, 1.2, 2.1, 2.3, 2.8, 7.1		
Lesson 9 *(2 sessions, 1 block)* Developing a Healthy Mind	1.1, 1.2		
Lesson 10 *(2 sessions, 1 block)* Expressing Emotions and Managing Stress	1.1, 1.2, 1.5		**Using Life Skills:** Using Goal-Setting and Decision-Making Skills: Managing Stress, p. 103 **Speaking Out:** Managing Stress, p. 106
Lesson 11 *(3 sessions, 1 block)* Dealing with Depression	1.1, 1.2, 1.5, 7.2		**Facts About:** Depression, p. 116 **Using Life Skills:** Accessing Valid Health Information, Products, and Services: Accessing Hotlines for Help, p. 120
Lesson 12 *(3 sessions, 1 block)* Dealing with Loss and Grief	1.5, 4.4, 8.1		**Health News:** Drug and Alcohol Use and Loss and Grief, p. 125 **Just the Facts:** Loss and Grief, p. 127

Key to Differentiated Instruction

L1 Level 1 activities should be appropriate for students with learning difficulties.

L2 Level 2 activities should be within the ability range of all students.

L3 Level 3 activities are designed for above-average students.

ELL ELL activities should be within the ability range of English language learners.

FAST FILE RESOURCES

INTRODUCING THE UNIT

Parent and Family Letter	p. 1	Health Behavior Contract	p. 3
Spanish Parent and Family Letter	p. 2	Unit Focus Transparency Master and Worksheet	p. 4

TEACHING THE UNIT LESSONS

Reproducible Student Pages	Lesson 8	Lesson 9	Lesson 10	Lesson 11	Lesson 12
Reading Strategy	p. 7	p. 21	p. 35	p. 49	p. 63
Vocabulary Practice	p. 8	p. 22	p. 36	p. 50	p. 64
Lesson Transparency Master and Worksheet	p. 9	p. 23	p. 37	p. 51	p. 65
Real-Life Health	p. 11	p. 25	p. 39	p. 53	p. 67
5-Minute Check	p. 15	p. 29	p. 43	p. 57	p. 71
Lesson Quiz	p. 17	p. 31	p. 45	p. 59	p. 72

CLOSING THE UNIT

Family Involvement Activity	p. 75	Health in the News	p. 85
Community Involvement Activity	p. 77	Health Career Research Activity	p. 87
Health Lab	p. 79	Unit Test A	p. 89
Activity: Strengthening Health Skills	p. 83	Unit Test B	p. 93

Technology

- **Interactive Chalkboard CD-ROM**
- **TeacherWorks™ CD-ROM**
- **StudentWorks™ CD-ROM**
- **Reading Essentials CD-ROM**
- **ExamView® Assessment Suite**

Glencoe Exclusive!

TeacherWorks™
All-In-One Planner and Resource Center

www.glencoe.com
- **Vocabulary Puzzlemaker**
- **Interactive Tutor**
- **Your Health Checklist**
- **Web Links**
- **Student Web Activities**

TEST YOUR EMOTIONS IQ

Use the three statements on the student page to initiate a class discussion about mental and emotional health. *Additional True/False statements are:*

4. **A person cannot become more resilient than he or she already is.**
   FALSE: There are several steps one can take to be more resilient: improve relationships with family members, acquire a mentor, make supportive friends, and ask for help.

5. **There are ways to protect your health during stressful times.**
   TRUE: Some actions you can take to protect your health are: be physically active, write in a journal, eat a healthful diet, and get plenty of rest and sleep.

6. **If a person was suicidal, he or she is suicidal for the rest of his or her life.**
   FALSE: Suicidal thoughts or behavior might be the result of a stressful life event. With help, a person who was suicidal can change his or her situation and outlook on life.

in the news Character versus Actions

Character Discussion Ask students if they agree with Helen Keller's statement about character. Have students discuss whether a person must experience suffering in order to have a strong character, and why or why not. Ask students how a person's choices affect his or her character. **L2**

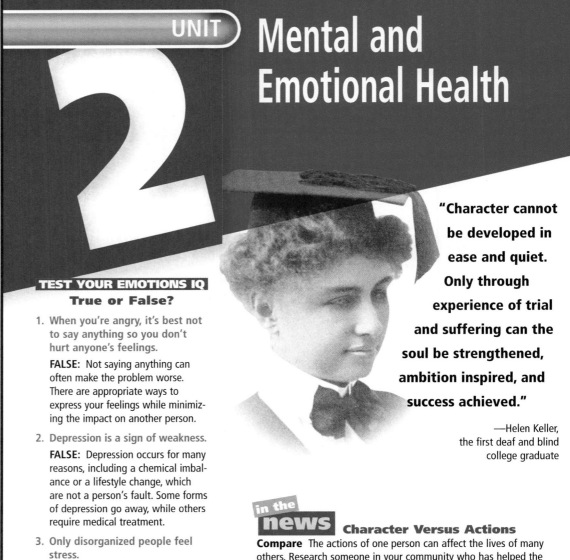

UNIT 2 Mental and Emotional Health

TEST YOUR EMOTIONS IQ
True or False?

1. **When you're angry, it's best not to say anything so you don't hurt anyone's feelings.**
   FALSE: Not saying anything can often make the problem worse. There are appropriate ways to express your feelings while minimizing the impact on another person.

2. **Depression is a sign of weakness.**
   FALSE: Depression occurs for many reasons, including a chemical imbalance or a lifestyle change, which are not a person's fault. Some forms of depression go away, while others require medical treatment.

3. **Only disorganized people feel stress.**
   FALSE: Stress is the result of feeling threatened or worried. Disorganization can increase stress, but organized people also can feel stress.

> "Character cannot be developed in ease and quiet. Only through experience of trial and suffering can the soul be strengthened, ambition inspired, and success achieved."
>
> —Helen Keller, the first deaf and blind college graduate

in the news Character Versus Actions

Compare The actions of one person can affect the lives of many others. Research someone in your community who has helped the community. Go to the library and ask a librarian to help you find information in local newspapers. What character traits does the person possess? How do these traits affect the person's actions? Prepare an oral report about the person and present it to the class.

LESSON 8	LESSON 9	LESSON 10
Developing Good Character	Developing a Healthy Mind	Expressing Emotions and Managing Stress

Two-Minute Unit Launcher

Demo Fill two clear drinking glasses with water so they are half-full of water. Ask students to describe how much water the glasses contain. Tell students that some people describe the glasses as being half full, while others describe the glasses as being half empty. Ask students what their responses mean in terms of how they view the world and their attitudes. Have students discuss whether they can change their views and attitudes and how this might help them to become more resilient. **L2**

EVALUATING MEDIA MESSAGES

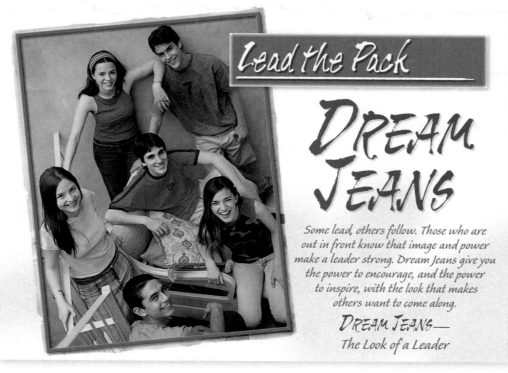

Lead the Pack

DREAM JEANS

Some lead, others follow. Those who are out in front know that image and power make a leader strong. Dream Jeans give you the power to encourage, and the power to inspire, with the look that makes others want to come along.

DREAM JEANS—
The Look of a Leader

 WHAT'S YOUR VERDICT?
To evaluate this advertisement, use the criteria for analyzing and evaluating health messages delivered through media and technology that you learned in Unit 1.

 Health Online

Visit www.glencoe.com to find regularly updated statistics on teen depression. Using the information provided, determine the answer to this question: How many teens suffer from depression?

Visit www.glencoe.com to use *Your Health Checklist* ✔, an interactive tool that helps you determine your health status.

LESSON 11
Dealing with Depression

LESSON 12
Dealing with Loss and Grief

Health Online

Answers Some signs of teen depression include a decline in school performance, withdrawal from friends and activities, feelings of sadness that last for weeks, weight or appetite changes, sleep disturbances, and agitation. Risk factors for teen depression include traumatic life events, academic or social problems, low serotonin levels, genetic predisposition, physical illness and disorders, and alcohol or other drug use. If teens know someone who exhibits these signs or risk factors, they should talk to a trusted adult.

 What's Your Verdict?

Advertising Appeals Ask students what method is being used to sell the jeans and what type of appeal is being made in the ad. For more information on evaluating advertisements, see Lesson 4 in Unit 1. Ask students: Do you think the ad is persuasive enough to convince you to purchase the jeans? Do you think it is persuasive enough to convince other teens to buy the jeans? Ask students why they are or are not affected by the appeal. **L2**

Health Journal

Write an Essay Ask students to write in their health journals about the effect of advertising on teens and their purchases. Have students respond to the statement: "The clothes make the person." Ask students what types of appeals advertisements make to get teens to buy items and whether they feel these appeals are effective. Have students explain their answers. **L2**

INTERACTIVE CHALKBOARD
with Image Bank

Unit Focus Transparency

Page 4, **Unit 2 Fast File Resources**

| UNIT 2 | Mental and Emotional Health |

UNIT FOCUS TRANSPARENCY

Maria's Schedule

THURSDAY
6:30–7:00 AM — go jogging
8:00–3:00 PM — school
3:00–5:00 PM — school play rehearsal
6:00–10:00 PM — childsit for neighbor (study for French test)
10:00 –11:00 PM — finish book report

As Maria looks over her schedule, her heart beats faster and her stomach starts to hurt. She is feeling stress about her busy day to come.

❶ What things on Maria's schedule will help her handle the effects of stress more easily?

❷ What changes could Maria make to her schedule to reduce her level of stress?

Meeks Heit Health & Wellness   UNIT AND LESSON TRANSPARENCIES

National Health Education Standards
Pages 72–73: 1.1, 1.2, 2.5, 3.1

73

LESSON 8

Developing Good Character

 Out of Time?

If time does not permit an in-depth study of this topic, use the following activities in this Teacher Wraparound Edition:
- Class Activity, p. 76
- Explain the Concept, p. 78
- Quick Demo, p. 79

1 Focus

HEALTH GOALS **Character** Have students respond to the Health Goals for this lesson by writing in their health journals values that contribute to good character and create a positive social-emotional environment. *Answers might include compassion, good citizenship, fairness, respect, responsibility, trustworthiness, and honesty.* **L2**

 ABOUT IT!

NHES Assessment/SCASS

Constructed Response Ask students to write in their health journals about a situation in which they witnessed good sportsmanship. **L1**

What You'll Learn

1. Discuss ways parents and guardians teach family values. *(p. 75)*
2. Identify traits and behaviors associated with having good character. *(p. 75)*
3. List and discuss ways to develop, maintain, or improve self-respect. *(p. 77)*
4. Describe responsible actions that promote positive self-esteem. *(p. 78)*
5. List ways a positive social-emotional environment improves health status. *(p. 79)*
6. List and discuss strategies to improve the social-emotional environment. *(p. 80)*

Why It's Important

There is a saying, "Actions speak louder than words." To have and display good character, your actions must be consistent with your beliefs.

Key Terms

- self-respect
- value
- good character
- self-control
- delayed gratification
- self-esteem
- positive self-esteem
- social-emotional environment
- social-emotional booster
- social-emotional pollutant

HEALTH GOALS
- **I will develop good character.**
- **I will interact in ways that help create a positive social-emotional environment.**

A high regard for oneself because one behaves in responsible ways is *self-respect*. Self-respect should not be confused with conceit. Conceit is excessive appreciation of one's worth. This lesson explains how to develop good character, improve self-esteem, and maintain self-respect. It also describes ways to improve the social-emotional environment.

 ABOUT IT!

Writing About Good Character Suppose your baseball team wins the championship game. Some of your teammates start to taunt the other team's players, calling them "losers." Your teammates urge you to join in. After you read the information about good character on page 75, write a response to this situation in your health journal.

National Health Education Standards—Guide for Lesson 8		
1.1	Predict how healthy behaviors can impact health status.	pp. 74, 75–78
1.2	Describe the interrelationships of emotional, intellectual, physical, and social health.	pp. 74, 78–80, 81
2.1	Analyze how family influences the health of individuals.	pp. 74, 75–77, 79, 80, 81
2.3	Analyze how peers influence healthy and unhealthy behaviors.	pp. 74, 75, 76–77, 81
2.8	Analyze the influence of personal values and beliefs on individual health practices and behaviors.	pp. 74, 75, 76–77, 81
7.1	Analyze the role of individual responsibility for enhancing health.	pp. 74, 75–78, 81

The Social-Emotional Environment

The quality of the contacts a person has with the people with whom he or she interacts is the **social-emotional environment.** Your interactions with members of your family influence your social-emotional environment. Your interactions with peers and adults in the community also have an influence. A positive social-emotional environment improves health status by allowing you and others to comfortably communicate needs, wants, and emotions.

How the Social-Emotional Environment Affects Health Status

Positive social-emotional environment
A positive social-emotional environment exists when you receive plenty of social-emotional boosters. A **social-emotional booster** is an interpersonal contact that helps a person feel encouragement and support, choose responsible behavior, and recognize options. In a positive social-emotional environment, people around you encourage you to take calculated risks, and praise you when you do something well. They recognize that you are special and compliment you on your actions. When people do these things, you feel connected and cared about. You are less likely to feel depressed or down over circumstances in your life.

Negative social-emotional environment
A negative social-emotional environment exists when you experience too many social-emotional pollutants. A **social-emotional pollutant** is an interpersonal contact that limits options or may cause a person to feel discouraged and alone or to choose wrong behavior. In this type of environment, people around you are disrespectful, put you down, or gossip about you. They try to manipulate and control you, or abuse you in some way.

If you live in a negative social-emotional environment, you must take action. If you do not take action, you can feel discouraged, unsupported, lonely, and alienated.

Ways a Positive Social-Emotional Environment Improves Health Status

- improves self-respect
- provides support for responsible behavior
- allows you to correct mistakes, forgive yourself, and move on
- helps you to be resilient
- helps you to be optimistic
- helps to prevent and relieve stress and depression
- helps prevent feelings of loneliness and alienation
- reduces the risk of psychosomatic diseases

LESSON 8 • Developing Good Character **79**

The Social-Emotional Environment

Quick Demo

Self-Esteem Fill two glasses with water and explain to students that the water represents a teen's self-esteem. Ask the class to give an example of a social-emotional booster. Place a drop of red food coloring in one glass to represent the social-emotional booster. Next, ask the class for an example of a social-emotional pollutant, and add a drop of blue food coloring to the other glass. Ask the students to note the effects of boosters and pollutants on self-esteem. **ELL**

5-Minute Check

Page 16, **Unit 2 Fast File Resources**

1. Why is it important to be resilient? *It improves self-confidence.*
2. How can taking a calculated risk help you develop positive self-esteem? *It helps you to learn not to be afraid of failure.*
3. What is the social-emotional environment? *the quality of the contacts a person has with the people with whom he or she interacts*
4. What is the difference between a positive social-emotional environment and a negative social-emotional environment? *A positive environment includes support, encouragement, and praise, and a negative environment displays disrespect, manipulation, or abuse.*
5. Name five ways that a positive social-emotional environment improves health status. *See page 79 for full list.*

⊕ Cross-Curricular Connections

Language Arts Have students write an essay about a literary character who acts as either a social-emotional booster or a social-emotional polluter. Ask students to describe the character's actions and discuss why the actions are social-emotional boosters or social-emotional pollutants. Students should include a discussion of how other characters in the story are affected by the person's actions. Ask students to consider these questions: How did the person's actions affect the self-esteem and self-respect of other characters in the story? Did any other characters act in ways they may not have, if it weren't for the person's boosters or pollutants? **L2**

Positive Interactions

Class Activity

Goal Ask students to give themselves three social-emotional boosters each day. Have students write them down and keep the list with them. Ask them to look at what they have written several times during the day for encouragement. At the end of one week, discuss as a class how this exercise made the students feel. **L2**

Class Discussion

List and Discuss Ask the class how they can improve their social-emotional environment. Record their answers on the chalkboard or on an overhead transparency and discuss which ways the students feel are the easiest to accomplish and which would be the most rewarding. **L2**

3 Assess

Vocabulary Practice

Page 8, **Unit 2 Fast File Resources**

Positive Interactions

There are strategies to improve the social-emotional environment. These strategies focus on improving your interactions with others. Practicing these strategies helps you create a social-emotional environment that will help you reach your goals.

How to Improve the Social-Emotional Environment

Did You Know?

Daily Social-Emotional Boosters You can improve your self-esteem by giving yourself three social-emotional boosters each day. Write them on a sheet of paper.

Minimize or avoid contact with people who put you down. Evaluate the positive and negative effects of various relationships, such as peers, family, and friends. Consider how these relationships affect your physical and emotional health. Minimize or avoid contact with persons who treat you with disrespect.

Use positive self-statements if you are with a person or group of persons who are negative. Evaluate the dynamics of your relationships with peers and family. Evaluate the dynamics of social groups to which you belong. If you cannot avoid negative people, say positive self-statements to yourself to avoid listening to their negative words.

▲ Making new friends can improve a teen's social-emotional environment.

Spend time with a mentor. The significant people in your life may not give you social-emotional boosters. They may ignore your needs, wants, and emotions. Find a mentor with whom you can spend time and get the social-emotional boosters you need. Communicate your needs, wants, and emotions to your mentor.

Join a support group. Within a support group, you can experience a positive social-emotional environment and get social-emotional boosters. You can practice expressing your needs, wants, and emotions in a safe setting.

Expand the network of people with whom you communicate needs, wants, and emotions. Remember, you need social-emotional boosters to maintain physical and emotional health. If you are not getting them, consider finding new friendships that provide them. Participate in new activities at school and in your community.

Give others social-emotional boosters. Contribute to the quality of the social-emotional environment by supporting and encouraging peers, friends, and family members. Encourage them to communicate their needs, wants, and emotions. When you do, you help others maintain their physical and emotional health.

80 UNIT 2 • Mental and Emotional Health

 Community Involvement

Mentor Discuss the role of a mentor in a person's life. A mentor is someone who provides support and guidance to another person who does not have the same amount of experience in a certain area. A mentor may be a teacher, a coach, an older classmate or teammate, or an adult at a workplace or volunteer site. Have students consider acquiring a mentor for some aspect of their lives. Students should outline their goals for having a mentor and make a plan to find a mentor. Ask students to write a list of benefits they would experience if they had a mentor. **L2**

8 STUDY GUIDE

Key Terms Review

Complete the fill-in-the-blank statements with the lesson Key Terms on the left. Do not write in this book.

delayed gratification
good character
negative self-esteem
positive self-esteem
self-control
self-esteem
self-respect
social-emotional booster
social-emotional environment
social-emotional pollutant
value

1. _____ is a person's belief that he or she is worthy and deserves respect.

2. _____ is a person's belief about his or her worth.

3. The _____ is the quality of the contacts a person has with the people with whom he or she interacts.

4. _____ is a person's use of self-control to act on responsible values.

5. A(n) _____ is a negative interpersonal contact that closes options.

6. _____ is the degree to which a person regulates his or her own behavior.

7. _____ is a high regard for oneself.

8. _____ is voluntarily postponing an immediate reward in order to complete a task before enjoying a reward.

9. A(n) _____ is an interpersonal contact that helps a person feel encouragement and support.

10. A(n) _____ is a standard or belief.

Recalling the Facts

11. What are two ways parents, guardians, mentors, and teachers teach values?

12. What are seven values that are building blocks for good character?

13. What are ten ways to improve self-respect?

14. What are six strategies that improve the social-emotional environment?

15. Discuss the three steps that can help you develop and maintain self-respect.

16. List three ways a positive social-emotional environment can improve health status.

17. Discuss the seven actions that help improve self-esteem.

18. Who or what are the influences on one's social-emotional environment?

Critical Thinking

19. How does communicating needs, wants, and emotions help improve the social-emotional environment?

20. How does the use of self-control and delayed gratification build good character?

21. How does taking calculated risks help a person improve his or her self-esteem?

22. How is resiliency related to self-esteem?

Activities

Responsible Decision Making

27. **Write a Skit** You are with your friend at the movie theater. Your friend suggests that you pay and go into the movie and then open the exit door so he or she can sneak in. What would you do? Refer to the Responsible Decision-Making Model on page 61 for help. Write a skit about this scenario and your decision.

Real-Life Applications

23. Why do you think treating others with respect helps you to respect yourself?

24. What belief statements can you use to help you have positive self-esteem?

25. How can you make your social-emotional environment more positive?

26. What is an example of a positive belief statement that promotes self-respect?

Sharpen Your Life Skills

28. **Access Health Information** Find an ad in the newspaper that shows a famous person promoting a product. What message is the ad conveying? How might this ad affect a teen's self-esteem? Write a new advertisement to sell the product in a way that would not affect a teen's self-esteem.

Visit www.glencoe.com for more *Health & Wellness* quizzes.

LESSON 8 • Study Guide **81**

LESSON 8 STUDY GUIDE

Key Terms Review

1. Positive self-esteem
2. Self-esteem
3. social-emotional environment
4. Good character
5. social-emotional pollutant
6. Self-control
7. Self-respect
8. Delayed gratification
9. social-emotional booster
10. value

Recalling the Facts

11. setting an example and setting standards for your behavior
12. compassion, good citizenship, fairness, respect, responsibility, trustworthiness, and honesty.
13. Refer to the Actions That Promote Self-Respect on page 77.
14. Refer to How to Improve the Social-Emotional Environment on page 80.
15. Make a character check, control the belief statements that motivate you, and choose actions that promote self-respect. See page 76 for a discussion of each.
16. See full list on page 79.
17. Refer to Actions That Promote Positive Self-Esteem on page 78.
18. family members, peers, adults in the community

Critical Thinking

19. Communication helps people to feel accepted and cared-for.
20. Both are often needed to act in responsible ways and to avoid making a decision based on an immediate desire.
21. Taking calculated risks helps build a person's confidence by allowing him or her to try something new without being afraid of failing.
22. Hanging on through a difficult situation builds self-confidence.

Real-Life Applications

23. Having respect for others shows that you value compassion and fairness. Others see your good character and you are proud of your behavior.

---

24. "I am a good friend." "I am honest."
25. Evaluate your friends and how they may act in a negative way. Don't spend time with others who don't respect you.
26. "I wouldn't let someone treat me badly."

Activities

Responsible Decision Making

27. It is not a responsible decision to help someone sneak in. It is against the law. Parents and guardians expect their children to be fair to others. It shows a lack of character to cheat someone else out of the cost of the movie.

Sharpen Your Life Skills

28. This health skills activity gives students a chance to develop communication skills (positive belief statements) that demonstrate consideration and respect for self.

If time does not permit an in-depth study of this topic, use the following activities in this Teacher Wraparound Edition:

- Explain the Concept, p. 84
- Class Discussion, p. 87
- Class Discussion, p. 90

1 Focus

HEALTH GOALS **Addictions** Have students respond to the Health Goals for this lesson by listing in their health journals characteristics of teens who are at risk for developing addictions. *Answers might include depression, negative self-esteem, guilt and shame, anger, poor coping skills, and difficulty with authority figures.* **L2**

Write ABOUT IT!

Journaling Have students write in their health journals about how to recognize the signs of addiction. Ask students to create a list of ways to identify the signs and symptoms of addiction. **L2**

LESSON 9

Developing a Healthy Mind

HEALTH GOALS
- I will develop healthful personality characteristics.
- I will choose behaviors to promote a healthy mind.

You will face many challenges in your life. Some challenges will be more difficult than others. The way you respond to challenges in your life is important. Every challenge is an opportunity to learn about yourself and to develop your potential.

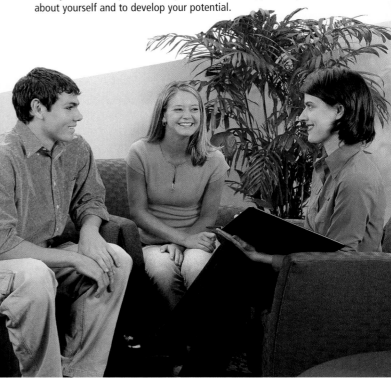

What You'll Learn

1. Identify influences on personality and describe the different personality types. *(p. 83)*
2. Discuss ways addictions can affect health status. *(p. 84)*
3. Identify types and signs of addictions and ways to avoid addictions. *(pp. 85, 87, 88)*
4. Discuss codependence. *(p. 88)*
5. Outline categories of mental disorders, giving examples of each. *(p. 89)*
6. Discuss mental-health services and treatment. *(p. 92)*
7. Identify strategies for coping with anxiety. *(p. 92)*

Why It's Important

The stoic philosopher Epictetus once said, "Men are disturbed not by things, but by the view which they take of them." Having a healthy mind helps you to take a positive view of things.

Key Terms

- personality
- attitude
- addiction
- perfectionism
- formal intervention
- relapse
- codependency
- support group
- mental disorder
- panic disorder

Write ABOUT IT!

Writing About Addictions Suppose a friend tells you that he thinks he is addicted to exercise. He says that he would rather exercise than spend time with his family or friends, and that he feels very anxious when he does not exercise. After you read the information about addictions on page 85, write a letter to your friend in your health journal about why you think he needs to get help.

National Health Education Standards—Guide for Lesson 9		
1.1	Predict how healthy behaviors can impact health status.	pp. 82, 83–88, 93
1.2	Describe the interrelationships of emotional, intellectual, physical, and social health.	pp. 82, 85, 89–91

Personality

A n individual's unique pattern of characteristics is called ***personality.*** Your personality is what makes you different from others. There are many influences on personality, including heredity, environment, attitudes, and behaviors.

What to Know About Personality

Heredity Your heredity helps determine your intellectual abilities, temperament, and talents. For example, your heredity influences your athletic ability and artistic capabilities. It influences the degree to which you are resilient.

Environment Your environment includes everything that is around you. Where you live and the people with whom you have contact influence your personality. Your environment influences the opportunities you have.

Attitudes The feeling or emotion a person has toward something or someone is an ***attitude.*** Your attitudes influence your personality.

Behaviors Your behavior is what you do. What you do influences your personality.

Personality Type

Your personality is different from your personality type. Personality type is a person's usual way of focusing energy, gathering information, making decisions, and getting work done. It is important to know and understand your personality type because it helps you understand yourself. You get a better grasp of how you approach and respond to people and things.

An understanding of personality type also helps you understand the people with whom you interact. You recognize ways you are different and alike. You understand the preferences of others.

Lastly, an understanding of personality type helps you improve your chance of working effectively and successfully with others. Being aware of your preferences and those of others helps you work more efficiently. You are better able to assign tasks. You have a better grasp of what roles people will play within a group setting.

Check Your Personality Type

There are four dimensions to personality type, including styles of energy focusing, information gathering, decision making, and work mode.

- **How You Focus Energy**
  (E) Extroverted: You are energized by people and things.
  (I) Introverted: You are energized by ideas and images.
- **How You Gather Information**
  (S) Sensing: You trust tangible information that you gather from your senses.
  (N) Intuitive: You give more weight to information from your insight and imagination.
- **How You Make Decisions**
  (T) Thinking: You base your

decisions on objective principles and facts.
  (F) Feeling: You trust your "gut" and weigh decisions against people issues and concerns.
- **How You Get Work Done**
  (J) Judging: Your approach to doing things is structured and organized.
  (P) Perceiving: Your approach to doing things is flexible. You adapt as you do things and prefer open-ended deadlines.

Source: Adapted from research by Carl Jung and the Myers-Briggs model of personality.

LESSON 9 • Developing a Healthy Mind **83**

Lesson Resource Manager

- **Unit 2 Fast File Resources**
  Reading Strategy, p. 21
  Vocabulary Practice, p. 22
  Transparency Master and Worksheet, p. 23
  Real-Life Health, p. 25
  Real-Life Health, p. 27
  5-Minute Check, p. 29
  Lesson 9 Quiz, p. 31
- **Unit 2 Transparency**
- **Lesson 9 Transparency**

- **Reading Essentials**
- **Technology**
  TeacherWorks™ CD-ROM
  StudentWorks™ CD-ROM
  Reading Essentials CD-ROM
  Exam*View*® Assessment Suite
  Vocabulary Puzzlemaker

Personality

2 Teach

Class Discussion

Personality Write the word "personality" on the chalkboard or overhead transparency. Under personality, write the words "heredity" and "environment." Ask the students to define personality. Discuss how heredity and environment influence personality. Ask the students which they think is more influential, heredity or environment. **L2**

Class Activity

Write Ask the students to write personality traits of someone whom they know who has a "good personality." Write the students' lists on the chalkboard. Ask the class to discuss why these are desirable traits. **L2**

INTERACTIVE CHALKBOARD with Image Bank

PowerPoint® Presentations

This CD-ROM is an editable Microsoft® PowerPoint® presentation that includes:
- Lesson presentations
- Lesson checks
- Interactive graphics
- 5-Minute Checks
- Image Bank
- All transparencies

CRISS Project

Vocabulary Use the Sentence Synthesis Strategy on page 16T to ensure that the students fully grasp the concepts related to mental disorders.

National Health Education Standards
Pages 82–83: 1.1, 1.4, 6.1

Addictions

Explain the Concept

Addiction Define addiction for the students. An addiction is a compelling desire to use a drug or engage in a specific behavior, continued use despite negative consequences, and loss of control. Explain that an addiction is not always substance-related, but can instead involve a behavior such as gambling or thrill-seeking.

Class Discussion

Characteristics of Addiction Have students read "At Risk for Addictions" on this page, which lists the characteristics that put a teen at risk for developing an addiction. Start a class discussion about how these characteristics could lead to an addiction. Some of these characteristics cannot be changed, such as genetic vulnerability or a traumatic childhood, but ask the students how a person who had some of the modifiable characteristics could trade them for more healthful behaviors. **L2**

NHES Assessment/SCASS

Selected Response To which of the following could a person become addicted?
A. drugs
B. exercise
C. perfectionism
D. *all of the above*

A compelling desire to use a drug or engage in a specific behavior, continued use despite negative consequences, and loss of control is an *addiction*. Some teens feel a compelling desire to drink alcohol or use other drugs when they have problems or feel bored, lonely, frustrated, or depressed. However, people can be addicted to things that are not substance-related, such as relationships, television, exercise, and shopping.

How Addictions Affect Health Status

An addiction can harm physical health. Using drugs, including nicotine and alcohol, can harm body organs or cause death. Exercising to extremes can cause injury or other health problems. Starving oneself can cause malnutrition and death.

An addiction can jeopardize safety. Teens who have a thrill-seeking addiction take unnecessary risks that might result in injury and death. Teens who use drugs might choose unsafe actions and have accidents. They might get into fights that result in injuries.

An addiction can harm relationships. Teens who have addictions focus their attention on drugs or on specific behaviors. This primary focus causes them to neglect other priorities. They neglect relationships. They deny and lie about their addictions.

An addiction can cause problems with the law. Drinking alcohol and gambling, including the purchase of lottery tickets, is illegal for minors. The use of marijuana, Ecstasy, and other drugs also is illegal. Teens might steal money to support their gambling addiction. All of these things can cause legal problems for teens.

An addiction can jeopardize financial health. Teens with shopping addiction might overspend, borrow credit cards, or steal to pay for purchases. Teens with drug addiction might spend large amounts of money on drugs. Teens with gambling addiction may continue betting when they do not have any more money. This can lead to large amounts of debt that will affect the teen's ability to buy a car or get a loan from a bank for school in the future.

At Risk for Addictions

Teens who are at risk for developing addictions may have one or more of the following characteristics:

- depression or a negative self-esteem
- genetic vulnerability
- feelings of guilt or shame
- traumatic childhoods
- feelings of tension, anxiety, boredom, or loneliness
- difficulty expressing feelings
- trouble managing anger

- trouble accepting responsibility for their actions
- a constant need for approval
- a need to control others
- poor coping skills
- difficulty with authority figures
- difficulty delaying gratification
- personal problems that they deny

84 UNIT 2 • Mental and Emotional Health

🛡 Sensitive Issues

Getting Help for Addictions Students might have family members or friends who have addictions. Students themselves might have addictions. Things that are important to teens can be addictive, such as exercise, shopping, eating, or dieting. Tobacco is addictive. Be aware that some students may have a need for help with an addiction of their own or want to know how to help someone close to them. Know what resources are available should a student ask for help.

National Health Education Standards

Pages 84–85: 1.1, 1.2, 1.4, 1.8, 5.1, 5.7

A Teen's Guide to Addictions

Drug addiction The compelling desire to use a drug even though it harms the body, mind, or relationships is *drug addiction.* Teens with drug addiction feel the need to drink alcohol or use other drugs when they are anxious, bored, frustrated, lonely, or depressed. They depend on alcohol or other drugs to change their moods. They drink alcohol or use other drugs to avoid facing problems and will usually deny that they drink alcohol or use other drugs for these reasons.

Exercise addiction The compelling desire to exercise is *exercise addiction.* Teens with exercise addiction make exercise the main focus of their lives. They exercise to relieve tension and to feel in control of their lives. They put their exercise routine ahead of family, friends, studying, and other responsibilities. They may push themselves to the limit and injure themselves. If they do not exercise, they are depressed, anxious, and unhappy and may have difficulty sleeping.

Gambling addiction The compelling desire to bet money or other things is called *gambling addiction.* Though you may think that a person with a gambling addiction spends much of his or her time in casinos, there are other ways of gambling that also can be addictive. Lotteries and sporting events are two other forms of gambling that can be addictive. Teens with gambling addiction often are bored and restless. They get a "high" when they place bets. Teens who develop gambling addiction can struggle to control the urge to gamble for the rest

of their lives. More than one-third of teens with gambling addiction have other addictions as well.

Nicotine addiction The compelling desire for nicotine is *nicotine addiction* or *nicotine dependence.* Nicotine is a stimulant drug found in tobacco products, including cigarettes and chewing tobacco. Teens addicted to nicotine may develop their schedule around smoking or chewing tobacco. They may rely on nicotine to wake up in the morning. They may smoke or chew to relieve tension or boredom.

Perfectionism The compelling desire to be flawless is *perfectionism.* Perfectionists are overly critical of themselves and of others. Nothing is ever good enough for them. Perfectionism is the result of feeling inadequate and insecure. Some teens become perfectionists because adults had unrealistic expectations of them during their childhood.

Relationship addiction The compelling desire to be connected to another person is *relationship addiction.* Teens with relationship addiction use relationships like they would drugs. When they feel depressed or insecure, contact with a specific person gives them a quick fix. But they feel better only for a brief time. They need the other person to "fill up" their emptiness. They feel a constant need to be with this other person. Teens with relationship addiction often are described as being needy. The person with whom they have a relationship feels suffocated and drained of energy.

Make the Connection

Alcoholism For more information on alcoholism, see page 419 in Lesson 37.

Quick Demo

A Magnetic Attraction You will need a block of wood and two magnets. Explain to the class that the block of wood represents a person who does not possess characteristics that put him or her at risk for addictions. One magnet represents a person who is at risk for addiction and the other magnet represents a behavior that can be addictive, such as gambling or drinking alcohol. Place the block of wood against the behavior magnet. Ask the class to note they are not attracted. Then place the two magnets together. Explain to the class that having risk factors for addiction does not guarantee that a person will become addicted to something, but it makes it much harder for that person to resist addictive behavior. **ELL**

Class Activity

Effects of Addiction Provide the students with a list of the addictions that are found on pages 85 and 86. Have students discuss how each addiction affects a person's physical health, safety, relationships with others, and legal and financial status. **L2**

INTERACTIVE CHALKBOARD with Image Bank

Teaching Transparency
Page 23, **Unit 2 Fast File Resources**

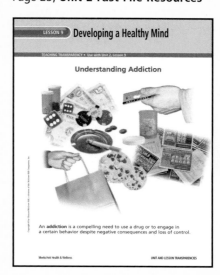

LESSON 9 Developing a Healthy Mind

TEACHING TRANSPARENCY • Use with Unit 2, Lesson 9

Understanding Addiction

An **addiction** is a compelling need to use a drug or to engage in a certain behavior despite negative consequences and loss of control.

Meeks Heit Health & Wellness   UNIT AND LESSON TRANSPARENCIES

⟨F⟩ **Cross-Curricular Connections**

Language Arts Ask students to write an essay about one of the addictions on pages 85 and 86. Have them address ideas about how these addictions may develop, the influences in society that might support the addiction, and how a person can resist the addiction. Ask them to address the legal implications that could come about as a result of an addiction, such as being caught driving while intoxicated. Finally, have students discuss the effects addiction may have on family and friends of a person who is addicted to a certain behavior or activity. **L2**

Teacher FYI

Multiple Addictions Explain to the class why a person with one addiction is more likely to develop other addictions. People can have certain genetic traits or personality characteristics that increase their risk for addictions. Some of these characteristics are depression, anxiety, difficulty expressing emotions or anger, poor coping skills, and the need to control others.

5-Minute Check

Page 29, Unit 2 Fast File Resources

1. What is personality? *It is an individual's unique pattern of characteristics.*

2. Why is it important to know and understand your personality type? *because it helps you to understand yourself and get a better grasp of how you approach and respond to people and things*

3. How can an addiction harm relationships? *People who have an addiction focus on the addiction and neglect and lie to the people in their lives.*

4. What are indicators of a relationship addiction? *Indicators might include one person feeling suffocated and drained of energy. The person with the relationship addiction acts needy and seems to be always in contact with the other person.*

5. What is a thrill-seeking addiction? *It is the compelling desire to take unnecessary risks.*

 Did You Know?

Gambling and Substance Addictions People addicted to gambling are more likely to become addicted to alcohol or other drugs.

Shopping addiction The compelling desire to purchase things is called *shopping addiction.* Teens with shopping addiction may describe themselves as "born to shop" and may "shop 'til they drop." These teens are insecure. Shopping gives them a quick fix for depressed feelings. Salespeople may give them special attention. They feel in control and powerful when they make purchases. After a shopping spree, they often feel guilty. Shopping addiction can lead to severe emotional and financial problems.

Television addiction and computer addiction Some teens are addicted to television or computers. *Television addiction* is the compelling desire to watch television. *Computer addiction* is the compelling desire to play computer games or engage in other computer activities. Teens with these addictions plan their schedules around television or computer use. They might watch television or be on the computer six to seven hours a day.

Some teens become addicted to gambling using instant lottery tickets. ▼

When they become anxious, lonely, or bored, they turn on the TV or the computer. They get a quick fix. They are unable to manage their time and get other things done. As a result, they have less time to be involved in school activities.

Thrill-seeking addiction The compelling desire to take unnecessary risks is called *thrill-seeking addiction.* Teens with thrill-seeking addiction enjoy scary situations. They are willing to take dangerous dares. During risky experiences, there are biochemical changes in the brain that can produce a pleasurable sensation. Some teens get hooked on these sensations and constantly seek these changes. Thrill-seeking becomes a quick fix. Teens with this addiction may take unnecessary risks and injure themselves.

Workaholism The compelling desire to work to fill an emptiness is called *workaholism.* Teens who are workaholics may feel the need to work whenever they are not in school. This may include excessive studying. This does not mean that all teens who study and get good grades are workaholics. It is healthy to set goals and work hard to reach them.

Teens who have workaholism, however, do not enjoy themselves when they are not working or studying. Working long hours keeps them from dealing with other aspects of their lives, such as emotions and relationships. They need the constant praise they may get from work. They get a high from work that helps them overcome feelings of depression and are anxious, tense, and upset when they are not working.

🏠 Family Involvement

Monitor and Discuss People can have an addiction to watching television or using their computers. They may deny their addiction. Have students analyze their need to watch television or use a computer. Ask the students to record in their health journals how much time they spend watching television and using the computer for purposes other than school or work over the course of a week. Have students share the results with their parents or guardian and ask for their reaction. Then, ask students to write a short report on the activity. Have students answer the following questions: Were you surprised at how much time you spend watching television and using a computer? Do think you spend too much time on these activities? Do you think it is healthful to spend a majority of your free time on these activities? Why or why not? **L2**

What to Do About Addictions

Having one or more addictions is a serious threat to a person's health. Be on the lookout for signs of addictions in yourself and in others. The following suggestions will help you recognize addictions and get appropriate treatment.

Stay informed. Review up-to-date information about addictions. Understand the causes and treatments of addictions.

Review the list of characteristics of teens who are at risk for developing addictions. Do any of these characteristics describe you, a friend, or a family member? If so, what can you do to protect yourself from addictions?

Recognize addictions in yourself and others. Seek help or encourage others to seek help to control their addictions.

Get help for addictions. Teens often deny addictions and refuse to get help. They may need to be confronted by parents, guardians, or other caring people.

A *formal intervention* is an action by people, such as family members, who want a person to get treatment. The people involved in a formal intervention prepare ahead of time. They might meet with a trained counselor. They are prepared to explain to the teen how his or her addiction affects them.

During a formal intervention, these people confront the teen by sharing their observations. They explain why treatment is needed.

▲ Sometimes a formal intervention is used to confront a teen with an addiction.

Page 92 in this lesson discusses treatment for addictions.

Teens who have been treated for an addiction may have a relapse. A *relapse* is a return to a previous behavior or condition. These teens return to their addiction when they feel lonely, depressed, or anxious. To avoid relapse, teens must stick to their plan for recovery.

Part of any recovery plan for teens with addictions is to have a support network. The purpose of a support network is to allow teens to feel secure enough to share their feelings and needs. People in the support network also provide encouragement.

Signs of Addiction

Any of the following symptoms are signs of addiction:

- having a compelling desire to take a drug or engage in a behavior
- taking a drug or engaging in a behavior instead of dealing with feelings of anxiety, depression, boredom, or loneliness
- feeling bad about oneself after taking a drug or engaging in a behavior
- taking a drug or engaging in a behavior even when there are negative consequences
- trying to stop taking a drug or engaging in a behavior, but being unable to do so

LESSON 9 • Developing a Healthy Mind **87**

Codependence

Codependency

S ome people get very involved with someone who has an addiction, whether the person's addiction is to alcohol, drugs, gambling, work, or another activity. They want to rescue the person and fix the person's problems. They become a codependent. **Codependency** is a problem in which a person neglects himself or herself to care for, control, or try to "fix" someone else.

What to Know About Codependency

People who are codependent are enablers. An **enabler** is a person who supports the harmful behavior of others. For example, an enabler might lend money to someone with a gambling addiction or make excuses for a friend who uses drugs. An enabler might praise someone who exercises to extremes.

These responses encourage people who have addictions to continue their addictions. People who are codependent are unable to share their feelings.

People with codependency may benefit from individual, family, or group therapy, which will be discussed later in this lesson. They also may benefit from being in a support group. A **support group** is a group of people who help one another recover from an addiction, a particular disease, or a difficult situation.

Recovery from codependency and codependent relationships involves developing a better sense of self, learning to share feelings, learning to stay focused on solving one's own problems, allowing other people to be responsible for their own lives, and using honest talk to confront people with problems.

Characteristics of Codependent People

People who are codependent usually:

- deny their feelings
- focus on fixing other people's problems
- try to control other people
- feel responsible for what other people say or do
- seek the approval of others
- have difficulty having fun

- have difficulty allowing others to care for them
- try to protect others from the harmful consequences of their behavior
- do not meet their own needs
- avoid living their own lives by concentrating on other people

▲ Support groups can help teens with codependency.

88   UNIT 2 • Mental and Emotional Health

Ⓓ Ⓘ Differentiated Instruction

Mental Disorders

A behavioral or psychological syndrome or pattern that occurs in an individual and that is associated with distress or disability or with a significantly increased risk of suffering, death, pain, disability, or an important loss of freedom is a **mental disorder.** The causes of mental disorders can be biological, psychological, and/or behavioral. Biological influences on mental disorders are caused by genes, physical injuries, and illnesses that affect the brain. Some causes include strokes, brain tumors, automobile accidents, alcoholism, sexually transmitted diseases, and meningitis. Psychological influences on mental disorders include stress, traumatic experiences, and poor coping skills.

A Guide to Mental Disorders

Anxiety disorders A disorder in which real or imagined threats prevent a person from enjoying life is an ***anxiety disorder.*** There are several forms of anxiety disorder.

A chronic or long-lasting state of anxiety, fear, and tenseness is called ***general anxiety disorder (GAD).*** People with this disorder feel anxious most of the time even when there is little or nothing to worry about. People with GAD usually have physical symptoms, such as fatigue, headaches, muscle tension, muscle aches, difficulty swallowing, trembling, irritability, sweating, increased heart rate, and hot flashes.

A disorder in which a person has persistent, unwelcome thoughts or images and engages in certain rituals is called ***obsessive-compulsive disorder (OCD).*** The disturbing thoughts or images are called obsessions. The rituals performed to try to prevent them are called compulsions. The rituals relieve anxiety temporarily, but they do not cause pleasure. People with this disorder spend large amounts of time engaging in the rituals.

A disorder in which feelings of terror strike suddenly and repeatedly with no warning is called ***panic disorder.*** These feelings are accompanied by panic attacks. A ***panic attack*** is a period of intense fear accompanied by bodily changes. Bodily changes may include increased heart rate, weakness, faintness, and dizziness. People who have panic disorder can't predict when a panic attack will occur. Symptoms usually peak in 10 minutes, but they may last longer.

A ***specific phobia*** is a disorder in which there is excessive fear of certain objects, situations, or people that pose little or no actual danger. The fear feels very real to the person, even though it is not realistic. A panic attack may occur when the feared object, situation, or person is near. The causes of specific phobias are not well understood. Examples of common phobias are fear of spiders or closed spaces.

A disorder in which a person is overly anxious and self-conscious in everyday social situations is called ***social anxiety disorder,*** or ***social phobia.***

Did You Know?

Mental Disorders in the U.S. Each year, roughly 26 percent of the adult U.S. population has a diagnosable mental disorder.

Reading Review

1. What is an addiction?
2. How can a support group help people with codependence?
3. What are the symptoms of a panic attack?

LESSON 9 • Developing a Healthy Mind **89**

Teacher FYI

Living with a Mental Disorder
Explain to students that people live with all kinds of health conditions. Often they must make adjustments in their lifestyle. For example, people who have diabetes learn to manage their condition with regular checkups and by controlling their diet. People who have mental disorders also can learn to manage their condition.

Reading Review

1. *a compelling desire to use a drug or engage in a specific behavior despite negative consequences and loss of control*
2. *by helping develop a better sense of self and teaching how to share feelings*
3. *intense fear accompanied by increased heart rate, weakness, faintness, or dizziness*

🔁 Cross-Curricular Connections

Psychology Assign the students to research one of the six anxiety disorders studied in this section. Students should define the disorder and describe the symptoms. Have students research the cause of the disorder and the recommended treatment. Ask students to compare this type of illness with another illness, such as cancer. Ask them to answer this question: Do you see any differences in the way people with mental disorders are treated, compared to the way people who have cancer or another "physical" illness are treated? Ask students to share their findings with the class. **L2**

National Health Education Standards
Pages 88–89: 1.1, 1.2, 2.1, 5.1

Explain the Concept

Eating Disorders Explain the difference between anorexia nervosa and bulimia. Anorexia nervosa is a disorder in which a person does not eat in order to lose weight and weighs 15 percent or more below the healthful weight for his or her age and gender. Bulimia is an eating disorder in which a person binges on food and then vomits or uses laxatives to rid the body of the food. Define the term "eating disorder" for the students and ask them to give reasons why teens may be at a higher risk than adults for experiencing eating disorders. You may want to review Lesson 29, which contains more information about various eating disorders, with the class.

Class Discussion

Eating Disorder Ask students to list factors that contribute to eating disorders. *Answers can include low self-esteem, lack of self-confidence, ads in magazines and on television, too much emphasis on being thin.* Write the students' answers on the chalkboard and discuss how students can identify this problem in themselves and others. Discuss ways they can find help for an eating disorder, or help someone change harmful eating habits. **L2**

Class Activity

Analyze Ask students to bring in magazine ads showing teens who are very thin. Explain to the class that bulimia is a problem many teens face and that those with bulimia often eat not just when they are hungry, but when they are angry, tired, sad, or lonely. Ask students to analyze the ads and discuss the following questions: Why might teens who have negative self-esteem reach for food after seeing these ads? What are healthful ways of dealing with feelings of sadness and negative self-esteem? How might the ads affect someone who has anorexia? **L2**

Make the Connection

Eating Disorders For more information on eating disorders, see page 332 in Lesson 29.

Physical symptoms are similar to other anxiety disorders. People with social phobia irrationally fear they are being watched and judged by others at all times and are terrified of being embarrassed or humiliated by their actions. Social phobia can be limited to one situation, such as public speaking, or it might include all social situations.

A disorder in which aftereffects of a terrifying event keep a person from living in a normal way is called ***post-traumatic stress disorder (PTSD)***. People with PTSD often have frightening thoughts and memories of an event. They may have nightmares and disturbing thoughts during the day. They may feel emotionally numb. PTSD can result from any number of traumatic incidents including events, such as war or abuse, or other causes, such as natural disasters or witnessing a bombing. Seeking professional help, developing stress-management skills, and talking to a responsible adult are ways to cope with anxiety.

Cognitive disorder A disorder in which a person's brain deteriorates in function is a ***cognitive disorder***. A condition in which brain deterioration affects memory, language, and reasoning is ***dementia***. Dementia differs from forgetfulness associated with aging, tiredness, and depression. Dementia progresses from mild through severe stages and is fatal. Alzheimer's disease is a common cause of dementia.

Conduct disorder A disorder in which a person regularly violates the rights of others and breaks social rules is a ***conduct disorder***. People with conduct disorder might bully others, start fights, or be cruel to animals. They might damage property, steal, or set fires. They might be deceitful. These people violate rules and may have little remorse for their wrong actions. They also may abuse alcohol and other drugs.

Eating disorders A mental disorder in which a person has a compelling need to starve, to binge, or to binge and purge, is an ***eating disorder***. To binge is to eat large amounts of food over a short period of time. To purge is to rid the body of food by vomiting or by using laxatives or diuretics. People who have eating disorders are more at risk for depression, anxiety, and substance abuse.

An eating disorder in which a person starves his or her body and weighs 15 percent or more below the healthful weight for his or her age and gender is called ***anorexia nervosa***. People with anorexia typically have a distorted body image, and see themselves as being overweight even though they are overly thin. They also may exercise to extremes, vomit, and use laxatives or diuretics.

An eating disorder in which a person binges and then purges is called ***bulimia***. People with bulimia binge on foods or eat large quantities of food. They will then purge by vomiting or using laxatives or diuretics.

A disorder in which people binge on large quantities of food is ***binge eating disorder***. This disorder can increase a person's risk for obesity and chronic diseases.

Mood disorders A mental disorder involving moods that are extreme is a ***mood disorder***. A mood disorder is sometimes called an affective disorder.

90   UNIT 2 • Mental and Emotional Health

Differentiated Instruction

Gifted and Talented Ask students to research why more females than males experience eating disorders. Have them write a short paper or create a multimedia presentation to report their findings. Ask them to include research about why more males are experiencing eating disorders in recent years. Have students include information on the causes and effects of eating disorders. Ask students to address the following questions: What effect do television shows and movies have on a teen's self-image? What about magazines and retail stores that target teens? Is the effect different for males and females? **L3**

A mood disorder called ***clinical depression*** is characterized by long-lasting feelings of hopelessness, sadness, or helplessness. People are considered clinically depressed if they have not had a recent trauma and still experience five of nine general symptoms for two weeks or more. General symptoms include deep sadness, apathy, fatigue, agitation, sleep disturbances, weight or appetite changes, lack of concentration, feelings of worthlessness, and morbid thoughts.

A disorder in which a person's moods vary from extreme happiness to extreme depression is called ***bipolar disorder.*** During the manic phase, the person may experience great joy for no reason and be very talkative and restless. During the depressive phase, the person is in a passive mood, has little energy, and may think of suicide. This phase ends when the person's mood swings back to the manic phase.

A type of depression that occurs when a person has reduced exposure to sunlight is called ***seasonal affective disorder (SAD).*** People with this disorder usually experience symptoms during the months when there is reduced sunlight. Symptoms include increased appetite, decreased physical activity, irritability, and general depression. Special light therapy for short periods daily will relieve many of these symptoms.

Personality disorders A disorder in which a person's patterns of thinking, feeling, and acting interfere with daily living is a ***personality disorder.***

A personality disorder in which a person's patterns of behavior are in conflict with society is called ***antisocial personality disorder.*** People who are antisocial are often hateful, aggressive, and irritable. They may be indifferent to others' needs and feel no remorse for their actions.

A disorder in which a person has sudden changes in mood, relationships, and behaviors is called ***borderline personality disorder (BPD).*** People with borderline personality disorder are impulsive. Their feelings toward family and friends can shift suddenly from love to anger. They fear abandonment. Among people with BPD, there is a high rate of self-injury with or without suicidal intent.

Schizophrenia A disorder in which there is a breakdown in logical thought processes is called ***schizophrenia*** (skiht suh FREE nee uh). The breakdown results in unusual behaviors. People with this disorder tend to have hallucinations, delusions, and a distorted perception of reality. Actions, words, and emotions are confused and usually are inappropriate. Schizophrenia is not curable, but it can be treated with medication.

Somatoform disorders A disorder in which a person has symptoms of disease but no physical cause can be found is a ***somatoform disorder*** (so MA tuh form). A disorder in which a person is constantly worried about illness is called ***hypochondria*** (hy puh KAHN dree uh). People with hypochondria misinterpret aches, pains, and other symptoms, and worry about developing an illness or disease although they are assured they are healthy.

▲ Teens with a distorted body image are at risk for developing an eating disorder.

Reading Review

1. What causes PTSD?
2. What are the symptoms of clinical depression?
3. How is schizophrenia treated?

LESSON 9 • Developing a Healthy Mind **91**

Reading Review

1. *experiencing a terrifying event*
2. *deep sadness, apathy, fatigue, agitation, sleep disturbances, weight or appetite changes, lack of concentration, feelings of worthlessness, and morbid thoughts*
3. *with medication*

🖤 **Health Project**

Staying Informed Ask students to make an informational poster or flyer about one of the disorders discussed in the section on mood disorders, personality disorders, or somatoform disorders. Have them identify the symptoms of the condition and include information about where someone can get help if they feel they have the disorder. Encourage students to include on the posters the idea that there is nothing wrong with seeking help if they recognize some of the symptoms in themselves. Hang the posters up in your class or hallway as a reference for other students. **L2**

Teacher FYI

Getting Help Many teens may feel embarrassed or ashamed about having symptoms of mental disorders described in this lesson. Explain to them that, as they have read in this lesson, mental-health problems are caused by very real, sometimes physical problems and that it is not a shameful thing to tell your parent, teacher, or doctor that you need help. Tell them to remember that 1 in 5 Americans have been diagnosed with a mental disorder. Encourage your students to seek out help if they recognize any of the symptoms discussed in this lesson.

3 Assess

Vocabulary Practice

Page 22, **Unit 2 Fast File Resources**

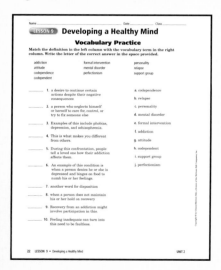

National Health Education Standards

Pages 92–93: 1.5, 3.2, 3.4

Mental-Health Services

Many people experience some anxiety and sometimes are apprehensive without any apparent cause. There are strategies for coping with this kind of anxiety. However, people who have anxiety disorders, other mental disorders, or addictions, benefit from treatment.

Did You Know?

The Homeless and Mental-Health Services An estimated 20 to 25 percent of homeless people suffer from mental illness. The Center for Mental Health Services (CMHS) supports programs to assist people who are homeless who suffer from mental illness.

Treatment for Mental Disorders and Addictions

Formal intervention A formal intervention may be needed to help people who deny their condition and refuse to get help.

Evaluation People who have mental disorders and addictions may need both a physical examination and a psychological or psychiatric evaluation. A physician can do the physical examination, discover or rule out physical causes for mental disorders, and prescribe medication, if necessary.

Other professionals, such as psychiatrists, psychologists, and social workers, also can help. A ***psychiatrist*** is a physician who specializes in the diagnosis and treatment of mental disorders and can prescribe medication. A ***psychologist*** is a professional who specializes in the diagnosis of and counseling for mental and emotional problems. This person cannot prescribe medications. A ***psychiatric social worker*** specializes in working with clients with mental and emotional problems.

Medication A physician or psychiatrist will determine if a person will benefit from taking prescription drugs. These drugs can take several weeks to become effective, and a person must be monitored for potential side effects while using them.

Inpatient and outpatient treatment Inpatient treatment involves staying at a hospital or other treatment facility during part or all of their treatment. Outpatient treatment involves living at home, but visiting a hospital, doctor's office, or other facility for treatment.

Therapy After an evaluation, an approach to treatment is outlined. People who have mental disorders and addictions may benefit from individual, group, or family therapy, or a combination of these therapies.

Support groups People who have mental disorders and/or addictions may benefit from being in a support group. There also are support groups for family members and friends.

Cross-Curricular Connections

History Ask students to research the history of mental disorders and mental-health services in America. Have them write a report focusing on the attitudes toward mental disorders and the types of treatment and medication used in the nineteenth and early twentieth centuries, and how these differ today. Ask them to address types of illnesses diagnosed as mental disorders in the past that today are not considered illnesses at all. Share some of the best reports with the class and discuss the reasons why mental disorders were misunderstood in the past. **L3**

9 STUDY GUIDE

addiction
anxiety disorder
attitude
codependency
formal intervention
mental disorder
panic disorder
perfectionism
personality
relapse
support group
workaholism

Key Terms Review

Complete these fill-in-the-blank statements with the lesson Key Terms on the left. Do not write in this book.

1. A(n) _____ is an action by people, such as family members, who want a person to get treatment.

2. _____ is a disorder in which feelings of terror strike suddenly.

3. _____ is an individual's unique pattern of characteristics.

4. _____ is a problem in which people neglect themselves to care for, control, or try to "fix" someone else.

5. A(n) _____ is a feeling or emotion toward someone or something.

6. A(n) _____ is when someone returns to a previous behavior or condition.

7. A(n) _____ is a compelling desire to use a drug or engage in a specific behavior, despite negative consequences.

8. The causes of _____ can be biological, psychological, and/or behavioral.

9. _____ is the compelling need to be flawless.

10. A(n) _____ is a group of people who help one another recover from an addiction, a particular disease, or a difficult situation.

Recalling the Facts

11. What influences personality?

12. How might addictions affect health status?

13. How might a person recover from codependence and having codependent relationships?

14. What is a cognitive disorder?

15. What are anxiety disorders?

16. What are five signs of an addiction?

17. What are types of treatment for mental disorders?

18. What are the main categories of mental disorders?

Critical Thinking

19. How do anxiety disorders and mood disorders differ? How are they the same?

20. Would a person in the northern or southern U.S. be more likely to suffer from seasonal affective disorder? Explain.

21. If a person looks of normal weight and has not lost weight, is it likely that he or she has anorexia nervosa? Explain.

22. Discuss why codependency is dangerous.

Real-Life Applications

23. Why do you think people with schizophrenia may have difficulty taking their medications regularly?

24. How do you think behaviors become addictive?

25. Why do you think so many people who have an addiction are in denial?

26. Why do you think a person with one addiction is at risk for other addictions?

Activities

Responsible Decision Making

27. **Role-Play** A community has a lottery that has grown to over $25 million. A teen plays the lottery every week and is in debt. He asks you to lend him money. Pair up with another student to role-play this situation. Refer to the Responsible Decision-Making Model on page 61 for help.

Sharpen Your Life Skills

28. **Advocate for Health** Choose one of the addictions described in this lesson. Prepare a collage of pictures that represents the addiction, including what the addiction focuses on, as well as possible health consequences of the addiction. Explain your collage to the class.

Visit www.glencoe.com for more *Health & Wellness* quizzes.

STUDY GUIDE

Key Terms Review

1. formal intervention
2. Panic disorder
3. Personality
4. Codependency
5. attitude
6. relapse
7. addiction
8. mental disorder
9. Perfectionism
10. support group

Recalling the Facts

11. heredity, environment, attitudes, and behaviors

12. harm physical health, jeopardize safety, harm relationships, cause problems with the law, and jeopardize financial health

13. Refer to page 88.

14. disorders in which a person's brain deteriorates in function

15. disorder in which real or imagined fears prevent a person from enjoying life

16. See the list on page 87.

17. formal intervention, evaluation, medication, inpatient or outpatient treatment, therapy, recovery plan, support groups

18. anxiety, cognitive, conduct, eating, mood, personality, schizophrenia, somatoform

Critical Thinking

19. Anxiety disorder exists when real or imagined fears prevent someone from enjoying life. Mood disorders involve moods that are extreme. They both affect quality of life.

20. northern, because this area receives less sunlight than the South

21. No, a person with anorexia generally is 15 percent or more below normal weight.

22. Codependent people neglect themselves and keep others from learning how to take care of themselves.

Real-Life Applications

23. Schizophrenia causes a breakdown in logical thought processes.

---

24. Behaviors may provide a "quick fix" that makes a person feel better.

25. Denial is easier than facing a problem.

26. Certain personality characteristics can make a person vulnerable to other addictions.

Activities

Responsible Decision Making

27. The teen has signs of gambling addiction. Loaning him money is not a responsible decision. It is not healthful for him to have this addiction. You should tell an adult so the teen can get help.

Sharpen Your Life Skills

28. Students' collages should include images of people engaged in an addictive behavior and negative consequences of the addiction. Have students discuss the different collages.

Expressing Emotions and Managing Stress

If time does not permit an in-depth study of this topic, use the following activities in this Teacher Wraparound Edition:

- Quick Demo, p. 96
- Class Discussion, p. 99
- Class Activity, p. 103
- Class Discussion, p. 105

1 Focus

HEALTH GOALS **Stress Management** Have students respond to the second Health Goal for this lesson by listing in their health journals five stress management skills. *Skills might include: talking to others, keeping a journal, keeping a budget, having good friends, and exercising.* **L2**

Write ABOUT IT!

Journaling Tell students that different people deal with stress in different ways, and that physical activity is just one option.

Expressing Emotions and Managing Stress

HEALTH GOALS
- **I will express emotions in healthful ways.**
- **I will use stress-management skills.**

Suppose someone asked you to write a "top ten list of ways for teens to maintain optimal health." Your list might include expressing emotions in healthful ways and having a plan to manage stress. This lesson explains the link between anger, stress, and health.

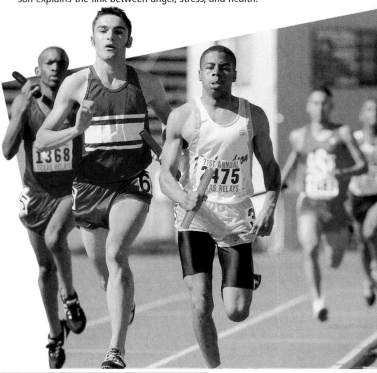

What You'll Learn

1. Explain the mind-body connection. *(p. 95)*
2. Outline guidelines for expressing emotions in healthful ways. *(p. 96)*
3. Discuss hidden anger, anger cues, and anger-management skills. *(pp. 97, 98)*
4. Explain the bodily changes caused by stress during each of the three stages of the general adaptation syndrome. *(p. 100)*
5. Explain ways that prolonged stress can affect health. *(p. 101)*
6. Identify life changes that are most stressful for teens. *(p. 102)*
7. List and discuss stress-management skills. *(pp. 104, 105)*

Why It's Important

Stress is linked to many of the ten leading causes of death, including heart disease, cancer, stroke, and injuries.

Key Terms

- emotion
- mind-body connection
- psychosomatic disease
- hidden anger
- hostility
- serotonin
- anger-management skills
- stress
- general adaptation syndrome (GAS)
- stress-management skills

Write ABOUT IT!

Writing About Managing Stress Suppose you are juggling a lot and you are starting to feel really stressed out. One of your classmates tells you that a good way to relieve stress is to get some exercise. She urges you to try running track after school to blow off some steam. What would you do? After you read the information on stress-management skills on page 104, write a response to this situation in your health journal.

National Health Education Standards—Guide for Lesson 10		
1.1	Predict how healthy behaviors can impact health status.	pp. 95–97, 103
1.2	Describe the interrelationships of emotional, intellectual, physical, and social health.	pp. 94, 95–97, 100–103, 107
1.5	Propose ways to reduce or prevent injuries and health problems.	pp. 94, 95, 96, 97, 98–99, 100–102, 103, 104–105, 106, 107

The Mind-Body Connection

A specific feeling is called an ***emotion***. You likely have experienced many emotions, such as anger, sadness, happiness, anxiety, or others. Did you know that there is a powerful connection between your thoughts, emotions, and bodily responses? What you think and feel can affect what happens to your body, and what happens in your body can affect how you think and feel.

What to Know About the Mind-Body Connection

The ***mind-body connection*** is the relationship between a person's thoughts, emotions, and bodily responses. Consider the following example. Suppose you are worried about a test tomorrow. The emotion of worry might trigger certain bodily responses, such as an increase in heart rate and blood pressure. If this continues, you might have difficulty getting a good night's sleep. You might be tired the next day because your emotional state triggered changes in your body.

Sometimes your emotional state can trigger illnesses and disorders. A ***psychosomatic*** (si koh suh MA tihk) ***disease*** is a physical illness or disorder that is caused or aggravated by emotional responses. Suppose you have an argument with a friend. You are upset about what was said. Your upset feelings might cause a headache or stomachache. Some teens have chronic physical conditions that are aggravated by emotions.

Asthma is a chronic condition in which breathing becomes difficult. A teen with asthma might be fearful of speaking in front of the class. When the teacher asks him to give a report, he might have difficulty breathing. His emotional state aggravated his asthma.

> **Make the Connection**
>
> **Influences on Health** For more information on influences on health, see page 35 in Lesson 4.

◄ Schoolwork and studying can be a source of stress, which can cause changes in the body.

Lesson Resource Manager

- **Unit 2 Fast File Resources**
  Reading Strategy, p. 35
  Vocabulary Practice, p. 36
  Transparency Master and Worksheet, p. 37
  Real-Life Health, p. 39
  Real-Life Health, p. 41
  5-Minute Check, p. 43
  Lesson 10 Quiz, p. 45
- **Unit 2 Transparency**
- **Lesson 10 Transparency**

- **Reading Essentials**
- **Technology**
  TeacherWorks™ CD-ROM
  StudentWorks™ CD-ROM
  Reading Essentials CD-ROM
  Exam*View*® Assessment Suite
  Vocabulary Puzzlemaker

The Mind-Body Connection

2 Teach

Class Discussion

Define Write the words *emotions, mind-body connection,* and *psychosomatic disease* on the chalkboard or on an overhead transparency. Ask students to give examples of different emotions and events that might trigger each. Next, have students explain the connection between mental and physical health, and ask them to give examples of psychosomatic diseases. **L2**

Class Activity

Write Ask students to think about a time in their lives when their emotions affected them physically. Have them write a short paragraph describing the situation and explain why they think they were affected physically. **L2**

PowerPoint® Presentations

This CD-ROM is an editable Microsoft® PowerPoint® presentation that includes:
- Lesson presentations
- Lesson checks
- Interactive graphics
- 5-Minute Checks
- Image Bank
- All transparencies

Discussion Refer to the AuthenticQuestions Strategy on page 17T to stimulate whole-class discussion on anger, anger management, and stress.

> **National Health Education Standards**
> Pages 94–95: 1.1, 1.2, 1.5

95

Expressing Emotions in Healthful Ways

Quick Demo

Expressing Emotions Model for your students different ways of reacting to a situation (some healthful, some not). Ask the students to decide which are healthful, and discuss how they could make the other reactions more healthful. *Some suggested statements: I am so angry at you right now! Why can't you just be on time? Let me get a good night's sleep and see how I feel in the morning. I'm going to go for a run and think this through. I'm going to get her back for this.* **L2** **ELL**

Class Activity

In Groups Have students divide into small groups and discuss the five guidelines for expressing emotions in healthful ways. Assign each group one of the guidelines and ask them to give reasons why each bullet point below the guideline is important. (You may want to give one group both number one and number two, since those lists are short.) For example, one group will list and discuss why it is important to talk to parents about emotions, find out more information before responding, and rehearse what they would say before responding. Then, have each group report to the class what they discussed about each guideline. **L2**

H ow well do you express your emotions? When you express your emotions, are your actions responsible? Do you think about protecting your health when you experience an intense emotional response? Review the five guidelines that appear below for expressing emotions in healthful ways.

1. Identify the emotion.
   - What emotion am I experiencing?

2. Identify the source of the emotion.
   - Why do I feel this way?

3. Decide whether or not you need to respond right away.
   - Should I talk to a parent, guardian, or other responsible adult about the emotions I am experiencing?
   - Should I try to sort out my emotions by myself?
   - How might my parent, guardian, or mentor respond?
     - Do I need more information before I respond? How do I get the information I need?
     - If I respond based on the way I am feeling right now, will I regret it later on?
     - Do I need to rehearse what I will say before I respond?

4. Choose a responsible and healthful response.
   - What I-message might I use? For more information on I-messages, see p. 98.
   - Would it be helpful if I discussed my feelings with someone I trust, such as a parent, guardian or mentor?
   - Would it be helpful to express my emotions by writing in a journal?
   - Could I write a poem, sculpt clay, or draw a picture to express my emotions?

5. Protect your health.
   - Do I need extra sleep? Am I sleeping too much?
   - Do I need to work off my strong emotions with exercise?
   - Do I need to dissipate my strong emotions by spending healthful time with relatives or friends?
   - Am I aware of any physical disorders that might be connected to the emotional response I am experiencing? If so, I may need to see a physician.
   - Am I able to function in daily activities? If not, I may need to ask my parent or guardian about counseling.
   - What healthful outlets can I use to help me deal with my emotions?
   - How might I deal with this emotion in the future?

STRESS in the Media **Writing Activity** Identify five characters in your favorite television shows that were involved in some sort of emotional situation. When faced with a problem, how did they react? Did they express the emotions in healthful ways, or did they lash out at others? Write an entry in your health journal about how you would have reacted in the situations they faced. Discuss your answers with your classmates.

Teacher to Teacher

Schedule Provide each student with a blank schedule grid for one week, beginning at 12:00 A.M. and ending at 11:59 P.M. each day. The student will record what he or she does during the week. At the end of the week, students can evaluate their schedule by answering the following questions: Are they getting enough sleep? Are they engaged in too many activities? Are their schedules causing stress in their lives? What can they do to reduce their level of stress? **L2** **ELL**

James Schwarz
Columbus South High School, Columbus, OH

Angry Feelings

The feeling of being irritated or annoyed is called *anger*. Anger usually is a response to being hurt, frustrated, insulted, or rejected. An *anger trigger* is a thought or event that causes a person to become angry. An *anger cue* is a body change that occurs when a person is angry. Anger cues are an example of the powerful mind-body connection.

What to Know About Hidden Anger and Hostility

Anger that is not recognized and is expressed in inappropriate ways is called *hidden anger*. The following types of behavior may be signs of hidden anger: being negative, making cruel remarks to others, being sarcastic, procrastinating, or blowing up easily.

If you have hidden anger, you may experience anything from tense facial muscles, stiff or sore neck and shoulder muscles, ulcers, or headaches to high blood pressure. Stress also may have a role in development of some types of cancer.

Some teens are always angry. This chronic state of anger is called *hostility*. Hostility is a physical state that places the body at greater risk of developing severe illness. The person's body is in overdrive and gets very little rest. The person's immune system, the body system that fights disease, is suppressed.

Teens who exhibit hostility have lowered brain serotonin levels. *Serotonin* is a chemical that is involved in controlling states of consciousness and mood. Teens with lowered brain serotonin levels can become very aggressive.

Teens with hidden anger may express their anger in harmful ways. *Projection* is blaming others for actions or events for which they are not responsible. *Displacement* is the releasing of anger on someone or something other than the cause of the anger. For example, a teen might be angry at a parent because the parent would not let them attend a concert. The teen might displace their anger and get into an argument with a friend. The teen might not be angry with the friend, but takes their anger out on the friend.

Some teens don't know they have hidden anger. This lesson can help you recognize hidden anger and learn how to express your anger in healthful ways.

Symptoms of Anger

- rapid breathing
- increased heart rate
- rise in blood pressure
- increased sweating from sweat glands in the face
- sweaty palms
- dryness of the mouth
- increased alertness
- decreased sensitivity to pain
- increased muscle strength as a result of increased availability of blood sugar to the muscles
- tensed eyebrows
- pursed lips
- reddening of the face

LESSON 10 • Expressing Emotions and Managing Stress   **97**

Angry Feelings

Quick Demo

Hidden Anger You will need two cans or plastic bottles of the same kind of soda. Slightly open one can to relieve pressure, but don't let the students know. Show the cans of soda to the class and explain that they represent two teens. Ask students if they can see any difference in the teens. Next, ask a student to feel both cans. He or she will report that one can is more flexible. Explain that this teen has anger-management skills. Show students you have relieved pressure by slightly opening the can. Explain that they can relieve pressure by practicing anger-management skills. Shake the other can and pretend you are opening it in front of the class. Students will jump back thinking it will explode. Explain that this can represents a teen with hidden anger. Anger builds up and might explode at any time. **ELL**

Cross-Curricular Connections

Language Arts Ask the students to write a short story in which one or more characters displays hidden anger and uses projection and/or displacement to express their emotions. Encourage students to be creative with their stories. Ask them to include suggestions as to why their character has a problem managing his or her anger. Encourage students to demonstrate a knowledge of anger-management skills by mentioning some in the stories. Ask volunteers to share their stories with the class. **L2**

National Health Education Standards
Pages 96–97: 1.1, 1.2, 1.5, 4.1, 4.4, 6.1

Anger-Management Skills

Performance Event Ask the students to select one of the ten methods of anger management listed on this page and the next. Then, have students write about a situation in which they have used this method to deal with their own anger. Let students know that their papers are confidential. **L2**

5-Minute Check

Page 43, **Unit 2 Fast File Resources**

1. Give an example of a mind-body connection. *Answers might include: worrying about a test causes a person to lose sleep.*

2. What is a psychosomatic illness? *It is a physical illness or disorder caused by or aggravated by emotional responses.*

3. Give an example of a psychosomatic disease. *Answers include: headache or stomachache.*

4. What are the five guidelines for expressing emotions in healthful ways? *Identify the emotion, identify the source of the emotion, decide to respond immediately or not, choose a healthful response, and protect your health.*

5. Explain how hidden anger can negatively affect health. *Answers include: tension, sore muscles, ulcers, headaches, high blood pressure, and possibly even cancer.*

Anger-Management Skills

t is not harmful to feel angry. Feeling angry is a normal and healthful response to some situations. However, to protect your health and your relationships it is important to control anger and to express anger in appropriate ways. *Anger-management skills* are healthful ways to control and express anger.

How to Use Anger-Management Skills

Keep an anger self-inventory. An anger self-inventory helps you process your anger. Answer the following questions when you experience anger cues: What symptoms are you experiencing? What are the possible causes of your anger? Has your anger been growing over time? Is your anger justified, or are you overreacting to a situation or person? If your anger is justified, examine appropriate ways to express it.

Use self-statements to control anger. Self-statements are words a person can say to himself or herself when experiencing anger triggers and cues.

Some examples of self-statements are "I can manage this situation. I will take a few deep breaths before I say anything, or I'll just count to ten."

Use I-messages instead of you-messages. An I-message can be used to express your anger about the behavior of another person. Using I-messages keeps communication lines open. The other person can respond without feeling threatened. Using you-messages puts the other person on the defensive. The person may become angry. This escalates a problem rather than beginning to resolve it. For example, you could say "You don't listen to me," or "I feel that we aren't communicating effectively." The second option is less likely to upset the other person.

Write a letter. Writing a letter to the person or persons with whom you are angry can be helpful. It gives you a "time-out" and helps you to think clearly. You can express your reasons for being angry without being interrupted. You can hold the letter until you cool down. You can share your letter with a parent, guardian, or mentor. You can make changes to your letter before sending it. You may even decide not to send the letter after you have written it.

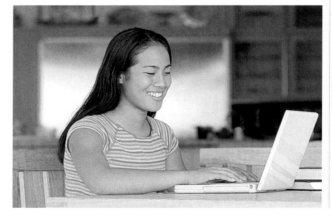
Writing a letter can help you manage anger. ▼

🔲 Family Involvement

Interview Ask students to interview family members about methods they use to manage feelings of anger. If students are unable to interview a family member, encourage them to talk to another trusted adult. Have students share the ten anger-management skills from this lesson, and encourage their family members to try to use these methods also. Ask students to write a short paper explaining some of the other methods they discovered after talking to their families and to describe how the methods in this lesson are working for them. Have students include the reasons why they think these skills help control anger. Remind students that there is no need to share any personal information with you or the class. **L2**

Write in a journal. Writing in a journal about anger can help you to keep track of when you feel angry and what you do about it. Write answers to the questions in the anger self-inventory. Review your answers to learn more about your anger. Share your journal with a parent, guardian, or mentor.

Reduce the effects of anger with physical activity. Vigorous physical activity keeps the body in good condition. It helps you maintain a healthful heart rate and blood pressure. When you experience anger cues, this will be helpful. Vigorous physical activity also uses up blood sugar. When you are angry, extra blood sugar is released into your bloodstream. This extra blood sugar goes to your muscles. By using your muscles, you use up this blood sugar.

Use other safe physical actions to blow off steam. Blow off steam in a physical way that will not have harmful consequences for you or others. Try to stomp on the floor, scream into a pillow, hit a pillow, or squeeze a tennis ball.

Breathe deeply. When you are angry, take a few seconds to breathe deeply. When you are angry or stressed, your breathing is typically faster and more shallow. Take a few deep breaths, counting to four as you inhale and again as you exhale. This can help you relax before you decide how to deal with your anger.

Keep a sense of humor. Telling a joke or poking fun at a situation (in a good-spirited way that does not attack others) can lighten up a situation. Laughing helps reduce the

▲ Sometimes laughter really is the best medicine.

effects of anger cues. However, don't joke about, poke fun at, or laugh at someone else. This might provoke someone else's anger.

Rehearse what to do in situations that you know are anger triggers. Think of situations that make you angry. Imagine what you would say and do in these situations to control your anger. Rehearse in front of a mirror or with a friend, parent, guardian, mentor, or counselor. You might want to write down what you would say and do. Read what you have written so you are prepared to act appropriately if the situation occurs.

Talk with a parent, guardian, or mentor. Sometimes talking through your anger helps to relieve it. Responsible adults can help you process anger. They can help you recognize anger triggers and cues. They can help you decide if your anger is justified or if you are overreacting. They can help you identify healthful ways to express your anger. They can give you feedback as to whether you are making improvements in controlling and expressing anger.

Contact Ask students to contact local agencies to identify programs for people who abuse family members and others as a result of anger that is not properly managed. Also, ask them to address the negative consequences of not managing anger, such as problems at work, problems with friends, and risking the health of family members. Have students research statistics on abuse in marriage and families, and report their findings to the class. **L3**

Class Discussion

Role-Play Provide the students with different situations in which someone can become angry. Ask students to role-play using anger-management skills to resolve the problem in a healthful manner. *Examples include: you find out that your sibling has given some of your CDs to a friend; a friend of yours spills soda inside your parents' car; your relay team loses a race because someone on the team is disqualified.* After the role-playing, have students discuss as a class why anger-management skills are helpful. **L2**

🏛 Community Involvement

Research Ask students to locate agencies within the community that provide anger-management counseling. Have students talk to someone at the agency who counsels on anger-management about the kinds of exercises used to help people control their anger. Ask students to gather information on the types of people who seek help at these agencies. Questions they might ask include: Are your clients mostly male, or mostly female, or do an equal number of men and women seek help managing anger? What is the reason that most people give for wanting to get help with anger-management? What is the easiest anger-management skill for your clients to learn? What is the hardest skill to learn? Have students present their findings to the class. **L3**

National Health Education Standards
Pages 98–99: 1.5, 6.3, 7.1

Stress

Define Write the words *stress, stressor, eustress,* and *distress* on the chalkboard or on an overhead transparency. Define each term for the class and give examples of each.

Quick Demo

GAS You will need a pitcher of water, a sponge, and a bowl. Ask a student to hold the sponge in the palm of the hand over the bowl. Explain that the sponge represents a person's body and the water is adrenaline that is released during the alarm stage of GAS. You will name a stressor and pour water on the sponge. The student will give a stress-management skill and squeeze out the water to show he or she has reduced the harmful effects of the stressor on the body. Repeat this process by giving stressors faster than the student can squeeze out the water. Ask students what happened. Explain that the effects of the stress on the body accumulated with the adrenaline and that this body is now in the exhaustion stage of GAS. A way to prevent this from happening is to have a stress-management plan in place before stress occurs. **ELL**

Stress

The response of the body to the demands of daily living is **stress**. A source or cause of stress is a **stressor**. Stressors may be physical, mental, social, or environmental. Exercising until you are exhausted is a physical stressor. Preparing for a difficult test is a mental stressor. Being introduced to someone new is a social stressor. Being in a room filled with cigarette smoke is an environmental stressor. When you experience stressors, changes occur in your body. A response to a stressor might be healthful or harmful. **Eustress** is a healthful response to a stressor. **Distress** is a harmful response to a stressor.

The General Adaptation Syndrome

Did You Know?

Categories of Stress
Stress can be acute or chronic. A source of acute stress is taking an exam. A source of chronic stress is providing long-term care for an ill family member.

The **general adaptation syndrome (GAS)** is a series of body changes that result from stress. The GAS occurs in three stages: the alarm stage, the resistance stage, and the exhaustion stage.

The alarm stage The first stage of the GAS, in which the body gets ready for quick action, is the **alarm stage.** During this stage, adrenaline is secreted into the bloodstream. **Adrenaline** is a hormone that prepares the body to react during times of stress or in an emergency. Sometimes the alarm stage is called the fight-or-flight response because it gets you ready to either take action or to run away to protect yourself. The following body changes occur in the alarm stage: pupils dilate to improve vision, hearing sharpens, saliva decreases, heart rate and blood pressure increase to stimulate blood flow to muscles, bronchioles dilate to increase oxygen supply to muscles, digestion slows to increase blood flow to muscles, and muscles tighten.

The resistance stage The second stage of the GAS, in which the body attempts to regain internal balance, is the **resistance stage.** The body no longer is in the emergency state. Adrenaline no longer is secreted. The following body changes occur in the resistance stage: pupils constrict, hearing is normal, saliva increases, heart rate and blood pressure decrease, bronchioles constrict, intestinal secretions increase to normal, blood flow to muscles decreases, and muscles relax.

The exhaustion stage The first two stages of the GAS are normal and healthful. When you experience a stressor, the alarm stage helps you respond. After your initial response, the resistance stage occurs, and your body regains internal balance. However, some people are not able to manage stress. As a result, their bodies are in the alarm stage for long periods of time. The **exhaustion stage** is the third stage of the GAS, in which wear and tear on the body increase the risk of injury, illness, and premature death.

Teacher to Teacher

Rotate Your Stress Away Create stations to practice different stress-management techniques. Station 1 is Music Therapy. Play soft, uplifting music or relaxation CDs. Station 2 is Laughter. Create a joke box filled with slips of paper with jokes that you have written. Each student reads a joke. Or play a CD of a family-friendly stand-up comedy routine. Station 3 is Art Therapy. Provide paper and pencils, pens, markers, and colored pencils so students can draw. Spend 8–10 minutes at each station. Have the students discuss how each activity made them feel. **L2 ELL**
Christy Rhoades
West Wilkes High School, Millers Creek, NC

How Stress Affects Health Status

This textbook is divided into ten areas of health. There are health goals for you to achieve and maintain for each of the ten areas. Having too much stress can interfere with these health goals. Consider the following effects of stress.

Stress and mental and emotional health Prolonged stress makes it difficult for you to think clearly and concentrate. It can keep you from having a healthy mind. If you do not manage your stress in healthy ways, your level of stress can build. If this happens, you might become edgy and express emotions in inappropriate ways. Prolonged stress increases the risk of depression and psychosomatic diseases. Physical illness and disorders, such as ulcers, headaches, and stomachaches are more likely. Other physical disorders, such as acne, asthma, and chronic fatigue syndrome are aggravated by stress. Prolonged stress makes it difficult to be resilient.

Stress and family and social health Some teens live in a stressful home environment. Other teens are in stressful relationships. These situations and other social stressors can increase the likelihood that you will become ill, and they also can hinder your immune system's ability to fight off infection and disease.

Stress and growth and development During puberty, hormones cause body changes. For example, growth hormones may cause you to experience a growth spurt. It is not uncommon for

teens to grow four inches taller in one year. Other hormones cause secondary sex characteristics to develop. Teens who cannot adjust to these changes may choose harmful ways of coping. For example, eating disorders are more common in teens who are uncomfortable with their body changes.

Stress and nutrition It is important to eat moderately and regularly when you are stressed because you may be less able to cope with stress if you are hungry. When you are stressed, your body secretes adrenaline. This causes the body to use up its supply of vitamins B and C. Eating healthful foods can replenish your supplies of vitamins B and C.

Many people consume caffeine. Caffeine is a stimulant found in chocolate, coffee, tea, some soda pops, and some prescription and over-the-counter drugs. It is best to be moderate in your consumption of caffeine because it stimulates the nervous system and may promote even more nervousness and stress.

Some people eat salty foods when they feel stressed. When you increase salt consumption, your body might retain fluids. This could increase your blood pressure. High blood pressure is a contributing factor to heart disease.

▲ Stress can deplete your body of certain vitamins. Eating healthful foods can help replenish your body's supply.

Reading Review

1. Describe the mind-body connection.

2. What are two symptoms of anger?

3. Describe the general adaptation syndrome.

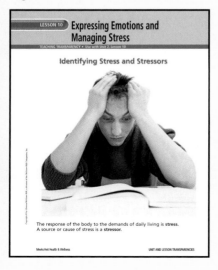
Other people respond to stress by eating large quantities of sweets. High concentrations of refined sugar may cause your body to increase its production of insulin, a hormone that helps your body use sugar in the blood. Too much insulin results in low blood sugar and will cause you to lose energy.

Stress and personal health and physical activity Recall that your body uses up vitamin C during stressful periods. Vitamin C helps your immune system to function well. Though exercise can be a positive outlet for stress, it also can harm the body if it is done in excess. Suppose you exercise to exhaustion when you are stressed. Too much exercise can affect your immune system, the body system that helps fight disease. You may become fatigued and run down.

Stress and alcohol, tobacco, and other drugs The use of drugs such as tobacco, marijuana, cocaine, alcohol, and tranquilizers may decrease your ability to cope with stress. Using tobacco, marijuana, or cocaine actually may cause a person to experience the alarm stage of the GAS. Alcohol and tranquilizers depress the part of the brain responsible for reasoning and judgment. Your decision-making skills may be affected. Some people use these substances as a way to escape their stress. Though they may feel that they escape while using these substances, the effects of the substances eventually wear off, and the problem or stressor is still there. They have not dealt with the stressor in a healthful way, and they have not done anything to resolve the issue. In reality, they likely have compounded the problem, and are putting themselves at risk for developing an addiction.

Stress and communicable and chronic diseases Periods of being overwhelmed and frustrated may cause the body's immune system to be suppressed. This results in lowered resistance to disease. You could become more susceptible to communicable diseases, such as flu and the common cold. Prolonged stress might affect a person's risk of cancer. Cancer cells are more likely to develop, multiply, and spread. Being stressed keeps the body in the alarm stage of the GAS. Heart rate and blood pressure remain high. This affects the heart and blood vessels. Cardiovascular diseases are more likely to occur.

Stressful Life Events

The following are life events that have been assigned numerical values. Complete the Using Life Skills activity on the next page using these values.

- Death of parent, sibling, boyfriend, or girlfriend — 100
- Divorce of parents — 65
- Pregnancy (or causing pregnancy) — 65
- Breakup with boyfriend or girlfriend — 60
- Jail term — 60
- Death of other family member — 60
- Beginning next level of school (entering high school) — 45
- Drug or alcohol use — 45
- Expelled from school or fired from work — 45
- Trouble at school — 40
- Serious health problem of a family member — 40
- Working — 35
- Gaining a family member — 35
- Change in financial state — 30
- Death of a close friend — 30
- Change in number of arguments with others — 30
- Sleep less than eight hours per night — 25
- Outstanding personal achievement — 25
- Change to new school — 10

102   UNIT 2 • Mental and Emotional Health

 Family Involvement

Survey Ask students to take home the Stressful Life Events list on page 102 and ask family members to circle stressors in their lives during the past twelve months (the list is geared to teens, but many events on the list apply to adults as well). Have students provide family members with the "scoring" information found on page 103 in Using Life Skills. If the family members score more than 150 on the survey, have students share some of the ideas in this lesson on dealing with stress. Have students write a summary of the activity. Remind the students that they do not need to share personal information with you or the class. **L2**

Activity: Using Life Skills

Using Goal-Setting and Decision-Making Skills: Managing Stress

Life changes can be a source of stress. While you can't always control these changes, you can control your response to them. These steps can help you become more aware of stressors in your life and to manage the effects of stress.

1 Write your health goal and make an action plan to meet your health goal. Decide upon the steps you will take to achieve your goal.

2 Identify obstacles to your plan. Read through the list of stressful life events on page 102. On a separate sheet, write down each change that applies to your life over the past 12 months, plus its point value. Add up your points.

3 If your total is less than 150, then you have experienced little change. If your total is over 250, then you have experienced many changes in your life.

4 Set up a time line to accomplish your health goal and keep a chart or diary in which you record progress toward your health goal. If your score is over 150, develop a plan to manage your stress. List actions you can take to cope with the stress and protect your health during stressful times.

5 Build a support system Surround yourself with family and friends to help you reach your goals.

6 Revise your action plan or time line, and reward yourself when you reach your health goal. Set a new health goal.

▲ Use the list of stressful life events on the previous page to compute your score.

Stress and consumer and community health Boredom is a stressor. Boredom results from a lack of challenge. People who are bored with their lives may turn to harmful behaviors. Shopping addiction, television addiction, computer addiction, and gambling addiction are more common in people who are stressed from boredom.

Stress and environmental health The environment includes everything around you. Pollutants are harmful substances in the environment. Pollutants may be in the air you breathe, the water you drink, or the food you eat. Pollutants activate the GAS. Loud noise, such as from rock music and concerts, heavy traffic, and airports, also initiates the alarm stage of GAS. If you are exposed to loud noises, you may be more likely to make mistakes and have accidents. Teens who smoke or who listen to loud music while driving have more accidents.

Stress and injury prevention and personal safety Stress is a major contributing factor in almost all kinds of accidents. Motor vehicle accidents are the leading cause of death in the 15–24 age group. People who are frustrated, aggressive, and angry because of stress in their lives may not be able to concentrate on safe driving. These people have higher accident rates.

Using Life Skills

Using Goal-Setting and Decision-Making Skills Have students focus on their support systems. Ask them to spend time thinking about the people in their lives who support them in difficult times. Have students choose one person and list the ways that person supports them when they are facing a stressful situation. Have students share the actions or qualities of the person that they feel help them the most. **L2**

Class Activity

Write a Plan To help students complete the activity on this page, have them first write a hypothetical stress-management plan. Have them choose one of the stressors listed on pages 101–103 and write about different ways they would cope with the difficult situation. **L2**

Teacher FYI

Stress Keep in mind that teens may be stressed by certain things that adults would not worry about. Peer pressure, the desire to do well in school and sports, and difficulties in relationships with friends or people they are dating can create a lot of stress for teens. Let your students know that even if they don't think their parents, guardians, or other adults will understand their stress, it is still important to talk to them about it and to learn how to manage it. Adults remember what it was like to be a teen, and students may be surprised at how much their parents or guardian can empathize with them.

DI Differentiated Instruction

Hearing Impairment For a student with a hearing impairment, stress is a common occurrence in his or her everyday life. It may stem from experiencing too much background noise in the classroom, the fear of social exclusion, the fear of missing what the teacher says, and many other situations that cause problems for people who have hearing impairment. Ask your student to reflect on the causes of his or her stress and to list those causes. Then, together, examine the list and discuss ways to eliminate or ease each stress factor. **L2**

National Health Education Standards
Pages 102–103: 1.1, 1.2, 1.5, 6.2, 6.3

Stress-Management Skills

Class Discussion

Budget Ask the class to give reasons why keeping a budget would prevent stress. Ask them to think about the consequences of not planning how to use their money. *Answers may include: avoiding debt and developing a sense of financial security.* **L2**

Class Activity

Instant Replay Ask the students to recall a stressful event and tell how they might have reacted differently if they could have used what they have learned about stress management. Remind students that they do not have to share personal information with you or the class. **L2**

Teacher FYI

Support Not all teens have an adult at home who will listen when they want to talk about something that is causing them stress. Emphasize to students that it is important to talk about problems with adults. Encourage them to talk about stressors with another trusted adult if they do not feel they are supported at home.

Stress-Management Skills

Throughout your life you will experience many stressors. You may not be able to control all of these stressors, but you can control your responses to them. *Stress-management skills* are techniques to prevent and deal with stressors and to protect one's health from the harmful effects produced by the stress response. People can use these skills to help them manage their stress every day, so stress does not continue to build to dangerous levels.

How to Prevent and Deal with Stressful Situations

Make the Connection

Time Management For more information on creating a time-management plan, refer to page 551 in Lesson 51.

Use responsible decision-making skills. When a situation is difficult and requires a decision, you will be less stressed if you approach the situation in a logical way. The Responsible Decision-Making Model gives steps to follow when you are stressed out but need to think clearly. Always use the six questions to evaluate the possible consequences of each decision. Refer to page 61 in Lesson 6 for a refresher on the six questions.

Keep a time-management plan. A time-management plan is a plan that shows how a person will spend time. Having a time-management plan helps keep you from being overwhelmed. Poor time management is a major stressor. However, people can develop time-management skills to help them prevent stress.

Keep a budget. A plan for spending and saving money is called a *budget*. Spending more money than you have is a major stressor. Knowing your income and expenses keeps you from spending money and regretting it later.

Talk with parents, a guardian, a mentor, or other responsible adults. You can benefit from the wisdom of adults. They can help you explore ways to deal with stressors. They can help you evaluate decisions you must make. They can provide support, encouragement, and suggestions.

Make sure you have a support network of friends. Friends can listen and offer suggestions. They can share healthful ways they dealt with similar experiences. When you have a support network of friends, you do not feel alone. You know others care about you and will be there for you during difficult times.

Cross-Curricular Connections

Math Have the students develop a budget for saving and spending income. Assign each student a different type of budget situation—some with more money and some with less. Base the numbers on a hypothetical situation in the future involving mortgage or rent, car payment, insurance, gas, food, entertainment, and utilities. Talk to the students about the risks of credit-card debt and include some sort of debt in their budget profiles. After they have created their budgets, have students share their ideas with the class and discuss how saving and planning their finances will help reduce stress. **L2**

How to Protect Health During Stressful Periods

Participate in physical activity. Regular physical activity helps the body regain internal balance during times of stress. Physical activity uses up the extra adrenaline and sugar released during times of stress. Take a walk or choose other activities when you feel stressed. Physical activity up to 24 hours after the onset of stress is beneficial.

Consider the other benefits of physical activity. If you are regularly physically active, your body may release beta-endorphins during and after your workout. Beta-endorphins are substances produced in the brain that create a feeling of well-being.

Regular physical activity will help you become physically fit. When you are physically fit, the stress response is not as great, your body regains internal balance more easily, and you have improved resistance to disease.

Write in a journal. Writing in a journal can help you organize your thoughts and feelings. You can review how a stressor is affecting you and learn more about how you cope.

Use breathing techniques. When you experience a stressor, your body begins the alarm stage of the GAS. Breathing techniques help to relax you and restore internal balance. Breathe in deeply through your nose, keeping your mouth shut. Then slowly blow the air out through your mouth. This breathing technique will calm you and help stop the alarm stage of the GAS.

Eat a healthful diet. Vitamin B is needed for a healthy nervous system. Vitamin C helps the immune system function. When you are stressed out, your body uses up an extra supply of these two vitamins. It is very important for you to replenish them by choosing foods that are good sources of these vitamins. You can make other changes in your diet. Reduce your intake of caffeine. Caffeine is found in coffee, tea, some soda pops, and chocolate. Decrease your intake of sugar.

Get plenty of rest and sleep. When you are stressed, your body is working extra hard. Your heart rate, breathing rate, and blood pressure are increased. Your muscles are tense. Getting rest and sleep keeps you from becoming too tired. When you are resting or sleeping, your blood pressure lowers, your breathing rate decreases, your heart rate slows, and your muscles relax.

When you feel stressed, taking a walk or engaging in another physical activity will use up the extra adrenaline that stress causes to be released ▼ in your body.

LESSON 10 • Expressing Emotions and Managing Stress   105

Family Involvement

Investigate Ask the students to read the labels on food and beverage containers at home to determine which items contain caffeine and large amounts of sugar or salt. Have the students also identify foods and beverages that contain vitamins B and C. Ask them to write a short paper summarizing the activity. Have them give suggestions about how they could improve their families' diets to lower stress. Remind students they do not need to share personal information about their families with you or the class. L2

105

SPEAKING OUT
Teens Talk About Health

Analyzing the Feature

Use the following questions to help students uncover the main point of this feature.

1. What is Olivia's first step when faced with a stressful situation? *to figure out why she is stressed*

2. Why is building confidence important when dealing with stress? *to be prepared for future problems*

3. For Olivia, what is the positive side of stress? *It has taught her to work well under pressure.*

 Journaling Activity

Ask students to think about a stressful situation that a friend is facing right now. Have them write about how they might help their friend by suggesting ways to cope with stress. **L1**

3 Assess

Vocabulary Practice

Page 36, **Unit 2 Fast File Resources**

National Health Education Standards
Pages 106–107: 1.5, 5.6

Olivia Walter
Managing Stress

> First you have to figure out why you're stressed about something. Then, take the steps necessary to solve the problem.

To Olivia Walter, dealing with stress is a lot like solving a problem. "First," she explained, "you have to figure out why you're stressed about something. Then, take the steps necessary to solve the problem."

Easier said than done If managing stress were easy, it wouldn't be a problem for so many young people. Olivia admits that. "When I'm stressed, I feel angry. If something is really bad," she added, "it can even seem hopeless for a while. But that makes me really want to solve the problem. And in that way, I guess stress has a positive side—it can lead to improvements."

The usual suspects What kinds of things cause Olivia to feel stress? It's the usual things: trouble with a homework assignment, tensions with family and friends. "It's personal stuff," Olivia said, "and school stuff, too."

Putting words into action Olivia described a typical stressful situation. "A friend and I got into an argument. I was feeling stressed because I thought our friendship was going to end. I felt angry, confused, and hurt because I didn't want to lose this friend."

At this point, Olivia decided to problem-solve and went to work. "First, I looked at the situation and tried to see what I could do to calm myself down," she explained. "When I was feeling calmer, I talked to my friend and we reconciled the problem. The way I had handled things like this in the past gave me confidence that I could handle this problem, too."

Building one's confidence Being confident that she can deal with stressful situations is a key for Olivia. Dealing with small things is good training for dealing with the more important problems. "With everyday things," she said "that confidence comes with experience. If you get good at the small things, when the big things come along, it's not as hard to solve them because you've had practice."

How does Olivia do it? "It's really important not to let things get blown out of proportion," she said. "Sometimes it's hard not to look at something in the worst light, but things usually aren't as bad as they seem." Her advice is to try to look at a situation realistically and objectively.

The bright side? Stress can even have an upside. "I'm good at working under a certain amount of pressure," Olivia explained. "So I guess you could say that's a good stress. I feel like I do my best work when I'm a little pressed for time."

 Journaling Activity

Think about a time when you had to deal with a stressful situation. Write in your journal about how you managed it. Were there things you'd do differently now? Why? Give yourself an overall grade for that situation.

106 UNIT 2 • Mental and Emotional Health

Health Project

Peer Mediation Encourage students to develop a peer-mediation group for your class that addresses actual problems that students are having. Another option is to set up a mock peer-mediation group in your class and create some situations to have the students help each other work through. Examples include two friends who are in an argument over who is working harder on a group project and two students who don't get along because of a rivalry on a sports team. Be sure the students follow the anger-management and stress-management skills outlined in this lesson as they help solve students' actual or hypothetical problems. **L2**

anger
anger-management
    skills
emotion
general adaptation
    syndrome (GAS)
hidden anger
hostility
mind-body
    connection
projection
psychosomatic
    disease
serotonin
stress
stress-management
    skills

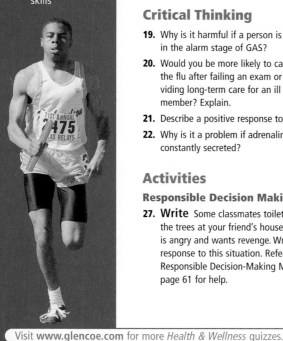

Key Terms Review

Complete the fill-in-the-blank statements with the lesson Key Terms on the left. Do not write in this book.

1. A chronic state of anger is _____.
2. The _____ is the relationship between a person's thoughts and emotions and bodily responses.
3. _____ are techniques to prevent and deal with stress and protect one's health during stressful periods.
4. A(n) _____ is an illness or disorder caused or aggravated by emotional responses.
5. A(n) _____ is a specific feeling.
6. _____ are healthful ways to control and express anger.
7. _____ is a chemical involved in controlling states of consciousness and mood.
8. _____ is anger that is not recognized and is expressed in inappropriate ways.
9. _____ is the response of the body to the demands of daily living.
10. The _____ is a series of body changes that result from stress.

Recalling the Facts

11. How does exercise help relieve stress and reduce the effects of anger?
12. What are the effects of stress during each of the three stages of the general adaptation syndrome?
13. What are ten stress-management skills?
14. What are the five guidelines for expressing emotions in healthful ways?
15. Name and discuss three symptoms of hidden anger.
16. What are the steps in keeping an anger self-inventory?
17. How might using you-messages escalate a problem?
18. How does stress affect mental and emotional health?

Critical Thinking

19. Why is it harmful if a person is constantly in the alarm stage of GAS?
20. Would you be more likely to catch a cold or the flu after failing an exam or after providing long-term care for an ill family member? Explain.
21. Describe a positive response to a stressor.
22. Why is it a problem if adrenaline is constantly secreted?

Real-Life Applications

23. How can you express emotions in healthful ways?
24. How might you manage anger?
25. Why do you think teens with hidden anger use projection or displacement instead of dealing with their anger?
26. What stress-management skills would you use if you felt stressed?

Activities

Responsible Decision Making

27. **Write** Some classmates toilet-papered the trees at your friend's house. Your friend is angry and wants revenge. Write a response to this situation. Refer to the Responsible Decision-Making Model on page 61 for help.

Sharpen Your Life Skills

28. **Advocate for Health** Prepare a pamphlet on stress-management skills that could be given to students in your school. Exchange your pamphlet with other students in your class and have them critique it.

Key Terms Review

1. hostility
2. mind-body connection
3. Stress-management skills
4. psychosomatic disease
5. emotion
6. Anger-management skills
7. Serotonin
8. Hidden anger
9. Stress
10. general adaptation syndrome (GAS)

Recalling the Facts

11. It uses up extra adrenaline and blood sugar produced during times of stress and anger, and releases beta endorphins.
12. Refer to page 100.
13. Refer to pages 104–105.
14. Identify the emotion, identify the source of the emotion, decide whether or not you need to respond right away, choose a responsible and healthful response, and protect your health.
15. being negative, being sarcastic, making cruel remarks to others
16. Identify symptoms you feel, think about possible causes, decide if your anger is justified, and examine appropriate ways to express it.
17. They put the other person on the defensive.
18. Stress makes it hard to think clearly and concentrate, and increases the risk of depression, headaches, ulcers, stomachaches, acne, asthma, and chronic fatigue syndrome.

Critical Thinking

19. It causes wear and tear on the body and increases the risk of injury, illness, and premature death.
20. Providing long-term care for an ill family member is more stressful than failing an exam.
21. Answers will vary.
22. It makes you more vulnerable to illness and injury.

Real-Life Applications

23. Answers will vary but may include: talking to others, writing in a journal, using art to express feelings.

---

24. Refer to pages 98–99.
25. They don't have anger-management skills.
26. Answers will vary but may include the stress-management skills on pages 104–105.

Activities

Responsible Decision Making

27. Expressing anger by getting revenge is not responsible, does not demonstrate good character, and is not safe. It is not a healthful way to express anger. The other anger-management skills identified on pages 98 and 99 might be mentioned.

Sharpen Your Life Skills

28. As students create their pamphlets, encourage them to include information on the physical and emotional effects of stress and ways teens can manage stress.

107

LESSON 11

Dealing with Depression

Out of Time?

If time does not permit an in-depth study of this topic, use the following activities in this Teacher Wraparound Edition:
- Class Activity, p. 109
- Teacher FYI, p. 111
- Explain the Concept, p. 117
- Class Discussion, p. 118

1 Focus

HEALTH GOALS **Resiliency** Have students respond to the Health Goals for this lesson by imagining that they just failed an exam. Ask what they can do to be resilient. *They can take steps to perform better on the next exam, such as studying more or getting a tutor. They can also talk to their parents or another trusted adult if they are feeling depressed about their grades.* **L1**

Write ABOUT IT!

Constructed Response Students' answers should include: They would ask their friend what is bothering them, and they would tell their friend that they are concerned. They also might tell their friend that they think he or she needs to seek professional help and/or talk to a trusted adult. **L2**

LESSON 11

Dealing with Depression

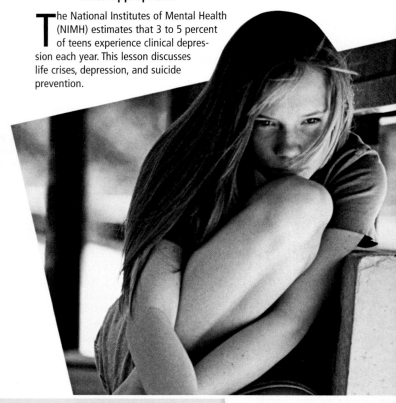

HEALTH GOALS
- I will be resilient during difficult times.
- I will seek help if I feel depressed.
- I will use suicide prevention strategies when appropriate.

The National Institutes of Mental Health (NIMH) estimates that 3 to 5 percent of teens experience clinical depression each year. This lesson discusses life crises, depression, and suicide prevention.

What You'll Learn

1. Discuss emotional responses used to cope with life crises. *(p. 109)*
2. Differentiate between kinds of depression, possible causes, symptoms, and treatments for depression. *(p. 110)*
3. Explain why being depressed puts teens at risk. *(p. 112)*
4. Identify strategies for coping with depression. *(p. 113)*
5. Identify warning signs for suicide and discuss suicide prevention strategies. *(p. 114)*
6. Discuss eight steps teens might take to be resilient. *(p. 118)*

Why It's Important

Teens who are depressed often fail to seek help. If their depression goes untreated, they are at risk for developing addictions, being ill, and making suicide attempts.

Key Words

- life crisis
- minor depression
- major depression
- cognitive behavior therapy
- antidepressant
- suicide
- parasuicide
- cluster suicides
- suicide prevention strategies
- resiliency

Write ABOUT IT!

Writing About Depression Suppose that lately one of your friends has seemed distracted. She has stopped hanging out with your group of friends and always looks sad when you see her. She says she is fine, and that she just does not want to socialize with anyone right now. What do you do? After you read the information about depression on page 110, write what you would say to your friend in your health journal.

National Health Education Standards—Guide for Lesson 11		
1.1	Predict how healthy behaviors can impact health status.	pp. 109, 111, 112, 114, 116, 118–120, 121
1.2	Describe the interrelationships of emotional, intellectual, physical, and social health.	pp. 110–116, 119, 120, 121
1.5	Propose ways to reduce or prevent injuries and health problems.	pp. 108, 109, 113, 115, 117, 118–119, 120
7.2	Demonstrate a variety of healthy practices and behaviors that will maintain or improve the health of self and others.	pp. 108, 113–115, 117–120, 121

Life Crisis

Sometimes life is difficult. Events happen over which you have no control—a loved one dies; a parent loses a job; an earthquake, fire, or tornado destroys your property. You might be in a car accident or turn on the television and view tragic world events. You might experience disappointments—you don't make an athletic team, your parents argue, your boyfriend or girlfriend breaks up with you. A *life crisis* is an experience that causes a high level of stress.

How to Cope with a Life Crisis

Most people respond to life crises by working through a series of five emotional responses. The five responses are listed below. A person has worked through a life crisis when he or she accepts what is happening, adjusts, and bounces back. This does not mean that he or she likes what has happened.

Emotional responses The following example illustrates how a teen might work though a life crisis. Suppose a teen's parents tell her they are getting a divorce. She *denies* that her parents will go through with the divorce. Then, her father moves out of the family home. She responds by *being angry* about what is happening. She might even act out her anger by breaking family rules.

Next, she responds by *bargaining,* or making promises, hoping it will change the outcome. Her promises might be motivated by guilt. She might feel she is partially at fault for her parents' failed marriage.

She then responds by *being depressed* when she recognizes nothing she can say or do will change the outcome. This period of sadness is necessary. Sadness helps her feel the pain and experience the loss of family life as she knew it. After a period of time, she begins *accepting* the fact that her parents are no longer together. She makes adjustments and bounces back.

This is only one example of a life crisis. But, the five emotional responses are the same responses that apply to other life crises. People of all ages experience these emotional responses. If you experience a life crisis, remember these emotional responses. Learning to work through feelings during difficult times helps you become emotionally mature.

Five Emotional Responses Used to Cope with Life Crises

People respond to life crises by working through the following emotional responses:

- **Denying** or refusing to believe what is happening
- **Being angry** about what is happening
- **Bargaining,** or making promises, hoping to change what is happening
- **Being depressed** when recognizing the outcome is unlikely to change
- **Accepting** what is happening, adjusting, and bouncing back

Source: These five stages have been adapted from Dr. Elisabeth Kübler-Ross's work on death and dying.

LESSON 11 • Dealing with Depression **109**

Lesson Resource Manager

- **Unit 2 Fast File Resources**
  Reading Strategy, p. 49
  Vocabulary Practice, p. 50
  Transparency Master and Worksheet, p. 51
  Real-Life Health, p. 53
  Real-Life Health, p. 55
  5-Minute Check, p. 57
  Lesson 11 Quiz, p. 59
- **Unit 2 Transparency**
- **Lesson 11 Transparency**

- **Reading Essentials**
- **Technology**
  TeacherWorks™ CD-ROM
  StudentWorks™ CD-ROM
  Reading Essentials CD-ROM
  ExamView® Assessment Suite
  Vocabulary Puzzlemaker

109

Depression

Class Discussion

Causes of Depression Ask students why they think that an inability to cope with a life crisis is a risk factor for depression. How does this risk factor relate to the five emotional responses to a life crisis? *One of the response stages is "being depressed." If a person is unable to cope with a life crisis, he or she can get stuck in this stage.* **L2**

Explain the Concept

Depression Students might think that a person who is depressed should be able to just "snap out of it." This type of thinking is one reason why people think it is embarrassing to suffer from the illness. In reality, depression is a serious mental disorder that needs to be treated. In fact, major depression is the leading cause of disability in the United States. Job and school performance often are affected when a person is depressed. The National Institute of Mental Health has a guide for employers and supervisors regarding employee depression.

Depression

I t is a normal reaction to feel angry or depressed while trying to adjust to a life crisis. For example, suppose a classmate was killed in a motor vehicle accident. You might feel angry about the accident. Later, you might feel sad and depressed because you will not see your friend again. Or, suppose a boyfriend or girlfriend breaks up with you to date someone else. You might feel angry, betrayed, and depressed. But what if you don't bounce back and continue to be depressed? Or what if you are depressed for two or more weeks for no specific reason?

What to Know About Depression

Some symptoms for depression are listed below. **_Minor depression_** is a mood disorder accompanied by feelings of hopelessness, sadness, or helplessness. It is diagnosed with two to four of the symptoms listed below that last for at least two weeks. Minor depression might go away, or it might become chronic. This means a teen continues to have mild depression. **_Dysthymic disorder_** is a long-lasting form of depression. With this disorder, an adult displays two or more of the symptoms listed below for the majority of days for two or more years; for children and teens, the time frame is one or more years.

Major depression is a mood disorder accompanied by long-lasting feelings of hopelessness, sadness, or helplessness. A teen is diagnosed as having major depression if he or she has at least five of nine general symptoms that last for at least two weeks. Some teens experience something called double depression. They have dysthymic disorder with periodic bouts of major depression.

What Causes Depression

Inability to cope with a life crisis Some teens are unable to get through life crises that most teens can cope with, such as the loss of a boyfriend or girlfriend, or moving to a new neighborhood. Some teens experience severe life crises, such as being a victim of crime, or being in a natural disaster, such as an earthquake, flood, or tornado. When teens cannot cope with a life crisis, they may develop a form of depression. Some teens develop post-traumatic stress disorder (PTSD) after experiencing a life crisis. Teens who have PTSD often are depressed.

Symptoms Used to Diagnose Depression

The American Psychiatric Association uses these symptoms to diagnose depression:

- deep sadness
- apathy
- fatigue
- agitation
- sleep disturbances
- weight or appetite changes
- lack of concentration
- feelings of worthlessness
- morbid thoughts

 Sensitive Issues

Life Crisis Some students may have experienced a recent life crisis and may still be experiencing levels of emotional responses. Students may have recently lost a family member or friend, experienced a parent losing a job, or experienced a natural disaster or an act of violence. Explain that students who are feeling depressed can talk to a trusted adult and can seek help from a mental-health professional. Have resources available for students who wish to talk with a health professional. Encourage students to discuss their feelings with a parent or guardian.

Changes in brain structure Changes in brain structure can increase risk for depression. During the teen years, the brain is still developing. Between the ages of 14 and 17, there is a "pruning" or clearing of the gray matter. The gray matter consists of closely packed and interconnected nerve cells. It is found in the outer layers of the cerebrum. The cerebrum is the largest part of the brain and controls the ability to memorize, think, and learn. Gray matter also is found in some regions deeper within the brain. The "pruning" process involves clearing out unused brain-cell connections from the gray matter. This clearing process prepares the brain for even deeper brain-cell connections. When this process is complete, teens can focus more intently and learn things more deeply. Scientists have learned that there is a significant increase in mental disorders, including depression, when this clearing-out process takes place. Research is being conducted to find out why.

Genetic predisposition The inheritance of genes that increase the likelihood of developing a condition is called *genetic predisposition.* Some teens may be genetically predisposed to having depression. The closer a teen is connected to a biological family member who is depressed, the greater the likelihood that the teen may become depressed. For example, a teen whose mother suffers from depression is more at risk than if the teen's aunt suffers from depression.

Low serotonin levels A chemical that is involved in controlling states of consciousness and mood is *serotonin.*

◀ Teens who are depressed may be distracted from everyday activities.

Serotonin levels fluctuate and are not the same in all people. Teens who have lowered serotonin levels are more at risk for depression.

Traumatic family events Teens who have experienced traumatic family events are at increased risk for depression. Examples of traumatic family events might include: parents' divorce; serious illness of a family member; the death of a family member; a parent losing a job; a family member going to jail; the murder, abduction, or sudden absence of a family member; a family member engaged in a war; or abuse by a family member (physical, emotional, or sexual).

Physical illness and disorders Teens who have certain physical disorders and are ill may experience depression. For example, heart disease, cancer, diabetes and stroke are related to depression. Some nutritional deficiencies, such as Vitamin B, also may increase the risk of depression.

Alcohol and other drug use Teens who drink alcohol and abuse other drugs have much higher rates of depression. Their brains are not yet fully developed, and depressant drugs have an even greater effect on their mood. Teens who suffer from depression and use alcohol and other depressant drugs become even more depressed.

Did You Know?

Gender and Depression Researchers have identified a gene variation that appears to increase depression risk more among women than men.

LESSON 11 • Dealing with Depression **111**

Why Being Depressed Puts Teens at Risk

Make the Connection

Addictions For more information on addictions, see page 84 in Lesson 9.

Most teens feel down in the dumps once in a while. In many cases, they bounce back after speaking with a parent, guardian, mentor, or other trusted adult and using coping strategies for depression. But, some teens do not bounce back from depressed feelings.

School performance Teens who are depressed may be tired and have difficulty concentrating. This affects their ability to memorize, think, and learn. They may be apathetic and have difficulty getting motivated to do school work. School absence and poor grades are warning signs of teen depression. Teens who do poorly in school limit the options they will have in the future.

Social isolation Teens who are depressed often withdraw from friends. They stop participating in enjoyable teen activities, such as

A teen who is depressed may not perform well in school. One warning sign of depression is a decrease in grades.

Reading Review

1. What are the five emotional responses people go through after a loss?
2. Name three symptoms of depression.
3. How can being depressed affect school performance?

athletic events, clubs, and get-togethers. This can make their depression worse. Teens who are socially isolated miss the opportunity to gain social skills, which makes it difficult for them to develop and maintain healthful relationships.

Drug addiction Drug addiction is the compelling desire to take a drug even though it harms the body, mind, and relationships. Teens who are depressed might depend on alcohol and use other drugs to escape from problems or change their mood.

Other addictions Teens might depend on certain behaviors to change their mood. Some of these behaviors, such as exercising, are normally healthful and may help with depression. However, when a specific behavior is taken to extremes, it can become an addiction.

Physical illnesses When teens are depressed, their body's immune system is suppressed. The immune system is less able to fight off pathogens. Teens who are depressed are more susceptible to colds and flu.

Mental disorders Teens who are depressed are at increased risk for having major depression in adulthood. They are also at increased risk for developing other mental disorders.

Suicide attempts Teens who are depressed have a sense of hopelessness and helplessness. When these feelings are coupled with other risk factors, such as drug use, eating disorders, or social isolation, the risk of making a suicide attempt increases.

Treatment for Depression

Teens who are depressed usually suffer for years before they are diagnosed. Few teens who need treatment for depression actually seek help. The following are types of treatment for depression.

Physical examination A physical examination is needed to evaluate health status. Poor health status, such as illness, might precede depression. Depression also might precede poor health status because it is associated with symptoms such as sleeplessness and loss of appetite. Depression also suppresses the immune system, which increases the risk of illness.

Therapy Teens who are depressed may benefit from therapy. ***Cognitive behavior therapy*** is a form of psychotherapy that involves behavior therapy and cognitive therapy. Other forms of therapy, such as individual counseling or a combination of therapy and medication, also can be beneficial. Therapy can help change a teen's hopeless and negative thinking. It can help a teen gradually resume former responsibilities and patterns of daily living.

Medication A physician will determine if a teen will benefit from taking prescription drugs for depression. An ***antidepressant*** is a drug used to relieve depression. There are different kinds of antidepressant drugs. Some antidepressants regulate serotonin levels, which play a role in regulating a person's mood. Antidepressant drugs can take several weeks to become effective, and require medical supervision to check for side effects.

Some of the antidepressant drugs prescribed by physicians have not yet been approved by the Food and Drug Administration for use by persons under 18. However, physicians might prescribe them in what is referred to as "off-label" use. This is a common procedure for prescription drugs that are being studied. The National Institutes of Health is still studying the long-term effects of several antidepressants when used by teens. Questions have been raised about the possible risks associated with the use of antidepressant drugs. Parents or guardians and teens should discuss the risks and benefits of antidepressant drug treatment with their physician.

◄ Antidepressant drugs are often used to treat depression in adults. The effects of these drugs on teens is still being researched.

Coping with Depression

These are strategies for coping with depression:

- Talk with a parent, guardian, mentor or other trusted adult.
- Stay connected with friends.
- Practice healthful behaviors, such as eating nutritious meals and getting exercise.
- Use anger-management skills. (Page 98)
- Practice stress-management skills. (Page 104)
- Avoid the use of alcohol and other drugs.
- Take steps to develop resiliency. (Page 118)
- Seek treatment if these strategies do not relieve depression.

LESSON 11 • Dealing with Depression **113**

🧍🧍 Healthy People 2010

Objective 18-9b *Increase the proportion of adults with recognized depression who receive treatment.*

According to the Healthy People 2010 report, about 20 percent of the United States population encounters mental illness each year. Of this percentage, over 19 million adults suffer from depression. However, the percentage of adults who are diagnosed with depression who also receive treatment is a little over 20 percent. Have students research depression and answer the following questions in a short report: How can drug use affect mental health and cause depression? How can they identify the signs of depression in friends, family, or themselves? How can they get help or help others who may be depressed? **L2**

Class Discussion

Treatments Write *physical examination, therapy,* and *medication* on the chalkboard or an overhead transparency. Ask students how these three areas can be part of treatment for depression. Record the students' responses and discuss how some forms of treatment work better for some people than for others. **L2**

Extension

Antidepressant Drugs Have students research antidepressant drugs and write a short report on their benefits and their side effects. Students should pay particular attention to how the antidepressants they are researching affect teens and whether the FDA has approved the antidepressants for use by teens. Students should present their findings to the class. **L2**

Teacher FYI

Side Effects There currently are no antidepressant drugs that are approved for use by people under the age of 18. The National Institute of Mental Health (NIMH) is investigating the effects of antidepressants on adolescents. The NIMH reports that some drug treatments, such as fluoxetine and paroxetine, have been shown to have a positive impact on adolescent depression.

National Health Education Standards
Pages 112–113: 1.5, 2.1, 2.3, 3.4, 7.2

Suicide

Class Activity

Community Resources Have the class compile a list of local suicide-prevention agencies and agencies that help people cope with depression. Students can use a phone book to find suicide-prevention hotlines and counseling services and agencies that specialize in helping people with depression. Students should locate phone numbers, addresses, and Web sites for each agency. Have students create a booklet that includes the names of the agencies, their phone numbers, addresses, and Web site addresses. Underneath this information, students should list the agencies' missions and the services they provide. Display the list in the classroom. **L2** **ELL**

5-Minute Check

Page 57, Unit 2 Fast File Resources

1. What is a life crisis? *an experience that causes a high level of stress*
2. What is major depression? *a mood disorder accompanied by long-lasting feelings of hopelessness, sadness, or helplessness*
3. What is genetic predisposition? *the inheritance of genes that increase the likelihood of developing a condition*
4. What are the three forms of treatment for depression? *physical examination to determine if there are physical causes for depression, therapy, medication*
5. Why should talk of a suicide attempt be taken seriously? *People who talk about suicide are crying out for help. They might make a suicide attempt.*

Suicide

The essayist and poet Joseph Addison once said, "The three grand essentials to happiness in life are something to do, something to love, and something to hope for." Having something to do, and doing it well, gives a person a feeling of accomplishment. Having people to love gives a person the opportunity to share feelings, hopes, dreams, and disappointments. Having something to hope for gives a person a reason to live. Teens who do not have things to do, people to love, and something to hope for can be at risk for making a suicide attempt.

Did You Know?

Causes of Death More people die from suicide than from homicide each year in the United States. Suicide is the third leading cause of death for Americans age 10–24.

What to Know About Suicide and Suicide Attempts

Suicide The intentional taking of one's own life is ***suicide.*** Some teens view suicide as a way to end depression, or as a way to escape problems. Other teens view suicide as a way to gain attention or a way to get even with those who have rejected them. But, suicide is the ultimate mistake—it can not be undone. Suicide is never the best choice.

Parasuicide A suicide attempt in which a person does not intend to die is ***parasuicide.*** Parasuicide is a cry for help. Teens who make a suicide attempt are depressed, discouraged, and lack hope. They want others to know that they are in a lot of pain. Some teens who make a suicide attempt and do not intend to die are not found in time. Their cries for help end in tragic death. Without help, teens who have attempted suicide once may attempt suicide again. For this reason, a suicide attempt or talk of a suicide attempt always must be taken seriously.

If you are depressed and have thoughts about suicide, seek help. You can call 1-800-SUICIDE toll free to speak with a trained individual. You also can find a mental-health professional in your area in your local phone book. Therapy and/or medication can help. Never make a suicide attempt, even as a way to get attention. Remember, you will not have a second chance if your attempt goes too far. Talk to a trusted adult if you have suicidal thoughts.

Cluster suicides A series of suicides occurring within a short period of time and involving people who are connected in some way are ***cluster suicides.*** Some teens make pacts or agreements. Other teens commit suicide in response to the suicide of a friend. Teens also might consider suicide after they learn about another teen's or a famous person's suicide.

If you know someone who has committed suicide, talk to your parents, a guardian, school counselor or other trusted adult. You might need help working through your feelings. If you learn about a suicide of a famous person, realize that this person made the ultimate mistake. Do not copy this mistake.

114 UNIT 2 • Mental and Emotional Health

Cross-Curricular Connections

Math Before students complete the following problem, have them guess what percent of teen deaths are due to injuries, homicide, and suicide and write it in their health journals. The top three causes of death in teens and young adults ages 15–24 are unintentional injuries, homicide, and suicide. Unintentional injuries caused roughly 45 percent of total deaths in this age group in 2001. In the same year, 3971 adolescents ages 15–24 committed suicide. There were 32,252 total deaths in this age group. What percent of total deaths in teens ages 15–24 were due to suicide? *about 12 percent* Ask students to write a one-page reflection after completing this problem. Have them discuss whether or not this result surprised them. **L2**

What to Know About Suicidal Tendencies

Teens who attempt suicide may have had a difficult life experience, such as a breakup of a relationship, an unplanned pregnancy, or failure at school. Teens are more likely to attempt suicide if they encounter any of the following experiences.

Abuse of alcohol and other drugs People who abuse alcohol and other substances often have other risk factors for suicide, such as social problems. Also, people who abuse substances can tend to be impulsive, which also has been linked to teen suicide.

Death of a parent, parental separation, or parental divorce These events can cause extreme stress in teens. Although these events are out of the teen's control, they may feel responsible in some way. Teens also may feel like the mental pain they are feeling will never go away.

Feelings of alienation and rejection Teens who do not have a supportive social-emotional environment and teens who feel that they have no one to talk to, are at greater risk for attempting suicide than teens who have a supportive network of family and friends.

Difficulty coping with body changes and sexuality Teens may be uncomfortable or unhappy with the changes that occur during puberty. They also may feel uncomfortable with their sexuality, and feel unable to ask questions or talk to someone about their feelings.

Depression Feelings of hopelessness or worthlessness that accompany depression also are risk factors for suicide. Although not everyone that suffers from depression attempts suicide, having depression increases the risk of suicide.

Impulsive and/or aggressive behavior Teens who are impulsive or aggressive do things without thinking them through first. They may make a suicide attempt without thoroughly thinking through the potential consequences of their actions.

Mental disorders A majority of people who have committed suicide either had a mental disorder or abused substances before they committed suicide.

Reading Review

1. What are some causes of depression?

2. Why might a teen who is depressed be at risk for addictions?

3. What are some risk factors for suicide?

How to Recognize Signs of Suicide

Teens who are thinking about making a suicide attempt often provide warning signs. By trying to warn others, they are crying out for help and hoping someone will step in and help them. Signs that a teen may be considering a suicide attempt include:

- making a direct statement about suicide, such as "I wish I was never born"
- making an indirect statement about suicide, such as "I wonder where I can get a gun."
- having a change in personality
- withdrawing from contact with family and friends
- losing interest in personal appearance
- being preoccupied with death and dying
- using alcohol and other drugs
- losing interest in schoolwork
- giving away possessions
- talking about getting even with others
- failing to recover from a disappointment or a loss
- running away from home
- having a close friend or relative who has committed suicide

LESSON 11 • Dealing with Depression **115**

115

FACTSABOUT
DEPRESSION

Teacher FYI

Exercise and Depression One benefit of exercise is improved mood. It is thought that a person who exercises can experience psychological benefits, such as an increased sense of self-control and self-esteem. Physiological effects, such as improved fitness and increased levels of neurotransmitters also can benefit a person who is depressed.

Investigating the Issue

- Encourage the person to see a health-care professional who can make a diagnosis and prescribe treatment. Discuss your concerns with a trusted adult. Listen to the person and offer encouragement when appropriate.
- Evidence shows a link between lowered amounts of serotonin and depression. SSRIs work by blocking the reuptake of serotonin. Serotonin builds up in the synapse between neurons, allowing a nerve impulse to pass.
- Student answers will vary. Some statistics include: approximately 10 percent of American adults experience a depressive illness in any given year; women experience depression twice as often as men; approximately 3 to 5 percent of American teens experience depression each year; in children, depression is one of the most commonly diagnosed mood disorders; an estimated 6 percent of Americans over age 65 experience depression in any given year.

FACTSABOUT
DEPRESSION

▲ This PET scan shows the brain of a depressed patient. Areas of low activity typically found in the brains of people suffering from depresssion are shown in red and yellow.

Depression is an illness that can affect both men and women at any age, or of any race, ethnicity, or economic group. It involves not only the body, but mood and thoughts as well. It is not a weakness, nor can it be willed away. People suffering from depression cannot just "pull themselves together" and recover. Depression needs to be treated with the help of health-care professionals that may include medical doctors, counselors, or therapists, all of whom work together with the patient and parents or guardians in the recovery process.

Causes While the exact cause of depression remains unknown, evidence that some types of depression, such as bipolar disorder, run in families indicates that genetics may play a role in the development of depressive disorders. Having low self-esteem or poor coping skills also may put people at a higher risk for developing a depressive disorder. Hormonal disorders may cause physical changes in the body that can lead to depression. Certain environmental factors can trigger the onset of depression. Depression may develop as a result of traumatic events, such as being a survivor of an attack. Stress at home, work, or school also may be involved in the development of depression.

Depression is a serious illness that should not go untreated. Some symptoms of depression were discussed on p. 110. Other signs and symptoms of depression include:

- feelings of guilt or worthlessness
- loss of interest or pleasure in activities or hobbies that were once enjoyed, such as sports or going out with friends
- thoughts of death or suicide
- difficulty making decisions
- feeling restless or irritable
- sleeping longer and more often

- experiencing other physical symptoms, such as headaches, stomachaches, or chronic pain that does not respond to treatment

Depression usually can be successfully treated with a combination of medication and therapy. The medication relieves the symptoms of depression, while therapy helps the patient learn coping mechanisms for dealing with life's problems. Therapy can help the patient move away from the negative thinking and behavior that often accompanies depression. Exercise has been shown to relieve symptoms of depression in some patients. A mental-health professional may suggest a patient include excercise along with other treatments.

Investigating the Issue

Visit www.glencoe.com to research more information about depression.

- What should you do if you suspect a friend or family member may be suffering from depression?
- How do medications, such as selective serotonin reuptake inhibitors (SSRIs), work to relieve the symptoms of depression?
- Research current statistics on depression. How often does depression occur in men, women, teens, children, and the elderly?

Use a software program to create a pamphlet about depression, including places to get help.

www.glencoe.com

 Teacher to Teacher

Suicide Draw a line on the chalkboard. Label one end *birth* and the other *death.* Name the person whose life the line represents. Have students list life events, such as graduation from high school, marriage, having children, and establishing a career. Write their responses in the correct order on the line. Create a narrative of the person's life, drawing on the life events the students listed. Then tell the class that the person you are describing actually committed suicide at the age of 14. Erase the life events that occur after this age. Explain that this person never experienced any of these life events. Ask the students to imagine that the person was a friend or family member and to write in their health journals how they feel about the person's suicide. **L1**

Virginia Donnelly
Walton Central High School, Walton, NY

Getting Help

Techniques that can be used to help prevent a person from thinking about, attempting, and completing suicide are *suicide prevention strategies*. If you know someone that is contemplating suicide, there are ways that you can help. Contact a suicide hotline for more information about ways to help a person who is thinking about suicide.

What to Know About Getting Help

Listen. If friends share their thoughts of suicide with you, listen to them and encourage them to talk to you. Use active listening skills. Remind them that suicide is not the answer, and point out the future events that they will miss if they commit suicide. Tell them how devastated their family and friends, including you, will be.

▲ If a friend shares thoughts of suicide with you, listen to him or her, tell a trusted adult, and urge your friend to call a suicide hot line.

Encourage them to seek help. Tell your friends that there are ways that depression can be treated. Remind them that their depressed feelings may not go away on their own. With treatment, they may be able to start enjoying life again. Refer them to a suicide hotline, where they can talk to a trained professional.

Tell a trusted adult. Do not promise your friends that you will keep their suicidal thoughts a secret. Tell your friends that you care too much about them to keep their secret. They may be upset at first, but remind them that you care and want them to continue to be a part of your life.

Suicide Prevention Strategies

If you are concerned about a teen:

- look for warning signs when a teen is depressed
- listen without giving advice
- take a suicide threat seriously
- ask if the teen has a specific plan and means to follow through
- do not be sworn to secrecy
- call a parent, a guardian, or other responsible adult immediately
- stay with the teen until professional help arrives

LESSON 11 • Dealing with Depression **117**

Getting Help

Class Activity

Role-Play Set up a scenario for students: A friend tells you she is considering suicide. She tries to make you promise not to tell. Have students role-play how they would handle this situation. Explain that in a situation such as this one, you must tell a trusted adult about your friend's thoughts of suicide in order to save her life. **L1**

Explain the Concept

Suicide Unfortunately, many people who attempt suicide do not seek professional help. If a teen knows someone who has talked about suicide, he or she needs to tell a trusted adult. Many people who attempt or complete suicide gave some indication of their intent before their attempt. Emphasize that any talk of making a suicide attempt must be taken seriously.

NHES Assessment/SCASS

Selected Response A friend has confided to you that he has been thinking about suicide. What should you do?
A. Use active listening skills.
B. Encourage your friend to seek professional help.
C. Tell a trusted adult.
D. *All of the above*

(DI) Differentiated Instruction

Gifted and Talented Have students research the number of teen suicide attempts in the country, in their state, and in their community. Students can use resources such as the Centers for Disease Control and Prevention and the National Institute of Mental Health to locate the information. Students should present the information in chart or graph form. Ask students to compare the average rates in the country, in their state and in their community. Students also can do research on whether the teen suicide attempt rate has been rising or falling in recent years. **L3**

National Health Education Standards

Pages 116–117: 1.1, 1.2, 1.3, 1.5, 2.3, 3.2, 3.4, 3.5, 4.1, 5.3, 5.5, 6.3, 7.2, 7.3, 8.1

Resiliency

"When the going gets tough, the tough get going." "Tough times never last, but tough people do." These sayings describe people who demonstrate resiliency. **Resiliency** is the ability to adjust, recover, bounce back, and learn from difficult times. Some teens are more resilient than others. Being resilient is a powerful protective factor. A **protective factor** is something that increases the likelihood of a positive outcome. Being resilient helps you cope with life crises. It helps prevent depression and suicide. If you have not been resilient in the past, you can work to increase your resiliency.

How to Be Resilient

Work on your relationships with members of your family. You are working on skills to gain independence from your parents or guardian. Yet, at the same time, you need to remain close to them. Feeling connected to family members gives you added strength during tough times. Family members can comfort you. They also can offer suggestions for coping with life crises. Do not wait for tough times to happen. Spend time talking to your parents or guardian and other family members every day. Share what is happening in your life—your successes and your difficulties. Be vulnerable and share fears and insecurities.

Develop a close relationship with a mentor. A responsible person who guides another person is a **mentor**. A coach, member of the clergy, teacher, counselor, principal, guardian, aunt, uncle, grandparent, or other responsible adult can be a mentor. Spend time with the person you choose as a mentor. Discuss difficult situations with your mentor. Get suggestions on ways to handle life crises. When you need someone to talk to, or are looking for advice, a mentor can help you get through difficult times. You might want to keep a journal of your daily successes and difficulties and discuss your journal with your mentor.

Choose friends who are supportive and who have responsible behavior. Select your friends wisely. Friends who choose responsible behavior will encourage you to make wise choices during difficult times. They will listen to your feelings. They might think of options you do not. Stay away from teens who behave in harmful ways.

Positive family relationships help teens ▼ develop resiliency.

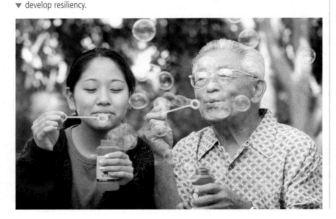

When you experience life crises, they might encourage you to participate in harmful behaviors.

Do not put off dealing with your feelings when a difficult situation arises. At first, you may respond to a difficult situation by denying what is happening. Do not get stuck in a state of denial. Get in touch with your feelings. Express any anger you feel in healthful ways. If you feel sadness or depression, share these feelings with your parents, guardian, mentor, or other trusted adult. Remember, tough times do not go away by pretending nothing is wrong. Face up to what is happening. Work through your feelings to gain acceptance and take responsible actions.

Avoid choosing harmful behaviors as a way of coping with tough times. You cannot adjust and bounce back from tough times by choosing harmful behaviors. Drinking alcohol or using other harmful drugs will interfere with your ability to make responsible decisions. Other addictive behaviors, such as gambling, smoking, and eating disorders will interfere with your ability to cope. These behaviors also are harmful to health. Stealing, lying, or breaking rules and laws will get you into trouble. Remember, harmful behaviors make the situation worse.

Ask for support when you need it. Reach out and ask for help during tough times. Some people do not ask for help, for fear they will look weak. Others feel that asking for help will show they are not in control. However, people who ask for help or support show that they are in control and are strong enough to know when to turn to another for support or assis-

tance. People that ask for help or support can deal with problems and move on. If they had not asked for help or support, they still may have been suffering from the problem. Willingness to ask for help is a key ingredient in developing resiliency.

▲ Teens who feel sad or depressed can find help by talking with their parent or guardian, or with another trusted adult.

Discuss available support groups with a parent, guardian, mentor, or other responsible adult. A group of people who help one another recover from an addiction, a particular disease, or a difficult situation is a ***support group.*** Sometimes it is helpful to be in a group with other teens who have experienced the same life crisis. You will not feel like you are the only one who has ever felt the way you do. Other teens can share their experiences with you. They can reassure you that they made it through a specific life crisis and you will too. Most support groups have guidelines concerning privacy. Those who attend agree not to share anything from the meeting outside the group.

Be involved in school activities. Don't withdraw from friends or stop participating in school activities. Being involved is an important way to feel connected to others. Being a member of a school team or participating in an activity gives you a sense of belonging.

LESSON 11 • Dealing with Depression 119

Using Life Skills

Accessing Valid Health Information, Products, and Services Step 5 of the Using Life Skills involves having students create a crisis resource handbook. After students create the handbook, ask them what they observed about obtaining the information. For example, ask them if it was easy or hard to find the contact information, and if they learned anything about information-gathering that they can use next time they do research on a topic.

3 Assess

Vocabulary Practice

Page 50, **Unit 2 Fast File Resources**

Activity: Using Life Skills

Accessing Valid Health Information, Products, and Services: Accessing Hotlines for Help

Most communities have suicide prevention or crisis intervention hotlines. A person calling the hotline can get immediate help in dealing with suicidal thoughts or an emotional crisis. Hotlines are an emergency health service. Here are some points that will help you use this service.

1 Identify health information, products, and services. Most hotlines are staffed by experienced volunteers, who are trained to listen to people in distress.

2 Many hotlines focus on specific problems, such as suicide or rape. Any information shared with hotline staff will be kept private. Callers do not need to give their name or other identification to a hotline counselor.

3 Hotlines give a person who is depressed or suicidal a chance to talk. Talking to someone about negative feelings that seem overwhelming can make a difference. They can provide comfort and perspective.

4 Locate health information, products, and services you need. Some hotlines, such as 1-800-SUICIDE (1-800-784-2433), are national. You can call these numbers toll-free. National hotlines can direct you to treatment services in your area. Other hotlines are offered by local hospitals, mental-health centers, and community organizations.

5 Evaluate health information, products, and services, and take action when health information is misleading and/or health products and services are unsatisfactory. To learn more about crisis hotlines that are available in your community, create a crisis resource handbook. List the name of the hotline, its phone number, and a few details about the service. To gather information for the handbook, check your local phone book. Make multiple copies of your crisis resource handbook. Place them at locations in your school and community where other teens will see them.

Make the Connection

Volunteering For more information on being a volunteer, see page 66 in Lesson 7.

Practice healthful behaviors. Remember the powerful mind-body connection. Your thoughts and emotions can trigger certain body responses. For example, the body's immune system might be suppressed during stressful times. Be proactive. Get plenty of exercise. Limit sedentary activities. Eat healthful foods. Avoid eating to manage stress. Practice stress-management strategies. Get plenty of sleep, and pay attention to grooming to keep a neat and clean appearance. Wear a favorite outfit and try to look your best.

Volunteer to help others. Acts of giving stimulate the brain to release endorphins. Endorphins are substances produced in the brain that create feelings of well-being. The release of endorphins helps produce a state in which a person feels increased energy, relaxation, and improved mood as a result of giving service to others. During tough times, it is helpful to have increased energy, relaxation, and improved mood. Helping others who are less fortunate can help you put your own troubles in perspective.

120 UNIT 2 • Mental and Emotional Health

Ⅾ️Ⅰ Differentiated Instruction

Physical Challenges Students who have physical challenges may have a difficult time completing the Using Life Skills activity. Assign students to groups of three or four and have them divide the project into parts. For example, one person can look in the phone book for community resources. Another student could record the names and numbers for the hotlines. Another student could type the list. The remaining student could do a 5-minute oral presentation that mentions some of the hotlines that were recorded in his or her group's handbook. **L1**

LESSON 11 STUDY GUIDE

antidepressant
cluster suicides
cognitive behavior
  therapy
genetic
  predisposition
life crisis
major depression
minor depression
parasuicide
protective factor
resiliency
suicide
suicide prevention
  strategies

Key Terms Review

Complete these fill-in-the-blank statements with the lesson Key Terms on the left. Do not write in this book.

1. _____ is therapy that helps teens identify and deal with sources of depression.

2. _____ is an experience that causes a high level of stress.

3. _____ are a series of suicides occurring within a short period of time involving people who are connected in some way.

4. _____ is the ability to adjust, recover, bounce back, and learn from difficult times.

5. _____ is a mood disorder accompanied by mild feelings of hopelessness, sadness, and helplessness.

6. A(n) _____ is a drug used to relieve depression.

7. _____ is a suicide attempt in which a person does not intend to die.

8. _____ are techniques that can be used to help prevent a person from thinking about, attempting, and completing suicide.

9. _____ is a mood disorder accompanied by long-lasting feelings of hopelessness, sadness, and helplessness.

10. _____ is the intentional taking of one's own life.

Recalling the Facts

11. What are the five stages of emotional response to life crises?

12. In what ways does being depressed put teens at risk?

13. What are strategies for coping with depression?

14. List suicide prevention strategies.

15. How might you develop resiliency?

16. What are the differences between minor depression, major depression, and dysthymic disorder?

17. What are the causes of depression?

18. Describe several methods of treating depression.

Critical Thinking

19. Discuss why a teen might consider attempting suicide after learning of a celebrity's suicide.

20. Why might a person with depression have changes in appetite or weight?

21. Why might a teen think that he or she is getting even with someone if he or she attempts suicide?

22. How does having a support system promote resiliency?

Real-Life Applications

23. Why might two people react differently to the same traumatic event?

24. How do you think exercise helps relieve symptoms of depression?

25. Why might a person who is depressed stop taking his or her medication a week or two after starting it?

26. Why do you think suicide rates are highest among the elderly?

Activities

Responsible Decision Making

27. **Write** You are feeling down because you did poorly on an exam. A classmate suggests that you drown your sorrows with a six-pack of beer. Write your response in your journal. Refer to the Responsible Decision-Making Model on page 61 for help.

Sharpen Your Life Skills

28. **Advocate for Health** Contact a local mental-health agency and find out how it is working to decrease the stigma associated with depression and suicide. Create an information packet on depression and suicide.

STUDY GUIDE

Key Terms Review

1. Cognitive behavior therapy
2. Life crisis
3. Cluster suicides
4. Resiliency
5. Minor depression
6. antidepressant
7. Parasuicide
8. Suicide prevention strategies
9. Major depression
10. Suicide

Recalling the Facts

11. denial, anger, bargaining, being depressed, and accepting
12. See page 112.
13. See page 113.
14. See page 117.
15. See pages 118–120.
16. See page 110.
17. See pages 110–111.
18. a physical examination, therapy, and medication

Critical Thinking

19. A teen may idolize the celebrity and want to copy his or her actions, or a teen may see the public mourn the celebrity and want to feel needed and wanted like the celebrity was.
20. Depressed people might eat more to try to cope with their feelings of worthlessness or less because they lose interest in eating.
21. The teen may think the person will feel sorry or guilty for what he or she did.
22. When you have supportive family members, friends, mentors, etc., they can help you work through difficult times. They can help you deal with problems and become more resilient.

Real-Life Applications

23. They may go through the five emotional responses differently. One may have a better support system than the other, one may be more resilient, etc.

24. Exercise can increase endorphins, which can elevate mood.
25. Antidepressant drugs can take several weeks to become effective in changing a person's mood. People may feel the drugs are not working and stop taking the medication.
26. An elderly person may face more stressful life crises, including death of a spouse, friend, or family member, or a serious illness.

Activities

Responsible Decision Making

27. Alcohol is a depressant drug and might cause you to be depressed. This might increase your risk of doing something destructive, such as harming yourself or others.

Sharpen Your Life Skills

28. Answers will vary.

Dealing with Loss and Grief

Out of Time?

If time does not permit an in-depth study of this topic, use the following activities in this Teacher Wraparound Edition:
• What Would You Do?, p. 122
• Family Involvement, p. 125
• Class Activity, p. 127
• Class Discussion, p. 128

1 Focus

HEALTH GOAL **Coping With Loss** Have students respond to the Health Goal for this lesson by identifying healthful ways to cope with loss and grief. *Some answers might include spending time with friends and family, sharing memories and your feelings of loss, allowing time to grieve, and continuing your daily routine.* **L2**

Write ABOUT IT!

Journaling Have students pretend that a friend or relative has recently lost a loved one. Students should write a letter to the friend or relative. Students' letters could offer support to the grieving friend or relative and share good memories about the person who has died. **L2**

LESSON 12

Dealing with Loss and Grief

HEALTH GOAL • **I will cope with loss and grief in healthful ways.**

There are times in life when you have no control over events that occur. Something may end before you are ready for it to end. Something may happen to someone you know or to you. Although you might not control the event, you can control the response to the event. This lesson focuses on loss and grief. You will learn causes of loss and grief that teens might experience. You will learn about the five stages of loss and grief. You also will learn how to respond to loss and grief in a healthful way.

What You'll Learn

1. Identify causes of loss and grief. *(p. 123)*
2. Identify symptoms of loss and grief. *(p. 124)*
3. Identify the five stages of loss and grief. *(p. 124)*
4. Discuss healthful ways to respond when someone close to you is dying. *(p. 126)*
5. Discuss healthful ways to respond when someone you know is grieving a loss. *(p. 126)*
6. Discuss healthful ways to respond when you are grieving a loss. *(p. 128)*

Why It's Important

No one goes through life without experiencing loss. But, loss is an opportunity to respond by being caring and compassionate. It is an opportunity for each of us to reach out to one another.

Key Terms

• loss
• grief
• anticipatory grief
• out-of-order death
• invincible
• empathy
• five stages of loss and grief

 ABOUT IT!

Writing About Grief Suppose that your friend's sister just died in a car accident. Your friend does not want to talk to anyone about it. Your friend's mother is concerned about her, because she does not sleep more than a few hours each night. Your friend is constantly doing something to keep herself busy. After reading the information about dealing with a loss on page 126, write a response to this situation in your health journal.

National Health Education Standards—Guide for Lesson 12		
1.5	Propose ways to reduce or prevent injuries and health problems.	pp. 122, 126–127, 128, 129, 130
4.4	Demonstrate how to ask for and offer assistance to enhance the health of self and others.	pp. 122, 124, 126–128, 129, 130, 131
8.1	Utilize accurate peer and societal norms to formulate a health-enhancing message.	pp. 120, 126–127, 129, 130

Loss and Grief

The feeling that occurs when someone dies or a life situation changes or ends is *loss*. Intense emotional suffering caused by a loss, disaster, or misfortune is *grief*. Grief experienced prior to a loss is *anticipatory grief*. It is the feelings a person has when he or she knows someone or something that is cherished or valued is about to die or change. No one goes through life without experiencing loss and grief.

What to Know About Loss and Grief

Causes of Loss and Grief

The causes of loss and grief include a change in the family, changes in living conditions, the death of a friend, suicide, the death of a well-known person, tragedies in the news, and the loss of special belongings.

Changes in the family Some family changes that cause feelings of loss and grief might include: death of a family member, divorce of parents, serious or terminal illness, or death of a family pet.

Changes in living conditions A change in living conditions can trigger feelings of loss and grief. A family member might lose a job or temporarily be laid off. The company the person worked for might close. There might be changes in economic conditions locally or nationally. As a result, a family's lifestyle might change. A family may go from having an income that allowed them to live comfortably to being strained financially. They may no longer be able to afford their house payments, and may have to move into a smaller house or an apartment. In severe situations, a family might be evicted from their house, apartment, or trailer, and may

become homeless or live in a shelter. Teens experience loss when these events take place. They grieve these losses. They might feel angry and depressed. Homelessness and poverty are major risk factors for teen depression.

Death of a friend The death of a friend is very traumatic. It is especially difficult when the friend is someone your age or younger. *Out-of-order death* is the death of a person that occurs at an unexpected time in his or her life cycle. Out-of-order death is traumatic. You grieve the loss of a friend and at the same time realize that you are not invincible. To view oneself as incapable of being harmed is to think you are *invincible.* If a teen dies in an automobile accident or from a terminal illness, then you realize that this could happen to you. You come face-to-face with your own mortality.

Suicide A suicide is the intentional taking of one's own life. When a suicide or several suicides (known as cluster suicides) occur, it is especially difficult for someone your age. You might wonder if you could have done anything to prevent the suicide(s).

Make the Connection

Suicide For more information on suicide, see page 114 in Lesson 11.

bar

LESSON 12 • Dealing with Loss and Grief   **123**

Loss and Grief

2 Teach

Class Activity

Write Have students describe in their health journals a situation in which they experienced loss and grief and explain how they responded to it. If students have not experienced a loss, have them write about how they think they might respond to a loss. **L2**

INTERACTIVE CHALKBOARD with Image Bank

PowerPoint® Presentations

This CD-ROM is an editable Microsoft® PowerPoint® presentation that includes:
- Lesson presentations
- Lesson checks
- Interactive graphics
- 5-Minute Checks
- Image Bank
- All transparencies

Discussion Refer to the KWL or KEL Charts Strategy on page 17T, and have students brainstorm things they know about loss and grief, what they want to know, and, after the lesson, what they have learned.

Lesson Resource Manager

- **Unit 2 Fast File Resources**
  Reading Strategy, p. 63
  Vocabulary Practice, p. 64
  Transparency Master and Worksheet, p. 65
  Real-Life Health, p. 67
  Real-Life Health, p. 69
  5-Minute Check, p. 71
  Lesson 12 Quiz, p. 72
- **Unit 2 Transparency**
- **Lesson 12 Transparency**

- **Reading Essentials**
- **Technology**
  TeacherWorks™ CD-ROM
  StudentWorks™ CD-ROM
  Reading Essentials CD-ROM
  ExamView® Assessment Suite
  Vocabulary Puzzlemaker

National Health Education Standards
Pages 122–123: 2.1, 2.3, 2.4

123

Reading Review

1. What is anticipatory grief?
2. What are three causes of loss and grief?
3. What are the five stages of loss and grief?

You might feel guilty because you are still alive. You might become angry because someone about whom you cared made this choice. You might feel sad and depressed. Most communities and schools offer counseling when teen suicide occurs. Teens need to talk through their feelings of grief.

Death of a well-known person Most likely, you have seen the reaction of the public to the death of a well-known person. This might be a politician, actress, actor, sports figure, or other person that the public has grown to know and love. Even though you do not know someone personally, you might experience loss or grief when a person dies. You imagine what it might be like to be a family member of the person. You feel their sense of grief and loss.

Tragedies in the news Most likely, you watched the extensive news coverage of the tragedies that occurred on September 11, 2001. You might have watched news coverage of wars, murders, terrorist bombings, tornadoes, floods, or earthquakes. These events can trigger feelings of loss and grief. You value human life and are saddened when life and property are lost. You have empathy for people who are affected by loss or death.

Symptoms of Loss and Grief

Symptoms of loss and grief include the following:

- numbness
- shock
- loss of appetite
- intestinal upsets
- sleep disturbances
- loss of energy

- shortness of breath
- confusion
- crying spells
- moodiness
- outbursts of anger
- depression

124 UNIT 2 • Mental and Emotional Health

Empathy is the ability to share in another person's emotions or feelings. Your empathy for others can cause you to experience loss and grief.

The end of something special Did you know that you also might experience loss and grief when something ends? For example, one day you will graduate from high school. This will end a period of your life that has been special. Even though you look forward to your future, you may have feelings of grief and loss. You are sad that you are leaving your school and your friends. Your parents or guardian might experience a similar loss when you move away from home. They experience emptiness because you are not there. They long for the days when you lived together and shared daily events. Yet, they look forward to sharing new opportunities with you.

The Five Stages of Loss and Grief

What happens when teens experience loss and grief? Teens will experience a variety of emotions that must be worked through before they can accept what has happened to them.

The *five stages of loss and grief* are psychological stages of grieving that include denial, anger, bargaining, depression, and acceptance. Refer to page 109 in Lesson 11 for definitions of the stages.

The amount of time you might spend in each stage of loss and grief will vary. You might backslide. For example, you might work through your feelings and gain acceptance, only to backslide to feeling depressed.

124

Or you might skip one stage and move to the next stage. Some teens get stuck in one of the five stages of loss and grief. Teens who become stuck in one of the five stages of loss and grief usually need help. These teens are unable to deal with the loss on their own. Therapists can help teens work through their feelings.

Dealing with a terminal illness The five-step grieving process can be illustrated by the example of people with terminal illnesses. If people are told by a doctor that they have a terminal illness, they may first refuse to believe that they are dying. They pretend that the information the doctor told them is wrong.

The second stage is anger. People with a terminal illness in this stage may direct their anger at their family, friends, physicians, or other medical professionals.

Anger can turn into bargaining. People who are dying try to avoid death by making deals and promises. When they realize bargaining will not change the outcome, they become depressed. Once a person who is terminally ill accepts that he or she is dying, he or she begins to say goodbye, share special feelings and thoughts with loved ones, and tries to enjoy the remainder of his or her life.

Different people may spend different amounts of time in each of the stages. Some people progress through the stages, while others get stuck or go backward. Family members and friends of people with terminal illnesses may go through similar stages of loss and grief.

www.glencoe.com

Drug and Alcohol Use and Loss and Grief

When a person suffers a loss, whether it is the death of a close friend or a move to a new location, he or she will commonly have feelings of grief.

Some people might self-medicate in an attempt to feel better or to escape the feelings of grief. Using alcohol or other drugs as a coping mechanism for feelings of grief is not a solution. Although these substances might produce a temporary feeling of relief, these substances will not help a person get through the grieving process. The feelings of grief remain after the effects of the drugs have worn off. In many cases, these substances actually may make a person feel worse, emotionally and physically, after their use.

Positive ways to cope with grief include talking about your feelings with people whom you trust. Expressing your feelings in writing, such as keeping a journal, can help as well. Grief counseling with a professional counselor or therapist also can be helpful for someone who is struggling with the grieving process.

 Visit www.glencoe.com for more information on how to deal with grief.

Projections of Alcohol Abuse and Dependence in the U.S.

Source: National Institutes of Health, 2000

Analyzing Graphs
Study the graph above and answer these questions.

1. Which group is projected to have the greatest number of people with alcohol dependence?

2. Which group is projected to have the least number of people abuse alcohol?

Analyzing Graphs
1. Caucasian males
2. African-American females

Project
Drug and Alcohol Abuse Have students research the effects of alcohol abuse on mental-health status. Ask students if there is a connection between substance abuse, depression, and suicide. Have students identify three healthy ways to deal with loss and grief. **L3**

NHES Assessment/SCASS

Selected Response In which of the following situations might a person experience anticipatory grief?

A. after leaving home for college

B. when a family member is terminally ill

C. upon learning of the death of a favorite celebrity

D. sudden death of a friend

Family Involvement

Loss Although students may not have personally experienced a loss, it is likely that someone in their family, such as a parent or grandparent, has experienced the death of someone close to them. Ask students to interview an adult family member to learn how they were able to cope with the loss of a close friend or family member. Have students prepare a list of questions before the interview and review the questions before the interview takes place. Have students write a summary of the interview in their health journals, if both the student and the family member is comfortable with the student doing that. **L2**

National Health Education Standards
Pages 124–125: 1.1, 1.2, 1.8, 2.1, 2.3, 2.4, 3.4, 4.4, 5.7, 7.2

NHES Assessment/SCASS

Constructed Response Discuss the suggested activities on this page. Have students write one to two paragraphs in their health journals in response to the following questions: Which activities would benefit a person who has a terminal illness? Which activities would benefit the person's family members and friends? Discuss how the activities are helpful. **L2**

5-Minute Check

Page 71, **Unit 2 Fast File Resources**

1. What is loss? *the feeling that occurs when someone dies or a life situation changes or ends*

2. List some symptoms of loss and grief. *Answers might include numbness, shock, anger, depression, moodiness, and loss of energy. See page 124 for the full list.*

3. Why might tragedies in the news trigger feelings of loss and grief? *A person might feel empathy for others experiencing a loss.*

4. Why is the use of alcohol and drugs not a good way to deal with loss? *Answers might include that they do not help a person recover from loss and grief and they might make a person feel worse.*

5. Why does our response to loss and grief differ? *Our response is based on who we are, whom or what we have lost, and how much our day-to-day life is changed.*

Dealing with a Loss

The response to loss and grief differs based on who we are, whom or what we have lost, and how much our day-to-day life is changed. The following information provides guidelines for responding when someone close to you is dying, when someone whom you know is grieving a loss, and when you are grieving a loss. Remember, everyone responds to loss and grief in his or her own way. If you have questions about your responses or those of someone else, talk to your parent, guardian, mentor, or other trusted adult.

Healthful Ways to Respond to a Loss

> **Make the Connection**
>
> **Listening Skills** For more information on using active listening skills, see page 41 in Lesson 5.

When someone close to you is dying When this happens, both you and the person who is dying experience anticipatory grief. The person who is dying grieves the loss of his or her life. You grieve the loss of the person you care about or love. The time you have left to be together and share becomes very special. You can make wise use of the precious moments you have.

Suppose the person about whom you care is in a coma. The time you have left to be together and share is very important. Frequent visits may be helpful to you and to the person who is dying. Many people who have come out of a coma remember words spoken to them. They also remember being comforted. You might hold this person's hand and speak to him or her. Expressing your feelings can help you and the person who is in a coma.

When someone you know is grieving a loss You may know someone who is grieving the loss of a close friend or loved one. You also can comfort this person. Make yourself available. Remember, friends support one another during difficult times. Another way to comfort the person is to do something thoughtful for the person. You might send a card or call the person. You might offer to help the person with meals or errands. You can show your support for someone who is grieving by attending memorial services, with permission of your parents or guardian.

What to Do If Someone You Know Is Dying

There are many ways you can show your love for someone who is dying:

- Spend time with the friend or family.
- Share your loving feelings and memories.
- Share your feelings of loss and pain.
- Encourage the person to talk about his or her death.
- Listen carefully to the person's feelings and thoughts about the past, present, and future.
- Reassure the person with affection, hold hands, or hug.
- Share your grief with family members and friends.
- Continue your daily routine if possible.
- Consider what you will do to keep alive the memory of the person.
- Allow yourself time to grieve.

126 UNIT 2 • Mental and Emotional Health

Differentiated Instruction

Gifted and Talented Have students interview a grief counselor at a local hospital or mental-health center. Students should prepare interview questions to determine why people use a grief counselor, the types of losses clients experience, and how the counselor is able to help. After the interview, have students create a multimedia presentation of their findings from the interview. **L3**

Just the FACTS: LOSS AND GRIEF

> **If a person doesn't cry, is he or she really grieving?**

The FACTS There are no rules about grieving and no "right" way to grieve. Each person experiences grief in his or her own way. Trying to behave according to the expectations of others during this difficult time only adds more stress to the situation. Some people suffer greatly, but they might express their feelings through art, writing, exercise, or another outlet. Other people, especially teenagers, might enter a state of denial and feel numb for weeks or months after a death or another loss. As the numbness fades, they may need support as they deal with their feelings.

> **Are people who cry after losing a loved one—or even a pet—weak?**

The FACTS This myth is the opposite of the first one—and just as hurtful. Crying is a healthful way to express emotions and helps to release bottled-up tension. Trying too hard to control painful emotions can block healing and make the process take longer. At the same time, there is no "correct" schedule for grieving. People let go of a loved one or pet or recover from another loss in different ways and are ready to let go at different times.

> **Does talking about a loss only make things worse?**

The FACTS Talking about a loss helps people begin to accept the new reality. If you know people who are grieving, encourage them to tell you about the loss, including what happened, when it occurred, how they reacted, and how they feel now. Invite them to share their memories of the person or pet. If everyone avoids the subject and pretends that nothing happened, a grieving person feels alone. He or she may think that no one else cared about the individual or pet who is gone. The grieving person also may begin to think that something is wrong with him or her because only he or she feels sad about the loss. This isolation can add to the person's grief.

Have empathy for the person's loss. Do not lessen the loss by making statements such as, "She would have wanted it this way," or "He is in a better place now." Instead say, "I am sorry you feel sad. I am here to support you." If you knew the person who has died, you can talk about good memories you have of that person. Often, it helps people who are grieving to know that others remember their loved one. It can also comfort them if you help them remember good times with their friend or loved one.

Encourage the person to talk about his or her grief, and be able to recognize signs of grief that are not healthful. A person who remains severely depressed or who relies on alcohol or other drugs may need help. Tell a responsible adult if you notice such behaviors.

Remember that people deal with a loss in different ways. Some people grieve publicly, while others prefer to grieve privately. Some people grieve for longer periods of time than others. Some people prefer to recall funny memories about a loved one, while others may need time to deal with their feelings before they can do this.

When a loved one is dying, it is important to spend time with him or her, and express your ▼ loving feelings.

LESSON 12 • Dealing with Loss and Grief   127

Grieving a Loss

Class Discussion

Ways to Handle a Loss On the student page, students will find suggestions on ways to handle loss. Ask students to read each suggestion and indicate which they have used in the past and how useful the methods were to them. If students have not experienced a loss, have them indicate which ways they think they would respond in the future. Students can write the techniques on a sheet of paper along with a numerical value of the usefulness of each. **L2**

3 Assess

Vocabulary Practice
Page 64, **Unit 2 Fast File Resources**

National Health Education Standards
Pages 128–129: 1.1, 1.5, 2.1, 2.3, 4.4, 7.2

128

Grieving a Loss

There are many things people do when grieving a loss. Some people turn to unhealthy outlets for their grief. However, there are many healthful ways to deal with grief. You can manage grief in a healthful way.

Taking time to grieve will help you deal with a loss. Spending time alone doing activities you enjoy can help you work through
▼ your feelings.

1. Talk with your parent, guardian, mentor or other trusted adult.

2. Ask your friends and family members to comfort and support you.

3. Have someone stay by your side for a period of time if you prefer to not be alone.

4. Give yourself time to grieve, including some "alone time."

5. Express your feelings in healthful ways.
   - Give yourself permission to cry.
   - Use I-messages to express feelings (Lesson 5, page 41).
   - Use anger-management skills if you are angry (Lesson 10, page 98).
   - Use strategies for coping with depression to help with your sadness (Lesson 11, page 117).
   - Write your feelings in a grief journal. Writing about feelings helps relieve sadness and depression.

6. Maintain a normal schedule and routine as much as possible.
   - Return slowly to your normal activities and daily routine to avoid becoming too tired.

7. Protect your health.
   - Physical activity will relieve tension and will give you a feeling of well-being. Physical activity can also help you deal with angry feelings and frustration.
   - Moderate your intake of sugar and caffeine. Eat a healthy, balanced diet. This reduces stress.
   - Maintain your normal sleep and rest schedule. Go to bed when you normally would sleep. Wake up when you normally would wake up. Avoid napping when you normally would be awake.
   - Use breathing techniques. Inhale with slow deep breaths through your nose. Slowly exhale through the mouth. Repeat four or five times.
   - Avoid harmful behaviors as ways of coping. For example, do not smoke, drink alcohol, or use other harmful drugs.

8. Seek professional help if you are unable to make adjustments or have lingering anger and depression.
   - Call a crisis hotline, or make an appointment to see a counselor. See a psychologist to talk about your feelings. You might need to be treated for depression.

GRIEF in the Media
Advocating for Health Every day on the national news, there is a report about someone or a group of people who have experienced a traumatic event in which a loved one was lost. How are they dealing with their loss? Create a pamphlet that explains how they can deal with their grief in healthy ways.

128   UNIT 2 • Mental and Emotional Health

(DI) Differentiated Instruction

Learning Disabilities Assign students to groups of three or four. Have students go through each point in the list on the student page and discuss how each point will help someone who is grieving. Have students create a "dealing with grief recipe" that lists at least four steps that will help someone deal with grief. Students should be able to identify why they chose the four steps they included in their recipe. **L1 ELL**

anticipatory grief
empathy
five stages of loss
    and grief
grief
invincible
loss
out-of-order death
suicide

Key Terms Review

Complete the fill-in-the-blank statements with the lesson Key Terms on the left. Do not write in this book.

1. A(n) _____ is the death of a person that occurs at an unexpected time in his or her life.

2. _____ is the ability to share in another person's emotions or feelings.

3. _____ is the feeling that occurs when something ends.

4. _____ is grief experienced prior to a loss.

5. The _____ are psychological stages of grieving that include denial, anger, bargaining, depression, and acceptance.

6. To think you are _____ is to view oneself as incapable of being harmed.

7. Intense emotional suffering caused by a loss, disaster, or misfortune is called _____.

Recalling the Facts

8. What are some causes of loss and grief in teens?

9. What are the five stages of grief?

10. How might you respond in a healthful way when someone close to you is dying?

11. How might you respond in a healthful way when someone you know is grieving a loss?

12. What are healthful ways to grieve a loss?

13. Why might teens grieve when a well-known person dies?

14. What is the difference between grief and anticipatory grief?

15. How do tragedies in the news trigger feelings of loss and grief?

16. Why does drug or alcohol use not help a person respond to a loss?

17. Does a teen who does not cry grieve as much as one who does if the two experienced the same loss? Explain.

18. Why is talking about a loss important?

Critical Thinking

19. Why would getting stuck in one of the first four stages of loss and grief be harmful to one's health?

20. Why might a person experience shortness of breath, loss of appetite, or intestinal upsets after experiencing a loss?

21. Does grieving always involve all five stages of loss and grief? Explain.

22. Why might feelings of loss or grief intensify during the holidays?

Real-Life Applications

23. Why do you think an out-of-order death is traumatic?

24. Why might a person with a serious illness respond by bargaining?

25. Why do you think some teens feel they are invincible?

26. What are some causes of out-of-order deaths in teens? How could the risk of some of those causes be reduced?

Activities

Responsible Decision Making

27. **Role-Play** A teen's grandmother is terminally ill. The teen tells you he is uncomfortable visiting her because he knows she is dying and does not want to see her. Pair up with a classmate for role-play. Refer to the Responsible Decision-Making Model on page 61 for help.

Sharpen Your Life Skills

28. **Comprehend Health Concepts**
The five stages of grief may be experienced when a person has a loss. Select a situation, other than death, which causes a person to grieve. Write an essay explaining what a person in this situation experiences based on the five stages of grief.

Visit **www.glencoe.com** for more *Health & Wellness* quizzes.

LESSON 12
STUDY GUIDE

Key Terms Review

1. out-of-order death
2. Empathy
3. Loss
4. Anticipatory grief
5. five stages of loss and grief
6. invincible
7. grief

Recalling the Facts

8. See pages 123–124.
9. denial, anger, bargaining, depression, and acceptance
10. See list on page 126.
11. See pages 126–127.
12. See page 128.
13. See page 124.
14. Anticipatory grief occurs before a loss, while grief occurs after a loss.
15. You feel empathy for the people affected by the tragedy.
16. Alcohol or drug use may delay the grieving process and may make them feel worse emotionally and physically.
17. People experience grief in different ways. There is no one right way to grieve.
18. Talking about a loss helps people begin to accept the new reality.

Critical Thinking

19. If you are stuck in one of the first four stages, you may be highly stressed. You would not have dealt with your feelings, and you may not be able to function as well in your everyday life.
20. The person's body is responding to the stress that a loss produces.
21. No. Everyone experiences at least some of the stages in response to a personal loss or tragedy.
22. The loss may have been close to a holiday, which may trigger memories and sadness; or a person may associate holidays with spending time with a person who has died.

Real-Life Applications

23. An out-of-order death means a person died young, such as a child dying before a parent. It is unexpected and shocking.

24. He or she may be unable to accept that the illness is out of their control and still think there is something they can do to fix it.

25. He or she may feel young, healthy, and capable of recovering from anything.

26. car accidents, homicide, or suicide; being safe, getting help to deal with anger, stress, or depression

Activities

Responsible Decision Making

27. It is healthful for the teen to share feelings of discomfort with a parent or guardian. Venting feelings of loss, anger, depression, and fear protects physical and emotional health.

Sharpen Your Life Skills

28. Answers will vary.

UNIT 2
STUDY GUIDE

Key Terms Review

1. h	6. c
2. e	7. j
3. l	8. g
4. b	9. i
5. d	10. f

Recalling the Facts

11. a standard or belief that is learned from parents, guardians, mentors, or teachers

12. Pay attention to your appearance, enjoy activities by yourself, write your feelings in a journal, etc. See page 77 for the full list.

13. a problem in which a person neglects himself or herself to care for, control, or try to "fix" someone else

14. See the list on page 87.

15. See page 97.

16. alarm stage, resistance stage, exhaustion stage

17. deep sadness, apathy, fatigue, agitation, sleep disturbance, weight or appetite changes, lack of concentration, feelings of worthlessness, morbid thoughts

18. See page 115.

19. numbness, shock, loss of appetite, intestinal upsets, sleep disturbances, loss of energy, shortness of breath, confusion, crying spells, moodiness, outbursts of anger, and depression

20. denial, anger, bargaining, depression, and acceptance

Critical Thinking

21. To have good character, you need to have high self-esteem and self-respect. If you do not have these, you are more likely to do things that do not demonstrate good character.

22. If you have a supportive network of family and friends, you likely will be more mentally healthy, which can help improve or maintain your physical health.

23. A person with an addiction may lack self-control when faced with a certain behavior or substance. This can translate into other parts of his or her life.

UNIT
2
STUDY GUIDE

Key Terms Review

Match the following definitions with the correct Key Terms. Do not write in this book.

a. good character *(p. 75)*
b. empathy *(p. 124)*
c. grief *(p. 123)*
d. life crisis *(p. 109)*
e. loss *(p. 123)*
f. mental disorder *(p. 89)*
g. mind-body connection *(p. 95)*
h. personality *(p. 83)*
i. resiliency *(p. 118)*
j. self-respect *(p. 74)*
k. stress *(p. 100)*
l. stress-management skills *(p. 104)*

1. an individual's unique pattern of characteristics
2. the feeling that occurs when something changes or ends
3. techniques used to prevent and deal with stress to protect one's health
4. a person's use of self-control to act on responsible values
5. an experience that causes a high level of stress
6. intense emotional suffering caused by a loss, disaster, or misfortune
7. a high regard for oneself because one behaves in responsible ways
8. the relationship between a person's thoughts, emotions, and body responses
9. the ability to adjust, recover, bounce back, and learn from difficult times
10. a mental or emotional condition that makes it difficult for a person to live in a normal way

Recalling the Facts

11. What is a value? *(Lesson 8)*
12. What are actions that show self-respect? *(Lesson 8)*
13. What is codependence? *(Lesson 9)*
14. What are signs of addiction? *(Lesson 9)*
15. What are signs of hidden anger? *(Lesson 10)*
16. What are the three stages of general adaptation syndrome? *(Lesson 10)*
17. What are symptoms used to diagnose depression? *(Lesson 11)*
18. What are warning signs that indicate a teen might make a suicide attempt? *(Lesson 11)*
19. What are symptoms of loss and grief? *(Lesson 12)*
20. What are the five stages of loss and grief? *(Lesson 12)*

Critical Thinking

21. How are self-respect and self-esteem related to good character? *(Lesson 8)*
22. Why does your social-emotional environment affect your health? *(Lesson 8)*
23. Why might having one addiction increase risk for development of another one? *(Lesson 9)*
24. Why is bipolar disorder dangerous to a person if he or she is not treated? *(Lesson 9)*
25. Why is it harmful to use projection and displacement to deal with angry feelings? *(Lesson 10)*
26. How can stress be positive? *(Lesson 10)*
27. How can a person with dysthymic disorder have a second form of depression? *(Lesson 11)*
28. How is being resilient related to good character? *(Lesson 11)*
29. How is health compromised if a person gets stuck in the anger stage of the five stages of loss and grief? *(Lesson 12)*
30. Why do some people grieve after the death of a well-known person? *(Lesson 12)*

Use **Interactive Tutor** at **www.glencoe.com** for additional help.

24. People with bipolar disorder have extreme highs and extreme lows. They can become suicidal during their depressive phase.

25. Both of these are ways that people use to avoid dealing with a situation. People have to deal with the problem to help deal with their anger.

26. When people feel stressed, it can be an opportunity for them to slow down, evaluate their lives, and make healthful changes.

27. A person with dysthymic disorder has long-term depression with two or more symptoms. He or she can also have bouts of major depression that are short-term, which would include five or more symptoms.

28. If you are resilient, you can overcome adversity. Overcoming adversity helps you develop good character.

Health Literacy Activities

What Do You Know?
Critical Thinking Work with your classmates to create a Top Ten List of Stressors. Form a team with five classmates. Compete against other teams to make a list of unique ways to overcome the stressors on the list.

Connection to World Cultures
Self-Directed Learning People throughout the world experience losses and life crises, such as earthquakes, famine, airplane crashes, floods, and deaths due to AIDS. Watch news coverage of world events, and select a life crisis that is happening in another part of the world. Write a news report about how the people are dealing with the crisis.

Family Involvement
Effective Communication Ask family members to participate in a family round table. Explain the five guidelines for expressing emotions in healthful ways. Then ask each family member to use an I-message to share his or her feelings about an event taking place in his or her life.

Investigating Health Careers
Responsible Citizenship Select a person who has a health career. Interview this person and ask the following questions: Why did you choose this career? How did you prepare for this career? What is the most stressful part of your job? How do you manage stress at your job? Share the information you gathered from the interview with your classmates.

Group Project
Problem Solving In order to improve the social-emotional environment, think of a younger person in your community for whom you could be a mentor. Suppose you were to spend an hour a week with this person for six weeks. On a sheet of paper, describe what you might do. Meet with a group of classmates to brainstorm ideas. Share your plan with your parents or guardian and consider acting on it. Visit www.glencoe.com for more information.

Standardized Test Practice

Reading & Writing

Read the following selection and answer the questions that follow.

Can you train your mind to control body responses? With biofeedback, a technique in which a person gets feedback on body responses by viewing measurements on monitors or other devices, or hearing specific sounds, this may be possible. Biofeedback training has been used to help people deal with stress. Biofeedback works by closely monitoring body functions and displaying the measurements taken in different ways. The subject becomes familiar with the kinds of external forces that cause the stress. For example, blood pressure can be displayed on a chart or meter, while an elevated heart rate can set off a bell or alarm.

Multiple Choice

1 In this paragraph, the word *elevated* means:
- **A** lower than normal
- **B** higher than normal
- **C** dangerous
- **D** changeable

2 Biofeedback training has been used to help people deal with:
- **A** Weight issues
- **B** Peer pressure
- **C** Stress
- **D** Conflict resolution

Open-Ended

3 Imagine you are developing a study to show the effect of biofeedback on stress. Write a paragraph describing a study you would design to test the effectiveness of biofeedback.

---

29. A person who is constantly angry is causing his or her body to continually react to the stressor and remain in the alarm stage of general adaptation syndrome.
30. People may feel connected in some way to the famous person, they may feel empathy for the family, or they may feel the loss is a loss to society because of the person's activities.

Health Literacy Activities

What Do You Know?
Lists will vary. Listen to groups to be sure that students are giving correct answers.

Connection to World Cultures
News reports will vary. Have students read their reports to the class and then have the class discuss various ways the world community can help populations in crisis.

Family Involvement
Answers will vary. Have students practice using I-messages in class so they can teach the skill to family members.

Investigating Health Careers
Students should share the results of their interviews with the class.

Group Project
Answers will vary, but might include working on schoolwork, talking about school and family, doing fun activities such as riding bikes, etc.

Standardized Test Practice

Reading & Writing

Multiple Choice
1. B   2. D

Open-Ended
3. Students' paragraphs should describe a study in which biofeedback is the only variable, or possible influence, on a disease or condition. Students should show awareness that only by isolating the effect of biofeedback can a study be valuable. Paragraphs should contain correct spelling, capitalization, punctuation, grammar, usage, and sentence structure.

Family and Social Health

STANDARDS AND FEATURES

Lesson	National Standards	State/Local Standards	Activities and Features
Lesson 13 *(3 sessions, 1 block)* Developing Healthful Family Relationships	1.2, 1.8, 2.1, 5.7		**Using Life Skills:** Using Communication Skills: Practicing Conflict Resolution, p. 146
Lesson 14 *(2 sessions, 1 block)* Adjusting to Family Changes	1.2, 2.1, 2.3		**Using Life Skills:** Using Communication Skills: Talking About Family Changes, p. 151
Lesson 15 *(2 sessions, 1 block)* Examining Dating and Friendships	1.8, 2.3, 4.1, 8.1		
Lesson 16 *(4 sessions, 2 blocks)* Practicing Abstinence from Sex	1.1, 1.5, 2.1, 2.3, 4.4, 8.1		**Using Life Skills:** Using Resistance Skills: Remaining Abstinent, p. 171 **Speaking Out:** Practicing Abstinence from Sexual Activity, p. 176
Lesson 17 *(2 sessions, 1 block)* Recognizing Harmful Relationships	1.1, 2.1, 2.3, 5.1		
Lesson 18 *(4 sessions, 1 block)* Preparing for Marriage and Parenthood	1.2, 1.5, 2.1		**Health News:** Marrying Later in Life, p. 191 **Facts About:** The Importance of Responsible Parenting, p. 193 **Using Life Skills:** Practicing Healthful Behaviors: Egg Baby Exercise, p. 200 **Just the Facts:** Pregnancy Myths, p. 202

Key to Differentiated Instruction

L1 Level 1 activities should be appropriate for students with learning difficulties.

L2 Level 2 activities should be within the ability range of all students.

L3 Level 3 activities are designed for above-average students.

ELL ELL activities should be within the ability range of English language learners.

FAST FILE RESOURCES

INTRODUCING THE UNIT

Parent and Family Letter	p. 1	Health Behavior Contract	p. 3
Spanish Parent and Family Letter	p. 2	Unit Focus Transparency Master and Worksheet	p. 4

TEACHING THE UNIT LESSONS

Reproducible Student Pages	Lesson 13	Lesson 14	Lesson 15	Lesson 16	Lesson 17	Lesson 18
Reading Strategy	p. 7	p. 21	p. 35	p. 47	p. 61	p. 73
Vocabulary Practice	p. 8	p. 22	p. 36	p. 48	p. 62	p. 74
Transparency Master and Worksheet	p. 9	p. 23	p. 37	p. 49	p. 63	p. 75
Real-Life Health	p. 11	p. 25	p. 39	p. 51	p. 65	p. 77
5-Minute Check	p. 15	p. 29	p. 43	p. 55	p. 69	p. 81
Lesson Quiz	p. 18	p. 31	p. 44	p. 57	p. 70	p. 83

CLOSING THE UNIT

Family Involvement Activity	p. 87	Health in the News	p. 97
Community Involvement Activity	p. 89	Health Career Research Activity	p. 99
Health Lab	p. 91	Unit Test A	p. 101
Activity: Strengthening Health Skills	p. 95	Unit Test B	p. 105

Technology

- **Interactive Chalkboard CD-ROM**
- **TeacherWorks™ CD-ROM**
- **StudentWorks™ CD-ROM**
- **Reading Essentials CD-ROM**
- **Exam*View*® Assessment Suite**

Glencoe Exclusive!

TeacherWorks™
All-In-One Planner and Resource Center

www.glencoe.com
- **Vocabulary Puzzlemaker**
- **Interactive Tutor**
- **Your Health Checklist**
- **Web Links**
- **Student Web Activities**

UNIT 3

Family and Social Health

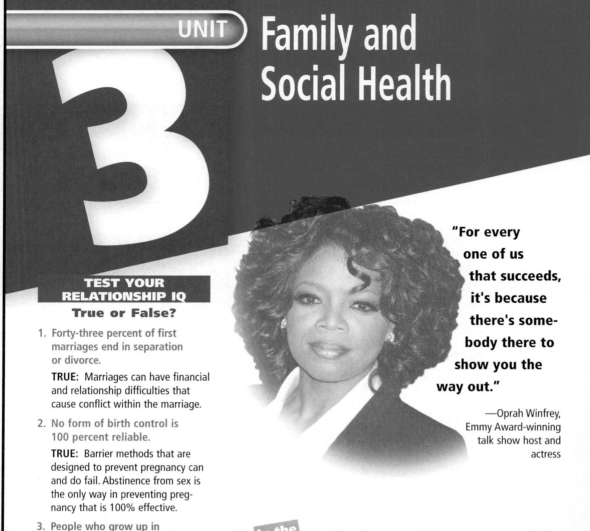

TEST YOUR RELATIONSHIP IQ

Use the three statements on the student page to initiate a class discussion about family and social health issues. *Additional True/False statements are:*

4. **75 percent of divorced persons eventually remarry.**
   TRUE: Of those 75 percent, 65 percent of the remarriages involve children from other marriages.

5. **If a parent loses a job, he or she can always find another job within a few weeks.**
   FALSE: In October of 2003, 23 percent of people who were unemployed had been looking for work for 27 weeks or longer.

6. **Half of the people in the United States are stepchildren, stepparents, stepsiblings, or other members of a stepfamily.**
   FALSE: One out of three Americans falls into one of those categories. Ten percent of children 18 years or younger live with their biological mother and stepfather, while 0.6 percent live with their biological father and stepmother.

 Abstinence Advocacy

Role Models Ask the students to discuss Oprah Winfrey's statement about the role others play in our own success. Ask students to identify positive role models for abstinence. **L2**

TEST YOUR RELATIONSHIP IQ
True or False?

1. **Forty-three percent of first marriages end in separation or divorce.**
   TRUE: Marriages can have financial and relationship difficulties that cause conflict within the marriage.

2. **No form of birth control is 100 percent reliable.**
   TRUE: Barrier methods that are designed to prevent pregnancy can and do fail. Abstinence from sex is the only way in preventing pregnancy that is 100% effective.

3. **People who grow up in dysfunctional families will not be able to adjust and succeed in life.**
   FALSE: Life is full of decisions. Teens who grow up in dysfunctional families can choose a more healthful path that will help them become successful.

"For every one of us that succeeds, it's because there's somebody there to show you the way out."

—Oprah Winfrey, Emmy Award-winning talk show host and actress

in the news **Abstinence Advocacy**

Explain Several individuals and groups have voiced their support for abstinence from sex before marriage. Research one of these groups or individuals and explain their reasons for supporting this choice. Do you agree or disagree with their opinion? Write your response in your journal, and explain why you agree or disagree.

LESSON 13	**LESSON 14**	**LESSON 15**
Developing Healthful Family Relationships	Adjusting to Family Changes	Examining Dating and Friendships

⧖ Two-Minute Unit Launcher

Activity Have students write down five qualities they find attractive in their friends. Students should then compose a list of what they feel are their own best qualities. Afterwards, have them compare their first list to their second list. Discuss or have the students write in their health journals what similarities and differences they found between the two lists. Ask students how their characteristics and their friends' characteristics complement each other. If the students' lists are similar, ask them why they think that is so. **L2**

EVALUATING MEDIA MESSAGES

Have YOU found that 'Special Someone'?

Have you sent the signals?
Have you seen the look?

Angela, the advice columnist for the next generation, knows what you need to do to find that special someone. From what to wear to how to act on the first date—follow her easy guidelines and you, too, will never be on the dating sidelines again.

 WHAT'S YOUR VERDICT?
To evaluate this advertisement, use the criteria for analyzing and evaluating health messages delivered through media and technology that you learned in Unit 1.

 Health Online

Visit **www.glencoe.com** to find regularly updated statistics on teen marriages. Using the information provided, determine the answer to this question: What percentage of teen marriages fail?

Visit **www.glencoe.com** to use *Your Health Checklist* ✔, an interactive tool that helps you determine your health status.

LESSON 16
Practicing Abstinence from Sex

LESSON 17
Recognizing Harmful Relationships

LESSON 18
Preparing for Marriage and Parenthood

UNIT 3 • Family and Social Health **133**

 Health Online

Answers Only 6 percent of all teenage girls and 2 percent of all teenage boys are married. Marriages of teens 14 to 17 years old are two to three times more likely to end in separation or divorce than adult marriages. Also, most teen marriages begin with a pregnancy, which can make marriage more difficult. Eight out of ten babies born to married 15- to 17-year-old mothers were conceived before marriage. Tell students that waiting to marry and to have children greatly increases the chance of a successful marriage and the ability of people to emotionally and financially care for children.

Developing Healthful Family Relationships

Out of Time?

If time does not permit an in-depth study of this topic, use the following activities in this Teacher Wraparound Edition:
- Family Involvement, p. 137
- Class Activity, p. 138
- Cross-Curricular Connections, p. 143
- Class Discussion, p. 145

1 Focus

HEALTH GOALS **Improve Relationships** Have students respond to the second Health Goal for this lesson by listing in their health journals ways they can try to improve a difficult family relationship. *Examples include talking to a family member about a problem or spending more time with family members.* **L2**

Write ABOUT IT!

Family Values Have students make a list of the values they have been taught at home. Then ask them to create a situation where one of these values might be tested, such as an offer of help to cheat on a test at school. Have students write about the situation and how they would handle it while being consistent with their families' values. **L2**

LESSON 13

Developing Healthful Family Relationships

HEALTH GOALS
- I will develop healthful family relationships.
- I will work to improve difficult family relationships.

Your family has a lot of influence on you. You learn ways of interacting from family members. This lesson focuses on family relationships. You will examine the role of parents and other family members. You will learn about skills and behaviors that are taught in healthful families. You will learn about difficult family relationships and ways to improve them.

What You'll Learn

1. Describe the roles of parents and guardians in promoting a healthful family. *(p. 135)*
2. Discuss the roles of extended family members in promoting a healthful family. *(p. 135)*
3. Explain twelve behaviors and skills children learn in healthful families. *(p. 136)*
4. Discuss ten causes of dysfunctional family relationships and identify steps to improve these relationships. *(p. 140)*
5. Discuss ten behaviors of codependent people. *(p. 143)*
6. Discuss the purposes of recovery programs. *(p. 146)*

Why It's Important

You can be a loving family member. ACT: choose healthful Actions, Commit to being loving, and pledge Time.

Key Terms

- family
- healthful family
- dysfunctional family
- affection
- work ethic
- abandonment
- enmeshment
- interdependence
- recovery program
- Alateen

Write ABOUT IT!

Writing About Values In healthful families, parents and/or guardians teach their children family values. Suppose a classmate asked you to do something that would conflict with family values. What would you do? Why might you discuss the situation with your parents or guardian? After reading pages 136–139 about the skills parents or guardians teach their children in healthful families, write a response to this situation in your health journal.

National Health Education Standards—Guide for Lesson 13		
1.2	Describe the interrelationships of emotional, intellectual, physical, and social health.	pp. 135–143
1.8	Analyze personal susceptibility to injury, illness, or death if engaging in unhealthy behaviors.	pp. 140–143
2.1	Analyze how family influences the health of individuals.	pp. 134, 135–143, 147
5.7	Evaluate the effectiveness of health-related decisions.	pp. 136–143, 147

Family Relationships

The basic unit of society is a *family.* It is the group of persons to which we belong. *Extended family members* are the members of a family in addition to parents, brothers, and sisters. An extended family may include: stepparents, stepbrothers, stepsisters, half-brothers, half-sisters, grandparents, aunts, uncles, cousins, nephews, and nieces. Some families include people who are not related by blood, marriage, or other legal procedure as members of their families.

What to Know About Family Roles

A *healthful family* is a family that practices skills that promote loving, responsible relationships. Healthful family relationships are ones that have a positive effect on physical and emotional health. In healthful families, parents and guardians teach their children these behaviors and skills: self-respecting behavior; healthful attitudes; effective communication; a clear sense of values; responsible decision making; ways to resolve conflict; effective coping skills; ways to delay gratification; ways to express affection and integrate love and sexuality; how to give and receive acts of kindness; a work ethic; and respect for authority.

Role of parents and guardians Parents and guardians teach their children the behaviors and skills listed above. They teach by (1) setting an example, (2) having discussions, (3) expecting behaviors and skills to be practiced, and (4) enforcing consequences when they are not.

Role of grandparents Grandparents reinforce the behaviors and skills taught by parents and guardians. Some grandparents help raise their grandchildren. Some children might live with their grandparents, who assume direct responsibility for teaching children the behaviors and skills listed in the left column.

Role of other family members Other family members practice the behaviors and skills taught by parents, guardians, and grandparents. They help each other interact in loving and responsible ways.

The Family Continuum

The Family Continuum shows two extremes of family life. Studying these two extremes—ideal and dysfunctional—is an important way to learn about relationships. A *dysfunctional family* is a family that does not promote loving, responsible relationships.

The family continuum indicates the degree to which a ▶ family promotes skills needed for loving, responsible relationships. Eight out of ten families rank in the middle of the continuum. They are not ideal, but neither are they completely dysfunctional.

Dysfunctional Family ◀ ▶ Ideal Family

Family Relationships

2 Teach

Class Activity

Extended Family Divide the class into groups, and have them discuss and list ways extended family members can support each other and ways extended family members contribute to healthful families. Then have each group report to the class what they have discussed.
L2 **ELL**

INTERACTIVE CHALKBOARD
with Image Bank

PowerPoint® Presentations

This CD-ROM is an editable Microsoft® PowerPoint® presentation that includes:
- Lesson presentations
- Lesson checks
- Interactive graphics
- 5-Minute Checks
- Image Bank
- All transparencies

CRISS Project
Journals Use the Teacher-Student Journal Strategy on page 17T for students to examine ways to promote healthful family relationships.

Lesson Resource Manager

- **Unit 3 Fast File Resources**
  Reading Strategy, p. 7
  Vocabulary Practice, p. 8
  Transparency Master and Worksheet, p. 9
  Real-Life Health, p. 11
  Real-Life Health, p. 13
  5-Minute Check, p. 15
  Lesson 13 Quiz, p. 18
- **Unit 3 Transparency**
- **Lesson 13 Transparency**

- **Reading Essentials**
- **Technology**
  TeacherWorks™ CD-ROM
  StudentWorks™ CD-ROM
  Reading Essentials CD-ROM
  ExamView® Assessment Suite
  Vocabulary Puzzlemaker

National Health Education Standards
Pages 134–135: 1.2, 1.5, 2.1, 7.2

Healthful Family Relationships

Class Discussion

Self-Respect Ask the class to identify examples of self-respecting behavior. Discuss why it is important. *Answers include taking good care of yourself; not allowing someone to treat you badly, either emotionally or physically; and acting in ways that will ensure others respect you. It is important to respect yourself so that others will respect you.* **L2**

Teaching Transparency

Page 9, **Unit 3 Fast File Resources**

T he connections a person has with family members are *family relationships.* Family relationships have an effect on a person's mental, emotional, and social health. What influences family relationships? Parents and guardians are the primary influence. They play the most direct role in teaching behaviors and skills to their children. Sometimes others—grandparents, foster parents, or other adults—play this role. How do you learn behaviors and skills from parents, guardians, or other significant adults responsible for guiding the family?

What to Know About Healthful Family Relationships

Learning self-respecting behavior Treating oneself in healthful and responsible ways is *self-respecting behavior.* It is an outgrowth of the ways you were treated by the adults who raised you. If you received love and felt accepted, then you began to feel good about yourself. If you were well-cared for, you learned how to take care of yourself. As a result, you learned how to treat yourself in healthful and kind ways. You learned to choose behaviors that would not harm you. When you learn to treat yourself in healthful and kind ways, you learn to expect the same from others.

Learning to value the needs of others Teens raised in a healthful family also learn the difference between self-respecting and self-centered behavior. *Self-centered behavior* is an action that fulfills personal needs with little regard for the needs of others. Self-centered behavior does not contribute to healthful family relationships.

Learning healthful attitudes toward sexuality The definition of *sexuality* is the feelings and attitudes a person has about his or her body, sex role, and relationships. Your sexuality is influenced from birth, when you are born either male or female. Your parents or guardians talk to you about your body and shape your attitudes about being male or female.

Learning healthful sex roles Parents and guardians influence your sex role. A *sex role* is the behaviors, attitudes, values, and beliefs that a particular cultural group considers appropriate for males and females on the basis of their biological sex. Your parents or guardians helped you learn about sex roles from a very early age. For example, you may have learned that it is acceptable for males and females to cry and share feelings. You may have learned that males and females are different, but deserve equal respect. In a healthful

🔹 Achieving Health Literacy

Effective Communicator Using the information in the Student Edition, have students create a newsletter for their community. Ask students to include the answers to the following questions in the newsletter:
1. What does it mean to have a healthy family relationship?
2. What does it mean to have an unhealthy family relationship?
3. How can a family work to improve relationships?
4. What are some important behaviors and skills learned in healthful family relationships?
Ask permission to display the newsletters in the school library. **L2**

family, parents or guardians discuss puberty with their teens. They explain the changes in feelings and emotions that accompany puberty. Their openness and sensitivity help teens understand the changes they are experiencing and learn how to accept their sexuality.

Learning effective communication skills Skills that help a person share feelings, thoughts, and information with others are *communication skills.* You first learn communication skills within your family. Suppose your parents or guardians use I-messages to express feelings and listen carefully when you speak. Then, as you begin to copy their way of communicating, you develop skills in communicating with others. Your parents or guardians also may demonstrate how to express anger, sadness, and disappointment in healthful ways. Then you learn healthful ways to express these emotions. In a healthful family, you feel secure practicing communication skills. You use these communication skills in other relationships.

Learning a clear sense of values A standard or belief is called a *value.* A value that is learned within a family is called a *family value.* In a healthful family, parents or guardians teach their children certain values. For example, your parents or guardians may value hard work, honesty, and close family relationships. They behave in ways consistent with these values. They work hard, are honest in their dealings with others, and spend time with members of their family. They discuss these values with you. You listen to what they say, and their behavior mirrors what they say. You observe their everyday behavior. You internalize their values and behave in similar ways. When you relate to others, you remember these family values. They become the standard for what you think and believe. You will have a clear sense of these values for the rest of your life.

Learning to make responsible decisions In a healthful family, parents or guardians serve as role models for decision making. You observe your parents or guardians using the decision-making process. They carefully evaluate options before deciding what to do. They weigh the consequences of possible actions. They make responsible decisions and teach you to do the same. Parents or guardians expect responsible behavior from their children. They set guidelines and make expectations clear. There are consequences for breaking family guidelines. You learn that there always are consequences for unhealthful behavior. This helps you when you are pressured by peers. You think about consequences and say "no" to wrong behaviors. When you have difficulty saying "no," you turn to your parents or guardians for support. When you make a mistake, your parents or guardians help you learn from the experience.

Learning to resolve conflicts A disagreement between two or more people or two or more choices is called a *conflict.*

Make the Connection

Making Responsible Decisions For more information on making responsible decisions, see page 61 in Lesson 6.

Parents who teach their children to value working hard will raise teens who are confident and ▼ motivated to succeed.

Quick Demo

Communication Make the following statements to the students and ask them to change the statements to I-messages in order to improve communication.
- "I hate my job! My boss is such a jerk!"
- "Be quiet, I can't hear the T.V."
- "You are always goofing off at school. Shape up."
- "No, I'm not mad. Just forget it."
L2

NHES Assessment/SCASS

Performance Event Have students write an essay discussing the four values they think are the most important to teach within a family. Ask students to describe why they chose the four values. After they have completed their essays, they can pair up with another student to analyze the values each one chose. Ask students which two values from their partner's list they believe to be most important and why. **L3**

Family Involvement

Interview Have students interview their parents or guardians about ways they teach their children healthful behaviors. Have the students list two healthful behaviors their parents or guardians focus on. Students also should describe how their parents or guardians focus on the behaviors. Have students turn in their lists without their names attached. Then read through the ideas for the class. Ask students what they observed in the answers. Ask them, for example, if the behaviors that parents or guardians mentioned were similar and if there was a common way they went about promoting these health behaviors. **L2**

National Health Education Standards
Pages 136–137: 1.2, 2.1, 4.1, 4.4

Delayed Gratification Define the term *delayed gratification* for students. Tell students that an example of delayed gratification is saving money from a job instead of spending it right away. If they do this, they could use it for something that is more expensive, like a car. Ask students to give other examples and the benefits that could occur. **L2**

NHES Assessment/SCASS

Constructed Response Ask the class to write one to two paragraphs about ways teens learn from their parents to cope with difficulty. Discuss the importance of these coping skills. *Answers may include encouraging teens to talk about their problems, and parents displaying good coping skills themselves.* **L2**

Class Activity

ACT Break the class into small groups and assign each one either Action, Commitment, or Time. Have the groups discuss and write down ways to fulfill each goal in the acronym ACT in their family relationships. Then have each group report their findings and write them on one large poster. Display the finished poster in the room for students to see. *Examples are: (Action) Don't lie to family members. Be kind to siblings. (Commitment) Try to help out more with household responsibilities. (Time) Ask parents to have a family movie or game night each week.* **L2**

National Health Education Standards

Pages 138–139: 1.2, 2.1, 2.3, 4.3, 5.7, 6.3

In every relationship there are conflicts. In a healthful family, parents or guardians teach their children to resolve conflicts in healthful ways. They listen to both sides of a disagreement and work to find an acceptable solution. In a healthful family, conflicts are resolved without violence. You learn healthful ways to resolve conflicts. The skills you learn from your family help you to resolve conflicts in other relationships.

Learning effective coping skills In Lesson 11 you learned the five emotional responses that people use to cope with a life crisis. They are: (1) denying or refusing to believe what is happening, (2) being angry about what is happening, (3) bargaining or making promises, hoping it will change what is happening, (4) being depressed when you recognize that the outcome is unlikely to change, and (5) accepting the situation, making adjustments, and then, bouncing back. In a healthful family, parents or guardians want to help their children develop emotional strength. They understand ways people deal with a life crisis. Suppose your parents or guardians encourage you to share your feelings during a life crisis.

In healthful families, parents or guardians help their children develop the confidence and emotional strength needed to understand why waiting until marriage to have sex is the right decision. ▼

You will learn how to cope during difficult times that you may experience later in your life.

Learning to delay gratification In a healthful family, parents or guardians teach their children the importance of delayed gratification. *Delayed gratification* is voluntarily postponing a reward in order to complete a task or responsibility before enjoying the reward. If you have learned to delay gratification, you are patient. You are not tempted to act immediately. Instead, you see the value in waiting until a more appropriate time. Being able to delay gratification is especially important in relationships. During your teen years you may experience sexual feelings and desires, but it is not appropriate for you to be sexually active. Waiting until marriage to express intimate sexual feelings protects your emotional and physical health and follows healthful family values.

Learning to express affection and integrate love and sexuality A fond or tender feeling that a person has toward another person is *affection.* In a healthful family, parents or guardians teach their children how to express affection. For example, your parents or guardians may hug you, kiss you goodnight or good-bye, or hold you when you are sad. Their expressions of warm feelings help you feel loved and help you develop a healthful attitude toward showing affection to loved ones. They also teach you appropriate ways to express affection. You learn who has the right to touch you, when, and how. For example, you may allow a doctor to touch certain parts of your

Cross-Curricular Connections

Math Invite a math teacher or banker to speak to your class about the power of compound interest. The speaker should include a numerical example, and should explain the process of how to figure out how much savings can be accumulated in 1 year, 5 years, and 20 years. This is a good example of delayed gratification as time has the greatest impact on how money grows. The speaker can explain the power of saving money early and the benefits of not withdrawing it for many years. Have the students do calculations in class. **L3**

body during a physical examination. However, you learn when it is not appropriate for someone to touch your body. In a healthful family, parents or guardians also teach their children that sex and love belong together in a committed marriage. You learn that sex belongs in marriage, and you practice delayed gratification of your sexual feelings.

Learning to give and receive acts of kindness In a healthful family, parents or guardians demonstrate acts of kindness and express thankfulness. They do kind things for family members and for other people in the community. They accept and are grateful for acts of kindness from others. As you observe your parents or guardians giving and receiving, you learn to act in similar ways. You are willing to give to others and express thankfulness. You learn the value of giving to others, and you are able to receive kind acts from others. Giving and receiving are both needed to sustain healthful relationships throughout life.

Learning a work ethic An attitude of discipline, motivation, and commitment toward tasks is a **work ethic.** In a healthful family, parents or guardians teach their children a strong work ethic. Parents and guardians work hard and serve as role models for their children. As you observe your parents or guardians displaying a strong work ethic, you learn to do your best and not give up when work is challenging. You learn the rewards that result from hard work. You learn to demonstrate a good work ethic by completing schoolwork, doing household chores,

participating in athletics and extracurricular activities, holding a part-time job, or doing volunteer work.

Learning to respect authority In a healthful family, children learn to respect authority. **Authority** is the power and right to apply laws and rules. Authority is first learned within the family. In a healthful family, children respect the authority of their parents or guardians. Parents or guardians set and enforce guidelines for behavior. For example, your parents or guardians may set a curfew. A **curfew** is a fixed time when a person is to be at home. You respect your parents or guardians and do not stay out past your curfew. You recognize that if you do, there will be consequences. Your parents or guardians will then use appropriate discipline, such as taking away certain privileges. In a healthful family, parents or guardians also serve as role models for their children. They, too, respect authority by obeying laws and rules. As you observe their behavior, you learn to obey laws and rules set by authority figures, such as teachers, principals, and police officers.

Reading Review

1. Name the qualities of a healthful family.

2. What are some ways that a healthful family expresses love and affection?

How to Be a Loving Family Member

Family relationships will not be perfect. Yet, the desire to have the best family life possible is worth the effort. Your task is to be the very best family member you can. Consider the following acronym: **ACT**

- Action: Choose actions that promote healthful family relationships.
- Commitment: Make a commitment to be a loving family member.
- Time: Spend time with your family.

Reading Review

1. *practices skills that promote loving responsible relationships; have positive effect on physical and emotional health*

2. *hugs, kisses, holding each other when they are sad*

INTERACTIVE CHALKBOARD with Image Bank

5-Minute Check

Page 15, **Unit 3 Fast File Resources**

1. How do parents and guardians teach their children healthful behaviors? *setting an example, having discussions, expecting skills and behaviors to be practiced, enforcing consequences when behaviors are not followed*

2. Name five examples of healthful family behavior. *Answers will vary, but should include behaviors from the list on pages 136–139.*

3. Why is it important for parents to teach their children healthful attitudes toward sexuality? *Parents can help children understand and feel more comfortable with the changes that are taking place during puberty.*

4. Why is it important for teens to learn to make responsible decisions? *As teens get closer to adulthood, they face more important decisions on their own. These decisions can affect their emotional and physical health.*

5. Name some places, other than a family, where respect for authority is important. *Answers may include: school, job, library, sports team, store, and a friend's house.*

Community Involvement

Work Ethic Ask the students to think about all the different settings or tasks where a work ethic is important in their community. *Examples: workplace, school, volunteering, athletics, house and yard work.* Have students write an essay that includes how a work ethic is important in these settings. Also have students include in their essays the problems associated with a bad work ethic, including how if everyone decided not to work hard, what would happen to the town or city where they live, and how the students would be affected. Have students send their essays to a community newspaper for possible publication. **L2**

Dysfunctional Family Relationships

Explain the Concept

Dysfunctional Family Define the term again to the class: a family that lacks the skills to promote loving and responsible relationships (see page 135). Parents in dysfunctional families often don't understand the importance of the 14 healthful behaviors described earlier in the chapter, or they don't know how to teach these behaviors to their children.

Class Discussion

Family Continuum Explain the idea of two extremes at each end of a line diagram (see page 135) and discuss that most families will fall somewhere in the middle. On the chalkboard draw an example of a continuum using sports teams placing at an event. Point out that there is only one team at the winning end and one at the losing end. Most teams fall in between. This is true of families as well. Then discuss the role of the coach in helping players develop skills. Compare the coach's job to that of parents, stepparents, and guardians. **L2** **ELL**

The term *dysfunctional family* was first used to describe families in which one or more family members had alcoholism. One or more family members responded to the problem with negative behaviors. As a result, there was dysfunction within the family. Today, the term dysfunctional family includes families who struggle with alcoholism or any of the problems listed in this section.

What to Know About Dysfunctional Family Relationships

 Make the Connection

Addictions For more information on addictions, see page 84 in Lesson 9.

Chemical dependence in the family The compelling desire to use a drug even though it harms the body, mind, or relationships is called *chemical dependence,* or drug addiction. The lives of family members who are chemically dependent become dominated by the need to obtain and use drugs.

The drugs, in turn, cause changes in thinking and behavior. Often, there is more of a risk for violence in families where there is drug abuse. Also, sexual abuse is more likely to occur in these families. Teens who are raised in a family in which there is chemical dependence are at risk for being harmed by violence. They may use drugs to cope with difficult situations. They also are more likely to be in trouble with the law.

There is evidence that chemical dependence may be an inherited tendency. Teens with a family history of chemical dependence who experiment with alcohol and other drugs have an increased risk of developing chemical dependence.

Teens and other family members may develop codependency. *Codependency* is a problem in which a person neglects himself or herself to care for, control, or try to "fix" someone else. Codependency will be discussed in greater detail later in this lesson.

Causes of Dysfunctional Families

The following are some of the problems that can cause dysfunction in a family:

- chemical dependence
- other addictions
- perfectionism
- violence
- physical abuse
- emotional abuse
- neglect
- sexual abuse
- abandonment
- mental disorders

140 UNIT 3 • Family and Social Health

 Differentiated Instruction

Gifted and Talented Assign students one of the following causes of dysfunctional families: chemical dependence, other addictions, perfectionism, violence, physical abuse, emotional abuse, neglect, sexual abuse, abandonment, or mental disorders. Have students create a concept map to illustrate how the main problem spreads from one family member to the next, and how it can affect the family as a whole. Students can present their concept maps to the class. **L3**

Other addictions in the family A compelling desire to use a drug or engage in a specific behavior, continued use despite negative consequences, and loss of control is an ***addiction.*** Besides chemical dependence, the following addictions can contribute to dysfunctional family life: eating disorders and food addiction, exercise addiction, gambling addiction, nicotine addiction, perfectionism, relationship addiction, shopping addiction, television addiction, computer addiction, thrill-seeking addiction, and workaholism.

A family member with an addiction becomes obsessed with his or her addiction. Family life is neglected. Teens who live with a family member who has an addiction may develop codependence. They may develop the same or other addictions as ways of coping with problems.

Perfectionism in the family Perfectionism is a common type of addiction. It is singled out for discussion because it is so common. ***Perfectionism*** is the compelling need to be flawless. Perfectionism goes beyond having high standards or wanting to do well. Parents or guardians who are perfectionists are overly critical of themselves and of their children. Teens who live with a perfectionist parent or guardian may feel inadequate and insecure. These teens also may become perfectionists. They may be overly critical of themselves and others and may never be satisfied with anything. Their behavior is self-destructive and harms relationships with others.

Violence in the family The use of physical force to injure, damage, or destroy oneself, others, or property is

violence. Abuse used by one person in a relationship to control the other is ***domestic violence.*** Domestic violence includes physical abuse, sexual abuse, and emotional abuse. A violent family member usually is very controlling. Sometimes, the violent family member abuses drugs. Often, other family members try to keep peace. They may blame themselves when the family member has violent outbursts. Between acts of violence, the violent family member may be kind, gentle, and apologetic, but the cycle of violence continues.

Teens who live in homes with domestic violence may be injured by the violence. They may copy the violent and controlling behavior. These teens are at risk for becoming juvenile offenders. A ***juvenile offender*** is a minor who commits a criminal act. Teens who are sexually abused are at risk for developing severe emotional problems, becoming pregnant, or becoming infected with HIV and other STDs.

Abuse in the family The harmful or cruel treatment of another person is called ***abuse.*** One type of abuse is ***child abuse,*** which is the harmful treatment of a minor. ***Spouse abuse*** is the harmful treatment of a husband or wife. ***Parent abuse*** is the harmful treatment of a parent. ***Elder abuse*** is the harmful treatment of an aged family member.

▲ Teens who live with violence in the home have a higher risk of becoming juvenile offenders. It is very important for these teens to talk to a trusted adult about their problems.

Did You Know?

Suicide Teens who are abused by a family member are more at risk for attempting suicide. It is especially important for these teens to talk about their problems with a trusted adult.

Reading Review

1. How can addiction cause dysfunction in a family?

2. Why are teens who live with violence in their homes at risk for other problems?

Teacher FYI

Family Violence Point out to the students that violence in the home may be more common than they think. According to a study published in 1999 by the National Institute of Justice and the Centers for Disease Control and Prevention, one in four women will be abused by her boyfriend or husband at some time in her life. A study by the National Child Abuse and Neglect Data System in 1999 found that the rate of child victims of violence and neglect was 11.8 children per 1000.

Extension

Addiction Have students research the number of Americans who have a substance addiction or other addiction, such as gambling. Have them write a paper summarizing what they have found and explaining ways they feel an addiction might affect a person's family life. **L3**

Reading Review

1. *A family member with an addiction often neglects the family. Other family members might develop codependence, or they might develop the same or other addictions.*

2. *Teens might be physically injured by the violence. They might copy the family member's behavior and get into trouble with the law. They also might develop emotional problems.*

Sensitive Issues

Student Privacy Some students might be dealing with some form of dysfunction in their families. When discussing dysfunction, be careful to avoid personal questions. Let students know that if they need to speak to you, their privacy is very important and will be respected by you as much as possible. Explain that you have an obligation to help them in situations of abuse or violence, and that you would have to report the abuse to the proper authorities. Have a list of trusted counselors and resources that students can access.

National Health Education Standards
Pages 140–141: 1.2, 1.8, 1.9, 2.1, 2.3, 5.7

Teens who have been abandoned by ▶ a parent can have difficulties with other relationships as a result. They may keep others at a distance, or become very emotionally needy.

Did You Know?

Abandonment Teens who have been abandoned are likely to act "tough," defy authority figures, refuse to follow school rules, and have a negative attitude.

An abusive family member is often controlling and moody. Sometimes, abusive family members are drug dependent. Their need for control and their moodiness increase when they are under the influence of drugs.

Teens who live with an abusive family member may be afraid and confused. They cannot understand the abuse. They want to believe they are loved. For this reason, they deny their feelings of fear and confusion and cover up what is happening. Often, they may blame themselves and believe they deserve the abuse.

Abandonment in the family When a person chooses to give up or refuses responsibility for those in his or her care, it is called ***abandonment.*** Parents who abandon their children are not available for them. They may abandon their children by their physical or emotional absence or both. Their absence from their children's lives may cause their children pain, suffering, and confusion. Children who have been abandoned may begin to feel unlovable, worthless, or guilty. They may think, "Why doesn't my parent want to be part of my life? What did I do wrong? I must not be lovable." They may experience the same feelings in other relationships. Teens who have been abandoned often have difficulty getting close to others. They may feel that if they get close to someone, that person also may abandon them. They may push away others. Or, they may be very needy emotionally. They may demand the attention of others to fulfill childhood needs that were not met.

Mental disorders in the family A behavioral or psychological syndrome or pattern that occurs in an individual and that is associated with distress or disability or with a significantly increased risk of suffering, death, pain, disability, or an important loss of freedom is a ***mental disorder.*** Families in which one or more family members have a mental disorder have special stressors. A family member may suffer from major depression. Other family members might respond in a healthful way. They are sensitive to this illness but do not let it dominate their lives. In a dysfunctional family, family members do not respond in a healthful way. They may feel responsible for the family member's depression and try to fix it themselves. They may allow the family member's depression to dominate family life.

Four Kinds of Abuse

Teens may have to deal with the following types of abuse in their families.

- Physical abuse is violent treatment that results in physical injury to the victim.
- Emotional abuse is belittling or verbally "putting down" another person, making a person feel worthless, or withholding love and affection in order to cause pain.
- Neglect is failure to provide proper care and guidance.
- Sexual abuse is sexual contact that is forced on a person, either through physical force, manipulation, or threats of harm.

142 UNIT 3 • Family and Social Health

Codependent Relationships

As stated earlier, codependency is a problem in which people neglect themselves to care for, control, or try to "fix" someone else. The Tree of Codependency, shown below, illustrates how dysfunctional family life can lead to codependency. The roots are labeled with behaviors that occur in dysfunctional families. The branches are labeled with feelings and behaviors that describe people who are codependent.

What to Know About Codependent Relationships

People who are codependent have difficulty with intimacy. **Intimacy** is a deep and meaningful kind of sharing between two people. Codependents avoid intimacy by going to extremes. They focus on pleasing others and deny their own needs, or they avoid being close to others to keep from being hurt.

The two sides of codependency—obsessing about the needs of others and avoiding others—are at the root of much unhappiness. **Enmeshment** is a condition in which a person becomes obsessed with the needs of another person and no longer can recognize his or her own needs. Codependent people may avoid intimacy by choosing relationships that offer little or no chance for closeness. Often, teens with codependency are more comfortable with someone who has problems.

In a healthful relationship, there is interdependence. **Interdependence** is a condition in which two people depend upon each other, yet each has a separate identity.

Tree of Codependency

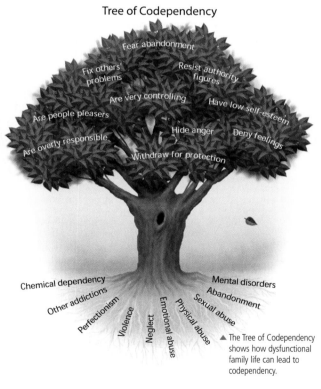

▲ The Tree of Codependency shows how dysfunctional family life can lead to codependency.

Codependent Relationships

Explain the Concept

Codependency Discuss the definition with the class. Codependency is a problem in which people neglect themselves to care for, control, or try to "fix" someone else. Examples of harmful ways of coping are denying the problem, using alcohol or drugs to try to ignore the problem, or turning to people who have harmful behaviors themselves for help with the problem.

Class Activity

Enmeshment and Interdependence Have student volunteers copy the following scenarios on notecards. Have volunteers read aloud the two roles in each scenario and then discuss as a class whether the characters have interdependence or enmeshment.

1. **Carlos:** I can't go out with you on Friday because my parents are having friends over and they want me there. Can we go to a movie on Sunday afternoon instead?
   Caitlin: Sure, I'll work on my report on Friday.
   Interdependence

2. **Mother:** I have a meeting at church on Thursday, so we'll have to go shopping this weekend.
   Teen: No! I have to have a new outfit for school on Friday!
   Mother: Alright, I'll see if I can change the meeting.
   Enmeshment

3. **Eddie:** I can't help you with your French homework tonight because I have a big project due tomorrow.
   Jenna: But you promised to help me every day!
   Eddie: OK, maybe I can just stay up later to work on my project.
   Enmeshment

◀▶ Cross-Curricular Connections

Language Arts Have students write a dialogue between two people who have a codependent relationship. Ask your students to refer to the Tree of Codependence diagram on this page and choose one or more behaviors to use in their dialogue. *Examples for the codependent speaker include: being overly responsible for a problem, being a people pleaser, hiding anger, or being very controlling.* Have students perform their dialogues for the class. Have the class identify the codependent behaviors that were illustrated in each dialogue. **L2**

National Health Education Standards
Pages 142–143: 1.2, 1.8, 2.1, 5.7

Improving Dysfunctional Relationships

1. Define the term *intimacy*. *a deep and meaningful kind of sharing between two people*

2. Explain the difference between enmeshment and interdependence. *Enmeshment is a condition in which a person becomes obsessed with the needs of another person and no longer can recognize his or her own needs. Interdependence is a condition in which two people depend upon one another, yet each has a separate identity.*

3. Who is involved in a formal intervention? *friends and family members of a person who needs professional help with addiction*

4. How does group therapy help people who are codependent? *It provides a place for codependent people to talk about their problems with others who have similar problems and to hear suggestions for ways to react in a healthful way.*

5. When trying to resolve a conflict, how can you set a positive tone? *listen without interrupting, acknowledge each other's feelings, avoid blaming*

Improving Dysfunctional Relationships

Suppose a teen is raised in a dysfunctional family and is codependent. The teen has difficulty maintaining healthful friendships at school. Is there any hope for the teen's recovery from codependency? Where can the teen find help? Can other family members learn how to relate in responsible and healthful ways? What steps can be taken to improve dysfunctional family relationships?

How to Improve Dysfunctional Family Relationships

If you have a dysfunctional family relationship, first identify the primary cause of dysfunction in the family (alcoholism, gambling, etc.). Then, try to recognize the harmful ways in which family members interact. Then, take responsibility for your behavior. Make sure you do not copy the harmful behavior of any family member. Also, you need to talk to a parent, guardian, mentor, or other trusted adult about getting help. Teachers and guidance counselors at school are able to listen to you and give advice. Be sure to talk to someone else if the first person you speak to does not help you.

Intervention Sometimes all family members agree that help is needed. Sometimes the family member with the primary problem, such as alcoholism, being abusive, or gambling, denies that there is a family problem and resists help. A trained therapist might work with other family members to plan a formal intervention. A *formal intervention* is an action by people, such as family members and friends, who want a person to get treatment. At a planned gathering, family members and others tell the person what they have observed and how they feel about it. They ask the person to get treatment. Some people need inpatient treatment, meaning they need to be admitted to a health-care facility that can help them with their problems. Also, they might need medical care. Other people need outpatient treatment only, meaning they would still live at home while being treated.

Therapy All family members who are codependent can benefit by getting help. Individual and group therapy can help with recovery. In individual therapy, a skilled therapist helps one family member learn healthier ways to express feelings and relate to others. In group therapy or family therapy, a skilled therapist works with a group or family at the same time. Those who participate in group therapy practice relating to one another within the safety of the group. Then, these new ways of relating are transferred into real-life situations.

Differentiated Instruction

Learning Disabilities To assist students with reading difficulties, provide those students who have reading difficulties with the questions to the 5-Minute Check ahead of time. Have students with reading difficulties fill in the answers as you lecture in class. Students can use the book to double-check if their answers are correct. Students can use the questions in the Lesson Study Guide to study for the exam. Provide students with the answers to the questions in the Lesson Study Guide. **L1 ELL**

Communication and Conflict Resolution in Families

Family conflicts don't have to turn into shouting matches or end with bad feelings. By using communication and decision-making skills, you can resolve conflicts in a responsible way. You can use communication skills and creative thinking to work out solutions that are acceptable to everyone involved in the conflict. Follow the steps below.

TABLE 13.1 Resolving Family Conflict Responsibly

Goal	Suggestions
Remain calm. Take time to cool off before trying to talk things through. Anger can get in the way of discussing a problem thoughtfully.	Find a cooling-off method that works for you. You might leave the room briefly, breathe deeply a few times, or take a quick walk.
Set a positive tone. Agree on some basic ground rules for your discussion. If each person agrees on the rules ahead of time, it is less likely that anger will get in the way.	Some good guidelines are to listen to the other person without interrupting, acknowledge each other's feelings, and avoid blaming.
Define the conflict and take responsibility for personal actions. Describe the problem.	Make "I" statements to help you focus on the conflict, not the other person.
Listen to the needs and feelings of others. Try to see the other person's point of view. This will help you understand why the other person feels the way he or she does.	Restate what you heard the other person say.
List and evaluate possible solutions. Brainstorm possible solutions with the other person.	Each solution should meet at least some of each person's needs. For example: • A teen could call home if they will be out after curfew on weekends. • A parent could allow a teen to stay out late once per month. • A teen could invite friends to his or her house instead of going out.
Agree on a responsible solution. Choose a responsible solution that hopefully satisfies both people. Each person must be willing to make some trade-offs, but each person will "win" something too.	Evaluate each solution above. Will it lead to an outcome that is safe, healthful, and legal? Does it show respect for both persons, follow family guidelines, and demonstrate good character?
Communicate. Strengthen the relationship and make future conflicts easier to work through.	Thank the other person for talking and for working things out.

Using Life Skills

Using Communication Skills Have the students think of an example of a family conflict. Ask them to write a journal entry about how the steps in the Using Life Skills can help solve the problem. **L2**

3 Assess

Vocabulary Practice

Page 8, **Unit 3 Fast File Resources**

Activity: Using Life Skills

Using Communication Skills: Practicing Conflict Resolution

Resolving conflict within families is not easy, but it can be done. Use these steps the next time you need to resolve a conflict: 1) remain calm; 2) set a positive tone; 3) define the conflict; 4) take responsibility for personal actions; 5) listen to the needs and feelings of others; 6) list and evaluate possible solutions; and 7) agree on a responsible solution.

1 To practice your conflict-resolution skills, role-play one of these situations. Use the steps outlined above.

- Frank's dad often complains that Frank plays his music too loud at home.

- Jane's sister, Anna, frequently borrows Jane's clothes without her permission.

2 Now try role-playing one of these situations using the steps outlined above.

- Mandy's mom feels that Mandy's grades would improve if she spent more time on her homework.

- Kate's parents are uncomfortable with one of her new friends, who often skips school.

3 Think of a conflict you are now involved in with a friend. Ask the other person to work on resolving the conflict with you, using the steps outlined above.

▲ By setting a positive tone and listening to the other person's point of view, you can resolve conflicts at home in a calm manner.

Recovery program Sometimes people join recovery programs. A *recovery program* is a group that supports members as they change their behavior to be more responsible. Today, there are many different recovery programs. *Alcoholics Anonymous (AA)* is a recovery program for people who are dependent on alcohol and other drugs. *Al-Anon* is a recovery program for people who have family members or friends who have an addiction. People who want to recover from codependency also attend Al-Anon. *Alateen* is a recovery program for teens who have family members or friends who have an addiction. Teens who want to recover from codependency also attend Alateen.

These programs are helpful for those who are codependent because they provide a place to meet other people with similar problems and they provide positive alternatives to harmful behavior. Teens can talk to a guidance counselor, a teacher, a clergy member, or another trusted adult for information on where to find these recovery programs.

For teens who have been raised in a dysfunctional family and for those who are codependent, communication is very important to finding ways to heal and to break free from the cycle of codependency. Talking openly and honestly about their problems will help teens develop ways of relating that are responsible and healthful.

146 UNIT 3 • Family and Social Health

Cross-Curricular Connections

Social Studies Assign students to groups of four. Have the groups research the history of recovery programs, such as Alcoholics Anonymous, Al-Anon and Alateen. Have groups report on where and why they were founded and discuss ways the programs have changed over the course of their histories. Students also should describe the main components of the recovery programs. If there are steps in the program, students should briefly describe them. Student groups can create multimedia presentations with the information they learned, and present their findings to the class. **L3**

National Health Education Standards

Pages 146–147: 1.5, 2.3, 3.4, 4.1, 4.3, 5.3, 5.5, 5.7, 6.3

abandonment
affection
Alateen
dysfunctional family
enmeshment
family
family relationships
healthful family
interdependence
recovery program
value
work ethic

Key Terms Review

Complete these fill-in-the-blank statements with the lesson Key Terms on the left. Do not write in this book.

1. _____ is a tender feeling a person has toward another.

2. A(n) _____ is the basic unit of society.

3. _____ is a relationship in which two people depend upon one another, yet each has a separate identity.

4. A(n) _____ is an attitude of discipline, motivation, and commitment toward tasks.

5. A(n) _____ is a family that promotes loving, responsible relationships.

6. _____ is refusing responsibility for those in your care.

7. A(n) —— is a group that supports people who want to change their behavior.

8. A(n) _____ is a family that does not promote loving, responsible relationships.

9. _____ is a recovery program for teens with a family member who has an addiction.

10. _____ is a condition in which a person is obsessed with the needs of others.

Recalling the Facts

11. What is the role of parents and guardians in a healthful family?

12. What are the roles of extended family members in a healthful family?

13. What are 14 skills children learn and practice in healthful families?

14. How does a parent teach self-respect?

15. What are three ways to be a loving family member?

16. What are ten causes of dysfunctional family relationships?

17. What are two ways people who are codependent avoid being close to others?

18. What initial steps might a teen take to improve dysfunctional family relationships?

Critical Thinking

19. Why is it important for teens to have self-respect?

20. Why are communication skills important?

21. Explore methods for addressing critical health issues within a dysfunctional family that is trying to improve its relationships.

22. Explain why it is important for teens who have been abused to talk about their problems.

Real-Life Applications

23. Give examples of how your extended family supports you.

24. Describe some ways to use communication to solve a current family conflict.

25. Why do you think some people develop a problem with enmeshment?

26. If you suspected that your best friend was being abused, what would you do?

Activities

Responsible Decision Making

27. **Write a Response** You spend the evening at a friend's home. Your friend tells you his brother has cocaine in his room. Write a response to this situation. Include what you will say to your friend about his brother and why you must not stay at his house. Refer to the Responsible Decision-Making Model on page 61 for help.

Sharpen Your Life Skills

28. **Analyze Influences on Health** Select two family sitcoms and ask your parent or guardian if it is OK to view them. Rate each show using the Guidelines for Analyzing Influences on Health on page 36. Do family members in the sitcom choose healthful behaviors? Where would you rank it on the Family Continuum?

Visit **www.glencoe.com** for more *Health & Wellness* quizzes.

---

26. Answers will vary, but can include: tell a trusted adult or refer them to a community organization

Activities

Responsible Decision Making

27. Emphasize the need to leave this friend's home right away and to share this informa-tion with their parents or guardian. The teen might tell the friend that his brother is harm-ing his health, and that it is illegal to have cocaine. You do not wish to stay in a house with illegal drugs in it.

Sharpen Your Life Skills

28. Answers will vary.

Key Terms Review

1. Affection
2. family
3. Interdependence
4. work ethic
5. healthful family
6. Abandonment
7. recovery program
8. dysfunctional family
9. Alateen
10. Enmeshment

Recalling the Facts

11. setting an example to follow, hav-ing discussions, expecting behav-iors and skills to be practiced, and enforcing consequences when they are not

12. to reinforce and practice behav-iors and skills taught by parents and guardians

13. See pages 136–139.

14. Parents care for you and teach you how to care for yourself; they love and accept you.

15. action, commitment, time

16. See pages 140–142.

17. focusing on trying to please another person or people and denying their own needs, or avoiding being close to another person or people to keep from being hurt

18. See page 144.

Critical Thinking

19. You must have self-respect if you want others to respect you.

20. If you have good communication skills, you can communicate your needs, wants, and feelings to improve family relationships.

21. Answers will vary.

22. Teens might blame themselves for the abuse. They need to under-stand they are not to blame.

Real-Life Applications

23. Answers will vary.

24. Answers will vary.

25. They may have a need to help others that they take a bit too far. They may feel better after helping others, and may develop a craving for this feeling.

LESSON 14

Adjusting to Family Changes

Out of Time?

If time does not permit an in-depth study of this topic, use the following activities in this Teacher Wraparound Edition:
- Using Life Skills, p. 151
- Family Involvement, p. 152
- Achieving Health Literacy, p. 153
- Class Activity, p. 155

1 Focus

HEALTH GOAL **Healthful Adjustments** Have students respond to the Health Goal for this lesson by listing in their health journals healthful ways to deal with family change. *Answers include talking to parents, asking for help, understanding how family changes will affect your life.* **L2**

Write ABOUT IT!

Answers Students' answers can include: keep in touch with the family member who is stationed away from home; keep a journal of family events to share with your family member when he or she returns; get in touch with other military families; share your feelings; limit the amount of media coverage that you watch; practice stress management skills. Encourage students to share some of these ideas if they know another teen who is adjusting to this family change. **L2**

What You'll Learn

1. Evaluate the effects divorce might have on teens and ways teens might adjust. *(p. 150)*
2. Discuss the effects of a single-custody family and ways teens might adjust. *(p. 152)*
3. Discuss effects of living in a stepfamily and ways teens might adjust. *(p. 153)*
4. Discuss having a family member in the military and ways teens might adjust. *(p. 154)*
5. Evaluate the effects on teens if a parent is in jail and discuss ways teens might adjust. *(p. 155)*
6. Evaluate the effect of a parent losing a job and ways teens might adjust. *(p. 156)*

Why It's Important

Understanding family changes helps teens to be resilient and protects physical and emotional health.

Key Terms

- marital separation
- divorce
- dissolution
- custodial parent
- joint custody
- visitation rights
- grandparents' rights
- single-custody family
- stepfamily
- foster care

148 UNIT 3 • Family and Social Health

HEALTH GOAL **• I will make healthful adjustments to family changes.**

This lesson discusses changes that may occur in family relationships. You will learn ways a teen might adjust if parents get a divorce, a teen lives in a single-custody family, a teen lives in a stepfamily, a parent loses a job, a family member is called to military duty, or a parent goes to jail. This information may help you if there are changes occurring in your family. It may help you understand and support other teens who might be adjusting to changes in their families.

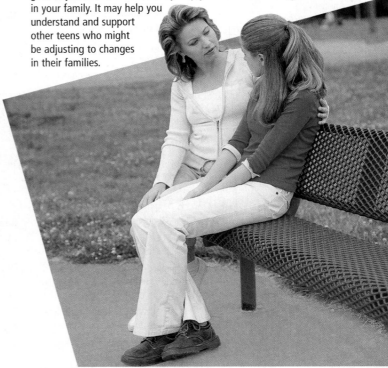

Write ABOUT IT!

Writing About Family Changes Suppose a friend has a family member called to active military duty. Your friend is unsure when she will be able to talk to her family member. She is afraid for her family member's safety. What are ways that you can help your friend adjust to this family change? After reading page 154, write a response in your health journal.

National Health Education Standards—Guide for Lesson 14		
1.2	Describe the interrelationships of emotional, intellectual, physical, and social health.	pp. 151, 156, 157
2.1	Analyze how family influences the health of individuals.	pp. 148, 150–156, 157
2.3	Analyze how peers influence healthy and unhealthy behaviors.	pp. 148, 150–151

Divorce

In order for marriages to succeed and be satisfying, married partners need to pay attention to the status of their relationship. When a relationship is neglected, the quality of the marriage declines and intimacy is lost. The most common stressors in marriage are changes in financial status, changes in living arrangements, changes in work situations, illness of a family member, abuse, infidelity, poor communication, and alcohol and other drug dependency.

What to Know About Divorce

If parents or stepparents have conflict A process in which married partners identify their problems, agree upon solutions, and reestablish intimacy is called **_marital conflict resolution._** The attitude of each partner is important in marital conflict resolution. In a healthful and caring marriage, each partner is willing to work on problems.

Sometimes, marriage partners need help with marital conflict resolution. They may need assistance identifying their problems or finding solutions. In some cases, one partner is aware of a problem, but the other partner does not recognize the problem. This is often the case in a marriage in which one partner abuses drugs or alcohol. The partner who abuses drugs or alcohol denies that a problem exists.

Outside intervention Outside intervention may be needed to help resolve the problem. A married couple may recognize a problem, but not be able to solve it themselves. A marriage counselor, such as a member of the clergy, psychologist, psychiatrist, or social worker, may help present possible solutions. If the solution involves new ways of behaving, the counselor may help one or both partners to change their behavior.

What Happens During Divorce

Married couples are not always able to solve problems and reestablish intimacy. About 43 percent of all first marriages end in marital separation and/or divorce. **_Marital separation_** is a cessation of cohabitation between a married couple by mutual agreement or judicial decree. **_Divorce_** is a legal way to end a marriage in which a judge or court decides the terms with respect to property, child custody, and spousal support. Most married couples who divorce experience a six-stage process.

Stage one The marriage deteriorates; partners show less affection and begin to detach from one another. Conflict resolution may be tried. The first stage may last up to several years.

Stage two One or both partners seek legal counsel. The different options for ending the marriage are examined. An **_annulment_** is a legal way to end a marriage when it is decided that the marriage was not legally binding. A **_dissolution_** is a legal way to end a marriage in which the marriage partners themselves decide the terms with respect to property, custody, and support.

Lesson Resource Manager

- **Unit 3 Fast File Resources**
  Reading Strategy, p. 21
  Vocabulary Practice, p. 22
  Transparency Master and Worksheet, p. 23
  Real-Life Health, p. 25
  Real-Life Health, p. 27
  5-Minute Check, p. 29
  Lesson 14 Quiz, p. 31
- **Unit 3 Transparency**
- **Lesson 14 Transparency**

- **Reading Essentials**
- **Technology**
  TeacherWorks™ CD-ROM
  StudentWorks™ CD-ROM
  Reading Essentials CD-ROM
  ExamView® Assessment Suite
  Vocabulary Puzzlemaker

Quick Demo

Divorce Rate Approximately 43 percent of all first marriages end in divorce or separation. Have half of the class stand. Explain that the students who are standing roughly represent the percentage of the total number of people in the class who might divorce or separate if they marry if the current rates continue. Review Lesson 18, "Preparing for Marriage and Parenthood," with the class, especially the section, "Success in Marriage."

PowerPoint® Presentations
This CD-ROM is an editable Microsoft® PowerPoint® presentation that includes:
- Lesson presentations
- Lesson checks
- Interactive graphics
- 5-Minute Checks
- Image Bank
- All transparencies

Note-Taking Use the SelectiveUnderlining/ Highlighting Strategy on page 16T to emphasize how family changes may affect teens and some ways in which they can adjust.

National Health Education Standards
Pages 148–149: 2.1, 2.3, 3.4, 4.1

Explain the Concept

Joint Custody Explain to the class that when joint custody is awarded, each parent has equal responsibility for the children in the family. The parents may share custody by alternating where the children live. This arrangement requires that meaningful communication and cooperation between the parents be maintained after the marriage has ended.

Class Activity

Grandparents' Rights Have students write an essay discussing why they believe courts are upholding grandparents' rights. Have them include thoughts about how they believe a teen might feel if he or she could not see a grandparent with whom he or she had had a relationship. **L2**

NHES Assessment/SCASS

Performance Task Divorce is very stressful on both parents and teens. It is important for teens to express their feelings in constructive ways. Have students create an artistic representation of the feelings that accompany divorce and other family changes. Projects may include drawings, paintings, sculpture, collages, creative writing, or musical expression. **L1** **ELL**

Make the Connection

Stress-Management Skills For more information on stress-management skills, see page 104 in Lesson 10.

Stage three In the third stage of divorce, issues regarding property and support payments are finalized. The property in a marriage usually refers to the home and household furnishings the couple owns, jewelry, cars, life insurance, money in savings accounts, stocks, and other investments. One partner may agree to pay spousal support to the other. Usually, the partner paying spousal support is the partner who has the greater ability to earn money.

Stage four In the fourth stage of divorce, issues of child custody, visitation rights, and child support are negotiated, and the divorce is finalized. *Single custody* is an arrangement in which one parent keeps legal custody of a child or children. The *custodial parent* is the parent with whom a child or children live and the parent who has the legal right to make decisions about the health and well-being of a child or children. *Joint custody* is an arrangement in which both partners keep legal custody of a child or children. A child or children may live with one parent or may alternate living arrangements, spending time with one parent and then the other. This arrangement requires that meaningful communication between the parents be maintained after the marriage has ended.

Visitation rights are guidelines set for the visitation of children by the parent who does not have custody. *Grandparents' rights* are the visitation rights with their grandchildren that courts have awarded grandparents when their son's or daughter's marriage ends.

Stage five In the fifth stage of divorce, each of the partners establishes a new identity with family, friends, and co-workers.

Stage six In the sixth stage of divorce, each of the partners makes emotional adjustments to the new lifestyle that results from being divorced. This stage of divorce affects both marriage partners and their children.

Effects of Divorce

The divorce of parents or guardians is a major life change. Recognizing the effects that divorce might have helps teens make adjustments.

Feeling a loss of control At least one of the married partners feels a divorce is for the best. Teens do not have control over the situation.

Spending less time with parents Divorced parents have additional responsibilities and less help in doing them. They may have less time to spend with teens. Any lack of parenting can take its toll on teens.

When Parents Divorce

The following are suggestions for teens whose parents divorce:

- Practice stress-management skills. You have experienced a major life stressor.
- Avoid using alcohol and other drugs.
- Recognize that becoming sexually active will not make you feel better. In most cases, it will make you feel more empty and alone.

- Choose healthful ways to express your anger. Participating in delinquent behavior will make life even more difficult for you.
- Be aware of your feelings of rejection and betrayal. Ask for help from friends, family, or teachers when you need it.

150 UNIT 3 • Family and Social Health

 Sensitive Issues

Student Privacy Divorce and remarriage are common and many students might be adjusting to these family changes. Be sensitive to this when discussing divorce and remarriage. Understand that some students might feel comfortable sharing their experiences, while others might wish to deal with their experiences privately. Avoid asking personal questions. Let students know that if they need to talk about a family change outside of class you will respect their privacy. Have a list of resources available for students to find additional help adjusting to divorce or remarriage.

Activity: Using Life Skills

Using Communication Skills: Talking About Family Changes

Family changes can leave you with feelings of anger, sadness, or fear. Talking about your feelings with those involved can help you adjust to the changes and feel more comfortable. Here are some ideas that can help.

1 **Identify your feelings.** To state your feelings accurately, try to use specific words, such as *threatened, confused, resentful, rejected, embarrassed,* or *fearful.*

2 **Choose the best way to communicate.** Use "I" statements when you express your feelings. Unlike a "you" message, an "I" message does not shame or blame the other person.

3 **Express your thoughts and feelings clearly.** Send a clear message. Make sure your tone of voice and body language match your spoken words. For example, if you say "I'm okay" but use an angry voice, you are sending a mixed message.

4 **Listen to the other person.** You also can encourage others to express their feelings by using "door openers," such as "You seem upset about losing your job."

5 **Make sure you understand each other.** Ask questions or restate what the other person has said. For example, "So you're saying I'll be able to stay at dad's every other weekend. That makes me feel better."

▲ Talking about your feelings with family and friends will help ease the anger, fear, or sadness you may feel due to family changes.

Declining academic performance Teens may experience a decline in grades during and after the divorce of parents. This usually is attributed to a lack of concentration.

Grieving Teens grieve the end of family life as they knew it. They may experience each of the five stages of grief at some point during the divorce process and after the divorce: denial, anger, bargaining, depression, and, finally, acceptance.

Acting out with harmful behaviors Some teens respond to the stress of divorce by acting out. These teens are at risk for becoming sexually active, abusing alcohol and other drugs, and developing delinquent behavior.

Resenting parental dating If parental dating begins before or soon after divorce, teens may feel angry. They may feel that a parent's boyfriend or

girlfriend caused the breakup of the parents' marriage. Some teens continue to hope for the reconciliation of parents for many years. They may be jealous of someone a parent dates.

Having difficulties in relationships Some teens have feelings of rejection and abandonment that affect their other relationships. For example, female teens may seek an older boyfriend to be a father figure that might now be missing. They are more likely to enter into harmful relationships and not end them. Male teens whose parents divorce may feel awkward in male/female relationships. Some hold back their feelings in dating and have difficulty trusting.

Having symptoms of anxiety and stress Teens whose parents divorce might have symptoms of anxiety and stress, including difficulty sleeping, feeling tired, and changes in appetite.

LESSON 14 • Adjusting to Family Changes   **151**

Single-Custody Families

Single-Custody Families

A family in which a child or children live with one parent who has custody is a *single-custody family*. A child or children may have two parents who are active in their lives, but only one parent has custody or legal responsibility for them. A *joint-custody family* is one in which parents share the living arrangement and legal responsibility for their child or children.

How to Adjust to Living in a Single-Custody Family

Some teens have lived in a two-parent household and then must adjust to living in a single-custody family. Recognizing the effects of living in a single-custody family can help them adjust more easily.

Change in standard of living In most cases, children raised in a single-custody family live with their mothers. Because women often experience a drop in their standard of living after divorce, children are likely to have a drop in their standard of living, too. In some cases, this puts them at risk for being economically disadvantaged.

This means they may lack some of the resources that other families have available, such as good medical care, clothing, food, and shelter. Children who live with their fathers also may experience economic hardships. Teens can adapt to changes in their standard of living by recognizing the financial pressures on their parents and discussing ways to control expenses.

Change in contact with role models In a two-parent, or joint-custody family,

there is both a male and a female role model. After divorce, some teens have little or no contact with one of their parents. In many cases, it is their father whom they see less often. Unless there are other family members in their lives, these teens may not experience the benefits of having both female and male role models. By talking to their parents about the change and scheduling time to be together, teens can spend more time with their parents. Also, teens can seek adult mentors through such organizations as Big Brothers and Big Sisters to help them adjust to a single-custody family.

Change in amount of parental supervision The single-custody parent may have the sole responsibility for supervising teens. If this parent works outside the home, there is less time for parental supervision of activities and schoolwork. This accounts for the finding that teens whose parents divorce spend less time with parents and are at risk for getting poor grades. Seeking extra help from teachers or a tutor may be helpful.

Stepfamilies

A marriage in which a previously married person marries again is called *remarriage*. A family consisting of the marriage partners, children that one or both of them had previously, and the children that they have by their marriage to one another is a *blended family* or *stepfamily* Some blended families include joint custody arrangements.

How to Adjust to a Stepfamily

There are many changes when a stepfamily is formed. Recognizing these changes and possible effects can help teens make adjustments.

Change in family rules When a stepfamily is formed, the parent and stepparent must determine what set of rules the children will follow. Often, children have been raised with specific rules that may not be the same as those in the stepfamily. Suppose one set of children in a blended family were raised with very clear guidelines in which consequences were identified for inappropriate behavior. However, the other children in the family had little discipline and were allowed to behave as they pleased. Blending these two sets of children into one framework for discipline requires adjustment.

Changes in budget Decisions about budget in a blended family can be challenging. Parents and stepparents have many decisions to make about how to spend money. The two sets of children may be used to having different guidelines for spending money.

Changes in family relationships Other issues that are important in blended families arise from the new relationships that are formed. The success of the blended family often depends on how stepsiblings interact. Clear guidelines for interactions are important.

Some teens who live in blended families feel resentment toward their stepparent. They may think that the stepparent does not like them, or that their stepparent does not treat them as they would like to be treated. However, with effective communication and mutual respect they can establish a healthful relationship with their stepparent.

Suggestions for Teens Whose Parents Remarry

The following suggestions will help teens adjust to a blended family:

- Respect the new guidelines for your behavior. You may not like the new rules, but you must obey them.
- Help your family follow a budget. Recognize that your parents have to provide for a larger family.
- Interact in healthful ways with your stepbrothers and stepsisters. Discuss guidelines for behavior when interacting with new siblings.
- Interact in healthful ways with your stepparent. Use effective communication skills and mutual respect to establish a healthful relationship with stepparents.

LESSON 14 • Adjusting to Family Changes **153**

🖋 Achieving Health Literacy

Problem Solver Have the students find a partner. Have them each take the survey below and compare their answers. Then ask them to negotiate and agree on only one way to answer each option. This exercise will help students understand how many issues must be negotiated in a blended family.

Survey questions: What are the rules at your house for each of these: bedtime; curfew; age allowed to date; computer in your room; eating out; having junk food in the house; when you do your homework; if you are allowed to have friends over without parents home; chores around the house; if you can play your stereo loudly; if your family eats meat; punctuality; and wake-up time on Saturdays. **L2**

If a Family Member Is Called to Military Duty

Explain the Concept

Military Duty Ask the students to raise their hands if they know someone in the military. Make sure students include people who serve in the National Guard and Reserves. Explain to the class what it means to be called to active duty. *Being called to serve in the military full-time. This may or may not require a person to relocate.* Explain that those in the Army Reserve can be called to active duty during times of crisis. **L2**

Class Activity

Journal Ask students to write in their health journals the thoughts and family news they would share with a family member who might be serving in the military. Ask the students to imagine how they would feel if a family member were stationed either overseas or in a different part of our country and they could not visit or talk to them regularly. Some students may actually have a family member in the military. They might share some letters or e-mails they have written to their family member. Keep in mind that this topic may be too sensitive for students who have a family member in the military; these students could do a different activity. **L2**

If a Family Member Is Called to Military Duty

Some teens have a family member who is called to military duty. A family member might have a military career with changing tours of duty, or might be in the reserves and be called to duty because of his or her military skill.

How to Adjust If a Family Member Is Called to Military Duty

Did You Know?

War Anxiety Research indicates that constant exposure to war-related news coverage heightens anxiety.

Understanding the possible effects when a family member is called to military duty will help teens make needed adjustments.

Loss of contact with the family member Family members who are called to military duty may serve in locations where they will not see or talk to their families for an extended period of time. Teens may feel sad and lonely during the family member's absence.

Loss of family income and change in living arrangements. When he or she was called to duty, the family member may have had another job. There may be a loss of income when the family member leaves. This may require changes in living arrangements.

Fear for the family member's safety A family member might be called to active duty in a place where there is terrorism, war, or other conflict. A person in the military may not be able to tell family and friends where he or she is, or what he or she is doing. For family members at home, the fear of the unknown can cause symptoms of stress and anxiety.

Symptoms of anxiety and depression Teens who are worried, fearful, and lonely may have symptoms of anxiety and/or depression. They may experience headaches, stomachaches, sleeplessness, tiredness, and changes in appetite. Also, they may have difficulty concentrating in school.

The following are suggestions for teens who have a family member called to military duty: Keep in touch with the family member by e-mail, telephone, or mail, if possible. Keep a journal of family events to share with the family member. Limit the amount of media coverage of military conflict you watch or read. Get in touch with other military families. This provides a support network for you and your family. Recognize symptoms of anxiety and practice stress-management skills. Share your feelings with family members and allow them to share their feelings with you. Ask for support when you need it. Share concerns with your teacher, guidance counselor, or coach.

 Community Involvement

Military Service Invite a person from the community who has recently served in the military to come to your class and speak about his or her experience. Ask the speaker to focus on his or her time away from family and how it affected both the family and the speaker. Ask students to prepare questions ahead of time to ask the speaker. Questions might concern active service, time away from family, and ways to make adjustments. Have students submit their questions before the speaker is scheduled to come, so that you can be sure students ask a variety of questions. **L2**

If a Parent Goes to Jail

Some teens have a parent or guardian who breaks the law. There may be sudden changes in family life. The police or FBI may come to the home. The parent or guardian may be arrested. There may be a long or short trial, followed by sentencing, and then jail time. This series of events can cause tremendous stress and anxiety for a family.

How to Adjust If a Parent Goes to Jail

When a parent goes to jail, it is especially stressful for teens. Understanding the possible effects can help teens adjust.

Loss of family income and change in living arrangements One of the immediate stressors may be a shortage of money, if the parent or guardian provided income for the family. Legal fees can be very expensive, and must be paid.

The loss of income may result in other changes. The family may have to move to another place or move in with relatives. If the parent or guardian who goes to jail is the only person providing care for a teen, that teen may end up living with other relatives or be placed in foster care. *Foster care* is an arrangement in which an unrelated adult assumes temporary responsibility for a child.

Criticism from society Teens who have a parent or guardian who is sentenced to jail may have to deal with criticism from society. It can be very embarrassing to listen to comments about the criminal behavior of a parent or guardian. Teens who have a parent or guardian in jail must recognize that they are not responsible for what has happened. They do not have to behave in similar ways.

Reduced contact Teens may or may not be permitted to visit the parent or guardian who is in jail. Some teens may be relieved that there is no contact. Often, teens may miss their parent or guardian.

Symptoms of anxiety and depression Teens may be lonely and depressed. They may fear for the safety of their parent or guardian in jail. Fear of the unknown creates additional anxiety. As a result, they may have difficulty concentrating. School performance might decline. They might experience other symptoms, such as sleeplessness, irritability, angry outbursts, tiredness, headaches, stomachaches, and other signs of anxiety and depression.

Did You Know?

Negative Influence Teens who have a parent or guardian in jail are more at risk for committing a crime themselves.

Suggestions for Teens Who Have a Parent in Jail

Discuss your feelings with another parent or guardian, mentor, or other trusted adult. Teens who have a parent in jail often feel ashamed, angry, confused, betrayed, and anxious.

- Ask questions: Will there be any changes in where I live? Will my family's financial situation change? What kind of contact am I allowed to have with my parent or guardian?

- Do not accept blame for the illegal actions of the parent or guardian. Remember, you did not commit a crime.
- Pledge that you will not engage in illegal behavior.

⚖️ Legal Issues

Criminal Acts Students might think that crimes are punished only by jail time. However, if a family member commits a crime, he or she might receive other sentences. In most states there are two different types of crime, as defined by the state criminal code. A misdemeanor is usually a crime that is punishable by less than one year in jail, depending on the class of misdemeanor. A felony crime is one that is punishable by more than one year in prison. Often, sentences for either a misdemeanor or a felony can be something other than jail or prison time, such as probation, fines, or community service.

If a Parent Goes to Jail

Teacher FYI

Criminal Behavior Teens whose parent or guardian commits a crime are more likely to commit a crime themselves. Often teens can feel responsible for their parent's crime, or feel that if they had acted differently, the crime would not have occurred. Emphasize to the class that they are not responsible for the actions of their parents. However, they do not automatically have the same tendencies toward crime if their parent is a criminal. They can choose to obey laws.

Class Activity

Journaling Emphasize the importance of communication when students are facing a problem that could cause a lot of stress in their family. Ask the class to write examples, in their health journals, of questions to ask and topics to bring up with a family member or other trusted adult who might help them deal with the stress if a parent was in jail. Ask them to list other people to whom they could talk if their parents were not available. Emphasize that this activity is a hypothetical situation and that students should respond to the situation as such. **L2**

National Health Education Standards
Pages 154–155: 1.2, 1.5, 2.1

155

If a Parent Loses a Job

Class Discussion

Ways to Help Have students discuss what they could do to help their families if one of their parents or guardians lost his or her job. *Answers will vary, but students might mention doing more chores, helping to care for younger siblings, giving their parent or guardian emotional support, or getting a part-time job.* **L2**

3 Assess

Vocabulary Practice

Page 22, **Unit 3 Fast File Resources**

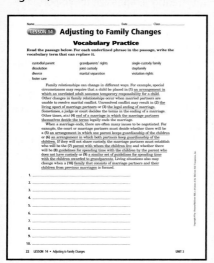

A teen's parent or guardian can lose his or her job. There are a number of reasons for why this might happen. A company or business might be acquired by another company. A company might downsize, or reduce its number of employees, for economic reasons. A parent or guardian might have poor job performance due to lack of skills or a problem, such as addiction.

How to Adjust If a Parent Loses a Job

When a parent loses a job, it has different effects on family members. Understanding the possible effects helps teens make adjustments.

The parent's feelings The loss of a job can be devastating to a parent or guardian. The parent or guardian who loses the job may become depressed and disappointed. He or she may lose self-confidence and feel embarrassed, or worry that family members and friends will lose respect for him or her. The person may be anxious and worried about how bills will be paid. He or she may need training for another job.

Loss of income A loss of income may require changes in living standards. Some families may experience homelessness due to unemployment. Some families may move in with other family members. For example, a teen may live with grandparents.

Fear of the unknown Teens who have a parent or guardian who has lost a job also may be anxious and worried. They may wonder: "What should I say to my parent or guardian?" "What should I say to other people?" "What changes will this bring about in where and how we live?"

Simple things, ▶ such as helping around the house more often, can make a big difference for a parent who is stressed or discouraged.

Suggestions for Teens When a Parent Loses a Job

The following suggestions will help ease stress and anxiety if a parent loses his or her job:

- Give your parent emotional support. Remember, you are on the same team. Encourage your parent.
- Discuss what to say to people outside the family. Your parent(s) can offer suggestions. You can discuss which family discussions are private and what information can be shared with others.
- Discuss what changes will occur in the family budget. Recognize that money might be tight. Do not spend money on things you do not need. Perhaps you can contribute money from a part-time job.

156 UNIT 3 • Family and Social Health

🎯 Differentiated Instruction

Behavioral Disorders Find an inexpensive reward that appeals to the student who has a behavioral disorder. Tell the student in advance that he or she must exhibit acceptable behavior during this exercise in order to receive the reward. Be certain the student understands what behaviors are acceptable in your class. Ask him or her to name some changes that might occur within a family that could raise emotional issues among family members. *Answers might include the divorce of one's parents, moving to a different location, or a parent losing a job.* **L2**

National Health Education Standards

Pages 156–157: 1.2, 1.5, 2.1, 4.1, 4.4, 8.4

annulment
custodial parent
dissolution
divorce
foster care
grandparents' rights
joint custody
marital conflict
    resolution
marital separation
single-custody family
stepfamily
visitation rights

Key Terms Review

Complete these fill-in-the-blank statements with the lesson Key Terms on the left. Do not write in this book.

1. _____ is an arrangement in which both parents keep legal custody of the children.

2. A(n) _____ ends a marriage and the marriage partners decide the terms.

3. _____ are guidelines set for the visitation of children by the parent who does not have custody.

4. A(n) _____ is the parent with whom children live and the parent who has the legal right to make decisions about the children.

5. A(n) _____ is a cessation of cohabitation between a married couple.

6. _____ is an arrangement in which an unrelated adult assumes temporary responsibility for a child.

7. A(n) _____ is a family in which a child or children live with one parent who has custody.

8. _____ is a way to end a marriage in which a judge or court decides the terms.

9. _____ are the visitation rights courts have awarded grandparents.

10. A(n) _____ consists of the marriage partners and their children from previous marriages.

Recalling the Facts

11. What are eight ways that the divorce of parents might affect teens?

12. What are five suggestions to help teens adjust to divorce?

13. What are five suggestions to help teens adjust to living in a single-custody family?

14. What are three ways having a stepfamily might affect teens?

15. What are some suggestions for teens whose parent loses a job?

16. How might a family member being called to military duty affect teens?

17. How might a teen adjust if a family member is called to military duty?

18. Name four ways having a parent in jail might affect teens.

Critical Thinking

19. Why do some teen females who do not have contact or have little contact with their father date older males?

20. How can teens find additional support and attention in a single-custody family?

21. Why do some teens whose parents get a divorce avoid social relationships?

22. How might children and teens in blended families benefit from having new family members?

Real-Life Applications

23. What do you think are some important questions for teens to ask if their parents are facing a divorce?

24. Why do you think illegal drug use puts an adult at risk for losing a job?

25. What would be some of your fears if a family member was on active military duty?

26. How could you help a friend adjust if his or her parent was sent to jail?

Activities

Responsible Decision Making

27. Write You have a friend whose parents are going through a difficult divorce. She seems depressed and you suspect that your friend is using alcohol. Write a response to this situation. Refer to the Responsible Decision-Making Model on page 61 for help.

Sharpen Your Life Skills

28. Use Communication Skills Imagine that you are a designer for a greeting card company. Design a greeting card to send to the families of those on active military duty. Refer to page 154 for information on having a family member in the military.

Visit **www.glencoe.com** for more *Health & Wellness* quizzes.

LESSON 14
STUDY GUIDE

Key Terms Review

1. Joint custody
2. dissolution
3. Visitation rights
4. custodial parent
5. marital separation
6. Foster care
7. single-custody family
8. Divorce
9. Grandparents' rights
10. stepfamily

Recalling the Facts

11. See pages 150–151.
12. See page 150.
13. See page 152.
14. See page 153.
15. See page 156.
16. loss of contact with the family member; loss of family income and a change in living arrangements; fear for the family member's safety; and symptoms of anxiety and depression
17. See page 154.
18. See page 155.

Critical Thinking

19. These female teens seek an older male boyfriend as a replacement figure for the father they do not see.
20. scheduling time with a parent, teacher, mentor, or tutor
21. These teens have felt rejected, betrayed, and abandoned and choose to fill up their time with activities that are not relationship-oriented. They fear getting hurt again.
22. Stepbrothers and stepsisters provide other family members with whom teens can participate in activities. They can become part of a teen's support network.

Real-Life Applications

23. With whom will I live; how often will I see the other parent?
24. Illegal drug use is linked to poor job performance and to missed days of work.
25. fear of loss of a family member, fear of losing touch, fear of change of living conditions

---

26. You can help your friend by being supportive. Tell him or her that he or she is not responsible for his or her parent's mistake. Encourage your friend to make healthful choices.

Activities

Responsible Decision Making

27. The friend does not share his or her emotions in healthful ways. The friend is at risk for hidden anger, which might produce many symptoms such as irritability, outbursts, headaches, sleeplessness, etc. The anger might be turned inward to self-destructive acts. You should tell a trusted adult if your friend is abusing alcohol.

Sharpen Your Life Skills

28. Answers will vary.

Out of Time?

If time does not permit an in-depth study of this topic, use the following activities in this Teacher Wraparound Edition:
- Class Activity, p. 159
- Health Project, p. 160
- Using the Table, p. 161
- Class Activity, p. 162

1 Focus

HEALTH GOALS **Dating Skills** Have the students respond to the second Health Goal for this lesson by listing in their health journals reasons why they need to develop dating skills. Reasons might include their own personal safety or reputation. **L2**

Write ABOUT IT!

Dating Guidelines Students should list questions such as: What are we planning to do on the date? How will we get where we're going? When will we be back? Will there be others present on the date? **L2**

Examining Dating and Friendships

HEALTH GOALS
- **I will develop healthful friendships.**
- **I will develop dating skills.**

A balanced relationship that promotes mutual respect and healthful behavior is a *healthful friendship*. Having balanced friendships improves the quality of your life. This lesson explains how to initiate friendships, carry on a conversation, and handle rejection. It includes dating guidelines to discuss with your parents or guardian and a Dating Skills Checklist to help you evaluate your dating skills.

What You'll Learn

1. List four questions to ask before beginning a friendship. *(p. 159)*
2. Discuss ways to initiate a friendship and healthful ways to respond to rejection. *(p. 159)*
3. Learn communication skills that encourage conversation. *(p. 159)*
4. Analyze how the age at which a teen begins to date might affect his or her physical and emotional health. *(p. 160)*
5. Establish dating guidelines with parents. *(p. 160)*
6. Evaluate your dating skills using the Dating Skills Checklist. *(p. 163)*
7. Discuss ways that balanced and one-sided friendships affect health status. *(p. 164)*

Why It's Important

There is a saying, "A friend is a gift you give yourself." You can have balanced friendships and healthful dating relationships.

Key Terms

- healthful friendship
- conversation
- rejection
- dating
- curfew
- dating skills
- balanced friendship
- one-sided friendship
- user

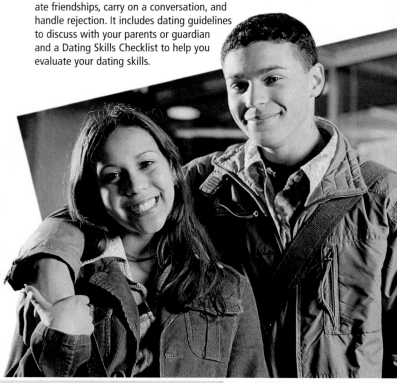

Write ABOUT IT!

Writing About Dating Guidelines Suppose you and a classmate want to go out on a date. Before you begin dating, your parents or guardian will set dating guidelines for you. Your parents or guardian will want to know details about your date. Read about dating guidelines on page 161 and make a list of questions in your health journal that you and your classmate might discuss.

National Health Education Standards—Guide for Lesson 15		
1.8	Analyze personal susceptibility to injury, illness, or death if engaging in unhealthy behaviors.	pp. 160, 162, 163, 165
2.3	Analyze how peers influence healthy and unhealthy behaviors.	pp. 159, 161, 162–163, 164, 165
4.1	Utilize skills for communicating effectively with family, peers, and others to enhance health.	pp. 158, 159, 162, 163, 165
8.1	Utilize accurate peer and societal norms to formulate a health-enhancing message.	pp. 158, 159, 162–163, 164, 165

Initiating Friendships

H ave you ever noticed that people often meet each other for the first time because they are talking about a similar interest? Friendships begin by using communication skills.

Communication Builds Friendships

There are questions to ask yourself about a person before beginning a friendship: What do I know about this person? Does this person have good character? Do my parents or guardian know this person? Will my parents or guardian approve of my spending time with this person? Pursue the friendship only if the person has good character and your parents or guardian approve.

How to initiate friendship There is an element of risk when you want to pursue a friendship. After all, you may not be certain that the person wants to pursue a friendship with you. The reward, however, is the opportunity to develop a new friendship. Ways to initiate a friendship include asking the person to enjoy a social activity with you and/or starting a conversation and asking questions to learn more about the person.

How to carry on a conversation If the person is receptive, your success in developing new friendships often depends on your ability to carry on a conversation. A *conversation* is a verbal exchange of feelings, thoughts, ideas, and opinions. The Conversation Keepers and Conversation Killers show what to do and what not to do when having conversations.

How to handle rejection Has someone you like ever ignored you? Has a friend or someone you thought was a friend failed to include you? Everyone experiences rejection at times. *Rejection* is the feeling of being unwelcome or unwanted. How do you respond to rejection? There are healthful ways for you to express your hurt, anger, and disappointment. Use I-messages to share your feelings with the person who rejected you. Share your feelings with a trusted adult. Remember that you are worthwhile even when a person does not want to be your friend or a friend does not include you.

> **Make the Connection**
>
> **A Good Listener** For more information on being a good listener, see page 44 in Lesson 5.

Conversation Keepers

Conversation Killers

The left column lists behaviors that keep a conversation going, while the right column lists behaviors that will make conversing hard.

Conversation Keepers	Conversation Killers
• asking questions	• talking about yourself
• showing interest in what someone else is saying	• appearing disinterested in what someone else is saying
• listening carefully	• interrupting someone
• responding to others	• changing the topic
• considering other ideas	• being a know-it-all
• encouraging another person	• complaining
• being positive	• talking about others
• making eye contact	• avoiding eye contact

LESSON 15 • Examining Dating and Friendships **159**

Lesson Resource Manager

- **Unit 3 Fast File Resources**
  Reading Strategy, p. 35
  Vocabulary Practice, p. 36
  Transparency Master and Worksheet, p. 37
  Real-Life Health, p. 39
  Real-Life Health, p. 41
  5-Minute Check, p. 43
  Lesson 15 Quiz, p. 44
- **Unit 3 Transparency**
- **Lesson 15 Transparency**

- **Reading Essentials**
- **Technology**
  TeacherWorks™ CD-ROM
  StudentWorks™ CD-ROM
  Reading Essentials CD-ROM
  ExamView® Assessment Suite
  Vocabulary Puzzlemaker

2 Teach

Class Activity

Conversation Exercise Have students choose a partner and ask each pair to have a conversation using the actions in the Conversation Keepers and Conversation Killers list on the student page. One student should follow suggestions listed as keepers and the other should follow actions listed as killers. Then after a few minutes have the students switch roles. After the exercise ask the class to discuss what they learned about making conversation. **L2**

INTERACTIVE CHALKBOARD with Image Bank

PowerPoint® Presentations
This CD-ROM is an editable Microsoft® PowerPoint® presentation that includes:
- Lesson presentations
- Lesson checks
- Interactive graphics
- 5-Minute Checks
- Image Bank
- All transparencies

Discussion Use the Seed Discussion Strategy on page 17T to initiate discussion about healthy relationships among teens.

> **National Health Education Standards**
> Pages 158–159: 2.3, 4.1, 4.3, 4.4, 8.1

Dating Guidelines

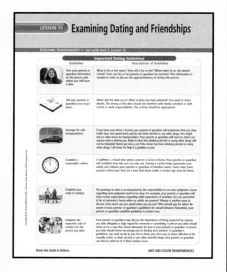
Dating Guidelines

Having social plans with a person in whom you are interested is ***dating.*** Teens may use other words instead of dating. Some teens refer to having a date as "going out" or "hanging out" or "seeing" someone. Spending time with people to whom you are attracted is a natural stage of adolescence. Before dating, it is helpful to know how to have healthful balanced friendships (see page 164). It is also helpful to communicate with parents.

What to Know About Dating Guidelines

> **Make the Connection**
>
> **Self-Esteem** For more information on self-esteem, see page 78 in Lesson 8.

When to begin dating A common concern of parents, guardians, and teens is identifying the appropriate time to begin dating. Parents and guardians do not want dating to interfere with their teen's education or emotional, social, and psychological development. Evidence shows that dating at a young age may have negative consequences.

Teens who begin dating before age 15 may seem to be confident and self-assured, but they can be more superficial than their peers. Early dating may interfere with the development of an independent identity. Teens who begin dating early may base their identity on their dating experiences rather than on developing their unique personality.

Parents or guardians are concerned about the effects of early dating on practicing abstinence from sex. Their concerns are backed up by research findings. Teens who begin dating at a young age and form steady relationships are more at risk for becoming sexually active. This increases their risk of becoming a teen parent and being infected with HIV or other sexually transmitted diseases.

Discuss the appropriate age to begin dating with your parents or guardian. Know that they want to protect you from the risks of dating too early.

Follow your parents' dating guidelines Before you begin dating, your parents or guardians will set dating guidelines for you. Their guidelines may include these sample dating guidelines. Share these dating guidelines with any person with whom you plan to have a date.

◀ Dating different people, casually, allows you to have fun and experience different dating situations while you're young.

160   UNIT 3 • Family and Social Health

Health Project

Dating Guidelines Have students form groups of 3–4 people and plan a presentation discussing the importance of dating guidelines to be given in another class at your school or possibly a middle school. Make sure students discuss the parents' or guardians' role in setting dating guidelines. They also should emphasize the importance of respect in a dating relationship. Students should create visual aids to emphasize the points shown in the table on p. 161. **L2**

TABLE 15.1   Important Dating Guidelines

Guideline	Description of Guideline
Give your parents or guardian information on the person with whom you will have a date.	What is his or her name? How old is he or she? Where does he or she attend school? How can his or her parents or guardian be reached? This information is needed in order to discuss the appropriateness of dating this person.
Tell your parents or guardian your exact plans.	When will the date occur? What activity has been planned? You need to share details. The timing of the date should not interfere with family activities or with school or work responsibilities. The activity should be appropriate.
Arrange for safe transportation.	If you have your driver's license, your parents or guardian will emphasize that you obey traffic laws and speed limits and do not drink alcohol or use other drugs. You might rely on older teens for transportation. Your parents or guardian will want to check out anyone who is driving you. Make it clear that drinking alcohol or using other drugs will not be tolerated. Never get into a car if the driver has been drinking alcohol or using other drugs. Call home for help if a problem occurs.
Establish a reasonable curfew.	A **curfew** is a fixed time when a person is to be at home. Your parents or guardian will establish how late you can stay out. Having a curfew helps guarantee your safety and relieves your parents or guardian of needless worry. Some cities have passed curfew laws that set a time that those under a certain age must be home.
Establish your code of conduct.	The privilege to date is accompanied by the responsibility to use wise judgment. Issues regarding wise judgment need to be clear. For example, your parents or guardian will have certain expectations regarding adult supervision of activities. Are you permitted to be at someone's home when no adults are present? Money is another issue to discuss. How much can you spend when you go out? Who should pay for what? Be aware of your parents' or guardian's guidelines for sexual behavior. Remember, your parents or guardian establish guidelines to protect you.
Establish the expected code of conduct for the person you date.	Your parents or guardian may discuss the importance of being respected by anyone you date. **Respect** is high regard for someone or something. A person you date should never act in a way that shows disrespect for you or your parents or guardian. A person you date should never encourage you to disobey your parents' or guardian's guidelines, say cruel words to you, hit or shove you, force you to show affection or be sexually active, or drink alcohol or use other harmful drugs. Your parents or guardian can discuss what to do if these actions occur.

LESSON 15 • Examining Dating and Friendships   **161**

Dating Skills

Explain the Concept

Casual Dating Explain to the class the difference between dating one person exclusively and dating a few people more casually. The benefits of dating casually include: different experiences with different people, more opportunity to grow as a person individually (such as becoming more socially adapted and able to communicate with a variety of people), learning to ask people out, and learning to accept rejection. Different dating experiences also help build self-confidence.

Class Activity

Role-Play Use role-playing to help students learn dating guidelines. Divide the class into pairs of students and have them role-play the following scenario. A student asks another student out on a date. Student #1 is very popular and Student #2 has liked #1 for a long time. Student #1 wants to pick up #2 for the date, steal some beer from his or her parents' garage and go to a party at another friend's house. Have student #2 respond to this request for a date by following the dating guidelines of his or her parents. Student #2 should make it clear that he or she is not interested in stealing, drinking, or going to a party where there will be others drinking. Student #2 might suggest that they do something else that night or another time, or say that he or she doesn't think dating this person is right for him or her at this time.
L2 **ELL**

S kills that help a person when he or she is dating are ***dating skills***. This two-page section includes questions and answers teens have about dating. Read through the problems and solutions below to learn more about dating. Then use the Dating Skills Checklist to rate your dating skills.

Check Out Your Dating Skills

Did You Know?

Internet Risks Some teens have been harmed by persons they met through the Internet. Remember, a person who contacts teens on the Internet could be a dangerous person pretending to make friendships.

Suppose you are dating only one person. Your parents discourage this steady relationship. They want you to go out with different people and spend more time with your friends. What are the advantages of dating several people versus dating one person seriously?

Dating only one person provides a comfort zone. You feel secure when you always have someone there for you. This person can help you feel accepted. But staying in the comfort zone has disadvantages too. During your teen years, you have the opportunity to practice your dating skills. You can take risks by asking out different people and accepting invitations. You can learn to handle rejection when someone does not want to go out with you. Different dating experiences help you meet new people and gain self-confidence.

Suppose there is someone in math class whom you think is attractive. You'd like to ask this person to a party your friend is having, but you get tongue-tied whenever you begin to speak. What can you do?

To calm your nerves, do a practice run first. Rehearse with a family member, trusted friend, or in front of a mirror how you will ask this person out. Be honest and share your feelings. It's OK to be up front and tell a person you wish to date that you are nervous. It will ease the tension. Then, take a deep breath, smile, and ask for the date. Now consider your dating attitude. If you ask someone for a date, do not consider yourself a success or failure based on the person's acceptance or rejection of your invitation. Instead, give yourself credit for doing the asking. Always remember, if a person turns you down for a date, it does not mean you are unlikable.

Suppose someone you have wanted to date asks you out. The plans involve going out with people who have a reputation for drinking. Should you accept the date?

Ask questions and get the facts before you accept the date. Explain that you do not drink and that you do not hang out with people who do. You need to know if there will be any drinking before you can accept. Your potential date may reassure you that there will be no alcohol. You need to make it clear that if there is drinking, you will leave immediately. You also may suggest going out with other people who do not drink. However, suppose your potential date does not reassure you that there will be no drinking. Turn down the date and do not be too disappointed. Remember, dating situations that include drinking lead to trouble.

Achieving Health Literacy

Problem Solver Have students create a skit about the following scenario: A classmate says that she has met a man on the Internet. She wants to meet the man at a restaurant over the weekend. Students' skits should include the dialogue between classmates, and should create an ending to the scenario. The skit should never include the student actually meeting the man at the restaurant; rather, the skits should focus on the classmates' discussion about why the student should not meet the man. Those reasons should include the danger to student's health and safety. Have students perform their skits for the class. **L2**

Suppose someone you do not like asks you out. How can you keep from hurting his or her feelings when you say "no" to the date?

Tune into your social graces and handle the situation with class. Thank the person for asking you. Say directly, but gently, that you are not interested in going out. Avoid dishonesty. For example, do not say you are busy when you are not.

Suppose you are at a party where teens are drinking alcohol or experimenting with other drugs. You tell your date you want to leave. Your date suggests staying another hour. Should you stay or make a fast exit?

Easy decision: make a fast exit. The faster you leave, the better. There can be serious consequences if you stay. Suppose someone calls the police to report alcohol and other drug use at the party. The police arrive and find teens drinking and using other drugs. You will appear guilty even though you did not drink or use drugs. People who hear about the party will believe you were drinking because you were at the party. Remember, your parents or guardian gave you the privilege to date. They believe that you are trustworthy and responsible. Now, what should you do if your date will not leave? Make a fast exit yourself. Call your parents or guardian, or another responsible adult to pick you up.

Suppose you have plans to go on a date with someone this Saturday. Then, you run into another person you like better. The second person asks if you have plans Saturday. Should you try to get out of your other plans?

Character is essential when dating. You must always treat people with respect. How would you feel if someone cancelled plans with you for someone he or she liked better? Always keep the commitments that you make to others. Set a date with the second person for a different night.

Suppose your friends talk about going out all the time, and you are not interested in dating. Is there something wrong with a person who is not interested in going out? Should that person go out anyway to keep up an image?

Going out, or dating, is a choice. Teens develop physically, mentally, and emotionally at different rates. Some teens will have developed an interest in dating while others have not. You may not be ready, or you may not be interested right now. Do not doubt yourself because you are not interested in dating. Do not date because you feel pressured to do so.

Reading Review

1. What are some of the benefits of waiting until age 15 to start dating?

2. What are some benefits of dating a few people casually instead of dating one person seriously?

Dating Skills Checklist

Rate your dating skills. Pat yourself on the back for each of the following statements that describes your behavior.

- I do not base my self-worth on my ability to get a date.
- I ask questions and get the facts before I accept a date.
- I decline a date when there will be pressure to drink or be sexually active.
- I honor my dating commitments and do not change plans if someone better comes along.
- I recognize the advantages of dating different people rather than having one serious boyfriend or girlfriend.
- I would make a fast exit from a date instead of being or staying in a situation that is against my parents' or guardians' guidelines.
- I would not hesitate to call my parents or guardian if I were on a date and needed help.
- I am comfortable staying home when I do not want to date.
- I am clear as to my expectations when I give or receive a gift in a dating situation.
- I am honest and kind when I turn down someone for a date.

LESSON 15 • Examining Dating and Friendships **163**

Quick Demo

Dating Early Draw a timeline on the board showing a person's lifeline from birth to age 80. Put an *X* in the time period from 15 to 20 years of age—the time period when many people begin to date—to demonstrate for the class how many more years they have to spend dating. People are marrying for the first time later in life now—often at age 30, 35, or 40.

Reading Review

1. *Teens who wait until the age of 15 can more readily develop an independent identity and will be more likely to practice abstinence from sex.*

2. *Dating casually will help you practice your dating skills, learn to handle rejection, meet new people, and gain self-confidence.*

Class Activity

Dating Skills Checklist Have students write down the Dating Skills Checklist on the student page and then answer "yes" or "no" to each item. Then have them identify the items to which they answered "no." Ask them to write suggestions for ways they could improve their behavior for each skill for which they answered "no." **L2 ELL**

Health Project

Dating Skills Have your students design and produce flyers to display around your school that list the Dating Skills Checklist on the student page. Have students identify at least one additional skill and add it to the list. Have students write their own heading and design the flyer as they choose. This project also can be done with 4–5 person teams in which the group writes an introduction together, one person does the layout on a computer, and others get permission and hang the flyers up around the school. **L3**

National Health Education Standards

Pages 162–163: 1.8, 1.9, 2.1, 2.3, 4.1, 4.2, 4.4, 5.7, 7.2, 8.1

Balanced Friendships

Extension

Fictional People Pleaser Have students select a book, TV show, or film that contains a character who is a people pleaser. (Students can find help in selecting a book or film at the school or community library.) Ask students to create a presentation about how the people-pleasing character tries to please people, how his or her actions affect his or her life and happiness, and how the people pleaser could learn to stand up for himself or herself. Have students share their presentations with the class. **L3**

3 Assess

Vocabulary Practice

Page 36, **Unit 3 Fast File Resources**

Name_____ Date_____ Class_____

LESSON 15 **Examining Dating and Friendships**
Vocabulary Practice

Write each term next to its definition below.

balanced friendship	dating	one-sided friendship
conversation	dating skills	user
curfew	healthful friendship	rejection

_____ 1. a person who does most of the receiving in his or her friendships

_____ 2. a relationship that promotes mutual respect and healthful behavior

_____ 3. having social plans with a person in whom you are interested

_____ 4. abilities that help a person when he or she is in a social situation with a person in whom they are interested

_____ 5. the feeling of being unwelcome or unwanted

_____ 6. a relationship in which two people give and receive acts of kindness with each other

_____ 7. a fixed time when a person is supposed to be at home

_____ 8. a verbal exchange of feelings, thoughts, ideas, and opinions

_____ 9. a relationship in which one person does most of the giving and the other person does most of the receiving

Answer the following question.

10. How can you tell if you have a balanced friendship with someone? How can you tell if a friendship is one-sided? Explain your answer.

_____

_____

_____

36 LESSON 15 • Examining Dating and Friendships   UNIT 3

Make the Connection

People Pleasers For more information on people pleasers, see page 179 in Lesson 17.

Balanced Friendships

A friendship in which two people give and receive acts of kindness with each other is a ***balanced friendship***. A friendship in which one person does most of the giving and the other person does most of the receiving is a ***one-sided friendship***. These two kinds of friendships have very different effects on your health.

What to Know About Friendships

How Balanced Friendships Affect Health Status

You give and receive in balanced friendships. For example, friends help celebrate success and listen to feelings of disappointment. Balanced friendships have positive effects on health status.

Emotional and physical health Acts of giving stimulate the brain to release endorphins. You feel increased energy, relaxation, and improved mood as a result of giving. Acts of receiving help you to feel cared about which makes you more resilient.

How One-Sided Friendships Affect Health Status

Some teens form one-sided relationships. Consider teens who do all or most of the giving in a relationship. There are at least two reasons why. First, teens who do most of the giving might be people pleasers. A ***people pleaser*** is a person who constantly seeks the approval of others. Teens who are people pleasers are usually insecure. They choose to do most of the giving so they will be liked and noticed by others. People who are takers often seek them out.

Another reason why some teens do most of the giving might be that they do not know how to receive acts of kindness from others. They are uncomfortable asking for support or accepting gifts or other kind gestures.

Teens who do most of the receiving in a relationship often are described as ***takers*** or ***users***. They take from others or use others to meet their needs. They are self-centered and selfish. One-sided friendships have negative effects on health status.

Emotional and physical health Teens who are people pleasers might feel others take advantage of them. This contributes to negative self-esteem. People pleasers often keep their feelings inside, which can cause headaches, stomachaches, and other stress-related symptoms. Teens who are takers have difficulty being close to others. This also contributes to negative self-esteem. Often, takers are controlling. They also can have stress-related symptoms.

Cross-Curricular Connections

Language Arts Have the students write two short fictional stories about two friends who have a balanced friendship and two friends who have a one-sided friendship. The plot of the stories should demonstrate the ways the friends either help and support each other, or the way one person uses the other unfairly. Students should create the stories for younger students, such as students in grades 1–4. Tell students their goal is to communicate the two ideas to younger students, so that younger students can identify problem friendships. **L2**

15 STUDY GUIDE

balanced friendship
conversation
curfew
dating
dating skills
healthful friendship
one-sided friendship
user
rejection

Key Terms Review

Write a sentence using each lesson Key Term correctly. Do not write in this book.

1. user
2. balanced friendship
3. curfew
4. conversation
5. healthful friendship
6. dating
7. one-sided friendship
8. dating skills
9. rejection

Recalling the Facts

10. What are four questions to ask yourself before beginning a friendship with someone?

11. What are three healthful ways to respond to rejection?

12. What are conversation keepers that encourage others to stay in a conversation with you? Name at least six.

13. What are conversation killers that discourage others to talk to you? Name at least six.

14. How might having balanced friendships affect a teen's emotional and physical health?

15. How might being a people pleaser affect a teen's emotional and physical health?

16. How might dating at an early age affect a teen's physical and emotional health?

17. What are six dating guidelines to discuss with your parents and/or guardian?

18. What are ten dating skills for you to consider?

Critical Thinking

19. List and explain some of the risks of dating someone who drinks alcohol or uses drugs.

20. Discuss why it is not a good idea for a person to talk about himself or herself all the time.

21. How might you evaluate the dynamics of social groups, such as groups of friends and people who are dating?

22. Why do people pleasers and users often become friends? How could a former people pleaser and user form a healthful relationship?

Real-Life Applications

23. What would you do if you went to a party with a date and some teens at the party had illegal drugs?

24. Why do you think parents and guardians set a curfew for teens?

25. What would you do if a friend always expected you to do what he or she wanted to do?

26. What would you do if your boyfriend or girlfriend began to say cruel things to you, treated you cruelly, or harmed you physically?

Activities

Responsible Decision Making

27. **Role-Play** You and a friend have not been invited to another friend's party. Your friend who was not invited wants to crash the party and cause a scene. Role-play the situation with a classmate. Refer to the Responsible Decision-Making Model on page 61 for help.

Sharpen Your Life Skills

28. **Advocate for Health** Review the dating skills on page 163. Pretend you are an advice columnist at a teen magazine. Write three letters for your column. Each letter should focus on a specific dating concern a teen might have. Then write a response to each of the letters.

Visit www.glencoe.com for more *Health & Wellness* quizzes.

LESSON 15 • Study Guide 165

LESSON 15
STUDY GUIDE

Key Terms Review

1. Answers will vary.
2. Answers will vary.
3. Answers will vary.
4. Answers will vary.
5. Answers will vary.
6. Answers will vary.
7. Answers will vary.
8. Answers will vary.
9. Answers will vary.

Recalling the Facts

10. What do I know about this person? Does this person have good character? Do my parents or guardian know this person? Will my parents or guardian approve of my spending time with this person?
11. See page 159.
12. See page 159.
13. See page 159.
14. See page 164.
15. See page 164.
16. See page 160.
17. See page 161.
18. See page 163.

Critical Thinking

19. You could face legal consequences. You place yourself in physical and emotional danger when you date someone who uses alcohol or drugs.
20. When you talk about yourself all the time, you do not encourage another person to join the conversation. This person will lose interest in you.
21. Answers will vary.
22. A people pleaser will constantly try to please a user. A user seeks a pleaser so that he or she can get what he or she wants. Answers will vary for the second question.

Real-Life Applications

23. You should leave the party.
24. Parents and guardians set a curfew to keep you safe. They want to know when you will return.
25. You might use an I-message to share your feelings. You might say that you want a more balanced friendship.

---

26. You should break up with him or her and tell a trusted adult about his or her behavior.

Activities

Responsible Decision Making

27. Role-plays will vary, but could include the following: Crashing the party and making a scene is not a responsible decision. It would be better to share an appropriate I-message with the friend having the party. Crashing the party also might not be safe. Others might become angry when you create a scene. This can lead to conflict. You do not show respect for yourself when you engage in this behavior.

Sharpen Your Life Skills

28. Answers will vary.

165

Practicing Abstinence from Sex

Out of Time?

If time does not permit an in-depth study of this topic, use the following activities in this Teacher Wraparound Edition:
- Health Goal, p. 166
- Explain the Concept, p. 168
- Teacher FYI, p. 168
- Using Life Skills, p. 171

1 Focus

HEALTH GOAL **PDA: Public Display of Affection** Have students respond to the Health Goal for this lesson by listing appropriate ways in which teens can display their affection for each other. **L2**

Write ABOUT IT!

Discussion Have students read the situation provided on the student page. Then discuss as a class how to go about setting limits for expressing physical affection. **L2**

LESSON 16

Practicing Abstinence from Sex

HEALTH GOAL • I will choose to practice abstinence from sex.

Voluntarily choosing not to be sexually active is ***abstinence from sex***. This lesson discusses the reasons why practicing abstinence from sex is the responsible choice for unmarried teens. You will learn how to set limits for expressing physical affection and how to say "no" if you are pressured to be sexually active. You will learn ten steps teens can take to change their behavior if they have been sexually active.

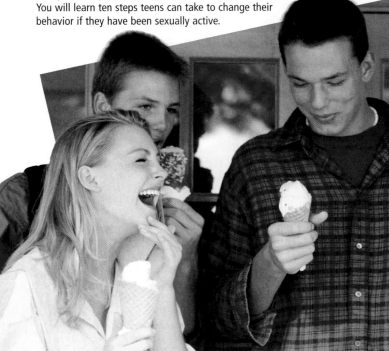

Write ABOUT IT!

Writing About Setting Limits Suppose you are very attracted to someone you are dating. This person is very attracted to you also. This person suggests setting guidelines for expressing physical affection. After reading the information on setting limits on page 167 and speaking with your parents or guardian, make a list of guidelines in your health journal that you might share with this person.

What You'll Learn

1. Identify guidelines for expressing physical affection. *(p. 167)*
2. Analyze reasons why practicing abstinence is a responsible choice for teens. *(p. 168)*
3. Analyze the benefits of practicing abstinence to protect emotional health and to prevent unplanned pregnancy and infection with STDs, including HIV. *(p. 168)*
4. Analyze the benefits of abstinence when dating in order to promote responsibility within marriage. *(p. 169)*
5. Demonstrate resistance skills to use if you are pressured to be sexually active. *(p. 172)*

Why It's Important

Abstinence from sex is the only method that is 100 percent effective in preventing pregnancy, STDs, and the sexual transmission of HIV.

Key Terms

- abstinence from sex
- respect
- sexual feelings
- responsible decision
- pelvic inflammatory disease (PID)
- legal age of consent
- reputation
- sexual fidelity

166 UNIT 3 • Family and Social Health

National Health Education Standards—Guide for Lesson 16		
1.1	Predict how healthy behaviors can impact health status.	pp. 166, 167–169, 172–175, 177
1.5	Propose ways to reduce or prevent injuries and health problems.	pp. 166, 167, 170, 171, 172–173, 174–175, 177
2.1	Analyze how family influences the health of individuals.	pp. 169–172, 174, 177
2.3	Analyze how peers influence healthy and unhealthy behaviors.	pp. 166, 167, 169–173, 174–175, 177
4.4	Demonstrate how to ask for and offer assistance to enhance the health of self and others.	pp. 166, 167, 169–173, 174, 175, 177
8.1	Utilize accurate peer and societal norms to formulate a health-enhancing message.	pp. 166, 167, 168–169, 170, 171, 172–173, 177

Setting Limits

E ach of us has a need to be liked, especially by those who are important to us. Liking includes both affection and respect. **Affection** is a fond or tender feeling that a person has toward another person. It is experienced as emotional warmth or closeness. Words such as "I like you" express affection. Physical touch can express affection. **Respect** is a high regard for someone or something.

How to Set Limits for Expressing Physical Affection

Staying in control In a relationship, there may be affection, respect, both, or neither. Knowing how to set limits for expressing physical affection helps you maintain self-respect and the respect of a dating partner. Setting limits helps you keep your sexual feelings under control. **Sexual feelings** are feelings that result from a strong physical and emotional attraction to another person. Sexual feelings may occur when you see a certain person, kiss or touch that person, look at a picture, or read certain material. These feelings are normal, but it is important to learn how to control them.

It is important for you to know how sexual feelings intensify when you express physical affection. Kissing and hugging may result in stronger sexual feelings.

Physical changes The couple's expressions of affection may not stop with a hug or casual kiss. Prolonged kissing can further intensify sexual feelings. Intimate expressions of physical affection can cause physical changes to occur in the body. This increases blood flow to the reproductive organs. In the male, the penis fills with blood and becomes erect. This intensifies sexual feelings in the male. In the female, there is increased blood flow to the vagina. This intensifies sexual feelings in the female.

Body's message vs. brain's message These physical changes prepare the body for sex even if the couple has pledged to practice abstinence. This is an important reason why you need to set limits for expressing physical affection. If you do not set limits, your body's message may attempt to override your brain's message, "I want to practice abstinence from sex."

> **Make the Connection**
> **Alcohol** For more information about how drinking alcohol affects thinking and decision making, see page 411 in Lesson 37.

Expressing Physical Affection

The following are guidelines that help you set and stick to limits for expressing physical affection.

- Limit your expressions of affection to holding hands, hugging, and casual kissing to keep your brain in control of your decisions and actions.
- Tell the person your limits before expressing affection.
- Do not date someone who does not respect your limits for expressing physical affection.
- Avoid drinking alcohol and using other drugs that impair your good judgment.
- Do not date someone who drinks alcohol or uses other drugs that impair his or her judgment.
- Stay in public places when on a date, such as the living room instead of a bedroom.

LESSON 16 • Practicing Abstinence from Sex **167**

Class Activity

Contract of Limitations Have students create a contract stating ways in which they can set and stick to limitations for expressing physical affection, based on the guidelines discussed in this lesson. Have them sign and date it, and if they have a significant other, have your students ask them to do the same. Have students involve their parents by asking them to witness and sign the contract also. **L2**

PowerPoint® Presentations

This CD-ROM is an editable Microsoft® PowerPoint® presentation that includes:
- Lesson presentations
- Lesson checks
- Interactive graphics
- 5-Minute Checks
- Image Bank
- All transparencies

Discussion Refer to the Think-Pair-Share Strategy on page 17T. Ask students to think about teens abstaining from sex, pair up to discuss their thoughts, and then participate in a whole-class discussion about the topic.

Lesson Resource Manager

- **Unit 3 Fast File Resources**
  Reading Strategy, p. 47
  Vocabulary Practice, p. 48
  Transparency Master and Worksheet, p. 49
  Real-Life Health, p. 51
  Real-Life Health, p. 53
  5-Minute Check, p. 55
  Lesson 16 Quiz, p. 57
- **Unit 3 Transparency**
- **Lesson 16 Transparency**

- **Reading Essentials**
- **Technology**
  TeacherWorks™ CD-ROM
  StudentWorks™ CD-ROM
  Reading Essentials CD-ROM
  ExamView® Assessment Suite
  Vocabulary Puzzlemaker

> **National Health Education Standards**
> Pages 166–167: 1.1, 1.5, 2.3, 4.2, 4.4, 7.1, 7.2, 8.1

Abstinence

Explain the Concept

Why Abstinence? Display for the class the six factors that determine if an action is a responsible decision. Then explain how abstinence affects each factor. Abstinence promotes health by protecting against STDs. Abstinence promotes safety by reducing the risk of emotional trauma. Abstinence follows laws by ensuring a person cannot be accused of having sex with a minor. Abstinence promotes respect for self and others by maintaining a person's good reputation and the good reputations of that person's friends. Abstinence follows parental or guardian guidelines by avoiding conflicts. Abstinence demonstrates good character by showing that a person has self-control and good values.

Teacher FYI

Some Are Waiting Students may say that more teens are having sex today than in the past. This is just a way to justify a decision to have sex. Tell your class that no matter what statistics say about how many teens are having sex, there will always be teens who understand the benefits of waiting to have sex. Emphasize to your students that they are definitely not alone by choosing to practice abstinence.

Abstinence

Throughout life, you will face many important decisions. The quality of your life will be determined by your decisions. Lesson 6 discussed how to make a responsible decision. A **responsible decision** is a choice that leads to actions that: 1) promote health, 2) protect safety, 3) follow laws, 4) show respect for self and others, 5) follow the guidelines of your parents and/or guardian, and 6) demonstrate good character. Practicing abstinence is a responsible decision for unmarried teens.

Why Practicing Abstinence From Sex Is a Responsible Decision

Make the Connection

Rape For more information about rape, see page 687 in Lesson 66.

Practicing abstinence from sex promotes health. By practicing abstinence, you protect your emotional health. Being sexually active interferes with your values and family guidelines. This clash in values can make you feel guilty. Being sexually active can lead to unplanned pregnancy and infection with sexually transmitted diseases, including HIV. These threats to health can make you fearful and anxious. Having sex outside of a loving, committed marriage increases your risk of feeling rejected, being compared to someone else, and feeling "used" by a partner. Practicing abstinence from sex protects you from these sources of emotional trauma.

By practicing abstinence, you will not become pregnant or get someone pregnant and become a teen parent. More than 1 million females under the age of 20 become pregnant annually. Many become pregnant more than once as teens. Fifty percent of teens who have a baby become pregnant again within two years of the baby's birth. When you practice abstinence from sex, you do not risk becoming pregnant or getting someone pregnant.

By practicing abstinence, you protect yourself from becoming infected with sexually transmitted diseases (STDs). To date, there is treatment, but no cure for genital herpes and genital warts. Teens infected with either of these STDs can have recurrences the rest of their lives. There is an increase in the number of cases of **pelvic inflammatory disease (PID)** in teen females. PID is a serious infection of the internal female reproductive organs, and can lead to sterility. When you practice abstinence, you protect yourself from infection with STDs, and you reduce the risk of becoming infected with HIV and developing AIDS.

When you practice abstinence from sex, you protect yourself from the sexual transmission of HIV. Millions are at risk because a person infected with HIV may not know it or may not tell a partner. To date, there is no effective cure for AIDS. Abstinence from sexual activity is the only method that is 100 percent effective in preventing pregnancy, the sexual transmission of STDs, including HIV, and the emotional trauma associated with adolescent sexual activity.

Sensitive Issues

Sexually Transmitted Diseases in Teenagers According to the Centers for Disease Control and Prevention, over one-half of newly reported sexually transmitted diseases are found in teenagers. This statistic makes it evident that you probably have students who are sexually active or who know someone who is sexually active. Also, you may have students who have been or are infected with some type of sexually transmitted disease. When discussing abstinence in class, care needs to be taken to avoid personal questions. Let students know that if they need to speak to someone, their privacy is important and will be respected by you. At the same time, have ready a list of trusted counselors and resources of which the students can make use.

Practicing abstinence from sex follows laws. You avoid being in situations in which you can be prosecuted for having sex with a minor. In many states, having sex with a person who has not reached the legal age of consent is considered corruption of a minor. In others, it is called statutory rape. The *legal age of consent* (which differs from state to state) is the age when a state considers a person legally able to give permission for sexual contact. A person can be prosecuted for having sex with a minor.

When you practice abstinence, there is no chance of having sex with an unwilling partner. You cannot be accused of rape.

Practicing abstinence from sex shows respect for self and others. You maintain a good reputation. *Reputation* is a person's overall character as judged by other people. Having a good reputation improves your relationships with peers. If peers know you practice abstinence from sex, they know that you protect your health and safety, and that you respect yourself and others. They know that you do not cave in to peer pressure and choose wrong actions.

Practicing abstinence from sex follows the guidelines of your parents and/or guardian. You avoid having conflicts with your parents or guardian because you follow their guidelines. Studies show that 97 percent of parents and guardians of teens want them to learn in school about the importance of abstinence from sex. Your parents or guardian want you to live a quality life. They know the serious consequences that can occur from being sexually active. They

want to protect you. By practicing abstinence, you are following your parents' or guardian's guidelines.

Practicing abstinence from sex demonstrates good character. You are self-disciplined and can delay gratification in order to uphold your values. A *value* is a standard or belief. *Character* is a person's use of self-control to act on responsible values. When you have good character, you uphold family values and practice abstinence from sex. You recognize the importance of delayed gratification. You postpone sexual intercourse until marriage. You concentrate on other aspects of your life, including dating relationships.

You promote dignity, respect, responsibility and sexual fidelity within marriage. *Sexual fidelity* in marriage is sexual faithfulness, and involves a promise to have sex only with one's marriage partner. It helps promote trust, a foundation for any strong marriage. Sexual fidelity helps protect the health of marriage partners. When marriage partners are faithful to one another, they do not need to worry about the sexual transmission of diseases. When teens practice abstinence from sex in their dating relationships, they reserve sex for the marriage relationship. This helps keep sex within marriage very special.

▲ The decision to practice abstinence from sex before marriage protects you from the risks of unplanned pregnancy, STDs, the sexual transmission of HIV, and possible prosecution for having sex with a minor.

Reading Review

1. When you are expressing physical affection, how can your body's message differ from your brain's message about limits that you have set for yourself?

2. What is PID? How does it affect a female's body?

LESSON 16 • Practicing Abstinence from Sex **169**

5-Minute Check

Page 55, **Unit 3 Fast File Resources**

1. Describe what abstinence from sex is. *It is the voluntary choice not to be sexually active.*

2. What are some guidelines that can help teens limit their expression of physical affection? *communicate to one another about their limitations, avoid alcohol and drugs, avoid someone who does not respect your views or drinks alcohol or uses drugs, stay in public places, and limit affection to holding hands and casual kissing*

3. How does abstinence from sex promote health? *You will not become pregnant or get someone pregnant; you will reduce the risk of contracting STDs or HIV; and you will protect your emotional health.*

4. Describe what the legal age of consent is. *It is the age when a person is legally able to give permission for sexual contact; this age differs from state to state.*

5. How does abstinence from sex promote respect for yourself and others? *You are able to maintain a good reputation for yourself and your friends.*

Reading Review

1. *Your body's message that it is ready to have sex can attempt to override your brain's message to practice abstinence.*

2. *pelvic inflammatory disease; it can lead to sterility*

 Family Involvement

Following Parental Guidelines Have students talk to their parents about dating, relationships, expressing physical affection, and abstinence. Parents should be asked to express their views on behaviors they would support and those that are unacceptable. The parents and teens should agree to be open to discussions about relationships. Encourage teens and their parents to draw up a contract that promises mutual respect and openness. **L2**

Saying No

Quick Demo

Model Model for students different responses they can use to resist peer pressure. Have students read aloud a line on this page that is used to try to convince someone to have sex. Then respond with a positive statement that counters the line and encourages abstinence. *Example: "Everybody else is doing it." "Just because he says everybody else is doing it, doesn't mean you have to. Do what you and your parents or guardian want you to do —which is practice abstinence—not what someone else wants."*

Class Activity

Developing Self-Respect Have each student put his or her name at the top of a blank sheet of paper. Then have them ask friends and family members to write two positive characteristics about them on the paper. Ask students to think about the characteristics their friends and family members listed on their papers. During the next class period, ask them to discuss how the lists make them feel. Ask if they were surprised by any of the comments on the paper. **L2**

Teaching Transparency

Page 49, **Unit 3 Fast File Resources**

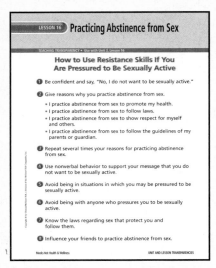

Saying No

The influence that people of similar age or status place on others to behave in a certain way is **peer pressure** Some peers influence you in positive ways. They encourage you to practice abstinence from sex. They want you to protect your health and safety, to follow laws and family guidelines, to show respect for yourself and others, and to demonstrate good character. Other peers pressure you to engage in harmful activity. They may pressure you to be sexually active. How can you resist this pressure?

How to Say "No" If You Are Pressured to Be Sexually Active

Focus on keeping your self-respect. Having high regard for oneself because one behaves in responsible ways is **self-respect.** If you respect yourself, others will respect you, too. Happiness is more a result of being respected for your values than being liked because you went along with the crowd. Consider what author Hugh Prather wrote in *Notes to Myself:* "The only way to be is me, then those who like me, like me." Do you understand what the quote means? Repeat it out loud.

The quote explains why you need to be yourself and act on your values. Unless you show others who you really are and what you really believe, they cannot really like you because they do not know the real you.

Do not be swayed to change your values. If you are challenged by peers to be sexually active, remember that you are the one who has to deal with the consequences of your actions. For example, if someone pressures you into staying out later than your curfew, you are the one who will be punished, not the person who talked you into it.

Giving in to peer pressure will not give you self-respect, and peers often lose respect for those who give in to peer pressure. Suppose you are known to practice abstinence from sex. Your peers will respect you for being able to resist the peer pressure to have sex. People often think that teens who spend time together behave in the same ways. By practicing abstinence, you protect the good reputation of your friends and those you date.

What Peers Might Say to Try to Convince You to Have Sex

Don't believe any of these lines!

- If you love me, you'll have sex with me.
- You can't get pregnant the first time.
- I'm safe. You won't get STDs or HIV.
- Everybody else is doing it.
- I'll always love you.
- Grow up, we're in high school.
- You got me all excited.
- If you won't do it, I'll find someone who will.
- You know you really want to—I can tell.
- I think you owe it to me.

Health Project

Peer Pressure Skits Have students break into groups and create a skit in which they portray someone resisting peer pressure. They need to include at least two peer pressure statements and use at least two resistance skills from pages 172–173. While the groups act out their skits, have the rest of the class analyze whether or not the resistance skills used were adequate. Ask students to make suggestions as to how the actors could have been more effective in resisting peer pressure. Point out that even though resistance skills are very effective, sometimes the best solution is to walk away from a situation. **L2**

Activity: Using Life Skills

Using Resistance Skills: Remaining Abstinent

On page 170 are ten lines that someone might use to pressure you to have sex. On page 47 in Lesson 5 are resistance skills. Use what you have learned as you do the following activity.

1 **Say "no" with self-confidence.** After you read the lines on page 170, write a reason you would say "no" to each. Give a different reason for each, using the reasons you learned in this lesson.

2 **Give reasons for saying "no."** Your teacher will ask you to form a small group with other students. Read each line and then have each student in your group tell the response he or she wrote. This will help you learn reasons other students might use when hearing the same line.

3 **Repeat your "no" response several times and use nonverbal behavior to match verbal behavior.** Practice resistance skills by using the lines and reasons in a role-play. One student will do the pressuring and another will use his or her reason to resist pressure. Student #1 will look directly at the other student, say "no," and then give his or her reason for saying "no." Then student #2 will give another line. Then, student #1 will repeat the same reason(s) again. Student #1 will try to influence the student giving the lines to practice abstinence.

4 **Avoid people who make wrong decisions, resist pressure to engage in illegal behavior, and influence others to make responsible decisions.** After several students engage in role-play, discuss other resistance skills. Brainstorm situations that might be avoided so that there will not be pressure to be sexually active.

Recognize lines peers might use to pressure you. A line is a short statement that may have a "hook" to it. A line may be intended to "hook" you and "reel" you into doing something you should not do. At the bottom of page 170 are ten lines designed to hook you into being sexually active. Do not get reeled in if someone tries to hook you by using one of these lines. A person who truly cares for you will not try to use a line or pressure you in any other way to have sex. A person who cares for you will respect your decision to practice abstinence.

Use resistance skills. Skills that help a person say "no" to an action or to leave a situation are **resistance skills.** Pages 172–173 contain a list of eight

suggested ways to resist peer pressure to be sexually active. Self-confidence is very important to successful resistance of peer pressure. The resistance skills that follow on the next page all require self-confidence. It is not always easy to say "no" to something that your friends want you to do. You must believe in yourself and trust that you have made the right decision. Having confidence in your decision to practice abstinence makes it easier to face any criticism you may hear from your peers. Confidence will help you avoid situations where you might be pressured to have sex, will help you use nonverbal behavior to support your choice of abstinence, and will help you influence your friends to practice abstinence from sex.

▲ Sharing your reasons for practicing abstinence from sex with friends, and role-playing different situations will help you build strong resistance skills and self-confidence.

Using Life Skills

Using Resistance Skills Have students follow the instructions given in steps 1–4. While still in groups, ask one or two pairs of students to reenact their conversations for the group. Ask them the following questions: How realistic were the responses? Do these resistance skills guarantee that a person will totally resist the peer pressure? *No, there is no guarantee, but they do help strengthen a person's resolve when facing peer pressure.* What are other factors that determine if someone will resist peer pressure? *self-respect, self-esteem, and self-confidence* **L2**

NHES Assessment/SCASS

Constructed Response Ask students to write one to two paragraphs in response to the following questions: What can happen if someone decides to have sex due to peer pressure? *They may contract an STD, become pregnant, or be emotionally unhappy due to the fact that they could not resist.* Why are people influenced by peer pressure? *They want to belong; they have low self-esteem; they believe they will earn more respect; they are afraid of losing their significant other.* Point out that real friends respect a person for his or her views and values, even if they do not agree with them. Also, tell students that withstanding peer pressure will strengthen their self-respect. **L2**

Achieving Health Literacy

Effective Communicator Have students work in groups to create pamphlets promoting resistance to negative peer pressure. The brochures should contain catchy phrases and examples of negative peer pressure statements and ways to resist them. They also should include reasons why people gain self-esteem by resisting negative peer pressure. Have students emphasize that everyone owns the choices he or she makes. Encourage students to be creative and use methods that advertising agencies use to promote their products. **L2 ELL**

National Health Education Standards
Pages 170–171: 1.5, 2.1, 2.3, 4.2, 4.4, 7.1, 8.1, 8.2

Class Activity

Collage of Confidence Have students look in newspapers and magazines to find pictures of people who project confidence. Have them also find some statements that emphasize self-confidence. After they have gathered all the material, have them make a collage and write about why they think the statements and pictures exemplify confidence. Ask students to include how working on this project made them feel and how they feel when they look at their finished collage. **L2**

Class Discussion

What About Your Kids? Ask students to imagine that they are older and married with children. Have them write down what types of expectations they would have for their children regarding peer pressure, relationships, abstinence, and sexual activity. Ask students to share their expectations and give some guidelines that would help children. Ask students to explain how they would discuss these issues with their children. **L2**

Resisting Peer Pressure

P eer pressure can be very difficult to ignore. Resistance skills will help you stay strong during times when peer pressure is at its worst. Stating exactly what you want or don't want will help you to stay confident. Give reasons for your decision to practice abstinence. Restate these reasons if necessary. This will make others take you seriously. Avoiding people and situations that might increase the pressure to have sex will make it easier to maintain your goal of abstinence. These resistance skills will help you reject peer pressure and keep the promise to yourself to practice abstinence.

How to Use Resistance Skills If You Are Pressured to Be Sexually Active

1. **Be confident and say, "No, I do not want to be sexually active."** Look directly at the person to whom you are speaking. State your limits for expressing physical affection.

2. **Give reasons why you practice abstinence from sex.** Use the six guidelines identified in the Responsible Decision-Making Model to develop your reasons for saying, "No, I do not want to be sexually active."

I practice abstinence to promote my health.
- I do not want to experience emotional trauma or feelings of guilt, fear, or rejection.
- I do not want to get pregnant or get someone pregnant.
- I do not want to become a teenage parent.
- I do not want to become infected with STDs, such as genital herpes and genital warts.

- I do not want to become infected with HIV and develop AIDS, a life-threatening disease.

I practice abstinence from sex to follow laws.
- I do not want my partner or myself to be prosecuted for having sex with a minor.
- I do not want to be accused of rape or to put myself in a situation in which I might be raped.

I practice abstinence from sex to show respect for myself and others.
- I want to protect my good reputation and the good reputation of others.

I practice abstinence from sex to follow the guidelines of my parents or guardian.
- I want to be self-disciplined and delay gratification in order to uphold my values.

172   UNIT 3 • Family and Social Health

Legal Issues

What Are The Laws Regarding Sex with a Minor in Your State? Have students research the laws regarding sex with a minor in your state and write an informative article to the school newspaper about the law and its purpose. You can suggest that students contact a local police station or state attorney's office for this information. Have students address these questions as part of their research: What is the legal age of consent for your state? Why is it important to have a legal age of consent? Who is protected by this law? **L3**

- I want to choose dating behavior that promotes dignity, respect, responsibility, and sexual fidelity within a marital relationship.

3. **Repeat several times your reasons for practicing abstinence from sex.**

For example, you might say, "No, I do not want to be sexually active. I practice abstinence from sex to promote my health. I do not want to experience emotional trauma or feelings of guilt, fear, or rejection. I do not want to get pregnant or get someone pregnant. I do not want to compromise my goals by becoming a teenage parent. I do not want to become infected with STDs, such as genital herpes and genital warts. I do not want to become infected with HIV and develop AIDS."

If you continue to get pressure, repeat this response several times. Each time you give the same response you will be more convincing.

4. **Use nonverbal behavior to support your message that you do not want to be sexually active.**

Do not behave in ways that go beyond what you've stated are your limits for affection. Strengthen your statement by always following what you have said.

5. **Avoid being in situations in which you may be pressured to be sexually active.**

Do not spend time in situations in which you might be vulnerable, such as being in someone's bedroom. Do not go to parties where teens will be drinking alcohol or using other drugs. Avoid watching movies and television shows that imply teen sex is OK.

6. **Avoid being with anyone who pressures you to be sexually active.**

Expect someone whom you are dating to respect your limits and do not date this person if she or he pressures you to have sex. Avoid being with teens who brag about "scoring" or having "sexual conquests." Date people your own age. Older people may exert additional sexual pressure. Pay attention to what your parents or guardian say when they advise against being with certain teens or adults.

7. **Know the laws regarding sex that protect you and follow them.**

Tell a parent, guardian, or other trusted adult if an adult makes sexual advances toward you. It is never appropriate for an adult to make sexual comments or advances toward a minor.

8. **Influence your friends to practice abstinence from sex.**

Be confident and share with friends your decision to practice abstinence from sex. Encourage a friend who is sexually active to change his or her behavior. They will respect your strength and self-confidence.

Did You Know?

Rape About two in ten females who first had sex before age 15 described it as involuntary. This means they were forced. Rape, whether of a minor or someone of legal age, is a criminal action with very serious consequences.

ABSTINENCE in the Media

Writing Activity Some movies and television shows portray teens having sex without showing any of the negative consequences. Choose a movie or TV show and write a newspaper article about the falsehoods portrayed by the movie or show with regard to sexual activity, abstinence, and young people. Present your article to the class. If possible, play some relevant scenes from the movie or show for the class and discuss your findings.

Extension

Abstinence Advocate Ask students to evaluate social activities in which teens in their community can participate. Have them develop a list of healthful activities in which teens can participate during a date. Finally, have students create a pamphlet to suggest these social activities and help promote abstinence from sex. **L3**

Class Discussion

Abstinence in the Movies Obtain clips from some popular movies with scenes that promote abstinence. Watch the scenes in class and discuss how realistic each scene is. Have students discuss how these scenes differ from those in movies that do not promote abstinence. Ask them to discuss how watching movies that promote abstinence can benefit teens. **L2**

NHES Assessment/SCASS

Performance Event Have students create a top ten list of why teenagers should abstain from sex and a list of statements that can be used to resist peer pressure. Encourage them to be creative and even use some appropriate humor to portray abstinence as a positive choice. **L2**

Health Project

In the News Have the students break into groups of four or five and create dialogue for a nightly news show. Have them create fictional stories that promote abstinence and ways to resist peer pressure to have sex. Also have them create pictures that they could use as background shots for the news stories. When the groups have gathered all their props, stories, and information, have two members act as anchors to tell the stories, two members videotape from different angles, and another act as producer or director. Encourage students to be realistic, professional, and to have fun. Show each group's tape to the class. **L2**

National Health Education Standards
Pages 172–173: 1.1, 1.5, 1.8, 1.9, 2.1, 2.3, 4.4, 5.7, 7.1, 7.2

Changing Behavior

Changing Behavior

Teens who have been sexually active can take steps to change their behavior. Changing behavior helps teens acknowledge that their health is important. They want to give up risk behaviors that might cause them to become infected with sexually transmitted diseases, including HIV, or to become pregnant or get someone pregnant. They acknowledge that it is wise to follow the guidelines of their parents or guardian. This helps them have a clear conscience. Although it is sometimes difficult to change behavior, it is worth making the change.

Steps Teens Can Take to Change Their Behavior If They Have Been Sexually Active

Did You Know?

Prevention Barrier protection and other contraceptive methods are not 100 percent effective in preventing pregnancy or the transmission of sexually transmitted diseases and HIV, the virus that causes AIDS. Abstinence from sex is the only method that is 100 percent effective in preventing pregnancy, STDs, and the sexual transmission of HIV.

Make a written list of your reasons for choosing abstinence from sex. Review this list often. The list will keep you aware of the risks you take when you are sexually active. For example, you may list "I do not want to become infected with HIV" or "I do not want to be pregnant or get someone pregnant."

Talk to a trusted adult about your behavior and your decision to practice abstinence. Your parents or guardian may be upset when they learn that you have been sexually active. However, they will support your decision to change your behavior. Remember, their role is to guide you. They can offer suggestions to strengthen you as you make changes. They can help you with the sexual relationship in which you were involved. They can help you decide what to do about this relationship. They can help you set new guidelines for expressing affection. They can discuss appropriate health care with you.

Consider the health consequences that may have occurred from being sexually active. You and any sexual partners you have had may be infected with one or more sexually transmitted diseases, including HIV. You or a partner may be pregnant. With your parents or guardian, discuss appropriate examinations and health care that may be required. If you are infected with an STD, including HIV, anyone who has been your sexual partner needs to be notified. This allows the person to get appropriate medical care.

Adhere to guidelines for expressing physical affection. Review the guidelines for expressing physical affection on page 167. Discuss these guidelines with your parents or guardians. Be honest about the people and situations that might tempt you or pressure you to break these guidelines. Discuss your plan for following these guidelines. Remember, your parents or guardian can help you.

174 **UNIT 3** • Family and Social Health

With approval of your parents or guardian, have a frank discussion with the person with whom you were sexually involved. Your parents or guardian may decide it is in your best interest not to have further contact with this person. But, if your parents or guardian agree to it, set a time and an appropriate place to have a frank discussion with this person. Share your reasons for making a renewed commitment to practice abstinence from sex. If your parents or guardian have decided that you should not see this person again, tell him or her.

With approval of your parents or guardian and if you are still dating, get reassurance from this person that he or she will practice abstinence from sex. Your partner must understand how serious you are about your renewed commitment to practice abstinence from sex. This means dating only persons who agree to practice abstinence from sex. You cannot put yourself back into a tempting situation or a situation in which you are pressured to change your mind.

Break off a relationship with a person who will not agree to practice abstinence from sex. Remember, you know your decision to practice abstinence from sex is responsible. Anyone who continues to pressure you to be sexually active is showing disrespect for you. End the relationship with this person.

Reevaluate the influence of the group of friends with whom you associate. Most people are drawn to friends who support what they are doing. Unfortunately, this often is the case with teens who are doing something wrong. These teens might be drawn to other teens who choose risk behaviors. They are comfortable because these teens support their wrong actions. Any time you need to change your behavior, it is best to look at the behavior of those with whom you are close. If they encourage you to change your behavior, they are truly "good" friends. If they encourage you to choose wrong actions, consider why they do so. Is it because they also want to choose wrong actions? An *enabler* is a person who supports the harmful behavior of others. Avoid being with friends who are enablers.

Be honest and direct about your commitment to practice abstinence from sex in new relationships. Get off to the right start when you begin new relationships. Adhere to the guidelines for expressing physical affection on page 167. Ask potential dating partners if they have made a commitment to practice abstinence from sex.

Avoid behaviors, such as drinking alcohol, using drugs, and being in tempting situations, that might impair your ability to practice abstinence from sex. You may have the best intentions and say that you will practice abstinence from sex, but certain behaviors, such as drinking alcohol or placing yourself in a tempting situation, may affect your ability to stick to what you say you will do.

▲ Once you have decided to practice abstinence from sex, you need to discuss it with the person you are dating. If he or she respects you, then he or she will respect your decision to practice abstinence.

Reading Review

1. Explain the quote, "The only way to be is me, then those who like me, like me."

2. How can practicing resistance skills prepare you for dealing with peer pressure?

3. Explain why teens who have been sexually active need to change their behavior.

LESSON 16 • Practicing Abstinence from Sex 175

Class Discussion

Difficulty Communicating Bring up a situation in which a teen wants to talk to his or her parents or guardian about sex, but doesn't know how to begin the conversation. Ask the class how they think the parents would feel and how the student would feel as well. Ask whether the topic is easy to discuss. *No, many people are uncomfortable with discussing many sexual topics.* Ask what the parents could do to make the communication process easier. *The parents could express their views in a calm and respectful way.* Ask what the student could do to make the communication process easier as well. *They, too, could voice their views in a respectful manner.* Explain to the class that when communicating about difficult and personal topics, a respectful and positive atmosphere can help make the conversation a lot easier, even though it still may be uncomfortable. **L2**

Reading Review

1. *It explains that you need to be yourself and act on your own values.*
2. *It will help you stay strong and confident during times of peer pressure.*
3. *It helps teens acknowledge that their health is important and that they want to give up risk behaviors.*

Cross-Curricular Connections

Language Arts Have students write a dialogue in which two friends are having a frank discussion about abstinence. Both friends have decided to abstain from sex, but one of them has a boyfriend or girlfriend who wants him or her to change that decision. The dialogue should include resistance skills and reasons for remaining abstinent that the friend who is feeling pressured can use to stick to his or her decision. The friends should conclude that the boyfriend or girlfriend must agree to practice abstinence or the relationship must be ended. Ask some students to volunteer to act out their dialogues in groups and have the whole class discuss the scenes. Ask students if they think it is important to have friends who practice abstinence and support others' decisions to practice abstinence. **L2**

National Health Education Standards
Pages 174–175: 1.1, 1.5, 1.8, 1.9, 2.1, 2.3, 4.4, 5.7, 7.1, 7.2

Analyzing the Feature

Use the following questions to help students uncover the main points of this feature.

1. **How did the research help Aaron decide to practice abstinence from sex?** *He did not want to contract an STD or cause an unplanned pregnancy.*

2. **What types of response did he receive?** *His family supported him 100 percent and most of his friends supported him.*

3. **What does Aaron believe he has gained from this decision?** *He has more confidence in himself.*

 Journaling Activity

Abstinence Ask students to discuss the conversations they have written in their health journals with the class. **L2**

3 Assess

Vocabulary Practice

Page 48, **Unit 3 Fast File Resources**

LESSON 16 **Practicing Abstinence from Sex**

Vocabulary Practice

Use the terms to fill in the blanks below. Some terms may be used more than once.

abstinence from sex | pelvic inflammatory disease (PID) | respect | sexual feelings
legal age of consent | reputation | responsible decision | sexual fidelity

1. A strong physical and emotional attraction to another person may result in _____

2. A(n) _____ is a choice that leads to actions that promote health and safety.

3. When you feel _____ for someone, you feel a high regard for him or her.

4. _____ is the only method that is 100 percent effective in preventing pregnancy and the transmission of STDs.

5. Your _____ may influence your relationships with your peers.

6. The _____ differs from state to state.

7. _____ promotes trust and protects the health of marriage partners.

8. _____ may occur when you see a certain person, look at a picture, or read certain material.

9. _____ is a sexually transmitted condition that affects females.

10. _____ is the voluntary decision not to be sexually active.

11. Having sexual contact with a person who is under the _____ is sometimes called statutory rape.

12. A person who makes a(n) _____ shows respect for self and others.

48   LESSON 16 • Practicing Abstinence from Sex   UNIT 3

National Health Education Standards

Pages 176–177: 4.4, 6.3, 7.2, 8.1, 8.2

SPEAKING OUT
Teens Talk About Health

**Aaron Brunson
Practicing Abstinence From
Sexual Activity**

> I didn't want any unplanned pregnancies or sexually transmitted diseases ruining my plans for the future.

It started out as a homework assignment. But for Aaron Brunson, it became a way of looking at life. When Aaron was searching for a research paper topic, his mom suggested abstinence. "I thought, 'OK, I don't know much about it, but I'll give it a try.'" Aaron used the resources of his local library, as well as the Internet, to learn about abstinence. He explained what happened next: "Doing my research for the paper, I decided it was a good thing to do. I didn't want any unplanned pregnancies or sexually transmitted diseases ruining my plans for the future."

What people say Not surprisingly, the reactions from Aaron's friends and family have been mixed. "My family has been really supportive," Aaron said. As for friends, "You get made fun of a little bit, but I also have friends who are 'on my side.' They support me and what I'm trying to do."

How important is not becoming a parent to Aaron's abstinence decision? "It's huge," he answered. "I want to become a doctor and it could really mess up my dreams and change my life."

Responding to media pressures Messages about sex are everywhere. How does Aaron react to messages on TV, in magazines, and in movies? "One thing I do is to try not to be around those kinds of pressures too much," Aaron said. "I'll turn off the TV if I have to."

Keeping on track What does Aaron believe he's gained from his decision? He explained it this way: "I believe in myself, which is a great thing for down the road. It's a hard decision to choose abstinence, and if I can do this, I'll have confidence that I can do other hard things in the future, like go to medical school. Practicing abstinence will keep me on the right track to what I want to be."

Helping others Keeping on the right track is something Aaron helps other young people do. "I teach some classes for high school and middle school kids. The program is sponsored by a local mental-health agency. I've also gotten some requests to do the programs in schools."

"The key to making an abstinence decision," said Aaron, "is to stick to it."

"Do what you believe if you think you're right," he added. "Don't be misled by what other people try to tell you. You'll know if what you're doing is right for you."

 Journaling Activity

Imagine that you, like Aaron, have been asked to speak to younger students about abstinence. What would you tell them? How would you answer their questions? Write an imaginary conversation, including several questions and answers.

176   UNIT 3 • Family and Social Health

Community Involvement

Abstinence Programs With their parents' or guardian's permission, have students ask local hospitals or health agencies if they can get involved with one of their abstinence from sex programs. Have the students write an essay about their experiences of teaching or working with the abstinence program. The essay should include factual information about the program itself and what their involvement was, including their responsibilities or assignments. Finally, students should express their feelings about the overall experience. **L3**

abstinence from sex
legal age of consent
peer pressure
pelvic inflammatory
    disease (PID)
reputation
respect
responsible decision
self-respect
sexual feelings
sexual fidelity

Key Terms Review

Match the definitions below with the lesson Key Terms on the left. Do not write in this book.

1. a person's character as judged by others

2. a choice that leads to actions that show good character

3. engaging in sexual activity only with one's marriage partner

4. a disease that can cause sterility in females

5. feelings that result from a strong physical and emotional attraction to another person

6. choosing not to be sexually active

7. a high regard for someone or something

8. the age when a state considers a person able to give permission for sexual contact

Recalling the Facts

9. What are some lines teens might say to try to pressure other teens to be sexually active?

10. What are four ways practicing abstinence from sex promotes your health?

11. Name six characteristics of a responsible decision.

12. What is the only 100 percent effective way to protect against STDs, HIV, and pregnancy?

13. What are two ways that practicing abstinence from sex helps you follow laws?

14. What are two ways practicing abstinence shows respect for yourself and others?

15. How does practicing abstinence from sex help you follow your family's guidelines?

16. What are two ways practicing abstinence from sex helps you demonstrate good character?

17. What are five guidelines to help you set limits for expressing physical affection?

18. What are eight resistance skills to use if you are pressured to be sexually active?

Critical Thinking

19. Why is it so important for teens to have self-respect?

20. Why should teens control sexual feelings?

21. How does the effectiveness of barrier protection and other forms of contraception in sexually transmitted disease, HIV, and pregnancy prevention compare to abstinence?

22. Name some things a teen parent might miss out on due to parenthood.

Real-Life Applications

23. What would you do if an adult asked you to have sex with him or her?

24. What are some limits you can set to avoid being in a tempting sexual situation?

25. If your best friend was being pressured for sex, what would you say to your friend?

26. How can you tell someone you are dating that you practice abstinence from sex?

Activities

Responsible Decision Making

27. **Write** You really like one of your classmates and now you are alone with this person for the first time. He or she wants to kiss you and touch you. You do not want to go beyond the limits for expressing affection you have set for yourself. Write a response to this situation. Refer to the Responsible Decision-Making Model on page 61 for help.

Sharpen Your Life Skills

28. **Advocate for Health** Pretend you are an advice columnist for a teen magazine. A sexually active teen wants to practice abstinence from sex. He wants to explain to his girlfriend why this is a responsible choice. Refer to the Responsible Decision-Making Model on page 61. Write a response that includes each of the six guidelines in the model.

LESSON 16 • Study Guide 177

Visit **www.glencoe.com** for more *Health & Wellness* quizzes.

Key Terms Review

1. reputation
2. responsible decision
3. sexual fidelity
4. pelvic inflammatory disease (PID)
5. sexual feelings
6. abstinence from sex
7. respect
8. legal age of consent

Recalling the Facts

9. Refer to the list on page 170.
10. protects emotional health; prevents pregnancy; reduces risk of STDs; reduces risk of HIV
11. See pages 168–169.
12. sexual abstinence
13. by avoiding the risk of having sex with a minor or being accused of rape
14. maintaining a good reputation for yourself and your friends
15. avoiding conflicts with your parents or guardian
16. you are self-disciplined; and you promote sexual fidelity within marriage
17. Refer to the list on page 167.
18. See pages 172–173.

Critical Thinking

19. It promotes healthful behavior, respect from others, and self-confidence.
20. so it is easier to limit physical affection
21. Abstinence is the only 100 percent effective way to protect against pregnancy and the sexual transmission of STDs, including HIV.
22. Answers will vary but may include going to school with your friends; playing sports or participating in other school activities; and going to parties.

Real-Life Applications

23. Tell the person that his or her behavior is both illegal and inappropriate, and to leave you alone. Then tell a trusted adult.
24. Answers will vary but may include only holding hands or kissing to show affection and avoiding using alcohol or drugs.

25. to stand up for himself or herself, that someone who respects him or her would never pressure him or her for sex
26. Be honest and tell the person the reasons you want to practice abstinence.

Activities

Responsible Decision Making

27. Let the person know that you have set some limitations for sexual contact. Let the person know that you like him or her a lot and would like to spend more time together, but that physical affection will have to follow your limits.

Sharpen Your Life Skills

28. Refer to pages 168–169 in this lesson for an outline of reasons why practicing abstinence is a responsible decision.

Recognizing Harmful Relationships

LESSON 17

Recognizing Harmful Relationships

Out of Time?

If time does not permit an in-depth study of this topic, use the following activities in this Teacher Wraparound Edition:
• Class Activity, p. 180
• Class Discussion, p. 182
• Class Activity, p. 184

1 Focus

HEALTH GOAL **Healthy Actions** Have students respond to the Health Goal for this lesson by writing in their health journals specific behaviors and actions that are characteristics of healthy relationships. Have students share at least one item from their lists with the class. Explain to students that they need to understand what a healthy relationship entails before they are able to recognize harmful relationships. **L2**

Write ABOUT IT!

Journaling Ask students to share their journal entries with the class. Ask whether they have ever been late or not shown up to meet a friend. Have them write in their health journals how they could change their own behavior to promote healthier relationships. **L2**

What You'll Learn

1. Describe behaviors typical of people who relate in harmful ways, including the people pleaser, the enabler, the clinger, the fixer, the distancer, the controller, the center, the abuser, the liar, and the promise breaker. *(p. 179)*
2. Explain why some people get involved in harmful relationships. *(p. 182)*
3. Evaluate the negative effects harmful relationships might have on health status. *(p. 183)*
4. Outline steps to take to end or change harmful relationships. *(p. 184)*

Why It's Important

Being in a harmful relationship can have a negative effect on a person's health status, so teens must evaluate their relationships to ensure they are positive.

Key Terms

• people pleaser
• enabler
• clinger
• fixer
• distancer
• controller
• center
• abuser
• liar
• promise breaker

HEALTH GOAL • I will recognize harmful relationships.

A connection a person has with another person is a ***relationship***. A relationship that promotes self-respect, encourages productivity and health, and is free of violence and/or drug abuse is a ***healthful relationship***. A relationship that harms self-respect, interferes with productivity and health, or includes violence and/or drug abuse is a ***harmful relationship***. This lesson will help you examine how harmful relationships affect health status.

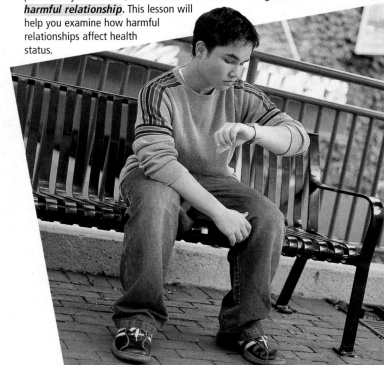

Write ABOUT IT!

Writing About Recognizing Harmful Relationships Suppose you are in a relationship with someone who does not show respect for you. The person might be late most of the time or be a "no show." The person might talk about you behind your back. After reading the information about changing harmful relationships on page 184, outline steps you might take to change this harmful relationship in your health journal.

National Health Education Standards—Guide for Lesson 17		
1.1	Predict how healthy behaviors can impact health status.	pp. 179–184, 185
2.1	Analyze how family influences the health of individuals.	pp. 178, 179–183, 185
2.3	Analyze how peers influence healthy and unhealthy behaviors.	pp. 178, 179–185
5.1	Examine barriers that can hinder healthy decision making.	pp. 178, 179–181

Harmful Relationships

A profile is a brief description of something or someone. The following ten profiles are brief descriptions of people who relate to others in harmful ways. Each is identified by a name others might use to refer to the person described. These profiles help you understand ways harmful behaviors can sabotage your chance to have healthful relationships. Do any of these profiles describe you or anyone you know?

Ten Profiles of People Who Relate in Harmful Ways

The people pleaser A person who constantly seeks the approval of others is the *people pleaser*. A people pleaser will do almost anything to be liked. This may include harmful behavior, such as using alcohol, using drugs, or engaging in sexual activity to please someone else. Often, other people describe a people pleaser as a "doormat" because they can walk all over the people pleaser with no consequences.

The people pleaser often lacks the self-confidence it takes to tell others what he or she thinks, wants, or needs. The people pleaser sabotages the chance to have healthful relationships because he or she does not demand respect from others.

The enabler A person who supports the harmful behavior of others is the *enabler*. The enabler may deny another person's harmful behavior. For example, the enabler may overlook another person's drinking, gambling, or cheating. The enabler may make excuses or cover up for another person. The enabler also may contribute to another person's harmful behavior. Sometimes it is much easier to act as an enabler than to stand up to a friend and tell him or her that his or her behavior is unacceptable.

A true friend will find the strength to be honest about another's harmful behavior. The enabler sabotages the chance to have healthful relationships when he or she does not expect other people to behave in responsible ways. As a result, the enabler cannot meet his or her own needs for attention, affection, and support.

The clinger A person who is needy and dependent is the *clinger*. The clinger feels empty inside and constantly turns to another person to feel better. When the clinger has this person's attention or affection, the clinger feels better, but no amount of attention or affection keeps the clinger fulfilled.

A relationship with a clinger is often very difficult because a clinger can be very demanding of others. The friend of a clinger can feel suffocated by the clinger's need for time and attention. The clinger sabotages the chance to have healthful relationships by not giving other people space. When people pull away, the clinger feels threatened and clings even more.

2 Teach

Explain the Concept

Where Do You Stand? Explain to students that everyone shares some qualities from each profile of people who relate in harmful ways and that this is normal. A problem may exist when someone exhibits the characteristics of one profile beyond moderation. Ask students to think about how some of their own qualities might fit some of the profiles.

INTERACTIVE CHALKBOARD with Image Bank

PowerPoint® Presentations
This CD-ROM is an editable Microsoft® PowerPoint® presentation that includes:
- Lesson presentations
- Lesson checks
- Interactive graphics
- 5-Minute Checks
- Image Bank
- All transparencies

Discussion Refer to the Sticky-Note Discussions Strategy on page 17T. Ask students to use sticky-notes to mark interesting paragraphs regarding harmful relationships that they would like to discuss in class.

Lesson Resource Manager

- **Unit 3 Fast File Resources**
  Reading Strategy, p. 61
  Vocabulary Practice, p. 62
  Transparency Master and Worksheet, p. 63
  Real-Life Health, p. 65
  Real-Life Health, p. 67
  5-Minute Check, p. 69
  Lesson 17 Quiz, p. 70
- **Unit 3 Transparency**
- **Lesson 17 Transparency**

- **Reading Essentials**
- **Technology**
  TeacherWorks™ CD-ROM
  StudentWorks™ CD-ROM
  Reading Essentials CD-ROM
  Exam*View*® Assessment Suite
  Vocabulary Puzzlemaker

Class Activity

Your Relationships Have students evaluate their relationships with friends and write a short essay on their findings. Ask them to consider if they act differently when they are with different people and whether they fit one profile with some friends and another with other friends. Ask students to think about why this might be so. Have students answer the following questions: Do they see any problems with their relationships? If so, how can they improve them? Some students may share personal information, so be sure to make clear to the students that you will keep everything confidential. **L3**

NHES Assessment/SCASS

Performance Event Find an example of a caricature of a certain profile in a newspaper or other media, and share it with the class. Then have the students pick a profile and draw a caricature or cartoon that illustrates it. Emphasize the use of symbolism and dialogue to communicate the point. **L2**

Did You Know?

Enmeshment A fixer usually has enmeshment. *Enmeshment* is a condition in which a person becomes obsessed with the needs of another person and no longer can recognize his or her own needs.

The fixer A person who tries to fix other people's problems is the *fixer.* The fixer takes on problems that are not his or her responsibility, but are the responsibility of another person. The fixer is quick to give advice. He or she will identify different possible solutions to the other person's problems and try them for the person. In the process of getting involved with someone else's problems, the fixer avoids his or her own feelings and problems. The fixer sabotages the chance to have healthful relationships because healthy people do not want others to solve their problems. Healthy people solve their own problems with the support of others. They do not want others to take over a situation.

The distancer A person who is emotionally unavailable to others is the *distancer.* The distancer may have been hurt by someone in the past and therefore, keeps other people from getting too close. The distancer may be too busy to spend time with other people, or may avoid sharing feelings. The distancer keeps others at a distance so he or she will not get hurt.

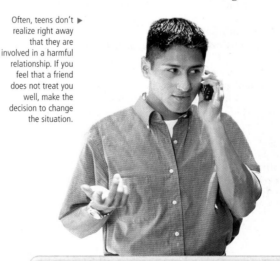

Often, teens don't realize right away that they are involved in a harmful relationship. If you feel that a friend does not treat you well, make the decision to change the situation.

The distancer sabotages the chance to have healthful relationships by not risking emotional involvement.

The controller A person who is possessive, jealous, and domineering is the *controller.* The controller seeks power. The controller may tell another person what to do, what to wear, and what to believe. The controller does not like to share the object of his or her attention with anyone else. The controller may monopolize a boyfriend's or girlfriend's time. The controller sabotages the chance to have healthful relationships by not respecting the interests or opinions of others.

Healthy people want to participate in the decisions made within a relationship. A person may be fearful of a controller, and with good reason. Those with the need to control may become violent. You may have seen media coverage of teens who harmed their boyfriend or girlfriend. In many instances, the teen causing the harm was a controller. There may have been signs of jealousy and possessive behavior before the harmful incident occurred, but they were not recognized or dealt with. Trust your feelings if you feel someone is being too jealous or possessive of you. Talk to a trusted adult.

The center A person who is self-centered is the *center.* It is as if the center is wearing a badge that says, "me, me, me." Talk to the center on the telephone and the center will do most of the talking. But the center will not show much interest in what you have to say. The center wants to do what the center wants to do, when the center wants to do it, and he or she is not too concerned about what other

ⓓⓘ Differentiated Instruction

Learning Disabilities Have students come up with characters from movies or books that match the different profiles of people who relate to others in harmful ways. Then have students describe each character and give examples of his or her behavior that match the profile. Ask students the following questions: How does that behavior affect the character? Are there any negative consequences to the harmful behavior in the story? Are there any negative effects on the character's health, either physically or emotionally, or on the health of other characters in the book or movie? Ask the students to decide if they think the outcome of the book or movie is realistic, considering the character's harmful behavior, and if not, how the story differs from reality. **L2**

people want to do or how other people feel. The center sabotages the chance to have healthful relationships by being so focused on being the center of attention that the needs of others are ignored. Others do not want to spend time with a person who can focus only on his or her own interests.

The abuser A person who is abusive is the ***abuser.*** The abuser may constantly put down others or cause others personal harm. The abuser may threaten others, begin fights, and act in violent ways. The abuser may force someone to have sex. Other people may find the abuser's behavior confusing. This is because the abuser may follow acts of abuse with periods of gentleness. However, the abusive behavior usually returns. An abuser may miss the chance to have healthful relationships by threatening and harming others.

Stay away from a person you suspect may be an abuser. This person can cause you physical or emotional harm. If someone is abusing you, either verbally or physically, immediately tell an adult you trust. It is never okay for someone to harm you. If the adult you go to for help does not help you end your relationship with an abuser, go to someone else who will.

The liar A person who does not tell the truth is the ***liar.*** Honesty is a foundation in any healthful relationship. People base their responses on what you tell them in your conversations and actions. When a liar does not tell the truth, other people make responses based on false information. Other people say and do things they might not have said or done had they

known the truth. This is exactly what the liar wants. The liar may lie about himself or herself to try to look good. For example, the liar may pretend to be something he or she is not, in order to impress others. His or her relationships are based on lies. The liar may have many friendships and relationships that are very shallow. These relationships lack a real connection or commitment because of the liar's actions. The liar avoids the truth to manipulate others into the responses he or she wants. The liar sabotages the chance to have healthful relationships by lying to others to get the response he or she wants.

The promise breaker A person who is not reliable is the ***promise breaker.*** The promise breaker will make plans with another person and be a "no show." The promise breaker often makes plans with another person and changes them if something better comes along. The promise breaker may agree to change annoying behaviors but does not make the changes. The promise breaker sabotages the chance to have healthful relationships by not keeping his or her word. Other people doubt the promise breaker's sincerity and commitment, which usually leads to ending the relationship.

▲ People doubt a promise breaker's sincerity and commitment, which usually leads to the end of a relationship.

Make the Connection

Media Television programs often have characters with some of these different profiles. For more information on ways to analyze messages in media, see page 558 in Lesson 52.

LESSON 17 • Recognizing Harmful Relationships **181**

INTERACTIVE CHALKBOARD with Image Bank

5-Minute Check

Page 69, **Unit 3 Fast File Resources**

1. **What defines a relationship as harmful?** *It is a relationship that harms self-respect, interferes with productivity and health, or includes violence and/or drug abuse.*

2. **What is a profile?** *A brief description of something or someone.*

3. **What is the difference between a people pleaser and a clinger?** *A people pleaser seeks approval from others, while a clinger is needy and dependent.*

4. **How do a fixer and a center differ?** *A fixer focuses on others while a center focuses on himself or herself.*

5. **How do promise breakers sabotage the chance to have healthful relationships?** *They do not keep their word, which causes other people to doubt their sincerity and commitment.*

Extension

Profiles on Television Have students watch several popular dramatic shows and choose a character from each show. For each character, have the students list personal characteristics, and explain which profile or profiles the character fits. Ask students to consider the following questions: What types of relationships does the character have? Are they realistic? Would the character be considered normal, eccentric, or unstable in the real world? **L3**

Health Project

Profile Examples Have students break into groups of four or five. Assign each group three different profiles of people who relate in harmful ways. The students are to create a skit or skits which demonstrate all three profiles. The skits can be about any type of relationship and can involve all three profiles in one skit, or students can do a separate skit for each profile. When they are finished writing their skits, have each group perform its skit or skits for the class. After each skit, have the class discuss the harmful relationship or relationships that were portrayed. Ask students to give examples of how each profiled personality could improve his or her harmful relationship. **L2**

National Health Education Standards
Pages 180–181: 1.1, 1.2, 2.3, 5.1, 7.2

Involvement in Harmful Relationships

Class Discussion

What Have You Seen? Students have been exposed to different types of relationships by their families, friends, and the media. Ask them for hypothetical examples of behaviors which demonstrate one of the match-ups in the text. Be sure to have an example to share with the students if no one can think of any. Ask students: How are these relationships harmful? *Answers will vary according to the examples.* Ask students: How can these relationships become healthy? *Answers will vary, according to the match-up profile.* Emphasize that for change to occur in relationships, both people must be willing to accept that there is something harmful in their relationship, be willing to communicate honestly with each other, and be willing to change themselves. **L2**

Teacher FYI

Abuse Victims Often, people who are abused by someone they are close to find themselves involved in other relationships in which they are mistreated. An abused person may begin to feel unworthy of being treated with respect and love. Therefore, abuse victims not only put up with abusive treatment, but may actually seek out people who mistreat them, because they don't think they deserve better treatment.

Involvement in Harmful Relationships

I t takes two people to have a relationship. What draws two people together? Is it by circumstance, such as being members of the same family? Being on the same athletic team at school? Having a part-time job at the same place? Or is it by choice? Two people are involved in a relationship because they are drawn to one another. It is important to understand the reasons why. Two people might be involved in a harmful relationship together because: 1) each one of them allows the other to play out a specific profile of harmful behavior, or 2) other people who expect healthful behavior avoid relationships with them.

Did You Know?

Responsibility An abuser often tries to blame the person he or she mistreats. The abuser might say, "You made me do it." Never accept responsibility for being abused by someone.

Why People Get Involved in Harmful Relationships

Match-up: a promise breaker and a people pleaser A promise breaker makes plans to go to a movie with a people pleaser. When the promise breaker gets another more interesting invitation, he or she cancels the plans. The people pleaser is angry but keeps the anger inside. The people pleaser accommodates the promise breaker and agrees to go to the movie at a later date.

Suppose you are a friend of the promise breaker. He or she mentions that he or she cancelled plans with someone to do something more interesting. Would you approve of what the promise breaker did? You do not know the other person in that relationship is a people pleaser, so you do not recognize that he or she also is relating in a harmful way. But if you knew the interaction of the two people in the relationship, you would have known that both people relate in harmful ways. The promise

breaker needs to learn to keep commitments. The people pleaser must set limits and share his or her feelings of anger and frustration.

Match-up: a controller and an enabler While controllers and enablers can be either male or female, in this match-up the controller is female and the enabler is male. The controller is a jealous teen female who demands all of her boyfriend's attention. She objects when he spends time with his friends. She has angry outbursts if a female classmate speaks to him.

The controller is very suspicious and accuses her boyfriend of seeing other girls. He is an enabler and makes excuses for her. He convinces himself "She loves me so much that she wants me with her all the time." He gives up his friends to spend all his time with her. He supports her wrong behavior. Suppose the male is your friend and he tells you about

---

 Sensitive Issues

Harmful Relationships When discussing harmful relationships with your students, be aware that it is likely that some of them are currently involved in a harmful relationship with someone. It may be at home, at school, or with a boyfriend or girlfriend. Encourage students to make a change if they feel they are involved in a harmful relationship. Let them know that parents, guardians, teachers, and guidance counselors are willing to help them take the steps necessary to change the relationship. Emphasize to students that personal privacy is important, but that if a teacher or other school employee learns of an abuse situation, that employee is legally required to share the information with authorities for the health of the student.

his girlfriend's love for him. From what he says, you might think he is in a very loving relationship. You might not recognize that this is a harmful relationship and that both of them relate in harmful ways. The girlfriend must respect her boyfriend's right to have friends and encourage him to run his own life. The boyfriend must take responsibility for his life and not deny his own feelings and needs.

Match-up: a clinger and a distancer
Although clingers and distancers can be either male or female, in this match-up the clinger is female and the distancer is male. The clinger is a female who was raised in a divorced family. Her father abandoned the family when she was ten years old, and she rarely speaks with him. She was very hurt and feels the loss of her father's presence in the home. Deep down, she fears that she will be abandoned again. As a result, she is afraid to be vulnerable and close. She becomes attracted to a distancer. The distancer is the perfect match because he is emotionally unavailable.

Both the clinger and the distancer are afraid to be close. They protect themselves in different ways. The clinger chases someone who cannot

be close. The distancer runs away from relationships and does not get emotionally involved with the clinger. Both the clinger and the distancer must change to have healthful relationships. The clinger must address the emptiness she feels and develop greater self-confidence. The distancer must address his fears of sharing feelings and becoming close to others.

Changing one's profile to fit different relationships There are many match-ups of people who relate in harmful ways, such as the center and the fixer, and a people pleaser and an abuser. It is important to know that a person can be described one way in one relationship and a different way in another relationship. For example, suppose a female has several close friends, but is an enabler only when she is with her boyfriend. She needs to examine this relationship to determine what causes her to relate in harmful ways.

Almost everyone has one or more qualities of the profiles described in this lesson. You may not fit a profile 100 percent, but do you recognize any of the harmful behaviors in your own actions? Use the steps on the following page to improve your relationships with others.

> **Make the Connection**
>
> **Self-Confidence** For more information on how to be more self-confident and assertive in your relationships with others, see page 48 in Lesson 5.

Reading Review

1. How does an enabler harm healthful relationships?

2. Why will certain people with harmful behaviors be drawn to one another?

How Harmful Relationships Affect Health Status

Mental-emotional health	Physical health	Family-social health
• anxiety and stress	• headaches	• lack of nurturing, supportive connections
• feelings of guilt and/or rejection	• stomachaches	• failure to develop appropriate social skills
• lack of self-confidence	• sleeplessness	
• negative self-esteem	• injuries from abuse	

LESSON 17 • Recognizing Harmful Relationships **183**

Class Activity
Warning Signs Have students choose two match-ups and create posters with the warning signs and consequences of these types of relationships. Encourage students to be creative and to use their imaginations in creating the posters. If they choose, students can use magazine or newspaper art or photographs, or draw illustrations to accompany the text. Have the students display the posters around the school for other students to read. **L2** **ELL**

NHES Assessment/SCASS
Constructed Response Ask students to write reasons why people might become involved in a harmful relationship. *It allows both people involved to play certain roles, or others who expect healthful behavior won't become involved with them.* Expand the assignment by asking the reasons why people would want to play a role such as a controller or a promise breaker. *Answers can include low self-esteem or lack of self-control, self-respect, and confidence.* **L2**

Reading Review

1. *Enablers may deny another person's harmful behavior. Enablers sabotage the chance to have healthful relationships when they don't expect responsible behavior from others, thus making it impossible to meet their own needs for attention, affection, and support.*

2. *They allow each other to play out specific roles, or other people who expect healthful behavior avoid relationships with them.*

Community Involvement

Abused Spouses Have students go to a local organization for abused spouses and interview a counselor about different types of harmful relationships. Students should ask the following questions: What are the most common profiles? Which profiles seem to be the most dangerous? Why do people who are abused stay with their abusive partner? What usually triggers the abused to get help? What are some ways in which their organization helps abuse victims? Is there anything teenagers can do to avoid abusive relationships? Have the students write a summary of their experience and what they learned. **L3**

National Health Education Standards
Pages 182–183: 1.1, 1.2, 2.1, 2.3

183

Class Activity

What If? Have students use the steps provided to create a scenario in which they are trying to change a relationship from harmful to healthful. Have them create a dialogue with the other person in the relationship that shares their concerns and expectations. Have the class evaluate volunteers' dialogues for directness and honesty. **L2**

3 Assess

Vocabulary Practice

Page 62, **Unit 3 Fast File Resources**

> Name_____ Date_____ Class_____
>
> **LESSON 17** **Recognizing Harmful Relationships**
> ### Vocabulary Practice
> Ideas expressed in words and phrases have similarities and differences. When you compare two ideas, you discuss the similarities between them. When you contrast two ideas, you tell how they are different. Compare and contrast the ideas expressed in the pairs of words and phrases listed below.
>
> | abuser | distancer | liar |
> | center | enabler | people pleaser |
> | clinger | fixer | promise breaker |
> | controller | | |
>
> 1. Compare and contrast the terms *enabler* and *fixer*.
>
> 2. Compare and contrast the terms *distancer* and *center*.
>
> 3. How is a *clinger* different from a *controller*?
>
> 4. Compare the terms *liar* and *promise breaker*.
>
> 5. Contrast the terms *people pleaser* and *abuser*.
>
> 62   LESSON 17 • Recognizing Harmful Relationships   UNIT 3

Changing Harmful Relationships

Suppose you recognize that you are involved in a harmful relationship that threatens your health status and that of the other person in the relationship. You can take steps to end or change the relationship. Your parents, guardian, and other responsible adults can help you.

1. Evaluate each of your relationships on a regular basis.
   - List ways you relate to others that worry you.
   - List ways other people relate to you that worry you.
   - Ask a parent, guardian, or other trusted adult to review the lists with you. This adult may recognize harmful behaviors in one of your relationships that you do not recognize.

2. Recognize when you must end a harmful relationship rather than work to change it.
   - End a relationship with anyone who chooses illegal behavior or threatens your health or safety.
   - End a relationship when your parents or guardian ask you to do so.
   - Get help from a trusted adult if the harmful relationship is with a family member.

3. Identify changes in behavior that must occur in any existing harmful relationship if you are to continue with the relationship.

- List changes you expect from yourself. For example, you might write, "I will not cancel plans if I have something better to do."
- List changes you expect the other person to make. For example, you might write, "I expect (person's name) to tell the truth at all times."

4. Talk to a parent, guardian, or other trusted adult about the changes you expect in the relationship.
   - Share your concerns about the relationship.
   - Share the behaviors you expect to change.
   - Share the behaviors you expect the other person to change.
   - Discuss whether your expectations are realistic.
   - Discuss whether or not it is wise to continue the relationship.

5. Have a frank discussion with the other person in the relationship in which you share your concerns and expectations.
   - Identify your concerns and your expectations.
   - Ask the other person to identify his or her concerns and expectations.
   - Discuss whether or not the relationship should be continued.
   - Make a plan to work on the relationship if you want to continue together.

6. Set a future date when you will evaluate the relationship again.
   - Evaluate whether or not your expectations have been fulfilled.

RELATIONSHIPS in the Media **Discussion** Think of a character in one of your favorite books or movies who fits one of the ten profiles for harmful behavior described in this lesson. How does his or her behavior fit the profile? How could he or she change in order to become more healthful in relationships? What are some of the reasons he or she relates in harmful ways? After you have considered these questions, break into small groups and discuss each person's character.

184   UNIT 3 • Family and Social Health

🖊 Achieving Health Literacy

Responsible Citizen Have the class write a series of feature articles for the school newspaper that discuss harmful relationships and how to avoid them. The articles should contain information about each profile, examples of possible dangerous match-ups, and ways to change a harmful relationship. Encourage students to be creative with the format of the articles. For example, they could use an advice column format to highlight different problems people have in relationships. Also, have students include information about how and where other students can get help to change or end a harmful relationship. **L2**

17 STUDY GUIDE

Key Terms Review

Match the mini-profiles below with the lesson Key Terms on the left. Do not write in this book.

abuser
center
clinger
controller
distancer
enabler
fixer
harmful relationship
healthful relationship
liar
people pleaser
promise breaker

1. a person who supports the harmful behavior of others
2. a person who is needy, dependent, and suffocates others
3. a person who ignores the needs of others and is self-centered
4. a person who is emotionally unavailable and pushes others away
5. a person who puts down, threatens, and harms others

6. a person who constantly seeks approval, is a "doormat," and will do almost anything to be liked
7. a person who is possessive, jealous, and domineering
8. a person who does not tell the truth
9. a person who takes over other people's responsibilities and often gives advice
10. a person who is unreliable and agrees to change behavior but does not do so

Recalling the Facts

11. What are two reasons people might get involved in harmful relationships?
12. What are four negative effects of harmful relationships on mental-emotional health?
13. What are four negative effects of harmful relationships on physical health?
14. What are six steps you might take to end or change a relationship?

15. What are three ways to evaluate your relationships on a regular basis?
16. What are three circumstances in which you should end a relationship?
17. How does an enabler sabotage healthful relationships?
18. How can your parents or guardian help if you need to change a relationship?

Critical Thinking

19. Why might a person act one way in one relationship and differently in another?
20. How can a person's role in his or her family affect his or her behavior with friends? Give an example.
21. How does a people pleaser differ from a clinger?
22. Why do you need to set a future date to evaluate the changes you have made to improve a harmful relationship?

Activities

Responsible Decision Making

27. **Role-Play** You invite a friend to a movie. She says she can't go because her new boyfriend gets jealous if she spends time with anyone else. This is causing problems with her family. Role-play the situation with a classmate. Refer to the Responsible Decision-Making Model on page 61 for help.

Real-Life Applications

23. Has a harmful relationship hurt your health? How?
24. How can you improve your behavior to have more healthful relationships?
25. Why do you think a center talks about himself or herself all the time?
26. Which profiled personality do you think is most dangerous to be involved with? Why?

Sharpen Your Life Skills

28. **Analyze Influences on Health** In a small group, select three television programs. Write descriptions of the shows and profiles of at least two of the characters. One of the characters in each program must fit one of the ten profiles of people who relate in harmful ways.

LESSON 17
STUDY GUIDE

Key Terms Review

1. enabler
2. clinger
3. center
4. distancer
5. abuser
6. people pleaser
7. controller
8. liar
9. fixer
10. promise breaker

Recalling the Facts

11. to play out a specific profile or because people who want healthful relationships avoid them
12. See the list on page 183.
13. headaches; stomachaches; sleeplessness; injuries from abuse
14. See page 184.
15. See step 1 on page 184.
16. if the other person chooses illegal behavior or threatens your health or safety, or when your parents or guardian ask you to do so
17. by not expecting others to behave in responsible ways
18. They can help you recognize harmful behaviors and help you end harmful relationships.

Critical Thinking

19. One friend may allow or expect certain behavior, but another friend does not.
20. A person who fits a certain type of profile within his or her family may continue this behavior in other relationships.
21. A people pleaser puts others' wishes ahead of his or her own. A clinger feels a need to stay very close to another person for security.
22. to establish a time frame in which the relationship is expected to improve

Real-Life Applications

23. Answers will vary but should include different types of physical and emotional effects students are likely to experience.
24. Answers will vary; discuss ways to improve behavior for each profile.

---

25. This person may be very insecure or self-centered.
26. abuser and controller because they may physically harm the other person

Activities

Responsible Decision Making

27. Tell your friend that a relationship with a controller is not healthful. Possessive behavior can lead to arguments, and sometimes, violence. Tell your friend she must involve her parents or guardians to help her end the relationship.

Sharpen Your Life Skills

28. Students can analyze the influence of characters by asking the questions in the Guidelines for Analyzing Influences on Health in Lesson 4.

Out of Time?

If time does not permit an in-depth study of this topic, use the following activities in this Teacher Wraparound Edition:
• Health Goals, p. 186
• Explain the Concept, p. 188
• Class Activity, p. 192
• Class Activity, p. 195

1 Focus

HEALTH GOALS **What Does Marriage Involve?** Have students respond to the first two Health Goals for this lesson by creating a list in their health journals of at least five skills they believe a couple should have when preparing for marriage and when preparing for parenthood. Make sure they include an explanation of each skill. As the lesson progresses, have them compare and contrast their list to the information given in the book. At the end of the lesson, have them write a comparison of what they thought before reading the lesson with what they have learned. Students should include the similarities and differences and what information was new to them. **L2**

Journaling Ask students to volunteer to share what they wrote in their health journals. Have the class discuss the responsibilities of parenthood. **L2**

Preparing for Marriage and Parenthood

HEALTH GOALS
• I will develop skills to prepare for marriage.
• I will develop skills to prepare for parenthood.
• I will choose to practice abstinence from sex to avoid the risks of teen marriage and parenthood.

Marriage and parenthood require commitment and sustained effort. You are not ready for these commitments right now.

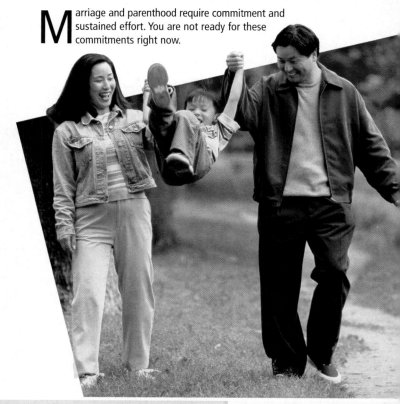

What You'll Learn

1. Explain the four kinds of intimacy in marriage. *(p. 187)*
2. Explain two ways to ensure that marriage will last. *(p. 188)*
3. Analyze ten factors that predict success in marriage. *(p. 192)*
4. Identify skills needed for responsible parenthood. *(p. 196)*
5. Discuss five examples of faulty thinking that lead to teen pregnancy. *(p. 198)*
6. Discuss the risks associated with being a teen parent. *(p. 202)*

Why It's Important

Training and skills are needed for two of life's most important jobs—being a marriage partner and a parent.

Key Terms

• intimacy
• developmental stages of marriage
• developmental task
• preventive discipline
• behavior modification
• logical consequences discipline
• faulty thinking
• generational cycle of teen pregnancy
• low birth weight
• toxemia of pregnancy

186 **UNIT 3** • Family and Social Health

Writing About Parenthood Think about what kind of parent you want to be in the future. Write about your thoughts on parenthood. Consider what goals you would have as a parent. After reading the information on being a responsible parent on pages 196–197, write in your health journal about the benefits and difficulties you might experience as a parent.

National Health Education Standards—Guide for Lesson 18		
1.2	Describe the interrelationships of emotional, intellectual, physical, and social health.	pp. 187, 188, 190–192, 196, 197, 203, 204
1.5	Propose ways to reduce or prevent injuries and health problems.	pp. 192, 196–197, 200, 203, 204
2.1	Analyze how family influences the health of individuals.	pp. 192–202, 203–205

The Marriage Relationship

You are not ready for marriage right now. However, your high school education is helping you prepare for your future. You are gaining information and skills to use as an adult. You already have learned something about marriage by observing your parents or guardian and other adults who are married or have been married. From them, you may have learned something about intimacy.

Intimacy in Healthful Marriages

Intimacy is a deep and meaningful kind of sharing between two people. There are many kinds of intimacy, but for marriage to be sustained over the years, four kinds of intimacy are of particular importance. The four kinds of intimacy are philosophical, psychological, creative, and physical.

Philosophical intimacy The sharing of beliefs and values is *philosophical intimacy.* Marriage partners share the values that determine their day-to-day priorities. For example, one partner might value his or her relationship with parents. As a result, spending holidays with parents becomes a priority for both partners.

Emotional intimacy The sharing of needs, emotions, weaknesses, and strengths is *emotional intimacy.* Marriage partners share their needs, their happiness, and their disappointments with each other. Emotional intimacy deepens through the years.

Creative intimacy The sharing of efforts to accomplish tasks and projects is *creative intimacy.* These tasks include running a household together, planning a vacation, and raising children. Marriage partners must work together with a willing attitude to have creative intimacy.

Physical intimacy The sharing of physical affection is *physical intimacy.* Physical intimacy includes a wide range of behaviors that express warmth and closeness. Marriage partners show physical affection when they touch, caress, hold hands, and kiss. Marriage partners express physical affection when they have sexual intercourse. The commitment that the marriage partners make to each other provides a sense of security to each partner. This enhances physical intimacy.

Having sex before marriage does not provide the security and intimacy that comes with the commitment of marriage. Dating couples can access the warmth and closeness that each partner feels for the other without having sexual intercourse. Fact: Sex before marriage does not predict sexual satisfaction during marriage. Remember, it is a responsible decision to wait until marriage to have sex.

2 Teach

Class Activity

Scenes of Intimacy Create four scenarios for each type of intimacy to read to the students. After you have read each one, have the students write down which type of intimacy they believe each scene represents. Then, go through the correct answers and explain why each scene relates to a specific type of intimacy. Explain what the main cues were. Emphasize to the students that each of these intimacies are important for a relationship to be healthful. **L2**

INTERACTIVE CHALKBOARD with Image Bank

PowerPoint® Presentations

This CD-ROM is an editable Microsoft® PowerPoint® presentation that includes:
- Lesson presentations
- Lesson checks
- Interactive graphics
- 5-Minute Checks
- Image Bank
- All transparencies

Journaling Refer to the Pre- and Post- Reading Responses Strategy on page 17T. Ask students to use their health journals to record what they know about teen marriages both before and after they read the lesson.

Lesson Resource Manager

- **Unit 3 Fast File Resources**
  Reading Strategy, p. 73
  Vocabulary Practice, p. 74
  Transparency Master and Worksheet, p. 75
  Real-Life Health, p. 77
  Real-Life Health, p. 79
  5-Minute Check, p. 81
  Lesson 18 Quiz, p. 83
- **Unit 3 Transparency**
- **Lesson 18 Transparency**

- **Reading Essentials**
- **Technology**
  TeacherWorks™ CD-ROM
  StudentWorks™ CD-ROM
  Reading Essentials CD-ROM
  Exam*View*® Assessment Suite
  Vocabulary Puzzlemaker

National Health Education Standards
Pages 186–187: 1.2, 4.4., 5.5, 5.7

The Marriage Commitment

Explain the Concept

Commitment Explain to the class that when two people get married they are making a commitment to each other to respect and support each other throughout the marriage. This promise is very serious, although it may be taken lightly by some people. When a person gets married, he or she promises to share the other person's problems, illnesses, debt, and sadness, as well as all the good times they will have together. When a spouse does not take this commitment seriously, he or she may begin to act on feelings, instead of the commitment made to the other partner.

Quick Demo

Scenes of Marriage Model for the students several scenarios of conflict that can happen in a marriage, including two different ways of resolving the conflict. *Example: A couple does not agree on how they should spend some extra money. One wants to go to Las Vegas with some friends, and the other wants to use the money as a down payment for a house. One result has the first person saying, "I don't care what you want. We're going." Another has him or her saying, "Let's use the money for the house, and I'll take my trip some other time."* Ask the class to decide which solutions are commitment-motivated, and which are feelings-motivated.

The Marriage Commitment

Today, because of rising divorce rates, it seems wise to examine two important ways marriage partners can help ensure that their marriage will last: marriage partners must be committed to actions that honor their wedding vows, and marriage partners must be committed to working together to master the major tasks of the five stages of marriage.

The Commitment to Honor Wedding Vows

When two people marry, they take vows, or make promises. This is called **commitment.** Yet, there are two ways partners can view marriage. One view of marriage is commitment-motivated: "I will behave in my marriage in the ways I have promised." Another view of marriage is feelings-motivated: "I will behave in my marriage according to how I feel at the moment."

Partners who are commitment-motivated behave as they say they will rather than as they happen to feel at the time. Suppose a partner does not "feel" like being supportive of the other person's needs, but uses self-discipline to do so to honor the marriage commitment. Suppose a partner does not "feel" like being sexually faithful, but uses self-discipline to say "no" to tempting situations. It is not always easy, but when a partner is supportive and faithful without feeling resentment, he or she indicates that the marriage commitment is a priority. These kinds of actions reinforce the marriage commitment.

But suppose a partner believes in a feelings-motivated marriage. This partner believes how he or she feels at any given moment determines his or her actions. The partner may not feel like being supportive or being sexually faithful. The partner decides to honor these feelings rather than the promises made in the wedding vows. The consequences are loss of trust, loss of security, and loss of commitment. Sexual infidelity also may bring an STD to the marriage. A commitment involves responsible actions. No one can promise how he or she will feel for a lifetime. One can promise how he or she will act.

The **developmental stages of marriage** are five stages of marriage in which couples must master certain tasks in order to develop and maintain intimacy. The tasks within each stage depend on the ages of the partners and the length of the marriage. The tasks are designed for people who marry in their twenties and stay married to the same person. People who marry younger or older may experience other stressors that affect the tasks.

 Family Involvement

What Does a Marriage Take? Have students interview a parent, guardian, or other responsible adult who is or has been married. Have them ask this person the following questions about the elements of a successful marriage: What factors have made your marriage successful or unsuccessful? What are some of the challenges that you have faced in marriage? How did you handle conflict within your marriage? What advice would you give to a couple planning to marry? With the permission of the person interviewed, students can write a summary of and response to their interview. **L2**

The Major Tasks of the Five Stages of Marriage

The first stage: the first two years
The newly married couple overcomes their idealistic notions of marriage and begins to form a family. The partners strive to:
- maintain individual identity as they form a family,
- develop cooperation and reduce the need to control one another,
- develop a sexual bond that leads to deeper intimacy,
- develop an effective decision-making style,
- recognize difficulties in their parents' marriages and anticipate how those difficulties might affect their marriage.

The second stage: the third through the tenth year
The couple gains a realistic view of one another and must settle into dealing with their individual weaknesses and make an effort to avoid dysfunctional behaviors. Their goals are to:
- recognize and confront the weaknesses of both partners,
- examine relationships and avoid dysfunctional behaviors,
- reaffirm commitment to sexual intimacy, including sexual fidelity,
- examine the influence of children on marriage and agree upon child-raising methods.

The third stage: the eleventh through the twenty-fifth year
The couple establishes and maintains individual identities and deals with issues of aging, adolescent children, and intimacy. They recognize the need to:
- maintain individual identities and develop mutual dependence,

- recognize that neither person will be perfect, and forgive mistakes,
- confront the crises of middle age, including aging, sexuality, and job and financial security,
- maintain and develop intimacy.

The fourth stage: the twenty-sixth through the thirty-fifth year
The couple must master tasks from the first three stages that were not previously mastered, confront changes in sexuality, and grieve over their losses. They determine to:
- reevaluate the tasks from the previous stages,
- recognize the physical changes that accompany aging and affect sexuality, and to rekindle romance,
- grieve over losses such as the death of parents and children leaving home.

The fifth stage: the thirty-sixth year and on
The couple finds new inspiration after the major life tasks have been completed, and they confront feelings about death. They agree to:
- prepare for retirement,
- renew intimacy and develop ways to continue sexual intimacy,
- prepare for death and for the death of the marriage partner.

▲ Successful marriages depend on commitment to marriage vows and dedication to facing life's changes together.

Reading Review

1. How does the marriage commitment enhance physical intimacy?

2. What are the tasks important to the first developmental stage of a healthful marriage?

LESSON 18 • Preparing for Marriage and Parenthood **189**

Class Activity

Timeline of Marriage Have the students create a timeline based on the five stages of marriage. Have them paraphrase the key points on their timelines and add art or photos or draw illustrations for each stage of the marriage. **L2** **ELL**

Explain the Concept

The First Stage Explain to the class why the tasks in the first stage of marriage are important. The first two years of a marriage often are difficult for a couple because they are getting used to living with another person, getting used to sharing space, and learning how to work together. These tasks are critical to a happy marriage as they help build confidence, trust, and intimacy.

Reading Review

1. *by providing a sense of trust and security for both partners*
2. *maintain individual identity; reduce the need for control and develop cooperation; develop a sexual bond; develop an effective decision-making style; and anticipate how difficulties in their parents' marriages might affect the marriage*

⊕ Cross-Curricular Connections

Social Studies Have students choose a country other than the United States and research how marriage is viewed in its culture and within its main religion. Research topics might include marriage and divorce statistics; average age at marriage for men and women; percentage of teen marriages; and a comparison of cultural practices regarding marriage to those of the United States. Ask students to give reasons why they think differences exist in different countries with regard to marriage. Have students share their information with the class perhaps in the form of a multimedia presentation. **L3**

National Health Education Standards
Pages 188–189: 1.2, 4.4, 5.7

Teen Marriage

Class Discussion

Healthful Relationships Have students list ways they believe they can develop healthful relationships with members of both sexes. *The list could include joining student organizations, attending student events, or being part of a sports team.* Ask students to discuss why it is important to experience healthful relationships with people of both sexes. *to understand more about the opposite sex, to learn more about yourself, and to learn how to communicate and how to develop friendships*
L2

5-Minute Check

Page 81, **Unit 3 Fast File Resources**

1. What is the difference between commitment-motivated and feelings-motivated marriages? *In a commitment-motivated marriage, actions are based on the vows made to your spouse. In a feelings-motivated marriage, actions are based on a person's feelings at the time.*

2. What is intimacy? *a deep and meaningful kind of sharing between two people*

3. What are the four types of intimacy? *philosophical, emotional, creative, and physical*

4. What happens during the first stage of marriage? *A couple overcomes their idealistic notions of marriage and begins to form a family.*

5. What happens during the second stage of marriage? *A couple gains a realistic view of one another; they must settle into dealing with their individual weaknesses and make an effort to avoid dysfunctional behaviors.*

Teen Marriage

Sociologist Robert Havighurst identified eight developmental tasks of adolescence. A *developmental task* is an achievement that needs to be mastered to reach the next level of maturity. Teens who marry do not have enough time to master the developmental tasks of adolescence before facing the responsibilities of marriage.

Why Teen Marriage Is Risky

Divorce More than 50 percent of teen marriages end in divorce.

One way to reduce the number of separations and divorces is to reduce the number of teen marriages. More than 50 percent of teen marriages end in divorce. There are many reasons why teen marriages do not succeed. Teens need to master the developmental tasks of adolescence before tackling the tasks that are appropriate for the stages of marriage. The following discussion explains why teen marriage interferes with mastering these tasks of adolescence and prevents a teen from reaching the next level of maturity necessary for a successful marriage.

Task 1: Develop healthful friendships with members of both sexes. Teen marriage doesn't give you time to do this. During adolescence, you need to have friendships with boys and girls. You need to learn how to communicate and how to develop friendships. Having friendships with members of both sexes helps you learn more about yourself, which is an important aspect of forming personal identity. Teen marriage cuts short the time you need to develop friendships with members of both sexes.

Task 2: Become comfortable with your maleness or femaleness. Teen marriage does not give you enough time to do this. Dating helps you learn to respond to people of the opposite sex.

Having the opportunity to date different people is very beneficial. Teens who marry pass up much of the fun that their peers have participating in social activities.

Task 3: Become comfortable with your body. Teen marriage doesn't give you enough time to do this. Your body is still growing and developing. Hormonal changes that accompany puberty cause new feelings as well as body changes. *Puberty* is the stage of growth and development when both the male and female body become capable of producing offspring. You need time to be comfortable with changes in your body. Teens who marry may do so only because they have a strong sexual attraction to one another. As a result, they may make mistakes in selecting a marriage partner.

Task 4: Become emotionally independent from adults. Teen marriage does not allow time for this. You are learning to be an adult and preparing to run your own life. During your teen years, you need the safety and security your parents or guardians provide. They help you practice becoming independent. Teens who marry are faced with adulthood without the safety and security of being parented themselves when they really need it.

190   UNIT 3 • Family and Social Health

⚖ Legal Issues

Teen Marriage Laws Have the students check the library for information regarding teen marriage in several different states. Ask them to answer the following questions: What laws govern teen marriage? What are the teen marriage laws in your state? Do different states have different laws concerning teen marriage? How are the laws alike and how are they different? Ask students to explain the importance of laws governing teen marriage. Ask them to think about some of the serious legal issues married teens may face, such as finding insurance coverage and paying their taxes. **L3**

Task 5: Learn skills you will need later for a successful marriage and parenthood. Teen marriage prevents this. Teens need to develop effective communication skills to help them achieve intimacy in adulthood. Teens also need to develop conflict-resolution skills to learn how to settle disagreements when they are married.

Task 6: Prepare for a career. Teen marriage does not allow for this. Your education should be a top priority. Your goal is to have the skills needed to get a job, support yourself, and become financially independent. Teens who marry usually have difficulty completing their education and finding a good job.

Task 7: Have a clear set of values to guide your behavior. Teen marriage does not give you time to do this. As an adolescent, you are beginning to achieve emotional independence from your parents or guardian. You gain confidence when you move from "these are my parents' or guardian's values" to "these are my values." Teens who marry may do so before they are certain of their own values. This can lead to making decisions you will regret later.

Task 8: Understand and achieve socially responsible behavior. Teen mariage does not give you time to do this. During early and middle adolescence, you may focus only on your needs. You may spend much time thinking about your appearance, your social life, and your friends. In the next few years, you will begin to look at the world around you and identify ways to be helpful. Teens who marry do not have the time to develop these skills. The demands of marriage, and possibly parenthood, take up all of their time.

www.glencoe.com

HEALTH NEWS

Marrying Later in Life

According to a report released by the Centers for Disease Control and Prevention's National Center for Health Statistics (NCHS), the younger a woman's age at the time of marriage, the more likely it is that the marriage will be disrupted, either by separation or divorce. The graph below shows the percentage of first marriages disrupted for different age groups of the woman at the time of marriage. Overall, marriages that occur when the woman is in her teens have the least likely chance of lasting. In the study done by the NCHS, during the first ten years, close to 50 percent of marriages that occurred when the woman was under the age of 18 had been disrupted. Of the marriages that occurred when the woman was 25 years or older, 24 percent had been disrupted during the first ten-year period.

Although the study does not offer any reasons as to why the marriages of younger women may be might unstable, a longer courtship and more maturity and life experience might allow couples to face the difficulties and responsibilities of marriage with more success.

Health Online   Visit www.glencoe.com for more information on the topic of marriage.

Failure Rate of First Marriages by Age of Bride

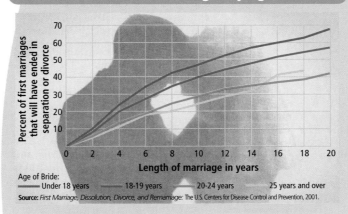

Percent of first marriages that will have ended in separation or divorce / Length of marriage in years

Age of Bride:
—— Under 18 years   —— 18-19 years   —— 20-24 years   —— 25 years and over

Source: *First Marriage, Dissolution, Divorce, and Remarriage:* The U.S. Centers for Disease Control and Prevention, 2001.

Analyzing Graphs

Study the graph above and answer these questions:

1. Which age group (at time of marriage) is most likely to still be married after 10 years of marriage?

2. Which group is most likely to be divorced or separated 20 years after marriage?

LESSON 18 • Preparing for Marriage and Parenthood   **191**

HEALTH NEWS

Analyzing Graphs
1. age group 25 and over
2. Even after 20 years of marriage, it is still age group 18 and under.

Project
Analyze Have students write about why they think it is true that the younger a woman is at the time she marries, the less likely it is that the marriage will last. **L2**

Class Discussion
Career Influence Have the class focus on task six, which is preparing for a career. Ask students to imagine that they were married while they were still in high school. Then ask if they think they would have enough time to finish school and prepare for the career they want. *It could be done, but it would take a lot more time and effort.* Ask students to explain how marriage might affect their plans for a career. *They would not make decisions for just themselves anymore, but would have to deal with their spouses' needs and desires as well. Also, they might not have the financial support of their families.* **L2**

DI Differentiated Instruction

Learning Disabilities Ask the class to stand and explain to them that they each represent a marriage between two teens. Have 30 percent of the class sit down. Tell them that this is the number of marriages that would fail within the first 5 years. Then, have 20 percent of the total number of students in the class sit down, and explain that this many more marriages will end in divorce or separation within 10 years. Ask another 20 percent of the total number of students to sit. In the end, only 30 percent of the class will be standing, and you can demonstrate for the class how high the risk of divorce is when teens marry. **L1 ELL**

National Health Education Standards
Pages 190–191: 1.2, 5.5, 5.7, 7.2

Success in Marriage

Class Activity

Your Expectations Have students answer the following questions in their health journals: How long do you believe a couple should be in a relationship prior to marriage? What are your attitudes about children and child-raising? What are your main interests? What are your positive qualities? What do you look for in a potential partner? Explain that the purpose of the exercise is to get students thinking about the issues and attitudes that affect a long-term commitment.
L2

Reading Review

1. *more than 50 percent*
2. *People who marry later in life have time to master the developmental tasks of adolescence before facing the responsibilities of marriage. Also, people who marry later in life have more maturity and life experience.*

Success in Marriage

D o you know a couple that has a long-lasting and satisfying marriage? Why do you think the couple's marriage has lasted through the years? What factors help to predict if a marriage will be long-lasting? The following discussion focuses on ten factors that might be used to predict success in marriage. Why is each factor important?

How to Predict Success in Marriage

Age Couples who marry during their teen years have a high divorce rate. Couples who marry when they are in their twenties or older usually enjoy more success. Marriage partners who are similar in age have greater success in marriage because they are at similar stages of development.

Reasons for marriage Couples who marry to love and nurture one another and to share intimacy are more likely to succeed at marriage than those who marry to escape a difficult and unhappy family situation, to hurt their parents, or to escape loneliness.

Length of the relationship and engagement Longer relationships and engagements provide the opportunity for couples to examine their relationship and to develop intimacy. Longer relationships usually are associated with success in marriage.

Similar attitudes about children and child-raising Discussing attitudes toward having and raising children contributes to a successful marriage. Couples should discuss these issues before they are married: if and when they want children, how many children they want, and how they intend to raise their children. Couples should work through any disagreement on these issues before they are married.

Similar interests Although marriages can sustain differences in interests, the old saying "opposites attract" may not apply when predicting success at marriage. Differences provide extra stressors that must be worked out.

Commitment to sexual fidelity Physical intimacy in marriage provides a closeness and a feeling of security. Sexual fidelity is important in establishing trust. Couples who honor a commitment to sexual fidelity and who trust each other are more likely to succeed at marriage.

Good character People who have good character make responsible decisions and are aware that their actions will affect their marriage.

Parents' success at marriage People whose parents are divorced are more likely to get divorced themselves. This may be because they have not lived in a family in which parents resolved conflicts and maintained their marriage.

Parental attitudes toward the potential marriage partner A marriage is more likely to succeed when a person's parents approve of the future husband or wife.

Careful selection of marriage partner A marriage is more likely to succeed when people are cautious when selecting a mate.

Reading Review

1. What percentage of teen marriages end in divorce?
2. Why does age affect the success of a marriage?

⚡ Health Project

Successful Marriage Have students conduct a survey of people who have volunteered to share information about their marriages. One requirement is that the subject considers his or her marriage to be a success. Students can canvas teachers, parents, guardians, other relatives, family friends, and neighbors. Have students ask those in the survey if they think they met each of the ten predictors of success listed on the student page. Have students summarize their findings and report to the class how often their interview subjects met the factors that predict a successful marriage. L3

National Health Education Standards
Pages 192–193: 1.2, 1.5, 2.1, 2.10, 5.5

FACTS ABOUT THE IMPORTANCE OF RESPONSIBLE PARENTING

▲ Spending time with parents every day is very important for children's and teens' development.

Like any other job, being a parent has its ups and downs. Some days, such as when a child says his or her first words, can be extremely rewarding. Other times, such as when a child is having a tantrum in the grocery store, can try a parent's patience. Being a responsible parent begins with a lifelong commitment to your child.

Parents provide children with basic survival needs, including food, medical care, and a safe environment. A parent may have help in meeting the basic needs of a child, whether it is in the form of support from other family members, advice from health-care professionals, financial assistance, or skills learned in a parenting class. Another aspect of child-rearing includes establishing positive social interaction between a parent and child. The more difficult aspects of parenting include establishing rules, setting limits, communicating with the child, and discipline. Parents influence every aspect of a child's development. They play a key role in the development of a child's self-esteem and confidence. They can teach their children to be responsible for themselves and their actions and to make responsible decisions. They help their children develop the communication and social skills that allow them to get along well with others.

What to expect Knowing what to expect during each stage of a child's growth and development can be helpful to a parent. This way a parent does not have unrealistic expectations about what a child can do, reducing some of the frustration that many parents experience. Knowing that children imitate the words and actions of those around them also can help remind parents that they are role models for their children. Children can learn respect for others, good sportsmanship, and how to handle their emotions by watching how their parents act in different situations. Providing a consistent, positive example for a child is an important aspect of parenting.

RPM3 The U.S. National Institute of Child Health and Human Development (NICHD) publishes a guideline to successful parenting that includes a five-part model called RPM3. The letters stand for Responding, Preventing, Monitoring, Mentoring, and Modeling. The RPM3 presents a comprehensive approach to the difficult job of parenting, including how to be consistent, how to help prevent problems from occurring, and how to be a responsible role model for a child.

Investigating the Issue

Visit www.glencoe.com for more information on parenting skills.

- Explain in more detail what each aspect of the RPM3 parenting model involves.
- Why is being consistent in setting and enforcing limits for a child important?
- Where can parents go if they need help with parenting skills?

Make a video showing how to childproof a home. If a video camera is not available, use a software program to make a pamphlet. Present the results of your project to your class.

FACTS ABOUT THE IMPORTANCE OF RESPONSIBLE PARENTING

Teacher FYI

Single Parents According to the U.S. Census Bureau, the percentage of children who live with two parents has been declining among all racial and ethnic groups. According to the "Families and Living Arrangements" section of the U.S. Census Bureau's annual Current Population Survey (CPS), in 2005 there were 12.9 million single parents in the U.S. Also, the number of single mothers (10.4 million) has remained relatively constant, while the number of single fathers has grown significantly over the past decade. Men now comprise one-fifth of the nation's single parents.

Investigating the Issue

- *responding to your child in an appropriate manner; preventing risky behavior or problems before they arise; monitoring your child's contact with his or her surrounding world; mentoring your child to support and encourage desired behaviors; and modeling your own behavior to provide a consistent and positive example for your child*
- *It teaches children discipline, self-respect, and to be responsible for themselves.*
- *They could go to other family members, a health-care professional, or a parenting class.*

Community Involvement

Parenting Help Have students go to a local organization that offers help for parents. Students should find out what type of assistance is offered to current or expectant parents, such as financial help, skills training, counseling, or formal parenting classes. Have students ask about the average age and marital status of the parents who seek assistance. Students should prepare a brief summary of their experience. Ask students to answer the following questions: Why is it important for a parent to have good parenting skills? Who suffers if parents do not have good parenting skills? **L-3**

Parenthood

Most teens look forward to having their driver's license. To get a driver's license, you must be a certain age, pass a written test, and pass a test for driving skills. Your driver's license indicates that you have the required knowledge and skills needed to be a responsible driver. If society requires such strict standards for those who want to drive a car, why are there no requirements for more important roles, such as supporting and caring for a child?

Before Becoming a Parent

Now, think about becoming a parent. A **_parent_** is someone who guides a child to responsible adulthood. There is no license that is required before becoming a parent. There is no written test and no test of parenting skills. Yet, being a parent is one of the most important tasks in society. How might a person prepare for parenthood? First, it is important to reach a certain age. You will be more successful as a parent if you wait until you are an adult. Being a teen parent is risky. Second, it is important to consider the three "Rs" before becoming a parent:

- The Reasons you want to have a child
- The Responsibilities you will have as a parent
- The Resources you will need to raise a child

Responsibilities of parenthood When people become parents, they take responsibility for raising a child. Whether the child is adopted or was conceived by them, there are certain promises parents should make. Parents should promise to set aside a quantity of time as well as quality time to spend with their children. They should learn about age-appropriate

Reasons People Want to Become Parents

Many times, the reasons people give for wanting to become parents center around themselves, not the best interest of a child.

To build up one's ego
- To have a child who looks like me
- To carry on the family name
- To have a child who will inherit the family business, money, or property

To compensate for something that is missing
- To improve one's marriage
- To make up for one's unhappy childhood
- To feel more secure as a male or female

To conform to what peers are doing or what others expect
- To please one's parents or guardian
- To do what one's peers are doing
- To avoid criticism for being childless

To love and guide someone
- To have the satisfaction of loving a child
- To help a child grow and develop
- To teach a child how to be responsible

Source: Adapted from Peck and Granzig, *The Parent Test,* 1978.

194 UNIT 3 • Family and Social Health

 Sensitive Issues

Teenagers in Single-Custody Homes According to the 2000 U.S. Census Bureau data, 30 percent (more than 21 million) of all children in the U.S. under 18 live with one parent. These statistics make it evident that you may have students who live in a single-custody home. When discussing responsible parenthood in class, care needs to be taken to avoid personal questions. Let students know that if they need to speak to someone, their privacy is important and will be respected by you. At the same time, have a list of trusted counselors and resources of which the student can make use.

development so that they can have realistic expectations for their children. They should teach their children rules to ensure their health and safety, and give love and affection freely. Parents should teach their children with a positive attitude, avoiding harsh criticism. They should teach their children their own moral and ethical values. They should teach self-discipline and self-control with effective discipline, not child abuse. Parents should provide economic security. They should recognize that their children have rights, and they should respect those rights. Parents should raise their children in a stable, secure family that is free from substance abuse (free from the abuse of alcohol, marijuana, and other drugs).

Resources needed for parenthood
Suppose a married couple wants to purchase a car. The cost of the car and various options for the car would be considered. If the purchase could not be financed, the decision to buy the car might have to be delayed. Financial resources also must be evaluated when a couple considers having a child. For many families, there is the additional cost of lost income during the mother's maternity leave. One of the parents may cut back to part-time work or stop working altogether after the birth of a baby. The first year of child rearing is very expensive. These financial considerations are a must when deciding if and when to become parents.

Financial costs of having a baby The financial costs of having a baby are very high. They include things you may not think about. People who are expecting a baby need to consider the

▲ Spending time with children is just as important when children are young as when they are teens.

cost of prenatal care for the mother-to-be, health and hospitalization insurance, and maternity clothes. There will be a cost for the delivery of the baby and postpartum (after the birth) care for the mother and baby in a hospital, birth center, or at home. There will be a cost for the hospitalization for the baby. Hospital and delivery fees can reach more than $10,000. If the parents do not have insurance to help cover some of this cost, they will be responsible for that bill. After the baby and mother come home from the hospital, there will be costs for pediatrician visits, well-baby checkups, required immunizations, and medications for the baby.

Parents also need to provide a safe and clean home for the baby. A baby will need a sturdy crib, bedding, linens, bathtub, stroller, high chair, chest, car seat, and toys. Parents must purchase clothing for the baby, diapers and/or diaper service, formula, food, and vitamins for the baby. Other necessary baby supplies that you might not think about are bottles, swabs, baby wipes, diaper rash ointment, tissues, powder, baby soap, and shampoo. Another very high expense to consider is the possible need for child care or day care.

LESSON 18 • Preparing for Marriage and Parenthood **195**

5-Minute Check

Page 82, **Unit 3 Fast File Resources**

1. **What are developmental tasks?** *achievements that need to be mastered to reach the next level of maturity*

2. **What is puberty?** *the stage of growth and development when both the male and female body become capable of producing offspring*

3. **Why must teens learn conflict-resolution skills?** *to learn how to settle disagreements now and when they are married*

4. **How does age affect the success of a marriage?** *Couples who marry in their twenties or older usually enjoy more success than those who marry in their teen years. Marriage partners who are similar in age have greater success in marriage because they are at similar stages of development.*

5. **What do the three "Rs" stand for as a parent?** *the reasons you want to have a child, the responsibilities you will have as a parent, and the resources you will need to raise a child*

Class Activity

The Estimated Price of Having a Child Have groups of students read the section on financial costs of having a baby. Have them research the cost of each item listed and then add them to come up with a total amount. Discuss as a class what the students found and explain that some of these items will be an expense until a child becomes an adult. **L2** **ELL**

🏠 **Family Involvement**

Decisions to Have Children Have students interview a parent, guardian, or responsible adult with children about the reasons he or she decided to have children. Have students tell the person that the questions will be very personal. Questions might include: Was it to build his or her self-esteem? Was it to fill a void in his or her life? Was he or she trying to conform to cultural or religious expectations? Did he or she want someone to love and guide? Is it a combination of factors? Students might also ask if the person planned to have children at a certain age or phase of his or her life, such as waiting until he or she owned a home. With the permission of the person who was interviewed, have the students summarize the answers and respond to their experience. **L2**

Responsible Parenting

Explain the Concept

Developing Intimacy Explain to students ways that a parent can develop intimacy with a child. Begin by listing a few ways to develop each of the four kinds of intimacy important for parents and children. An example of philosophical intimacy is to be consistent when disciplining your child. An example of emotional intimacy would be to have dinner as a family and talk about the day's joys and worries. An example of creative intimacy would be to take a class with your child and learn together. And an example of physical intimacy would be to give your child a hug.

Extension

Tips from the Media Have students browse through some magazines published for parents and select an article that interests them. Ask them to read the article and write a short summary of it, and then compare it to the information they have learned in this lesson about responsible parenting. Students also can evaluate the quality of the information in the article by using the skills they learned in Lesson 4, "Analyzing Influences on Health." **L3**

Responsible Parenting

Parenting involves more than having loving feelings for a child. Being a responsible and caring parent is not an easy task. It involves having parenting skills. Parenting skills focus on developing intimacy with a child, caring for a child as the child grows and develops, and helping a child to develop self-discipline and self-control.

What to Know About Parenting Skills

You are not ready to be a parent right now, but you can have experiences with children and practice some parenting skills. Perhaps you have a younger brother or sister, or you spend time childsitting. What might you do to learn about the following parenting skills?

Develop intimacy with a child. This lesson has focused on the reasons for becoming a parent, the resources needed, and the responsibilities involved. Developing intimacy with a child is one of the responsibilities and joys of parenting. The early lessons about intimacy that a child learns from parents influence his or her ability to become intimate with others.

Philosophical intimacy is the sharing of beliefs and values. Responsible parents teach their children beliefs and values. They discipline their children when they act in wrong ways, which helps them know how to behave. It helps them develop good character.

Emotional intimacy is the sharing of needs, emotions, weaknesses, and strengths. Responsible parents are trustworthy and accepting. Their children can talk to them about sensitive topics. Responsible parents encourage and support their children when their children have disappointments.

Creative intimacy is the sharing of efforts to accomplish tasks and projects. Responsible parents give their children their first feelings of teamwork. They ask their children to help with tasks in the home. They share fun projects.

Physical intimacy is the sharing of physical affection. Responsible parents express physical affection for children in appropriate ways. Babies who receive soft touches, are spoken to, held, and looked at frequently by the mother and father in the first few days of life, cry less and smile and laugh more than babies who are not treated in these ways. Children who

Cross-Curricular Connections

Language Arts Begin with a discussion about positive parenting. Parents and guardians are the most influential people in a child's life, and they serve as role models for a child whether their actions are positive or negative. Have students write a letter to their future children that includes a pledge of positive parenting. Give students some examples of parent pledges such as: I will set aside time to spend with you; I will give you love and affection; I will teach you rules to ensure your safety; I will recognize that you have rights, and
I will respect those rights; I will teach you with a positive attitude, avoiding criticism. Have students write their letters and then discuss some of their ideas about what positive parenting means to them. **L2**

(adapted from *Comprehensive School Health Education: Totally Awesome Strategies for Teaching Health,* by Linda Meeks, Philip Heit, and Randy Page) are loved learn to trust and to feel secure in ways of expressing affection. They are able to receive affection from others.

Care for a child as the child grows and develops. Responsible parents help their children develop emotional, social, verbal, intellectual, and motor skills by providing appropriate activities to stimulate their children's growth. They understand that age-appropriate skills help keep their children safe from harm.

They understand emotional development and reassure their children if they are fearful or anxious. They obtain medical help for their children when needed.

Help a child develop self-discipline and self-control. Responsible parents discipline their children. *Discipline* is training that develops self-discipline and self-control. *Preventive discipline* is training in which a parent explains correct behavior and the consequences of wrong behavior.

Suppose a child gets a new bicycle for his or her birthday. The parent explains his or her expectations. For example, the parent says he or she expects the child to put away the bicycle after riding it. The parent further explains that if the bicycle is not put away, the child will not be permitted to ride the bicycle for three days.

Behavior modification is a disciplinary technique in which positive rewards are used to encourage desirable behavior and negative consequences are used to stop undesirable behavior. For example, a parent might praise a child for remembering to put away his or her bicycle. The parent might plan a special reward.

◄ Teaching a child self-discipline and self-control is one of a parent's most important responsibilities.

On the other hand, the parent wants to change undesirable behavior. The child who leaves the bicycle in an unsafe place may not be permitted to ride the bicycle for three days.

Logical consequences discipline is a disciplinary technique in which the child is allowed the opportunity to experience the results of undesirable behavior so that he or she will want to change the undesirable behavior.

An example might be a child who frequently forgets to take his or her homework project to school on the day it is due. The child calls the parent and asks the parent to bring the forgotten homework to school. The parent disciplines the child by refusing to deliver the homework. The child experiences the consequences, losing points for being late with the project. As a result, the child is not as forgetful in the future.

Reading Review

1. Why is the first year of parenthood often very expensive?

2. Name some of the most important responsibilities of a parent.

Teaching Self-Discipline and Self-Control

The parents who are most effective in helping their children learn self-discipline and self-control are those who:

- set limits for their children,
- are consistent in their actions,
- are neither too strict nor too permissive,
- discuss acceptable behavior with their children,
- listen to their children and pay attention to their feelings.

LESSON 18 • Preparing for Marriage and Parenthood **197**

Class Discussion

Breaking Curfew Provide the following situation: A teen has broken curfew and twice has been late getting home. His or her parents are very angry. Have the students break into groups and answer the following questions: How can the parents use the following forms of discipline to deal with the teen's behavior: preventive discipline, behavior modification, or logical consequences discipline? Which form of discipline would be most effective and why? After the groups have discussed the issue, have a class discussion about their opinions. **L2**

Reading Review

1. *There is the cost of lost income during a mother's maternity leave, one parent may cut hours from his or her job or stop working outside the home altogether, and there are many new baby-related expenses.*

2. *developing intimacy with a child, caring for a child as the child grows and develops, and helping a child develop self-discipline and self-control*

⚖ Legal Issues

Responsible Parenting Laws and state agencies work to protect children against inadequate parenting. Explain to your students that not only is it their moral responsibility to care for their child, but their legal responsibility as well. Parents can be prosecuted, jailed, and/or have their children taken from them for not providing adequate care. Discuss with the class some situations in which a parent would lose custody of a child. Examples include not providing an environment free of drug abuse or neglecting a child's basic needs for food, clothing, or healthcare. Ask students if they think parents should be held legally responsible for such things as a crime committed by the child, a child's truancy, or a child's drug addiction. Discuss the role of parents in preventing these kinds of problems. **L2**

National Health Education Standards
Pages 196–197: 1.2, 1.5, 2.1

Teen Pregnancy

Teacher FYI

Teen Pregnancies According to the Campaign for Our Children, the children of adolescent mothers are at increased risk for dropping out of school as adolescents. Also, 50 percent of adolescents who have a baby become pregnant again within two years of the baby's birth. In 2002, 21.3 percent of all births to young women, ages 15–19, in the U.S. were repeat births.

Class Discussion

Teen Parents Ask the class to list some of the responsibilities they would have as a teen parent. As they begin to name some, make sure to fill in anything they may overlook. *Responses should include: feeding the baby many times during the day, changing as many as 10–12 diapers per day, waking up in the night to comfort and feed the baby, bathing the baby, doing laundry for the baby, and taking the baby to the doctor for well-care and in times of illness. Emphasize to students that they would have very little free time, if any, as a teen parent.* **L2**

Teen Pregnancy

D
o you usually consider the consequences of your behavior? Do you gather facts before you act? **Faulty thinking** is a thought process in which a person ignores or denies factors or believes false information. Faulty thinking is dangerous. It can lead to actions that cause you and others harm. It is a factor in teen pregnancy and parenthood.

Why Teens Become Pregnant

> **Make the Connection**
>
> **Health Advocate** For more information on becoming a health advocate who encourages teens to practice abstinence from sex to avoid teen pregnancy, see page 65 in Lesson 7.

Faulty thinking: I can have a baby now. My mother had a baby when she was a teen and she managed OK. The cycle that occurs when a teen whose mother was a teen parent becomes pregnant is the *generational cycle of teen pregnancy*. This cycle has heartbreaking consequences.

According to the Alan Guttmacher Institute, only 70 percent of teen females who have babies finish high school. The likelihood that any of these teen females will get a higher education is very slim.

As a result, the downward cycle of low income and poverty begins for a teen mother and her baby. She is less likely to marry or stay married to the baby's father than is a female who has her first baby in her twenties. By the time her baby is five years old, a teen mother is less likely to own a home or have savings in the bank than a female who waits to have a baby.

Now, suppose the teen mother has a daughter and raises her with limited financial resources, and then the daughter also becomes pregnant as a teen. The cycle of low income and poverty is perpetuated and continues from one generation to the next.

If you are female, and your mother was a teen parent, do not repeat this pattern. Your mother loves you and is glad she has you. However, if you

> ## Did You Know?
>
> **Abandonment**
> Pregnancy is a key factor in terminating relationships, as more than 85 percent of all males who impregnate a teen female will eventually abandon her.

wait until you are older to have a daughter or son to love, you are more likely to have the resources you need to raise your child. Wait to finish school, get a job, get married, and then have a baby.

Faulty thinking: I'll be the center of attention if I have a baby. Perhaps you have read about an unmarried actress who has a baby. Her pregnancy received a lot of publicity. Keep in mind that she also may have a full-time nanny, cook, and housekeeper to care for her needs and the needs of her baby. She is not frazzled and struggling to make ends meet. After all, she is rich and famous, which is a major reason she is the center of attention as an unmarried mother.

Perhaps you know a teenager who has a baby. Maybe everyone makes a fuss over the baby when the mother is around. This makes the teen mother the center of attention, but only for a brief moment. Consider what a teen mother's life is like most of the time. She must spend her time preparing formula, changing diapers, and comforting a crying baby who will not sleep. She has little, if any, social life.

The brief moments of attention you might receive if you have a baby right now are just that—brief. After the novelty wears off, you have a

 ## Achieving Health Literacy

Critical Thinker Give students the following scenario: A male classmate with a macho attitude brags he can have any girl he wants. He says he does not care if a girl gets pregnant. He says it is the girl's responsibility to avoid pregnancy. Have students explain why his thinking is irresponsible and his behavior is high-risk. Ask them to list some of the risks he is taking and what the consequences for him and for anyone he dates might be if he continues his high-risk behavior. Ask the class to think about why this teen acts the way he does. Ask students to discuss his behavior with regard to self-respect and respect for others. **L2**

baby who is depending upon you to meet his or her every need. As a teen, you have many needs of your own. You have needs to stay in school, enjoy social activities, and learn skills for a career. You can't meet those needs and also meet the needs of a baby.

Faulty thinking: I (she) won't get pregnant if it's our first time. One out of ten females becomes pregnant before the age of 20. How many of these females planned on getting pregnant? Very, very few. Every day there are teens who become pregnant who believed "it won't happen to me."

The fact is that a female can become pregnant the first time she has sex. She can become pregnant even if she is being careful. She can become pregnant even if her partner says he is being careful.

Any time sperm enter a woman's vagina, or are deposited near it, there is a chance of pregnancy. Don't be fooled by faulty thinking about how pregnancy occurs.

Don't take chances and do not allow someone else to persuade you to take chances. Being careful is not an option. Practice abstinence. When you practice abstinence, a female cannot get pregnant, and a male cannot get a female pregnant.

Faulty thinking: I can drink alcohol and still stay in control of my decisions about sex. Alcohol is a depressant drug that numbs the part of the brain that controls reasoning and judgment. The inner voice that says, "I want to practice abstinence" is dulled when you drink alcohol.

Drinking alcohol is very risky, and it is illegal for someone your age.

Drinking alcohol is especially risky when you choose abstinence and your partner is trying to pressure you to be sexually active.

Many teens who are sexually active were drinking alcohol the first time they had sex. They didn't intend to have sex. Do not drink alcohol or try to get someone to drink alcohol in order to persuade the person to have sex.

If someone wants you to drink alcohol so that your decision-making ability will be affected, recognize how little respect that person has for you. A person who does not respect you may try to use you. A person who respects you will not pressure you to do anything that you do not want to do.

Make the Connection

Pregnancy For more information on pregnancy, see page 246 in Lesson 21.

◄ Having a child to care for can interfere with your plans for the future.

Using Life Skills

Practicing Healthful Behaviors Have students read the activity and follow the instructions provided. Ask them to pretend to shop for their "child" and keep track of everything they would need to buy for their child during the week of the activity. Ask them to include this information and answer the following questions in their health journals: How much time did you spend shopping and running errands for your baby? Are you surprised at how much money you would need to care for a baby for one week? Why or why not? **L2**

Teacher FYI

U.S. Teen Pregnancy According to the National Campaign to Prevent Teen Pregnancy, although rates in the U.S. are declining, the U.S. has the highest rate of teen pregnancy in the industrialized world. In fact, the U.S. teen pregnancy rate is nearly double Canada's, at least four times that of France and Germany, and more than eight times that of Japan.

Activity: Using Life Skills

Practicing Healthful Behaviors: Egg Baby Exercise

Being a parent, especially the parent of a new baby, is a big job. Babies require constant care and attention. In this activity, you will see how much work it is to be the parent of a newborn infant by looking after an egg baby for one week. If you want to write a health behavior contract for this activity, follow these steps: 1) Write your name and the date 2) Write the healthful behavior you want to practice as a health goal 3) Write specific statements that describe how this healthful behavior reduces health risks 4) Make a specific plan for recording your progress and 5) Complete an evaluation of how the plan helped you accomplish the health goal.

1 Flip a coin to find out the sex of your baby. Let heads be female, and tails be male.

2 For your egg baby, use a fresh egg that has had the insides blown out of it. Rinse the egg thoroughly. Add a face and hair to your baby. Then, create a realistic carrier for it. Make sure the carrier is padded so the baby will be safe.

3 Be with your baby. For one week, you must never leave your baby unattended. If you must be away from your baby, "hire" a sitter. The sitter may look after the baby for no more than three hours at a time.

4 Keep a journal of your thoughts and feelings as you look after your egg baby. Think about questions like these: What would it be like to feed and diaper your baby? How would you feel if your baby cried all night the night before a test at school? How much money would you have to spend on your baby each week?

5 At the end of the week, meet in groups to discuss what life with a real baby might be like. Share excerpts from your journal.

▲ The egg baby exercise helps teens to understand the responsibility of caring for an infant.

Faulty thinking: It's up to her to set the limits; after all, "boys will be boys." For conception to occur, a sperm must fertilize an egg. In other words, it takes two to have a baby. Although the female carries the unborn child, the male also is responsible for the pregnancy. The male and female are legally and morally responsible for the baby when it is born. If you are a male, think ahead about the need a baby has for a father. The close bonding of a baby with a father helps the baby develop self-confidence. In addition to emotional support, a father helps provide financial support for his family. Do you really believe that the female is the only person responsible when pregnancy occurs? Are you aware that laws have been passed that require you to financially support a baby who is yours, even if you are still in high school and/or unemployed?

A teen male should be proud of the way he lives his life. He must value respectful relationships, the institution of marriage, and fatherhood. He must treat every female with respect. He should not see "how far he can go" sexually without weighing the risks. He must take responsibility, set limits, and practice abstinence. A teen male must recognize the significance of fatherhood. A teen male is not ready to provide the emotional and financial support that a mother and baby need.

Cross-Curricular Connections

Social Studies Have students choose another industrialized country and research teen pregnancy issues in that country. They should collect the following information: teen pregnancy statistics, organizations dedicated to controlling teen pregnancy, and any changes in teen pregnancy statistics in recent years. Have the students theorize why the country they are studying has fewer or higher numbers of teen pregnancies than the United States. Also ask students to address what role the media might play in the number of teen pregnancies in the United States and other countries. Students can share multimedia presentations on their findings with the class. **L3**

Why Teen Pregnancy Is Risky

A chance that is not worth taking after the possible outcomes are considered is an **unnecessary risk**. The possible outcomes of teen pregnancy and parenthood are included in the discussion that follows. These outcomes are reasons to choose to practice abstinence from sex to avoid the risks of teen pregnancy and parenthood.

Risks Associated with Being a Baby Born to Teen Parents

A discussion of teen pregnancy and parenthood often begins with the risks to the teen mother and father. But let's think about the baby. Teens are at risk for producing unhealthy babies. Caring and responsible people consider the effects of their behavior on others.

Low birth weight A teen female's body still is developing and maturing. For proper growth, her body needs adequate and balanced nutrition. Many teen females do not have healthful habits. Since a developing baby relies on the mother-to-be for its nutrition, whatever the mother-to-be eats, smokes, or drinks gets into the baby's bloodstream. A baby may be inadequately nourished for six to eight weeks or more before the mother-to-be knows she is pregnant. Often, pregnant teens delay getting prenatal care. Many teens do not receive any prenatal care. As a result, teen mothers are at risk for having a baby with a low birth weight. A *low birth weight* is a weight at birth that is less than 5.5 pounds. Low-birth-weight babies are more likely to have physical and mental problems than do babies of normal birth weights.

Damaged hereditary material The health habits of a teen father-to-be also affect a developing baby. The habits of the father-to-be affect the quality of the hereditary material contained in his sperm. Some substances that can damage a male's sperm are related to poor lifestyle choices, such as smoking, drinking alcohol, and taking other drugs. Lead, pesticides, benzene, and anesthetic gases also can damage sperm.

Inadequate parenting skills Parenting takes knowledge and skill. Babies born to teen parents are at risk of having parents with inadequate parenting skills. Teens are not prepared to be responsible for a child 24 hours a day. They have other responsibilities that include school, his or her social development, and other learning experiences. Having a baby in addition to those responsibilities can be overwhelming to a teen, and the baby can suffer as a result.

Did You Know?

Babies' Health The incidence of low birth weight among babies born to teens is more than double the rate for adult mothers. The death rate (within 28 days of birth) is almost 50 percent higher among babies born to teens.

LESSON 18 • Preparing for Marriage and Parenthood **201**

Why Teen Pregnancy Is Risky

Class Discussion

Teen Parenthood Ask students what their life goals are and list them on the chalkboard. Ask students how these goals can be achieved. *Answers will vary.* Ask students to consider how having a child as a teenager affects their dreams for the future. *Parenthood requires time and money.* Explain to the class that life as a teenager is full of decisions and risks. Calculated risks can affect your life somewhat, but having a child as a teenager will change your life completely. **L2**

Extension

Low Birth Weight Problems Have students look up specific information on low birth weight babies and answer the following questions: What percentage of babies born in the U.S. have low birth weight? What are the specific physical problems that low birth weight babies can have? What are the specific mental problems that low birth weight babies can have? Students should present their findings comparing normal weight children to low birth weight children in the form of charts or graphs. **L3**

Teacher to Teacher

The Rose This activity demonstrates how sexual activity can affect your emotional health. You will need a long-stemmed rose with the thorns removed. Start on one side of the room and have students pass the rose around. Each student should pull one petal from the rose. The petals will probably be gone before the rose makes one trip around the room. Draw an analogy between the loss of the petals and a person who has one sexual encounter after another. With each encounter, a person gives away part of himself or herself. Eventually the person is emotionally empty. Emphasize to your students that being emotionally empty is not a healthful state. **L1**
Denise Fountain
South Cobb High School, Austell, GA

Just the FACTS:

Pregnancy Myths Have students read each question in Just the Facts and tell whether they agree or disagree with the implications of the questions. The discussion may uncover misconceptions students have about pregnancies. **L2**

Reading Review

1. *A teenage mother is less likely to finish high school or obtain a higher education degree, which can affect whether she will be able to find a job and what her salary will be.*

2. *He is legally and morally responsible for the child. He should provide financial, as well as emotional, support.*

3 Assess

Vocabulary Practice

Page 74, **Unit 3 Fast File Resources**

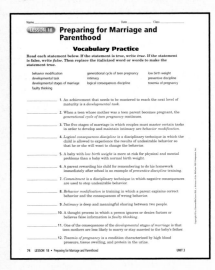

Name_____ Date_____ Class_____

LESSON 18 Preparing for Marriage and Parenthood

Vocabulary Practice

Read each statement below. If the statement is true, write *true.* If the statement is false, write *false.* Then replace the italicized word or words to make the statement true.

behavior modification
developmental task
developmental stages of marriage
faulty thinking

generational cycle of teen pregnancy
intimacy
logical consequences discipline

low birth weight
preventive discipline
toxemia of pregnancy

___ 1. An achievement that needs to be mastered to reach the next level of maturity is a *developmental task.*

___ 2. When a teen whose mother was a teen parent becomes pregnant, the *generational cycle of teen pregnancy* continues.

___ 3. The five stages of marriage in which couples must master certain tasks in order to develop and maintain intimacy are *behavior modification.*

___ 4. *Logical consequences discipline* is a disciplinary technique in which the child is allowed to experience the results of undesirable behavior so that he or she will want to change the behavior.

___ 5. A baby with *low birth weight* is more at risk for physical and mental problems than a baby with normal birth weight.

___ 6. A parent rewarding his child for remembering to do his homework immediately after school is an example of *preventive discipline* training.

___ 7. *Commitment* is a disciplinary technique in which negative consequences are used to stop undesirable behavior.

___ 8. *Behavior modification* is training in which a parent explains correct behavior and the consequences of wrong behavior.

___ 9. *Intimacy* is deep and meaningful sharing between two people.

___ 10. A thought process in which a person ignores or denies factors or believes false information is *faulty thinking.*

___ 11. One of the consequences of the *developmental stages of marriage* is that teen mothers are less likely to marry or stay married to the baby's father.

___ 12. *Toxemia of pregnancy* is a condition characterized by high blood pressure, tissue swelling, and protein in the urine.

74 LESSON 18 • Preparing for Marriage and Parenthood   UNIT 3

National Health Education Standards

Pages 202–203: 2.1, 4.4, 5.5, 8.2

Just the FACTS: PREGNANCY MYTHS

❝Isn't it her responsibility if she gets pregnant?❞

the FACTS If you father a child, that child is yours to support until he or she is at least 18, no matter how old you are. Government agencies help mothers establish the paternity (father's identity) of their children. A mother also is required to pay support if the father is raising the child. Sometimes child support is gathered by deducting it directly from the parent's paycheck. So, if she gets pregnant, it's your responsibility, too.

❝Won't he marry me if I get pregnant with his child?❞

the FACTS In 2000, more than 33 percent of all births were to unmarried mothers. When these babies were born, only one-third of the mothers were living with the baby's father and no other adult. About 51 percent of these new mothers were not living with the baby's father at all. One-third of this group of mothers lived alone with their babies.

❝She can't get pregnant if she's having her period, right?❞

the FACTS Any time sperm enter a woman's vagina, or are deposited near it, there is a possibility she could become pregnant. This is because sperm can live inside her body for several days. Since a woman has no way of knowing exactly when she has ovulated, or will ovulate again, the possibility of pregnancy exists. The only way to make sure you won't get pregnant, or get someone pregnant, is to avoid having sexual relations.

Risks Associated with Being Teen Parents

For females Pregnancy places many demands on a female's body. The demands on a female who is a teen are even greater because her body is still growing. A pregnant teen is at risk for developing anemia and toxemia of pregnancy. ***Anemia*** is a condition in which the oxygen-carrying pigment in the blood is below normal. If the pregnant teen is anemic, the developing baby will be seriously affected because the baby depends on the mother's blood for oxygen and nutrients. ***Toxemia of pregnancy*** is a disorder of pregnancy characterized by high blood pressure, tissue swelling, and protein in the urine. If severe, toxemia of pregnancy can progress to seizures and coma.

Pregnant teens and teen mothers are at risk in other ways. Pregnancy and parenthood disrupt education and career plans. Dating opportunities are limited for a teen raising a child. She does not have as much time or money as her peers.

For males Teen fathers have the responsibility of providing for the care of their babies. Some states have passed laws that require teen fathers to pay child support until their child is 18. They are less likely to graduate from high school or college than their peers who did not become fathers when they were teens.

Teen fathers usually do not marry the mother of their children. As a result, teen fathers often spend little time with their children. Children do not thrive as well when there is a lack of contact with their father. Fathers also can feel the emptiness of not being close to their children.

Reading Review

1. Why is the generational cycle of teen pregnancy linked to low income and poverty?

2. In what ways is a male teen responsible for a baby he helps conceive?

202 UNIT 3 • Family and Social Health

Achieving Health Literacy

Critical Thinker Have students write down the following information on a piece of paper: They are 30 years old and are successful. Next, have them outline their success by writing down their marital status, the number of children they have, the education and training they have completed, jobs that they have had, their income, hobbies and leisure activities, and awards and recognitions they have received. Finally, have them cross out items on their outline that would not be a reality if they became a teen parent. Have students express their reactions to the loss of life goals. **L2**

LESSON 18 STUDY GUIDE

behavior
    modification
commitment
developmental
    stages of
    marriage
developmental task
faulty thinking
generational cycle of
    teen pregnancy
intimacy
logical consequences
    discipline
low birth weight
parent
preventive discipline
toxemia of
    pregnancy

Key Terms Review

Complete these fill-in-the-blank statements with the lesson Key Terms on the left. Do not write in this book.

1. The _____ are five stages of marriage in which couples must master certain tasks to develop and maintain intimacy.

2. _____ is a disciplinary technique in which negative consequences are used to stop undesirable behavior.

3. _____ is a deep and meaningful kind of sharing between two people.

4. A(n) _____ is a weight at birth that is less than 5.5 pounds.

5. _____ is a disciplinary technique in which the child is allowed to experience the results of undesirable behavior.

6. _____ is a thought process in which a person ignores or denies factors or believes false information.

7. A(n) _____ is an achievement needed to reach the next level of maturity.

8. _____ is training in which a parent explains correct behavior and the consequences of wrong behavior.

9. _____ is a disorder of pregnancy characterized by high blood pressure, tissue swelling, and protein in the urine.

10. The _____ occurs when a teen whose mother was a teen parent becomes pregnant.

Recalling the Facts

11. What are four kinds of intimacy in marriage?

12. What are ten factors that can be used to predict success in marriage?

13. What are two ways that marriage partners can ensure that their marriage will last?

14. What are the three "Rs" to consider before becoming a parent?

15. What are three skills needed for responsible parenthood?

16. What are five examples of faulty thinking that can lead to teen pregnancy?

17. What are the risks associated with being born to teen parents?

18. What are the risks for a teen father?

Critical Thinking

19. Why are wedding vows important to a married couple?

20. Using the information in this lesson, distinguish between a dating relationship and a marriage.

21. Analyze how abstinence promotes emotional health and the prevention of pregnancy.

22. How does behavior modification differ from logical consequences discipline?

Real-Life Applications

23. How do you think a person would feel if his or her spouse was not sexually faithful?

24. Does a mother or a father have more responsibility for their baby? Explain.

25. How would your life be different if you were the parent of a six-month-old baby?

26. Name some things you would have to do without if you were a teen parent.

Activities

Responsible Decision Making

27. **Role-Play** Suppose a classmate tells you she wants to get pregnant and have a baby. Her boyfriend just told her he wants to date others, and she thinks getting pregnant will help her keep him. Role-play the situation with a classmate. Refer to the Responsible Decision-Making Model on page 61 for help.

Sharpen Your Life Skills

28. **Access Health Information** Laws have been passed to require fathers to pay child support for their children who are under 18 years of age, even if the fathers are still in high school and/or are unemployed. Research the child support laws of the community where you live.

Visit **www.glencoe.com** for more *Health & Wellness* quizzes.

LESSON 18 • Study Guide 203

LESSON 18 STUDY GUIDE

Key Terms Review

1. developmental stages of marriage
2. Behavior modification
3. Intimacy
4. low birth weight
5. Logical consequences discipline
6. Faulty thinking
7. developmental task
8. Preventive discipline
9. Toxemia of pregnancy
10. generational cycle of teen pregnancy

Recalling the Facts

11. philosophical, emotional, creative, and physical
12. See page 192.
13. honor their wedding vows, and work together to master the developmental stages of marriage.
14. reasons, responsibilities, and resources
15. developing intimacy with a child; caring for a child; and teaching discipline and self-control
16. See pages 198–200.
17. If the mother doesn't have adequate prenatal care, the baby may have a low birth weight; the father's health habits may affect the quality of his hereditary material; and the parents may have poor parenting skills.
18. See page 202.

Critical Thinking

19. Vows show that each person is promising fidelity and support to the other.
20. A dating relationship does not require the serious commitment that a marriage does.
21. Abstinence from sex protects you from emotional trauma and from feeling used and prevents pregnancy.
22. Behavior modification rewards desirable behavior and punishes undesirable behavior. Logical consequences discipline allows a person to experience the results of undesirable behavior so that he or she will want to change behavior.

Real-Life Applications

23. betrayed, helpless, lack of confidence, angry, jealous, unloved
24. Both parents are equally responsible, emotionally and financially, for their baby.
25. The baby's needs would come before your own. You would have very little free time.
26. Answers should include a social life and disposable income.

Activities

Responsible Decision Making

27. This is faulty thinking. A person who doesn't want to date you will not want to marry you and care for a baby.

Sharpen Your Life Skills

28. Have students report on some of the problems facing your community regarding the enforcement of these laws.

203

UNIT 3
STUDY GUIDE

Key Terms Review

1. e	6. h
2. c	7. i
3. d	8. j
4. f	9. k
5. b	10. g

Recalling the Facts

11. self-respecting behavior, to value the needs of others, healthful attitudes toward sexuality, healthful sex roles, effective communication skills, a clear sense of values, responsible decision making, how to resolve conflicts, effective coping skills, how to delay gratification, how to express affection and integrate love and sexuality, how to give and receive acts of kindness, a work ethic, respect for authority

12. chemical dependence, other addictions, perfectionism, violence, abuse, abandonment, and mental disorders

13. change in family rules, changes in budget and guidelines for spending money, changes in family relationships

14. talking about yourself only, appearing disinterested in what someone else is saying, interrupting someone, changing the topic, being a know-it-all, avoiding eye contact, talking about others, and complaining

15. Give your parents or guardian background information on the person with whom you will have a date, tell your parents or guardian your exact plans, arrange for safe transportation, establish a reasonable curfew time, establish your code of conduct, establish the expected code of conduct for the person you date.

16. Limit your expressions of affection to holding hands, hugging, and casual kissing; tell a person your limits before expressing affection; do not date someone who does not respect your limits for expressing physical affection; avoid drinking alcohol and using other drugs; do not date someone who drinks alcohol or uses other drugs; and stay in public places when on a date.

17. See pages 172–173.

18. See page 184.

19. See page 192.

20. the reasons you want to have a child, the resources you will need to raise a child, and the responsibilities you will have as a parent.

Critical Thinking

21. Children need a good example to learn good values.

22. self-respect, a good reputation, tenacity, and a sense of accomplishment

23. Children who don't have both parents in their lives may not experience the benefits of having both female and male role models.

24. Communication can help clear up any misunderstandings and can help you to feel more confident.

25. Yes, because he or she seeks to please others, but doesn't feel worthy of others pleasing him or her.

26. It can result in others treating you unfairly in school, at home, or in your community.

UNIT 3
STUDY GUIDE

Key Terms Review

Match the following definitions with the correct lesson Key Terms below. Do not write in this book.

a. abstinence from sex *(p. 166)*
b. dating *(p. 160)*
c. enabler *(p. 179)*
d. family *(p. 135)*
e. grandparents' rights *(p. 150)*
f. intimacy *(p. 187)*
g. legal age of consent *(p. 169)*
h. low birth weight *(p. 201)*
i. one-sided friendship *(p. 164)*
j. people pleaser *(p. 179)*
k. reputation *(p. 169)*
l. sexual fidelity *(p. 169)*

1. the visitation rights with grandchildren that courts have awarded grandparents
2. a person who supports the harmful behavior of others
3. the basic unit of society
4. a deep and meaningful sharing between two people
5. having social plans with a person in whom you are interested
6. a weight at birth that is less than 5.5 pounds
7. a friendship in which one person does most of the giving
8. a person who constantly seeks the approval of others
9. a person's overall character as judged by others
10. the age when a person is legally able to give permission for sexual contact

Recalling the Facts

11. What are 14 skills children learn and practice in healthful families? *(Lesson 13)*
12. What are seven causes of dysfunctional family relationships? *(Lesson 13)*
13. How might having a stepfamily affect teens? *(Lesson 14)*
14. What are "Conversation Killers" that discourage good conversation? *(Lesson 15)*
15. What are six dating guidelines to discuss with your parents or guardian? *(Lesson 15)*
16. What are six guidelines to help you set limits for expressing physical affection? *(Lesson 16)*
17. What are eight resistance skills to use if you are pressured to be sexually active? *(Lesson 16)*
18. What are six steps to take to end or change a harmful relationship? *(Lesson 17)*
19. What are ten factors that can be used to predict success in marriage? *(Lesson 18)*
20. What are the three "R's" to consider before becoming a parent? *(Lesson 18)*

Critical Thinking

21. Why is it important for parents or guardians to teach values to their children? *(Lesson 13)*
22. What are the benefits of a strong work ethic? *(Lesson 13)*
23. Why is it important for a teen to seek out a mentor or positive role model if he or she does not see one of his or her parents very often due to divorce? *(Lesson 14)*
24. Why is it healthful to talk about the situation if you feel rejected by someone? *(Lesson 15)*
25. Is a people pleaser likely to have low self-esteem? Why or why not? *(Lesson 15)*
26. How might having a bad reputation limit a teen's opportunities? *(Lesson 16)*
27. How are sexual fidelity and trust linked within a marriage? *(Lesson 16)*
28. Name the benefits of watching television characters who relate in healthful ways. *(Lesson 17)*
29. Why is it important for children to learn about emotional intimacy? *(Lesson 18)*
30. How might a parent or guardian use logical consequences discipline (other than the ways explained in the text) to get a child to change wrong actions? *(Lesson 18)*

Use **Interactive Tutor** at **www.glencoe.com** for additional help.

Health Literacy Activities

 What Do You Know?
Problem Solving Write several factual questions about teen pregnancy and teen marriage that are intended to stump the class. Form teams with classmates and compete by answering the other teams' questions. Tabulate the correct answers to determine the winner.

 Connection to Language Arts
Self-Directed Learning Select a book on relationship skills (love, friendship, dating, marriage, parenthood, harmful relationships, codependence, or family changes). Select a book written by a person with professional credentials. Read the book and write a review of it.

Family Involvement
Critical Thinking Interview a parent, guardian, or other adult who has a satisfying marriage. Ask this person about the elements of a successful marriage. Compare these factors with the factors identified in this unit. Write a paper in which you describe the factors you believe to be most important.

Investigating Health Careers
Responsible Citizenship Research a career of interest to you that has to do with helping families. Then prepare an index card titled "What's My Career?" On one side of the index card, write three facts pertaining to the career you investigated. On the other side of the card, write the name of the career. The class will play "What's My Career?" and try to guess the career you selected based on the three facts.

Group Project
Effective Communication Form a group with classmates. Design a pamphlet that includes information on practicing abstinence from sex. Discuss reasons why abstinence is a responsible decision. Identify lines teens might use to pressure other teens to become sexually active. If possible, use a computer to design your pamphlet. Create a graphic for the cover of the pamphlet. Visit www.glencoe.com for more information.

27. Sexual fidelity in marriage is a way of demonstrating the love and trust that each person pledged to the other in their vows of marriage.
28. You might copy the behavior of the television characters who have healthful ways of relating. This would have a positive effect on your relationships.
29. Children will feel comfortable coming to parents with serious problems and questions as they grow and mature
30. Answers will vary, but should provide an example such as not replacing a dessert if it falls on the floor because the child was playing with it.

Health Literacy Activities

What Do You Know?
Students should choose questions on such topics as statistics on teen sex and pregnancy and marriage and divorce rates.

Connection to Language Arts
Students can select a book on a topic related to any of the lessons in this unit. You might want to have them get into small groups to share their critiques. The members of the small groups might then discuss what they found most interesting about each book presented.

Family Involvement
Students can ask this person about the ten factors that predict success in marriage and report on if they match this person's experience. Have students share their findings.

Investigating Health Careers
Students should choose careers that relate to helping families on a daily basis: nurse, doctor, psychologist, counselor, social worker, teacher, day-care worker.

Group Project
Have students review the What You'll Learn in Lesson 16. Have them try to cover as many of the objectives as possible. Ask them with whom they might share this pamphlet. Explain that sharing this pamphlet with others is using health advocacy skills.

Standardized Test Practice

Read the following selection and answer the questions that follow.

Reading & Writing

Marriage is an important institution to most peoples of the world. A common thread is that marriage is approved by law and by the society, and involves some kind of ceremony. However, customs and traditions can vary among different cultures. For example, in some societies that have little contact with other groups of people, it is expected that young people marry someone from his or her own tribe or group. This practice is called *endogamy*. The opposite practice, *exogamy*, expects people to marry outside the group to avoid the danger of marrying a close relative. Another difference lies in how mates are chosen. In some societies, marriages are arranged by parents or extended family members. In other societies young people choose their own marriage partners.

 www.glencoe.com

Multiple Choice

1 What kind of pattern does the writer use to organize the information in the paragraph?
A main idea and supporting details
B chronological order, from oldest to most recent
C geographical order, from nearest to farthest away
D comparing and contrasting

2 According to this paragraph, which of these statements is true?
A Most societies practice endogamy.
B Americans have very different ideas about marriage.
C Most societies share the idea that marriage is approved by law and involves a kind of ceremony.
D Exogamy is the more successful marriage model.

Open-Ended

3 The paragraph discusses exogamy and endogamy. Write a paragraph about the risks and the benefits of marrying within a small group or outside a small group.

UNIT 3 • Study Guide 205

Standardized Test Practice

Reading & Writing

Multiple Choice
1. D   2. C

Open-Ended
3. Students' paragraphs should discuss the risks and benefits of endogamy and exogamy. For example, endogamy could be dangerous because the group would not have a large gene pool. However, a group might find security in practicing endogamy, since they would not have to merge with other groups. Paragraphs should contain correct spelling, capitalization, punctuation, grammar, usage, and sentence structure.

Growth and Development

UNIT 4 ORGANIZER

STANDARDS AND FEATURES

Lesson	National Standards	State/Local Standards	Activities and Features
Lesson 19 *(4 sessions, 1 block)* Keeping Your Body Healthy	1.5		**Facts About:** Heart Disease, p. 211
Lesson 20 *(3 sessions, 1 block)* Learning About the Reproductive Systems	1.5, 6.1		**Just the Facts:** Reproductive Systems, p. 229 **Using Life Skills:** Practice Healthful Behaviors: Performing Breast Self-Exams, p. 233 **Using Life Skills:** Practice Healthful Behaviors: Performing Testicular Self-Exams, p. 239
Lesson 21 *(2 sessions, 1 block)* Learning About Pregnancy and Childbirth	1.1, 1.4, 1.5, 1.6, 1.9, 2.10, 3.3, 3.4, 8.1		**Using Life Skills:** Accessing Valid Health Information, Products, and Services: Research a Pregnancy Topic, p. 249
Lesson 22 *(1 session, 1 block)* Caring for Infants and Children	1.5, 3.5, 4.1, 7.1, 7.2		**Speaking Out:** Childsitting, p. 260
Lesson 23 *(1 session, 1 block)* Developing Learning and Planning Styles	7.1, 7.2		**Health News:** Maslow's Theory of Human Development, p. 267
Lesson 24 *(2 sessions, 1 block)* Aging Healthfully	7.1, 7.2		**Using Life Skills:** Advocating for Health: Volunteering to Help Older Adults, p. 273

Key to Differentiated Instruction

L1 Level 1 activities should be appropriate for students with learning difficulties.

L2 Level 2 activities should be within the ability range of all students.

L3 Level 3 activities are designed for above-average students.

ELL ELL activities should be within the ability range of English language learners.

FAST FILE RESOURCES

INTRODUCING THE UNIT

Parent and Family Letter	p. 1	Health Behavior Contract	p. 3
Spanish Parent and Family Letter	p. 2	Unit Focus Transparency Master and Worksheet	p. 4

TEACHING THE UNIT LESSONS

Reproducible Student Pages	Lesson 19	Lesson 20	Lesson 21	Lesson 22	Lesson 23	Lesson 24
Reading Strategy	p. 7	p. 21	p. 35	p. 47	p. 59	p. 71
Vocabulary Practice	p. 8	p. 22	p. 36	p. 48	p. 60	p. 72
Transparency Master and Worksheet	p. 9	p. 23	p. 37	p. 49	p. 61	p. 73
Real-Life Health	p. 11	p. 25	p. 39	p. 51	p. 63	p. 75
5-Minute Check	p. 15	p. 29	p. 43	p. 55	p. 67	p. 79
Lesson Quiz	p. 17	p. 32	p. 44	p. 56	p. 68	p. 81

CLOSING THE UNIT

Family Involvement Activity	p. 85	Health in the News	p. 95
Community Involvement Activity	p. 87	Health Career Research Activity	p. 97
Health Lab	p. 89	Unit Test A	p. 99
Activity: Strengthening Health Skills	p. 93	Unit Test B	p. 103

Glencoe Exclusive!

TeacherWorks™
All-In-One Planner and Resource Center

Technology

- **Interactive Chalkboard CD-ROM**
- **TeacherWorks™ CD-ROM**
- **StudentWorks™ CD-ROM**
- **Reading Essentials CD-ROM**
- **ExamView® Assessment Suite**

www.glencoe.com
- **Vocabulary Puzzlemaker**
- **Interactive Tutor**
- **Your Health Checklist**
- **Web Links**
- **Student Web Activities**

TEST YOUR GROWTH IQ

Use the three statements on the student page to initiate a class discussion about healthful growth and development. *Additional True/False statements are:*

4. **All teens go through puberty at the same time.**
   FALSE: Girls will begin to notice changes between the ages of 8 and 15 and boys between the ages of 12 and 15.

5. **A female's missed period always means she is pregnant.**
   FALSE: A missed period does not always indicate a pregnancy. A female may skip a period because of stress, diet, physical activity, or illness.

6. **Many teen fathers will not graduate from high school.**
   TRUE: Many states have passed laws requiring teen fathers to pay child support, so teen fathers often will drop out of school to earn money to support their children.

in the news Talented Teens

Compare and Contrast Ask students what they think Maya Angelou's statement means. Discuss with students a list of teens who are well-known for a particular talent. Then, ask what things they may have in common and what things may be different. **L2**

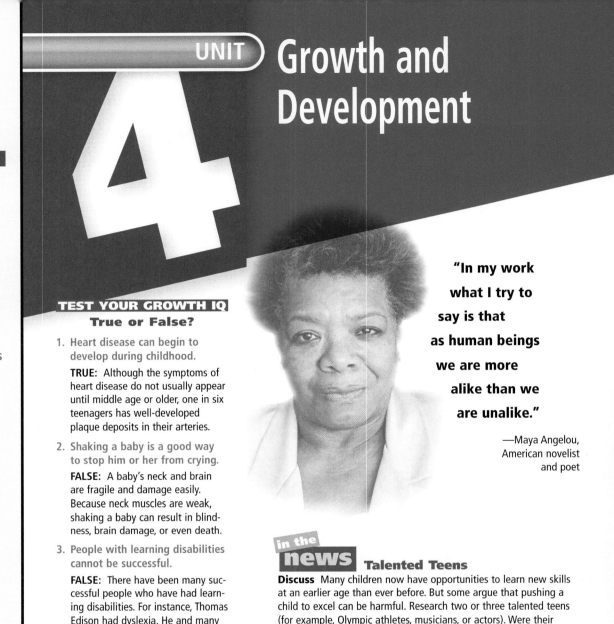

UNIT 4 Growth and Development

TEST YOUR GROWTH IQ
True or False?

1. **Heart disease can begin to develop during childhood.**
   TRUE: Although the symptoms of heart disease do not usually appear until middle age or older, one in six teenagers has well-developed plaque deposits in their arteries.

2. **Shaking a baby is a good way to stop him or her from crying.**
   FALSE: A baby's neck and brain are fragile and damage easily. Because neck muscles are weak, shaking a baby can result in blindness, brain damage, or even death.

3. **People with learning disabilities cannot be successful.**
   FALSE: There have been many successful people who have had learning disabilities. For instance, Thomas Edison had dyslexia. He and many others had significant accomplishments despite their disabilities.

> "In my work what I try to say is that as human beings we are more alike than we are unalike."
>
> —Maya Angelou, American novelist and poet

in the news Talented Teens

Discuss Many children now have opportunities to learn new skills at an earlier age than ever before. But some argue that pushing a child to excel can be harmful. Research two or three talented teens (for example, Olympic athletes, musicians, or actors). Were their opportunities positive or negative, or a combination of both? Discuss your findings with your class as part of an oral report.

LESSON 19	**LESSON 20**	**LESSON 21**
Keeping Your Body Healthy	Learning About the Reproductive Systems	Learning About Pregnancy and Childbirth

206 UNIT 4 • Growth and Development

 Two-Minute Unit Launcher

Discussion Ask students to discuss television or movie depictions of adolescents or teen characters in books that they have read. Have students explain what positive and negative experiences that adolescents may have during puberty were depicted or described. Ask students if they think it is harder to be a teen in today's society than it was when their parents or grandparents were teenagers, and if so, why. Ask students what kinds of things they wish were different. Discuss with students how their bodies change over time and the importance of thinking about the future of their body systems. **L2**

EVALUATING MEDIA MESSAGES

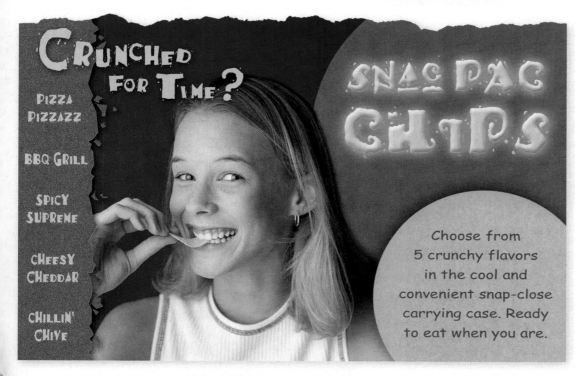

CRUNCHED FOR TIME?

PIZZA PIZZAZZ

BBQ GRILL

SPICY SUPREME

CHEESY CHEDDAR

CHILLIN' CHIVE

SNAC PAC CHIPS

Choose from 5 crunchy flavors in the cool and convenient snap-close carrying case. Ready to eat when you are.

 WHAT'S YOUR VERDICT?
To evaluate this advertisement, use the criteria for analyzing and evaluating health messages delivered through media and technology that you learned in Unit 1.

Visit www.glencoe.com to find regularly updated statistics on U.S. life expectancy. Using the information provided, determine the answer to this question: How has U.S. life expectancy changed in the last 50 years?

Visit www.glencoe.com to use *Your Health Checklist* ✔, an interactive tool that helps you determine your health status.

LESSON 22
Caring for Infants and Children

LESSON 23
Developing Learning and Planning Styles

LESSON 24
Aging Healthfully

Health Online

Answers According to the Centers for Disease Control and Prevention (CDC), life expectancy in the United States has increased by approximately 8 years over the last 50 years. The increase has occurred for both sexes and for different races. The increase in life expectancy has been somewhat greater for African-Americans (approximately 10 years) than for Caucasians (7 to 8 years). Despite the bigger increase for African-Americans, life expectancy is still almost 6 years longer for Caucasians than for African-Americans in this country.

 What's Your Verdict?

Ads Food items are advertised on television and in magazines. Have students bring in an advertisement about one of their favorite foods. Have each student present his or her ad to the class, stating what he or she thinks the advertisement is trying to say. Ask students in the class to provide feedback to see if they feel the same way. Have students determine whether any of the ads attempt to manipulate students to eat unhealthful foods. Ask students to look back at Lesson 4 for information about the ten advertising appeals. **L2**

Health Journal

Write an Essay Have each student choose a life skill he or she is interested in making a permanent part of his or her life. Ask each of them to write an essay in his or her health journal about why he or she thinks it is so important and how it will help improve his or her health status. **L2**

INTERACTIVE CHALKBOARD
with Image Bank

Unit Focus Transparency
Page 4, **Unit 4 Fast File Resources**

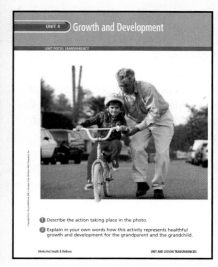

UNIT 4 Growth and Development

UNIT FOCUS TRANSPARENCY

❶ Describe the action taking place in the photo.
❷ Explain in your own words how this activity represents healthful growth and development for the grandparent and the grandchild.

Meeks Heit Health & Wellness   UNIT AND LESSON TRANSPARENCIES

National Health Education Standards
Pages 206–207: 1.1, 2.5, 2.6, 3.1

Keeping Your Body Healthy

Out of Time?

If time does not permit an in-depth study of this topic, use the following activities in this Teacher Wraparound Edition:
- Health Goal, p. 208
- Family Involvement, p. 211
- Class Discussion, p. 214
- Class Activity, p. 222

1 Focus

HEALTH GOAL **Healthy Body Systems** Have students respond to the Health Goal for this lesson by discussing choices they can make to keep their bodies healthy. *Answers may vary, but should include diet, exercise, and avoiding risk behaviors.* **L2**

Write ABOUT IT!

Journaling After students read about the muscular system, have them write in their health journals what they know about the importance of a warm-up before exercising. Have small groups discuss how they would respond to their friend's decision and how they would try to convince him or her of the importance of stretching. **L2**

LESSON 19

What You'll Learn

1. Identify behaviors to keep your cardiovascular, nervous, and immune systems healthy. *(pp. 210, 213, 214)*
2. List behaviors important to the health of your respiratory, skeletal, and muscular systems. *(pp. 215, 216, 217)*
3. Identify behaviors important to the health of your endocrine and digestive systems. *(pp. 219, 221)*
4. List behaviors important to the health of your integumentary and urinary systems. *(pp. 223, 224)*

Why It's Important

Think about a car. Many parts need to work together to keep it running well. Your body also has many parts that make up your body systems, which need to work together to keep you well.

Key Terms

- cardiovascular system
- nervous system
- immune system
- respiratory system
- skeletal system
- muscular system
- endocrine system
- digestive system
- integumentary system
- urinary system

Keeping Your Body Healthy

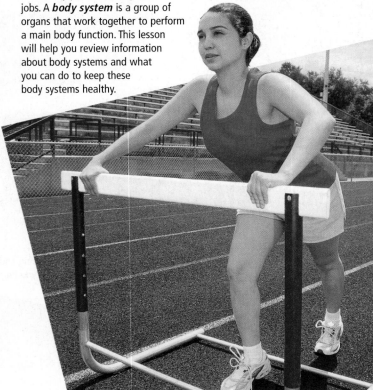

HEALTH GOAL • **I will keep my body systems healthy.**

Your body is made of cells, tissues, and organs that form body systems. A *cell* is the smallest living part of the body. An *organ* is a body part consisting of several kinds of tissue that do particular jobs. A *body system* is a group of organs that work together to perform a main body function. This lesson will help you review information about body systems and what you can do to keep these body systems healthy.

Write ABOUT IT!

Writing About Stretching Suppose one of your friends says she is not going to warm up and stretch before the big track meet. She says that warming up wastes valuable energy that she could use for running. After you read the information on the muscular system on page 217, write a response to this situation in your health journal.

National Health Education Standards—Guide for Lesson 19		
1.5	Propose ways to reduce or prevent injuries and health problems.	pp. 208, 210, 213, 215, 217, 219, 221, 223, 224, 225

The Cardiovascular System

The body system that transports nutrients, gases, hormones, and cellular waste products throughout the body is the **cardiovascular system.** The cardiovascular system consists of the blood, blood vessels, and the heart.

What to Know About the Cardiovascular System

Blood Your blood carries nutrients, oxygen, carbon dioxide, and cellular waste products to and from your body cells. The average-sized adult body has about ten pints of blood. Blood is composed of plasma and blood cells. **Plasma** is the liquid component of blood that carries blood cells and dissolved materials. It is about 95 percent water. Plasma contains two major types of blood cells—red blood cells and white blood cells. Plasma also consists of particles called platelets. A **platelet** is a particle that helps the blood clot. Blood clots stop the bleeding when blood vessels are injured.

A **red blood cell** transports oxygen to body cells and removes carbon dioxide from body cells. Red blood cells contain hemoglobin. **Hemoglobin** is an iron-rich protein that helps transport oxygen and carbon dioxide in the blood. New red blood cells are constantly produced in bone marrow, which is the spongy material inside some bones.

A **white blood cell** is a blood cell that attacks, surrounds, and destroys pathogens that enter the body and prevents them from causing infection.

A **pathogen** is a germ that causes disease. The number of white blood cells in your blood increases when you have an infection.

Blood vessels There are three major types of blood vessels—arteries, veins, and capillaries. An **artery** is a blood vessel that carries blood away from the heart. Arteries have thick muscular walls that move blood between heartbeats. A **coronary artery** supplies nutrients and oxygen to the heart muscle. A **pulmonary artery** carries blood from the heart to the lungs, where it absorbs oxygen and releases carbon dioxide.

Vein
Artery
Heart

► The cardiovascular system consists of blood, arteries, veins, and the heart.

LESSON 19 • Keeping Your Body Healthy **209**

Lesson Resource Manager

- **Unit 4 Fast File Resources**
  Reading Strategy, p. 7
  Vocabulary Practice, p. 8
  Transparency Master and Worksheet, p. 9
  Real-Life Health, p. 11
  Real-Life Health, p. 13
  5-Minute Check, p. 15
  Lesson 19 Quiz, p. 17
- **Unit 4 Transparency**
- **Lesson 19 Transparency**

- **Reading Essentials**
- **Technology**
  TeacherWorks™ CD-ROM
  StudentWorks™ CD-ROM
  Reading Essentials CD-ROM
  ExamView® Assessment Suite
  Vocabulary Puzzlemaker

The Cardiovascular System

2 Teach

Teacher FYI

Anemia Anemia is a condition in which the amount of hemoglobin in the body, and the number of red blood cells that carry it, fall below normal. This causes the body to get less oxygen, which can lead to feelings of fatigue, weakness, loss of concentration, and dizziness, as well as more serious symptoms. Anemia can affect anyone, but people with kidney disease, diabetes, cancer, heart disease, rheumatoid arthritis, and inflammatory bowel disease are at the highest risk.

INTERACTIVE CHALKBOARD with Image Bank

PowerPoint® Presentations

This CD-ROM is an editable Microsoft® PowerPoint® presentation that includes:
- Lesson presentations
- Lesson checks
- Interactive graphics
- 5-Minute Checks
- Image Bank
- All transparencies

Note Taking Refer to the Two-Column Notes: Main Idea-Detail Strategy on page 16T and ask students to list the body systems in the left-hand column and list the components of each system in the right-hand column.

National Health Education Standards
Pages 208–209: 1.5

209

1. What is the function of blood? *It carries nutrients, oxygen, carbon dioxide, and cellular waste to and from body cells.*

2. What is a red blood cell? *It transports oxygen to and removes carbon dioxide from body cells.*

3. What is the function of a white blood cell? *It attacks, surrounds, and destroys pathogens and prevents them from causing infection.*

4. What are important differences between the three major types of blood vessels? *Arteries carry blood away from the heart and have thick walls, veins return blood to the heart and have thinner walls, and capillaries connect veins and arteries and have thin walls that allow transfer of oxygen, carbon dioxide, and waste.*

5. How does oxygen get into the blood? *Carbon dioxide is released and oxygen is absorbed as blood circulates in capillaries around the air sacs in the lungs.*

Reading Review

1. *blood, blood vessels, and heart (see pages 209–210)*
2. *the force of blood against the artery walls*

Teaching Transparency

Page 9, **Unit 4 Fast File Resources**

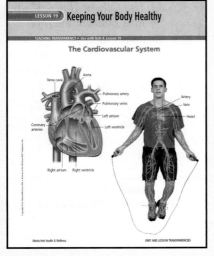

LESSON 19 **Keeping Your Body Healthy**

The Cardiovascular System

Aorta
Vena cava
Coronary arteries
Right atrium
Right ventricle

Pulmonary artery
Pulmonary veins
Left atrium
Left ventricle

Blood is pumped ▶ from the right ventricle of the heart through the pulmonary artery to the lungs.

Reading Review

1. Name and describe the parts of the cardiovascular system.

2. What is blood pressure?

A **vein** is a blood vessel that returns blood to the heart. Veins have thinner walls than arteries. A **capillary** is a tiny blood vessel that connects arteries and veins. Capillaries have thin walls that allow the transfer of nutrients, oxygen, carbon dioxide, and cellular waste between the blood and the body cells.

Heart A four-chambered muscle that continually pumps blood throughout the body is called the **heart.** The two upper chambers are **atria.** The two lower chambers are **ventricles.** The heart is divided into the right atrium and ventricle and the left atrium and ventricle. Blood that is poor in oxygen, returning from the body, flows constantly into the right atrium and ventricle.

From the right ventricle, blood is pumped through the pulmonary artery to the lungs. Carbon dioxide is released and oxygen is absorbed as the blood circulates in capillaries around the air sacs in the lungs. This oxygen-rich blood flows into the left atrium and ventricle. Contractions of the left ventricle pump the blood through the aorta to the body. The **aorta** is the main artery in the body. The aorta branches into smaller arteries through which blood flows to all parts of the body.

Heart rate is the number of times the heart contracts each minute. **Pulse** is the surge of blood that results from the contractions of the heart. **Blood pressure** is the force of blood against the artery walls.

How to Keep Your Cardiovascular System Healthy

The following are some of the ways you can keep your cardiovascular system healthy:

- Reduce the amount of fat in your diet.
- Reduce the amount of salt in your diet.
- Exercise regularly to strengthen your heart muscles.
- Avoid using tobacco products because they increase blood pressure.
- Maintain a healthful weight.
- Practice stress-management skills

210   UNIT 4 • Growth and Development

 Healthy People 2010

Objective 19-10 *Increase the proportion of persons age 2 years and older who consume 2400 mg or less of sodium daily.*

Presently, 21 percent of people age 2 years and older consume 2400 mg or less of sodium daily, and the Healthy People 2010 target is 65 percent. Have students record their daily sodium intake using the sodium listing in the nutrition facts panel on the labels of food that they eat. They also can ask for nutrition information at restaurants. Then have students list ideas that would help them and others decrease the amount of sodium they consume. If sodium information is not available for a certain food they consume, students should make an estimate. Discuss with students the relationship between sodium, high blood pressure, and cardiovascular disease. **L2**

FACTSABOUT HEART DISEASE

The most common type of heart disease is coronary heart disease, also referred to as coronary artery disease (CAD). There are two coronary arteries that branch from either side of the ascending aorta at the top of the heart. The coronary arteries are the vessels that supply the heart muscle with oxygenated blood.

With age, these arteries, which are normally elastic, harden and lose their elasticity. This condition is known as arteriosclerosis (ar TEER ee o skluh ROH suhs). A form of arteriosclerosis, called atherosclerosis (a thuh roh skluh ROH suhs), involves the buildup of deposits within the coronary arteries.

As these deposits accumulate on the interior walls of these vessels, the diameter of the arteries decreases, restricting and blocking the flow of blood to the heart muscle. The effects of atherosclerosis on the coronary arteries results in CAD.

Cholesterol Excess cholesterol, which comes from foods we ingest, also is deposited in arteries. Although some cholesterol is needed by the body to make cell membranes and some hormones, it is needed only in small amounts.

As the flow of blood to the heart is restricted, the heart's ability to pump effectively is reduced. This can lead to a condition called angina (an JI nuh), in which a person may feel pain in the chest, left shoulder, and left arm. Angina also can result in a heart attack, in which some of the heart muscle tissue actually dies from a lack of proper blood supply.

Symptoms of CAD These can range from not having any symptoms or discomfort at all to shortness of breath and fatigue, or to mild or severe chest pain.

Risk factors Can the development of CAD be avoided? The risk factors for CAD include: age, family history of heart disease, high blood cholesterol, smoking, high blood pressure, diabetes, overweight/obesity,

▲ An electrocardiogram (ECG) is a graphic representation of electrical impulses that reflect the action of the heart.

and physical inactivity. Some of these factors, such as age and family history, are not in your control. Many of the others can be controlled through diet, regular exercise, and controlling diabetes or other relevant medical conditions.

CAD is the leading cause of death for both men and women in America today. More than 13 million Americans suffer from CAD. Practicing positive health behaviors, such as following a well-balanced diet and exercising regularly, can help reduce your risk of developing CAD later in life.

Investigating the Issue

Visit www.glencoe.com to research more information about coronary artery disease.

- How can risk factors, such as blood cholesterol levels, blood pressure, and weight, be controlled?
- What effect does stress have on the development of CAD?
- What role, if any, does gender play in the risk of developing CAD?

Create a presentation that outlines health behaviors that everyone in your family can follow to reduce the risk of CAD. In your presentation, be sure to address risk factors such as smoking, physical inactivity, and high blood pressure.

FACTSABOUT HEART DISEASE

Quick Demo

Fatty Buildup Place a fried food, such as potato chips, on a piece of colored paper or brown paper towel. After five minutes, remove the food and show students what is left behind. The fried foods leave an oily stain on the paper, which means there is fat in the food. Foods that contain oils also increase deposits on artery wall linings. This harms the arteries.

Investigating the Issue

- *These risk factors can be controlled through diet, exercise, other lifestyle choices, and medication, if necessary.*
- *Stress causes the body to release adrenaline and increase heart rate and blood pressure, all of which place an increased demand on the heart muscle. Over time, artery walls thicken and harden in response to high blood pressure. Stress also may cause people to make harmful lifestyle choices, such as skipping exercise or smoking.*
- *Men have a higher risk of heart attack than women. However, after the age of 65, the risk of developing heart disease is the same for both men and women when other risk factors are similar.*

Family Involvement

Family Heart Health History Have students interview family members about any history of heart disease. Students who are not living with their biological families may ask if anything is known about the history of heart disease in their biological families. If not, they can ask about heart health history in their adoptive families. Students may see a pattern of heart disease in their families. Help them realize that genetics is one important factor, but that there are positive steps they can take to reduce the risk of heart disease. They can examine their family's diet and exercise habits, and identify positive behaviors that reduce the risk of cardiovascular disease. Ask students to add any new information they discover to their family health histories and personal health records. **L2**

National Health Education Standards
Pages 210–211: 1.5

The Nervous System

NHES Assessment/SCASS

Performance Task Have students research information about the right brain and the left brain with respect to personality traits. Ask students to answer this question: What kinds of tests can be used to determine if a person is left-brained or right-brained? With permission from their parents or guardians, students should take one of these tests. When they have the results, have students write an essay evaluating how their results relate to their personality traits. Ask students if they see a correlation to their preferred methods of problem-solving and communication. Encourage students to include illustrations with their essays.
L3

Explain the Concept

Nervous System Explain the relationship between the central nervous system and the peripheral nervous system, and how they work together. Sensory signals from the peripheral nervous system travel to the central nervous system, which sends motor signals back to cause an appropriate reaction.

The Nervous System

The body system that carries messages to and from the brain and spinal cord and all other parts of the body is the **nervous system**. The nervous system is composed of two divisions—the central nervous system and the peripheral nervous system.

What to Know About the Nervous System

The **central nervous system** consists of the brain and spinal cord. The **peripheral nervous system** is made up of nerves that branch out from the central nervous system to muscles, skin, internal organs, and glands. Your sense organs continually send messages, such as odors, sights, or tastes, to your brain through the peripheral nervous system. Your central nervous system, in turn, relays responses to these messages to your muscles and glands as your body responds to changes in your environment.

Brain The mass of nerve tissue that acts as the control center of the body is called the **brain.** The human brain weighs about three pounds and can store more information than all the libraries in the world put together. Your brain creates ideas and controls thinking, reasoning, movement, and emotions. The brain has three major parts—the cerebrum, the cerebellum, and the brain stem.

The **cerebrum** is the largest part of the brain and controls the ability to memorize, think, and learn. The cerebrum also determines a person's intelligence and personality. It consists of two halves, called hemispheres. The right hemisphere controls the left side of the body, and the left hemisphere controls the right side of the body. The **cerebellum** is the part of the brain that controls and coordinates muscle activity. It also helps you maintain your balance.

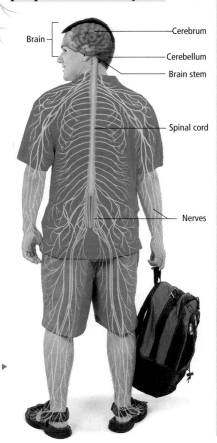

Did You Know?

Concussion A brain injury that sometimes results in a loss of consciousness is a concussion. An impact creates a sudden movement of the brain within the skull.

Brain — Cerebrum
— Cerebellum
— Brain stem
— Spinal cord
— Nerves

◀ The nervous system is made up of the central nervous system (the brain and spinal cord) and the peripheral nervous system (nerves).

🔻 Health Project

Skits The brain creates ideas and controls thinking, reasoning, movement, and emotions. Have students consider the short-term and long-term effects of alcohol on the brain. Ask students whether these effects could be permanent. Have groups of students create skits in which one or more friends try to convince another friend who is considering drinking alcohol why he or she should not do so. In the skits, students should explain the effects of alcohol on the brain. They also can describe the negative effects that excessive alcohol use can have on other aspects of one's life, such as relationship problems and poor performance at school or work. By the end of the skit, the friend should decide not to drink alcohol. Skits could be performed for the class and possibly videotaped to share with other classes or groups. **L3**

Your ability to catch a ball is a function of your cerebellum. The **brain stem** is the part of the brain that controls the functions of the internal organs.

Spinal cord The column of nerve cells that extends downward from the brain is the **spinal cord.** Your spinal cord carries messages to and from your brain and all parts of your body. It keeps your brain informed of changes in your body and in your environment. Your spinal cord is protected by your vertebrae.

Nerve cells The nervous system is composed of cells called neurons. A **neuron** is a nerve cell that is the structural and functional unit of the nervous system. Some neurons in the spinal cord may be several feet long. A neuron consists of a cell body, an axon, and dendrites. A **cell body** is the main body of the neuron. An **axon** is an elongated fiber that carries impulses away from the cell body to the dendrites of another neuron. **Dendrites** are branching fibers that receive impulses and carry them to the cell body.

Sensory and motor neurons work together to help you respond to your environment. **Sensory neurons** carry impulses from the sense organs to the spinal cord and brain. **Motor neurons** carry responding impulses to muscles and glands from the brain and spinal cord. Motor neurons cause responses in muscles and glands.

Reflex action Have you ever touched something hot and quickly pulled away from it? You experienced a reflex action. A **reflex action** is an involuntary action in which a message is sent to the spinal cord, is interpreted, and is responded to immediately.

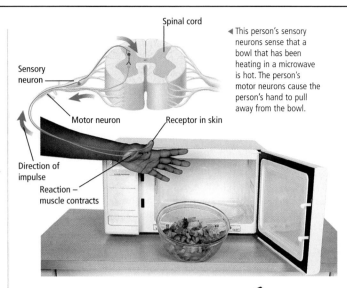

Spinal cord

Sensory neuron

Motor neuron

Receptor in skin

Direction of impulse

Reaction – muscle contracts

◀ This person's sensory neurons sense that a bowl that has been heating in a microwave is hot. The person's motor neurons cause the person's hand to pull away from the bowl.

Sensory neurons carry the message that you touched a hot surface to your spinal cord and brain. Your brain interprets the message. Motor neurons carry the message back to your muscles. You respond by moving your hand. Reflex actions do not involve conscious thought and take only a fraction of a second. Reflex actions help keep you safe.

Reading Review

1. What is the difference between the central nervous system and the peripheral nervous system?
2. What is a reflex action?

How to Keep Your Nervous System Healthy

The following suggestions will protect your nervous system:

- Wear a protective helmet for sports.
- Avoid diving into shallow water or water of unknown depth.
- Use a safety belt.
- Follow directions for taking any medications that affect the nervous system.
- Avoid drinking alcohol and using other drugs that impair the functions of the brain.
- Follow directions for using household products that contain chemicals that may affect the nervous system.

LESSON 19 • Keeping Your Body Healthy **213**

The Immune System

Quick Demo

Spread of Germs Place glitter on an object like a desk, pencil sharpener, or doorknob at the beginning of class. Have a student volunteer touch or use the object and then shake hands with another student. Have the students look at how the glitter has spread, and use this to discuss the spread of germs. **ELL**

Explain the Concept

Bacteria Not all bacteria are pathogens (germs that cause disease). There are "good" bacteria. "Good" bacteria help to break down food in the process of digestion. They also are used in the production of some foods, and to help recycle waste.

Class Discussion

Immunization Shots Many students remember receiving immunization shots. Discuss with students what those shots do and why it is important to require students to have them before they enter school. *Immunization shots are important because they help prevent outbreaks of preventable diseases among school students. Be sensitive to the fact that some students do not get the shots for medical or religious reasons.* **L2**

Reading Review

1. *a germ that causes disease*
2. *the body's resistance to disease-causing agents*

214

The Immune System

The Immune System

The body system that removes harmful organisms from the blood and combats pathogens is the *immune system*. The immune system is composed of lymph, lymph nodes, lymph vessels, tonsils, the thymus gland, and the spleen.

Make the Connection

Immune System For more information on the immune system, see page 485 in Lesson 44.

What to Know About the Immune System

The immune system protects your body from pathogens. A pathogen is a germ that causes disease. When white blood cells attack pathogens, the pathogens are filtered into the lymph. *Lymph* is a clear liquid that surrounds body cells and circulates in lymph vessels. Lymph carries harmful pathogens and other small particles to lymph nodes. A *lymph node* is a structure that filters and destroys pathogens. The *spleen* is an organ on the left side of the abdomen that filters foreign matter from the blood and lymph.

Immunity is the body's resistance to disease-causing agents. White blood cells are formed in bone marrow and circulate in the blood. These white blood cells are changed to T cells within the *thymus gland.* A *T cell* is a white blood cell that destroys pathogens. A *B cell* is another kind of specialized white blood cell that produces antibodies. An *antibody* is a special protein that helps fight infection.

Reading Review

1. What is a pathogen?
2. What is immunity?

Lymph node
Thymus gland
Spleen
Lymph vessel

▲ The immune system protects your body from pathogens.

How to Keep Your Immune System Healthy

The following are ways to keep your immune system healthy:

- Choose foods that are high in protein and vitamin B.
- Keep accurate records of all immunizations.
- Get plenty of rest and sleep.
- Exercise to keep bones dense and to protect bone marrow.

Healthy People 2010

Objective 14-27a *Increase routine vaccination coverage levels for adolescents who have had three or more doses of the hepatitis B vaccine.*

In a 1997 baseline survey, parents reported that 48 percent of adolescents age 13 to 15 years had received three or more doses of the hepatitis B vaccine. The Healthy People 2010 target is 90 percent. Assuming that only 48 percent of the adolescents in their community have had three or more doses of the hepatitis B vaccine, have students work in groups to list ways that the community could work to reach the objective by 2010. Have students answer these questions: Whom do they think they should target with the message to increase immunization? Adolescents? Their parents? Parents of younger children? Health professionals? Others? Have students create a print, radio or television public service announcement about this issue. **L2**

The Respiratory System

The body system that provides body cells with oxygen and removes carbon dioxide that cells produce as waste is the *respiratory system.* Air enters through your nose or mouth when you inhale. Mucus in the nasal passages and sinuses warms and moistens the air and traps dust particles and pathogens. *Mucus* is a thick secretion that moistens, lubricates, and protects mucous membranes. A *mucous membrane* is a type of tissue that lines body cavities and secretes mucus.

What to Know About the Respiratory System

Air moves from your nose or mouth through your pharynx to your trachea. The *epiglottis* is a flap that covers the entrance to the trachea when you swallow. When you inhale, the epiglottis opens and air flows into the trachea. The *trachea* is a tube through which air moves to the bronchi and lungs. The trachea is lined with cilia. *Cilia* are hairlike structures that remove dust and other particles from the air.

The *bronchi* are two tubes through which air moves to the lungs. The *lungs* are the main organs of the respiratory system. As the bronchi enter each lung, they branch to form bronchioles. The *bronchioles* are small tubes that branch to form alveoli. *Alveoli* are microscopic air sacs. The walls of the alveoli are so thin that oxygen and carbon dioxide easily pass through them.

Two exchanges take place in the alveoli. Oxygen passes from the alveoli into your capillaries and carbon dioxide passes from your capillaries into the alveoli. You exhale carbon dioxide. Blood rich in oxygen flows from your lungs to your heart.

Epiglottis
Nasal cavity
Mouth
Pharynx
Trachea
Larynx
Bronchiole
Lungs
Alveoli

◀ The respiratory system provides body cells with oxygen and removes carbon dioxide that cells produce as waste.

How to Keep Your Respiratory System Healthy

The following are ways to keep your respiratory system healthy:

- Do not smoke.
- Avoid breathing secondhand smoke.
- Do not inhale harmful drugs.
- Avoid breathing polluted air.
- Exercise regularly.
- Avoid inhaling harmful chemicals.
- Seek medical help for respiratory infections.

LESSON 19 • Keeping Your Body Healthy **215**

The Respiratory System

Class Activity

Respiratory System Model Have students create models of the respiratory system. They should include lungs, bronchi, trachea, epiglottis, and any other parts that they can incorporate. For example, students could use balloons for the lungs, straws or small cardboard tubes for bronchi, a paper towel roll for the trachea, and a piece of cardboard, stiff paper, or plastic to cover the end of the trachea for the epiglottis. By using tape and cardboard or stiff paper rolled up, they should be able to connect the parts so that the lungs will inflate, at least a little, if they blow into their models. They should be able to describe the movement of oxygen and carbon dioxide through their models. **L2 ELL**

Teacher FYI

Influenza Pandemic Some respiratory illnesses, such as colds, are mild. Others, such as influenza or pneumonia, can be severe or life threatening. In 1918 and 1919, an influenza pandemic killed between 20 and 40 million people and infected millions around the world. More people were killed by influenza during the pandemic than in World War I or by the bubonic plague in the 1300s.

Cross-Curricular Connections

Science Have students create a map or chart that shows the differences in air pollution in different areas of the country or world. Ask them to list the major causes of air pollution in different areas. *car exhaust, industrial emissions, power plants, volcanic ash, other causes* Ask students to list ways in which we can work to improve the quality of the air. Have students answer these questions: How does breathing polluted air affect our health? What groups of people may have more severe problems when breathing polluted air? *people who have asthma or other respiratory ailments, the elderly* **L2 ELL**

National Health Education Standards
Pages 214–215: 1.5

The Skeletal System

Explain the Concept

Cartilage and Joints Cartilage is soft, connective tissue that acts as a cushion in the joints. Students may know some places where there is cartilage in their bodies, but not others. Cartilage can be found in joints, disks in the spine, the nose, and the ears. Three different types of joints in the body are ball and socket, hinge, and pivot.

Teacher FYI

Cracking Knuckles Cracking knuckles has not been clearly linked to causing arthritic problems. The popping or cracking sound is normal. When a joint is pulled, lower pressure is created in the joint area, causing tiny air bubbles to break. That is the noise people hear.

Reading Review

1. *protects vital organs, works with muscles to produce movement, produces blood cells*
2. *ligaments*

NHES Assessment/SCASS

Selected Response Which body system produces blood cells?
A. cardiovascular system
B. immune system
C. *skeletal system*
D. endocrine system

The Skeletal System

The body system that serves as a support framework, protects vital organs, works with muscles to produce movement, and produces blood cells is the *skeletal system.*

What to Know About the Skeletal System

Bone is the structural material of the skeletal system. **Periosteum** (per ee AHS tee um) is a thin tissue that covers bone and contains nerves and blood vessels. **Bone marrow** is soft tissue in the center of most bones where both red and white blood cells are formed.

Cartilage is soft, connective tissue on the ends of some bones. It also acts as a cushion where bones meet, such as in the knee and hip joint. Cartilage disks between vertebrae serve as shock absorbers. A **ligament** is a tough fiber that connects bones together. A **joint** is the point where two bones meet. There are several types of joints in your body.

Reading Review

1. List three functions of the skeletal system.
2. What connects bones?

How to Keep Your Skeletal System Healthy

The following are ways to keep your skeletal system healthy:

- Choose foods rich in calcium, phosphorus and vitamin D.
- Exercise to strengthen joints.
- Wear protective equipment and well-cushioned, properly fitting shoes and warm up before exercising.
- Sit, stand and walk with correct posture. Participate in screening for scoliosis.

Phalanges — Metacarpals
Carpals — Ulna
Radius — Humerus
Skull
Clavicle (collarbone) — Scapula (shoulder blade)
Sternum — Rib cage
Illium — Vertebrae (spinal column)
Sacrum — Coccyx (tailbone)
Ischium
Femur — Patella
Tibia — Fibula
Tarsals
Phalanges   Metatarsals

▲ The skeletal system serves as a support framework for your body.

Teacher to Teacher

Making a Human Skeleton Materials: scissors, tape or glue, picture of a skeleton. Have students draw each bone in the skeleton diagram above. Then they can number each bone so that bones with consecutive numbers belong next to one another. They may want the same bones on each side of the body, such as an arm or leg bone, to have the same number and a letter (R or L) to indicate which side it belongs on. Have students cut out all of the bones and tape or glue together a model, then arrange the bones in the correct order by matching up consecutive numbers and label each bone. **L2** **ELL**
Aron Fass
Port Isabel High School, Port Isabel, Texas

The Muscular System

The body system that consists of muscles that provide motion and maintain posture is the *muscular system*. There are more than 600 muscles in your body.

What to Know About the Muscular System

Muscles are divided into two major groups: voluntary and involuntary. A *voluntary muscle* is a muscle a person can control. Muscles in your arms and legs that help you move are voluntary muscles. An *involuntary muscle* is a muscle that functions without a person's control. Muscles in your stomach and other internal organs are involuntary muscles.

There are three types of muscle tissue in your body. *Smooth muscle* is involuntary muscle tissue found in many internal organs. *Skeletal muscle* is voluntary muscle tissue that is attached to bone. *Cardiac muscle* is specialized muscle tissue found only in the heart. It is unique from other muscle tissue because of its structure. Contractions in cardiac muscles are generated by nerve stimulation.

A *tendon* is tough tissue fiber that attaches muscles to bones. Skeletal muscles work in pairs to move your body. One muscle in the pair contracts and shortens, while the other relaxes and lengthens.

◄ The muscular system consists of muscles that provide motion and maintain posture.

Frontalis
Triceps brachii
Deltoid
Pectoralis (chest muscle)
Latissimus dorsi
Biceps brachii
Sternocleidomastoid (neck)
Rectus abdominis (abdominal muscles)
Gluteus maximus
Sartorius
Rectus femoris
Quadriceps (front of the thigh)
Biceps femoris (back of thigh)
Gastrocnemius (calf muscle)

(The dotted lines are used for muscles that are on the back side of the figure and can't be seen from the front.)

Did You Know?

Muscles Muscles shorten and lengthen because of elasticity in muscle fibers. This allows movement at the joints.

How to Keep Your Muscular System Healthy

The following are ways to keep your muscular system healthy:

- Discontinue exercise if you have a muscle injury.
- Warm up and stretch before exercise.
- Exercise different muscle groups regularly.
- Maintain your desirable weight.
- Bend at the knees and keep your back straight when lifting heavy objects.
- Select foods and beverages containing carbohydrates and proteins for energy and muscle development.
- Sleep on a firm mattress.

LESSON 19 • Keeping Your Body Healthy **217**

The Muscular System

Class Activity

Muscle Types Have students work in groups to design a poster that defines a type of muscle (skeletal, smooth, cardiac), where it can be found, its function, and whether it is voluntary or involuntary. Posters should include a drawing or diagram as well as text with information about the type of muscle. Posters can be displayed or presented in class. **L2 ELL**

Extension

Muscle Growth Have students research why a muscle gets larger with exercise. They also can gather information from Unit 6 about the effects steroids have on muscles. Ask students to answer these questions: Is there a limit on how large muscles can become? What differences in muscle growth are there between men and women? How large might a specific muscle, such as a biceps, become in a bodybuilder? Have students bring in notes on their findings and discuss this topic as a class. **L3**

DI Differentiated Instruction

Physical Challenges If you have a student in your class who has a physical disability, pair him or her with another student. Have them work together to list exercises and then come up with ways to adapt the exercises so the physically challenged student can perform them. The pair should consult with a physical therapist or an occupational therapist to evaluate their exercises and for additional activities the physically challenged student could use in order to keep himself or herself in the best possible health. **L2**

National Health Education Standards
Pages 216–217: 1.5

217

The Endocrine System

5-Minute Check

Page 16, **Unit 4 Fast File Resources**

1. Where are hormones produced? *in the endocrine system*

2. How do hormones work? *They act as chemical messengers that are released into the blood to control body activities.*

3. How does the pancreas affect the blood? *It releases the hormone insulin to help regulate blood sugar level; if there is not enough insulin, a person will develop diabetes mellitus.*

4. What happens when adrenaline is released into the bloodstream? *heart rate and blood pressure increase*

5. What hormones are produced by the ovaries and testes and what is the shared function of these hormones? *In females, ovaries produce estrogen. In males, testes produce testosterone. These hormones produce the secondary sex characteristics. (Lesson 20 has additional information on this topic.)*

NHES Assessment/SCASS

Performance Event Have students draw an outline of a human body and then draw the location of each gland in the endocrine system using the diagram on this page. Have them develop a chart that lists each gland, the hormone it produces, and the function of the hormone. **L2 ELL**

The Endocrine System

The body system that consists of glands that produce hormones is the ***endocrine system.*** A group of cells that secretes hormones is a ***gland.*** A chemical messenger released into the bloodstream is a ***hormone.*** Hormones control many body activities.

Did You Know?

Hormones Hormones circulate throughout the body in the bloodstream. However, each hormone targets only certain organs or tissues.

What to Know About the Endocrine System

Labels: Pituitary gland, Parathyroid glands, Thyroid gland, Thymus, Adrenal glands, Pancreas, Ovaries

Testes

▶ The endocrine system consists of glands that produce horomones.

Pituitary gland The endocrine gland that produces hormones, which control growth and other glands is the ***pituitary gland.*** The pituitary gland is located below the hypothalamus in the brain and is about the size of a pea.

Hormones from the pituitary gland influence growth, metabolism, development of the reproductive organs, uterine contractions during childbirth, and many other body functions.

The pituitary gland often is called the master gland because it releases hormones that affect the function of other glands.

Thyroid gland The endocrine gland that produces thyroxin is the ***thyroid gland.*** A hormone that controls metabolism and calcium balance in the body is ***thyroxin.*** The rate at which food is converted into energy in body cells is ***metabolism.*** The thyroid gland is located near the upper portion of the trachea.

Parathyroid glands The endocrine glands that secrete hormones, which control the amount of calcium and phosphorus in the body are the ***parathyroid glands.*** There are four parathyroid glands that are located on the thyroid gland. Each parathyroid gland is about the size of a grain of rice.

⚡ Health Project

Stress Have groups of students research the effects that stress has on a particular body system. Include information on health problems associated with stress. Each group also should research one technique to reduce stress levels. Each group can develop a poster or other visual aid to present its research to the class. Students may want to try appropriate stress-reduction techniques, such as listening to a relaxation tape in class or at home. Ask students if they felt relaxed after trying the technique. **L2**

Pancreas The gland that produces both digestive enzymes and insulin is the *pancreas.* The digestive enzymes produced by the pancreas are essential to the digestion of food.

Insulin is a hormone that regulates blood sugar level. If the pancreas fails to produce enough insulin, a person develops diabetes mellitus. *Diabetes mellitus* is a disease in which the body produces little or no insulin. Diabetes will be discussed further in Lesson 48.

Adrenal glands The endocrine glands that secrete several hormones, including adrenaline, are the *adrenal glands.* A hormone that prepares the body to react during times of stress, danger, or in an emergency is *adrenaline.* When adrenaline is secreted into the bloodstream, both heart rate and blood pressure increase.

The adrenal glands also secrete hormones that affect the body's metabolism. There are two adrenal glands in the body, located on each kidney.

Ovaries There are two ovaries in the female body. The *ovaries* are female reproductive glands that produce ova and estrogen. *Ova* are egg cells, or female reproductive cells.

Estrogen is a hormone produced by the ovaries that stimulates the development of female secondary sex characteristics and affects the menstrual cycle.

Testes There are two testes in the male body. The *testes* are male reproductive glands that produce sperm and testosterone. *Testosterone* is a hormone that produces the male secondary sex characteristics.

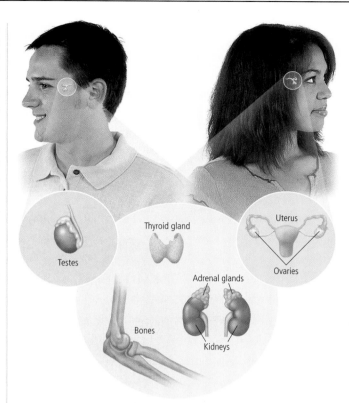

▲ Pituitary hormones have many functions. They regulate the development of bones and muscles; affect the reproductive organs; affect the functioning of the kidneys, the adrenal gland and the thyroid glands; and stimulate the uterus to contract during childbirth.

How to Keep Your Endocrine System Healthy

The following are important ways to keep your endocrine system healthy:

- Have regular medical checkups.
- Perform testicular self-examinations each month.
- Keep track of the length and dates of your menstrual cycles.

LESSON 19 • Keeping Your Body Healthy **219**

Teacher FYI

Diabetes Diabetes mellitus is a disease in which the body produces little or no insulin. Type 1 (5–10 percent of people who have diabetes) is controlled by receiving insulin injections. There is no cure for Type 1 diabetes. Type 2 (most common, 90–95 percent of people who have diabetes), also called adult-onset diabetes, can be controlled with medication, diet, and exercise.

Quick Demo

Fight or Flight Response Ask students to clear their desks and take out a sheet of paper and a pencil or pen. Have them write their names on top and number from 1–10 down the left-hand side of the page. Students will assume they are having a pop quiz. Have students write the answers to difficult questions you ask. Ask students to describe how they are feeling —physically and emotionally—at this moment. *Students may write that they are nervous and anxious and that their heart is beating faster, they are breathing faster, and they have sweaty palms.* Explain that this is an example of the "fight or flight" response that our bodies experience in reaction to stress. Also explain that this is not a "real" quiz.

Class Activity

Endocrine Gland Have students get into pairs to create flash cards listing an endocrine gland on one side and its hormone and function on the other side. Then have them test each other using the cards. This activity will help students in the class who learn best with visual cues. **L2 ELL**

National Health Education Standards

Pages 218–219: 1.5

The Digestive System

Class Activity

Digestive System Organize the class into groups and assign each group a part of the digestive system. Have the groups research the role their part plays in the digestive process and create a presentation. Have the students determine the appropriate order in which groups should present their findings to the class. **L2**

Quick Demo

Enzymes at Work Provide students with a pretzel or cracker and ask them to chew it up without swallowing it. Ask students to think about how the taste changes over time. *salty taste at first and then a sweet taste* Tell students that this is an example of how enzymes in the saliva begin to break down food for the digestion process. There are enzymes in the stomach and small intestines to break food down even further. **ELL**

The Digestive System

The body system that breaks down food into nutrients that can be used by the body is the *digestive system*. The digestive system also allows nutrients to be absorbed by body cells and waste materials to be eliminated from the body. *Digestion* is the process by which food is changed so that it can be absorbed by body cells.

What to Know About the Digestive System

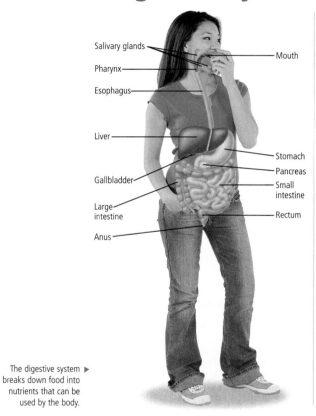

Salivary glands
Pharynx
Esophagus
Liver
Gallbladder
Large intestine
Anus
Mouth
Stomach
Pancreas
Small intestine
Rectum

► The digestive system breaks down food into nutrients that can be used by the body.

Mouth When food is chewed in the mouth, teeth break it into smaller pieces. The *salivary glands* are glands in the mouth that release saliva, which contains a chemical that begins the digestion of carbohydrates. *Saliva* is a fluid that helps soften food so that it can be swallowed more easily.

Approximately 10,000 microscopic taste buds are on the tongue. Each taste bud contains 50–100 receptor cells. A tiny hair extends from each receptor cell. When the hairs are stimulated by food, they send nerve impulses to the brain that register one of four basic flavor sensations: sweet, salty, sour, or bitter.

Esophagus When you swallow food, it moves into the esophagus. The *esophagus* is a tube that connects the mouth and the stomach. Food passes to your stomach by the process of peristalsis. *Peristalsis* (per uh STAHL suhs) is a series of involuntary muscle contractions. Peristalsis can move food to your stomach even if you are standing on your head.

⊂ Cross-Curricular Connections

History Divide students into groups and have the groups do research on how meals have changed over time. Ask students answer these questions: What types of foods do Americans no longer eat and why? How is food prepared differently today as compared to 20, 30, or 50 years ago? What was done to preserve foods 50 years ago? Which techniques, if any, do Americans continue to use the same way now? What are the effects of newer preservation techniques on the quality of food that is processed for mass production in today's world? Can trends in public health, such as increasing rates of heart disease, diabetes, and obesity, be linked to trends in dietary preferences? Group reports can be multimedia to provide a broad picture. **L2**

Stomach The organ that releases acids and juices that mix with food and produce a thick paste called chyme (KIM) is the *stomach.* The stomach produces a layer of mucus to protect its lining from the strong acids released in digestion. After about four hours of churning the food, muscle contractions force the food into the small intestine.

Small intestine The coiled tube in which the greatest amount of digestion and absorption take place is the *small intestine.* The small intestine is about 21 feet long and is lined with villi. *Villi* are small folds in the lining of the small intestine that increase the surface area and allow more food to be absorbed. Several enzymes are produced in the lining of the small intestine. An *enzyme* is a protein that regulates chemical reactions.

Liver The gland that secretes bile to help break down fats, maintain blood sugar level, and filter poisonous wastes is the *liver.* Bile flows to the small intestine to help in the digestion of fats. Bile is stored in the gallbladder, which is a small sac-like organ located under the liver.

Pancreas The gland that produces both digestive enzymes and insulin is the pancreas. Enzymes from the pancreas break down proteins, starches, and fats from food in the small intestine.

Large intestine After food passes through the small intestine, it enters the large intestine, also called the colon. The *large intestine* is a tube extending from the small intestine in which undigested food is prepared for elimination from the body. When the large intestine is full, it contracts, and solid wastes leave the body through the rectum and anus. The *rectum* is the lower end of the large intestine that stores wastes temporarily. The *anus* is the opening to the outside of the body at the end of the rectum.

Make the Connection

Health Behavior Contracts For more information on making a health behavior contract to keep your body systems healthy, see page 32 in Lesson 3.

Reading Review

1. What is digestion?
2. What are the four basic flavor sensations detected by taste buds?

TABLE 19.1 Keep Your Digestive System Healthy	
Healthful Behavior	**Description of Healthful Behavior**
Fiber-rich foods	Choose a variety of foods every day and eat plenty of foods that contain fiber. Whole-grain breads and cereals, as well as fruits and vegetables, are good sources of fiber. Fiber stimulates digestive tract muscles.
Enjoyment	Chew slowly and enjoy your food. Do not rush to finish a meal. Chew food well and avoid indigestion. Avoid arguments when eating.
Fluids	Drink at least six to eight glasses of water each day. Water is involved in many body functions, including digestion and maintaining normal body temperature.

Small Intestines Bring in a rope or string that is 21 feet long to show students the length of the small intestines. Select two students to hold the ends of the rope, standing 21 feet apart. Tell students that the greatest amount of digestion and absorption takes place in the small intestine.

Teacher FYI

Drinking Alcohol When people drink alcohol, 20 percent of the alcohol is absorbed in the stomach (food in the stomach will slow this rate down) and 80 percent is absorbed in the small intestine. (See Lesson 55 for additional information.)

Reading Review

1. *the process by which food is broken down into nutrients so that it can be used by the body*
2. *sweet, salty, sour, bitter*

Using the Table

Healthful Behaviors Ask students to review the healthful behaviors in Table 19.1. Ask students these questions: Do you engage in these behaviors on a daily basis? If not, what changes could you make in your daily routines to help keep your digestive systems healthy? Have students write their responses in their health journals. **L2**

(DI) Differentiated Instruction

Hearing Impairment Students who are hearing impaired may learn material more easily if it is in a visual format. Provide each of five groups of students with a sheet of paper with a digestive system organ listed on the top (mouth, stomach, small intestine, liver, colon). Ask students to draw a diagram of the organ and write a description of what that organ does in the digestion process. They also should list ways to keep the entire digestive system healthy. Display the pages in the classroom. **L2**

National Health Education Standards
Pages 220–221: 1.5

The Integumentary System

The Integumentary System

Quick Demo

Sweat Glands Place a latex glove on your hand for 5 minutes, then remove the glove and discuss the changes in the skin that take place. *The hand will become warm and sweaty, and the skin may become wrinkled.* Discuss where sweat glands are located and how they work. If there are enough gloves, this is an activity the whole class could do. Be sure to ask students if they are allergic to latex if you do this.

Teacher FYI

Sweat Sweating gives our bodies the ability to get rid of waste and to control temperature. Sweat is also a home for bacteria that can produce body odors. Bathing or showering daily, along with the use of antiperspirant and/or deodorant, can help reduce the development of body odor.

Class Activity

Promote Healthy Skin Care Have students design posters or brochures to promote healthy skin care and skin safety. Students should use computer graphics, drawings, or pictures from magazines to help make the project interesting. **L2**

The body system that covers and protects the body and consists of skin, glands associated with the skin, hair, and nails is the ***integumentary*** (in TEG yuh MEN tuh ree) ***system.*** The skin performs several functions that are essential for survival.

What to Know About the Integumentary System

The largest organ in the body is skin. It contains nerve cells that help you detect pain, pressure, touch, heat, and cold. Skin protects some body parts against injury, serves as a protective layer that keeps microorganisms from entering the body, and helps maintain a healthful body temperature.

Skin helps with the removal of wastes from the body and helps you sense the environment. It also helps

The integumentary system consists of skin, glands associated with ▼ the skin, hair, and nails.

protect you from ultraviolet radiation because of the presence of melanin. ***Melanin*** is a pigment that gives the skin its color.

Two layers Skin is made up of two layers. The ***epidermis*** is the outer layer of skin cells. These cells are constantly shed and replaced. The epidermis does not contain blood vessels or nerve endings. New skin cells are produced in the deepest layer of the epidermis. The ***dermis*** is a thick layer of cells below the epidermis that contains sweat glands, hair follicles, sebaceous (oil) glands, blood vessels, and nerves.

Glands A gland that aids the body in getting rid of wastes, such as salt, is a ***sweat gland.*** Sweat glands also help cool the body by releasing sweat through pores to evaporate on the surface of your skin.

A ***sebaceous gland*** is a small oil-producing gland that helps protect the skin. ***Sebum*** is the oil produced by sebaceous glands. Sebaceous glands are usually found together with hair follicles, though some exist in hairless areas. Below the dermis is the subcutaneous layer. The ***subcutaneous layer*** is a layer of fatty

Labels on figure: Sebaceous gland, Epidermis, Dermis, Hair follicle, Hair, Sweat gland, Nerves, Artery, Vein

🛡 Sensitive Issues

Body Image Body image can be a sensitive issue, and the discussion of skin conditions may make some students uncomfortable. The discussions of acne, scars, burns, warts, moles, and birthmarks should take place with an effort to not single out a particular student with a particular skin condition. This also would be a good time to dispel myths about how some conditions are acquired. For example, some people get plantar warts from walking barefoot in a locker room, in contrast to the belief that warts come from touching toads.

tissue located below the dermis. A large portion of the body's fat is stored in this layer.

Birthmarks and Scars Because skin is the largest organ in the body, it also is the most vulnerable organ. There are several types of conditions that affect the skin. Common skin conditions include birthmarks and scars. A birthmark is an area of discolored skin that is present at birth. Birthmarks include different types of freckles and moles and may be removed by a physician. A scar is a mark left on damaged tissue after the tissue has healed. If a person is cut or has a severe burn, a scar may develop. Some people are more likely than others to develop scars.

Warts Warts and acne are other common skin conditions. A *wart* is a contagious growth that forms on the top layer of the skin. Warts are caused by a viral infection. They usually grow in groups and can be spread by contact. Warts can be treated with over-the-counter drugs. However, if warts spread, they should be treated by a physician.

Acne A skin disorder in which hair follicles or pores in the skin become plugged with sebum is *acne.* Acne may be prevalent during adolescence because hormonal changes stimulate the sebaceous glands to produce sebum. A *pustule* is a dome-shaped lesion that contains pus consisting of white blood cells, dead skin cells and bacteria. The plug may close the pore, causing it to swell, creating a whitehead. If the pore is open, it is commonly called a blackhead because the surface of the plug has a dark appearance. Blackheads are not caused or colored by dirt.

Acne can last through early adulthood. Acne may be aggravated by application of oil-based makeup, suntan oil, or hair products.

Ringworm A skin condition that causes small, red, ring-shaped marks on the skin is *ringworm.* Ringworm is caused by a fungal infection and can be spread by physical contact. Physicians usually treat ringworm with ointments or creams. However, severe cases of ringworm may require treatment with antifungal tablets.

Nails and hair Nails and hair also are part of the integumentary system. *Nails* are made up of dead cells and keratin, a tough protein. *Hair* is a threadlike structure consisting of dead cells filled with keratin. Hair protects skin from harmful sun rays and helps maintain body temperature. Hair varies in color, texture, and amount for each person. From 100,000 to 200,000 hairs may be on your head. Each hair grows from a follicle. A *hair follicle* is a depression on the surface of the dermis that contains nutrients a hair needs to grow. The roots of hairs are made up of living cells.

Blisters Blisters are caused by pressure or friction that causes fluid to collect between the layers of the skin.

Reading Review

1. How does skin aid the body in getting rid of wastes?

2. What causes warts?

How to Keep Your Integumentary System Healthy

The following tips will help you keep this body system healthy:

- Wear sunscreen with an SPF of at least 15 when you are exposed to the sun.
- Examine skin monthly for any changes in moles, warts, or freckles.
- Follow directions when using makeup.
- Shower or bathe each day.
- Eat foods containing vitamin A.
- Seek proper medical care for skin rashes.
- Wash hair regularly.
- Treat dandruff with appropriate products.

LESSON 19 • Keeping Your Body Healthy **223**

Achieving Health Literacy

Critical Thinker Ask students to make a list of things they could do to take care of their skin. Ask them to consider things such as how much time they spend in the sun, whether or not they use sunscreen, and whether or not they examine their skin for changes in moles. They should also consider other habits, such as how often they shower or bathe and wash their hair, and whether they eat enough foods containing vitamin A. Look into problems associated with the lack of taking care of the skin. Have each student choose one behavior from the list and create a health behavior contract. **L2**

Quick Demo

Dehydration Show two containers of fluid that are different shades of yellow. Use the darker container to illustrate the color of urine when a person is dehydrated (toxins can build up). Adding water will make the color lighten to a pale yellow color, similar to urine in a properly hydrated person.

Reading Review

1. *removes liquid wastes from the body and maintains the body's water balance*
2. *It damages the kidneys.*

3 Assess

Vocabulary Practice
Page 8, **Unit 4 Fast File Resources**

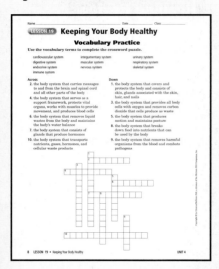

National Health Education Standards
Pages 224–225: 1.5

The body system that removes liquid wastes from the body and maintains the body's water balance is the **urinary system.** The organs of the urinary system are the kidneys, ureters, bladder, and urethra.

What to Know About the Urinary System

Kidneys An organ that filters the blood and excretes waste products and excess water in the form of urine is a **kidney.** A pale yellow liquid composed of water, salts, and other waste products is **urine.** The body has two kidneys. They lie on either side of the spinal column just above the waist.

Ureters A narrow tube that connects a kidney to the urinary bladder is a **ureter** (YUR uh tur). Two ureters carry urine from the kidneys to the urinary bladder.

Urinary bladder The muscular sac that stores urine is the **urinary bladder.** As the urinary bladder fills with urine, it expands. During urination, urine is forced out of the bladder into the urethra.

Urethra The narrow tube extending from the urinary bladder to the outside of the body, through which urine passes out of the body is the **urethra** (yu REE thruh).

The urinary system ► consists of the kidneys, the ureters, the bladder, and the urethra.

Reading Review

1. Name two functions of the urinary system.
2. How can high blood pressure affect the urinary system?

Kidney

Vein

Ureter

Artery

Urethra

Urinary bladder

How to Keep Your Urinary System Healthy

These two tips will help you keep this body system healthy:

- Drink plenty of water a day, especially in hot weather or when doing physical activity.
- Maintain a healthful blood pressure, as high blood pressure damages the kidneys.

▲ To keep your urinary system healthy, make sure you stay hydrated.

🏠 Family Involvement

Drinking Water Consuming plenty of water each day can help to keep the urinary system healthy. Have students discuss water consumption with their families. Each family member should monitor his or her water intake for several days by keeping a record of how much water and other beverages he or she drinks during each day. Then, the family should determine whether each person is meeting the water drinking goal. If not, they should work together to try to increase the water intake of each family member while cutting back on sugary drinks like sodas and sweetened juice. Have the student ask each family member if he or she has experienced any health benefits after several days of increased water intake, such as fewer headaches or better digestion. Students should note these benefits as motivations for continuing to drink more water. **L2 ELL**

cardiovascular
    system
central nervous
    system
digestive system
endocrine system
immune system
integumentary
    system
muscular system
nervous system
peripheral nervous
    system
respiratory system
skeletal system
urinary system

Key Terms Review

Match the following definitions with the lesson Key Terms on the left. Do not write in this book.

1. produces a hormone that controls growth
2. includes ligaments and joints
3. contains cells that transmit messages to body parts
4. includes plasma and hemoglobin
5. helps the body remove liquid wastes
6. the main organs are the lungs
7. helps provide motion and maintain posture
8. covers and protects the body
9. includes antibodies that fight infection
10. produces enzymes that break down proteins and starches

Recalling the Facts

11. What is the function of white blood cells?
12. List three ways to keep your integumentary system healthy.
13. What is the difference between pulse and blood pressure?
14. What are three types of muscle? How are they different?
15. Describe the exchange that occurs in the alveoli.
16. What is the function of the urinary system?
17. Why is it important to eat foods that contain fiber?
18. Name and describe the five functions of the brain.

Critical Thinking

19. How are sensory and motor neurons similar? How are they different? How do they work together?
20. How are the cardiovascular and immune systems related?
21. Explain the relationship between the muscular and the skeletal systems in the way they function.
22. Explain how the integumentary and urinary systems have a common function.

Real-Life Applications

23. Why would having a hyperventilating person breathe into a paper bag be helpful?
24. Investigate what options are available to you if you injure the cartilage in your knee joint.
25. How might eating too fast affect your digestive system?
26. Explain why physical activity might be beneficial to a person recovering from coronary artery disease.

Activities

Responsible Decision Making

27. **Journaling** You are going to a midday baseball game with a friend. The weather is going to be hot and sunny. Your friend tells you that you should protect yourself from the sun so that you don't get sunburned. What should you do? Write a response to this situation in your journal. Refer to the Responsible Decision-Making Model on page 61 for help.

Sharpen Your Life Skills

28. **Analyze Influences on Health** Set up six or eight stations. Choose an activity (such as push-ups or jumping jacks) for each station. Circulate through the stations. Record your heart rate before and after each activity. Allow two minutes at each station. A rest station is last. Evaluate your results. Did your heart rate differ? Discuss how the heart reacts to activity and then recovers.

Visit **www.glencoe.com** for more *Health & Wellness* quizzes.

Key Terms Review

1. endocrine system
2. skeletal system
3. nervous system
4. cardiovascular system
5. urinary system
6. respiratory system
7. muscular system
8. integumentary system
9. immune system
10. digestive system

Recalling the Facts

11. See page 209.
12. See page 223.
13. See page 210.
14. See page 217.
15. See page 215.
16. See page 224.
17. See page 221.
18. See pages 212–213.

Critical Thinking

19. Both carry impulses between the brain and spinal cord and other parts of the body. Sensory neurons carry impulses from sense organs to brain and spinal cord, and motor neurons carry impulses from brain and spinal cord to muscles and glands.
20. Both systems transport materials throughout the body. Nutrients, gases, hormones, and cellular waste products circulate in the cardiovascular system. Lymph circulates in the immune system.
21. They work together to produce movement.
22. Both remove wastes from the body.

Real-Life Applications

23. By breathing into and out of the paper bag, exhaled carbon dioxide is re-inhaled. This will help restore the balance of gases (oxygen and carbon dioxide) in the blood.
24. Many treatments, such as arthroscopy, are available for cartilage renewal and repair.
25. It might overfill and/or overwhelm the digestive tract. Digestion is a complex process with specialized functions.

---

26. Physical activity can help to reduce cholesterol, which can help keep arteries clear.

Activities

Responsible Decision Making

27. Your friend is right because overexposure to the sun can increase the risk of developing skin cancer. When in the sun, cover the skin by doing things such as wearing a hat and a long-sleeved shirt, and use sunscreen.

Sharpen Your Life Skills

28. Students should find that their heart rates increase when they engage in physical activity and decrease again when they rest.

LESSON 20

Learning About the Reproductive Systems

Out of Time?

If time does not permit an in-depth study of this topic, use the following activities in this Teacher Wraparound Edition:
- Health Goals, p. 226
- 5-Minute Check, p. 228
- Just the Facts, p. 229
- Class Activity, p. 232
- Class Discussion, p. 235

1 Focus

HEALTH GOALS **Protect Reproductive Health** Have students respond to the Health Goals for this lesson by discussing methods people may use to keep their reproductive systems healthy. *See pages 232 and 240 for coverage of methods.* **L2**

Write ABOUT IT!

Journaling Student journal entries may include the fact that physical changes that occur in a male during puberty become noticeable between the ages of 12 and 15. These changes are affected by heredity, diet, health habits, and health status. Your classmate may simply be a "late bloomer," and it is unkind and shows poor character to make fun of him. **L2**

LESSON 20

What You'll Learn
1. Discuss physical and emotional changes during puberty. *(pp. 227, 235)*
2. Describe the functions of the female and male reproductive organs. *(pp. 228, 236)*
3. Identify concerns of reproductive health. *(pp. 230, 238)*
4. Identify ways to protect reproductive health. *(pp. 232, 240)*

Why It's Important
Your body is going through many dynamic changes. What causes these changes? How will they affect you? This lesson will provide answers.

Key Terms
- puberty
- ovaries
- Fallopian tube
- uterus
- Pap smear
- testosterone
- epididymis
- vas deferens
- prostate gland
- Cowper's glands

Learning About the Reproductive Systems

HEALTH GOALS
- I will recognize habits that protect female reproductive health.
- I will recognize habits that protect male reproductive health.

During adolescence, the female and male bodies mature and develop secondary sex characteristics. Females and males become capable of reproduction, even though they are not prepared to become parents. This lesson discusses the reproductive systems and reproductive health.

Write ABOUT IT!

Writing About Puberty Suppose that one of your classmates doesn't seem to be physically developing as fast as the rest of the students. He is shorter and thinner than the other boys, and his voice is constantly cracking. Some of your classmates make fun of him. After reading the information about puberty in males on page 235, write an entry in your health journal about why your classmates should not make fun of the boy.

National Health Education Standards—Guide for Lesson 20		
1.5	Propose ways to reduce or prevent injuries and health problems.	pp. 226, 232, 233, 239, 240, 241
6.1	Assess personal health practices and overall health status.	pp. 232–233

Puberty in Females

E ach stage of life is a process of change. The stage of growth and development when both the male and female body become capable of producing offspring is *puberty*. During puberty, a female experiences physical and emotional changes.

What to Know About Puberty in Females

When a female is around eight years old, the pituitary gland increases its production of a hormone called follicle-stimulating hormone (FSH). FSH causes ovaries to secrete estrogen. **Estrogen** is a hormone produced by the ovaries that stimulates the development of female secondary sex characteristics and affects the menstrual cycle. **Secondary sex characteristics** are physical and emotional changes that occur during puberty.

How to manage emotions During puberty, a female may notice that she has sudden emotional changes and sexual feelings. Estrogen and other hormones cause these changes as hormone levels fluctuate. Everyday occurrences may produce intense feelings.

A female may be puzzled by some of her emotional reactions, but she should know that most changes in mood are normal. She must take responsibility for behaving responsibly even though her emotional reactions may change rapidly.

The increase in estrogen also produces sexual feelings. Sexual feelings result from a strong physical and emotional attraction to another person. Females must set limits, stick to these limits, and practice abstinence.

How to accept physical changes Physical changes that occur during puberty become noticeable between the ages of 8 and 15. This maturing process is affected by heredity, diet, health habits, and health status. For example, a female with an inadequate diet may mature more slowly. A female who overtrains for a sport may have a delayed menstrual cycle.

During puberty, a female must become comfortable with her maturing body. **Body image** is the perception a person has of his or her body's appearance. A female is more likely to have a positive body image when she is well-educated about her body. She should try not to compare her body to those of other females the same age. Knowing that females mature at different rates can help a female avoid comparisons. She should ask her parents, guardian, or physician when she has questions about her growth and development.

Did You Know?

Brain Power Puberty also is a time of intellectual growth.

Reading Review

1. What is estrogen?
2. How may the maturing process be affected?

Female Secondary Sex Characteristics

Physical changes that occur during puberty:

- increase in height
- widening of the hips
- softer and smoother skin
- growth of pubic and underarm hair
- increase in breast size
- enlargement of external genitalia
- formation of mature ova
- beginning of menstruation

LESSON 20 • Learning About the Reproductive Systems **227**

Puberty In Females

2 Teach

Reading Review

1. *a hormone produced by the ovaries that stimulates the development of female secondary sex characteristics and affects the menstrual cycle*
2. *by heredity, diet, health habits, and health status*

INTERACTIVE CHALKBOARD with Image Bank

PowerPoint® Presentations

This CD-ROM is an editable Microsoft® PowerPoint® presentation that includes:

- Lesson presentations
- Lesson checks
- Interactive graphics
- 5-Minute Checks
- Image Bank
- All transparencies

CRISS Project

Discussion Refer to the Authentic Questions Strategy on page 17T and instruct students to write down questions they have about the reproductive systems as they read.

Lesson Resource Manager

- **Unit 4 Fast File Resources**
  Reading Strategy, p. 21
  Vocabulary Practice, p. 22
  Transparency Master and Worksheet, p. 23
  Real-Life Health, p. 25
  Real-Life Health, p. 27
  5-Minute Check, p. 29
  Lesson 20 Quiz, p. 32
- **Unit 4 Transparency**
- **Lesson 20 Transparency**

- **Reading Essentials**
- **Technology**
  TeacherWorks™ CD-ROM
  StudentWorks™ CD-ROM
  Reading Essentials CD-ROM
  ExamView® Assessment Suite
  Vocabulary Puzzlemaker

National Health Education Standards
Pages 226–227: 1.5

The Female Reproductive System

Explain the Concept

Fallopian Tube The Fallopian tube also is called the oviduct or the uterine tube. The use of different terms for the same body part may confuse some students.

INTERACTIVE CHALKBOARD
with Image Bank

5-Minute Check

Page 29, **Unit 4 Fast File Resources**

1. What is puberty? *the stage of growth and development when both the male and female body become capable of producing offspring*
2. During what age range do most females reach puberty? *Physical changes usually occur between ages 8 and 15.*
3. What is body image? *the perception a person has about his or her body's appearance*
4. List the secondary sex characteristics for females. *increased height, widening hips, softer and smoother skin, growth of pubic and underarm hair, increase in breast size, enlargement of external genitalia, formation of mature ova, and onset of menstruation*
5. What are the internal female reproductive organs? *ovaries, Fallopian tubes, uterus, and vagina*

The Female Reproductive System

T he reproductive system is a major body system. Reproduction is the mechanism that maintains life from one generation to another. The **female reproductive system** consists of organs in the female body that are involved in producing offspring.

What to Know About the Female Reproductive System

Did You Know?

Slow Traveling
An ovum may take several days to move through a Fallopian tube.

External female reproductive organs
The external female reproductive organs are called the vulva. The vulva consist of the mons veneris, the labia majora, the labia minora, the clitoris, and the hymen. The **mons veneris** is the fatty tissue that covers the front of the pubic bone and serves as a protective cushion for the internal reproductive organs.

During puberty, hair begins to cover both the mons veneris and the labia majora. The **labia majora** are the heavy folds of skin that surround the opening of the vagina. The **labia minora** are two smaller folds of skin located within the labia majora. The clitoris and the openings of the urethra and the vagina are located within the labia minora.

The **clitoris** is a small structure located above the opening of the urethra. The **hymen** is a thin membrane that stretches across the opening of the vagina. The hymen has small openings in it. Some females do not have a hymen. Other females break or tear the hymen when they ride bicycles or horses or exercise strenuously.

Internal female reproductive organs
The internal female reproductive organs are the ovaries, Fallopian tubes (also known as oviducts), uterus, and vagina. The **ovaries** are female reproductive glands that produce ova and estrogen. The ovaries are situated in the lower abdomen. A female is born with between 200,000 and 400,000 immature ova in her ovaries. About 375 of these ova will mature and be released in a female's lifetime. During puberty, the ova begin to develop. Each developing ovum is enclosed in a small, hollow ball called a follicle. Each month

Fallopian tube
Ovary
Uterus
Cervix
Bladder
Vagina

▲ The internal female reproductive organs are the ovaries, the Fallopian tubes, the uterus, and the vagina.

Sensitive Issues

Reproductive Health Male and female reproductive health can be quite embarrassing for some students to discuss in a classroom environment. Provide a way for students to ask questions anonymously during this lesson. Each student can write one or more questions, fold the paper, and pass it to you. Emphasize that students should not write their names on the papers. You can choose some questions to answer at the end of class or during the next class meeting. Alternatively, students could write questions or concerns in their health journals and turn these in for you to write responses. **L1**

Just the FACTS: REPRODUCTIVE SYSTEMS

❝If a female's menstrual periods stop, isn't it is just one less thing for her to worry about?❞

the FACTS Missed periods can be a sign of trouble, including unplanned pregnancy. Excessive dieting and/or exercising also can cause a female to stop having periods. Other causes include emotional stress, depression, and the use of tranquilizers or antidepressants. A missed period usually is not a cause for celebration—it's often a warning that the body is struggling to meet its needs, physically or emotionally.

❝Should a healthy female not have menstrual cramps?❞

the FACTS Menstrual cramps are a sign that a female is healthy and ovulating. Still, not all healthy females experience cramps, and the severity varies from female to female and from one period to another. These cramps are caused when the uterus contracts to shed its lining. Severe cramps can be due to disease, such as endometriosis, a condition in which the uterine lining moves outside the uterus. Severe cramps do not automatically signal the presence of a disease. A physician can determine whether or not a disease is causing the cramps. For most females, a warm bath, moderate exercise, and ibuprofen help reduce the pain.

❝Can young males get testicular cancer?❞

the FACTS Testicular cancer is the most common cancer in males ages 20 to 34, the second most common cancer in males ages 35 to 39, and the third most common cancer in males ages 15 to 19. The testicles, the male sex glands that produce sperm, are located in the scrotum. Most cases of testicular cancer are first found by the male. About 90 percent of these cases begin as a painless or uncomfortable lump on a testicle or with swelling of a testicle. The number of deaths due to testicular cancer is dropping because of improved detection and treatment.

during a regular menstrual cycle, an ovum matures and is released from its follicle. *Ovulation* is the release of a mature ovum from one of the two ovaries.

When an ovum is released from an ovary, it enters one of the Fallopian tubes. A *Fallopian tube* (oviduct) is a tube through which an ovum moves from an ovary to the uterus. A female has two Fallopian tubes—thin tubes

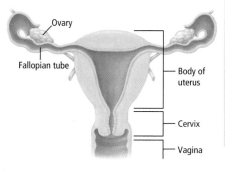

Ovary

Fallopian tube

Body of uterus

Cervix

Vagina

about four inches long. Each tube is close to an ovary. The end of each tube is shaped like a funnel.

During the menstrual cycle, a mature ovum moves toward the uterus. If fertilization occurs, it usually occurs in a Fallopian tube. An ovum that is not fertilized either disintegrates in the uterus or leaves the body during menstruation.

The *uterus* is a muscular organ that receives and supports the fertilized ovum during pregnancy and contracts during childbirth to help with delivery. The *cervix* is the lowest part of the uterus that connects to the vagina. The *vagina* is a muscular tube that connects the uterus to the outside of the body. The vagina is the female organ for sexual intercourse, the birth canal, and the passageway for the menstrual flow.

Reading Review

1. What are the names of the external female reproductive organs?

2. Where does fertilization usually occur?

Just the FACTS:

Reproductive Systems Learning about reproductive health is very important for adolescents. Choices they make today can have positive or negative consequences for their future reproductive health. Have students read each statement in Just the Facts and state why they agree or disagree. Have students identify health facts that support their positions. The discussion may uncover misconceptions students have about reproductive health. **L2**

Teacher FYI

Missed Periods In addition to the reasons listed in the first fact on the student page, a missed period may be caused by a hormone imbalance, or by polycystic ovary syndrome (PCOS). PCOS also may cause some degree of unwanted body hair and fertility problems.

Reading Review

1. *The vulva is the external female reproductive organ. It consists of the mons veneris, the labia majora, the labia minora, the clitoris, and the hymen*

2. *in a Fallopian tube*

Differentiated Instruction

Visual Impairment Ask at a local doctor's office if they would allow you to use one of their charts depicting the reproductive system. These large charts are typically found on the walls in doctors' offices and might enable a student with a visual impairment to better understand the lesson. Also, plastic molds are available in educational supply stores for understanding through tactile examination. Referring to the charts during class lectures and discussions also will benefit English language learners. **L2 ELL**

National Health Education Standards
Pages 228–229: 1.9, 2.6, 3.4

Female Reproductive Health

Female Reproductive Health

During adolescence, females start to take more and more responsibility for their own health care. The following questions and answers provide information on female reproductive health.

Did You Know?

Pap Smears The death rate from cervical cancer has decreased by 70 percent since the 1940s because of increased Pap smear screening.

What to Know About Female Reproductive Health

What products can be used to absorb the menstrual flow? Pads, panty shields or liners, and tampons are products that can be used to absorb the menstrual flow. A pad is a thick piece of cotton that is worn inside underpants, which absorbs the menstrual flow as it leaves the vagina. A pad should be changed every four to six hours. A panty shield or liner is a thin strip of cotton that is worn inside underpants to collect the menstrual flow. It is usually worn on days when flow is light and may be worn with a tampon for extra protection.

A tampon is a small tube of cotton placed inside the vagina to absorb the menstrual flow. The tampon collects the menstrual flow before any of the flow leaves the vagina. A female who wears a tampon can swim during her period without fear that the menstrual flow will get on her bathing suit or into the water. Tampons should be changed at least every four to six hours.

How can menstrual cramps be reduced? Some females have painful menstrual cramps caused by contractions of the uterus. This is normal.

A warm bath and moderate exercise may relieve the cramps. Reducing the amount of caffeine and sodium in the diet also may reduce menstrual cramps. A female can speak with her parents, guardian, or physician about using medications, such as ibuprofen, that help reduce menstrual cramps.

What is premenstrual syndrome (PMS)? A combination of physical and emotional symptoms that affect a female a week to ten days prior to menstruation is *premenstrual syndrome (PMS).* These symptoms may include weight gain, mild to severe menstrual cramps, bloating, swollen breasts, headache, backache, constipation, mood swings, cravings, anxiety, and depression.

A female can help reduce weight gain, bloating, and swelling by avoiding caffeine and salt. This reduces the chances that she will retain fluids. She also can exercise regularly to produce beta-endorphins that improve mood and reduce anxiety and depression. A physician can prescribe medications to lessen the symptoms of PMS.

Legal Issues

Toxic Shock Syndrome (TSS) In 1980, over 800 cases of TSS were reported to the Centers for Disease Control and Prevention (CDC). This was a big jump from the numbers in earlier years. Studies were conducted to determine risk factors for TSS and one factor was the use of super-absorbent tampons made from new materials. Those tampons were discontinued by the manufacturers. In 1982, the Food and Drug Administration (FDA) began requiring TSS warning labels and labels advising women to choose the lowest absorbency tampon necessary on tampon packaging. An information sheet was also included inside packages telling women that the TSS risk would be reduced by not using tampons or alternating them with sanitary pads. In part because of changes in tampon materials and education, the numbers of cases of TSS dropped to fewer than 10 per year in the late 1990s.

What causes a missed menstrual cycle?
The absence of menstruation is *amenorrhea* (ay me nuh REE uh). The menstrual cycles of some females do not begin at puberty. This type of amenorrhea may be caused by underdeveloped female reproductive organs, poor general health, and/or emotional stress. Some females miss additional menstrual cycles after their first menstrual cycle. This type of amenorrhea is often caused by pregnancy, a reduction in red blood cell levels resulting from stress, overtraining, eating disorders, drastic weight loss, or anemia.

What does a pelvic examination include? An examination of the internal female reproductive organs is a *pelvic examination.* A Pap smear usually is done when this examination is performed. A *Pap smear* is a screening test in which cells are scraped from the cervix and examined to detect cervical cancer.

What is a yeast infection? A yeast infection is a vaginal infection caused by a fungal organism. Symptoms include a thick, malodorous discharge, vaginal and labial itching, and painful urination. If you suspect you have a yeast infection, see your doctor. He or she will probably prescribe an over-the-counter ointment or prescription pill that will eliminate the infection.

What is toxic shock syndrome (TSS)? A severe illness that results when vaginal bacteria secrete a toxin that gets into the bloodstream is *toxic shock syndrome (TSS).* The incidence of TSS in the U.S. is 1–2 per 100,000 women ages 15–44. Most TSS cases occur in females who are using tampons. Early flulike symptoms of TSS include a high fever of more than 102°F, vomiting, diarrhea, dizziness, fainting, and a rash that resembles sunburn. A female's blood pressure may drop suddenly. Complications of TSS include kidney and heart failure and difficulty breathing. Females should change tampons often. Regular absorbency tampons that are changed often are better than superabsorbent tampons that are worn for longer periods of time.

A pad should be worn at night instead of a tampon. Tampon use should be discontinued if fever or other signs appear. Prompt medical care is needed if symptoms occur.

What is female infertility? A condition of the reproductive system that impairs the ability of a female to become pregnant is *infertility.* Conception, or fertilization, depends on many factors, such as the production of a healthy ovum by the female and healthy sperm by the male, and unblocked Fallopian tubes that allow the sperm to reach the ovum. Infertility is not the same as sterility, which is the inability to conceive under any circumstances.

The most common female factor in infertility is associated with ovulation. An ovum may not be released each menstrual cycle, menstrual periods may be irregular, or Fallopian tubes may be blocked.

A female can control some of the risks of infertility, including sexually transmitted diseases, tobacco and marijuana use, intense exercise over a period of time, and excessive use of alcohol. Other factors are poor general health, stress, eating disorders, drastic weight loss, and anemia.

Make the Connection

PID For more information about pelvic inflammatory disease (PID), see page 499 in Lesson 46.

Reading Review

1. What is PMS?
2. What are the symptoms of TSS?

Explain the Concept
Pelvic Exam Explain that this is a regular examination by a medical professional that should begin once a female's parents or guardian and physician decide she should start to have them, a female reaches age 18, or a female becomes sexually active. The exam includes a physical exam and an internal exam that is used to detect cervical cancer.

Teacher FYI
Bladder Infections A bladder infection is a bacterial infection that is more common in females than males because a female's urethra is much shorter than a male's, which increases the likelihood of infection. A prescription antibiotic is an appropriate treatment. A yeast infection is a fungal infection of the vaginal area that can be treated with over-the-counter medication for three to seven days.

Reading Review

1. *Premenstrual syndrome (PMS) is a combination of physical and emotional symptoms that affect a female a week to ten days prior to menstruation.*
2. *fever higher than 102°F, vomiting, diarrhea, dizziness, fainting, and a rash that resembles sunburn*

Health Project

Infertility Have students work together in groups to research the underlying causes of and available treatments for male and female infertility. Report information may include the options available to couples who are not able to conceive a child. You might want to encourage different groups to focus on different aspects of infertility, such as problems with ovulation, problems with implantation or uterine structure, or hormonal issues that cause problems after fertilization has occurred (for women) or problems with sperm production or other issues (for men). Other groups could focus on other aspects of infertility. After the research is complete, have students present the information in a newsletter format.
L2

National Health Education Standards
Pages 230–231: 1.8, 1.9, 3.4, 3.5

Protecting Female Reproductive Health

Class Activity

Protecting Reproductive Health Have female students put the tips for protecting reproductive health on this page in order from those they are most likely to do to those they are least likely to do. Then have them explain why they ordered the tips as they did. Ask students to answer these questions: What is it about the tips that are listed as least likely that makes them unlikely to be done? How might they remove barriers to do more of the listed tips? Ask male students to do the same thing with their list of tips on page 240. **L2**

NHES Assessment/SCASS

Performance Task Have students investigate the future problems that can occur with their reproductive health when they contract an STD, such as chlamydia, gonorrhea, syphilis, or genital warts. *Answers may vary, but may include sterility, ectopic pregnancy, miscarriage, stillbirth, fetal illness, mental disability, or death.* **L3**

Teaching Transparency

Page 23, **Unit 4 Fast File Resources**

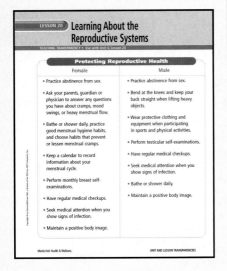

Protecting Female Reproductive Health

Protecting and maintaining the health of your reproductive system is important, not only at your present age, but also over your entire life span. How well you protect your reproductive health now will influence your health as you grow older.

How to Protect Female Reproductive Health

> **Make the Connection**
>
> **Abstinence** For more information about abstinence from sex, see page 168 in Lesson 16.

Practice abstinence from sex. Abstinence from sex is choosing not to be sexually active. Practicing abstinence prevents teen pregnancy and infection with sexually transmitted diseases.

Make a note of any questions you have about cramps, mood swings, or heavy menstrual flow. Share this information with your parents or guardian and your physician.

Practice good menstrual hygiene habits. Change your pad, panty shield, or tampon every four to six hours. Wear a pad or panty shield at night to reduce the risk of toxic shock syndrome (TSS). Change underpants often and wash your genitals daily to avoid vaginal odor.

Choose habits that prevent or lessen menstrual cramps. Exercise regularly and reduce the amount of caffeine and salt in your diet. Reducing the amount of caffeine in your diet also will help reduce the number of benign fibrocystic lumps that sometimes form in breast tissue.

Keep a calendar to record information about your menstrual cycle. Keep track of the number of days in each cycle. Keep track of the number of days that you menstruate. Know the date of your last menstrual period.

Perform monthly breast self-examinations. Safeguard your health by performing a breast self-examination each month after your menstrual flow stops.

Have regular medical checkups. Take the calendar on which you have recorded information about your menstrual cycles with you to your medical checkup. Go over the recorded information with your physician. Your parents or guardian and your physician will determine the appropriate age for you to begin having a pelvic examination and Pap smear.

Seek medical attention when you show signs of infection. Vaginal discharge, lumps, and rashes are symptoms of infection. You may have a yeast infection or a sexually transmitted disease.

Differentiated Instruction

Gifted and Talented Have students research screening tests, such as the Pap smear for cervical cancer and the PSA test for prostate cancer. Have students answer these questions: When were these tests developed? When did they start to become widely used? How accurate are the tests? What types of errors can occur and how frequently? How has the tests' use affected the incidence of these diseases and the prognosis for people who have them? How does their use affect health-care costs (including the costs of the tests themselves and any savings from earlier diagnosis, etc.)? Have students write a report that discusses these issues, as well as the process of developing acceptance for screening tests. **L3**

Activity: Using Life Skills

Practice Healthful Behaviors: Performing Breast Self-Exams

You can help safeguard your health by doing a regular self-exam of your breasts. The self-exam can help you detect lumps or changes that could be a sign of cancer. Cancer treatment is more effective when the cancer is detected early. The self-exam takes only a few minutes. If you would like to make a health behavior contract, follow these steps. 1) Write your name and the date. 2) Write the healthful behavior you want to practice as a health goal. 3) Write specific statements that describe how this healthful behavior reduces health risks. 4) Make a specific plan for recording your progress. 5) Complete an evaluation of how the plan helped you accomplish the health goal.

1 Do the self-exam once a month approximately a week after menstruation ends.

2 To feel the right breast, place your right hand behind your head and use your left hand. To feel the left breast, reverse this procedure.

3 In the shower or bath, feel each breast with three fingers, holding them flat. Move your fingers in a circular, clockwise motion over the entire breast area. Start at the outside and move toward the nipple. Include the area between the breast and the armpit and the armpit itself. Press firmly enough to feel the tissue of your breast. Check for any lumps or changes in breast tissue.

4 Repeat step 3 while lying down. Place a pillow behind your shoulder on the side you are checking.

5 Stand in front of a mirror, with your arms at your sides, and observe your breasts. Look for any changes in size or shape, such as puckering, swelling, dimpling, or changes in the skin texture or in the nipple.

6 Clasp your hands behind your head. Press your hands forward. Look again for any changes in size or shape of the breasts.

7 With your arms at your sides, gently squeeze each breast just behind the nipple. Check for any discharge.

8 If you discover any changes or something abnormal, talk to your doctor.

▲ Resources are available to help you learn how to perform a breast self-exam.

Breast cancer Breast cancer is one of the most common types of cancer in women. According to the National Cancer Institute, the following are risk factors for developing breast cancer: being over the age of 50; having no pregnancies; having a first child after the age of thirty; having a family history of breast cancer especially among immediate family members such as a mother or sister.

In addition to conducting breast self-examinations, it is important to have regular medical checkups. While most breast lumps are not cancerous, many females will develop breast cancer.

There are several options in treating breast cancer. In a lumpectomy, the lump itself and a small amount of surrounding tissue are removed. In a partial mastectomy, the lump, some breast tissue, the lining over the chest muscles beneath the tumor, and some lymph nodes are removed. In a total mastectomy, the entire breast and possibly a few lymph nodes may be removed. These procedures may be followed by chemotherapy or radiation. It is important to understand that with early detection and treatment, the chances of successfully treating breast cancer increase.

LESSON 20 • Learning About the Reproductive Systems **233**

Achieving Health Literacy

Self-Directed Learner Encourage females to learn how to perform breast self-exams. They should make sure to practice each step until they are comfortable with the process. They also should plan when they will perform the exam each month. Some students may be hesitant to do so for fear of finding cancer. Reassure them by explaining that self-examination is about knowing what is normal, so if things change at some point in their life, they may have an easier time detecting it. Ask students to write a list in their health journals of reasons that would motivate them to practice self-examination regularly. Reasons may include to be there for family and friends, to prevent illness from disrupting future plans, and to set a good example for others. **L2**

Explain the Concept

Female Reproductive Cycle

Menstruation begins at the onset of puberty for females and will continue until they reach menopause later in life. Not all females have a cycle that is regular in terms of number of days between periods, missing periods, length of periods, or symptoms during periods.

Class Discussion

Menstrual Cycle Discuss the normal changes that occur during the average 28-day process and what things could cause changes in the cycle. Ask students to answer these questions: Other than pregnancy, what factors might cause a woman to miss a period? What symptoms might some females notice during their cycles in addition to bleeding at menstruation? **L2**

NHES Assessment/SCASS

Selected Response What is the name of the temporary gland that secretes progesterone to support a pregnancy?

A. uterus
B. *corpus luteum*
C. ovum
D. Fallopian tube

Reading Review

1. *It helps a woman detect lumps or changes that could be a sign of cancer.*
2. *Abstinence prevents pregnancy, STDs, the sexual transmission of HIV, and emotional trauma associated with adolescent sexual activity.*
3. *every 28 days*

The Menstrual Cycle

The monthly series of changes that involves ovulation, changes in the uterine lining, and menstruation is the *menstrual cycle.* The period in the menstrual cycle in which the unfertilized egg and the lining of the uterus leave the body is *menstruation.*

What to Know About the Menstrual Cycle

Reading Review

1. How does doing a breast self-exam reduce health risks?
2. List health risks that can be avoided by practicing abstinence.
3. How often do most women have their period?

Record information about your menstrual cycle on a calendar and take it to your medical checkups.

Females often describe menstruation as their "period." The menstrual cycle usually occurs over 28 days. This means a female will have her period every 28 days. However, many teens have irregular cycles and the length of their menstrual cycles varies. Menstruation usually lasts about five days; however, the number of days also may vary. Refer to the outline that follows for the series of changes that occur during a 28-day menstrual cycle. Pages 232–233 in this lesson discuss female reproductive health and how to protect it.

Days 1–5 Menstruation occurs. The menstrual flow consists of about two ounces of blood. Some females may notice small particles. These are small pieces of uterine lining. At the same time, a new ovum is maturing in the ovary.

Days 6–12 The uterine lining begins to thicken. The uterus prepares for ovulation and the possibility that an ovum will be fertilized.

Days 13–14 Ovulation occurs. A follicle in an ovary bursts, and an ovum is released into one of the Fallopian tubes.

Days 15–20 The corpus luteum secretes hormones to support a pregnancy. The *corpus luteum* is a temporary gland that secretes progesterone. The corpus luteum is formed when the remains of the burst follicle close. *Progesterone* is a hormone that changes the lining of the uterus. As the uterine lining changes, it prepares to support a fertilized ovum. If an ovum is fertilized, the corpus luteum continues to secrete progesterone throughout pregnancy.

Days 21–28 The corpus luteum disintegrates if an ovum is not fertilized. Progesterone is no longer secreted. The cells in the lining of the uterus die without progesterone. The unfertilized ovum disintegrates. The menstrual cycle begins again with menstruation.

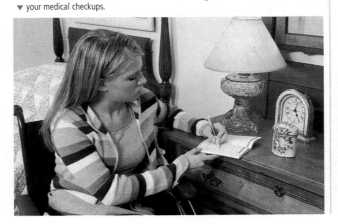

234 UNIT 4 • Growth and Development

Cross-Curricular Connections

Social Studies Have students research how females are treated during their menstrual cycle. In some countries or cultures, the first menstrual cycle is celebrated, and in other countries or cultures menstruating women must go to a special place away from others. Students also could research how treatment during menstruation may have changed over the course of history. Use care when discussing this topic so as not to embarrass students of other nationalities. Have students write a magazine article describing their findings. **L3**

Puberty in Males

P uberty is the stage of growth and development when both the male and female bodies become capable of producing offspring. It is a period of great physical and emotional changes.

What to Know About Puberty in Males

During puberty, the male's pituitary gland increases its production of a hormone called luteinizing hormone (LH). LH travels through the bloodstream to the testes and causes them to secrete testosterone.

Testosterone is a hormone that produces the male secondary sex characteristics. Secondary sex characteristics are the emotional and the physical changes that occur during puberty.

How to manage emotions During puberty, a male may notice that he has sudden emotional changes and sexual feelings. Testosterone is responsible for causing these changes. As testosterone levels fluctuate, a male experiences sudden changes in his emotions.

A male may become angry or say things he does not mean to say. He may feel insecure or edgy for no reason. He may be puzzled when he has such intense feelings, but he should know that changes in emotions are normal during puberty.

Males are accountable for the way they respond to emotional changes. Lesson 10 explains how to express emotions in healthful ways.

The increase in testosterone that happens during puberty also produces

sexual feelings. Sexual feelings result from a strong physical and emotional attraction to another person. Males must learn to set limits, stick to these limits, and practice abstinence. Lesson 16 explains how to set limits and how to resist pressure to be sexually active.

How to accept physical changes Physical changes that occur in a male during puberty become noticeable between the ages of 12 and 15. The maturing process that happens in puberty is affected by several factors, including heredity, diet, health habits, and health status.

For example, a male who regularly lifts weights may develop a more muscular body than a male who does not. Another example is a male who is short for his age. He may have biological relatives who also are short.

Did You Know?

Voice Change As a male matures, his voice has a deeper tone and his Adam's apple becomes more prominent.

Male Secondary Sex Characteristics

Following are some physical changes that occur during puberty:

- increase in height
- longer and heavier bones
- broader shoulders
- thicker and tougher skin
- deepened voice

- growth of facial hair, pubic hair, and body hair
- enlargement of penis, scrotum, and testes
- formation of sperm

LESSON 20 • Learning About the Reproductive Systems   **235**

Puberty in Males

Class Discussion

Puberty Ask students to discuss how males and females can deal with the physical and emotional changes that take place during puberty. Draw a Venn diagram on the chalkboard with one circle for females and one for males. The circles should overlap. Physical and emotional changes that occur during puberty can be written in the appropriate circle or the overlap to indicate whether they affect females, males, or both. **L2**

NHES Assessment/SCASS

Constructed Response Have students look at the lists of male and female (page 227) secondary sex characteristics and compare and contrast them. Ask students which characteristic changes are common to both sexes at puberty. *Both sexes experience changes in skin and hair growth.* Ask students which characteristic changes differ between males and females. Have students write the answers to these questions in their health journals. **L2**

Family Involvement

Changes Over Time Have students discuss with family members changes in the appearances of young males and females today versus when the students' grandparents were growing up. Have students answer these questions: What things are different today in terms of age at puberty, size, nutrition, involvement in sports, and environment? What might be causing the differences? What other types of appearance changes, if any, such as permanent body changes like piercings or tattoos, come up in the discussion with family members? Have a class discussion to share what was learned from students' families. **L2**

National Health Education Standards
Pages 234–235: 1.7, 2.3

The Male Reproductive System

The Male Reproductive System

Class Discussion

Sperm Path Ask students to discuss the path sperm travel before exiting the body. Have students describe which body parts sperm travel through and what happens in each area. **L2**

Teacher FYI

Variocele A variocele is a varicose vein that develops in the scrotum. In some cases, a variocele can lead to male infertility problems. Surgery to repair the variocele can improve fertility.

Class Discussion

Body Image Have students look through magazines and discuss the body image messages they see for both males and females. Ask students to answer these questions: Are the messages the same for both sexes? Are they realistic? Do people in magazines look like many of the people that students see in their community? If not, why not? **L2** **ELL**

The male reproductive system consists of organs in the male body that are involved in producing offspring. The physical changes that produce sexual maturity are caused by the increased production of male hormones.

What to Know About the Male Reproductive System

Did You Know?

Sexual Maturity Sexual maturity usually occurs later in males than in females.

External male reproductive organs The external organs of the male reproductive system are the penis and the scrotum. The *penis* is the male sex organ used for reproduction and urination. The *scrotum* is a saclike pouch that hangs under the penis and holds the testes. The scrotum helps regulate the temperature of the testes.

The *testicles* are male reproductive glands that produce sperm cells and the hormone testosterone. The scrotum hangs from the body so that the testes have a temperature 3–5 degrees lower than the rest of the body. If it becomes too cool, the scrotum will contract, bringing the testes closer to the body for warmth. Sperm are protected in this way.

Sperm are male reproductive cells. A sperm is made up of a head, which contains the nucleus of the cell; a body; and a tail. A sperm measures about 1/6000th of an inch long. Sperm make up about 2–5 percent of semen.

Internal male reproductive organs The internal male reproductive organs include the testes, seminiferous tubules, epididymis, vas deferens, seminal vesicles, ejaculatory duct, prostate gland, Cowper's glands, and urethra.

The testes are divided into several sections that are filled with seminiferous tubules. The *seminiferous* (se muh NIH fuh ruhs) *tubules* are a network of coiled tubules in which sperm are produced. *Spermatogenesis* (spur mah tuh JE nuh suhs) is the process by which sperm are produced. Sperm development is a result of a hormone produced by the pituitary gland.

After sperm are produced in the seminiferous tubules, they move by contractions from the testes to the epididymis. The *epididymis* (e puh DIH duh mus) is a comma-shaped structure along the upper rear surface of the testes. Sperm mature in the epididymis. Some sperm are stored in the epididymis, but most move to the vas deferens after they mature.

The *vas deferens* are two long, thin tubes that act as a passageway for sperm and a place for sperm storage. They extend from the epididymis in the scrotum up into the abdomen. The walls of the vas deferens are lined with cilia.

Differentiated Instruction

Hearing Impairment Hearing impaired students may learn better with visual cues and when topics are broken down into smaller chunks of information. Have students work in pairs to create flash cards of the male and female reproductive system. The body part listed on one side can be defined on the other side. Have students work in pairs to test each other on identifying parts of the reproductive systems. They can review the material again at home. **L2** **ELL**

Explain the Concept

Urethra Although most parts of the reproductive systems are different for males and females, both sexes have a urethra. The urethra is much longer in males than in females. In males, the urethra carries both urine and semen, whereas in females, the urethra carries only urine.

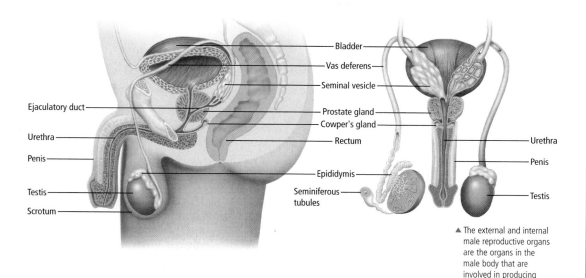

▲ The external and internal male reproductive organs are the organs in the male body that are involved in producing offspring.

The contractions of the vas deferens, along with the action of the cilia, help transport sperm. In the abdomen, the vas deferens circle the bladder and connect with the ducts of the seminal vesicles to form the ejaculatory duct.

The *seminal vesicles* are two elongated saclike glands at the base of the bladder that secrete a fluid rich in sugar that nourishes the sperm and helps them move. They contribute up to 60 percent of the fluid in ejaculate.

The *ejaculatory duct* is a short, straight tube that passes into the prostate gland and opens into the urethra. The urethra serves as a passageway for sperm and urine to leave the body.

The *prostate gland* is a gland that produces a fluid that helps keep sperm alive. The prostate gland is about the size of a chestnut. The prostate gland is located beneath the bladder and surrounds the urethra. Without the fluid from the prostate gland, fertilization would be almost impossible because many sperm would die.

The *Cowper's glands* are located beneath the prostate gland. The Cowper's glands are two small glands about the size of peas that secrete a clear, lubricating fluid into the urethra as part of the semen.

Semen is the fluid that is released by the reproductive tract. Semen contains sperm and fluids from the seminal vesicles, prostate gland, and Cowper's glands.

An *erection* is a process that occurs when the penis swells with blood and elongates. An erection may be followed by ejaculation.

Ejaculation is the passage of semen from the penis and is a result of a series of involuntary muscular contractions. After ejaculation, the penis returns to a nonerect state.

Quick Demo

Lifting Technique Bring a large, empty or light box into the classroom to demonstrate appropriate lifting technique. Be sure to bend your knees and keep your back straight so you lift with your legs, not with your back. Lifting objects correctly can help prevent an inguinal hernia.

Reading Review

1. *a hormone that produces the male secondary sex characteristics*
2. *the testes*
3. *the process by which sperm are produced*

Reading Review

1. What is testosterone?
2. What are the male glands that produce sperm cells?
3. What is spermatogenesis?

🗂 Family Involvement

Family Reproductive Health History Have students interview family members for any history of reproductive diseases, such as prostate or breast cancer. Students who are not living with their biological families may ask if anything is known about the history of reproductive diseases in their biological families. If not, they can ask about reproductive health history in their adoptive families. Students also could ask about any fertility issues in the family, such as genetic birth defects or history of miscarriage or stillbirth. Other topics they can examine are their family members' diets and exercise habits. A healthful diet and regular exercise can help reduce the risk of developing some cancers, including breast cancer. Ask students to add any new information they discover to their family health histories and personal health records. **L2**

Male Reproductive Health

There are many physical changes that an adolescent male experiences that are a normal part of maturing. The following questions and answers provide information on issues related to male reproductive health.

What to Know About Male Reproductive Health

What is circumcision? The end of the penis is covered by a piece of skin called the foreskin. *Circumcision* is the surgical removal of the foreskin from the penis. This procedure usually is performed on the second day after birth. Circumcision may reduce the risk of urinary infections and cancer of the penis. Males who are not circumcised should pull the foreskin back and cleanse the penis regularly to prevent smegma from collecting. *Smegma* (SMEG muh) is a substance that forms under the foreskin, consisting of dead skin and other secretions.

What causes an inguinal hernia? In a developing fetus, the testes pass from the abdomen into the scrotum through the inguinal canal during the seventh month of pregnancy. Then the inguinal canal closes to keep the intestines from also passing into the scrotum. In some males, the inguinal canal does not completely close off. The intestines pass into the inguinal canal and the male develops an inguinal hernia. An *inguinal hernia* is a hernia in which some of the intestine pushes through the inguinal canal into the scrotum. Lifting heavy objects sometimes stresses this area and is the cause of the hernia. An inguinal hernia may be painful. It can be repaired surgically.

How can having mumps after puberty cause sterility? Mumps is a viral infection that affects the salivary glands. Mumps usually occurs in childhood. There is a vaccine to prevent mumps, but some people do not get mumps in childhood, nor do they get the mumps vaccine. If a male has mumps after puberty, the virus can affect the testes. The virus causes swelling of the testes. The seminiferous tubules may be crushed and become incapable of producing sperm. This causes sterility. *Sterility* is the inability to produce offspring.

Why should males have a digital rectal examination? Prostate cancer is the second most common cancer in males. A major symptom of prostate cancer is an enlarged prostate. Physicians use digital rectal examinations to examine males for symptoms of prostate cancer. A *digital rectal examination* is an examination in which the physician inserts a finger into the rectum and examines

 Cross-Curricular Connections

Social Studies Have students research the cultural reasons for family beliefs about male circumcision. Small groups of students may study different cultures and write a report describing their findings. Have groups study cultures from different parts of the world. Then, discuss the similarities and differences between cultures, including circumcision rates, age at circumcision, and rituals associated with the procedure, as well as any other interesting facts they find. Ask students if they found information about the historical origins of the traditions in the culture they studied. Be sensitive when discussing this topic so as not to embarrass students from different cultures. **L3**

Activity: Using Life Skills

Practice Healthful Behaviors: Performing Testicular Self-Exams

You can help safeguard your health by doing a regular exam of your testicles. The exams can help you detect lumps or changes that could be a sign of cancer. Cancer treatment is more effective when the cancer is detected early. Each self-exam takes only a few minutes. If you would like to make a health behavior contract, follow these steps. 1) Write your name and the date. 2) Write the healthful behavior you want to practice as a health goal. 3) Write specific statements that describe how this healthful behavior reduces health risks. 4) Make a specific plan for recording your progress. 5) Complete an evaluation of how the plan helped you accomplish the health goal.

1 Do the self-exam once a month after a bath or shower.

2 Examine each testicle one at a time with both hands. Gently roll each testicle between the thumb and fingers. Becoming familiar with how your testicles feel will help you spot changes.

3 When you are examining your right testicle, prop your right leg on a chair or stool. Place your left leg on the chair or stool when you are examining your left testicle.

4 Find the epididymis, which feels like a cord behind each testicle. Next, find the vas deferens, which is above the epididymis in each testicle. It feels like a smooth, firm tube.

5 Feel the front and side of each testicle. If you notice any hard lumps, tenderness, or unusual changes, contact your physician.

the internal reproductive organs and the rectum for irregularities. The American Cancer Society recommends that males over the age of 40 have a digital rectal examination annually. Having a PSA (Prostate Specific Antigen) test also is recommended for males over 50. A male should have this test at age 40 if there is a family history of prostate cancer. This blood test detects if protein production in the prostate is elevated. If it is, it can mean that cancer of the prostate exists.

What is testicular self-examination? Testicular cancer is one of the most common cancers among males between the ages of 15 and 34. The best way to detect testicular cancer is by doing regular testicular self-examinations. A *testicular self-examination* is a screening procedure for testicular cancer in which a male checks his testes for lumps or tenderness. If detected early, testicular cancer has a high rate of cure. Teen males should begin the habit of performing testicular self-examination.

What is male infertility? Infertility is a condition in which the ability to produce offspring is impaired. The prime cause of male infertility concerns his sperm. Sperm may be affected by mumps, sexually transmitted diseases, injuries, or hormone disorders.

Some risks of infertility can be controlled. These include exposure to STDs, tobacco and marijuana use, intense exercise over a period of time, and excessive use of alcohol.

▲ Publications are good sources of information on how to perform a testicular self-exam.

Reading Review

1. What is one possible cause of an inguinal hernia?
2. What is a PSA test?

Achieving Health Literacy

Effective Communicator Have students research and write a biographical magazine article about a celebrity who has had testicular cancer. Examples of celebrities whom they could choose are bicyclist Lance Armstrong, figure skater Scott Hamilton, comedian Tom Green, football players Brian Piccolo or Dan Turk or golfer Todd Barranger. The articles should include as much detail as students can find about the age at diagnosis, type of testicular cancer, treatment received, and the outcome of treatment. Students should be encouraged to share their article with family and friends to increase awareness of testicular cancer. **L2**

Reading Review

1. *It keeps your external reproductive organs clean to prevent infection and odor.*
2. *discharge from the penis, tenderness in the scrotum, lumps, and rashes*

3 Assess

Vocabulary Practice

Page 22, **Unit 4 Fast File Resources**

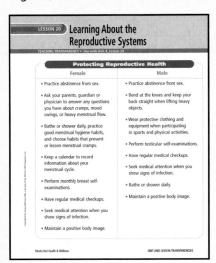

LESSON 20 **Learning About the Reproductive Systems**

TEACHING TRANSPARENCY • Use with Unit 4, Lesson 20

Protecting Reproductive Health

Female	Male
• Practice abstinence from sex.	• Practice abstinence from sex.
• Ask your parents, guardian or physician to answer any questions you have about cramps, mood swings, or heavy menstrual flow.	• Bend at the knees and keep your back straight when lifting heavy objects.
• Bathe or shower daily, practice good menstrual hygiene habits, and choose habits that prevent or lessen menstrual cramps.	• Wear protective clothing and equipment when participating in sports and physical activities.
	• Perform testicular self-examinations.
• Keep a calendar to record information about your menstrual cycle.	• Have regular medical checkups.
• Perform monthly breast self-examinations.	• Seek medical attention when you show signs of infection.
• Have regular medical checkups.	• Bathe or shower daily.
• Seek medical attention when you show signs of infection.	• Maintain a positive body image.
• Maintain a positive body image.	

Meeks Heit Health & Wellness.

UNIT AND LESSON TRANSPARENCIES

The care given to one body system affects the entire body. Protecting the reproductive system will help maintain and promote overall health now and in the future. Having regular check-ups is an important part of protecting health.

How to Protect Male Reproductive Health

Make the Connection

Healthful Behaviors For more information on practicing healthful behaviors, see page 27 in Lesson 3.

Practice abstinence from sex. Abstinence from sex is choosing not to be sexually active. Practicing abstinence prevents teen pregnancy and infection with sexually transmitted diseases, including HIV.

Bend at the knees and keep your back straight when lifting heavy objects. Use the correct technique when lifting heavy objects to help prevent the risk of an inguinal hernia.

Wear protective clothing and equipment when participating in sports and physical activities. Athletic supporters can be worn to provide extra support for the penis and testes. You should wear protective equipment, such as a cup, to prevent injury to these organs.

Perform testicular self-examinations. Testicular cancer is one of the most common cancers in younger males. Teen males should examine their testes for lumps and tenderness.

Have regular medical checkups. Your physician will perform an examination and discuss the ways your body is changing. Your physician also will answer any questions you have.

Seek medical attention when you show signs of infection. A discharge from the penis, tenderness in the scrotum, lumps, and rashes are symptoms of sexually transmitted diseases (STDs).

Bathe or shower daily. Keep your external reproductive organs clean to prevent infection and odor.

Maintain a positive body image. During puberty, a male must become comfortable with his maturing body. Body image is the perception a person has of his or her body's appearance. A male is more likely to have a positive body image when he is knowledgeable about his body. For example, he should be aware that the growth spurt in males occurs later than it does in females and that males mature at different rates. A male should try not to compare his body to those of other males. A teen male should not compare his body to a professional athlete's body. Professional athletes are older and have completed training programs that have affected their bodies. A male should ask his parents, guardian, or physician questions he has about growth and development.

Reading Review

1. Why is a daily bath or shower a good plan?
2. What are symptoms of sexually transmitted diseases?

Healthy People 2010

Objective 25-12 *Increase the number of positive messages related to responsible sexual behavior during weekday and nightly prime-time television programming.*

The Healthy People 2010 document states that "television messages hold the potential to promote responsible sexual behaviors, such as abstinence . . ." Ask students if they know of any TV shows that promote abstinence. If they do, discuss the messages they send. Ask students how citizens could increase the number of TV shows that promote abstinence. *Answers might include: Watch shows that promote abstinence so their ratings will go up and TV networks will note their popularity and perhaps create more shows that promote abstinence. Another answer might be to write to networks and ask for more shows that promote abstinence.* **L3**

National Health Education Standards

Pages 240–241: 1.5

Key Terms Review

Match the following definitions with the lesson Key Terms on the left. Do not write in this book.

corpus luteum
Cowper's gland
epididymis
Fallopian tube
ovaries
Pap smear
prostate gland
puberty
testicles
testosterone
uterus
vas deferens

1. a comma-shaped structure along the upper rear surface of the testes

2. the stage of growth and development when females and males are able to reproduce

3. secrete a clear, lubricating fluid into the urethra

4. receives and supports a fertilized ovum

5. another name for an oviduct

6. produces a fluid that helps keep sperm alive

7. act as a passageway for sperm to travel

8. a screening test to detect cervical cancer

9. produce ova

10. hormone that produces male secondary sex characteristics

Recalling the Facts

11. What accounts for the fluctuating emotions in adolescents?

12. What are the symptoms of TSS?

13. What are the changes that occur during adolescence? Why are they important?

14. What is a Pap smear?

15. What is spermatogenesis?

16. What are four risk factors for breast cancer?

17. How often should a female conduct a breast self-examination?

18. What can males and females do to protect their fertility?

Critical Thinking

19. List three ways to protect your reproductive health. Explain why each is important and how you will plan to make each one part of your daily activity.

20. Why is a testicular self-examination important for a male?

21. How is the prostate gland related to fertilization?

22. Discuss how being aware of your reproductive health will help prepare you for adulthood.

Real-Life Applications

23. Why might moderate exercise help relieve menstrual cramps?

24. Explain the connection between abstinence and HIV infection.

25. How will protecting your reproductive system help you maintain and promote your overall health now and in the future?

26. Why are you more apt to have a positive body image when you are educated about your anatomy and physiology?

Activities

Responsible Decision Making

27. **Write** Your friend John tells you that his older brother had recently noticed that he had a lump next to one of his testicles. It is not painful, so his brother has decided that he will not do anything about it. Write a letter explaining to John why you think it is important for his brother to have a medical checkup. Refer to the Responsible Decision-Making Model on page 61 for help.

Sharpen Your Life Skills

28. **Use Communication Skills**

Suppose you are a physician who writes a column for a women's magazine. Respond to a letter from a woman who has been trying to lose weight in a hurry. She skips breakfast and lunch and exercises for two hours every day. She feels tired and has missed her last two menstrual periods. She has not been sexually active. She wants to know why she hasn't had a period.

Visit **www.glencoe.com** for more *Health & Wellness* quizzes.

Key Terms Review

1. epididymis
2. puberty
3. Cowper's gland
4. uterus
5. Fallopian tube
6. prostate glands
7. vas deferens
8. Pap smear
9. ovaries
10. testosterone

Recalling the Facts

11. estrogen, testosterone, and other hormones
12. See page 231.
13. See pages 227 and 235.
14. a screening test for cervical cancer
15. See page 236.
16. See page 233.
17. once a month
18. See pages 231 and 239.

Critical Thinking

19. See pages 232 and 240 for females and males, respectively.

20. It is a safeguard against cancer and other problems, and makes it possible to get medical help in an early stage of a problem.

21. The prostate gland produces a fluid that helps keep sperm alive. Live sperm are essential for fertilization to occur.

22. Awareness of reproductive health can prepare you for maintaining your health and for becoming a parent in the future.

Real-Life Applications

23. Moderate exercise improves circulation, provides a feeling of well-being, and relieves anxiety.

24. Abstinence prevents sexual transmission of HIV.

25. Infections or diseases of the reproductive system can affect your overall health now and in the future.

26. Having an understanding of what changes to expect during puberty will help people to adapt and to manage emotional changes. Teens will understand that people mature at different rates and will avoid comparing themselves with others.

Activities

Responsible Decision Making

27. A lump in the testicle could be an indication of testicular cancer. The earlier testicular cancer is detected and treated, the greater the chance of recovery.

Sharpen Your Life Skills

28. In the response, students might include concerns that amenorrhea is a sign that the body is struggling to meet its needs. The woman should eat healthy meals and exercise more moderately.

Learning About Pregnancy and Childbirth

 Out of Time?

If time does not permit an in-depth study of this topic, use the following activities in this Teacher Wraparound Edition:

- 5-Minute Check, p. 244
- Class Discussion, p. 246
- Class Activity, p. 247
- Family Involvement, p. 250

1 Focus

HEALTH GOAL **Learn About Pregnancy and Childbirth** Have students respond to the Health Goal for this lesson by asking them why learning about pregnancy and childbirth might be important for them as teenagers. Answers may vary, but should include: *to help prevent an unplanned pregnancy, or to have knowledge about prenatal care so that they will have a healthy baby when they are older.*
L2

 ABOUT IT!

Journaling Student responses should indicate that they encourage the aunt to talk to her doctor. Some prescription medications can cause birth defects or other problems for the mother or fetus.
L2

LESSON 21

Learning About Pregnancy and Childbirth

HEALTH GOAL • **I will learn about pregnancy and childbirth.**

Knowing about the human body also entails learning about conception and childbirth. In this lesson, you will learn about heredity and the process of development. You will discover facts about the way a cell grows and develops into a human being.

What You'll Learn

1. Explain how a baby is conceived and how the baby's sex and inherited traits are determined. *(p. 243)*
2. Explain how pregnancy is determined. *(p. 246)*
3. Explain why prenatal care is important. *(p. 248)*
4. Describe the three stages of labor. *(p. 250)*

Why It's Important

The understanding of growth and development begins with pregnancy. Understanding how pregnancy occurs and the importance of a healthy pregnancy is an important step in a healthy development throughout the life cycle.

Key Terms

- fertilization
- chromosome
- gene
- amniocentesis
- ultrasound
- embryo
- placenta
- fetal alcohol syndrome (FAS)
- labor
- afterbirth

 ABOUT IT!

Writing About Parenthood Suppose your aunt and uncle announce that they are having a baby. Your aunt wants to keep taking a certain prescription medication during her pregnancy. She does not think it is important to tell her physician what she wants to do. After reading the information about prenatal care on pages 248 and 249, write an entry in your health journal about what you might advise your aunt to do.

National Health Education Standards—Guide for Lesson 21					
1.1	Predict how healthy behaviors can impact health status.	pp. 248–249	2.10	Analyze how public health policies and government regulations can influence health promotion and disease prevention.	p. 248
1.4	Analyze how genetics and family history can impact personal health.	pp. 243, 244, 245	3.3	Determine the accessibility of products and services that enhance health.	p. 249
1.5	Propose ways to reduce or prevent injuries and health problems.	pp. 248–249, 253			
1.6	Analyze the relationship between access to health care and health status.	p. 249	3.4	Determine when professional health services may be required.	p. 251
1.9	Analyze the potential severity of injury or illness if engaging in unhealthy behaviors.	pp. 248, 253	8.1	Utilize accurate peer and societal norms to formulate a health-enhancing message.	pp. 248–249

Conception and Heredity

The union of an ovum and a sperm is *conception*, or **fertilization**. One ovum matures and is released from an ovary each month. Once an ovum is released, it enters a Fallopian tube (sometimes called an oviduct). As the ovum moves through the Fallopian tube, it can be fertilized if sperm are present. Conception usually occurs in the upper-third portion of a Fallopian tube.

What to Know About Conception and Heredity

At conception, heredity is determined. *Heredity* is the passing of characteristics from biological parents to their children. All body cells, except sperm and ova, contain 23 pairs of chromosomes. A *chromosome* is a threadlike structure that carries genes. A *gene* is a unit of hereditary material.

Chromosomes in men and women In a female, the 23 pairs of chromosomes are identical. In a male, one pair of chromosomes is not made up of identical chromosomes.

In both males and females, one pair is called the sex chromosomes. In females, the pair of sex chromosomes is identical and is called XX. Every ovum produced by a female contains an X chromosome.

In males, the pair of sex chromosomes is not identical and is called XY. Sperm produced by a male contain either an X chromosome or a Y chromosome which determines a baby's sex.

The presence of a Y chromosome is essential for the development of male characteristics and the presence of an X chromosome is essential for the development of female characteristics. The sex of a baby is determined by the sex chromosome from the father. When a sperm fertilizes an ovum, a full complement, or set, of 46 chromosomes (23 from the father and 23 from the mother) is present in the resulting cell.

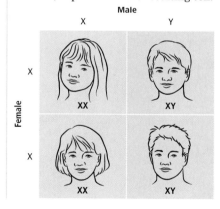

Male

	X	Y
Female X	XX	XY
X	XX	XY

◄ The sex of a baby is determined by the possible combinations of the X and Y chromosomes.

2 Teach

Class Activity

Heredity Have students bring in pictures of parents and their children to look for shared characteristics. They could bring in pictures of themselves and their parents. Alternatively, they could find pictures of celebrity parents and their children in magazines. This topic needs to be handled sensitively so that students who are not living with their biological parents do not feel bad. **L2 ELL**

PowerPoint® Presentations

This CD-ROM is an editable Microsoft® PowerPoint® presentation that includes:
- Lesson presentations
- Lesson checks
- Interactive graphics
- 5-Minute Checks
- Image Bank
- All transparencies

Discussion Refer to the Read-and-Say-Something Strategy on page 17T. Have groups of students silently read the information under each subtopic, then take turns saying one thing about the subtopic until it has been thoroughly covered.

National Health Education Standards
Pages 242–243: 1.5

Did You Know?

Chromosome Count Some genetic disorders are the result of abnormal chromosome numbers. Down syndrome, for example, involves an extra chromosome.

If a sperm with an X chromosome fertilizes an ovum, the resulting cell will have an XX pair of sex chromosomes. A fertilized ovum with an XX set of chromosomes develops into a female. If a sperm with a Y chromosome fertilizes an ovum, the resulting cell will have an XY pair of sex chromosomes. A fertilized ovum with an XY set of chromosomes develops into a male.

Genes All chromosomes carry genes that contain hereditary material. Sex-linked characteristics are hereditary characteristics that are transmitted on the sex chromosomes. For example, the X chromosome carries genes for traits such as color vision and blood clotting. The Y chromosome does not carry matching genes for those or other traits. Therefore, when the X and Y chromosomes are present together, the genes on the X chromosome control those traits.

A dominant gene influences a child's appearance.

Inherited characteristics Inherited characteristics are determined by genes carried on chromosomes. Genes are arranged on chromosomes somewhat like beads on a necklace. Just as chromosomes are paired, so are genes.

There are two genes for every trait. One is located on each chromosome that makes up a pair.

If the maternal and paternal genes for a trait are different, one will override the other. A ***dominant gene*** is a gene that overrides the expression of the other gene. A ***recessive gene*** is a gene whose expression is overridden by the other gene.

For example, a paternal gene for brown eyes might line up with a maternal gene for blue eyes. In this case the gene for brown eyes will keep the gene for blue eyes from being expressed.

The gene for brown eyes is dominant. The gene for blue eyes is recessive because it is not expressed when the dominant gene for eye color is present.

If an offspring inherits recessive genes for eye color from both parents, the offspring will have blue eyes. Other examples of dominance in humans are curly hair over straight hair and dark hair over blond hair.

Genetic counseling A couple may receive genetic counseling to prepare for parenthood. In some cases, a physician may recommend that a pregnant female have a test for possible genetic defects. ***Genetic counseling*** is a process in which a trained professional interprets medical information concerning genetics to prospective parents.

244 UNIT 4 • Growth and Development

Health Project

Genetic Disorders Have students research genetic disorders and how they develop. Some disorders that they could study include hemophilia, albinism, Huntington disease, muscular dystrophy, Down syndrome, sickle-cell anemia or phenylketonuria (PKU). Ask students to answer these questions: What is currently being done to prevent or detect the disorders? What can be done to help those who have the disorders? Have students create a visual aid to assist in sharing their projects with the class. Genetic disorders need to be handled sensitively in class, as students may have a genetic disorder or know someone who does. **L3**

◀ Ultrasound examination is a painless procedure.

Quick Demo

Ultrasound If available, share pictures of an ultrasound to see if students can identify what they are looking at. Ultrasounds that clearly show different body parts—such as the spine, hand, foot, heart, and face—would be ideal, but not necessary.

NHES Assessment/SCASS

Selected Response Which of these traits is determined by genes on the X chromosome only?

A. hair color
B. eye color
C. hair texture
D. *color vision*

Reading Review

1. *the sex chromosome it receives from the father*
2. *A dominant gene overrides the expression of a recessive gene.*
3. *Amniocentesis involves inserting a needle through the uterus to extract fluid from the amniotic sac. The fluid contains genetic information. Ultrasound uses high-frequency sound waves to provide an image of the developing baby.*

Amniocentesis (am nee oh sen TEE suhs) is a diagnostic procedure in which a needle is inserted through the uterus to extract fluid from the amniotic sac. The *amniotic sac* is a pouch of fluid that surrounds a fetus. The extracted fluid contains valuable genetic information about the fetus.

Cells extracted from the amniotic fluid are analyzed to determine if any genetic defects are present. The sex of the fetus also may be revealed.

If necessary, the procedure is performed in the second trimester of a pregnancy. Amniocentesis usually is safe for both the mother and the fetus. It is recommended for women over 35 and women who are at risk for giving birth to a baby with genetic or chromosomal disorders.

Ultrasound is another diagnostic procedure used to monitor the fetus. With ultrasound, high-frequency sound waves are used to provide an image of the developing baby. Then, the physician evaluates the image.

Ultrasound can be used to confirm pregnancy and to confirm that the pregnancy is within the uterus, rather than in the Fallopian tube (a condition known as an ectopic pregnancy). Ultrasound also can be used to assess the size and growth of the fetus and to help a doctor diagnose any problems the mother might be having.

This ultrasound procedure often takes place in the first trimester of a pregnancy. Further ultrasounds during the pregnancy help monitor the growth of the fetus.

The procedure is safe for both the mother and the fetus. With ultrasound, some problems can be diagnosed before birth and some can even be treated while the fetus is still in the uterus.

Ultrasound also reveals the sex of the fetus and if there is more than one fetus in the uterus. Knowing ahead about the presence of a birth defect is helpful in planning how to care for the baby after birth.

Make the Connection

Body Systems For more information on the female reproductive system, see page 228 in Lesson 20.

Reading Review

1. What determines the sex of a baby?
2. How does a dominant gene differ from a recessive gene?
3. How does amniocentesis differ from ultrasound?

LESSON 21 • Learning About Pregnancy and Childbirth **245**

Sensitive Issues

Birth Defects There may be some students who have birth defects or have siblings or other relatives with birth defects. Use care to avoid personal questions and to lead discussions away from a specific student who may have an apparent birth defect. Keep in mind that some birth defects are not apparent, so affected students may feel uncomfortable even though others do not realize why they would. In advance, find magazine articles about children who have birth defects who are not related to any of your students in order to keep the discussion away from students' personal experiences. **L2**

National Health Education Standards

Pages 244–245: 1.4

Pregnancy

Class Discussion

Pregnancy Ask students to discuss the difference between pregnancy indicators and symptoms of pregnancy. *An indicator of pregnancy may be a missed period, but symptoms include tender breasts, fatigue, appetite change, and morning sickness.* **L2**

Class Activity

Ask an Expert If possible, bring in a speaker who can answer student questions about pregnancy and childbirth. The expert could be a nurse, doctor, midwife, etc. Students may list some questions ahead of time to get the discussion started. **L2**

Teaching Transparency

Page 37, **Unit 4 Fast File Resources**

Pregnancy

After conception, a fertilized ovum continues to divide and move through the Fallopian tube. The cell divisions form a cluster of cells by the time they reach the uterus. These cells attach to the endometrium, which is the lining of the uterus. An *embryo* is a developing baby through the second month of growth after conception. A *fetus* is a developing baby from the ninth week after conception until birth.

What to Know About Pregnancy

Did You Know?

Eating Habits Poor eating habits before and during a pregnancy can harm both the mother and the fetus.

The outer cells of the embryo and the cells of the endometrium form the placenta. The *placenta* is an organ that anchors the embryo to the uterus. Other cells form the umbilical cord. The *umbilical cord* is a rope-like structure that connects the embryo to the placenta. The mother's blood carries nutrients and oxygen to the embryo or fetus through the umbilical cord until birth. Waste products from the embryo move through the cord to the mother's bloodstream to be excreted.

How pregnancy is determined The first sign that indicates pregnancy is the absence of a menstrual period. However, a missed period does not always indicate pregnancy. A female may skip her menstrual period because of stress, diet, physical activity, or illness.

If conception has occurred, a female usually has other symptoms of pregnancy. She may have excessive tenderness in her breasts, fatigue, a change in appetite, and morning sickness. Morning sickness is nausea and vomiting during pregnancy. Some pregnant females have spotting or light, irregular menstrual flow.

A female who misses a period and also has other symptoms of pregnancy should have a pregnancy test. This test is used to detect a hormone that is present a few days after fertilization. A physician or nurse practitioner can administer this test and send it to a lab for confirmation.

Some home pregnancy tests also are sold in drugstores. Home pregnancy tests may not always be reliable soon after a missed period. A pregnancy should always be confirmed by a physician or a nurse.

Pregnancy usually lasts nine months. Each nine-month period is divided into trimesters or three-month periods.

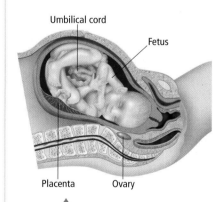

Umbilical cord

Fetus

Placenta   Ovary

A fetus is well-nourished and protected in the uterus.

Health Project

Careers Involving Pregnancy Ask students to research all of the possible careers associated with pregnancy, from pre-conception to well after the birth of the child. Some examples include an obstetrician, family practice physician, neonatologist, fertility specialist, labor and delivery nurse, postpartum nurse, midwife, nurse practitioner, doula, pediatrician, lactation consultant, nutritionist, etc. Career choices can be drawn from a hat, or given to the teacher as students research areas of interest, so the same career will not be repeated in the presentations. Students may try to interview someone in the chosen career to find out the responsibilities of the job, and other pertinent information. The presentation of information can include posters, brochures, newsletter articles, or oral reports. **L2**

The first trimester The first three months after conception are the first trimester. At the end of the first month, the embryo has a heartbeat, a two-lobed brain, and a spinal cord.

By the end of the second month, the embryo is recognizable as a human and is called a fetus. After two months, the embryo has started to form arms and legs as well as fingers, ears, and toes. The fetus can be visibly identified as a male or female. By the end of the first trimester, the heart has four chambers.

The second trimester By the end of the fourth month, fingernails, toenails, eyebrows, and eyelashes have developed. Teeth begin to form, lips appear, and head hair may begin to grow. Movement of the fetus can be felt by the mother. The fetus can bend its arms and make a fist. During the fifth month, the heartbeat can be detected by a stethoscope.

The third trimester If a baby is born prematurely at the beginning of the seventh month, it has a 20 percent chance of surviving. Optimum development occurs at about 40 weeks after conception.

A ***premature birth*** happens when a baby is born before 37 weeks of pregnancy. A premature baby has not had time to fully develop all body systems. For example, underdeveloped lungs are a usual problem in premature babies.

A baby born between 38 and 40 weeks of pregnancy is considered to be full-term. Full-term babies usually are 19 to 21 inches long and might weigh between six and nine pounds by the end of the third trimester.

◄ The embryo in this photo is less than 1 inch long. By the end of the first trimester, the fetus is about three inches long and weighs about an ounce.

◄ By the end of the second trimester, the fetus is about 12 inches long and weighs about one pound.

◄ By the end of the third trimester, the baby is ready to be born.

Reading Review

1. What is the function of the umbilical cord?

2. During which trimester can the fetus be identified as a male or female?

LESSON 21 • Learning About Pregnancy and Childbirth **247**

Prenatal Care

NHES Assessment/SCASS

Performance Task Prenatal care can begin before a female becomes pregnant. Have students write a dialogue between a doctor and a patient that gives advice on what things a female can do before conception to help in conceiving and delivering a healthy baby. **L2**

Explain the Concept

Birth Complications Explain the difference between premature birth—birth of the baby before it is fully developed, at less than 38 weeks from conception—and low birth weight—weight at birth that is less than 5.5 pounds. A premature baby may have a low birth weight, but not all premature babies are under 5.5 pounds. Also, some full-term babies have low birth weight.

Extension

Prenatal Exams Have students contact medical offices where women receive prenatal care. They should find out the typical schedule for prenatal appointments and tests, such as the glucose tolerance test for gestational diabetes. Have students answer these questions in a short report: How often do pregnant women have checkups? Does the frequency change as the pregnancy progresses? What tests are most pregnant women given, and when and how often are those given? **L2**

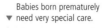

Prenatal Care

The care that is given to the mother and baby before birth is *prenatal care.* Prenatal care includes routine medical examinations, proper nutrition, reasonable exercise, extra rest and relaxation, childbirth and child-care education, avoidance of drugs and other risk behaviors, and the practice of common sense.

What to Know About Prenatal Care

A well-balanced diet is important to a pregnant female. Premature birth or low birth weight may result when a developing baby does not receive adequate nutrients.

Premature birth is the birth of a baby before it is fully developed—less than 37 weeks from the time of conception.

A **low birth weight** is a weight at birth that is less than 5.5 pounds. Premature birth and low birth weight are associated with mental disability and infant death.

A pregnant female needs to check with her physician before she takes any prescriptions or over-the-counter drugs. Drugs present in the mother's bloodstream can pass into the devel-

Babies born prematurely need very special care.

oping baby's bloodstream and harm the baby. For example, tranquilizers taken early in pregnancy can cause birth defects. Some drugs prescribed for acne and hormones, such as those in birth control pills also can cause birth defects. Aspirin may interfere with blood clotting in both the pregnant female and her developing baby.

A female should not drink alcohol during pregnancy. **Fetal alcohol syndrome (FAS)** is the presence of severe birth defects in babies born to mothers who drink alcohol during pregnancy. FAS includes damage to the brain and to the nervous system, facial abnormalities, small head size, below normal I.Q., poor coordination, heart defects, and behavior problems.

A pregnant female should not smoke or inhale smoke from tobacco products. Females who smoke have smaller babies who are more unhealthy than babies of nonsmoking females. Babies born to mothers who smoke also may be at risk for heart disease in adulthood. Smoking and breathing smoke increase the risk of complications, miscarriage, and stillbirth during pregnancy.

A **miscarriage** is the natural ending of a pregnancy before a baby is developed enough to survive on its own outside the mother's body. A stillbirth is the birth of a dead fetus.

248 UNIT 4 • Growth and Development

Legal Issues

Birth Defect Causes The Surgeon General first advised women not to drink alcoholic beverages during pregnancy in 1981 because alcohol consumption may lead to birth defects. The Surgeon General's warning on all alcoholic beverages was first required in 1989. It states: "According to the Surgeon General, women should not drink alcoholic beverages during pregnancy because of the risk of birth defects." Alcohol consumption among pregnant women decreased after warning labels appeared, but it has started to rise again. Some groups are suggesting changes to make the warnings more visible on labels as a way to try to decrease consumption again. Some states also require that establishments where alcoholic beverages are sold must post health warning signs.

Activity: Using Life Skills

Accessing Valid Health Information, Products, and Services: Research a Pregnancy Topic

There are many sources available for information about pregnancy. To be a good researcher, you will need to look through multiple sources of information to ensure that you get all the facts. Evaluate the information. If you are using your research to write a paper, be sure to cite your sources.

1 Identify health information, products, and services you need. Head to the library. The library is a great place to start your information search. With library books, it's a good idea to check the publication date listed in the front of each book. Health information changes quickly, so the statistics and health facts you find in some library books may be out-of-date if the book is more than five years old.

2 Find health information, products, and services. You will find information on pregnancy topics at www.glencoe.com.

4 Talk with a medical specialist if possible, at his or her convenience. Have your questions prepared in advance and in writing. Be sure to thank the person. If a medical specialist is not available, be sure that your library research is thorough.

3 Visit the bookstore. Most bookstores have a pregnancy book section. It usually is located near the children's books and may be part of a larger section called Parenting and Family.

5 Evaluate health information, products, and services and take action when health information is misleading and/or health products and services are unsatisfactory. Keep careful records of all your sources, including titles and authors or Web sites. Keeping records on index cards is one convenient method.

▲ Use every resource available to you to obtain information on the topic you have chosen.

A pregnant female should not use other harmful drugs, such as marijuana, crack, cocaine, or heroin. Babies born to mothers who use these drugs can be born prematurely and have low birth weight. These babies may be born addicted to drugs.

Some research indicates that caffeine may be linked to birth defects. Caffeine is found in coffee, chocolate, cola drinks, tea, and some prescription and over-the-counter drugs. A mother-to-be should follow her physician's advice about caffeine.

One nutrient known to prevent birth defects is folic acid. Folic acid is the chemical form of folate, which is found in green leafy vegetables, citrus fruits, and legumes. Folate aids in cell division, and consuming foods high in folate reduces a woman's chance of having a child with spina bifida and other abnormalities of the spine and brain.

The U.S. Public Health Service recommends that all women of childbearing age, who are capable of becoming pregnant, consume 0.4 mg of folic acid per day to help prevent neural tube defects. For pregnant or lactating women, the daily value increases to 0.8 mg per day. It is especially important that women consume sufficient folate before they become pregnant.

Reading Review

1. What is prenatal care?
2. What is fetal alcohol syndrome (FAS)?

www.glencoe.com

LESSON 21 • Learning About Pregnancy and Childbirth **249**

 Community Involvement

Resources Have students gather information about resources in your community that are available to assist parents before, during and after they have their child. These could include medical resources, such as county public health programs, as well as information, emotional support, and assistance, such as transportation to medical appointments. Mothers, particularly those having their first babies, may also appreciate knowing about fun things to do, such as mother-and-child classes and activities. Have students create a list of resources and how to access them; have them get permission to put the list of resources on display in a public place, such as a community library. **L2**

Childbirth

Childbirth

Explain the Concept

Amniotic Sac Rupture When the amniotic sac ruptures, it often is referred to as a woman's water breaking or as the rupture of membranes. Students may have heard those phrases. For some women, there is not a gush, but a slow leak, which they may not recognize as the rupture of the amniotic sac. If the sac does not rupture on its own, the doctor may rupture it with a special instrument to speed up labor.

Class Discussion

Childbirth Depictions Ask students to recall depictions of childbirth that they have seen in movies or on television. Compare those depictions with information that they have been learning in class. Ask students to answer these questions: In what ways did the depictions seem accurate? In what ways were they inaccurate? What did they leave out? **L2**

Class Activity

Timeline Using a piece of roll paper or butcher block paper, have a group of students construct a timeline from conception to birth including changes that occur in the fetus as well as in the mother. They may include drawings or pictures from magazines, as well as text information. **L2 ELL**

The process of childbirth is called *labor*. During labor, muscular contractions of the uterus start, become more intense, last longer, and become more frequent. The amniotic sac may rupture shortly before or after labor begins. A discharge or gushing of water from the vagina indicates the sac has broken. Bloody show, which is the discharge of the mucous plug that sealed the cervix during pregnancy, also may be experienced.

What to Know About Childbirth

Labor is considered to have three distinct stages.

Stage 1: Dilation of the cervix The first stage of labor is the longest stage. The length of this stage varies considerably. It can last from two hours to many hours. Dilation or widening of the cervix occurs. The cervical opening enlarges eight to ten centimeters—wide enough for the baby to move through.

Stage 2: Delivery of the baby The second stage begins when the cervix is completely dilated and ends with the delivery of the baby. The baby moves farther down the birth canal, usually head first. The mother pushes, and the muscles in the uterus contract to push the baby out.

Crowning is the appearance of the baby's head during delivery. Once the baby has been eased out of the birth canal and begins to breathe on its own, the umbilical cord is cut.

Stage 3: Delivery of the placenta The third stage of labor is the expulsion of the afterbirth. The *afterbirth* is the placenta that is expelled after delivery. If this does not occur naturally, the physician removes it.

▲ The cervix begins to dilate during the first stage of labor.

▲ The baby moves down the birth canal and is born during the second stage of labor.

 Family Involvement

Interviewing Family Ask students to interview a family member or friend on the experience of childbirth. Students should prepare several questions ahead of time that can be used in the interview. Some possible questions students could ask are: How long did labor last? How much of the labor was intense and how much was not as bad? How long did pushing last (if it was a vaginal birth)? How long did you spend in the hospital or birthing center? Who was with you during labor and delivery? Were there any complications? Students should prepare a written report and can volunteer to share stories with the class, if both the subject of the interview and the student are comfortable with sharing that information. **L2 ELL**

When the baby is breathing on its own, the umbilical cord is clamped and cut off. A stump remains on the navel. It dries up and falls off in a few days. A physician gives the baby an Apgar score.

The *Apgar score* is a rating of physical characteristics of an infant at one and five minutes after birth. Another score is given at 10 minutes if there are problems with the baby. Characteristics, such as heart rate, color, respiratory effort, and reaction to sucking, are scored and used to predict the health of the baby. A score of 7–10 is normal, 4–7 might need some resuscitative measures, and 3 and below require immediate resuscitation.

The *postpartum period* is the span of time that begins after the baby is born. Hormones produce changes in the mother's body. The breasts secrete a watery substance believed to provide the baby with immunity to certain diseases.

The breasts also secrete a hormone that stimulates the breasts to secrete milk. Some studies show that breast-fed babies have fewer cases of

▲ In the third stage of labor, the uterus continues to contract to expel the placenta.

respiratory illnesses, skin disorders, constipation, and diarrhea.

Multiple births Some pregnancies result in the birth of two or more babies at the same time. Two babies born at the same time are called twins.

Identical twins develop from the same ovum and sperm. Identical twins develop when one fertilized ovum divides at an early stage of development and the two cells divide and develop separately. This results in twins of the same sex who have identical chromosomes and are very similar in appearance.

Fraternal twins develop when two ova are released from an ovary and are fertilized at the same time by different sperm. The twins may or may not be the same sex and usually do not look alike.

Three babies born at the same time are called triplets, four are quadruplets, five are quintuplets, and six are sextuplets. Multiple births of more than three babies are rare.

Childbirth classes Childbirth classes are available to prepare prospective parents for the birth of their baby. Hospitals, health centers, and other organizations offer these classes. The classes include detailed information about the process of childbirth. A nurse or other health-care practitioner is available to answer questions and to help with concerns.

Special exercise classes also are offered for pregnant females to help them stay fit during pregnancy and prepare for childbirth. A female should obtain permission from her physician before participating in exercise classes.

Make the Connection

Healthful Behaviors For more information on practicing healthful behaviors, see page 27 in Lesson 3.

Reading Review

1. What are the three stages of labor?

2. What is the Apgar score?

3. What is the difference between identical twins and fraternal twins?

Pregnancy Complications Have students research additional pregnancy complications, such as gestational diabetes, preeclampsia, pre-term labor, intrauterine growth retardation, or infection with group B strep. Have students give oral presentations to their classmates, and then compile the information into a booklet describing the various complications and how they are handled. **L3**

Class Discussions

Cesarean Sections C-sections account for about 25 percent of births. Ask students to give some reasons why a C-section may be required. *The unborn baby is too large to pass through the mother's pelvis, vaginal delivery is too dangerous for the baby and/or mother, or the baby is not in the correct position.* **L2**

3 Assess

Vocabulary Practice

Page 36, **Unit 4 Fast File Resources**

National Health Education Standards

Pages 252–253: 1.1, 1.5, 1.9

Complications During Pregnancy and Childbirth

Ectopic pregnancy Ectopic pregnancy, which can be caused by tissue scarring from STDs, is a pregnancy that occurs outside of the uterus. The embryo becomes implanted in the Fallopian tube or another location in the abdomen. Symptoms include cramping, severe abdominal pain, and spotting. Surgery often is needed to remove the embryo. An ectopic pregnancy can be fatal to females.

Rh incompatibility Rh incompatibility is a mismatch between the blood of a pregnant female and the blood of the developing baby. The female's blood produces an antibody that attacks a substance in the developing baby's blood. Rh incompatibility may occur when a female's blood is Rh negative and the developing baby's is Rh positive. The condition can be treated and an injection of an anti-body to the Rh factor is given to the female to prevent risk during future pregnancies.

Toxemia of pregnancy Toxemia of pregnancy is a condition characterized by a rise in the pregnant female's blood pressure, swelling, and leakage of protein into the urine. Untreated toxemia can result in the death of the female or the developing baby.

Miscarriage Miscarriage is the natural ending of a pregnancy before a baby has developed enough to survive on its own. Miscarriages occur most often during the first trimester. They may be caused by a defect in the fetus or a medical condition of the fetus or pregnant female. Signs of miscarriage include cramping, severe pain, spotting, and bleeding.

Cesarean section Cesarean section is a procedure in which a baby is removed from the mother by making an incision through the mother's abdomen and uterus and removing the baby. A cesarean may be performed if an unborn baby is too large to pass through the mother's pelvis, is not positioned correctly, or the physician determines that a vaginal delivery may be dangerous to the health of the mother or the baby. Recovery time from a cesarean delivery is longer than recovery from a vaginal delivery.

Stillbirth Stillbirth is a fully developed baby that is born dead. Stillbirth may be caused by a defect in the baby or a medical condition of the baby or the pregnant female.

In an ectopic pregnancy, as the embryo develops, the Fallopian tube expands, causing potentially serious ▼ consequences.

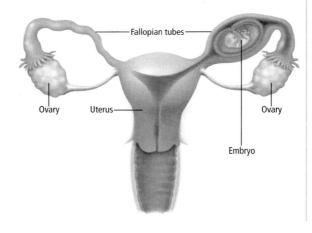

Fallopian tubes

Ovary   Uterus   Ovary

Embryo

252   UNIT 4 • Growth and Development

🏃 Healthy People 2010

Objective 16-5 *Reduce maternal illness and complications due to pregnancy.*

In 1998, the rate of maternal illness and complications was 31.2 per 100 deliveries. The 2010 target goal is 24 per 100 deliveries. The Healthy People 2010 document states that ectopic pregnancy, caused mainly by preventable tubal scarring due to pelvic inflammatory disease (PID) caused by chlamydia and gonorrhea, was responsible for many of these complications. Discuss these statistics with students and remind them that the only 100 percent effective method to prevent unplanned pregnancy, STDs, and the sexual transmission of HIV is abstinence. **L2**

afterbirth
amniocentesis
chromosome
embryo
fertilization
fetal alcohol
   syndrome
gene
labor
miscarriage
placenta
premature birth
ultrasound

Key Terms Review

Explain the relationship between the pairs of lesson Key Terms given below. Do not write in this book.

1. gene—chromosome
2. embryo—fetal alcohol syndrome (FAS)
3. placenta—afterbirth
4. fertilization—labor
5. amniocentesis—ultrasound

6. afterbirth—labor
7. embryo—fertilization
8. fetal alcohol syndrome—ultrasound
9. placenta—embryo
10. amniocentesis—gene

Recalling the Facts

11. Explain why the resulting chromosome number in a fetus is the same as the parents' chromosome number.
12. What are dominant genes? Give two examples.
13. How are a fetus' sex and inherited traits determined?
14. What are six complications of pregnancy?

15. What is one unique aspect of each trimester of pregnancy?
16. Why is it important to begin prenatal care as soon as a female finds out she is pregnant?
17. How can taking a childbirth class promote a healthful pregnancy?
18. How can cigarette smoke affect a developing embryo or fetus?

Critical Thinking

19. Why should a female in late pregnancy seek medical help if the amniotic sac ruptures?
20. Why is fertilization in a blocked Fallopian tube dangerous both to the pregnant female and to the fetus?
21. In what ways is a pregnant female's diet important to the health of the fetus?
22. How are ova and sperm different from other body cells?

Real-Life Applications

23. What arguments would you use to try to dissuade a pregnant female from using harmful drugs?
24. How would you persuade your pregnant sister that her diet has an effect on her fetus?
25. Explain the concerns you might have about a baby born prematurely.
26. Discuss why a mother and baby are taken to a hospital even if the baby is born on the way.

Activities

Responsible Decision Making

27. **Write** You go to lunch with a family friend who is pregnant. Several people are waiting in line for a table. The host explains that you can have a table right now if you want to sit in the smoking section. The family friend is uncomfortable standing. Write a response to this situation. Refer to the Responsible Decision-Making Model on page 61 for help.

Sharpen Your Life Skills

28. **Use Communication Skills**
Warnings on alcohol and tobacco products describe why it is harmful for pregnant women to use these products. Draw a picture of a warning label with text that emphasizes the risks of smoking, being around second hand smoke, or drinking during pregnancy.

Visit **www.glencoe.com** for more *Health & Wellness* quizzes.

LESSON 21 • Study Guide   **253**

LESSON 21
STUDY GUIDE

Key Terms Review

1. Chromosomes carry genes.
2. FAS causes severe birth defects to an embryo.
3. The afterbirth is the placenta when it is expelled after delivery.
4. Fertilization begins a pregnancy and labor ends a pregnancy.
5. Both are diagnostic procedures to monitor a fetus.
6. Afterbirth is expelled when labor is completed.
7. Fertilization of an ovum creates an embryo.
8. An ultrasound can reveal birth defects caused by FAS.
9. The placenta anchors the embryo to the uterus.
10. During amniocentesis, fluid is extracted that carries genetic information about a fetus.

Recalling the Facts

11. See page 243.
12. See page 244.
13. See pages 243–244.
14. See page 252.
15. See page 247.
16. See pages 248–249.
17. See pages 248–249.
18. See page 248.

Critical Thinking

19. It is a sign that labor is about to begin or has begun, so a female needs medical assistance to ensure the delivery of a healthy baby.
20. When a fetus develops in a Fallopian tube, the tube can burst, causing serious internal consequences for the female. A fetus has no chance of surviving.
21. A developing fetus is completely dependent on the pregnant female for adequate nourishment.
22. All body cells contain 23 pairs of chromosomes, except sperm and ova, which contain 23 each.

Real-Life Applications

23. Babies can be born premature with low birth weight and addicted to drugs.
24. Explain that the developing baby gets all its nutrition from the mother.

---

25. Some organs in a premature baby are not fully developed, so the baby can struggle to function normally in many ways.
26. Medical personnel can check the mother and baby for any complications.

Activities

Responsible Decision Making

27. Do not sit in the smoking section. Smoke can harm the embryo or fetus. The restau-rant may be able to provide a place for your pregnant friend to sit down while you are waiting for a table.

Sharpen Your Life Skills

28. The labels should include information about how smoking, inhaling secondhand smoke, or drinking alcohol can lead to health problems for the fetus.

LESSON 22

Caring for Infants and Children

HEALTH GOALS
- I will learn about the growth and development of infants and children.
- I will provide responsible care for infants and children.

A person who provides care for infants and children during a short absence of a parent or guardian is a *childsitter*. This lesson describes how to prepare to be a childsitter. You will learn how to care for infants and young children from birth to eight years old.

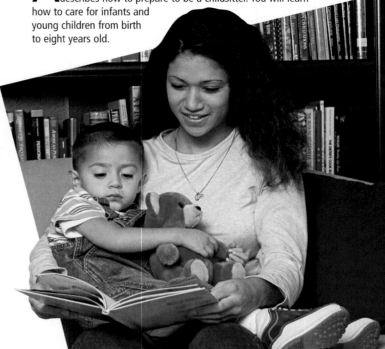

What You'll Learn

1. Describe what to know to be a good childsitter. *(p. 255)*
2. Describe ways to care for infants and toddlers. *(p. 256)*
3. Describe ways to care for young children. *(p. 258)*

Why It's Important

Perhaps you have been or will be asked to look after a child. You will need to know how to act responsibly. This information also will help you if you become a parent one day.

Key Terms

- childsitter
- sudden infant death syndrome (SIDS)
- time out

Writing About Childsitting Suppose that one night you are childsitting for your younger sister and she does not want to go to bed because she is frightened. Review the information about caring for young children on page 258, then write an entry in your health journal about what you would do to calm your younger sister so that she could fall asleep.

Caring for Infants and Children

 Out of Time?

If time does not permit an in-depth study of this topic, use the following activities in this Teacher Wraparound Edition:
- Teacher FYI, p. 255
- Class Discussion, p. 256
- Quick Demo, p. 257
- Class Activity, p. 258

1 Focus

HEALTH GOALS Responsible Childsitting Have students respond to the Health Goals for this lesson by listing the qualities that make a good childsitter. *Qualities might include patience, kindness, maturity, and having a lot of energy.* **L2**

Write ABOUT IT!

Journaling Ask students to write a response to this scenario in their health journals. Student responses may include: "talk quietly to my sister and show her I am not afraid, find out why she is afraid," "move any object that frightens her out of her sight" or "give her a favorite toy or stuffed animal to hold." **L2**

National Health Education Standards—Guide for Lesson 22		
1.5	Propose ways to reduce or prevent injuries and health problems.	pp. 257, 258–259, 261
3.5	Access valid and reliable health products and services.	pp. 255, 261
4.1	Utilize skills for communicating effectively with family, peers, and others to enhance health.	pp. 255, 256, 258–260
7.1	Analyze the role of individual responsibility for enhancing health.	pp. 255–259, 261
7.2	Demonstrate a variety of healthy practices and behaviors that will maintain or improve the health of self and others.	pp. 255–259, 261

254

Childsitting

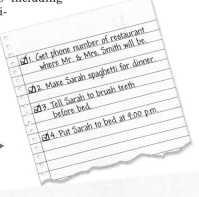

C hildsitting, also known as babysitting, is a task that requires a great amount of responsibility. It means more than watching a child. Understanding how to follow safety rules when watching a child is a must. Knowing what steps to take in an emergency also is a must.

A Childsitter's Checklist

A responsible childsitter is prepared. It is your responsibility to obtain the information you need before you childsit.

Qualifications You have taken a first aid course and are familiar with universal precautions. You also have completed a childsitting course offered by the American Red Cross or by another organization.

Personal You have your parents' or guardian's approval to childsit and you check to make sure you will be available to childsit. You discuss with the child's parents or guardian the hours you will childsit and the payment you expect. You arrange for transportation to and from the job.

The child (or children) You meet the child or children and learn their name(s) and age(s). You know when mealtime, naptime, and bedtime are. You also know which activities are allowed and which are not, and you know what the child's or children's favorite activities and toys are.

Possible health needs You know what health problems, such as allergies, the child has, and you know what medications he or she might need.

Details You familiarize yourself with the home and where everything is. If there is a pet, you discuss pet rules.

You check about the privileges you will have, such as the use of the telephone. You ask if you are allowed to have visitors and if you are welcome to eat any food in the refrigerator. You know what time to arrive and what time you expect the parents or guardian to be home.

Information You know emergency telephone numbers including police, fire, and poison control. You know if 911 service is available. You know the name and number of the child's physician.

☑ 1. Get phone number of restaurant where Mr. & Mrs. Smith will be.
☑ 2. Make Sarah spaghetti for dinner.
☑ 3. Tell Sarah to brush teeth before bed.
☑ 4. Put Sarah to bed at 9:00 p.m.

► A checklist is a good way to remind yourself of your responsibilities.

Characteristics of a Childsitter

A responsible childsitter is:

- observant and alert
- calm during emergencies
- able to follow instructions
- trained in first aid
- able to recognize safety hazards
- able to communicate with adults
- able to communicate with young children
- able to supervise young children
- patient and friendly

LESSON 22 • Caring for Infants and Children **255**

Lesson Resource Manager

- **Unit 4 Fast File Resources**
  Reading Strategy, p. 47
  Vocabulary Practice, p. 48
  Transparency Master and Worksheet, p. 49
  Real-Life Health, p. 51
  Real-Life Health, p. 53
  5-Minute Check, p. 55
  Lesson 22 Quiz, p. 56
- **Unit 4 Transparency**
- **Lesson 22 Transparency**

- **Reading Essentials**
- **Technology**
  TeacherWorks™ CD-ROM
  StudentWorks™ CD-ROM
  Reading Essentials CD-ROM
  ExamView® Assessment Suite
  Vocabulary Puzzlemaker

2 Teach

NHES Assessment/SCASS

Performance Event Have students write a "help wanted" ad for a child-care provider. They should include a detailed description of the job duties, the personal qualities or characteristics desired, the number of hours required, the times, and the rate of pay. **L2**

Teacher FYI

Babysitting Training The American Red Cross offers a course in babysitter training. The course instructs potential babysitters in a variety of areas, including: interviewing for babysitting jobs, choosing appropriate toys and games, performing first aid, diapering and feeding techniques, and handling bedtime issues.

INTERACTIVE CHALKBOARD with Image Bank

PowerPoint® Presentations

This CD-ROM is an editable Microsoft® PowerPoint® presentation that includes:
- Lesson presentations
- Lesson checks
- Interactive graphics
- 5-Minute Checks
- Image Bank
- All transparencies

Discussion Use the KWL Strategy on page 17T to determine what the students already know and what they would like to learn about infant and child care, and then what they learned in the lesson.

Infants and Toddlers

Explain the Concept

Infants and Children Infants differ from older children in many ways: physically, cognitively, socially, and intellectually. Infants are capable only of very basic functions, and their primary interactions are based on survival. They cry when they need something, such as food, a clean diaper, or human interaction.

Class Discussion

Spoiling Children Have students discuss whether or not they think infants can be spoiled. They need to consider the cognitive development of infants, as well as their physical and emotional capabilities. **L2**

Teacher FYI

Shaken Baby Syndrome According to the National Center on Shaken Baby Syndrome, shaken baby syndrome is the most common cause of infant mortality in the U.S. and accounts for the most long-term disability in infants and young children due to physical abuse. There are between 600 and 1400 cases per year, approximately 20 percent of which are fatal. The highest incidence of cases occurs between the ages of six weeks and four months, the time when babies are most likely to cry for long periods of time.

Infants and Toddlers

Infants, or babies, share some common characteristics. So do toddlers. Learn the following common characteristics so you will know what to expect from infants and toddlers in your care.

How to Care for Infants and Toddlers (Birth to Three Years)

Newborns to one-year-olds Infants and babies need to feel secure and like to be with people. They cry when they are hungry or uncomfortable. They like to touch and hold things, to look at their hands and faces, and to put things in their mouths.

One- to three-year-olds Children this age need to feel secure. They want to be independent. They want to eat, drink, and get dressed without help. They like to play, build things, and watch what other children are doing. They like to do the same thing over and over again and may have temper tantrums if they don't get what they want.

A responsible childsitter never leaves an infant or toddler alone. A responsible childsitter never shakes or hits an infant or toddler. Even gently shaking a young child can cause severe head and neck injury known as shaken baby

▲ Babies always have favorite toys.

syndrome. Consult a parent or guardian if an infant or child persists in a behavior you find difficult or inappropriate.

You need certain skills to provide responsible care for an infant or toddler. Consult the childsitter's list of skills for infant and toddler care, shown below, to make sure you have the skills needed.

A Childsitter's Skills for the Care of Infants and Toddlers

You know how to pick up and hold a baby. You slide your arm under the baby's body. You cradle the baby against your body, or support the baby against your shoulder. You always support the baby's head with one hand. You also support the shoulders. You are careful when touching the two soft spots on the top of the baby's head.

You know what to do when a baby cries. You determine if the baby is too warm, too cold, hungry, teething, or ill. Is the diaper wet or soiled? You take the appropriate action.

🔁 Cross-Curricular Connections

Social Studies Have groups of students research child-care practices in other cultures. Each group should choose a different culture to study. Try to include cultures from many different parts of the world. Have them research: Which child-care practices are similar to how they were raised? Which practices are different? How do different practices affect children's development? Are there any long-term differences in abilities due to different child-care practices? If not, at approximately what age do most children have similar abilities? Have each group prepare a written report or poster, then present their findings to the class. **L2**

◄ A three-year-old is becoming better coordinated.

You know what to do if you think an infant or toddler is sick. You call the parents or guardian, tell them the symptoms, and follow their advice.

You know how to diaper a baby. You wash your hands and have ready what you need: diaper, baby wipes, ointment, cotton balls, and safety pins for cloth diapers. You clean the baby's bottom and put on a clean diaper. You dispose of the soiled diaper appropriately and wash your hands again.

You know how to bathe a baby. If the umbilical cord is still present, you give only a sponge bath. Otherwise, you bathe the baby in a small tub or sink. You have warm water, a soft washcloth, and baby soap ready. You place the baby in the water while supporting the baby's head. After washing, you rinse the baby with clean, warm water from a cup. You wrap the baby in a towel and make sure the baby's head is covered.

You know how to give a baby a bottle. You ask the parents or guardian for instructions to prepare the bottle and you follow them. You make sure the bottle nipple is always full of milk.

You know how to burp a baby. You put a towel on your shoulder and hold the baby upright. You support the baby's head and back and gently pat the baby's back.

Or you lay the baby face down on your lap and gently pat the back. Or you sit the baby on your lap and support the baby's chest while gently patting the back.

Sudden Infant Death Syndrome

The sudden and unexplained death of an infant younger than one year of age is **sudden infant death syndrom (SIDS).** SIDS is responsible for over 3,000 deaths each year in the United States. It is a leading cause of death among babies between the ages of two and four months.

Cause of SIDS The cause of SIDS is not known for sure. It is currently believed that SIDS results when a baby has difficulty controlling certain body functions, such as breathing. When a baby is put to sleep face down, the risk of SIDS increases. If you childsit a baby, check with the parents about how they put their baby to sleep.

Make the Connection

Childhood Illnesses For more information on childhood illnesses and diseases, see page 491 in Lesson 45.

Reading Review

1. List three characteristics of one-year-olds to three-year-olds.
2. Why is it wrong to shake an infant or toddler?

Reducing the Risk of SIDS

The following are the American Academy of Pediatrics' guidelines for reducing the risk of SIDS.

- Babies should sleep on their backs, not their stomachs.
- Make sure babies sleep on a firm surface, not on a waterbed, a soft mattress, a pillow, a fluffy blanket, or a comforter. Stuffed toys, pillows, and blankets should not be placed in the crib with babies.
- Babies should be kept warm, but not too warm. Keep their room temperature so that it feels comfortable to you.
- Babies should be kept in a smoke-free zone.
- If a baby seems sick, his or her doctor should be called right away. Babies need to receive their shots on schedule.
- Regular prenatal care also can help reduce the risk of SIDS. For the baby's well-being, the mother should not smoke or use alcohol or drugs during pregnancy.

LESSON 22 • Caring for Infants and Children   **257**

Young Children

NHES Assessment/SCASS

Constructed Response Young children are influenced by what adults say and do. When students childsit, small children may view them as adults. Have students write one to two paragraphs about how young children's behavior or language can be influenced by inappropriate language or by viewing adult music videos. **L2**

Class Activity

Children's Activities Have students break into four small groups. Two of the groups should create a list of 6–8 activities that would be fun and appropriate for 3–5 year olds. The two remaining groups should do the same for 5–8 year olds. Each group should share their list with the class. The other groups should judge whether or not the activities are both fun and appropriate. **L2**

Extension

Hand Washing Have students research the importance of hand washing as it pertains to diaper changing. Have them research what infections can be passed through fecal matter, what infections can be passed from the caregiver to the baby, and what infections can be passed from the baby to the caregiver. **L3**

You need certain skills to provide responsible care for young children who are three to eight years old. A responsible childsitter never leaves a young child alone. A responsible childsitter never shakes or hits a young child. You need to consult a parent or guardian if a young child persists in a behavior you find difficult or inappropriate. Consult the list of Childsitter's Skills for the Care of Young Children, on this page, to make sure you have the necessary skills.

Did You Know?

Imaginations Four-year-olds have vivid imaginations.

Four- to five-year-old children love to play with friends.

How to Care for Young Children (Three to Eight Years)

Three- to five-year-old children share common characteristics, as do five- to eight-year-olds.

Three- to five-year-olds Children in this age range enjoy playing with friends and communicating with others. They like to learn numbers and play simple games. They like to be independent and do things for themselves. They like to learn new words and names for things. They can be very active and very aggressive.

Five- to eight-year-olds Children this age need to socialize with others besides family members. They want to be a part of conversations with family members. They usually have more self-confidence than do three- to five-year-olds. They like to ask questions about almost everything and are influenced by what adults say and do.

A Childsitter's Skills for the Care of Young Children

You know what to do when a child is afraid. You talk quietly with the child and show the child that you are not afraid. You find out exactly why the child is afraid. If an object frightens the child, you move it out of the child's sight. You give the child a favorite toy or stuffed animal to hold.

You know what to do if a child has a tantrum. You ask the parents or guardian ahead of time how to respond to a tantrum. You find out why the child is angry. You tell the child calmly that a tantrum is not appropriate or acceptable.

🍎 Teacher to Teacher

Motivation Have students imagine that they are childsitting. Write the following on an overhead transparency and ask them which of these four rewards would encourage them to be the best childsitter they could be: 1. payment for childsitting; 2. the affection of the children they are childsitting; 3. the respect of peers when they hear the student has been trusted to childsit; 4. the pride of their parents or guardian when they learn the student has been trusted to childsit. Have students rank each reward from 1–4 (1 = highest, 4 = lowest). Then, put a tally on the overhead transparency displaying the rankings and discuss each example. This will enable students to see that each person may be motivated by different rewards to reach a certain outcome. **L2**
Sherrie MacKinney
Trinity Area School District, Washington, PA

◄ Young children enjoy learning new tasks.

You tell the child that you will not pay attention to his or her wants until the tantrum stops. If it does not stop in a short amount of time, you tell the child that he or she will have a time out. *Time out* is a calming-down period of time. You tell the child that he or she may play again after becoming calm.

You know how to help a young child learn. You smile at the child. You talk to the child and play games with him or her. You use safe toys and games that interest the child.

You know what to do when a child refuses to go to bed. You find out if the child does not want to be left alone or is afraid of the dark. You read the child a story to help the child relax, or you sit and quietly talk to the child. You assure the child that you will be close by and will check on him or her again soon.

You know what to do if you think a young child is sick. You call the parents or guardian. You describe the signs and symptoms you have observed. You follow the parents' or guardian's instructions about what steps to take.

You know how to be safe around water. Watching a child around water requires 100 percent of your attention. In just a matter of seconds, a child can go from your sight and fall into a swimming pool. At a beach, a child can wander off and be lost in a crowd. Always be aware of where a child is.

You know how to be safe near streets. Children like to play outdoors whenever possible. A child can run into a street and be at risk.

Let a child know that running into a street is not allowed. Be nearby in case the child does not listen to you or obey you.

You know how to be aware of potential hazards. If a child rides a bike, make sure a helmet is worn. The child may tell you that he or she is not required to wear a helmet. However, your responsibility is to be sure the child is safe. Choose another activity that would not be a hazard.

You know to be aware of stray animals. When you are outdoors, you do not allow a child to approach a stray animal. You do not know which animals are friendly and which are not. Walk with the child in another direction if you notice an animal without an owner.

You know about having other friends around. You check with the child's parent or guardian about being allowed to get together with a friend who also is childsitting.

Parents and guardians will not always allow this because it is easy to become sidetracked and then full attention is not given to the child. Remember, your first responsibility is to the child you are watching.

Did You Know?

Sleep Six-year-old children may need 10–12 hours of sleep to be at their best.

Reading Review

1. What are three characteristics of three- to five-year-olds?

2. What is a time out?

LESSON 22 • Caring for Infants and Children 259

Analyzing the Feature

Use the following questions to help students uncover the main points of this feature.

1. According to Mericya, what quality do good childsitters have? *a lot of imagination*
2. Why did Mericya say she doesn't yell at kids? *They get scared easily.*
3. What other qualities did Mericya name as important? *being patient and being prepared*

📓 Journaling Activity

Have students write about a positive experience they have had while being cared for by a childsitter. **L2**

3 Assess

Vocabulary Practice

Page 48, **Unit 4 Fast File Resources**

Mericya Meza
Childsitting

> **❝ . . . sitting for younger kids is fun . . . because I play with them a lot. I like to do what they like to do. ❞**

What's the single most important qualification to be a good childsitter? One experienced sitter, Mericya Meza, had a quick answer: "Patience, a whole lot of patience!" That patience has helped Mericya become a popular childsitter in her neighborhood and among her friends and relatives.

A teen in demand Mericya sits for younger cousins, nieces and nephews, and "all sorts of little neighbors" in her family's apartment complex several times a week. Most of her work is during the evening, so balancing sitting and studying can sometimes be a challenge.

The good and the bad Mericya remembered the babysitters she herself had as a young child. "The good ones seemed to have a lot of imagination," she said. "They knew what kinds of things kids liked, what they thought was fun."

As for the not-so-good sitters, Mericya remembers them expecting her to sit quietly in a chair. In her own childsitting jobs, Mericya tries to keep her experiences in mind. "One of the reasons I think sitting for younger kids is fun is because I play with them a lot. I like to do what they like to do. I like little kids," she added. "I get along with them pretty well."

Different challenges While sitting for infants has its own challenges, older children can be even tougher. She described why: "Older kids are just into more stuff, you know? After a while, having a lot of kids crying or just messing with things and breaking stuff, can really test your patience." But Mericya has another rule she always follows. "I don't yell at kids," she explained.

"They can get scared pretty easily, and they remember things like that the next time you come over."

Mericya relies on the fact that she is bilingual to help her in her childsitting duties.

Prepared for almost anything Although she's never had to deal with a serious injury or other emergency while babysitting, Mericya is prepared. She learned CPR and other first aid techniques. She also has learned from her own mom how to deal with the many bumps, bruises, and scrapes that are a part of growing up. "That's where a babysitting course could come in handy," she said. In fact, Mericya is thinking about becoming a children's nurse. "It's a way to help kids and their families when they really need help," said Mericya.

📓 Journaling Activity

What do you think is the most important quality people who work with children need? Write a journal entry giving reasons for your opinion.

260 UNIT 4 • Growth and Development

 ### Community Involvement

Professional Child-Care Centers Have students interview people who work in a local child-care center. Tell students to ask them these questions: Why did you choose this career? Do you need to have specific training or educational background to work with children? Are there any licensing or certification requirements? What do you like most about your job? What do you like the least? How do you handle uncooperative children and uncooperative parents? Students should prepare a written report similar to a newspaper or magazine interview. **L3**

childsitter
sudden infant death
syndrome (SIDS)
time out

Key Terms Review

Complete these fill-in-the-blank statements with the lesson Key Terms on the left. Do not write in this book.

1. _____ is the sudden and unexplained death of an infant.

2. A _____ is a person who assumes a great amount of responsibility.

3. If a child has a tantrum, he or she might need a _____.

Recalling the Facts

4. What are three things you must do to be prepared to childsit?

5. List seven skills of a responsible childsitter for infants and toddlers.

6. What are the characteristics of newborns to one-year-olds?

7. What are the characteristics of young children three to five years old?

8. What emergency telephone numbers do you need to know if you are a childsitter?

9. What is shaken baby syndrome?

10. Why put babies to sleep on their backs?

11. What are two things you might do for a child who is afraid?

12. What do each of the initials in SIDS mean?

13. What should you do when a baby cries?

14. What age baby does SIDS usually affect?

15. When should a young child wear a helmet?

16. What is your first responsibility when you childsit?

17. What is important when giving a baby a bottle?

18. What may cause a child to have a tantrum?

Critical Thinking

19. What are three reasons a parent or guardian might ask a childsitter not to have visitors while childsitting?

20. In what ways do children benefit when they are cared for by a qualified, responsible childsitter?

21. Why is it important to end a child's tantrum?

22. How might teens meet the qualifications of a responsible childsitter if there are not any childsitter courses available in their community?

Activities

Responsible Decision Making

27. **Write** You are childsitting for a baby. You are giving the baby a bath. The telephone rings. The phone is in the next room. What should you do and why? Write a paragraph in your journal on this topic. Refer to the Responsible Decision-Making Model on page 61 for help.

Real-Life Applications

23. Is it more difficult to childsit for an infant or for a young child? List your reasons.

24. Choose the three characteristics of a responsible childsitter that you consider to be the most important. Give your reasons.

25. Why do you think some teens think that childsitting is an easy job?

26. If your friend is a childsitter and he or she thinks childsitting is an easy job, how would you convince your friend that child-sitting is a serious job?

Sharpen Your Life Skills

28. **Use Communication Skills** You have learned skills for responsible childsitting. Develop a pamphlet, including a cover, title, table of contents, and responsibilities of a childsitter. Ask your teacher for permission to give a copy of your pamphlet to students who are interested in childsitting.

Visit **www.glencoe.com** for more *Health & Wellness* quizzes.

LESSON 22 • Study Guide 261

Key Terms Review

1. Sudden infant death syndrome (SIDS)
2. childsitter
3. time out

Recalling the Facts

4. See page 255.
5. See pages 256–257.
6. See page 256.
7. See page 258.
8. See page 255.
9. See page 256.
10. It reduces the risk of SIDS.
11. See page 258.
12. sudden infant death syndrome
13. See page 256.
14. younger than one year
15. when riding a bike
16. the child's safety
17. See page 257.
18. anger or frustration

Critical Thinking

19. A visitor may take your attention away from the child, may not know appropriate ways to interact with a child, and may act in ways that the parent does not want the child to imitate.

20. Qualified childsitters may teach children new things, including important social skills and make their time together fun.

21. Calming the child may prevent injury to the child or someone else.

22. Teens may be able to learn first aid and CPR at a hospital. They could learn about infants and children from parents, friends, or experienced child-care workers.

Real-Life Applications

23. Answers will vary. For infants: more dependent on childsitter to do things, cannot tell you what may be wrong. For children: get into more stuff, may try to test your patience, get scared easily.

---

24. Answers will vary. Possible answer: observant, alert, and trained in first aid.

25. Some teens may not have considered how much you have to know and how infants and young children can be challenging to care for.

26. You may show him or her information from a childsitting course or a list of things he or she should know to childsit responsibly. Ask what he or she would do in an emergency.

Activities

Responsible Decision Making

27. Never leave a baby alone in a bathtub. The child could drown.

Sharpen Your Life Skills

28. The pamphlets that your students create might include qualifications, what you should know about the children, and necessary skills for taking care of children of various ages.

261

LESSON 23

Developing Learning and Planning Styles

Out of Time?

If time does not permit an in-depth study of this topic, use the following activities in this Teacher Wraparound Edition:

- Class Activity, p. 263
- Achieving Health Literacy, p. 264
- Family Involvement, p. 266
- Class Discussion, p. 267

1 Focus

HEALTH GOALS **Learning Style** Have students respond to the first Health Goal for this lesson by identifying their own personal learning style. Have them list three activities or strategies they currently use to help them learn. *Activities may include role-playing, tape recording, or taking notes.* **L2**

Write ABOUT IT!

Journaling Student responses may include: having their friend describe the painting aloud, talking with their friend about what they think about the painting, having their friend associate the painting with a feeling he or she gets when viewing it. **L2**

LESSON 23

What You'll Learn

1. Discuss the four learning styles and tips for each. *(p. 263)*
2. List ways to achieve the eight developmental tasks of adolescence. *(p. 264)*
3. Discuss five keys to unlock the door to a successful future. *(p. 266)*
4. Explain how to set goals and make plans to achieve them. *(p. 267)*
5. Discuss four common learning disabilities and the learning support available for people who have learning disabilities. *(p. 268)*

Why It's Important

As you grow and develop, you experience different changes. Knowing about these changes helps you adjust to them more easily. As a result, you can more easily reach your goals.

Key Terms

- learning style
- independent
- developmental tasks of adolescence
- sex role
- body image
- goal
- action plan
- dyslexia
- attention-deficit/hyperactivity disorder (ADHD)

Developing Learning and Planning Styles

 HEALTH GOALS
- I will develop my learning style.
- I will achieve the developmental tasks of adolescence.

The way a person gains and processes information is a ***learning style***. In this lesson, you will be given tips that will help you gain and process information. You also will learn about different kinds of learning disabilities, and you will learn to master tasks that help you become independent. To be ***independent*** is to be able to rely on oneself.

Writing About Learning Styles Suppose you are at a museum with your friend. Your friend does not understand a painting you are looking at. You know that your friend is not a visual learner. Read the information about learning styles on page 263, then write an entry in your health journal about what you would do to help your friend understand the painting.

National Health Education Standards—Guide for Lesson 23		
7.1	Analyze the role of individual responsibility for enhancing health.	pp. 264–266
7.2	Demonstrate a variety of healthy practices and behaviors that will maintain or improve the health of self and others.	pp. 263–266

Learning Styles

E ducators have identified four kinds of learners. You may recognize yourself as one of these kinds of learners in the discussion that follows. Pay attention to the list of tips that maximize learning for your learning style.

What to Know About Learning Styles

Visual learners A person who learns best by seeing or creating images and pictures is a *visual learner*. Visual learners picture the words they read or hear and store what is seen, read, or heard in images and pictures rather than in words. Visual learners perform better on written tests than on oral tests. Visual learners tend to prefer watching an activity before doing it themselves.

Tips for visual learners Take notes and review them often. Color code or highlight notes to be reviewed. Make a mental picture of key words.

Kinesthetic learners A person who learns best by acting out something, touching an object, or repeating a motion is a *kinesthetic learner*. Kinesthetic learners remember objects they have touched and remember facts from being in role-play. Kinesthetic learners perform better on tests requiring demonstration rather than on oral or written tests. Kinesthetic learners tend to figure things out as they go along, rather than read directions first.

Tips for kinesthetic learners Role-play situations in which you recall facts. Associate information with a feeling or a smell. Demonstrate concepts you have learned.

Auditory learners A person who learns best by listening or by discussing a topic is an *auditory learner*. Auditory learners remember what they hear and can repeat word-for-word what someone else says. They perform better on oral tests than on written tests. Auditory learners tend to be talkative and may think out loud.

Tips for auditory learners Tape record information that you need to recall. Play the tape several times when studying. Read or say information aloud to yourself. Study by having someone give you an oral test.

Global learners A person who learns best by combining visual, auditory, and kinesthetic ways of learning is a *global learner*.

Tips for global learners Assess which learning style works best for you for specific situations.

Visual learners benefit from class
▼ demonstrations.

LESSON 23 • Developing Learning and Planning Styles **263**

Lesson Resource Manager

- **Unit 4 Fast File Resources**
  Reading Strategy, p. 59
  Vocabulary Practice, p.60
  Transparency Master and Worksheet, p. 61
  Real-Life Health, p. 63
  Real-Life Health, p. 65
  5-Minute Check, p. 67
  Lesson 23 Quiz, p. 68
- **Unit 4 Transparency**
- **Lesson 23 Transparency**

- **Reading Essentials**
- **Technology**
  TeacherWorks™ CD-ROM
  StudentWorks™ CD-ROM
  Reading Essentials CD-ROM
  Exam*View*® Assessment Suite
  Vocabulary Puzzlemaker

Learning Styles

2 Teach

Class Activity

Learning Styles Have students give specific examples of activities that could be done with each of the learning styles listed. *An example for a kinesthetic learner would be to make up a story about what to do in the case of a sports injury.* **L2**

Quick Demo

Using the Tips Use a page of notes and show students how to use at least one of the tips for each type of learner. For example, you can color-code or highlight for a visual learner; have students act out a story to help a kinesthetic learner; read the notes aloud or sing them as a song for an auditory learner. **ELL**

INTERACTIVE CHALKBOARD with Image Bank

PowerPoint® Presentations

This CD-ROM is an editable Microsoft® PowerPoint® presentation that includes:
- Lesson presentations
- Lesson checks
- Interactive graphics
- 5-Minute Checks
- Image Bank
- All transparencies

Note-Taking Refer to the Two-Column Notes: Conclusion-Support Strategy on page 16T. Have students write what type of learner they are in the left column and evidence to support that conclusion in the right column.

National Health Education Standards
Pages 262–263: 4.1, 6.3

Developmental Tasks

Class Activity

Healthful Friendships Have students write an essay about an ideal situation in which two teens meet and become best friends. Ask students to answer these questions in their essays: How would these friends feel about each other? What kind of personal information would they share with each other? How long would they need to know each other before they became best friends? **L2**

Class Discussion

Healthful Relationships Have students discuss how developing healthful relationships during adolescence can affect the relationships they have as adults. Ask them to explain how the relationships they develop during adolescence might affect their marriage or their career. **L2**

NHES Assessment/SCASS

Constructed Response Bring in examples of personal ads selected from a local paper for students to examine. Caution: Evaluate them in advance to be sure that they are appropriate for your classroom. Have students create their own personal ad for a best friend. They should include the qualities and characteristics they would look for in a best friend. **L1**

Developmental Tasks

Achievements that need to be mastered to become a responsible, independent adult are the *developmental tasks of adolescence*. Robert Havighurst, a sociologist, identified eight developmental tasks that you need to master. These tasks are listed below.

How to Achieve Developmental Tasks

Making healthful friendships is an important developmental task. ▼

Task 1: Develop healthful friendships with members of both sexes. Healthful friendships involve mutual respect, flexibility, trust, honesty, and the opportunity to share feelings. Through friendships, you learn how to communicate effectively, cooperate, and resolve conflict. These skills will help you in the workplace and if you marry. Friends provide support and companionship throughout life.

Task 2: Become comfortable with your maleness or your femaleness. The way a person acts and the feelings and attitudes he or she has about being male or female is a *sex role*. Your sex role was influenced by the way adults in your life have related to one another. As a result, you have beliefs about the ways males and females should behave toward one another. Adolescence is a good time to test your attitudes and beliefs.

Participate in social activities you enjoy. They provide an opportunity to observe and react to how you interact with others.

Task 3: Become comfortable with your body. Adolescence is a period of transition that involves physical, social, emotional, and intellectual changes. You experience secondary sex characteristics and your body becomes adultlike. You are capable of producing offspring, although you are not ready to marry and have children. During adolescence, you must become comfortable with the ways in which your body changes. You must develop a positive body image. *Body image* is the perception a person has of his or her body's appearance. Be proud that your body is male or female.

Task 4: Become emotionally independent from adults. Your parents or guardian have provided emotional security throughout your childhood. They have shielded you and helped you sort out things. As an adult, you can still stay close to them. However, the balance of responsibility now starts to shift to you.

You may still ask for feedback but must become responsible for yourself and independent from your parents or guardian.

⚓ Achieving Health Literacy

Effective Communicator Discuss with students the skills involved in being a good conversationalist. These skills include asking questions, showing interest in what someone else is saying, listening carefully, responding to others, considering other ideas, encouraging another person, being positive, sharing your ideas, encouraging someone to talk, and making eye contact. Have students consider their last few conversations and rate them in their health journals based on these criteria. Ask students to answer these questions: Which skills do they use regularly? Are there some that they feel they need to try to use more often? How do their conversations differ when they are talking to different people, such as their friends, teachers, siblings, or parents or guardians? **L2**

Task 5: Learn skills you will need later if you marry and become a parent. As an adolescent, you are learning about intimacy. *Intimacy* is a deep and meaningful kind of sharing between two people. *Self-disclosure* is the act of making thoughts and feelings known to another person. During adolescence, you practice self-disclosure. Self-disclosure may bring you closer to someone. Sometimes the other person disappoints you. These kinds of experiences help you learn to trust your instincts about people. You learn with whom you can share feelings. Later on, this helps you select a marriage partner with whom you can be intimate.

During adolescence, you also can practice relating to infants and young children. You can learn skills that will help you if you become a parent in the future.

Task 6: Prepare for a career. During adolescence, you gain skills and knowledge about yourself to help you prepare for a career. Consider what you want to do next. Do you need to continue your education to be able to get the kind of job and income you want? Will you attend college or a vocational school? Is there some other training in which you are interested?

Make careful selections when planning your high school courses. Talk to adults engaged in the type of career that interests you. You may want to be a volunteer or get a part-time job to gain experience.

Task 7: Have a clear set of values to guide your behavior. Your parents or guardian have taught you a set of values to guide your behavior. As a child, you learned what values are

important. You knew what behaviors were expected of you.

To know about values is to have values in your head. However, as you mature, values must be in your heart as well. During adolescence, these values must move from your head to your heart. You must believe in these values. You must want them to guide your behavior. To want to practice values because you believe in them is to have values in your heart.

Task 8: Understand and achieve socially responsible behavior. To be a responsible adult, you must have a social conscience. A *social conscience* is a desire to contribute to society and to live a socially responsible life. To do this, you must move beyond thinking about yourself to thinking about the lives of others. What can you do to enrich the quality of life within your home, school, family, community, nation, and world?

You may decide to do volunteer work, give blood on a regular basis, donate money to charities, or initiate a project that will improve your community.

▲ There are many ways to be socially responsible.

Make the Connection

Healthful Friendships Refer to page 164 in Lesson 15 to investigate how you can form healthful friendships.

Reading Review

1. What are developmental tasks?

2. How might you get experience in a career that interests you?

Reading Review

1. *achievements that need to be mastered to become a responsible, independent adult*

2. *volunteer or get a part-time job in the field*

NHES Assessment/SCASS

Selected Response Volunteering, giving blood, donating money, and improving your community are behaviors that demonstrate:

A. intimacy

B. *social conscience*

C. self-disclosure

D. emotional independence

🏛 Community Involvement

Social Responsibility One of the developmental tasks of adolescence is to achieve social responsibility. Have students decide on a task they can complete that will enrich the quality of life for someone in their home, school, community, or nation. Once they have completed that task, they should write a short reaction paper or perform a skit expressing what they have learned from their experience and how helping others made them feel. For example, students could plant flowers for an elderly neighbor or help a sibling reorganize or redecorate his or her room in their home. **L2**

National Health Education Standards
Pages 264–265: 2.8, 7.1

Your Future

5-Minute Check

Page 67, Unit 4 Fast File Resources

1. Which type of learner would benefit from bringing a tape recorder to class? *an auditory learner*
2. What are the benefits of healthful friendships? *you learn how to communicate effectively, cooperate, and resolve conflict*
3. What is body image? *the perception a person has of his or her body's appearance*
4. What is a risk of practicing self-disclosure with someone? *He or she may disappoint you.*
5. What does it mean to have a social conscience? *to have a desire to contribute to society and to live a socially responsible life*

Using the Table

How to Plan for a Successful Future
Have students choose three of the keys to success to write about. Have them explain why these elements will help them plan for a successful future.
Answers will vary. **L2**

Teaching Transparency

Page 61, Unit 4 Fast File Resources

You may have many questions about your future and how you will prepare for it. What you do now will help determine what your future will be. You might get valuable insight into different careers by participating in volunteer activities while you are still in school.

How to Plan for a Successful Future

Keep a journal about your interests, work or volunteer experiences. Work with your school guidance counselor to focus on academic, personal, social, and career development. Ask for advice in choosing the courses for a career that interests you and work hard in those courses.

There are five keys that can help you unlock the door to a successful future.

TABLE 23.1 Five Keys to a Successful Future

 Key 1: Assess your strengths, weaknesses, and interests. Try to find where your strengths lie. Take tests prepared by professionals especially designed to do that. Talk to your parents or guardian or school counselor. Ask your counselor about interest inventories that are designed to help you.

 Key 2: Identify and use resources. Make things happen for yourself. Find people who can advise you about your goals and help you reach them. Use community resources, such as the library or youth center.

 Key 3: Set goals, make plans to reach them, and develop a positive attitude. Consider ways to improve yourself. Set new short-term and long-term goals. Remember, what you believe, you can achieve. Be an "I can" person.

 Key 4: Develop a work ethic and keep your priorities in order. A *work ethic* is an attitude of discipline, motivation, and commitment toward tasks. Having a work ethic increases your self-respect. Others know they can count on you. Carefully pick and choose what your priorities are. Which things must you do, and which can you give up? The ability to prioritize will help you be successful.

 Key 5: Manage your time wisely. Time management is critical in school, on the job, and in your personal life. Create a realistic schedule. Determine how much time you need to spend on school and work to be successful. Determine how much time you need for family responsibilities. Then you will know how much time you have for your social life.

266 UNIT 4 • Growth and Development

🏠 Family Involvement

Interview Ask students to interview an adult in their household about his or her goals. These may include different types of goals, such as career or educational goals, financial goals, or personal goals. Have students ask the person they are interviewing these questions: What goals did he or she have when the person was an adolescent? Did he or she meet those goals? If so, how? If not, why not? What are his or her current short- and long-term goals? What are his or her plans to meet these goals? Has he or she seen any progress toward these goals? Does he or she have a time frame for when he or she expects to meet these goals? Ask students to write a newspaper-style article about the interview that incorporates the answers to the above questions. **L2**

How to Set Goals and Make Plans to Achieve Them

Is there something you want to achieve now or in the future? Wishing and hoping will not help. You need to set goals. A ***goal*** is a desired achievement toward which a person works. A ***short-term goal*** is something a person plans to achieve in the near future. A ***long-term goal*** is something a person plans to achieve after a period of time. Setting and achieving personal goals need not be an overwhelming task.

State your goal. Write it down. Be specific. Share your goal with your parents or guardian. Is your goal clear? Is it realistic? Is it achievable?

Make an action plan. A detailed description of the steps a person will take to reach a goal is an ***action plan.*** You may need to set short-term goals to make progress toward a long-term goal.

Identify obstacles to your action plan. Ask yourself what might keep you from being able to do what you plan to do.

Set up a timeline. When will you begin? When do you hope to achieve your goal? Is the timeline realistic?

Keep a chart or diary. Record your progress toward your goal. Seeing progress will encourage you.

Build a support system. Ask people who will help you reach your goal for ideas and help.

Revise your goal, plan, or timeline if necessary. If you need to make changes, do so. Do not give up on your goal. Do not lower your standards.

www.glencoe.com

Maslow's Theory of Human Development

In the 1950s, psychologist Abraham Maslow (1908-1970) began to introduce his theory of human development, that humans have certain basic needs that must be met before they can go on to fulfill other needs. He presented his theory in the form of a pyramid or hierarchy of needs. A person must meet the needs of each level before going on to the next higher level.

The lowest level of the pyramid consists of the fulfillment of physiological needs, such as hunger, thirst, and sleep. The second level addresses safety needs. A person has to feel safe and secure in his or her environment. The third tier includes the need to feel a sense of belonging and acceptance from others. Self-esteem needs, such as the need to achieve and gain approval and recognition, make up the fourth level.

The top level consists of self-actualization needs. Maslow explained that these needs are the needs a person feels to reach his or her potential to the fullest. Maslow believed that a self-actualized person is one who accepts himself or herself—someone who is independent and is sympathetic to and promotes the welfare of others. A self-actualized person has a tendency to form meaningful relationships with a few people rather than maintain superficial, shallow friendships with many people.

 Health Online Visit www.glencoe.com for more information on growth and development.

Self-Actualization Hierarchy

Analyzing the Diagram

Study the diagram to the right and answer these questions:

1. Which levels of the pyramid involve needs for air and shelter?

2. How many levels of human basic needs are represented in the pyramid?

Self-actualization

Esteem

Belongingness and love

Safety

Physiological needs

LESSON 23 • Developing Learning and Planning Styles **267**

Analyzing Graphs

1. first level, second level
2. five

Project

Biography Have students research the life of Abraham Maslow and write a one-page biography. Have students include the answers to these questions in the biography: What was his educational background? Was he famous for anything else? Was his theory of human development widely accepted? **L3**

Explain the Concept

Short Term versus Long Term Tell students that short-term goals are goals that you may be able to reach within the next year or two. Examples might be preparing for the SAT test or shaving 30 seconds off of your time running a mile. Tell students that long-term goals are goals that will not be met for quite some time. Examples may include finishing college or starting a family.

Class Discussion

Hierarchy of Needs Have students discuss Maslow's theory of human development. Ask students if they agree with his theory. Have them give reasons why or why not. Ask students if they believe most people reach the highest level and if most individuals become self-actualized. **L2**

Ⓓ Differentiated Instruction

Learning Disabilities Have groups of students make posters displaying each of the five levels of Maslow's pyramid. Each group should work on one of the levels. Students can write a summary statement at the bottom of their poster and then combine the posters to make a storyboard to help the whole class review this topic. Display the storyboard in the classroom, possibly as a bulletin board display. **L2 ELL**

National Health Education Standards
Pages 266–267: 6.1, 6.2, 6.3, 7.1, 7.2

3 Assess

Vocabulary Practice

Page 60, **Unit 4 Fast File Resources**

Name_____ Date_____ Class_____
LESSON 23 Developing Learning and Planning Styles
Vocabulary Practice
Explain the relationship between the pairs or groups of words given below. Include a definition of each vocabulary term as part of your answer.

action plan — dyslexia — independent
attention deficit disorder (ADD) — goal — learning style
body image — hyperactive — sex role
developmental tasks of adolescence

1. goal—action plan
2. sex role—body image
3. independent—developmental tasks of adolescence
4. hyperactive—attention deficit disorder
5. learning style—dyslexia

60 LESSON 23 • Developing Learning and Planning Styles   UNIT 4

Learning Disabilities

A disorder in which a person has difficulty acquiring and processing information is a *learning disability.* If a person is diagnosed with a learning disability, counselors, school psychologists, teachers, and tutors can work with the person and his or her parents or guardian to make a plan to increase learning.

Did You Know?

Learning Disability Dyslexia is a common learning problem that occurs in children and adults with normal vision and normal intelligence.

What to Know About Learning Disabilities

Schools may offer classes for students with learning disabilities in which the teaching techniques are adapted to the needs of the students who require help. Many students with learning disabilities remain in the same classroom with other students. Their teachers provide special help when needed.

Some students with learning disabilities may get extra help outside of the classroom with a speech pathologist or a reading specialist. Many students have a tutor. A *tutor* is a person who works with individual students to help them with schoolwork.

Dyslexia A learning disability in which a person has difficulty spelling, reading, and writing is *dyslexia.* People who have dyslexia may reverse letters and numbers. They may read from right to left.

Tutoring is available for students who need extra assistance. ▶

Attention-deficit hyperactivity disorder A learning disability in which a person is restless and easily distracted is *attention-deficit hyperactivity disorder (ADHD).*

People who have ADHD cannot keep their attention focused on what they are doing. People with this disorder are also *hyperactive,* which means they have difficulty sitting or standing still for long periods of time.

Tracking disorder A learning disability in which a person has difficulty looking at and following an object is *tracking disorder.* People who have this disorder skip letters, words, and lines as they read.

Five facts To be more sensitive to people with learning disabilities, remember the following five facts. If you have a learning disability, these facts may help you understand yourself.

People with learning disabilities

1. are capable of learning,
2. can learn strategies that help them acquire and process information,
3. may need a tutor and/or special education classes,
4. need support and encouragement from classmates and family, and
5. can be very successful.

268   UNIT 4 • Growth and Development

♥ Sensitive Issues

Disabilities Many students with a variety of disabilities are now being mainstreamed into regular classrooms. It is important to address the issue of disabilities with all students while making sure not to draw undue or unwanted attention to those students with disabilities. Some students with disabilities that are not apparent may try to hide them, so it may not be obvious to others why this topic would make them uncomfortable. Discuss disabilities with respect to a nonspecific or possibly fictional student. Try to emphasize the list of positive facts above rather than the difficulties faced by those with disabilities.

23 STUDY GUIDE

action plan
attention-deficit
    hyperactivity/
    disorder (ADHD)
body image
developmental tasks
    of adolescence
dyslexia
goal
hyperactive
independent
learning style
sex role
tracking disorder

Key Terms Review

Match the definitions below with the lesson Key Terms on the left. Do not write in this book.

1. the way you gain and process information

2. a learning disability in which a person has difficulty spelling, reading, and writing

3. to not be able to sit or stand still for long periods of time

4. a desired achievement toward which you work

5. achievements that need to be mastered to become a responsible, independent adult

6. the detailed description of the steps to take to reach a goal

7. a learning disability in which a person is restless and is easily distracted

8. the perception a person has of his or her body's appearance

9. the way a person acts and the feelings he or she has about being male or female

10. to be able to rely on oneself

Recalling the Facts

11. What are four types of learning styles? Give a tip for each.

12. What does it mean to develop a work ethic?

13. What is Maslow's definition of a self-actualized person?

14. Describe how a person can keep his or her priorities in order.

15. State five facts that apply to people who have learning disabilities.

16. What are five ways to unlock the door to a successful future?

17. How can you set and achieve a goal?

18. What are four common types of learning disabilities?

Critical Thinking

19. What does it mean to have values in your heart as well as in your head?

20. Why is it important to understand what learning disabilities are? What learning support is available to students with learning disabilities?

21. Consider Developmental Tasks 1 and 7 in Havighurst's list of developmental tasks. How are they related?

22. Compare a visual learner with an auditory learner and a kinesthetic learner.

Real-Life Applications

23. In what way would keeping a journal help you achieve Developmental Task 4 in Havighurst's list of developmental tasks?

24. What is your learning style? What changes can you make in the way you study to maximize your learning?

25. As you think about your own goals, what first steps should you take to reach them?

26. What kind of volunteer work might you choose to prepare for a career?

Activities

Responsible Decision Making

27. **Describe** You have a test tomorrow. Your friend suggests studying together and quizzing each other. However, you know you study best when you outline the material you need to learn. Describe how you would respond to this situation. Refer to the Responsible Decision-Making Model on page 61 for help.

Sharpen Your Life Skills

28. **Set Health Goals** Refer to page 266 about planning for the future. Take a sheet of paper and number one through five. Next to each number, write a strength you have and think about how you can use this strength toward your future. Write a one-page journal entry on this topic.

Visit **www.glencoe.com** for more *Health & Wellness* quizzes.

LESSON 23 • Study Guide **269**

STUDY GUIDE

Key Terms Review

1. learning style
2. dyslexia
3. hyperactive
4. goal
5. developmental tasks of adolescence
6. action plan
7. attention-deficit/hyperactivity disorder (ADHD)
8. body image
9. sex role
10. independent

Recalling the Facts

11. See page 263.
12. See page 266.
13. See page 267.
14. See page 266.
15. See page 268.
16. See page 266.
17. See page 267.
18. See page 268.

Critical Thinking

19. It means to believe in values and want them to guide your behavior, as well as knowing them.

20. Understanding what learning disabilities are can make you more sensitive to people with learning disabilities. Learning support available to those with learning disabilities includes special classes, speech pathologists, reading specialists, and tutors.

21. Task 1 relates to healthful friendships and Task 7 with having values. These are related because you can choose friends who share important values so that they will not ask you to behave in ways that are contrary to your values.

22. Visual learners learn better using images and perform better on written tests. Auditory learners learn better by listening and perform better on oral tests. Kinesthetic learners learn better using role-play and perform better on tests requiring demonstration.

Real-Life Applications

23. If you keep a journal, you can note decisions that did not turn out as you expected and analyze what you might have done differently.

24. Answers will vary.

25. Answers will vary. First steps may include assessing your strengths and interests and identifying and using resources.

26. Answers will vary.

Activities

Responsible Decision Making

27. You can study by yourself and outline the material or you can outline the material first and then quiz each other.

Sharpen Your Life Skills

28. The lists students create will vary, but should include both their strengths and how they can be used in the future.

Out of Time?

If time does not permit an in-depth study of this topic, use the following activities in this Teacher Wraparound Edition:

- Class Discussion, p. 271
- Class Activity, p. 274
- Class Discussion, p. 274
- Class Discussion, p. 276

1 Focus

HEALTH GOALS **Healthful Aging** Have students respond to the first Health Goal for this lesson by listing reasons why they should develop habits that promote healthy aging. *Reasons might include that health habits can affect a person's biological and social age.* **L2**

Write ABOUT IT!

Journaling Student responses may include encouraging their grandparents to eat a healthful breakfast, follow the Dietary Guidelines, exercise regularly, choose activities to keep the mind alert and maintain or more fully develop healthful relationships with family and friends. **L2**

LESSON

Aging Healthfully

HEALTH GOALS
- I will develop habits that promote healthful aging.
- I will share with my family my feelings about death and dying.

There are several ways to measure a person's age. ***Chronological age*** is the number of years a person has lived. ***Biological age*** is a measure of how well a person's body systems are functioning. ***Social age*** is a measure of the activity level engaged in on a daily basis. Nothing can be done to change your chronological age. However, your health habits can affect your biological and social ages. This lesson includes facts about aging and discusses the end of the life cycle—death.

What You'll Learn

1. Describe the physical, mental, and social changes that occur in middle and late adulthood. *(pp. 271–273)*
2. Identify ten habits that promote healthful aging. *(p. 274)*
3. Discuss factors and resources to consider if you are a caregiver. *(p. 275)*
4. Discuss death and issues surrounding death, such as life support systems, living wills, and hospice care. *(p. 276)*

Why It's Important

Everyone goes through the aging process. If you understand this process, you will be better able to deal with the different stages you and others will face throughout the life cycle.

Key Terms

- chronological age
- biological age
- gerontology
- dementia
- caregiver
- hospice
- terminal illness
- legal death
- living will
- coma

Write ABOUT IT!

Writing About Aging Suppose your grandmother and grandfather do not seem to be as happy or active as they used to. They often say that they don't have enough to do during the day. Read the information on healthful aging on page 274, then write an entry in your health journal about what you could do to help your grandparents age healthfully.

National Health Education Standards—Guide for Lesson 24		
7.1	Analyze the role of individual responsibility for enhancing health.	pp. 271–274, 279
7.2	Demonstrate a variety of healthy practices and behaviors that will maintain or improve the health of self and others.	pp. 270, 273

Aging

The study of aging is called ***gerontology***. A person who specializes in the study of aging is a ***gerontologist***. Some gerontologists believe that aging begins the day you are born. Others believe that aging begins when you stop growing. Physical, mental, and social changes occur during middle and late adulthood.

What to Know About Aging

As a person ages, body systems also age. Changes are caused by heredity and other factors.

The cardiovascular system The heart may become less efficient. Blood may not circulate well. Blood vessels may lose elasticity and become clogged, causing increased blood pressure. Resting heart rate may increase and oxygen consumption may decrease. To lessen changes, older people need to maintain a desirable weight, exercise regularly, and follow a low-fat diet.

The nervous system Reaction time slows. Short-term memory may change, but not intelligence. The senses of touch, taste, smell, and hearing may be affected by loss and degeneration of nerve cells. This loss may cause Parkinson's disease. ***Parkinson's disease*** is a brain disorder that causes muscle tremors, stiffness, and weakness. To lessen changes, older people need to exercise their minds and bodies regularly.

The immune system This system becomes less efficient. Older people have less resistance to infectious diseases and are more likely to develop chronic diseases. A ***chronic disease*** is an illness that develops and lasts over a long period of time.

To lessen changes, older people need to have regular physical examinations, follow a healthful diet, and get flu shots regularly if advised to do so by a physician.

The respiratory system Lungs become less elastic and may not be able to hold the normal volume of air. Older people may experience shortness of breath and have an increased risk of chronic bronchitis, emphysema, and flu. ***Chronic bronchitis*** is a recurring inflammation of the bronchial tubes. ***Emphysema*** is a condition in which alveoli lose their ability to function. To lessen changes, older people need to use caution in severe weather, avoid secondhand smoke, exercise regularly, and not smoke.

Your health habits affect your biological and social ages. ▼

LESSON 24 • Aging Healthfully **271**

▲ Exercising the mind is important to a person of any age.

The skeletal system Bones become less dense, and when broken, take longer to heal. *Arthritis,* a painful inflammation of the joints might develop. Females, especially, may develop osteoporosis.

Osteoporosis is a disease characterized by low bone mass and deterioration of bone tissue. To lessen changes, older people need to maintain a desirable weight, exercise regularly, and choose foods with calcium.

The muscular system Muscle mass and strength decrease. Body composition changes and the percentage of body fat increases. To lessen changes, older people need to exercise regularly and lift objects correctly.

The endocrine system There may be changes in the secretions of hormones. Some people who are overweight or who have a hereditary tendency may develop diabetes mellitus. *Diabetes* or *diabetes mellitus* is a disease in which the body produces little or no insulin or cannot properly use insulin. To lessen changes, older people need to maintain a desirable weight and have regular blood tests.

The digestive system Metabolism slows, and weight may increase. Fewer nutrients are absorbed from foods. The liver may be less effective as it breaks down toxic substances. Some older people have difficulty digesting fatty foods. Gum disease and the loss of teeth may make it difficult to eat. Some older people may lose their appetites, eat less, and become malnourished.

Reading Review

1. How does aging affect the cardiovascular system?
2. What is emphysema?

To lessen changes, older people need to maintain a desirable weight, follow a balanced diet, limit alcohol consumption, and eat smaller meals more often.

The integumentary system Skin becomes drier and may wrinkle. Age spots may appear. Extended exposure to sunlight earlier in life may affect how skin ages. Hair thins and grays. Some males become bald, and some females develop bald spots. To lessen changes, older people need to wear sunblock and a hat to reduce exposure to ultraviolet radiation, and use lotions to prevent dry skin.

The urinary system The size of the bladder may decrease causing more frequent urination. Kidneys also may produce less urine. To lessen changes, older people need to drink at least eight glasses of water each day.

The reproductive system Fewer sex hormones are produced. Male testosterone levels decline with age. *Menopause* is a decrease in estrogen and the cessation of the menstrual cycle. During menopause, some females experience hot flashes, depression, insomnia, headaches, fatigue, and short-term memory loss. Some disease processes, such as osteoporosis, worsen as estrogen decreases. Some females choose hormone replacement therapy. *Hormone replacement therapy (HRT)* is synthetic estrogen and/or progestin given to reduce the symptoms of menopause and decrease osteoporosis. There is evidence that this type of therapy may be linked to a slightly increased risk of heart disease, strokes, breast cancer, and blood clots, as well as other risks.

272 UNIT 4 • Growth and Development

Activity: Using Life Skills

Advocating for Health: Volunteering to Help Older Adults

Volunteering to help an older adult can be a rewarding experience. As a young person, you can supply energy, companionship, and entertainment. This can make an older adult's life easier and more enjoyable. You also will have the satisfaction of knowing you are making a difference in another person's life. Here are some ideas to guide you in volunteering to help older adults.

1 Some older people live with family, some live in their own homes, and some may live in nursing homes or assisted-care facilities. They may welcome your interest and assistance wherever they live.

2 **Select a health-related concern.** List possible ways to make a difference in someone's life. Think about volunteering at organizations as well as helping individuals you know personally.

3 **Gather reliable information.** List possible ways to help, such as reading, talking, helping with chores, cleaning, or telephoning.

4 **Identify your purpose and target audience.** Identify one or two actions on the list that best fit your interests and personality. Decide how much time you have for this volunteer activity. Contact an organization and explain your interests.

5 **Develop a convincing and appropriate message.** Clarify exactly what your commitment is and your schedule for helping. Plan to show up on time and be prepared for your tasks. Talk with your friends about volunteering and share what you learned from your experience. How could you improve the experience?

Mental Changes in Middle and Late Adulthood

As people age, they may lose some short-term memory. Some people develop dementia. **Dementia** is a general decline in all areas of mental functioning.

Alzheimer's disease is a type of dementia. **Alzheimer's disease** is a progressive disease in which protein plaque and tangles form in the brain reducing nerve cell connections, nerve cells degenerate, and the brain shrinks in size. Symptoms vary, but there are usually three stages.

In the first stage, people are forgetful, lose interest, and feel anxious and depressed. In the second stage, people are disconnected and restless and have increased memory loss, especially for recent events. In the third stage, people become very disoriented, confused, and completely dependent on others. Older people should work to stay mentally sharp by using their mental skills.

Social Changes in Middle and Late Adulthood

People who are aging need friends with whom they can talk and engage in social activities. Most older people who stay active socially have better mental and physical health. Some older people suffer from depression. **Major depression** is long-lasting feelings of hopelessness, sadness, or helplessness. Exercise, therapy, and prescription medications are used to treat major depression.

Did You Know?

Alzheimer's Disease
Alzheimer's disease is rare in both young and middle-aged people.

Using Life Skills

Advocating for Health Many senior citizens benefit from having a pet. Contact your local humane society and a local senior citizen facility to determine if you could initiate a visiting program between seniors and students with animals at the humane society. Be sure to get permission from the students' parents or guardians first.

Class Discussion

Age and Beauty Many products claim to reduce wrinkles, fade age spots, and prevent balding. Have students discuss why these products might appeal to people who are showing signs of aging. Ask students why products like these have become big business. See the ten Advertising Appeals on page 38 in Lesson 4 for more information on advertising for these kinds of products. **L2**

Quick Demo

Healthful Aging Show students examples of activities that older people can use to maintain their mental skills. Examples may include doing crossword puzzles, math problems or multiplication tables, reading an engrossing book, and learning another language. **ELL**

Family Involvement

Write a Letter Senior citizens enjoy getting mail from family and friends. They grew up before cell phones and e-mail, so letter writing was a common form of communication for them. Have students write a letter to a grandparent, elderly relative, or family friend. The students should let them know how they are doing and what activities they currently are involved in. They also may want to share an amusing story or tell about a movie or book that they enjoyed recently. The recipient also may appreciate hearing about a favorite shared memory. **L2**

National Health Education Standards
Pages 272–273: 1.1, 1.2, 4.1, 4.4, 7.1, 7.2

Healthful Aging

Class Activity

Write an Essay Have students write an essay in which they discuss the statement by Joseph Addison: "The three grand essentials to happiness in life are something to do, someone to love, and something to hope for." **L2**

Class Discussion

Healthful Aging Divide students into five groups. Assign each group two habits that promote healthful aging. Have them discuss the negative health effects that might occur if these habits are not followed. Students should share their ideas with the other groups. **L2** **ELL**

Explain the Concept

Chronic Disease Tell students that a chronic disease is long-lasting and slow-progressing. Many elderly people suffer from these afflictions. The most common chronic diseases are heart disease, cancers, stroke, chronic obstructive pulmonary disease, and diabetes.

Teaching Transparency

Page 73, **Unit 4 Fast File Resources**

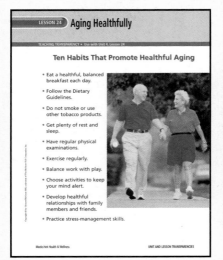

Healthful Aging

D o you want to age in a healthful way? Practice the ten habits that promote healthful aging that are listed below. Consider the words of essayist Joseph Addison: "The three grand essentials to happiness in life are something to do, something to love, and something to hope for."

How to Promote Healthful Aging

Early and middle adulthood The three grand essentials provide vitality and satisfaction throughout life. You need something worthwhile and satisfying to do to stay healthy. In early and middle adulthood, you may be engaged as a parent, or in a career.

Late adulthood During late adulthood, you may enjoy satisfying hobbies and volunteer work. You also need someone to love to stay healthy. You will have better health if you stay involved with family and friends. These people help you feel loved and supported. They encourage you.

Something to hope for You also need something to hope for in order to stay healthy. Having something to look forward to gives you a reason to take care of yourself. Right now, you may look forward to a social or athletic event. You may look forward to graduating from high school and continuing your education. These events give you a reason to keep going. As you age, having a reason to keep going is very important. Elderly people who have something to look forward to—the birth of a grandchild or the graduation of a grandchild—also benefit.

Both grandparent ▶ and grandchild benefit when they spend time together.

Ten Habits That Promote Healthful Aging

Make these habits part of your life to promote healthful aging.

- Eat a healthful, balanced breakfast each day.
- Follow the Dietary Guidelines.
- Do not smoke or use other tobacco products.
- Get plenty of rest and sleep.
- Have regular physical examinations.

- Exercise regularly.
- Balance work with play.
- Choose activities to keep your mind alert.
- Develop healthful relationships with family members and friends.
- Practice stress-management skills.

274 UNIT 4 • Growth and Development

⊕ Cross-Curricular Connections

Social Studies Have groups of students research agencies that provide age-related services, such as the Social Security Administration, Medicare, or AARP. Ask students to answer these questions: When and why was each agency originally created? Who is eligible? What benefits are provided for those who are eligible? What do people have to do in order to access the services provided by each agency? Have each group create a pamphlet or brochure that communicates what they have discovered. Groups should share their pamphlets with the rest of the class. **L3** **ELL**

Being a Caregiver

A s people age, they may require special care. Most older people turn to family members and friends for assistance and support. A *caregiver* is a person who provides care for a person who needs assistance.

What to Know About Being a Caregiver

Most people are caregivers for an elderly family member at some time in their lives. Your family may provide care for a relative right now. Resources for caregivers are listed below.

Senior centers Senior centers are facilities where older people can be involved in classes and social activities. Most centers provide meals.

Transportation assistance Some community agencies and senior centers provide transportation.

Friendly visitors Friendly visitors or companions volunteer to regularly visit older people who are alone.

Telephone reassurance programs Telephone reassurance programs are staffed by volunteers who regularly call older people who are alone.

Home-delivered meals Organizations such as Meals-on-Wheels deliver food to older people.

Gatekeeper programs People who work for the postal service or a public utilities company may be trained to notice changes that might affect the needs of the elderly and to report these changes.

Home health-care organizations These organizations offer a variety of services, including nursing care, medical treatment, and therapy in the home.

Personal emergency response devices These mechanical devices help older people call for help if they are not able to reach or dial the telephone.

Adult day care programs These programs provide health care, social activities, meals, therapy, and transportation.

Respite care Respite care is care provided by someone to relieve a caregiver of caregiving responsibilities.

Nursing homes or convalescent centers These facilities provide 24-hour care. Medical care is provided at nursing homes.

Hospice care Special care for people who are dying and for their families is available in a hospice.

Considerations for Caregivers

Six factors to consider when you are a caregiver for a family member:

- the type of care the family member needs
- the type of care the family member will accept
- the cost of the type of care needed
- the insurance coverage and financial resources of the family member
- the type of care you can provide
- the type of care provided by resources in the community

LESSON 24 • Aging Healthfully **275**

Death and Dying

Class Discussion

Living Wills Have students discuss the importance of having a living will, when people should make out their living wills, and how a living will will benefit a dying person's family members.

Reading Review

1. *mechanical or other means to support life*
2. *A living will tells what treatment a person wants, whereas a regular will tells how to distribute possessions.*

3 Assess

Vocabulary Practice
Page 72, **Unit 4 Fast File Resources**

Death and Dying

The permanent cessation of all vital organs is *death*. At one time, a person was pronounced dead when his or her heart and lungs stopped functioning. But today, life support systems can prolong life by keeping the heart and lungs functioning. A *life-support system* is mechanical or other means to support life.

What to Know About Death and Dying

Many people want to be near family and friends at the time of their death. They might use a hospice.

Hospices A facility for people who are dying and their families is a *hospice.* Two criteria must be met before a person is eligible to use a hospice. A person must have a terminal illness. A *terminal illness.* is an illness that will result in death. A person also must be expected to die in less than six months. Hospices can provide support at a hospital, another facility, or in someone's home. When possible, care is provided in the person's home. Usually, medications are given to keep the person as comfortable as possible. Family members and friends stay with the dying person. Hospice workers assist the family.

Death Life-support systems brought about a need to define death in legal terms. *Legal death* is brain death or the irreversible stopping of circulatory and respiratory functions. *Brain death* is the irreversible cessation of all functions of the entire brain, including the brain stem.

Living wills People are living longer than they did in the past, causing them to think about issues related to life-support systems and legal death.

People now have the right to make living wills. A *living will* is a document that tells what treatment a person wants in the event that he or she no longer can make decisions. A living will differs from a regular will. A regular will tells how a person wants his or her possessions to be distributed.

A living will focuses on medical treatment issues. A person may name someone to make decisions about medical treatment if he or she cannot do so. For example, a person in a coma cannot make his or her own decisions. A *coma* is a state of unconsciousness.

In a living will, a person also may make a request for medical nonintervention. A *request for medical nonintervention* is a person's refusal of specific life-support systems when there is no reasonable expectation of recovering or regaining a meaningful life. A person can state which life-support systems he or she does not want. These may include antibiotics, machine or forced feedings or fluids, cardiac resuscitation, respiratory support, or surgery. The request also may state that treatment be limited to providing comfort, such as the administration of painkillers.

Reading Review

1. What is a life-support system?
2. How does a living will differ from a regular will?

276 UNIT 4 • Growth and Development

⚖ Legal Issues

Legal Death Have students investigate their state's interpretation of legal death. Have students answer these questions: What are their state's laws dealing with living wills? Do they recognize them as legally binding documents? What types of information and preferences may be included in a living will? Are there any required elements to make the living will valid? Are there any circumstances under which parts of a living will may be disregarded? What if there is no living will? Who is legally responsible for making decisions for a dying individual? Have students give multimedia presentations on their findings. **L3**

biological age
brain death
caregiver
chronic disease
chronological age
coma
dementia
gerontology
hospice
legal death
living will
terminal illness

Key Terms Review

Explain the relationship between the pairs of lesson Key Terms below. Do not write in this book.

1. chronological age—biological age
2. living will—terminal illness
3. caregiver—hospice
4. gerontology—dementia
5. legal death—coma

Recalling the Facts

6. Give examples of a physical change, a mental change, and a social change that occur in middle and late adulthood.
7. What is the relationship between Alzheimer's disease and dementia?
8. What are ten habits that promote healthful aging?
9. Describe two legal definitions of death.
10. Discuss three issues related to death.
11. What is the difference between a living will and a regular will?
12. What is a request for medical nonintervention?
13. Name three resources available for caregivers. Name one main service of each.
14. How is clinical depression treated?
15. How might aging affect the immune system?
16. What is a life-support system?
17. What are the criteria for using a hospice?
18. What are the three grand essentials for happiness?

Critical Thinking

19. Why might some gerontologists think that aging begins at birth?
20. How might physical exercise benefit the respiratory system of an older adult?
21. Why is it important to know what resources for caregiving are available?
22. Explain the relationship between chronological age and biological age. Consider a person whose chronological age is less than his or her biological age. How might the difference be changed?

Real-Life Applications

23. Why do you think "something to hope for" is a grand essential for happiness?
24. What do you think this sentence means: "Life-support systems brought about a need to define death in legal terms?"
25. How would you try to convince a grandparent that exercise is beneficial?
26. Your aunt is a caregiver for her mother. List ways you might offer respite care to help your aunt.

Activities

Responsible Decision Making

27. **Write** You are the caregiver for your elderly grandparent who has Alzheimer's disease. A friend who stops by suggests taking a ride. Your friend assures you that you will be back before your grandparent misses you. Write a response to this situation. Refer to the Responsible Decision-Making Model on page 61 for help.

Sharpen Your Life Skills

28. **Analyze Influences on Health** Many elderly people seem to benefit from having a pet. Contact a local veterinarian and a person who works in a senior citizen facility that allows pets or encourages people to bring pets to visit. Summarize what you learn from talking to them.

Visit www.glencoe.com for more *Health & Wellness* quizzes.

LESSON 24 • Study Guide **277**

LESSON 24
STUDY GUIDE

Key Terms Review

1. See page 270.
2. A living will focuses on medical treatment decisions for a person who has a terminal illness.
3. A caregiver provides care for any person who needs assistance. Hospice care assists those who are dying.
4. Gerontology is the study of aging. Dementia may occur as people age.
5. Legal death is brain death or the irreversible stopping of circulatory and respiratory functions. A coma may precede death.

Recalling the Facts

6. See pages 271–273.
7. See page 273.
8. See page 274.
9. See page 276.
10. See page 276.
11. See page 276.
12. See page 276.
13. See page 275.
14. See page 273.
15. See page 271.
16. See page 276.
17. See page 276.
18. See page 274.

Critical Thinking

19. Changes in the body always are occurring.
20. Exercise strengthens the lungs so they can work more efficiently.
21. Knowing the resources will make it easier to get help, if needed.
22. See page 270.

Real-Life Applications

23. It gives you a reason to take care of yourself, and may encourage an optimistic attitude.
24. Life-support systems sometimes can prolong basic body functions in a person who would otherwise be dead. Thus, a legal definition of death is required to determine when to stop life-support systems and to read wills.
25. See pages 271–273 for information on exercise benefits.

---

26. You could offer to stay with her mother to give your aunt a break, or to run errands to save her time and energy.

Activities

Responsible Decision Making

27. One's first commitment is to a family member and the trust that a parent has instilled.

The grandparent may have a sudden need for assistance. If you were not there, the grandparent might try to walk without assistance and risk falling and injury.

Sharpen Your Life Skills

28. Answers will vary.

UNIT 4
STUDY GUIDE

Key Terms Review

1. k
2. l
3. i
4. e
5. f
6. c
7. d
8. h
9. a
10. j

Recalling the Facts

11. Have regular medical checkups, perform testicular self-exam for males, keep track of length and dates of the menstrual cycle for females.
12. Drink at least 6–8 glasses of water each day, maintain healthful blood pressure.
13. holds the testes and regulates their temperature
14. receives and supports a fertilized egg during pregnancy and contracts during childbirth to help with delivery
15. It can detect the presence of a birth defect, which can be helpful in planning how to care for a baby after birth.
16. They enjoy playing with friends and communicating with others; they like to learn numbers, play simple games, and be independent.
17. A visual learner learns best by seeing images, and an auditory learner learns best by listening to or discussing a topic.
18. A global learner learns best by studying the big picture and relating learning to personal experience.
19. arthritis and osteoporosis
20. Dementia and Alzheimer's disease are two mental conditions that can affect people in middle and late adulthood.

Critical Thinking

21. To reduce the risk of heart disease, you can reduce fat and salt in your diet, exercise regularly, avoid using tobacco products, maintain a healthful weight, and practice stress management.
22. If you dive into shallow water, you might hit your head and injure your spinal cord.
23. The body would not produce enough insulin, which would lead to developing diabetes. There also would be problems with digesting food without the enzymes produced in the pancreas.

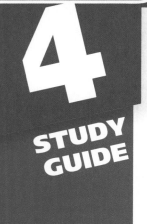

UNIT 4 STUDY GUIDE

Key Terms Review

Match the following definitions with the correct Key Terms. Do not write in this book.

a. conception *(p. 243)*
b. chromosome *(p. 243)*
c. coma *(p. 276)*
d. dementia *(p. 273)*
e. gerontology *(p. 271)*
f. goal *(p. 267)*
g. independent *(p. 262)*
h. ovaries *(p. 228)*
i. prostate gland *(p. 237)*
j. puberty *(p. 227)*
k. time out *(p. 259)*
l. ultrasound *(p. 245)*

1. a calming down period of time
2. high frequency sound waves that make a picture
3. the male part of the body that makes a fluid to keep sperm alive
4. the study of aging
5. what a person who wants to achieve something later in life has
6. the union of an ovum and a sperm
7. general decline in all areas of mental functioning
8. the female part of the body that produces ova and estrogen
9. carries genes
10. the stage of development when both the male and female body become capable of producing offspring

Recalling the Facts

11. What are three ways to keep the endocrine system healthy? *(Lesson 19)*
12. What are two ways to keep the urinary system healthy? *(Lesson 19)*
13. What are two purposes of the scrotum? *(Lesson 20)*
14. What are two functions of the uterus? *(Lesson 20)*
15. Why is an ultrasound important? *(Lesson 21)*
16. What are two characteristics of three-to-five-year-olds? *(Lesson 22)*
17. What is the difference between a visual learner and an auditory learner? *(Lesson 23)*
18. How does a global learner differ from a visual learner, an auditory learner and a kinesthetic learner? *(Lesson 23)*
19. What are two conditions that affect the skeletal system during aging? *(Lesson 24)*
20. What are two mental changes that can occur during middle and late adulthood? *(Lesson 24)*

Critical Thinking

21. What can you do to help keep yourself from becoming a victim of heart disease? *(Lesson 19)*
22. How could diving into shallow water negatively affect your nervous system? *(Lesson 19)*
23. What would happen if a person's pancreas was not functioning? *(Lesson 19)*
24. How would you convince a friend that being sexually active is harmful to health? *(Lesson 20)*
25. Discuss the relationship between body image and sex role. *(Lesson 23)*
26. What could you say to persuade a pregnant female not to use alcohol or drugs? *(Lesson 21)*
27. Discuss the importance of finding the reason for an infant's constant crying. *(Lesson 22)*
28. Discuss the responsibilities of caring for an infant. *(Lesson 22)*
29. Explain how an action plan would help prepare you for a career as an adult. *(Lesson 23)*
30. Explain why physical exercise is vital to growing old healthfully. *(Lesson 24)*

Use **Interactive Tutor** at **www.glencoe.com** for additional help.

24. Students may respond that sexual activity can lead to unplanned pregnancies and sexually transmitted diseases. STDs can lead to sterility and other future health problems.
25. Body image is the perception a person has about his or her body's appearance. Sex role is a way a person acts and the feelings and attitudes he or she has about being male or female. A person's perception of his or her body, particularly as it undergoes changes during adolescence, is closely related to how he or she feels about maleness or femaleness. Becoming comfortable with both one's body and sex role will help with adjustment during adolescence.
26. Alcohol and other drugs can pass from the mother's bloodstream to that of the developing embryo or fetus, thereby possibly causing harm.

What Do You Know?

Critical Thinking Write a factual question about growth and development. Form teams with classmates and compete by answering the other teams' questions. Tabulate the correct answers to determine a winner.

Connection to Language Arts

Effective Communication Write an essay to describe how you can be of help to an elderly person. Your essay should have ten facts that identify positive actions you can take. You can share your essay with a parent.

Family Involvement

Problem Solving Your younger sister has accepted her first job as a childsitter. Write her a note that explains the five most important things she should know to be a responsible childsitter.

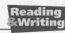

Investigating Health Careers

Responsible Citizenship Obtain permission from your parent, guardian, or teacher to interview a professional who works with students who have learning disabilities. Prepare by making a list of at least five questions to ask. Share the questions and answers with classmates.

Group Project

Self-Directed Learning Work with a group to prepare a resource guide of services for older people in your community. For example, someone will look up agencies that deal with different aspects of health, such as the American Cancer Society. Another person may look for resources that focus on services for the elderly, such as an organization that delivers meals. Visit www.glencoe.com for more information.

Standardized Test Practice

 Reading & Writing

Read the following selection and answer the questions that follow.

The word *hospice* comes from the Latin word *hospitium,* which means "guesthouse." It is related to our word *hospitality.* During the Middle Ages, a hospitium offered a safe place to stay for travelers who were on pilgrimages to religious sites. Today's hospices date from the 1960s in England. The first U.S. hospice was opened in New Haven, Connecticut, in 1974. Since that date, the number has grown to more than 3000 hospices throughout the country. Some people may be surprised to learn that 80 percent of hospice care is provided in patients' homes. The rest of hospice activities take place in separate facilities or in regular hospitals. Together, U.S. hospices serve over half a million dying people and their family and friends each year. Many of these family members are teenagers. Hospice workers and volunteers can offer support to teens and help them deal with their grief over the loss of loved ones.

Multiple Choice

1 Which of the following statements describes a way that modern hospices are similar to the hospitiums of the Middle Ages?

A Both are operated by religious groups.

B Both offer facilities and support to dying people.

C Both offer care in patients' homes.

D Both provide a safe and welcoming place for people to stay.

2 According to this paragraph, which of these statements is true?

A There are over half a million hospices in the United States.

B Hospices offer services to dying people only.

C Hospices for dying people have existed since the Middle Ages.

D Most hospice care is provided in patients' homes.

Open-Ended

3 What are some special challenges hospices face in dealing with teenagers who have lost loved ones? Write a paragraph that describes some of these challenges.

 www.glencoe.com

UNIT 4 • Study Guide   279

Standardized Test Practice

Reading & Writing

Multiple Choice

1. D   2. D

Open-Ended

3. Students' paragraphs should give examples of challenges facing grieving teens and how hospices can help them address these issues. Issues students may cite include the lack of meaningful support groups for teens, lack of life experience in dealing with unhappy events, role confusion, emotional immaturity, and the complicating role of existing conflicts. Paragraphs should contain correct spelling, capitalization, punctuation, grammar, usage, and sentence structure.

---

27. Infants cry to communicate a need. If an infant is crying constantly, it indicates that something is wrong. It may be that the baby is ill or needs something.

28. An infant is extremely dependent on a childsitter. An infant can only cry to communicate a need, so childsitters need to be vigilant in understanding what a baby needs. Caregivers need to know how to hold, diaper, bathe, feed, and burp a baby, as well as how to put a baby to bed and what to do if a baby is sick.

29. An action plan can help because you can make short-term goals, such as taking appropriate classes in high school and college, to help reach your long-term goal to have a career.

30. Exercise helps all the systems of the body stay strong.

Health Literacy Activities

What Do You Know?

Questions will vary. Listen to the game to be sure that students are giving correct answers.

Connection to Language Arts

Helpful actions in students' essays will vary, but may include things like helping to clean the home, having a conversation, playing games, reading newspaper articles, or raking leaves.

Family Involvement

Student notes will vary, but may include first aid and CPR; health needs of children; emergency contacts, including pediatrician and parents; skills to care for infants and toddlers; skills to care for older children.

Investigating Health Careers

Questions will vary, but may include: What types of learning disabilities do your students have? What types of activities do you do to help these students? What do you like about your career? What don't you like? What college classes did you need to take to prepare for this career? Are other educational requirements, such as professional exams, required?

Group Project

Information contained in resource guides will vary, but should include local resources, as well as some regional or national ones. Guides may include some resources that provide services, and others that provide information.

279

STANDARDS AND FEATURES

Lesson	National Standards	State/Local Standards	Activities and Features
Lesson 25 *(5 sessions, 2 blocks)* Choosing Healthful Foods	1.1, 2.10, 7.1		**Using Life Skills:** Analyzing Influences on Health: Comparing Food Labels, p. 292
Lesson 26 *(4 sessions, 1 block)* Following Dietary Guidelines	1.1, 1.5, 2.10		**Facts About:** Eating Right For Life, p. 298
Lesson 27 *(3 sessions, 1 block)* Using Diet to Guard Against Disease	1.1, 1.5, 7.2		**Health News:** Omega-3, p. 305
Lesson 28 *(4 sessions, 2 blocks)* Developing Healthful Eating Habits	1.1, 1.5, 7.1, 7.2		**Speaking Out:** Sports and Nutrition, p. 315 **Using Life Skills:** Practicing Healthful Behaviors: Planning a Day's Menu, p. 317 **Just the Facts:** Food Myths, p. 321
Lesson 29 *(3 sessions, 1 block)* Maintaining a Healthful Weight	1.5, 1.7, 3.4		**Using Life Skills:** Using Goal-Setting and Decision-Making Skills: Calculating Caloric Needs, p. 327

Key to Differentiated Instruction

L1 Level 1 activities should be appropriate for students with learning difficulties.

L2 Level 2 activities should be within the ability range of all students.

L3 Level 3 activities are designed for above-average students.

ELL ELL activities should be within the ability range of English language learners.

FAST FILE RESOURCES

INTRODUCING THE UNIT

Parent and Family Letter	p. 1	Health Behavior Contract	p. 3
Spanish Parent and Family Letter	p. 2	Unit Focus Transparency Master and Worksheet	p. 4

TEACHING THE UNIT LESSONS

Reproducible Student Pages	Lesson 25	Lesson 26	Lesson 27	Lesson 28	Lesson 29
Reading Strategy	p. 7	p. 21	p. 33	p. 45	p. 59
Vocabulary Practice	p. 8	p. 22	p. 34	p. 46	p. 60
Transparency Master and Worksheet	p. 9	p. 23	p. 35	p. 47	p. 61
Real-Life Health	p. 11	p. 25	p. 37	p. 49	p. 63
5-Minute Check	p. 15	p. 29	p. 41	p. 53	p. 67
Lesson Quiz	p. 17	p. 30	p. 42	p. 56	p. 69

CLOSING THE UNIT

Family Involvement Activity	p. 73	Health in the News	p. 83
Community Involvement Activity	p. 75	Health Career Research Activity	p. 85
Health Lab	p. 77	Unit Test A	p. 87
Activity: Strengthening Health Skills	p. 81	Unit Test B	p. 91

Technology

- **Interactive Chalkboard CD-ROM**
- **TeacherWorks™ CD-ROM**
- **StudentWorks™ CD-ROM**
- **Reading Essentials CD-ROM**
- **ExamView® Assessment Suite**

Glencoe Exclusive!

TeacherWorks™
All-In-One Planner and Resource Center

www.glencoe.com
- **Vocabulary Puzzlemaker**
- **Interactive Tutor**
- **Your Health Checklist**
- **Web Links**
- **Student Web Activities**

UNIT 5

Nutrition

TEST YOUR NUTRITION IQ

Use the three statements on the student page to initiate a class discussion about nutrition. *Additional True/False statements are:*

4. **Eating any amount of bread will make you fat.**
   FALSE: Eating too many calories causes weight gain, no matter what types of food the calories come from.

5. **It is always better to choose chicken over beef or pork.**
   FALSE: Chicken is sometimes a more healthful choice than beef or pork, but lean cuts of beef or pork may have less fat than chicken with the skin on it or chicken that has been breaded and deep-fried in oil.

6. **Eating whole fruits and vegetables is preferable to drinking fruit and vegetable juice.**
   TRUE: Whole fruits and vegetables not only have fewer calories than a glass of juice, but are also a good source of fiber. Many juice drinks contain added sugar.

in the news Eating Disorders

Role Models Ask students if Abby Wambach's statement about healthy eating habits has affected how they think about dieting. Ask them to think of examples in the media of diets that encourage unhealthy eating habits or eating disorders. Discuss all forms of media including radio, movies, TV shows, magazines, and music videos. **L2**

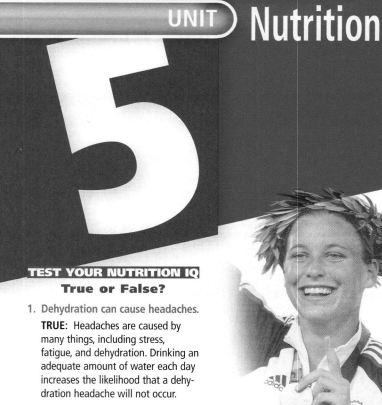

UNIT 5 Nutrition

TEST YOUR NUTRITION IQ
True or False?

1. **Dehydration can cause headaches.**
   TRUE: Headaches are caused by many things, including stress, fatigue, and dehydration. Drinking an adequate amount of water each day increases the likelihood that a dehydration headache will not occur.

2. **A meal is not healthy if it contains meat.**
   FALSE: Although in large quantities meat is not healthy for the body, it is a healthy choice if eaten in moderation. The MyPyramid food guidance system suggests eating 5 1/2 oz. of lean protein daily, of which meat is one of the choices.

3. **Breakfast is a very important meal of the day.**
   TRUE: Eating breakfast can result in higher test scores, a more positive attitude, more energy, an overall better diet, and a healthier body weight.

> **"If you can stick to basic, healthy eating habits, it will go a long way toward achieving fitness. Diet is only as complicated as you make it."**
>
> —Abby Wambach, professional soccer player and Olympic gold medalist

in the news Eating Disorders

Discuss Anorexia and other eating disorders continue to be a serious problem for teenagers, despite media efforts to educate about healthy body image. Research one media campaign, such as a radio or television ad. List ways the campaign discourages the eating disorder and discuss how effective you feel the media campaign is.

LESSON 25	**LESSON 26**	**LESSON 27**
Choosing Healthful Foods	Following Dietary Guidelines	Using Diet to Guard Against Disease

⏳ Two-Minute Unit Launcher

Demo Have students bring in current copies of popular fashion magazines. Ask students to flip through the magazines and have them vote on whether the models shown are the size of "normal" men and women. Ask the students why they think most models are so thin and whether looking at these models makes them feel bad about their own bodies. Talk about body image and how to feel good about one's body. Stress that the models in fashion magazines are, for the most part, underweight (for women) or overly muscular (for men). In other words, fashion models are not a reflection of reality and in many cases owe their appearance to unhealthful eating and/or exercise habits. **L2**

EVALUATING MEDIA MESSAGES

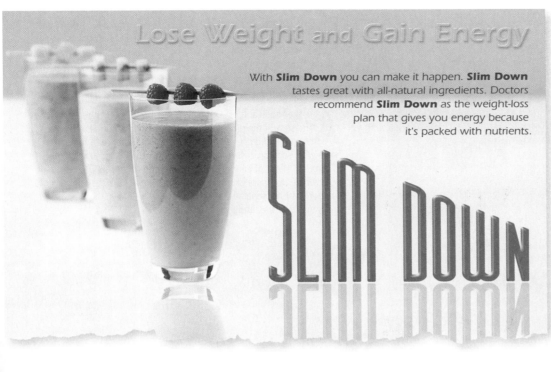

Lose Weight and Gain Energy

With **Slim Down** you can make it happen. **Slim Down** tastes great with all-natural ingredients. Doctors recommend **Slim Down** as the weight-loss plan that gives you energy because it's packed with nutrients.

SLIM DOWN

 WHAT'S YOUR VERDICT?
To evaluate this advertisement, use the criteria for analyzing and evaluating health messages delivered through media and technology that you learned in Unit 1.

Visit **www.glencoe.com** to find regularly updated statistics about teens and nutrition. Using the information provided, determine the answer to this question: What percentage of U.S. teens regularly eat healthfully?

Visit **www.glencoe.com** to use *Your Health Checklist* ✔, an interactive tool that helps you determine your health status.

LESSON 28
Developing Healthful Eating Habits

LESSON 29
Maintaining a Healthful Weight

Answers According to Healthy People 2010, 23 percent of teens aged 12–19 reported eating two or more daily servings of fruit and 38 percent reported three or more servings of vegetables. Thirty-four percent of teens aged 12–19 reported consuming less than 10 percent of calories from saturated fats. According to a Surgeon General Report on Mental Health, about 3 percent of young women have one of the three main eating disorders: anorexia nervosa, bulimia nervosa, or a binge-eating disorder. The average age of people who have these eating disorders is 17.

 What's Your Verdict?

Evaluating Food Advertisements
Have students review all advertisements in three different popular magazines. Ask students to answer these questions in their health journals: How many total advertisements were there? How many of them were for food? How many of those were for a product that would promote good nutrition? How many were for weight-loss products, and what claims did they make? Were certain types of products advertised more often in certain types of magazines? Have students discuss their findings in class. **L2**

Health Journal

Write an Essay Have students write an essay on their views of the responsibility the media has when it comes to negatively influencing people's health. Cigarette ads were banned from TV when the public discovered the health risks associated with smoking. Ask students to answer this question in their essays: Should junk food ads be banned because of their association with being overweight and obese? **L3**

INTERACTIVE CHALKBOARD
with Image Bank

Unit Focus Transparency

Page 4, **Unit 5 Fast File Resources**

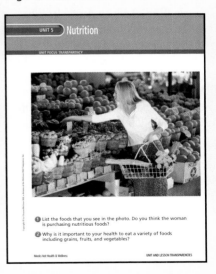

National Health Education Standards
Pages 280–281: 1.1, 2.5, 2.6, 3.1

Out of Time?

If time does not permit an in-depth study of this topic, use the following activities in this Teacher Wraparound Edition:
- Cross-Curricular Connections, p. 284
- Class Activity, p. 285
- Family Involvement, p. 289
- Teacher to Teacher, p. 290

1 Focus

HEALTH GOALS **Healthful Foods** Have students respond to the first Health Goal for this lesson by listing in their health journals reasons why it is important to eat foods that are healthful and contain nutrients. *Reasons may include maintaining good overall health, having energy, maintaining a healthful weight, and not having a vitamin deficiency.* **L2**

 ABOUT IT!

Journaling Have students describe what "calories from fat" means in their health journals (have them read page 290 to find this answer). Ask them to write if it is better if this number is larger or smaller. Also have students describe what trans-fatty acids are in their health journals. **L2**

LESSON 25

Choosing Healthful Foods

What You'll Learn

1. Identify the functions and sources of proteins, carbohydrates, and fats. *(pp. 283–285)*
2. Identify the functions and sources of vitamins, minerals, water, and herbal supplements. *(pp. 286–289)*
3. List and describe the five elements required on all food labels. *(p. 290)*
4. Discuss other information found on food labels. *(p. 291)*

Why It's Important

You need to understand body fuel as much as a car racer needs to understand the fuel needed for his car. With this knowledge, you can give your body the fuel it needs to function, grow, and repair itself properly.

Key Terms

- nutrient
- calorie
- protein
- amino acids
- carbohydrate
- fiber
- vitamin
- mineral
- herbal supplements
- protein supplements

HEALTH GOALS
- I will select foods that contain nutrients.
- I will evaluate food labels.

Are the foods and beverages you consume in a day healthful? The sum of the processes by which humans, animals, and plants consume and use food is *nutrition.* A substance in food that helps with body processes is a *nutrient.* Energy is measured in calories. A unit of energy produced by food is a *calorie.* In this lesson you will learn the six categories of nutrients and the functions and sources of the nutrients.

 ABOUT IT!

Writing About Evaluating Food Labels Suppose that you are going to have a backyard picnic with some of your friends. While you are shopping for food for the picnic, you notice that Brand X of pasta salad contains more calories and fat than Brand Y, because Brand X contains trans-fatty acids. After reading the information on fats on page 285, write an entry in your health journal about which brand of pasta salad you would chose.

National Health Education Standards—Guide for Lesson 25		
1.1	Predict how healthy behaviors can impact health status.	pp. 283–289
2.10	Analyze how public health policies and government regulations can influence health promotion and disease prevention.	pp. 290–292, 293
7.1	Analyze the role of individual responsibility for enhancing health.	pp. 283–287, 289

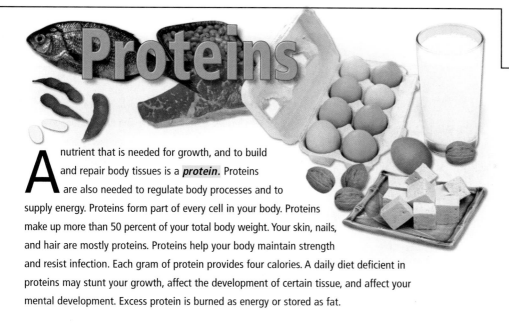

Proteins

A nutrient that is needed for growth, and to build and repair body tissues is a **protein.** Proteins are also needed to regulate body processes and to supply energy. Proteins form part of every cell in your body. Proteins make up more than 50 percent of your total body weight. Your skin, nails, and hair are mostly proteins. Proteins help your body maintain strength and resist infection. Each gram of protein provides four calories. A daily diet deficient in proteins may stunt your growth, affect the development of certain tissue, and affect your mental development. Excess protein is burned as energy or stored as fat.

What to Know About Proteins

There are two kinds of proteins: complete proteins and incomplete proteins.

Complete protein A protein that contains all of the essential amino acids is **complete protein.** The building blocks that make up proteins are **amino acids.** Examples of complete proteins are meat, fish, poultry, milk, yogurt, and eggs. The soybean is the only plant food that provides all nine of the essential amino acids. Your body needs 20 amino acids to function properly. Your body can produce only 11 of these amino acids. The nine amino acids the body cannot produce are **essential amino acids.** These nine essential amino acids must come from the foods you eat.

Incomplete protein A protein from plant sources that does not contain all of the essential amino acids is an **incomplete protein.** Incomplete

◀ Meats contain complete proteins.

proteins from plant sources fall into three general categories: grains (whole grains, pastas, and corn), legumes (dried beans, peas, and lentils), and nuts and seeds. Different plant sources of incomplete proteins can be combined to obtain all of the essential amino acids you need.

Reading Review

1. Name the two kinds of protein.
2. How many amino acids are essential?
3. Name three sources that are considered complete proteins.

LESSON 25 • Choosing Healthful Foods **283**

Lesson Resource Manager

- **Unit 5 Fast File Resources**
  Reading Strategy, p. 7
  Vocabulary Practice, p. 8
  Transparency Master and Worksheet, p. 9
  Real-Life Health, p. 11
  Real-Life Health, p. 13
  5-Minute Check, p. 15
  Lesson 25 Quiz, p. 17
- **Unit 5 Transparency**
- **Lesson 25 Transparency**

- **Reading Essentials**
- **Technology**
  TeacherWorks™ CD-ROM
  StudentWorks™ CD-ROM
  Reading Essentials CD-ROM
  ExamView® Assessment Suite
  Vocabulary Puzzlemaker

2 Teach

Teacher FYI

Proteins Proteins have several important functions in the body. They are part of the structural framework of the body, including keratin in skin, hair, and nails, and collagen in bone and other connective tissues. Myosin and actin are the two main proteins that compose muscle fibers and allow for the contraction of muscles.

Reading Review

1. *complete and incomplete*
2. *nine*
3. *Answers should include three of the following: meat, fish, poultry, milk, yogurt, and eggs.*

PowerPoint® Presentations

This CD-ROM is an editable Microsoft® PowerPoint® presentation that includes:
- Lesson presentations
- Lesson checks
- Interactive graphics
- 5-Minute Checks
- Image Bank
- All transparencies

CRISS Project

Note-Taking Refer to the Selective Underlining/ Highlighting Strategy on page 16T. Ask students to name the important categories of nutrients discussed in the lesson, as well as important details about each nutrient.

National Health Education Standards
Pages 282–283: 1.5, 3.1, 6.3

283

Carbohydrates

Carbohydrates

A nutrient that is the main source of energy for the body is a **carbohyrate** (kahr boh HY drayt). Carbohydrates include sugars, starches, and fiber. Carbohydrates supply four calories of energy per gram of food. Your body can store only limited amounts of carbohydrates. Excess carbohydrates are stored as fat. Sources of carbohydrates include vegetables, beans, potatoes, pasta, breads, rice, bran, popcorn, and fruit.

What to Know About Carbohydrates

There are two types of carbohydrates: simple carbohydrates and complex carbohydrates.

Simple carbohydrates Sugars that enter the bloodstream rapidly and provide quick energy are considered *simple carbohydrates.*

Simple carbohydrates provide calories but few vitamins and minerals. Sugars are found naturally in fruits, honey, and milk. Processed sugar, or table sugar, is added to food during processing. Processed sugar is found in cakes, candy, and other sweet desserts, as well as in ketchup, spaghetti sauce, and soda pop.

Complex carbohydrates Starches and fibers are considered *complex carbohydrates.* Most of the calories in your diet should come from complex carbohydrates. Sources of complex carbohydrates include grains, such as bread and pasta, and vegetables, such as potatoes and beans.

A food substance that is made and stored in most plants is a *starch.* Starches provide long-lasting energy.

When you eat complex carbohydrates, they are changed by saliva and other digestive juices to a simple sugar called *glucose.* Some glucose is used by cells to provide energy and heat. The remaining glucose is changed to glycogen.

Glycogen is stored in the muscles. When you need energy, glycogen is converted to glucose.

Fiber The part of grains and plant foods that cannot be digested is called *fiber.* Fiber also is known as roughage. There are two types of fiber—soluble and insoluble. Fiber helps move food through the digestive system. Insoluble fiber helps prevent constipation and other intestinal problems by binding with water. When you eat foods that contain fiber, you feel full. Eating foods with soluble fiber reduces your blood cholesterol level and your risk of developing heart disease. Good sources of fiber include wheat, bran, barley, rye, oats, whole grain pasta, breads and cereals, popcorn, brown rice, seeds, dried beans, fruit, and vegetables.

Insoluble fiber binds with water to help produce bowel movements. Insoluble fiber is associated with reduced risk of colon cancer. Good sources of insoluble fiber are wheat products, leafy vegetables, and fruits.

Soluble fiber is associated with reduced levels of cholesterol. Good sources of soluble fiber include oatmeal, beans, and barley.

Cross-Curricular Connections

Geography Have students investigate the main sources of simple and complex carbohydrates consumed in areas of the world, such as the Caribbean, Africa, the Pacific islands, and Asia. Ask students to find out what foods are more readily available in these areas compared to the United States. Have students create a map of the world to display in the classroom. Assign one or two countries to a student. Have students find a picture or draw the food or foods that are associated with that country. Have students paste their food drawing(s) to the classroom world map, and write a short caption about the food, including whether it is a source of simple or complex carbohydrates. **L3**

Fats

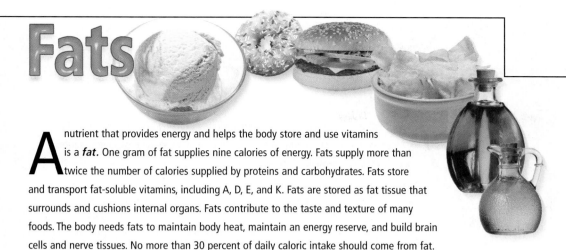

A nutrient that provides energy and helps the body store and use vitamins is a *fat.* One gram of fat supplies nine calories of energy. Fats supply more than twice the number of calories supplied by proteins and carbohydrates. Fats store and transport fat-soluble vitamins, including A, D, E, and K. Fats are stored as fat tissue that surrounds and cushions internal organs. Fats contribute to the taste and texture of many foods. The body needs fats to maintain body heat, maintain an energy reserve, and build brain cells and nerve tissues. No more than 30 percent of daily caloric intake should come from fat.

What to Know About Fats

Saturated fat A type of fat found in dairy products, solid vegetable fat, and meat and poultry is a *saturated fat.* Saturated fats usually are in solid form when at room temperature. Saturated fats contribute to the level of cholesterol that is in a person's blood. A fat-like substance made by the body and found in certain foods is *cholesterol* (kuh LES tuh rohl). Cholesterol in food is called dietary cholesterol. Dietary cholesterol is found in foods of animal origin, such as meats and dairy products. A person's blood cholesterol level is a combination of dietary cholesterol and cholesterol produced by the body. Blood cholesterol level can be lowered by eating fewer saturated fats.

Unsaturated fat A type of fat obtained from plant products and fish is called *unsaturated fat.* Unsaturated fats are usually liquid at room temperature. There are two types of unsaturated fats: polyunsaturated fats and monounsaturated (mahn oh uhn SACH uh rayt id) fats. Polyunsaturated fats include sunflower, corn, and soybean oils. Monounsaturated fats include olive and canola oils. Visible fat is fat that can be seen when looking at food. For example, you can see fatty areas on some meats and grease on potato chips. Invisible fat is fat that cannot be seen when looking at food. For example, a piece of cake contains eggs and shortening.

Trans-fatty acids Fatty acids that are formed when vegetable oils are processed into solid fats, such as margarine or shortening are called *trans-fatty acids.* This process is called *hydrogenation* and it makes the liquid oils more solid, more stable (increases the shelf life of the food product), and less greasy tasting. Many foods contain trans-fatty acids. Trans-fatty acids are found in vegetable shortening, some margarines, crackers, cookies, donuts, snack foods, and other foods. The body handles trans-fatty acids in the same way that it handles saturated fats. Trans-fatty acids appear to raise blood cholesterol levels. You can identify foods which contain trans fat by looking on the labels for "partially hydrogenated vegetable oil" or "vegetable shortening."

Did You Know?

Fat Free Products that claim to be "fat free" aren't necessarily free of fat. By law there have to be less than .5 g of fat per serving, but the serving size indicated on the label can be much smaller than what people normally eat.

LESSON 25 • Choosing Healthful Foods **285**

Fats

Explain the Concept

Unsaturated Fats Students might think that all types of fats are bad for their health. However, monounsaturated and polyunsaturated fats, found in some oils and nuts, can actually reduce the risk of developing cardiovascular disease. The American Heart Association recommends replacing saturated fats with these two types of fat to help lower cholesterol.

Class Activity

Substitutions Present students with the following list of foods that are high in fat. Have them brainstorm foods they can substitute that contain less fat.

Whole milk or cream: *replace with 1% or skim milk*

Fried foods: *replace with steamed or broiled foods*

Cooking with lard, butter, or palm oil: *replace with olive, canola, sunflower, corn, or soybean oil*

Sour cream or mayonnaise: *replace with low-fat yogurt, low-fat cottage cheese, or low-fat sour cream* **L2**

🚹🚺 Healthy People 2010

Objective 19-8 *Increase the proportion of persons aged 2 years and older who consume less than 10 percent of calories from saturated fat.*

According to the USDA's 1996 Continuing Survey of Food Intake by Individuals, 36 percent of persons aged 2 years and older consumed less than 10 percent of daily calories from saturated fat. The target for 2010 is 75 percent. Have students write a paragraph that contains suggestions as to how this goal can be met. For example, baking, broiling, and roasting are cooking methods that reduce fat. Olive oil has the highest amount of monounsaturated fat and the lowest amount of saturated fat. In their paragraphs, have students outline ideas on how their families, school, or community can reduce saturated fats in their diets. **L2**

National Health Education Standards

Pages 284–285: 1.1, 1.7

285

Vitamins

NHES Assessment/SCASS

Performance Event Have students construct a table for the vitamin B complex using the material presented in the text. Have students create a concept map illustrating each of the B vitamins and foods that contain the B vitamins. **L2**

Reading Review

1. *fat-soluble and water-soluble*
2. *A, D, E, K*
3. *B complex and C*

INTERACTIVE CHALKBOARD with Image Bank

5-Minute Check

Page 15, Unit 5 Fast File Resources

1. Explain the difference between a complete protein and an incomplete protein. *A complete protein is a protein that contains all of the essential amino acids. An incomplete protein is a protein from plant sources that does not contain all of the essential amino acids.*

2. What does the body use carbohydrates for? *energy*

3. Why is it important to get enough fiber in your diet? *Fiber helps move food through the digestive system and prevent constipation and other intestinal problems.*

4. What is saturated fat? *a type of fat found in dairy products, solid vegetable fat, and meat and poultry*

5. Compare and contrast fat-soluble vitamins and water-soluble vitamins. *Both are needed by the body to function properly. Fat-soluble vitamins are dissolved in fat and can be stored by the body; water-soluble vitamins dissolve in water and cannot be stored in adequate amounts.*

A nutrient that helps the body use carbohydrates, proteins, and fats is a **vitamin.** Vitamins provide no energy to the body directly, but help unleash energy stored in carbohydrates, proteins, and fats.

What to Know About Vitamins

There are two types of vitamins: fat-soluble vitamins and water-soluble vitamins.

Fat-soluble vitamins A vitamin that dissolves in fat and can be stored in the body is a **fat-soluble vitamin.** There are four fat-soluble vitamins: A, D, E, and K.

Water-soluble vitamins A vitamin that dissolves in water and cannot be stored by the body in significant amounts is a **water-soluble vitamin.** Vitamin C and B complex vitamins are examples of water-soluble vitamins. Vitamin C helps strengthen blood vessel walls, strengthens your immune system, and aids in iron absorption. Vitamin C can be found in citrus fruits, green leafy vegetables, potatoes, and tomatoes.

Reading Review

1. Name the two types of vitamins.
2. What vitamins are considered fat-soluble vitamins?
3. What vitamins are considered water-soluble vitamins?

Vitamin B complex Vitamin B_1, also called thiamin, is necessary for the function of nerves and can be found in whole-grain cereals and breads, poultry, and eggs. Vitamin B_2, also called riboflavin, helps the body use energy and can be found in milk, eggs, whole-grain cereals and breads, and leafy green vegetables. Vitamin B_3 is also known as niacin. This vitamin can be found in yeast, wheat germ, fish, and dairy products. Vitamin B_6 helps the body use fat and take in protein and can be found in foods such as whole grain cereals and breads, and leafy green vegetables.

Vitamin B_9, also called folacin, is necessary for the formation of hemoglobin in red blood cells. Vitamin B_9 can be found in green vegetables, liver, and whole-grain cereals and breads. Vitamin B_{12} is necessary for the formation of red blood cells and can be found in meat and dairy products.

Biotin is necessary for normal metabolism of carbohydrates and can be found in green vegetables, bananas, and peanuts. Pantothenic acid is necessary for production of RNA and DNA, and can be found in milk, whole-grain cereals and breads, and green vegetables.

The bulleted list in "Fat-Soluble Vitamins" identifies fat-soluble vitamins and their functions and lists their sources.

Fat-Soluble Vitamins

Fat solubles include vitamins A, D, E, and K.

- Vitamin A: Keeps eyes, hair, and skin healthy and can be found in dairy products, fruits, and green and yellow vegetables.
- Vitamin D: Aids in formation of bones and teeth; found in meat and dairy products.
- Vitamin E: Helps form and maintain cells; found in green vegetables and whole-grain cereals.
- Vitamin K: Necessary for normal blood clotting; found in leafy, green vegetables and cheese.

286 UNIT 5 • Nutrition

 Achieving Health Literacy

Self-Directed Learner Have students investigate different types of malnutrition, such as kwashiorkor, marasmus, or vitamin deficiencies. Ask students what circumstances could cause people to suffer from malnutrition. Students also could research problems of malnutrition in different areas of the world. Ask students what is being done, or what can be done, to address these problems. Have students create a newspaper article containing information about malnutrition. Have students share their newspaper articles with the class. **L2**

Minerals

A nutrient that regulates many chemical reactions in the body is a *mineral*. There are two types of minerals: macro minerals and trace minerals. Minerals are naturally occurring inorganic substances. Small amounts of some minerals are essential in metabolism and nutrition.

What to Know About Minerals

Macro minerals Minerals that are required in amounts greater than 100 mg are considered *macro minerals*. Examples of macro minerals are calcium and sodium. Calcium, which builds up bones and teeth, can be found in milk, cheese, legumes, soybean products, and green, leafy vegetables.

Magnesium is necessary for chemical reactions during metabolism. Good sources include soy products, whole grains, beans, nuts, seeds, fruit, and green leafy vegetables. Phosphorus builds bones, teeth, and cells. It can be found in milk, meats, poultry, legumes, and cheese. Potassium, which keeps fluids balanced within cells, can be found in green vegetables, legumes, and fruit.

Sodium is necessary for water balance in cells and tissues and for nerve cell conduction. Sodium can be found in table salt, high-salt meats, cheese, and crackers. Sulfur builds hair, nails, and skin and can be found in meats, milk, eggs, legumes, nuts, cheese, and brown sugar.

Trace minerals Minerals that are needed in very small amounts are called *trace minerals*. Examples of trace minerals are iron and zinc. Trace minerals are as important to the body as macro minerals.

Did You Know?

Good Nutrition
National Nutrition Month (March) is a campaign to focus attention on the importance of making informed food choices and developing sound eating and physical activity habits.

TABLE 25.1   Types of Trace Minerals

Trace Mineral and Function	Sources
Copper: Necessary for production of hemoglobin in red blood cells	Red meat, liver, seafood, poultry, nuts, and legumes
Iodine: Necessary for production of the thyroid gland hormone	Iodized salt, milk, cheese, fish, whole-grain cereals and breads
Iron: Aids red blood cells in transporting oxygen	Liver, red meats, fish, eggs, legumes, and whole-grain products
Manganese: Aids in synthesis of cholesterol and normal function of nerve tissue	Whole-grain products, leafy green vegetables, fruits, legumes, nuts
Zinc: Necessary for digestive enzymes and healing wounds	Seafood, red meats, milk, poultry, eggs, whole-grain cereals and breads

LESSON 25 • Choosing Healthful Foods **287**

(DI) Differentiated Instruction

Behavioral Disorders If time permits, take a few minutes each day to speak privately with a student who has a behavioral disorder regarding his or her behavior in your class. Along with the regular homework assignments on healthy foods found in this lesson, give the student an alternative to an unacceptable behavior to try for homework. Ask the student to let you know how it worked during your next class together. The student will know you care and that you are trying to help. **L1**

Minerals

Class Activity

High Blood Pressure Hypertension, or high blood pressure, is a type of cardiovascular disease that affects not only the heart and blood vessels but other organ systems as well. Although sodium is essential to proper body functioning, when ingested in high amounts it can adversely affect blood pressure. The Daily Recommended Intake of sodium for adults is less than 2,400 mg per day. Ask students how much sodium they are getting in their diets. Tell them that they can read food labels to help them determine how much sodium they are consuming daily.

Provide students with a label from an empty bag of potato chips and a soft drink can. Ask students how many milligrams of sodium are in one serving of each product and how many servings of each they consume in a day. **L2**

Teacher FYI

Anemia Anemia is a condition in which red blood cells are not supplying body cells with enough oxygen. Iron-deficiency anemia is the most common form of anemia. The condition is more common in women than men. It is the iron in hemoglobin that oxygen bonds with to be carried throughout the body. The oxygen-carrying capacity of the blood is reduced if there is an iron deficiency.

Causes for iron-deficiency anemia include too little iron in the diet, poor absorption of iron by the body, and blood loss. Symptoms include fatigue, pale skin color, weakness, brittle nails, and shortness of breath. Increasing the amount of iron in the diet and taking oral iron supplements usually can alleviate the condition.

National Health Education Standards
Pages 286–287: 1.1, 7.1

Herbal Supplements

S upplements that contain extracts or ingredients from the roots, berries, seeds, stems, leaves, buds, or flowers of plants are ***herbal supplements.*** Herbal supplements come in many forms, including tablets, capsules, powders, gelcaps, and liquids. They are sold in health food stores, grocery stores, gyms, and through mail-order catalogs, the Internet, and television programs.

What to Know About Herbal Supplements

Make the Connection

Calorie Burning For more information on participating in regular physical activity to burn calories, see page 367 in Lesson 33.

Herbal supplements are officially classified as foods and not as drugs. As a result of the passage by the U.S. Congress of the Dietary Supplement Health and Education Act (DSHEA) in 1994, herbal supplements are classified as foods and not as drugs. This means that herbal or dietary supplements do not have to be proven safe or screened by the Food and Drug Administration (FDA) before they can be placed on the market. In October 2003, the FDA filed a suit against several pharmaceutical companies to prevent the sale and distribution of unapproved and misbranded products.

Creatine An amino acid that is made in the liver, kidneys, and pancreas is called ***creatine.*** It also is found naturally in meat and fish. It also is a popular dietary supplement. Many teenagers use creatine as a way to increase their performance in sports or as a way to become more muscular. It is recommended that creatine only be taken under medical supervision. There is suspicion that excessive creatine use could be linked to such adverse effects as cramping, diarrhea, nausea, dizziness, dehydration, incontinence, muscle strain, high blood pressure, and abnormal liver and kidney function.

Protein supplements A product taken orally that contains proteins that are intended to supplement one's diet and are not considered food are ***protein supplements.*** Many who consume these soy and whey energy drinks or powders believe that the protein helps them to build muscle. Health and fitness experts say that the amount of protein needed each day is about one gram of protein per pound of body weight. Most people easily meet or exceed this requirement. Any excess protein is converted to fat and not to muscle.

Questions To Ask Before Taking A Supplement

Below are questions that one should ask before taking a supplement.

- Do I know what ingredients are contained in the supplement?
- Have I consulted my doctor about taking this supplement?
- Have I discussed my intention to use this supplement with my parents or guardian?
- Do I know that this supplement is safe and that it works?

- Does the product make claims that seem too good to be true (e.g., "miracle cure," "easy muscle gain," "effortless weight loss," "special ingredient")?
- Do I know if this supplement can interact with the foods that I am eating and the drugs that I am taking?

Cross-Curricular Connections

Science St. John's Wort, *Hypericum perforatum,* is an herb that has been used to treat depression, although many scientists and physicians are skeptical about the effectiveness of herbal supplements. Although how it works is not entirely understood, some recent scientific evidence has indicated that the herb works by preventing neurons from reabsorbing the neurotransmitter serotonin from the synapse. This process is similar to how other drugs work, specifically selective serotonin reuptake inhibitors (SSRIs), which are effective in treating depression. St. John's Wort is also being tested to determine whether it could be an effective treatment for other disorders such as social phobia and obsessive-compulsive disorder. Have students research the effect a dietary or herbal supplement (such as St. John's Wort) has on the brain and nervous system. Have students create drawings illustrating their findings. **L3**

Water

A nutrient that is involved with all body processes is *water*. Water makes up the basic part of the blood, helps with waste removal, regulates body temperature, and cushions the spinal cord and joints. Water makes up more than 60 percent of body mass. Water carries nutrients to all body cells and waste products from the cells to the kidneys. Water leaves the body in the form of perspiration and urine.

What to Know About Water

Dehydration You can live without other nutrients for months, but you can survive without water only for about three days. You may begin to feel tired when your body gets even a little low on water. A condition in which the water content of the body has fallen to an extremely low level is *dehydration* (dee hy DRAY shuhn). Dehydration is caused by lack of water intake, a dry environment, fever, vomiting, or diarrhea. Your sense of thirst often tells you when your body needs water. But sometimes you do not feel thirsty yet you are dehydrated. For example, hot weather and exercise can cause dehydration before you even realize that you are thirsty.

Common signs of dehydration include fatigue, dry mouth, dizziness, weakness, flushed skin, headache, blurred vision, difficulty swallowing, dry skin, rapid pulse, and infrequent urination. Research has correlated high fluid intake with a lower risk of kidney stones, and colon and bladder cancer. You lose a significant amount of water daily through perspiration, urine, bowel movements, and exhalation.

How much water is needed? It is important to drink an adequate amount of water a day. Good sources of water include juice, milk, soup, and frozen juice pops. Water also is found in many foods, such as fruits and vegetables. Do not substitute soda pop for water. Soda pop and drinks containing caffeine act as diuretics. A product that increases the amount of urine excreted is a *diuretic* (di yuh REH tihk).

Why drink water when you are sick? When you have certain symptoms of disease or illness, it is especially important to drink water and other clear liquids. Fever, vomiting, and diarrhea cause water loss and put people at risk for dehydration. Drinking water or other liquids can replace the fluids lost through these symptoms and help regulate body temperature. If you have a cold, drinking water can help loosen mucus and carry away the debris of infection.

How to get an adequate amount of water a day There are many tips to increase your water intake. Some tips include carrying a squeeze bottle filled with water, eating water-rich fruits and vegetables, and taking drinks from the water fountain.

Reading Review

1. What are signs of dehydration?

2. Water is what percent of body mass?

LESSON 25 • Choosing Healthful Foods **289**

Water

Quick Demo

Dehydration and Blood Viscosity
Blood plasma is about 90 percent water. As the body loses water during dehydration, the blood thickens, making it harder for the heart to pump blood through the body.

Demonstrate the idea of increased viscosity to students by boiling the water out of a small amount (about 3 or 4 ounces) of orange juice or tomato juice. Continue to stir the juice as it boils. After about 2 ounces of water has boiled off, the remaining liquid will be visibly thickened compared to the original viscosity. Allow students to see this comparison. **ELL**

Class Activity

Journaling Have students record how much water and juice they drink in a day. Some students may need to drink more water than others if they are very physically active. Have students set a goal to drink a certain number of glasses of water each day. Ask students what changes they will have to make to meet this goal. **L1** **ELL**

Reading Review

1. *fatigue, dry mouth, dizziness, weakness, flushed skin, headache, blurred vision, difficulty swallowing, dry skin, rapid pulse, and frequent urination*

2. *more than 60 percent*

 Family Involvement

Nutrition Encourage students to sit down with their families and evaluate the nutritional value of the food, including snacks and meals, that they are eating. Have students answer the following questions: Are the meals well-balanced? How much fruit and vegetables and how many grains are included in daily meals? How can the family work together to improve the nutritional value of meals? Have students and their parents or guardian make a plan to improve the nutritional value of their meals. Students and their families could create a healthful menu for one week. Once families try out the menu, have them discuss long-term changes in the families' diets. **L2**

National Health Education Standards
Pages 288–289: 2.10, 6.3

Food Labels

Quick Demo

Nutrition Density Select three or four items of foods that have roughly the same number of calories. For example, a 12 oz can of pop, an 8 oz glass of milk, and a 12 oz can of orange juice all have about the same amount of calories. Have students list the vitamins and minerals that are in each food item according to the label. Students should recognize that although all the food items contain the same number of calories, they do not have the same amounts of nutrients. **L2** **ELL**

Class Discussion

Serving Size The FDA allows serving sizes to be expressed either in common household measures (the English system) or metric measures. Household measures include ounce, pound, pint, and gallon. Metric measurements include gram, kilogram, liter, and kiloliter. Many people do not understand how to convert metric measurements to English measurements, and thus they can be fooled by metric measurements on food labels. Advise students that an understanding of the metric system will increase their ability to accurately read food labels, especially serving sizes. Ask students how serving size can affect the number of calories, amount and kind of fat, and amount of nutrients they consume. *If students do not understand the true size of a "serving size," they may end up consuming more calories and fat than they had planned.* **L2**

Food Labels

A panel of nutrition information required on all processed foods regulated by the Food and Drug Administration (FDA) is a *food label*. A food label is required by law to include the following elements: name of the food; net weight or volume; name and address of manufacturer, distributor, or packager; ingredients; and nutrient content.

What to Know About Food Labels

Nutrition facts The title of the information panel that is required on most foods is called the *nutrition facts*.

Serving size The listing of the amount of food that is considered a serving is called the *serving size*. Look carefully at the amount listed for the serving size. The serving size may be smaller than the amount you actually consume. The serving size listings on food labels are now uniform for similar products. The servings are determined by the Food and Drug Administration (FDA), not by the manufacturer of the product.

Servings per container The listing of the number of servings in the container or package is called the *servings per container.* The number can be deceiving. Suppose you drink a bottle of juice. You might glance at the label and see the number 90 next to the category "calories." So, you might think the bottle contains 90 calories. But, check the servings per container. If the bottle contains two servings, you actually are consuming 180 calories. Multiply the calories and nutrients by the number of servings per container to determine the total number of calories and nutrients in a container or package.

Calories listing The listing of the number of calories in one serving of the food is called the *calories listing.*

Calories from fat The listing of the number of calories from fat in one serving of the food is called *calories from fat.*

Percent Daily Value The portion of the daily amount of a nutrient provided by one serving of the food is called *Percent of Daily Value.* For total carbohydrates, dietary fiber, vitamins, and minerals, your goal is to have the foods you eat each day add up to 100 percent. The Percent Daily Value is based on dietary goals recommended for most adults and children over age four.

Notice that the footnote states that the Percent Daily Values are based on a diet of 2000 calories. Your recommended diet may consist of more or less than 2000 calories. Extremely active people may need an intake of 2500 calories. Maximum recommended limits for total fat, saturated fat, cholesterol, and sodium are listed for both a 2000-calorie and 2500-calorie diet. Values for vitamins A and C and the minerals calcium and iron are required on all food labels. Values for other vitamins and minerals may be added but are not required by law.

Nutrition facts are required on most foods. ▼

Nutrition Facts

Serving Size 1/2 cup (114g)
Servings Per Container 4

Amount Per Serving		
Calories 90	Calories from Fat 30	
		% Daily Value*
Total Fat 3g		5%
Saturated Fat 0g		0%
Cholesterol 0mg		0%
Sodium 300mg		13%
Total Carbohydrate 13g		4%
Dietary Fiber 3g		12%
Sugars 3g		
Protein 3g		

Vitamin A	80%	•	Vitamin C	60%
Calcium	4%	•	Iron	4%

*Percent Daily Values are based on a 2,000 calorie diet. Your daily values may be higher or lower depending on your calorie needs:

	Calories:	2,000	2,500
Total Fat	Less than	65g	80g
Sat Fat	Less than	20g	25g
Cholesterol	Less than	300mg	300mg
Sodium	Less than	2,400mg	2,400mg
Total Carbohydrate		300g	375g
Dietary Fiber		25g	30g

Calories per gram: Fat 9•Carbohydrate 4•Protein 4

 Teacher to Teacher

Food Label Analysis To help students understand how to read and analyze a food label, have them use a food label (not from a soft drink or candy bar) and record the following information on a separate piece of paper: food item; serving size; number of servings per container; calories per serving; total carbohydrates, protein, and fat grams; calories from carbohydrates, proteins, and fats; percent of calories from carbohydrates, proteins, and fats; and the amount of sodium per serving. Have students write a one-page paper on whether they feel that the food is nutritious and why they feel that way. Students should turn in the label with their completed assignment. **L2** **ELL**

Annette Cook
Eisenhower High School, Yakima, WA

Decoding Food Labels

A long with nutrition facts, other information can be found on a food label. This information may be included on the nutrition facts panel. Or, it may be found elsewhere on the packaging. Included in this information is a listing of ingredients, food additives, and other important facts.

How to Be Food Label Savvy

A food label is not required on fresh fruits and vegetables, food served in restaurants, fresh meats, foods in very small packages, foods sold by vendors, bakery and deli products, and coffee or tea.

Ingredients listing Almost all foods must have an ingredients listing. The parts that make up the particular food are *ingredients.* Ingredients are listed by weight, beginning with the ingredient that is present in the greatest amount. This listing is not a part of the nutrition facts, but is found elsewhere on the label.

Check the dates Information involving dates may be included on the food label. "Sell By" is the last date by which the product should be sold (although it can be stored past this date). "Best If Used By" is the date by which the product should be used to ensure quality. "Expiration Date" is the date after which the product should not be used.

Food Health Claims

Healthy A food product that claims the food to be "healthy" must be low in fat, low in saturated fat, and no more than 60 mg of cholesterol per serving.

Fat free A product that claims to be "fat free" must have less than .5 g of fat per serving.

Low fat A food that claims to be "low fat" must have 3 g of fat, or less, per serving.

Lean A product that claims to be "lean" must have less than 10 g of fat, 4.5 g of saturated fat, and no more than 95 mg of cholesterol per serving.

Light A product that claims to be "light" must have one-third the calories or no more than half the fat or sodium of the regular version.

Cholesterol free A product that claims to be "cholesterol free" must have less than 0.5 mg of cholesterol and 2 g of fat or less of saturated fat per serving.

_____ free Any product that claims to be fat, sodium, cholesterol, sugar, or caffeine "free" must adhere to the guideline that the product has no amount or only a negligible amount of fat, cholesterol, sodium, sugar, or caffeine.

Fresh Any product that claims to be "fresh," must be raw, unprocessed, contain no preservatives, or never have been frozen or heated.

A Low Fat Food!

Low in cholesterol

Low Sodium

No Sugar Added

No MSG

No Preservatives

> **Make the Connection**
>
> **Ads** For more information on how to evaluate food products advertisements, see page 37 in Lesson 4.

> **Ingredients:** Diced Tomatoes, Tomato Puree, High Fructose Corn Syrup, Salt, Extra Virgin Olive Oil, Dehydrated Onions, Dehydrated Garlic, Basil, Lemon Peel, Calcium Chloride, Dehydrated Red Bell Peppers, Citric Acid, Oregano, Modified Cornstarch, Natural Flavor

◄ An ingredients listing must be included on almost all foods.

LESSON 25 • Choosing Healthful Foods **291**

Decoding Food Labels

INTERACTIVE CHALKBOARD with Image Bank

5-Minute Check

Page 16, **Unit 5 Fast File Resources**

1. Explain the difference between macro minerals and trace minerals. Give an example of each. *Macro minerals are required in amounts greater than 100 mg. Examples include calcium, magnesium, phosphorus, potassium, sodium, and sulfur. Trace minerals are needed only in very small amounts. Examples include copper, iodine, iron, manganese, and zinc.*

2. Why is it important to do research before taking an herbal supplement? *Herbal supplements are not regulated by the FDA in the same manner as other drugs are.*

3. What is dehydration? *a condition in which the water content of the body has fallen to an extremely low level*

4. Explain the relationship between serving size, servings per container, and calories. *The amount of calories is given per serving size. If a container has more than one serving, the number of servings eaten at one sitting must be used to calculate the total number of calories ingested.*

5. What is the difference between a "lean" product and a "light" product? *A lean product must have less than 10 g of fat, 4.5 g of saturated fat, and no more than 95 mg of cholesterol per serving. A light product must have half the calories or no more than half the fat or sodium of the regular version.*

👪 Family Involvement

Fruits Have students inventory their homes for availability of fruits. Have students keep track of the amount and if the item is fresh, frozen, or canned for each fruit. Have students discuss their inventory with their parent or guardian. Fresh fruits usually contain more vitamins than canned or frozen fruits. Canned fruits are often higher in calories because of the syrup used in the canning process. Frozen fruits can lose some of their nutritional value in the process of being frozen. Fresh fruits can sometimes be a better source of nutrition than canned or frozen fruits if the nutritional value of the canned or frozen fruits has been compromised by added fats or sodium. **L2**

> **National Health Education Standards**
>
> Pages 290–291: 1.5, 1.7, 2.10

Analyzing Influences on Health Have students compare the food labels of at least five foods in their home. Students should record calories, fats, proteins, carbohydrates, vitamins and minerals. Have them record their findings in their health journals. **L2**

3 Assess

Vocabulary Practice

Page 8, **Unit 5 Fast File Resources**

Activity: Using Life Skills

Analyzing Influences on Health: Comparing Food Labels

The front of a food package may boast that the food is good for you. The only way to tell for sure, though, is to read the nutrition facts. While few foods are all good or all bad, comparing nutrition facts on food labels can help you to make healthy choices about what you eat.

1 Identify people and things that might influence you. Study both nutrition facts labels below. Label 2 is from a package of chocolate-chip cookies. Label 1 is from a package of oat-and-honey granola bars.

2 Evaluate how the influence might affect your health behaviors and decisions. Note the serving size for each food. Be sure to compare nutrition facts for the same amount of each food.

3 Take special note of the saturated fat content of the two foods. Choose the food with the lower percent (%) daily value. Eating too much fat in your teens can lead to high cholesterol and other health problems when you're older.

4 Compare the Percent Daily Values for dietary fiber and sugars. Generally, foods that are high in fiber and low in sugar are more healthful.

5 To practice comparing food labels, answer these questions. Compare one cookie to one granola bar. Which product has more saturated fat? Which product has more sugar? Which product has more calories per serving? Notice that a serving on the granola bars label is defined as two bars. Would the answers to any of the above questions change if you compare two granola bars to one cookie?

6 Choose positive influences on health and protect yourself from negative influences on health. Based on the answers to these questions, which food would you choose and why?

Nutrition Facts Serving size: 2 bars (42g).
Amount Per Serving: **Calories** 180, Fat Cal. 50, **Total Fat** 6g (9% DV), Sat. Fat 0.5g (3% DV), **Cholesterol** 0mg (0% DV), **Sodium** 160mg (7% DV), **Total Carb.** 29g (10% DV), Dietary Fiber 2g (8% DV), Sugars 11g, **Protein** 4g, Iron (6% DV). Percent Daily Values (DV) are based on a 2,000 calorie diet.
Carbohydrate Choices: 2

◄ Learning how to compare ► food labels helps you make food choices.

Nutrition Facts Serv. size: 1 cookie (16g), Servings Per Container: 4, Amount Per Serving: **Calories** 80, Fat Cal. 35. **Total Fat** 3.5g (5% DV), Sat. Fat 1g (5% DV), **Cholest.** 0mg (0% DV), **Sodium** 70mg (3% DV), **Total Carb.** 10g (3% DV), Fiber less than 1g (2% DV), Sugars 6g. **Protein** less than 1g, Vitamin A (0% DV), Vitamin C (0% DV), Calcium (0% DV), Iron (2% DV). Percent Daily Values (DV) are based on a 2,000 calorie diet.

Less _____ Any product that claims to have "less" of a nutrient or of the number of calories of the regular version of a food product must have at least 25 percent less of a nutrient or calories than the regular version.

High _____ Any product that claims to be "high" in a particular nutrient, such as "high in calcium," must supply at least 20 percent or more of the percent daily value of a particular nutrient per serving.

Food additives Food labels must list additives. Substances intentionally added to food are *food additives.* Food additives may add nutrients, flavor, color, or texture. They may prevent spoilage or help foods age quickly. They also improve taste and appearance.

Foods may be enriched or fortified to add to the nutrient value. An *enriched food* is a food in which nutrients lost during processing are added back into the food. A *fortified food* is a food in which nutrients not usually found in the food are added. For example, some orange juice products are fortified with calcium.

 Community Involvement

Environment Have students survey their community for places where fresh fruits and vegetables are available. Have students answer the following questions: How many supermarkets are within a 5-mile radius of your house? What is the quality of the fresh fruits and vegetables at each grocery store? Are there any food stands that sell fruits and vegetables nearby? Are there fruits and vegetables at gas stations or convenience stores? Have students create a map of their community, illustrating places in the community where fruits and vegetables are available. **L2**

National Health Education Standards

Pages 292–293: 1.1, 1.5, 2.10, 3.1, 6.1, 6.3

amino acids
calorie
carbohydrate
fiber
herbal supplements
ingredients
mineral
nutrient
nutrition
protein
protein supplements
vitamin

Key Terms Review

Complete these fill-in-the-blank statements with the lesson Key Terms on the left. Do not write in this book.

1. A _____ is a substance in food that helps with body processes.

2. A _____ is a unit of energy produced by food and used by the body.

3. A _____ is a nutrient that is needed for growth and to build, repair, and maintain body tissues.

4. _____ are the building blocks that make up proteins.

5. A _____ is a nutrient that is the main source of energy for the body.

6. _____ is the part of grains and plant foods that cannot be digested.

7. _____ are supplements that contain extracts or ingredients from plants and do not have to be proven safe by the FDA.

8. Soy and whey in pre-made energy drinks or powders are the forms in which _____ are usually found.

9. A water-soluble or fat-soluble _____ is a nutrient that helps the body use carbohydrates, proteins and fats.

10. A macro or trace _____ is a nutrient that regulates many chemical reactions in the body.

Recalling the Facts

11. What function does saturated and unsaturated fat play in our diet?

12. What required elements can be found on food labels?

13. What are examples of macro minerals and trace minerals and which is more important?

14. Why should people drink water when they are sick?

15. Why do you need foods and beverages each day that are sources of water-soluble vitamins?

16. What is the difference between a complete protein and an incomplete protein?

17. What are some common symptoms of dehydration?

18. How many amino acids are essential?

Critical Thinking

19. Why is it important to eat a well-balanced meal?

20. Discuss why it is important to limit intake of trans-fatty acids and saturated fats.

21. Explain why teens should not take creatine in order to improve muscular strength.

22. How much water do people lose daily through normal body functions?

Real-Life Applications

23. How can one determine the calories in a product?

24. Name three foods that are high in saturated fats that can be found in your school cafeteria.

25. What are foods that you can add to your diet to increase dietary fiber?

26. What questions should you ask while reviewing an herbal supplement product?

Activities

Responsible Decision Making

27. **Journal** During sports practice at school, you feel dizzy and weak. Write a response to this situation. Refer to the Responsible Decision-Making Model on page 61 for help.

Sharpen Your Life Skills

28. **Practice Healthful Behaviors** Use page 286 to evaluate your vitamin intake. After you complete your analysis, write a one-page paper on your findings.

Visit **www.glencoe.com** for more *Health & Wellness* quizzes.

LESSON 25 • Study Guide 293

Key Terms Review

1. nutrient
2. calorie
3. protein
4. Amino acids
5. carbohydrate
6. Fiber
7. Herbal supplements
8. protein supplements
9. vitamin
10. mineral

Recalling the Facts

11. See page 285.
12. See page 290.
13. Macro: calcium and sodium. Trace: iron and zinc. Trace and macro minerals are equally important even though you need only a very small amount of trace minerals.
14. because when you are sick you are at risk for dehydration, and water hydrates you and carries away the debris of infection
15. Water-soluble vitamins cannot be stored by the body in significant amounts and must be replenished every day.
16. Complete proteins contain all the essential amino acids, while incomplete proteins do not contain all the essential amino acids.
17. fatigue, dry mouth, dizziness, weakness, flushed skin, headache, blurred vision, dry skin, rapid pulse, and frequent urination
18. Nine amino acids are essential.

Critical Thinking

19. A well-balanced meal helps you obtain the vitamins, minerals, carbohydrates, proteins, and fats that your body needs.
20. Trans-fatty acids and saturated fats appear to raise blood cholesterol levels.
21. Creatine use could be linked with cramping, diarrhea, nausea, high blood pressure, abnormal liver and kidney functions, and other problems.
22. You lose roughly ten 8 oz glasses of water daily.

Real-Life Applications

23. Find the calories per serving on the food label and multiply this by the number of servings.
24. french fries, pizza, cookies
25. wheat products, vegetables, and fruit
26. See list on page 288.

Activities

Responsible Decision Making

27. Ask to take a water break because you are experiencing signs of dehydration.

Sharpen Your Life Skills

28. Answers will vary.

293

Following Dietary Guidelines

Out of Time?

If time does not permit an in-depth study of this topic, use the following activities in this Teacher Wraparound Edition:
- Health Goals, p. 294
- Health Project, p. 296
- Class Activity, p. 297
- Using the Table, p. 297

1 Focus

HEALTH GOALS **Healthful Diets** Have students respond to this lesson's Health Goals by taking time to write in their health journals what they normally eat each day. Encourage students to recall what they have eaten each day for the past few days and to include all of this in their health journals. After the students have read further in the lesson, they will be able to see if their normal diet follows MyPyramid and the Dietary Guidelines. **L1**

Write ABOUT IT!

Journaling Students might tell their friends that they want to include more nutritious options for the picnic. They also might say that eating more nutritious foods gives you more energy, which you will need for your active day. **L2**

Following Dietary Guidelines

HEALTH GOALS
- I will eat the recommended number of servings from the MyPyramid food guidance system.
- I will follow the Dietary Guidelines.

This lesson discusses the MyPyramid food guidance system and Dietary Guidelines. The ***Dietary Guidelines*** are recommendations for diet choices among healthy Americans who are two years of age or older. These guidelines are a result of research done by the United States Department of Agriculture and the United States Department of Health and Human Services.

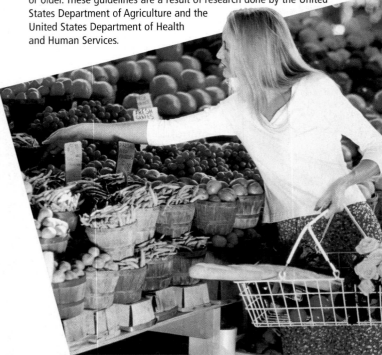

What You'll Learn

1. Identify the recommended number of daily servings for each food group in the MyPyramid food guidance system. *(p. 295)*
2. List examples of foods from each of the food groups in MyPyramid. *(p. 296)*
3. List and describe the Dietary Guidelines. *(p. 299)*
4. Explain how to use the Dietary Guidelines. *(p. 299)*
5. Explain how to follow a vegetarian diet. *(p. 300)*

Why It's Important

You are what you eat. You need to eat a variety of foods to obtain the nutrients your body needs for optimal health.

Key Terms

- Dietary Guidelines
- food group
- MyPyramid
- saturated fat
- cholesterol
- vegetarian diet
- vegan diet
- lacto-vegetarian diet
- ovo-lacto-vegetarian diet
- semi-vegetarian diet

Write ABOUT IT!

Writing About Following Dietary Guidelines Suppose you are grocery shopping for a picnic with your friends. Your friends put potato chips, candy bars, and high-calorie prepackaged sandwiches in their shopping carts. They urge you to do the same. After reading the information about Dietary Guidelines on page 299, write an entry in your health journal about why you should resist pressure and stick to the Dietary Guidelines.

National Health Education Standards—Guide for Lesson 26		
1.1	Predict how healthy behaviors can impact health status.	pp. 295–300, 301
1.5	Propose ways to reduce or prevent injuries and health problems.	pp. 294, 296–300, 301
2.10	Analyze how public health policies and government regulations can influence health promotion and disease prevention.	pp. 295–298, 301

The Food Groups

A category of foods that contain similar nutrients is a **food group.** There are six food groups as illustrated by MyPyramid. Each group has recommended servings per day depending on your age, size, sex, and level of activity.

What to Know About Each Food Group

Grains Every day you should eat at least 3 oz of whole-grain cereals, bread, crackers, rice, or pasta. These foods are good sources of vitamins, minerals, and complex carbohydrates. They provide fiber, iron, and vitamin B. A 1 oz serving equals 1 slice of bread, or 1 cup of ready-to-eat cereal, or 1/2 cup of cooked cereal, rice, or pasta.

Vegetables You need 2 1/2 cups each day from the vegetable group. These foods are low in fat and calories. They are good sources of vitamins A and C and minerals. Eat a variety from this food group, including dark green vegetables like broccoli and spinach, orange vegetables like carrots and sweet potatoes, and dry beans and peas.

Fruits You need 2 cups each day from the fruit group. Fruits are low in fat, and they are good sources of vitamins A and C, potassium, and carbohydrates. Choose a variety of fruits, whether fresh, frozen, canned, or dried, but go easy on fruit juices.

Milk You need to consume three cups a day of milk, yogurt, and other dairy products. These foods are good sources of calcium and protein. Select low-fat or fat-free versions of milk products to limit your fat intake. People who don't drink milk can choose lactose-free products or other foods and beverages fortified with calcium.

Meat and beans You need to eat at least 5 1/2 oz every day from the food group that includes meat, poultry, eggs, fish, beans, peas, nuts, and seeds. These foods are good sources of protein, B vitamins, iron, and zinc. To help limit fat intake, choose low-fat or lean meats and poultry, and bake, broil, or grill the food instead of frying it. It is important to choose more fish, beans, peas, nuts, and seeds to boost your intake of essential fatty acids.

Oils Most teens need to consume about 5 teaspoons per day of oils, which are found in nuts, fish, cooking oil, and salad dressings. Oils provide essential fatty acids and vitamin E. Oils are different from solid fats, which contain more saturated and trans fats and cholesterol. These tend to raise "bad" cholesterol levels in the blood and increase the risk for heart disease.

Did You Know?

Cola Facts A 12-oz can of non-diet cola contains about 9 teaspoons of sugar, 150 calories, and has no real nutritional value.

Make the Connection

Health Information For more information on accessing valid health and nutrition information, see page 20 in Lesson 2.

LESSON 26 • Following Dietary Guidelines **295**

Lesson Resource Manager

- **Unit 5 Fast File Resources**
  Reading Strategy, p. 21
  Vocabulary Practice, p. 22
  Transparency Master and Worksheet, p. 23
  Real-Life Health, p. 25
  Real-Life Health, p. 27
  5-Minute Check, p. 29
  Lesson 26 Quiz, p. 30
- **Unit 5 Transparency**
- **Lesson 26 Transparency**

- **Reading Essentials**
- **Technology**
  TeacherWorks™ CD-ROM
  StudentWorks™ CD-ROM
  Reading Essentials CD-ROM
  ExamView® Assessment Suite
  Vocabulary Puzzlemaker

The Food Groups

2 Teach

NHES Assessment/SCASS

Performance Task Have students choose a fruit or vegetable and research the nutrients found in the food as well as its health benefits and health drawbacks if it is overeaten. Students also can investigate recipes that include the food item. Students may discover that different types of their chosen food item are found in different parts of the world. Students can present their findings to the class. **L2**

INTERACTIVE CHALKBOARD with Image Bank

PowerPoint® Presentations

This CD-ROM is an editable Microsoft® PowerPoint® presentation that includes:
- Lesson presentations
- Lesson checks
- Interactive graphics
- 5-Minute Checks
- Image Bank
- All transparencies

Summarizing Refer to the Read-Recall-Check-Summarize Strategy on page 16T. After students read the lesson, ask them to brainstorm about the main details of each food group, go back to their reading to check the accuracy of the details, and then brainstorm notes to write a summary of each food group and its place in MyPyramid.

National Health Education Standards
Pages 294–295: 1.5, 2.10, 6.3, 8.2

295

Explain the Concept

Fatty acids Review the difference between oils and solid fats as presented in this lesson. Solid or saturated fats are found in animal products such as butter, cheese, and meat. Oils are derived from some plant sources, nuts, and fish.

Class Discussion

Food Groups Have the students refer to their health journal entries from this lesson's Health Goal. Encourage students to give examples of foods they have eaten in the past week. Discuss where these items fall in MyPyramid and how students can better follow the food guidelines. **L2** **ELL**

Teaching Transparency

Page 23, **Unit 5 Fast File Resources**

Reading Review

1. *five food groups*
2. *grains; vegetables; fruits; milk; meat and beans*

Reading Review

1. How many food groups are illustrated in MyPyramid?
2. Name the food groups of MyPyramid.
3. How much of each food group is recommended per day?

Discretionary calories Depending on your level of physical activity and the foods you choose from the other groups, you have a certain amount of "extra" calories that you can use. Assume that your daily consumption of the recommended foods in MyPyramid amounts to 1800 calories, but you burn 2000 calories a day. That means you have 200 discretionary calories that you can consume.

What to Know About the MyPyramid Food Guidance System

MyPyramid is a guide that recommends the kinds and amounts of foods to eat each day and emphasizes physical activity. A balanced diet includes servings from the five food groups. The greatest number of servings of food you eat each day should come from the widest sections of MyPyramid. The orange band on the far left of the pyramid is the grains group.

MyPyramid ▶ stresses the importance of healthy food choices and daily physical activity.

Health Project

Promoting Healthy Eating at School Divide the class into groups. Have each group look at a different day or week of the school cafeteria menu. Students should compare what is offered to the Dietary Guidelines. Groups also should investigate what other options are available for lunch and which options most of their fellow students choose. Have groups present their findings to the class. The class should discuss whether there are healthier options available to students than what they normally choose. Discuss how they can promote healthier eating to their fellow students. Students could make posters to start a healthy eating campaign in the school. **L2**

To its right is the vegetable group (in green) and the fruits group (in red). The wide blue band is the milk group, and the purple band on the far right is the meat and beans group. The narrow yellow band (between the fruits and milk groups) represents the oils group. It is so thin because people require such a small amount of oils, and most Americans already consume enough oil in the foods they eat.

Serving Size Guidelines

A serving is a specific amount of food that is indicated on the nutrition label. MyPyramid shows a range of servings for each major food group.

The number of servings that is right for you depends on how many calories you need, which in turn depends on your age, sex, size, and how active you are. Almost everyone should have at least the number of servings in the ranges. The following calorie level suggestions are based on the 2005 recommendations of the U.S. Department of Agriculture (USDA) Center for Nutrition Policy and Promotion.For adults and teens:

- 1800 calories is about right for many active young girls, sedentary teen girls, and sedentary women.

- 2200 calories is about right for most active adolescent girls, active women, sedentary teen boys, and sedentary men.

- 3000 calories is about right for many active teenage boys and active men.

If you eat a larger portion of a food than the serving size, you should count it as more than one serving. For example, a sandwich has two servings of bread. The top slice and bottom slice are each one serving.

Did You Know?

Serving Sizes Commonly available food portions are much larger than serving sizes for MyPyramid. For example, many bagels are as much as four times the serving size for MyPyramid.

TABLE 26.1	Sample Diets for a Day at Three Caloric Levels		
Food Groups	Lower Caloric Level (about 1800)	Moderate Caloric Level (about 2200)	Higher Caloric Level (about 3000)
Grains	6 oz	7 oz	10 oz
Vegetables	2.5 cups	3 cups	4 cups
Fruits	1.5 cups	2 cups	2.5 cups
Milk	3 cups	3 cups	3 cups
Meat and beans	5 oz	6 oz	7 oz

Differentiated Instruction

Learning Disabilities Pair a student who has learning disabilities with a student who does not have learning disabilities. Have students bring food magazines to class. Students should create a poster that illustrates healthful choices. Have students write captions beside foods describing possible vitamins or minerals that are found in that particular food. For example, milk contains calcium, which is essential for strong, healthy bones. **L1** **ELL**

Teacher FYI

Sedentary A sedentary person or lifestyle is one that is characterized by a lack of physical activity. A sedentary lifestyle increases the risk of heart disease and obesity. Physical activity can be derived not only from sports but also from work and household chores.

Class Activity

Journaling Have students write in their health journals their level of physical activity and which level of caloric intake they feel they fit into. Encourage students to seek advice from their family, the school nurse, or their family physician to help determine their caloric needs. **L2**

Using the Table

Food Journal Have students review the food journal entries they have been making. Students should compare these to the table on this page. They should analyze their entries to see if they have been eating the correct amount of each food group based on their personal recommended caloric intake. If not, students should note in their health journals what changes they can make in their eating habits to reach this goal. **L2**

Class Activity

Food Journal Have students monitor their eating habits for a week by writing down foods they ate, quantity of food they ate, and time of day they ate the food. Encourage students to be honest. Have students keep a separate journal for this activity. At the end of the week, have students examine their weekly diet. Have students answer the following questions: How many fruits and vegetables did you eat on an average day? How much milk and how many dairy products did you eat? How many sweets and how much soda did you consume? Students can use the journal to plan more balanced meals for themselves in the future. **L2** **ELL**

National Health Education Standards
Pages 296–297: 1.1, 1.5, 2.10

FACTSABOUT

EATING RIGHT FOR LIFE

Class Discussion

Eating Right for Life Engage the class in discussing why caloric and nutrient needs change during different stages of life. Students should expand on ideas given in the student text. List stages of life, such as infancy, teenage girls, teenage boys, pregnancy and nursing, active men and active women, and older adults, on the chalkboard. Write the students' ideas in the proper category, or break the class into groups; each group can discuss a different life stage and report back to the class. **L2**

Investigating the Issue

- *Student answers will vary, but may include ideas such as eating less fats and sugars, eating more fruits and vegetables, or eating more grains.*
- *A deficiency in vitamin D results in rickets, or soft bones. A deficiency in vitamin C results in scurvy, the symptoms of which include poor wound healing, loosened teeth, and swollen gums.*
- *Babies experience rapid growth and development, which affects their nutritional needs. Babies need more fat for energy and good sources of iron and calcium for proper development of body systems.*

FACTSABOUT
EATING RIGHT FOR LIFE

▲ Apples contain antioxidants, which can reduce cancer risks.

Caloric Intake Providing the right amount of nutrients and calories for your body is an essential part of maintaining good health. Your nutritional and caloric requirements change throughout the course of your life, depending on which stage of development you are in, how active you are, or if you become pregnant.

Nutritional needs of infants and children During their first few years, babies experience rapid growth. They need good sources of iron and calcium, as well as fat, in their diets. Infant formulas and baby food are specially formulated to meet the nutritional requirements of this age group. It is recommended that mothers breastfeed for the first six months. Breast milk helps fight infant infections, such as ear infections, diarrhea, allergies, and pneumonia. Breast milk also promotes digestion and absorption of nutrients. Children between the ages of two and eight years old need between 1000 and 2000 calories of food per day. The U.S. Department of Agriculture (USDA) recommends that the bulk of these calories be obtained from grains such as those found in bread, cereal, rice, and pasta. Fruits, vegetables, and dairy products, which provide a source of calcium for growing bones, also are an important part of a child's diet. Children also need enough iron to help prevent anemia. Dietary sources of iron include lean meats, shellfish, and cereals fortified with iron.

Nutritional needs of teen girls, active women, and most men Teen girls, active women, and most men need about 2200 calories per day. Iron and calcium are still important nutrients needed by the body of older children, teens,p and adults. Calcium helps protect against osteoporosis. Women who are pregnant need extra amounts of iron and folic acid. Evidence shows that folic acid is important to the proper development of nervous tissue and the spinal cord in fetuses. A deficiency in folic acid during pregnancy

can lead to serious spinal cord defects in newborn babies. Dietary sources of folic acid include green leafy vegetables, broccoli, breads, dried beans, and citrus fruits.

Nutritional needs of teen boys and active men Teen boys and active men need about 3000 calories per day. It is also important for adults over the age of 50 to get enough calcium, which helps keep bones strong and prevents the development of osteoporosis. Older adults and people who have little exposure to sunlight need to take a vitamin D supplement. Sunlight is a natural source of vitamin D. Vitamin D is required for the proper absorption of calcium into the body.

Investigating the Issue

Visit www.glencoe.com for more information on the nutritional requirements of your body.

- What changes could you make to your diet so that it better fulfills the USDA recommendations?
- What are some of the effects of vitamin deficiencies, such as vitamin D and vitamin C, on the body?
- Why do babies have different nutritional needs than adults?

Create a poster that summarizes the nutritional requirements of teens. Include information about what role each nutrient plays in the development of a healthy body. Display the poster in your classroom.

 www.glencoe.com

 Family Involvement

Family Discussion Encourage students to take their food journals home to discuss with their families. Students can discuss food guidelines and any changes they would like to make in their eating habits. Changes in eating habits will need the cooperation and support of family members, especially in regard to meals prepared at home. Have students work with parents to discuss meal options. Students could be responsible for helping to prepare at least one meal each week. **L1**

Dietary Guidelines

Recommendations for diet choices among healthy Americans who are two years of age or older are the Dietary Guidelines. They are a result of research done by the U.S. Department of Agriculture and the U.S. Department of Health and Human Services. These guidelines are updated every five years.

What to Know About the Dietary Guidelines

The USDA's Dietary Guidelines are designed to promote health. When you follow the guidelines, you obtain the nutrients your body needs and reduce the risk of developing certain diseases.

Make the Connection

Alcohol For more information on the effects of alcohol, see page 411 in Lesson 37.

TABLE 26.2 Dietary Guidelines	
Guidelines	**Description of Guideline**
Adequate Nutrients/ Food Safety	Eat a variety of nutrient-dense foods and beverages and adopt a balanced eating pattern based on MyPyramid. See Lesson 28 for information on how to reduce the risk of microbial food-borne illness.
Weight Management/ Physical Activity	Balance calories consumed from foods and beverages with calories expended. Engage in regular physical activity to promote health, psychological well-being, and a healthy body weight.
Food Groups to Encourage	Consume a variety of fruits and vegetables, whole-grain products, and 3 cups per day of fat-free or low-fat milk or milk products.
Fats	Choose a diet low in fat and cholesterol. A fat-like substance made by the body and found in certain foods is *cholesterol*. A type of fat from dairy products, meat, and poultry is called *saturated fat.*
Carbohydrates/ Sodium and Potassium	Choose fiber-rich foods and avoid sugars and caloric sweeteners. Consume potassium-rich foods such as fruits and vegetables. Choose and prepare foods with little salt.
Alcoholic Beverages	Do not drink alcohol, or drink sensibly and in moderation (if you are an adult).

LESSON 26 • Following Dietary Guidelines **299**

Vegetarian Diets

Teacher FYI

Healthful Weight By eliminating meat, vegetarians limit the amount of saturated fat they are eating, but they still must be aware of food choices to maintain a healthful weight. Choosing low-fat dairy products and plenty of fruits and vegetables while avoiding junk food is essential to maintaining a healthful weight.

3 Assess

Vocabulary Practice

Page 22, **Unit 5 Fast File Resources**

Name	Date	Class

LESSON 26 Following Dietary Guidelines

Vocabulary Practice

Answer the questions below. Include a definition of each vocabulary term as part of your answer.

cholesterol	lacto-ovo vegetarian diet	semi-vegetarian diet
Dietary Guidelines	lacto-vegetarian diet	vegan diet
food group	saturated fat	vegetarian diet
MyPyramid		

1. What is the relationship between the different *food groups* and *MyPyramid*?

2. What is a *vegetarian diet*?

3. Compare the *Dietary Guidelines* and *MyPyramid*.

4. Compare and contrast the following: *lacto-vegetarian diet, lacto-ovo vegetarian diet, and semi-vegetarian diet*.

5. Contrast the terms *cholesterol* and *saturated fat*.

22 LESSON 26 • Following Dietary Guidelines   UNIT 5

Vegetarian Diets

A diet in which vegetables are the foundation and meat, fish, and poultry are restricted or eliminated is a **vegetarian diet**. There are four kinds of vegetarian diets. A diet that excludes foods of animal origin is a **vegan diet**. A diet that excludes eggs, fish, poultry, and meat is a **lacto-vegetarian diet**. A diet that excludes fish, poultry, and red meat is a **ovo-lacto-vegetarian diet**. A diet that excludes red meat is a **semi-vegetarian diet**.

What to Know About Vegetarian Diets

Health benefits Vegetarian diets have some health benefits. Animal products are sources of fats, saturated fats, and cholesterol. A diet low in fats, saturated fats, and cholesterol helps reduce blood cholesterol. You are less likely to develop high blood pressure, heart disease, diabetes, and breast and colon cancer. It also is easier to maintain a healthful weight. Of course, a person can eat red meat occasionally and still obtain these health benefits.

How to Include More Vegetables in Your Diet

The following suggestions are creative and tasty ways to get more vegetables onto your plate:

- Create a salad. Try red leaf lettuce, spinach, bean sprouts, zucchini, cauliflower, peas, mushrooms, or red or yellow peppers.
- Select main dishes containing vegetables, such as pasta primavera, meatless chili, or minestrone soup.
- Make a sandwich containing vegetables, such as bean sprouts, spinach leaves, cucumbers, or carrot slices.
- Drink 100 percent vegetable juice instead of soda pop.
- Snack on raw carrot sticks, broccoli, cauliflower, celery sticks, and cucumber slices.

Discussing choices Teens who choose a vegetarian diet should discuss their choice with their parents or guardian and a physician or dietitian. Teens need to get enough protein, B vitamins, and calcium for growth and development. Foods of animal origin are a source of complete protein.

Incomplete proteins Foods of plant origin are sources of incomplete protein. Teens who do not eat foods of animal origin must combine different sources of incomplete protein to get enough protein in their diet. Two sources of incomplete protein can be combined to provide all the essential amino acids needed. For example, a teen might eat a vegetable burger and a serving of beans at the same meal, or vegetarian chili topped with cheese.

Because foods of animal origin are the source of vitamin B_{12}, a physician or dietitian may recommend vitamin supplements. Dairy foods are the best source of calcium. Teens who eliminate or restrict dairy products must discuss with a physician or dietitian how to get enough calcium.

Cross-Curricular Connections

Social Studies People from different cultures choose to follow a vegetarian diet for many different reasons. These reasons range from health concerns to environmental concerns as well as concern for animals and religious beliefs. Encourage the students to offer additional reasons why someone from another culture might choose a vegetarian diet. Divide the class into groups, and have each group of students choose a different culture to investigate. Each group can report its findings to the class, perhaps by preparing a vegetarian dish from the culture they are researching to share with the class. **L2**

National Health Education Standards

Pages 300–301: 1.1, 1.5, 2.10, 3.4, 6.3, 7.2, 8.2

Key Terms Review

Complete these fill-in-the-blank statements with the lesson Key Terms on the left. Do not write in this book.

cholesterol
Dietary Guidelines
food group
Food Guide Pyramid
lacto-vegetarian diet
ovo-lacto-vegetarian diet
saturated fat
semi-vegetarian diet
sodium
vegan diet
vegetarian diet

1. A(n) _____ is a category of foods that contain similar nutrients.

2. The _____ is a guide that tells how many servings from each food group are recommended each day.

3. A _____ is a diet in which vegetables are the foundation.

4. A _____ is a diet that excludes foods of animal origin.

5. A _____ is a diet that excludes eggs, fish, poultry, and meat.

6. A _____ is a diet that excludes fish, poultry, and red meat.

7. A _____ is a diet that excludes red meat but includes other kinds of meat.

8. The _____ are recommendations for diet choices among healthy Americans who are two years of age or more.

9. _____ is a type of fat from dairy products, solid vegetable fat, and meat and poultry.

10. _____ is a fat-like substance made by the body and is found in certain foods.

Recalling the Facts

11. What are the recommended number of daily servings for each food group in MyPyramid?

12. What constitutes a serving size for each group in MyPyramid?

13. What is a mineral found in table salt and in prepared foods?

14. What are the vitamins and nutrients found in each food group?

15. What percentage of the total calories you eat should come from fat?

16. What are the nutritional needs of teen girls and teen boys? Of active men and active women?

17. Why are the food groups arranged as they are in MyPyramid?

18. What are three foods that belong to each food group in MyPyramid?

Critical Thinking

19. How many servings of each of the food groups would a moderately active teenage girl need each day?

20. Why is it important to eat food items from each of the food groups in MyPyramid?

21. Why should you limit your intake of fats, oils, and sweets?

22. Why should you follow the Dietary Guidelines?

Real-Life Applications

23. How might you obtain adequate protein and amounts of B and C vitamins on a vegetarian diet?

24. Why do you think it is important to balance the food you eat with physical activity?

25. Why do you think it is important to choose a diet with plenty of grain products?

26. Why do you think it is important to choose a diet low in fat and saturated fat?

Activities

Responsible Decision Making

27. **Evaluate** Suppose you eat dinner and are trying to eat from MyPyramid. Your friends prefer to eat junk food. Write a response to this situation. Refer to the Responsible Decision-Making Model on page 61 for help.

Sharpen Your Life Skills

28. **Practice Healthful Behaviors** Ask your parent or guardian for permission to prepare a balanced and healthful menu for your family, using what you have learned about the food groups. Explain to your family why you chose the foods you did.

Visit www.glencoe.com for more *Health & Wellness* quizzes.

Key Terms Review

1. food group
2. MyPyramid
3. vegetarian diet
4. vegan diet
5. lacto-vegetarian diet
6. lacto-ovo-vegetarian diet
7. semi-vegetarian diet
8. Dietary Guidelines
9. Saturated fat
10. Cholesterol

Recalling the Facts

11. See page 296.
12. See page 295.
13. sodium
14. See page 295.
15. Thirty percent or less of the total calories one eats should come from fat.
16. See page 298.
17. The colored bands represent the number of servings and variety of foods one should eat per day.
18. See page 295.

Critical Thinking

19. At least 6 oz. grains, 2$\frac{1}{2}$ cups vegetables, 2 cups fruit, 3 cups milk, and 5$\frac{1}{2}$ oz. meat and beans.
20. Each food group offers different amounts of proteins, carbohydrates, fats, vitamins, and minerals needed by the body.
21. Fats, oils, and sweets are associated with obesity and heart disease.
22. The Dietary Guidelines are designed to promote health. When you follow the guidelines, you obtain the nutrients your body needs and reduce the risk of developing certain diseases.

Real-Life Applications

23. Combine different sources of incomplete proteins. You may need to consult a physician and consider taking vitamin supplements.

24. Activity helps people maintain a healthful weight, strengthens the heart, and tones the body.

25. to obtain fiber that might reduce the risk of colon cancer

26. A diet high in fat, saturated fat, and cholesterol increases the risk of heart disease, cancer, and obesity.

Activities

Responsible Decision Making

27. Tell your friends that you are trying to eat foods from MyPyramid and do not want to eat unhealthful foods.

Sharpen Your Life Skills

28. Answers will vary.

Using Diet to Guard Against Disease

Using Diet to Guard Against Disease

Out of Time?

If time does not permit an in-depth study of this topic, use the following activities in this Teacher Wraparound Edition:

- Health Goal, p. 302
- Explain the Concept, p. 304
- Community Involvement, p. 304
- Health Project, p. 306

1 Focus

HEALTH GOAL **Journaling** Have students respond to the Health Goal for this lesson by writing in their health journals what changes to their diet and lifestyle they can make to reduce their risk of disease. **L2**

NHES Assessment/SCASS

Constructed Response Student answers might include increased intake of calcium-rich foods, such as dairy products. **L2**

Using Diet to Guard Against Disease

HEALTH GOAL • I will follow a healthful diet that reduces the risk of disease.

Your diet affects your health status right now, as well as in the future. Having a healthful diet right now helps reduce your risk of developing certain diseases as an adult, including cancer, cardiovascular disease, diabetes, hypoglycemia, and osteoporosis. It also is important to know how to deal with food allergies and intolerances.

What You'll Learn

1. Discuss dietary guidelines to reduce the risk of developing cancer. *(p. 303)*
2. Discuss dietary guidelines to reduce the risk of developing cardiovascular diseases. *(p. 304)*
3. Discuss dietary guidelines to reduce the risk of developing osteoporosis. *(p. 306)*
4. Discuss diet recommendations for people with diabetes or hypoglycemia. *(p. 307)*
5. Discuss ways to avoid reactions to food allergies and intolerances, including lactose intolerance and celiac disease and reactions to MSG. *(p. 308)*

Why It's Important

A healthful diet can reduce your risk of getting cancer, cardiovascular diseases, diabetes, hypoglycemia, and osteoporosis.

Key Terms

- antioxidant
- cardiovascular disease
- atherosclerosis
- sodium
- osteoporosis
- diabetes
- hypoglycemia
- food allergy
- food intolerance
- lactase deficiency
- celiac disease

Writing About Using Diet to Guard Against Disease Suppose that several people in your family have had osteoporosis, and you want to lower your chances of having it. After you read the information about diet and osteoporosis on page 306, write an entry in your health journal to answer this question: How could you change your diet to help you prevent this disease?

302 UNIT 5 • Nutrition

National Health Education Standards—Guide for Lesson 27		
1.1	Predict how healthy behaviors can impact health status.	pp. 303–307
1.5	Propose ways to reduce or prevent injuries and health problems.	pp. 302, 303, 304–305, 307, 309
7.2	Demonstrate a variety of healthy practices and behaviors that will maintain or improve the health of self and others.	pp. 304–307, 309

Diet and Cancer

The National Academy of Sciences, the National Cancer Institute, and the American Cancer Society are organizations that have examined the role of diet in preventing cancer. You can reduce the risk of developing cancer by practicing the following dietary guidelines.

What to Know About Diet and Cancer

Diets high in antioxidants have been associated with decreased rates of esophagus, lung, colon, and stomach cancer. An **antioxidant** (an tee AHK suh duhnt) is a substance that protects cells from being damaged by oxidation. Antioxidants prevent cell damage and repair damaged cells. Their actions help prevent healthy cells from becoming cancerous cells. Vitamins C, E, and A, and the mineral selenium are antioxidants.

TABLE 27.1 Tips to Reduce the Risk of Cancer		
	Dietary Guideline	**Description**
	Avoid obesity.	Obesity is a body weight that is 20 percent or more than desirable body weight. Being obese increases the risk of developing cancers of the uterus, breast, gallbladder, prostate gland, and colon.
	Eat several servings and a variety of fruits, vegetables, and fiber-rich foods each day.	Especially eat *cruciferous* (kroo SIH fuh ruhs) vegetables such as cauliflower, broccoli, and brussels sprouts. Fruits and vegetables provide antioxidants that reduce the risk of developing cancers. Fiber is the part of grains and plant foods that cannot be digested. Eating fiber-rich foods helps you have a daily bowel movement, which reduces the risk of developing cancer of the colon and rectum.
	Limit fat intake and the consumption of foods that are smoked, salted, or nitrate-cured.	Limiting the amount of fat you eat helps reduce the risk of developing cancers of the breast, prostate gland, and colon. Limiting your consumption of foods that are smoked, salted, or nitrate-cured helps reduce the risk of developing cancers of the esophagus and stomach.
	Do not drink alcohol as a teen.	Alcohol consumption robs the body of vitamins needed for optimal health. When you avoid drinking alcohol, you reduce the risk of developing cancers of the liver, throat, mouth, breast, and stomach.

LESSON 27 • Using Diet to Guard Against Disease **303**

Lesson Resource Manager

- **Unit 5 Fast File Resources**
  Reading Strategy, p. 33
  Vocabulary Practice, p. 34
  Transparency Master and Worksheet, p. 35
  Real-Life Health, p. 37
  Real-Life Health, p. 39
  5-Minute Check, p. 41
  Lesson 27 Quiz, p. 42
- **Unit 5 Transparency**
- **Lesson 27 Transparency**

- **Reading Essentials**
- **Technology**
  TeacherWorks™ CD-ROM
  StudentWorks™ CD-ROM
  Reading Essentials CD-ROM
  ExamView® Assessment Suite
  Vocabulary Puzzlemaker

Diet and Cancer

2 Teach

Using the Table

Creating a Menu Have the students construct a full day's menu using the table as a guideline. Make sure the day's meals utilize all the guidelines to create a healthful diet. **L2** **ELL**

PowerPoint® Presentations

This CD-ROM is an editable Microsoft® PowerPoint® presentation that includes:
- Lesson presentations
- Lesson checks
- Interactive graphics
- 5-Minute Checks
- Image Bank
- All transparencies

Note-Taking Refer to the Two-Column Notes: Main Idea-Detail Strategy on page 16T. Ask students to make two columns on their paper. On the left side, have them write the names of the diseases discussed in the lesson and, on the right side, have them write some dietary means to reduce the risk of disease.

National Health Education Standards
Pages 302–303: 1.1, 1.5

Diet and Cardiovascular Disease

Teaching Transparency

Page 35, **Unit 5 Fast File Resources**

LESSON 27 **Using Diet to Guard Against Disease**

TEACHING TRANSPARENCY • Use with Unit 5, Lesson 27

Assessing Cancer Risk Factors

Tips to Reduce the Risk of Cancer

Dietary Guideline	Description
Avoid obesity.	Obesity is a body weight that is 20 percent or more than desirable body weight. Being obese increases the risk of developing cancers of the uterus, breast, gallbladder, prostate gland, and colon.
Eat several servings and a variety of fruits, vegetables, and fiber-rich foods each day.	Especially eat cruciferous vegetables such as cauliflower, broccoli, and brussels sprouts. Fruits and vegetables provide antioxidants that reduce the risk of developing cancers. Fiber is the part of grains and plant foods that cannot be digested. Eating fiber-rich foods helps you have a daily bowel movement, which reduces the risk of developing cancer of the colon and rectum.
Limit fat intake and the consumption of foods that are smoked, salted, or nitrate-cured.	Limiting the amount of fat you eat helps reduce the risk of developing cancers of the breast, prostate gland, and colon. Limiting your consumption of foods that are smoked, salted, or nitrate-cured helps reduce the risk of developing cancers of the esophagus and stomach.
Do not drink alcohol as a teen.	Alcohol consumption robs the body of vitamins needed for optimal health. When you avoid drinking alcohol, you reduce the risk of developing cancers of the liver, throat, mouth, breast, and stomach.

Meeks Heit Health & Wellness   UNIT AND LESSON TRANSPARENCIES

Explain the Concept

Cardiovascular Blockages Explain to students that problems with blood flow are responsible for a large number of health problems. Students may not realize that health problems such as stroke and heart attacks both result from blockages in the bloodstream, and that blood pressure is an indicator of how well the cardiovascular system is working.

Quick Demo

Blood Pressure Ask the school nurse to visit your class and bring a blood pressure cuff with him or her. Have the nurse demonstrate for students how blood pressure is taken and describe what both numbers of a blood pressure reading indicate. Ask the nurse to provide a table showing which blood pressure readings are considered healthy. **ELL**

Diet and Cardiovascular Disease

A disease of the heart and blood vessels is ***cardiovascular disease (CVD),*** which also is called heart disease. Cardiovascular diseases are a leading cause of premature death and disability. You can reduce the risk of developing premature cardiovascular diseases by practicing the following dietary guidelines.

What to Know About Diet and Cardiovascular Disease

> **Make the Connection**
>
> **CVD** For more information on cardiovascular disease, see page 515 in Lesson 47.

Limit fat and cholesterol intake. A fat-like substance made by the body and found in some foods is ***cholesterol.*** Eating foods that are high in saturated fats and cholesterol may cause plaque to form on artery walls. Plaque is made up of cholesterol, fatty substances, cellular waste products, calcium, and other substances. A disease in which there is a build up of plaque on artery walls is ***atherosclerosis*** (ah thuh roh skluh ROH suhs). When a person has atherosclerosis, the diameter of the artery becomes narrow. Blood pressure increases because blood is flowing through a narrower opening in the artery. Pressure may rupture the plaque causing a blood clot that blocks the artery or that breaks off, circulates in the bloodstream, and lodges in the bloodstream. An ***embolism*** is the blockage of an artery by a clump of material traveling in the bloodstream. If the blockage is in an artery in the brain, a person could have a stroke. If the blockage is in an artery in the heart, a heart attack could occur. A blockage in the lung is called a ***pulmonary embolism.***

Increase your intake of foods and beverages containing antioxidants. Antioxidants help prevent wear and tear in blood vessels. You can obtain antioxidants in your diet by: eating carrots, sweet potatoes, and squash to obtain vitamin A; eating citrus fruits, such as oranges and pineapples, to obtain vitamin C; and eating green vegetables, nuts, and whole-grain cereals and breads to obtain vitamin E.

How to Limit Fat Intake

Less than 30 percent of total calories per day should come from fat. Below are suggestions to limit fat intake.

- Limit your intake of cooked lean meat, poultry, and fish to 5 1/2 oz per day.
- Broil, bake, or steam food rather than fry it.
- Trim fat from meats before cooking.
- Trim fat from poultry before cooking.
- Limit your intake of egg yolks; consider using egg substitutes.
- Limit your intake of high-fat processed meats, such as hot dogs and bologna.
- Substitute fruits and low-fat yogurt for high-fat desserts.
- Substitute turkey, such as turkey hot dogs and turkey chili, for red meat.
- Substitute nonfat or low-fat dairy products for whole-milk dairy products, such as low-fat yogurt for ice cream, skim milk for whole milk, reduced-fat mayonnaise for regular mayonnaise, low-fat or non-fat cheese for regular cheese.
- Substitute fruits and vegetables for high-fat snacks, such as potato chips.

304 UNIT 5 • Nutrition

 Community Involvement

Accessibility of Restaurants Accessibility is an important factor in determining eating habits. People are more likely to eat foods that are easily accessible. If a deli is within a short drive, but a fast-food restaurant is miles away, you are more likely to go to the deli. Have students calculate the number of fast-food chains and sit-down restaurants that are within 10 miles of their home. Ask them which places they visit most often and why. Have students present a poster of the restaurants that are frequently visited and the reasons for visiting. Ask students to consider whether their restaurant choices were based on convenience, or the availabilty of healthful menu choices, or both. **L2**

Limit your intake of sodium. A mineral your body needs only in small amounts is **sodium.** The recommended daily allowance of sodium is three grams. Some teens consume many times this amount.

Too much sodium can affect people in different ways. It may cause some people to retain body fluid and, as a result, have increased blood pressure. You can limit your sodium intake by eating fresh rather than canned foods. Salt is usually added to canned foods as a preservative. Select prepared foods that are labeled low-salt or salt-free, such as canned corn that is low-salt and unsalted popcorn. Avoid eating foods on which you can see the salt, such as pretzels and nuts coated with pieces of salt. Do not add salt to food. Season foods with herbs and spices rather than with salt and limit your intake of salty foods, such as bacon, barbecue sauce, chips, crackers, hot dogs, processed meats, ketchup, canned meat, and mustard. Sodium appears in food as sodium bicarbonate, monosodium glutamate, sodium nitrite, sodium propionate, and sodium citrate.

Include flax, soy, canola, olive, and fish oils in your diet. The unsaturated fats in these foods can help prevent heart disease, lower bad cholesterol (LDL) and increase good cholesterol (HDL). LDL is associated with an increased risk of CVD, while HDL lowers the risk of CVD. Substitute oils high in soy, canola, and olive oil for polyunsaturated oils (e.g., corn, safflower, sunflower), saturated oils (e.g., palm, coconut), and trans fats. High levels of favorable fish oils are found in salmon, trout, mackerel, and sardines.

 www.glencoe.com

Omega-3

Did you know that eating fish at least twice a week helps keep your heart healthy? Some fish, such as mackerel, lake trout, herring, sardines, albacore tuna, and salmon are high in two omega-3 fatty acids. A third, less potent omega-3 fatty acid comes from soybeans, canola, walnuts, and flaxseed, as well as from the oils made from those beans, nuts, and seeds. Omega-3 fatty acids are used by the body to make nerve tissue in the retina of the eye and the brain. The body cannot manufacture omega-3 fatty acids. Our only source is from the foods we eat.

Omega-3 fatty acids decrease the incidence of blood clot formations, which can cause heart attacks and strokes. They are involved in the reduction of fat and cholesterol levels as well as slowing the rate at which plaque may be deposited on the interior walls of arteries. The deposition of plaque in arteries can lead to conditions such as heart disease, angina, and heart attack. Omega-3 fatty acids also decrease the risk of irregular heartbeat, which can cause death. They are also noted to be involved in lowering blood pressure slightly. The American Heart Association recommends that people eat at least one serving of fish that are high in omega-3 fatty acids at least two times per week.

 Visit www.glencoe.com for more information on diet and heart disease.

The Benefits of Having Fish in One's Diet

21% 1-3 Times per month*

34% >5 Times per week*

29% Once per week*

31% 2-4 Times per week*

◄ The 2002 Nurses' Health Study found an inverse relationship between fish consumption, omega-3 fatty acids and coronary heart disease (CHD) in women. The more fish women ate, the lower their risk of CHD was.

*as compared to females who ate fish once per month or less

Source: The Journal of the American Medical Association, *Nurses' Health Study*, 2002.

Analyzing Graphs

Study the graph above and answer these questions:

1. Which group received the most benefits from eating fish?

2. Compare the CHD risk for women who eat fish 1 to 3 times per month with women who ate fish less than once per month.

Analyzing Graphs

1. Women who ate fish more than 5 times per week.
2. Women who eat fish 1 to 3 times per month have a 21 percent less chance of developing CHD than do women who eat fish less than once per month.

Project

Fish and Omega-3 Have students do research to find the levels of omega-3 fatty acids present in different kinds of fish. Compare the levels of omega-3 fatty acids in various fish that could be ordered in a restaurant and show how much portions would have to vary to get the same amount of omega-3 fatty acids when ordering different kinds of fish. **L3**

Quick Demo

Circulatory Blockage Explain or demonstrate that the circulatory system operates much like drinking from a straw. When the system, or straw, becomes blocked, the force necessary to keep the liquid flowing must increase. In a circulatory blockage, that increased force causes stress on the heart muscle. **L2** **ELL**

Differentiated Instruction

Gifted and Talented Research shows that although eating fish benefits the heart and other parts of the circulatory system, many pollutants that can cause health problems are present in fish. Have students contact a local environmental protection agency to find out what kinds of pollutants are found in fish, and what types of fish contain the highest levels of pollutants. Encourage students to think critically about this information and make conclusions about including fish in their diet. Have students create a news broadcast illustrating the information that was obtained from their research. **L3**

National Health Education Standards

Pages 304–305: 1.1, 1.5, 2.1, 7.2

305

Diet and Osteoporosis

Class Activity

Sources of Calcium Have students research sources of calcium such as milk, cheese, broccoli, and bread. Ask students to answer this question: Which of these sources has the highest amount of calcium per serving? Have students compile the results of their research into a large poster that shows which foods are the best sources of calcium. Display the poster in your classroom. **L2**

5-Minute Check

Page 41, **Unit 5 Fast File Resources**

1. What is an antioxidant? *a substance that protects cells against damage from oxidation*
2. How does eating a variety of foods contribute to a healthy diet? *Eating a variety of foods increases the variety of nutrients that the body receives and helps prevent certain diseases.*
3. What is atherosclerosis? *a disease in which plaque deposits on artery walls*
4. In what two ways can atherosclerosis contribute to bad health? *It can narrow arteries, causing increased blood pressure; pieces of plaque also can break off and cause an embolism, stroke, heart attack, or pulmonary embolism.*
5. What kinds of fats should be especially limited in a healthy diet? *polyunsaturated, saturated, and trans fats*

1. *cardiovascular disease (CVD)*
2. *plaque builds up on the artery walls*
3. *Antioxidants prevent wear and tear in blood vessels.*

A disease characterized by low bone mass and deterioration of bone tissue is **osteoporosis.** Osteoporosis causes bones to become brittle and fracture easily. Females are ten times more likely to have severe osteoporosis than are males.

What to Know About Diet and Osteoporosis

Calcium and phosphorus form the hard substance in bone. Calcium is a mineral that is essential to bone growth. A deficiency of calcium, especially in females, increases the risk for osteoporosis. There are many good sources of calcium, including yogurt, milk, cheese, and leafy, green vegetables.

Adolescence is a time when an inadequate calcium intake can contribute to osteoporosis later in life. Bone growth occurs more rapidly in teenagers than it does during any other time in life.

Bones approach maximum density during childhood, adolescence, and young adulthood. Obtaining enough calcium during adolescence is critical to reduce the risk of osteoporosis.

Other ways to avoid osteoporosis Besides making sure that one eats a balanced diet rich in calcium, other ways to help prevent osteoporosis include engaging in weight-bearing exercise, avoiding smoking, and utilizing bone density testing and medications when appropriate.

Bone loss In both men and women, bone mass usually peaks between the ages 25 and 35. For women, an average bone loss before menopause is 1–1.25 percent a year, but it increases to 3–4 percent after menopause.

Heart disease and hormonal replacement A woman's estrogen production is reduced when she reaches menopause; thus, the body cannot use calcium effectively and the result is an increased risk of osteoporosis. In the past, it was commonly believed that hormonal replacement (estrogen and progesterone) would improve osteoporosis as well as decrease risk for heart disease.

Some scientists have found that hormonal replacement therapy actually increases the risk for heart disease, stroke, and cancer in some women.

▲ Consumption of dairy products in adolescence is important for reducing the risk of osteoporosis.

Reading Review

1. What is the leading cause of premature death and disability?
2. What happens during atherosclerosis?
3. What function do antioxidants play in blood vessels?

Health Project

Calcium-Enriched Products The importance of calcium as a part of diet has caused many food companies to incorporate calcium into their products. Have students explore their local supermarket or drug store to find food products that have been enriched with dietary calcium. Some foods might include cereals and breads. These items usually are labeled as "enriched." Have students create a list of products that have been enriched with calcium. Have students share their list with their classmates. **L2**

Diet, Diabetes, and Hypoglycemia

A disease in which the body either produces little or no insulin or cannot properly use insulin is called diabetes mellitus or **diabetes. Insulin** is a hormone that regulates the blood sugar level. Without treatment, a person with diabetes will have a high blood sugar level. Being overweight increases your risk of developing one form of diabetes. Diabetes is treated with diet, exercise, medications, or insulin.

What to Know About Diet, Diabetes, and Hypoglycemia

Dealing with diabetes A physician and dietitian can work with someone with diabetes to make a plan. The person may be advised to eat complex carbohydrates and protein to provide long-lasting energy; limit simple carbohydrate intake, especially sweets; eat six small meals a day to maintain a constant blood sugar level; have regular examinations to test blood sugar levels and reevaluate diet; and maintain desirable weight.

Who is at risk? Diabetes is associated with increased risk of blindness, cardiovascular disease, kidney failure, amputation of toes and legs, and premature death. Lifestyle facts such as lack of physical activity and obesity greatly increase the risk for diabetes. The early signs of diabetes are frequent urination, excessive thirst, cravings for sweets, and weakness.

Hypoglycemia A condition in which there is too much insulin in the body, causing the blood sugar level to be low is called **hypoglycemia** (hi poh gli SEE mee uh). Normally, when a person eats, the blood sugar level increases. As the blood sugar level increases, the pancreas secretes insulin into the bloodstream. When proteins and complex carbohydrates are eaten, insulin is secreted at a slower rate. People with hypoglycemia experience a rapid increase in blood sugar followed by a sudden drop. When their blood sugar level drops, they feel dizzy, weak, irritable, and confused. They may have headaches and feel hungry. To relieve these symptoms, they need to eat again to restore their blood sugar level.

Did You Know?

Diabetes The number of children and teens who are developing type 2 diabetes—a form of diabetes usually diagnosed in adults—is growing. More young people are developing type 2 diabetes because more of the U.S. population is becoming overweight, a condition that increases a person's risk of developing diabetes.

Guidelines for People with Hypoglycemia

People with hypoglycemia follow a diet similar to people who have diabetes and may follow the same guidelines:

- Eat complex carbohydrates and protein to provide long-lasting energy.
- Limit the amounts of sweets. Simple sugars increase blood sugar and the need for insulin.
- Eat six small meals a day to maintain a constant blood sugar level.
- Have regular examinations to test blood sugar levels and reevaluate diet.
- Maintain a desirable weight.

LESSON 27 • Using Diet to Guard Against Disease   307

Diet, Diabetes, and Hypoglycemia

Teacher FYI

Diabetes There are three types of diabetes:

- Type I diabetes: People born with type I diabetes are unable to produce insulin. Approximately 5–10 percent of Americans with diabetes have type I.
- Type II diabetes: Commonly called "adult onset" diabetes, this condition results from increased insulin resistance. Type II diabetes is linked with excessive weight gain and is becoming more common.
- Gestational diabetes: Approximately 4 percent of pregnant women develop gestational diabetes, in which hormones that support the development of the fetus also create insulin resistance for the mother.

Extension

Glycemic Index The glycemic index is a measure of how different foods affect blood sugar levels. Have students research the glycemic index and find the values of several foods. Students may be surprised to find that several foods, like white potatoes, actually have a higher index number, or affect blood sugar more dramatically, than plain table sugar. **L3**

🔖 Family Involvement

Diabetes and Other Chronic Diseases Many people do not know their family health history. Have students evaluate what chronic diseases run in their family. With a parent or guardian, have students develop a family tree illustrating relatives who have had diabetes or other chronic diseases, such as high cholesterol, high blood pressure, heart disease, or cancer. If a student is not living with his or her biological parents, the student can ask his or her guardian or adopted parents what they know about his or her family's health history. Ask students what behaviors they could practice to reduce their risk. Have students write a disease prevention plan in their health journals. Students could also create a disease prevention contract. **L2**

National Health Education Standards

Pages 306–307: 1.1, 1.5, 1.7, 3.4, 7.2

Food Allergies and Intolerances

Explain the Concept

Lactase Deficiency Explain that lactase deficiency is one of the most common food intolerances. Some children are born without the ability to make lactase. Even those with normal milk tolerance start losing the ability to make lactase after age two. Lactase deficiency has been linked genetically, and it is much more common in African-Americans, Native Americans, and Asian-Americans.

Reading Review

1. *an abnormal response to food that is triggered by the immune system*
2. *a condition in which lactase is missing*
3. *headaches, feelings of warmth, and chest pain*

3 Assess

Vocabulary Practice

Page 34, **Unit 5 Fast File Resources**

National Health Education Standards

Pages 308–309: 1.7, 2.10, 3.4, 4.1, 4.2, 4.4, 6.3

308

Food Allergies and Intolerances

You may have felt ill after eating a food and wondered if you were allergic to it. An abnormal response to food that is triggered by the immune system is a *food allergy.* Food allergies can cause severe illness, or even death.

What to Know About Food Allergies and Intolerances

A person who suspects he or she has a food allergy should see a physician. If a food allergy is diagnosed, the physician may recommend that the person completely avoid the food causing the allergy, or prescribe medication.

Food Allergies

Symptoms The most common foods that cause allergic reactions in adults are shellfish, peanuts, fish, and eggs. Symptoms of food allergies include: diarrhea, swelling, sneezing, itching, and nausea.

Food Intolerances

What many people think is a food allergy is actually a *food intolerance,* which is an abnormal response to food that is not caused by the immune system. It merely means that a food is not tolerated well.

Lactase deficiency A condition in which lactase, an enzyme that breaks down the milk sugar present in the cells of the small intestine, is missing is called ***Lactase deficiency.*** This condition results in the inability to digest lactose. This is called ***lactose intolerance.*** As the undigested lactose moves through the lower gastrointestinal tract, it releases products that are gaseous and cause discomfort, such as abdominal pain, bloating, and diarrhea. Lactase deficiency is the most common form of food intolerance. Drinking skim or low-fat milk will not help. It is not the fat, but the lactose, that causes the symptoms.

Celiac disease A condition in which a person is intolerant to gluten is called ***celiac*** (SEE lee ak) ***disease.*** Gluten is a part of wheat, rye, barley, and certain other grains. The symptoms of celiac disease include tiredness, breathlessness, weight loss, diarrhea, vomiting, and abdominal pain.

MSG A common cause of food intolerance is ***Monosodium glutamate*** (MSG). A flavor enhancer added to many foods, it can cause headaches, feelings of warmth, and chest pain in some people. MSG is often added to Chinese and other Asian foods. Sulfites added to foods also may cause food intolerance. Sulfites can be found in wines, potatoes, and packaged foods.

Make the Connection

Health Behavior Inventory For more information on how to complete a health behavior inventory, see page 27 in Lesson 3.

Reading Review

1. What is a food allergy?
2. What is meant by lactase deficiency?
3. What are some side effects people exhibit who are intolerant to MSG?

308 UNIT 5 • Nutrition

⚖ Legal Issues

Peanut Allergies Some people suffer from potentially lethal peanut allergies. Because peanuts are so prevalent in consumer products, manufacturers are required to put a warning label on their products if they are even manufactured in the same facility as a product containing peanuts. People with peanut allergies must be very cautious, because ingesting even a small amount of peanut residue can prove deadly. Because of the severity of the allergy, some school cafeterias no longer sell peanut products.

27 STUDY GUIDE

antioxidant
atherosclerosis
cardiovascular
  disease
celiac disease
diabetes
embolism
food allergy
food intolerance
hypoglycemia
lactase deficiency
lactose intolerance
osteoporosis

Key Terms Review

Complete these fill-in-the-blank statements with the lesson Key Terms on the left. Do not write in this book.

1. A(n)_____ is a substance that protects cells from being damaged by oxidation.

2. _____ is a disease of the heart and blood vessels and can be termed heart disease.

3. _____ is a disease in which plaque deposits on artery walls and can lead to high blood pressure.

4. _____ is characterized by low bone mass and is related to deficiency in calcium.

5. _____ is a disease in which the body either produces little or no insulin or cannot use insulin.

6. _____ is a condition in which the pancreas produces too much insulin.

7. A(n)_____ is an abnormal response to food that is triggered by the immune system.

8. A(n)_____ is an abnormal response to food that is not caused by the immune system.

9. _____ is a condition in which lactase is missing, causing discomfort when eating or drinking dairy products.

10. _____ is a condition in which a person is intolerant to gluten.

Recalling the Facts

11. What four dietary guidelines can you follow to reduce the risk of developing premature cardiovascular disease?

12. How can you limit your fat intake?

13. What are dietary sources of omega-3 fatty acids, and why are they good for you?

14. What kinds of diet recommendations do people with diabetes and hypoglycemia follow?

15. To what foods are people often allergic or intolerant?

16. Which vitamins are considered antioxidants?

17. What four dietary guidelines can you follow to reduce the risk of developing cancer?

18. Which cancer risks can you reduce by following the above guidelines?

Critical Thinking

19. Explain why it is important to limit the amount of fat and cholesterol in your diet.

20. If a teen girl does not eat dairy products and vegetables, but starts to eat them in her 30s, has she protected herself against osteoporosis?

21. Why are antioxidants important?

22. Describe how increasing your intake of omega-3 fatty acids can improve your health.

Real-Life Applications

23. What are foods in your school cafeteria that are rich in omega-3 fatty acids?

24. What are foods that are in your school cafeteria that are low in cholesterol?

25. If you or a loved one were diagnosed with diabetes, what would you do?

26. Why do you think it is important to recognize symptoms of food allergies or food intolerance?

Activities

Responsible Decision Making

27. **Explain** Suppose you have lactase deficiency. You accept a dinner invitation at a friend's house. The main dish is cheese-heavy lasagna. Write a response to this situation. Refer to the Responsible Decision-Making Model on page 61 for help.

Sharpen Your Life Skills

28. **Make Responsible Decisions** Your family invites one of your friends to go on vacation. Your friend has diabetes. How might you consider your friend's dietary needs as you plan ahead for the vacation? List actions you might take.

Visit **www.glencoe.com** for more *Health & Wellness* quizzes.

LESSON 27 • Study Guide **309**

STUDY GUIDE

Key Terms Review

1. antioxidant
2. Cardiovascular disease
3. Atherosclerosis
4. Osteoporosis
5. Diabetes
6. Hypoglycemia
7. food allergy
8. food intolerance
9. Lactase deficiency
10. Celiac disease

Recalling the Facts

11. Limit fat and cholesterol intake; increase intake of antioxidants; limit sodium; and include flax, soy, canola, olive, and fish oils in your diet.

12. See list on page 304.

13. See page 305.

14. Eat complex carbohydrates; limit total carbohydrate intake, especially sweets; eat six small meals a day; have regular examinations to test blood sugar levels; maintain desirable weight.

15. shellfish, peanuts, fish, eggs, milk, gluten/wheat and other grains, MSG, and sulfites

16. vitamin A; vitamin C; vitamin E

17. See page 303.

18. cancer of the uterus, breast, gall bladder, prostate gland, colon, rectum, esophagus, stomach, liver, throat, and mouth

Critical Thinking

19. Fat and cholesterol may cause plaque to form on artery walls.

20. Because bone growth occurs more rapidly in teens than it does later in life, she should have eaten calcium-rich foods when she was a teen to get the most protection against osteoporosis.

21. Antioxidants prevent cell damage and repair damaged cells, which helps prevent cancer.

22. See page 305.

Real-Life Applications

23. Answers will vary.
24. Answers will vary.
25. See page 307.
26. You can avoid foods to which you are allergic or intolerant, thus preventing health problems.

Activities

Responsible Decision Making

27. Tell your host that you are lactose intolerant. Ask if they would be offended if you ate a salad or something else instead of lasagna.

Sharpen Your Life Skills

28. Answers will vary.

Developing Healthful Eating Habits

Out of Time?

If time does not permit an in-depth study of this topic, use the following activities in this Teacher Wraparound Edition:
- Class Discussion, p. 314
- Journaling Activity, p. 315
- Class Activity, p. 316
- Cross-Curricular Connections, p. 320

1 Focus

HEALTH GOALS **Health Benefits** Have students respond to the first Health Goal for this lesson by listing the benefits of developing healthful eating habits. *Benefits might include avoiding chronic disease.* **L2**

Write ABOUT IT!

Discuss After students have read the lesson, have them discuss what they would do when faced with the choice of whether or not to use dietary supplements to improve their athletic performance. Ask them to discuss both positive and negative aspects of using dietary supplements to boost their performance. **L2**

LESSON 28

Developing Healthful Eating Habits

 HEALTH GOALS
- I will develop healthful eating habits.
- I will protect myself from food-borne illnesses.
- I will follow Dietary Guidelines when I eat out.

Consider your eating habits. Do you eat healthful foods for breakfast, snacks, lunch, and dinner? Does your exercise or sport routine require that you change your eating habits? You need to understand why you eat and how to plan to eat healthful foods and safe foods at home and other places.

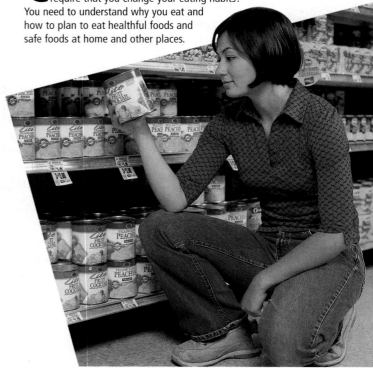

What You'll Learn

1. Explain what motivates people to eat. *(p. 311)*
2. List guidelines to follow when planning healthful meals. *(p. 312)*
3. Discuss how some supplements and dietary behaviors affect performance in sports. *(p. 314)*
4. Discuss guidelines to follow when eating out. *(p. 316)*
5. List three examples of healthful foods that can be ordered at various ethnic restaurants. *(p. 319)*
6. Outline ways to protect yourself from food-borne illnesses. *(p. 320)*
7. Explain five ways food can become contaminated. *(p. 322)*

Why It's Important

Be aware of what you eat because what you eat affects how you feel and perform.

Key Terms

- metabolism
- megadosing
- electrolyte
- carbohydrate loading
- protein loading
- food-borne illness
- salmonellosis
- botulism
- E coli
- gastroenteritis

 Write ABOUT IT!

Writing About Healthful Eating Suppose that you play school sports and want to improve your performance. You have heard teammates talk about sports drinks, energy bars, carbohydrate and protein loading, and supplements. After reading the information about nutrition and sports on page 314, write an entry in your health journal about how you can maintain healthful eating habits while playing sports.

National Health Education Standards—Guide for Lesson 28		
1.1	Predict how healthy behaviors can impact health status.	pp. 310, 311–314, 316–322, 323
1.5	Propose ways to reduce or prevent injuries and health problems.	pp. 310, 312–313, 317, 318, 320–321, 322, 323
7.1	Analyze the role of individual responsibility for enhancing health.	pp. 310, 312–314, 316–319, 322, 323
7.2	Demonstrate a variety of healthy practices and behaviors that will maintain or improve the health of self and others.	pp. 310, 312–322, 323

Why People Eat

The physiological need for food is **_hunger_**. Sometimes you eat because you are hungry. At other times, you eat even though you are not hungry. Do you decide to eat because you are hungry or because of other factors?

What Motivates People to Eat

Suppose you feel rejected, depressed, anxious, bored, or lonely. There are better ways to handle these feelings than by eating. When you rely on eating to cope, you develop harmful eating habits. Some teens develop eating disorders when they focus on eating or starving as a way of coping.

Motivation factors You need to eat when you are hungry. You also need to eat to obtain the nutrients necessary for good health. But you do not need to eat to manage stress. You do not need to eat when the sight or smell of food tempts you, or when you feel rejected, depressed, anxious, bored, or lonely. You do not need to eat to have something to do at a party where you feel uncomfortable, or because the people around you are eating.

Eating habits To develop healthful eating habits, you must understand why you eat. You must plan breakfast, lunch, dinner, and snacks to satisfy hunger. It is a misconception that our energy needs are primarily physical. Much of our total energy is emotional, the kind of energy we display as hope, faith, enthusiasm, passion, fun, and resilience. You must recognize when you are eating for reasons other than hunger. Then you must evaluate whether eating for this reason benefits your health or harms your health.

◀ It is important to understand what motivates you to eat.

Hunger or Something Else?

Examine the ten situations below. Hunger motivates you to eat in the first five situations mentioned. In the last five situations, it is something else that motivates you to eat.

- You have not eaten since last night. You eat breakfast.
- You eat a sports nutrition bar after playing soccer.
- You are growing rapidly. You eat an extra serving of vegetables for dinner.
- You have a lunch break at school. You eat the lunch you packed this morning.
- You cannot eat before taking a physical exam. You eat shortly after the exam.

- You are stressed about a test tomorrow. You eat chips.
- You feel rejected when you are not invited to a party. You treat yourself to a large order of fries.
- You feel insecure at a party. You nibble on snack mix.
- You feel depressed. You eat a carton of ice cream.
- You just ate dinner. You then eat several slices of pizza with friends.

LESSON 28 • Developing Healthful Eating Habits **311**

Class Activity
Alternatives to Eating Have students get into groups and brainstorm ideas that would be healthful, enjoyable alternatives to eating when they are bored, lonely, sad, or angry. **L2**

Class Discussion
TV Commercials Have students describe food commercials they have seen on TV. Discuss the different advertising strategies companies most often use to market food products. Ask students which strategies they think are most effective and why. **L2**

PowerPoint® Presentations

This CD-ROM is an editable Microsoft® PowerPoint® presentation that includes:
- Lesson presentations
- Lesson checks
- Interactive graphics
- 5-Minute Checks
- Image Bank
- All transparencies

CRISS Project

Discussion Refer to the Think-Pair-Share Strategy on page 17T, and ask students to think about healthy eating habits. Then pair students to pool their knowledge, and finally, involve everyone in a whole-class discussion.

Lesson Resource Manager

- **Unit 5 Fast File Resources**
  Reading Strategy, p. 45
  Vocabulary Practice, p. 46
  Transparency Master and Worksheet, p. 47
  Real-Life Health, p. 49
  Real-Life Health, p. 51
  5-Minute Check, p. 53
  Lesson 28 Quiz, p. 56
- **Unit 5 Transparency**
- **Lesson 28 Transparency**

- **Reading Essentials**
- **Technology**
  TeacherWorks™ CD-ROM
  StudentWorks™ CD-ROM
  Reading Essentials CD-ROM
  Exam*View*® Assessment Suite
  Vocabulary Puzzlemaker

National Health Education Standards
Pages 310–311: 1.1, 1.2, 1.5, 7.1, 7.2

Healthful Breakfast and Lunch

The word breakfast means "break the fast." Your body has been fasting (going without food for several hours) during the night and is running out of energy. Eating a healthful breakfast gives you the energy you need to begin your day. Remember that lunch also is a must. A well-balanced lunch provides energy for your afternoon activities.

How to Plan a Healthful Breakfast and Lunch

Make the Connection

Setting Health Goals For more information on how to set health goals, see page 57 in Lesson 6.

The rate at which food is converted into energy in body cells is called *metabolism.* During the night, your metabolism has slowed. Eating a healthful breakfast helps you feel alert. As your body begins to use the nutrients in foods, your metabolism speeds up. Follow the Dietary Guidelines in Lesson 26 when choosing foods and beverages for breakfast.

The energy gained from breakfast is used to keep you active throughout the morning. You need lunch to remain alert and to be able to focus on schoolwork throughout the afternoon. If you skip lunch, you may experience a mid-afternoon slump. Follow the Dietary Guidelines when choosing foods and beverages for lunch.

Breakfast and lunch dos and don'ts For both breakfast and lunch, you should eat fruits and vegetables or drink fruit or vegetable juices. Also eat foods high in proteins and foods that are sources of grains and fiber. Limit fatty, greasy, or fried foods, as well as salt-cured foods.

TABLE 28.1	Excuses for Skipping Breakfast
Possible Excuse	**Get the Facts Straight**
I have no time to eat breakfast.	Prepare breakfast the night before. Choose foods that are easy to prepare, such as skim milk, juice, and low-fat peanut butter on whole-grain bread.
I will lose weight if I skip breakfast.	Eating breakfast "jump starts" metabolism and burns calories. Skipping breakfast usually causes a person to eat more calories during the rest of the day.
I don't like breakfast foods.	Eat other healthful foods for breakfast, such as tuna fish, veggie pizza, or beans and rice.

Healthful Dinner and Snacks

Breakfast will help you start your day. Dinner will help "fuel" you to complete your day. A healthful dinner helps you complete your daily nutrition requirements. It is as important for snacks to be nutritious as it is for your breakfast, lunch, and dinner to be nutritious.

How to Plan a Healthful Dinner and Snacks

Eating a healthful dinner Evaluate the foods you have eaten during the day. Then, for dinner, select foods that provide the nutrients you did not eat at breakfast, lunch, and between meals. (See Lesson 25 for nutritional requirements.) Dinner should not make up more than one-third of your daily caloric intake.

Dinner dos and don'ts Dinner is a meal where you should round out your daily requirements. Try to eat a variety of foods. It is best to eat early in the evening rather than close to bedtime. Your body will not have a chance to use the food as energy, and if the stored food is not used for energy, it will convert to fat. Avoid drinking caffeine or eating spicy foods for dinner if you have difficulty sleeping.

Having healthful snacks When you eat snacks, you should do so to stop hunger and to get the needed servings from MyPyramid. See Lesson 26. Do not snack because you are bored, lonely, anxious, or depressed. Do not snack just to take a break from hard work, such as homework.

Snacking for these reasons leads to harmful eating habits. Always follow the Dietary Guidelines in Lesson 26 when choosing snacks.

Healthful snack choices When you snack, choose foods that are low in sugar, fats, and salt. Select foods such as fat-free yogurt, rice cakes, fruit, low-fat peanut butter, plain popcorn, cottage cheese, low-salt pretzels, bagels, veggies, and bean dip. Other nutritious foods include low-fat granola, low-sugar cereals, juice, crackers, and low-fat cheese.

Did You Know?

Sugar Content One 12-oz can of soda pop contains about 150 calories or the equivalent of over 10 teaspoons of sugar.

Making the Most of the Munchies

It is important to choose snacks that are good for your health.

- Select snacks that provide the servings you need from MyPyramid. For example, if you have not eaten three to five servings of vegetables, you might choose to snack on raw broccoli.
- Limit snacks that have a high level of sugar.
- Limit snacks that have a high level of fats and saturated fats.
- Limit snacks that have a high salt content.
- Carry healthful snacks with you so you won't be tempted to go to the vending machine.

LESSON 28 • Developing Healthful Eating Habits **313**

Healthful Dinner and Snacks

Class Activity

Word Search Have students create a word search puzzle using at least 20 foods that would be included in a healthful dinner or eaten as a healthful snack. Have students exchange puzzles with a classmate, and then complete. **L2** **ELL**

INTERACTIVE CHALKBOARD with Image Bank

5-Minute Check

Page 53, **Unit 5 Fast File Resources**

1. What is metabolism? *the rate at which food is converted into energy in body cells*
2. What is a good reason to eat? *because you're hungry and to obtain the nutrients necessary for good health*
3. How much of your daily caloric intake should dinner constitute? *one-third or less*
4. What are poor reasons for snacking? *being bored, lonely, anxious, or depressed*
5. When is the best time to eat dinner? *early in the evening*

ⓓⓘ Differentiated Instruction

Learning Disabilities Have students cut out pictures of healthful foods from magazines. They need to find foods from all of the groups represented in MyPyramid. The number of pictures for each food group should correspond to the number of recommended servings. They can paste or glue the pictures to a poster board and then label each photo with the food group and the appropriate serving size. The posters should be displayed in the classroom. **L1** **ELL**

National Health Education Standards
Pages 312–313: 1.1, 1.2, 1.5, 7.1, 7.2

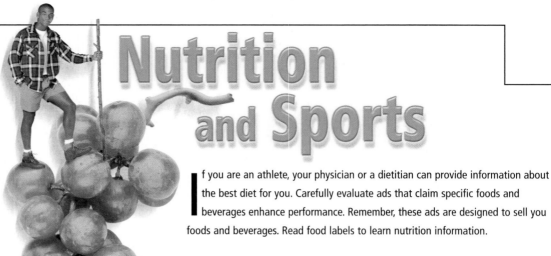

Nutrition and Sports

I f you are an athlete, your physician or a dietitian can provide information about the best diet for you. Carefully evaluate ads that claim specific foods and beverages enhance performance. Remember, these ads are designed to sell you foods and beverages. Read food labels to learn nutrition information.

What to Know About Nutrition and Sports

Vitamin supplements A substance that is added to the diet to increase the total dietary intake is a *supplement.* Taking vitamins in excessive amounts is *megadosing.* To date, there is no evidence that megadosing will improve your performance in sports. Taking specific vitamins in excess can be harmful to your health.

Salt tablets A teen also might try to enhance performance by taking salt tablets. Most teens get ten times the salt that is needed. However, many teens do not replace the water they lose through physical activity. Forget the salt tablets and drink plenty of water.

Sports drinks Advertisements may claim that sports drinks help replace electrolytes lost during physical activity. An *elecrolyte* is a nutrient that becomes electrically charged when in a solution, such as a bodily fluid. Sodium and potassium are electrolytes. They need to be balanced for a normal heartbeat. A physician or dietitian can advise you on your electrolyte balance. Eat foods with potassium, follow the Dietary Guidelines in Lesson 26 for salt intake, and drink plenty of water.

Energy bars Always read the food label before purchasing an energy bar. Many energy bars contain lots of sugar and are high in calories. Some energy bars are made from fruits, nuts, and grain. Some contain more protein than carbohydrate.

Carbohydrate loading An eating strategy in which a few days of a very low carbohydrate intake is followed by a few days of a very high carbohydrate intake is *carbohydrate loading.* This strategy is supposed to load the muscle with glycogen prior to strenuous physical activity. Experts have mixed opinions about the advantages of carbohydrate loading.

Protein loading An eating strategy in which extra protein is eaten to increase muscle size is *protein loading.* Eating extra protein does not increase muscle size—exercise increases muscle size. Athletes participating in some sports may need to *"make weight,"* or maintain a certain weight. Regular exercise and a balanced diet is the safest way to maintain a certain weight.

1. What is hunger?
2. What is an electrolyte?

 Health Project

SPEAKING OUT
Teens Talk About Health

Christina Chung
Sports and Nutrition

> **❝I do pay attention to food labels so I know what's in the food I'm eating.❞**

For Christina Chung, eating right for basketball is a lot like eating right for everything else. Whether you're in training for a sport or getting ready for an important exam, eating the right things puts you a step ahead by getting you physically and mentally prepared for the task at hand.

"I like to eat a variety of healthy foods anyway," she said, "so it's not really a question of changing what I eat or trying to eat certain things." Christina also advises against skipping meals. "If you do," she warned, "it's a lot easier to get weak and tired, not only for sports, but for studying too. When you get hungry after skipping a meal, you're more likely to eat practically anything, which is usually foods low in nutrients and high in calories."

Little interest in supplements Christina hasn't noticed a lot of her friends and classmates using supplements to improve athletic performance. "Vitamins, salt tablets, and those kinds of things don't seem to be that common at my school," she says. On the other hand, a lot of the athletes on teams at Christina's school do drink sports drinks before, during, and after games. Others prefer fruit juice drinks.

"Coaches and trainers are a good source of nutritional information," she says. "Most have some background in how to shape a diet so an athlete can reach his or her peak performance. That includes drinking lots of plain water."

Many different ways to eat right Of course, there's more than one way to eat right. "My family is Korean-American," Christina explained, "so we eat a lot of Korean food. That kind of food has a lot of meat in it, but the meat is often grilled, broiled, or baked to eliminate the extra fat." But, there's one food that's not on Christina's recommended list: candy.

Get help from labels Christina does take advantage of information that's easy to find. "I do pay attention to food labels so I know what's in the food I'm eating," she said. "I look for low-sodium, low-fat foods containing little sugar."

According to Christina, people should take advantage of an opportunity for good nutrition, whether they're playing basketball or taking a test. Eating right today will ensure that in the future, you will be physically and mentally strong.

Journaling Activity

Eating right and avoiding foods that aren't good for you can be pretty challenging, especially if you're busy with sports, classes, work, or other activities. Discuss with a friend ways you could help yourself follow good nutrition guidelines. Then make a list in your health journal of things you might be willing to try in your own life to help make sure you get the advantage that comes from eating right.

SPEAKING OUT

Analyzing the Feature

Use the following questions to help students uncover the main points of this feature.

1. Why should students avoid skipping a meal? *They are more likely to feel weak, tired, or to eat almost anything.*
2. Where can students go for nutritional advice? *to a coach or an athletic trainer*
3. What is one food that is not on Christina's recommended list? *candy*

Journaling Activity

Missed Meals Have students write in their health journals the circumstances under which they miss or skip a meal. Have them keep track for a week. Discuss students' journal entries in class. Ask students if they noticed any trends or patterns and what they could do to avoid skipping meals when encountering similar circumstances in the future. **L2**

Extension

Supplements Have students conduct a school survey to compare the number of students who use some type of supplement to improve athletic performance with those who do not use supplements. When all data are collected, have students share their findings in the form of a graph or chart. **L3**

👫 Healthy People 2010

Objective 19-16 *Increase the proportion of work sites that offer nutrition or weight-management classes or counseling.*

Have students contact companies in the area where they live. They should interview a person at each company about nutrition and weight-management programs that are provided for the company's employees. Interview questions should include: Is this program available for employees and their families? Does the program incorporate physical activity? Is counseling available for those individuals who are concerned about how nutrition and weight affect their overall health? As a class, discuss ways to encourage companies to increase the number of classes that are offered. **L2**

National Health Education Standards
Pages 314–315: 1.1, 1.2, 2.1, 2.2, 7.2

Eating Out

Eating Out

Whether you're with family or friends, in some locations the sheer number of restaurants from which to choose can be overwhelming. When you eat out, be careful to choose foods that adhere to the Dietary Guidelines in Lesson 26.

What to Know About Eating Out

Suppose you are at a favorite restaurant. The waiter or waitress gives you a few minutes to glance at the menu before taking your order. There are so many choices. Where do you start? How do you choose? There are no good foods or bad foods, but there are guidelines to follow when ordering from a restaurant menu.

Number of servings Order foods and beverages that help you get the appropriate number of servings from each food group in MyPyramid. See Lesson 26. Follow the Dietary Guidelines and choose foods that are low in fat, saturated fat, cholesterol, sugar, and salt, and include fruits, vegetables, and grains.

Check the menu. When eating out, see if there are foods that are designated as "heart healthy" or "light." Ask questions when you are uncertain about the ingredients in foods. This helps you avoid foods to which you may have a food allergy or food intolerance.

Food preparation Request that your food be prepared in a healthful way. For example, ask if a food can be prepared without butter or salt, or broiled

instead of fried. When ordering hamburger or ground sirloin, ask that it be cooked well-done.

Healthy breakfast choices Remember, for breakfast you are "breaking your fast." Eating out can be a challenge, but there are healthy choices. Try to avoid high-calorie, high-fat foods, such as French toast, hash browns, muffins, donuts, and breakfast sandwiches.

Breakfast meat choices If you have meat, select Canadian bacon. It is higher in protein and lower in fat than sausage or regular bacon. Choose an egg-white or egg-substitute omelette with peppers, onions, and tomatoes.

Other good breakfast choices Choose fresh fruit with cottage cheese or yogurt for added protein. Oatmeal is high in fiber and low in fat and sodium. Another good choice is a bagel with low-fat jam or fruit spread rather than high-fat and high-calorie cream cheese or butter.

Healthy lunch choices Lunch can be a challenge because we usually eat lunch with friends or co-workers, and it can be hard to make healthful food choices in social situations.

Lunch meat choices Try to order meats that have little fat. A turkey breast sandwich is a healthful choice. Combine red meat with turkey or ask for less meat.

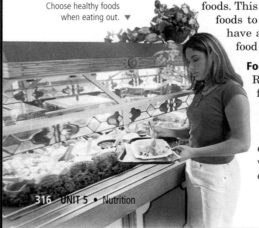

Choose healthy foods when eating out. ▼

Activity: Using Life Skills

Practicing Healthful Behaviors: Planning a Day's Menu

Think of planning your daily diet as a puzzle. You have all the pieces you need from MyPyramid. You simply need to put them into place throughout your day.

1 If you are going to write a health behavior contract, write your name and the date, and write the healthful behavior you want to practice as a health goal. Make a plan for what you are going to eat tomorrow. Make sure you follow MyPyramid.

2 Remember to vary your food choices. Instead of having four apples in one day, have a variety of fruit.

3 Write specific statements that describe how this healthful behavior reduces health risks. Choose a variety of foods with different colors. Don't eat a one-color lunch (macaroni and cheese and a banana) when you can paint your plate with color (apples, grapes, and oranges).

4 Be adventurous. Experiment with new and different ethnic foods. Try papaya, mango, cantaloupe, or kiwi to meet your fruit requirements. Eat asparagus, artichokes, or okra to meet your vegetable needs.

5 Learn how much food equals one serving to make sure you are counting correctly.

6 Make a specific plan for recording your progress and complete an evaluation of how the plan helped you accomplish the health goal. Tomorrow evening, write down everything you ate throughout the day. Check what you actually ate against MyPyramid (in Lesson 26) and your menu. How well did you do? What areas need work? Write a one-page summary describing what you observed about your eating habits.

▲ Vary your food choices when planning your meals.

Tuna and chicken salads are great choices if you limit the amount of the mayonnaise or other salad dressing. With any sandwich, choose nutrient rich, whole-wheat or multi-grain bread.

Other good lunch choices Soups are good choices, but watch the sodium. Beans are high in fiber and low in fat. Limit the amount of fried foods you eat. An occasional fried food can be a healthy choice if it keeps you from overeating. Request vegetables or fruit instead. Be aware that some salads—for example, chef's, Caesar, and taco—are high in calories and fat.

Healthy dinner choices Dinner menus usually offer many choices and servings are larger than those at breakfast and lunch. In many restaurants, half-portions are available.

Dinner meat choices Try chicken cooked in a variety of ways—baked, roasted, or grilled. Avoid fried and deep-fried chicken, which contain a lot of fat. Choose a smaller portion of a steak and eat a large salad with little or no dressing to fill you up. Have grilled pork chops and cut off the fat. Fish can be a low-fat, protein-packed choice if prepared without any fatty sauces. Have it grilled, broiled, baked, or boiled instead of fried.

Other good dinner choices Steamed vegetables are a great source of fiber. Leave off the butter. For dessert, choose fresh fruit, low-fat frozen yogurt, or sorbet. Split a dessert with a friend.

Don't be shy about asking for substitutions or about ingredients and preparation. Look for symbols to identify low-fat, healthful selections.

LESSON 28 • Developing Healthful Eating Habits **317**

Using Life Skills

Practicing Healthful Behaviors Once students have observed their eating habits, they should evaluate whether there is an area in which they need to improve. They should make a commitment to make one small change in their eating habits at a time. Have students make a written plan that outlines how they will accomplish their goal. **L2**

5-Minute Check

Page 54, **Unit 5 Fast File Resources**

1. What is megadosing? *taking vitamins in excessive amounts*
2. Name two electrolytes. *sodium and potassium*
3. Why should people carefully read the labels of energy bars before purchasing one? *Many energy bars contain a lot of sugar and are high in calories.*
4. What would be a good choice of meat when eating out? *turkey, chicken, pork, fish, or lean cuts of beef*
5. When dining out at dinnertime, how could you ensure that you don't overeat? *Ask for a half portion.*

Family Involvement

Dining Out The next time students go out to dinner with their families, encourage them to set a good example for family members by making healthful food choices. Students can share tips with family members for choosing low-fat, more nutritious choices. Students may offer their families suggestions such as: If the menu choices are too tempting, have them place their order ahead of time so when they arrive, they don't have to look at the menu. The students can politely request that an item be prepared differently, i.e., baked instead of broiled, or dressing on the side. If a bread basket is provided, have the students ask that there only be one serving per person, or ask the server not to bring the bread at all. **L2**

National Health Education Standards

Pages 316–317: 1.1, 1.5, 1.7, 6.2, 6.3, 7.1, 7.2

Fast Food

Extension

Research Have students investigate the connection between diet, heart disease, and cancer. Students should concentrate on how the decisions about food that a person makes on a day-to-day basis can affect health. Ask students to investigate the consequences of regularly choosing foods that contain high amounts of fat, salt, and sugar. Students should write an essay describing their findings. Their essay also should include healthy choices of foods that might decrease the risk of developing heart disease and cancer. **L3**

Teaching Transparency

Page 47, **Unit 5 Fast File Resources**

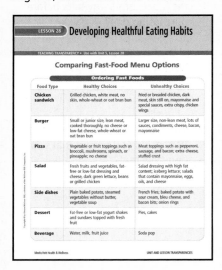

LESSON 28 **Developing Healthful Eating Habits**

TEACHING TRANSPARENCY • Use with Unit 5, Lesson 28

Comparing Fast-Food Menu Options

Ordering Fast Foods		
Food Type	Healthy Choices	Unhealthy Choices
Chicken sandwich	Grilled chicken, white meat, no skin, whole-wheat or oat bran bun	Fried or breaded chicken, dark meat, skin still on, mayonnaise and special sauces, extra crispy, chicken wings
Burger	Small or junior size, lean meat, cooked thoroughly, no cheese or low-fat cheese, whole-wheat or oat bran bun	Larger size, non-lean meat, lots of sauces, condiments, cheese, bacon, mayonnaise
Pizza	Vegetable or fruit toppings such as broccoli, mushrooms, spinach, or pineapple; no cheese	Meat toppings such as pepperoni, sausage, and bacon; extra cheese, stuffed crust
Salad	Fresh fruits and vegetables, fat-free or low-fat dressing and cheese, dark green lettuce, beans or grilled chicken	Salad dressing with high fat content; iceberg lettuce; salads that contain mayonnaise, eggs, oils, and cheese
Side dishes	Plain baked potato, steamed vegetables without butter, vegetable soup	French fries; baked potato with sour cream, bleu cheese, and bacon bits; onion rings
Dessert	Fat-free or low-fat yogurt shakes and sundaes topped with fresh fruit	Pies, cakes
Beverage	Water, milk, fruit juice	Soda pop

Meeks/Heit Health & Wellness   UNIT AND LESSON TRANSPARENCIES

Fast Food

Food that can be served quickly is *fast food*. Fast food includes TV dinners and foods served at fast-food restaurants. Fast foods are convenient and quick, but they can be expensive. They also can be high in calories, fat, and sodium.

How to Order Fast Foods

There are three guidelines to follow when ordering fast foods. First, ask the fast-food restaurant to provide nutrition information about the foods and beverages it serves. Second, choose foods and beverages that help you get the appropriate number of servings from each food group in MyPyramid. And third, follow the Dietary Guidelines in Lesson 26.

Did You Know?

Food Content Foods advertised as fat-free may contain a high number of calories.

Chicken choices Order grilled chicken. Limit fried and breaded chicken. Choose white meat over dark meat. Remove the skin or order skin-free. Order chicken sandwiches without mayonnaise and special sauces. Choose a whole-wheat or oat bran bun for additional fiber. Skip the fried and fattening chicken wings. Remember that extra crispy usually means extra fattening.

Burger bests Order the small or junior size burger—the smaller the burger, the lower the fat, calories, and sodium content. Order your burger lean and emphasize that it should be cooked thoroughly. Choose a whole-wheat or oat bran bun for additional fiber. Order burgers without mayonnaise and special sauces. Use small amounts of condiments for flavor. Order low-fat cheese to get calcium or skip the cheese to lower the fat content. Skip bacon. Remember that a single burger at a fast-food restaurant can range from 7 to 19 grams of fat.

Pizza picks Try pizza without cheese. Limit pepperoni, sausage, and bacon. Order vegetables, such as broccoli, peppers, mushrooms, or spinach. Add pineapple for an extra serving of fruit. Skip extra cheese and stuffed crust because they add extra fat.

Salad smarts Load up on fresh vegetables. Choose fat-free or low-fat salad dressings. Add fresh fruit. Order low-fat or fat-free cheese. Choose dark green lettuce instead of iceberg lettuce. Add beans or grilled chicken as a protein source. Remember that, just because it says salad, it doesn't mean low-fat. Many salads may contain lots of mayonnaise, eggs, oils, and cheese.

Side dish selections Eat a salad with low-fat or fat-free dressing. Choose a plain baked potato instead of french fries. Skip the sour cream, bleu cheese, and bacon bits on baked potatoes. Have a side of steamed vegetables without butter. Choose vegetable soup on the side. Limit fried sides, such as onion rings. Don't add extra salt.

Dessert and drink decisions Limit soda pops. Choose fat-free or low-fat yogurt shakes and sundaes. Drink fruit juice. Top yogurt sundaes with fresh fruit. Limit pies, cakes, and other fatty desserts. Remember that if it is sweet, it probably is sugary. Watch out for the sugar content in fast-food desserts and beverages.

Cross-Curricular Connections

Math Have students create a graph or chart that illustrates the ratio and percentage of students in their class that eat fast food and prepackaged food seven, five, three, and at least one day per week. Have students count off to determine the total number of students in the class. Ask all students who eat fast food or prepackaged food every day of the week to stand. Students should determine both the ratio and the percentage of students standing. Ask all students to be seated. Ask students to stand if they eat fast food or prepackaged food five days per week. Continue to repeat for the rest of the given days. All results should be displayed in a graph or chart. Instead of having students stand, you could have students anonymously record their answers on a piece of paper. Collect the papers and have students tally the responses. **L2 ELL**

Ethnic Foods

Food that is customary for members of a specific culture is called *ethnic food*. When you eat ethnic foods, make choices that help you get the appropriate number of servings from each food group.

What to Know About Ethnic Foods

Today we have a wide variety of foods from which to choose. Ethnic foods can be purchased in almost any form—boxed, frozen, dried, canned, or fresh. Many ethnic restaurants offer many food choices, which is like visiting a country you have never experienced before. The Guide to Ethnic Food identifies food as Asian/Pacific, European, African/ Middle Eastern, and North and South American. Foods in the first column are healthful choices. Foods in the second column are higher in fat, cholesterol, sugar, or salt and should be eaten in moderation. When choosing ethnic foods, follow the same Dietary Guidelines and selection of foods from MyPyramid as presented in Lesson 26.

TABLE 28.2 Guide to Ethnic Food Choices

	Healthful Choices	Moderate Use Foods	FYI
Asian/ Pacific	Steamed white or brown rice, broiled fish and chicken, tofu, miso (bean paste) soup, broth-based soups	Foods cooked in oil, such as egg rolls or tempura, soy sauce, creamy sauces	Soy sauce and pickled foods are high in sodium.
European	Pasta with vegetables, marinara sauce, broiled or steamed chicken and seafood, salads, antipasto, vegetables, fruit	Pasta with cream sauce, gravy, pastry, sausage, food cooked in oil or fat, ice cream	Ratatouille, a Mediterranean vegetable dish, is a delicious way to provide servings of vegetables.
African/ Middle Eastern	Steamed white or brown rice, broiled fish and chicken, chickpeas, greens, vegetable curries	Fried meat, cured meat products, curries	Curries made with coconut milk are higher in fat than tomato-based curries.
North and South American	Beans and whole grains, rice, grilled chicken or fish, corn tortillas, salsa, steamed vegetables	Fried foods, cream-based soup, hard cheese, mayonnaise-based salad dressing	Fajitas without cheese are usually lower in fat and calories than enchiladas.

Teacher FYI

Dietary Guidelines The first document to provide the basis for sound nutritional planning was developed in 1977 by the Senate Select Committee on Nutrition and Human Needs. This document was titled Dietary Goals for the United States. This was replaced with a more recent document titled Dietary Guidelines for Americans. This document has undergone several revisions and was developed by the United States Department of Agriculture in conjunction with the Department of Health, Education, and Welfare, which is now called the Department of Health and Human Services.

Using the Table

Ethnic Foods Have students use the table to identify at least one food that they like from each ethnic group, or at least would be willing to try. Have students use the phone book to identify and locate a restaurant nearby that serves each type of ethnic food. Encourage them to try a wide variety of international dishes whenever the opportunities occur. **L2**

Sensitive Issues

Ethnicity Although the European culture still dominates our society, many other cultures and ethnic groups are becoming more familiar to most Americans. Have students bring in a recipe for a dish that is a cultural staple for the ethnic group to which they belong. Each student can describe the ingredients in his or her dish to the rest of the class. Because customs differ among ethnic groups, do not force anyone to share who is reluctant to share or may be unable to share due to other factors. Explain to students that many ethnic foods have become familiar staples in the diets of Americans of all backgrounds. Compile a cookbook containing the recipes. **L2**

National Health Education Standards
Pages 318–319: 1.1, 1.5, 7.1, 7.2

Food-Borne Illnesses

Food-Borne Illnesses

ESCHERICHIA COLI
LISTERIA MONOCYTOGENES
SALMONELLA
CAMPYLOBACTER

Have you ever felt ill after you have eaten? Perhaps you thought, "It must have been something I ate." You may have contracted a food-borne illness. A ***food-borne illness*** is an illness caused by consuming foods or beverages that have been contaminated with pathogens, which are germs that cause disease. This illness is referred to as food poisoning.

How to Protect Yourself from Food-Borne Illnesses

Did You Know?

Preserving Foods
You should keep hot food hot at 140°F or higher, and keep cold food cold at 40°F or cooler because harmful bacteria grow at room temperature.

A food-borne illness may develop from one-half hour to several days after eating food contaminated with germs. Common symptoms of food-borne illness are cramps, nausea, diarrhea, vomiting, and fever. If symptoms are severe, or the person is young, elderly, or pregnant, prompt medical care is needed. Treatment includes drinking fluids and bed rest.

There are three serious food-borne illnesses. ***Salmonellosis*** (sal muh neh LOH suhs) is a food-borne illness in which the bacterium *salmonella* contaminates water, kitchen surfaces, eggs, and raw chicken, seafood, and other meats. ***Botulism*** (BAH chuh lih zuhm) is a food-borne illness in which the bacterium *Clostridium botulinum* produces a toxin that contaminates improperly canned foods. The toxin attacks the victim's central nervous system. Because the disease develops rapidly, prompt medical care is essential. A specific strain of the bacterium *Escherichia coli* (also known as ***E coli***) can contaminate undercooked meat, especially hamburger, causing a severe form of food poisoning.

A common, sometimes food-borne illness that can be caused by viruses or bacteria is ***gastroenteritis*** (gas tro en tuh RI tuhs). Gastroenteritis causes inflammation of the stomach and the small and large intestines.

Food safety at the store Check expiration dates, and to not buy outdated foods. Choose canned foods and packages that are free of dents, cracks, rust, holes, bulges, and tears. Check that products marked "keep refrigerated" are stored in a refrigerated case and that frozen foods are frozen solid. Open egg cartons to check that eggs are whole, clean, and chilled.

Food safety in the refrigerator Try to keep your refrigerator temperature between 35°F and 45°F. Keep your freezer thermometer at or below O°F. Pay attention to the "use by" date and the "keep refrigerated" instructions on all food labels.

Food safety in the kitchen Always wash your hands with hot, soapy water for at least 20 seconds before preparing food. Wash hands, cooking utensils, and surfaces after contact with raw eggs, raw chicken, and all other raw meats. Keep raw meat, chicken, and fish juices from contact with other foods. Do not use the same sponge or towel on other surfaces or

---

🔗 Cross-Curricular Connections

Science Have students research and locate pictures of each of the bacteria listed that cause disease. Students should discuss the mode of transmission, how the disease affects the body, safety precautions, and preventive measures. Students should check with their biology teacher to see if there are slides of bacteria that can be examined under a microscope. They should especially look for slides of bacteria that cause salmonellosis, botulism, and gastroenteritis, as well as slides of the E coli bacteria. Students also might check with the media specialist in your library about the availability of other resources on the same topic. **L2**

Just the FACTS: FOOD MYTHS

"Are there 'good' foods and 'bad' foods?"

The FACTS There is no reason to completely avoid any foods, including bread and pasta. To stay healthy, you must eat a balanced diet of starchy foods; lots of fruits and vegetables; some meat, fish, and dairy products; and only small amounts of fat and sugar. At the same time, there definitely are good diets and bad diets. Bad diets encourage you to eat unbalanced meals that put your health at risk and may result in only temporary weight loss.

"Is red meat bad for you?"

The FACTS Red meat contains the protein you need to stay healthy. Meat is a complete protein, containing all the amino acids, while many other sources of protein, such as beans, are incomplete. Lean red meat, with all visible fat removed, has only 4 to 8 g of fat per 100 g. Skinned poultry can have as little as 1 to 3 g of fat, but if you eat the skin and the fat underneath it, the amount of fat in a serving of chicken or turkey can be much higher. In the same way, vegetarian dishes that are fried or made with cheese, oil, nuts, pastry, or creamy sauces can be high in fat—higher than a serving of lean red meat.

"Is fruit good for you only if it is fresh?"

The FACTS One heaping tablespoon of dried fruit offers as much fiber and as many vitamins (except vitamin C) and minerals as a whole serving of fresh fruit. Canned and frozen fruits contain the same amount of vitamins and minerals as fresh fruit. Fruit juices that contain 100 percent fruit juice are also a good source of vitamins. Some fruit juices contain vitamin C, but only if the juice is fresh—vitamin C is lost in processing. Some juices are fortified with vitamin C. Of course, most juice has no fiber. Some dietitians recommend using fruit juice as only one serving of fruit a day. The other servings can be fresh, dried, canned, or frozen.

---

items, such as cooking utensils, after cleaning surfaces on which there was raw food. Before preparing food, cover cuts or sores with bandages or plastic gloves. Thaw frozen foods in the microwave or in the refrigerator—never at room temperature. Wash fruits and vegetables with running water. Cook eggs until they are firm, not runny. Do not taste foods that are not cooked thoroughly.

Food safety on the table Place cooked food in a clean dish for serving. Do not use the same unwashed plate for both preparing and serving foods. Rinse utensils before using. Do not let cooked food sit at room temperature for more than two hours. Keep hot foods hot, and cold foods cold.

Inspect leftovers. Are the leftovers in your refrigerator always OK to eat? How long will foods last before they should be discarded? If foods or beverages look or smell unusual, throw them out. Check the following list for storage times for specific foods.
- Milk: four to five days after the sell-by date
- Orange juice: up to a week after opening
- Refrigerated raw chicken: one to two days
- Cooked chicken: three to four days
- Hard cheese: three to four weeks after opening
- Cold cuts and hot dogs: three to five days
- Eggs: three weeks
- Ground beef: one to two days

Just the FACTS:

Food Myths Some students may think that all carbohydrates are bad for you. Complex carbohydrates that come from fruits and whole grains should be included in a well-balanced diet. Have students read each of the statements in "Just the Facts" and tell whether they agree or disagree. The discussion might uncover other misconceptions the students have about nutrition.

Teacher FYI

United States Department of Agriculture The Food Safety and Inspection Service (FSIS), the public health agency in the USDA, ensures that meat and poultry products are safe, wholesome, and correctly labeled and packaged. Under the Federal Meat Inspection Act and the Poultry Products Act, FSIS inspects all raw meat and poultry sold in interstate and foreign commerce and monitors meat and poultry products after they leave federally inspected plants.

Class Activity

Word Game Have students divide into groups and play a question/answer game using the terms associated with food-borne illnesses. One group of students will give the term for a food-borne illness. The other group will give the question regarding a food-borne illness associated with the term. For example, one term might be botulism. The question would be "What food-borne illness produces a toxin that contaminates improperly canned foods?" Allow students to devise the rules of the game. Allow for friendly competition, with praise and reward for each student who participates. **L2**

⚖️ Legal Issues

Timeline Have students research the legal history of food safety in our country. They should investigate the important laws and regulations regarding food safety and when they were enacted. Students might divide into groups to research laws regarding food safety during different time periods. After the research is complete, have students create a timeline showing the most important legislation concerning food safety regulations. They can create the timeline using a different sheet of construction paper to represent each period of time. The sheets can be connected together to display the timeline on a wall in the classroom or hallway. **L3**

National Health Education Standards
Pages 320–321: 1.1, 1.5, 7.2

Sharing Food Safely

NHES Assessment/SCASS

Performance Task Have students create skits in which someone wants to share food improperly. Have them create each of the scenarios listed in the table. They should practice being tactful but assertive when dealing with these "offenders." Have students individually evaluate each skit on whether it demonstrates good decision making and communication skills. **L2**

3 Assess

Vocabulary Practice
Page 46, **Unit 5 Fast File Resources**

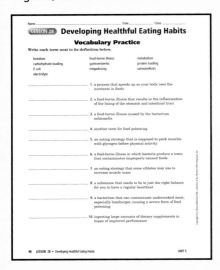

There are many situations when you eat with other people. Some situations afford opportunities to contaminate foods and beverages. Beware of the following food safety offenders.

What to Know About Sharing Food Safely

We often share food with others without giving it a second thought. Sharing food under certain circumstances can be a big source of transferring germs from one person to another.

TABLE 28.3 Sharing Food Safely		
	Description	Proper Way to Share
	The "double dipper" puts a piece of food into a dip and takes a bite. Then he or she puts the same piece of food back in the dip and finishes it. Double dipping contaminates food with germs. Other people who eat the same dip ingest these germs.	Don't double dip. Put a scoop of dip on your own plate to use for dipping.
	The "pop swapper" drinks from another person's can, glass, or bottle. Germs get on the can, glass, or bottle. Another person drinks from the same can, glass, or bottle. This person ingests germs.	Don't pop swap. Pour a beverage into a separate glass when you share a beverage.
	The "careless cook" tastes foods as he or she prepares them. Germs get into the foods as they are prepared.	Don't be a careless cook. Use a clean utensil each time you taste foods you are preparing.
	The "container contaminator" takes a sip or bite from a container of food and puts it back for others. This contaminates foods and beverages with his or her germs.	Don't be a container contaminator. Use a glass or clean utensil to take a sip or bite of food.
	The "bite burglar" takes a bite of another person's food and gives it back or takes bites off another person's plate. This person contaminates other people's food with his or her germs.	Don't be a bite burglar. Cut off a piece of food or use a clean utensil and put a portion on your own plate before eating.

322 UNIT 5 • Nutrition

Sensitive Issues

Cold Sores Have students discuss how they would handle a situation in which a friend of theirs asks for a sip of their soda. The student notices that his or her friend has a herpes blister (a.k.a. cold sore) on his or her lip. Ask students if they would let the friend have a drink and then throw the rest away; just say "no" to the friend; or, tell the friend they don't want to catch the virus from him or her. Discuss with students the health risks involved with sharing their friend's drink regardless of the cold sore. The cold sore is a sign of infection, but many organisms are passed from person to person without any noticeable signs. Explain that saying "no" is the best way to protect their health and the health of their friend. **L2**

botulism
carbohydrate loading
E coli
electrolyte
food-borne illness
gastroenteritis
hunger
make weight
megadosing
metabolism
protein loading
salmonellosis
supplement

Key Terms Review

Complete the fill-in-the-blank statements with the lesson Key Terms on the left. For statements marked with an *, indicate if there is any evidence it will improve performance in sports. Do not write in this book.

1. _____ is the rate at which food is converted into energy in body cells.

*2. _____ is taking vitamins in excessive amounts.

3. A(n) _____ is a nutrient that becomes electrically charged when in a solution, such as bodily fluid.

*4. _____ is an eating strategy in which a few days of very low carbohydrate intake is followed by a few days of very high carbohydrate intake.

*5. _____ is an eating strategy in which extra protein is eaten to increase muscle size.

6. A(n) _____ is an illness caused by consuming foods or beverages that have been contaminated with pathogens.

7. _____ is a food-borne illness from undercooked chicken, eggs, and other meats.

8. _____ is a food-borne illness from improperly canned foods.

9. A(n) _____ is a substance that is added to the diet to increase the total dietary intake.

10. _____ is a common, sometimes food-borne illness that can be caused by viruses or bacteria.

Recalling the Facts

11. What kinds of feelings motivate people to eat besides hunger?

12. What is the least expensive way to replace electrolytes?

13. What can you do to protect yourself from food-borne illnesses?

14. What is a fast food?

15. What is a supplement?

16. What is the recommended storage time for refrigerated milk and refrigerated eggs?

17. What are three serious food-borne illnesses?

18. Why is grilled chicken a better food choice than fried chicken?

Critical Thinking

19. Why is it important to not skip breakfast?

20. Why is it important to have a balance of electrolytes in the body?

21. Discuss what teens would look for on the nutrition label of an energy bar that they want to eat to provide long-lasting energy. What would teens want to avoid?

22. What are some healthful snacks teens can substitute for high sugar or salty snacks?

Real-Life Applications

23. You want to eat ice cream. Is that hunger or something else? Explain.

24. Why should you be very cautious about drinking so-called energy and performance-sports drinks?

25. What are some healthful things you can do when ordering from a restaurant menu?

26. What are some healthful things you can do when ordering fast food?

Activities

Responsible Decision Making

27. **Communicate** You see your friend taking vitamins in excessive amounts on a daily basis. Write a response to this situation. Refer to the Responsible Decision-Making Model on page 61 for help.

Sharpen Your Life Skills

28. **Access Health Products** Make a list of items served at a fast-food restaurant that contain a healthful amount of fat and sodium. Share the information with your classmates.

Visit **www.glencoe.com** for more *Health & Wellness* quizzes.

LESSON 28 • Study Guide **323**

Key Terms Review

1. Metabolism
2. Megadosing
3. electrolyte
4. Carbohydrate loading
5. Protein loading
6. food-borne illness
7. Salmonellosis
8. Botulism
9. supplement
10. Gastroenteritis

Recalling the Facts

11. feeling rejected, depressed, anxious, bored, or lonely
12. Eat foods with potassium, follow Dietary Guidelines for salt intake, and drink plenty of water.
13. See pages 320–321.
14. food that can be served quickly
15. something that is added to the diet to enhance performance
16. milk—4 to 5 days after sell-by date; eggs—3 weeks
17. salmonellosis, botulism, and gastroenteritis
18. Grilled chicken contains less fat than fried chicken.

Critical Thinking

19. jump starts metabolism and burns calories, skipping usually causes a person to eat more calories later
20. Electrolytes need to be in just the right balance for you to have a normal heartbeat.
21. Look for one with more grams of protein and less sugar.
22. See page 313.

Real-Life Applications

23. A taste for a certain food is not a physiological need for the food.
24. They might be loaded with sugars and caffeine, and can dehydrate the body.
25. Follow Dietary Guidelines; be aware of "heart-healthy" or "light" foods; ask questions about ingredients in foods.

26. Ask for and read provided menu nutrient information; don't super size; avoid mayonnaise, creamy dressings, extra cheese, chicken skin, and fried foods; choose salads, vegetables, grilled meat, fat-free or low-fat yogurt shakes and sundaes, and whole wheat and low-fat breads when possible; limit fatty desserts.

Activities

Responsible Decision Making

27. Students' responses will vary but should include that taking vitamins in excess is not a responsible decision.

Sharpen Your Life Skills

28. Your students' lists will vary depending on the fast foods they are familiar with.

323

LESSON 29

Maintaining a Healthful Weight

Out of Time?

If time does not permit an in-depth study of this topic, use the following activities in this Teacher Wraparound Edition:

- Class Activity, p. 326
- Class Activity, p. 329
- Class Discussion, p. 333
- Explain the Concept, p. 335

1 Focus

HEALTH GOALS **Health Effects of Eating Disorders** Have students respond to the second Health Goal for this lesson by listing the negative health effects of eating disorders. *Effects might include damage to the heart, kidneys, and other organs.* **L2**

Write ABOUT IT!

Discuss Ask if any students would like to share their lists. Good behavior might include recognizing that there is a problem and eating regular amounts in social situations. However, continuing to have binge episodes is not healthful behavior. Using the information in this lesson, discuss with students the physical and emotional consequences a person suffers as a result of continued episodes of binge eating. **L2**

LESSON 29

Maintaining a Healthful Weight

HEALTH GOALS
- **I will maintain a desirable weight and body composition.**
- **I will develop skills to prevent eating disorders.**

A diet and exercise plan to maintain a desirable weight and body composition is *weight management.* If you maintain a desirable weight, you have a better chance of avoiding many preventable diseases, such as diabetes and heart disease.

Write ABOUT IT!

Writing About Bingeing Suppose that you eat regular amounts when you are with other people, but you binge in private. You feel guilty about it and keep promising yourself that you'll never do it again, but you continue having binge episodes. After you read the information about binge eating on page 336, think about your choices and make a list in your health journal of what you should change about your behavior.

What You'll Learn

1. Discuss ways to determine desirable weight and body composition. *(p. 325)*
2. Outline steps to follow for healthful weight gain and weight loss. *(p. 328)*
3. Evaluate common weight-loss strategies *(p. 330)*
4. Discuss risks for developing eating disorders. *(p. 332)*
5. Discuss facts about anorexia nervosa and bulimia. *(p. 334)*
6. Discuss binge eating disorder and obesity: the causes, symptoms, associated health problems, and treatment. *(p. 336)*

Why It's Important

Proper weight management can help you look and feel your best. Getting caught up in fad diets or eating disorders can be disastrous for your health and wallet.

Key Terms

- body composition
- basal metabolic rate (BMR)
- caloric intake
- caloric expenditure
- overweight
- obesity
- eating disorder
- anorexia nervosa
- bulimia
- binge eating disorder

324 UNIT 5 • Nutrition

	National Health Education Standards—Guide for Lesson 29	
1.5	Propose ways to reduce or prevent injuries and health problems.	pp. 324, 325–326, 327, 328, 329, 333, 334, 335, 338
1.7	Compare and contrast the benefits of and barriers to practicing a variety of healthy behaviors.	pp. 329, 330–331, 332–333, 334, 335, 338
3.4	Determine when professional health services may be required.	pp. 325, 328–331, 334–336, 337

Weight and Body Composition

The first step in weight management is to determine your desirable weight and body composition. ***Desirable weight*** is the weight that is healthful for a person. ***Body composition*** is the percentage of fat tissue and lean tissue in the body. A physician and dietitian can help you. Factors that determine what your desirable weight should be include age, height, gender, body frame, basal metabolic rate, and activity level.

How to Determine Desirable Weight and Body Composition

The physician or dietitian will ask your age and measure your height and current weight.

Body frame The approximate weight and density of the bone structure is your ***body frame.*** The size and thickness of bones vary from person to person.

You can determine if you have a small, medium, or large body frame by either measuring the circumference of your wrist or by measuring the breadth of your elbow. There are standard measurements for both male and female body frames in relation to the person's height. A doctor can help you with this measurement.

Basal metabolic rate The number of calories the body uses at rest is the ***basal metabolic rate*** (BAY suhl·meh tuh BAH lik·RAYT) **(BMR).** A unit of energy produced by food and used by the body is a ***calorie.*** There are tests to determine thyroid gland function and BMR. A physician will determine if these tests are necessary.

The physician or dietitian will ask about your activity level. Physical activity increases BMR.

Body composition A physician or dietitian will emphasize the importance of having a healthful body composition. Percentage of body fat can vary. There are two kinds of body fat. ***Essential body fat*** is the amount of body fat needed for optimal health.

A caliper is one tool used to measure percentage
▼ of body fat.

2 Teach

Class Discussion

Desirable Weight Have the class discuss why there are so many factors that determine a person's desirable weight. Have them discuss how each of the factors affects how much a person should weigh. Ask students if there are any other factors that should be considered that were not on the list.
L2

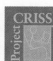

INTERACTIVE CHALKBOARD
with Image Bank

PowerPoint® Presentations

This CD-ROM is an editable Microsoft® PowerPoint® presentation that includes:
- Lesson presentations
- Lesson checks
- Interactive graphics
- 5-Minute Checks
- Image Bank
- All transparencies

Journals Refer to the Teacher-Student Journal Strategy on page 17T. Ask students to share their ideas on teens and eating disorders in their health journals.

Lesson Resource Manager

- **Unit 5 Fast File Resources**
  Reading Strategy, p. 59
  Vocabulary Practice, p. 60
  Transparency Master and Worksheet, p. 61
  Real-Life Health, p. 63
  Real-Life Health, p. 65
  5-Minute Check, p. 67
  Lesson 29 Quiz, p. 69
- **Unit 5 Transparency**
- **Lesson 29 Transparency**

- **Reading Essentials**
- **Technology**
  TeacherWorks™ CD-ROM
  StudentWorks™ CD-ROM
  Reading Essentials CD-ROM
  Exam*View*® Assessment Suite
  Vocabulary Puzzlemaker

National Health Education Standards

Pages 324–325: 1.1, 1.2, 1.5, 6.1, 7.2

Make the Connection

Physical Activities For more information on physical activities that help you reduce or maintain a healthful percentage of body fat, see page 375 in Lesson 34.

For example, fat-soluble vitamins must be dissolved in fat before they can be used. *Adipose* (A duh pos) *tissue* is fat that accumulates around internal organs, within muscle, and under your skin. Suppose you have a high percentage of adipose tissue. Your risk of developing cardiovascular diseases, cancer, diabetes, and arthritis increases.

A healthful percentage of body fat for teen males is about 11 to 17 percent. A healthful percentage of body fat for teen females is about 16 to 24 percent. There are different tests to measure your percentage of body fat. One test uses calipers to measure the thickness of skinfolds. A more accurate test involves underwater weighing. If you want to quickly determine if you have too much body fat, pinch a fold of skin on your upper arm. Estimate the thickness. You may have an excess of body fat if you pinch more than one inch.

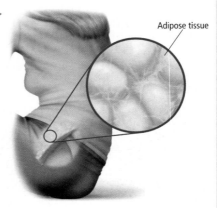

Adipose tissue ▶ is found in many areas of the body.

Adipose tissue

How to make a weight management plan A weight management plan is based on caloric intake and caloric expenditure. *Caloric intake*

Weight Management Plan		
	Caloric intake	Caloric expenditure
Monday		
Tuesday		
Wednesday		
Thursday		
Friday		
Saturday		
Sunday		

▲ A weight management plan can be used to help you evaluate your caloric intake and your caloric expenditure.

is the number of calories a person takes in from foods and beverages. *Caloric expenditure* is the number of calories a person uses for BMR, digestion, and physical activity. To maintain weight, your caloric intake must be the same as your caloric expenditure.

To gain weight, your caloric intake must be greater than your caloric expenditure. To lose weight, your caloric intake must be less than your caloric expenditure.

To make a weight management plan, you must know about calories and body fat. The energy equivalent of one pound of body fat is equal to 3500 calories. To gain one pound, increase caloric intake by 3500 calories and maintain the same amount of activity. To lose one pound, decrease caloric intake by 3500 calories and maintain the same amount of activity or increase caloric expenditure by 3500 calories. Also, regular exercise will increase the proportion of weight loss from body fat.

Activity: Using Life Skills

Using Goal-Setting and Decision-Making Skills: Calculating Caloric Needs

Factors such as age, activity, and metabolic rate affect how many calories you can consume each day. Follow the four steps below to find out how many calories you need to maintain your current weight. Your doctor can give you more exact numbers, but use these formulas as estimates. Keep in mind that what you eat is just as important as how much you eat, so try to make nutritious choices.

1 Calculate your basal metabolic rate (BMR), which is how many calories your body uses to stay alive and to perform most basic functions. Females should multiply their body weight (in pounds) by 10 to get calories for BMR. Males should multiply their body weight (in pounds) by 11 to get calories for BMR.

2 Then factor in calories that you use when you are physically active. Inactive people should multiply the calories for BMR (from step 1) by 0.3 to get calories for physical activity. People who are moderately active should multiply the calories for BMR by 0.5. People who are very active should multiply the calories for BMR by 0.75.

3 Next, calculate how many calories your body needs to digest food. Add the calories for BMR to the calories for physical activity. Multiply that number by 0.1 to get the calories needed to digest food.

4 Lastly, add it all together to get your total: Add calories for BMR (from step 1), calories for physical activity (from step 2), and calories to digest food (from step 3) to get the total calories you need each day.

▲ Read food labels to determine the number of calories per serving.

Goal setting When planning any type of goal setting, it is best to create a health contract or some type of plan. Start by writing your name and date. Then write the health behavior you want to practice as a health goal. Perhaps you want to reduce your caloric intake by 500 calories each day in order to lose weight. This would be your health goal. Next, write specific statements that describe how this healthful behavior reduces health risks. If you are overweight, reducing caloric intake and reducing weight will reduce your risk of developing heart disease, high blood pressure and other preventable illnesses. You will then need to make a specific plan for recording your progress. This may be done on a daily or weekly basis, but should be a part of your contract. Set a target date to evaluate your progress, stating how the plan helped you accomplish your health goal.

Decision-making skills You have set a goal and developed a plan. Next, think of decisions you make that might interfere with your progress. Are you placing yourself in situations that will help you reduce your caloric intake? Making responsible decisions regarding your caloric needs can help you reach your goal.

LESSON 29 • Maintaining a Healthful Weight   **327**

Gaining Weight

Class Activity

Weight-Gain Products Have students visit a local nutrition store or look in the nutrition aisle of a local grocery store to see the kinds of products available that claim to help people gain weight. Ask students the following questions: What kind of products are there that promote weight gain? What claims do these products make? What forms do the products come in? Bars? Pills? Powdered drink mixes? Have students compile a list of products and their ingredients. **L2**

Class Discussion

Unhealthy Weight Gain Have students discuss some unhealthy ways to gain weight. *eating too many sweets and fatty foods and not following dietary guidelines* What might be a negative health effect of gaining weight improperly? *Some of the foods consumed might add fat to the body but not muscle.* **L2**

Extension

Increasing Muscle Mass Have students develop a workout program that would help increase muscle mass. Ask how that workout would differ from a program designed to help someone lose weight. **L3**

Reading Review

1. *Desirable weight is weight that is healthful for a person based on age, height, gender, body frame, basal metabolic rate, and activity level.*
2. *Body composition is the percentage of fat tissue and lean tissue in the body.*

A body weight that is 10 percent or more below desirable body weight is *underweight*. People who are underweight may be malnourished. *Malnutrition* is a condition in which the body does not get the nutrients required for optimal health. In most cases, people who are malnourished have inadequate vitamin and mineral intake. Teens who are malnourished may not have the nutrients needed for proper growth. They may lack energy.

How to Gain Weight

There are other reasons why teens may be underweight. They may have a disease or an eating disorder. Teens who are underweight should have a physical examination to determine the cause. They should work with a physician and/or dietitian to develop a healthful plan for weight gain.

How to Gain Weight Healthfully

Begin your weight gain program with a physical examination by a physician. Have a physician or dietitian determine the number of pounds you need to gain. He or she can help you design a plan for weight gain. Remember, the energy equivalent of 1 pound of body fat is equal to 3500 calories.

Increase food intake. Suppose you want to gain 5 pounds. You may want to gain 1 pound a week for five weeks. You will need to increase your caloric intake by 3500 calories a week to gain a pound each week. This means you need to take in 500 more calories each day (3500 calories divided by seven days = 500 calories). You can do this by increasing the number of servings from each food group in MyPyramid. Eat extra servings of bread, cereal, rice, and pasta. Increase your servings of fruits and vegetables. Drink more milk. Eat more yogurt and cheese. Increase your portions of meat, poultry, fish, dry beans, eggs, and nuts.

Follow the Dietary Guidelines. Even though you want to gain weight, you must follow the Dietary Guidelines. You do not want to develop harmful eating habits that are difficult to break. For example, you do not want to pig out on french fries with a lot of salt. Choose low-fat and lean foods from the meat, poultry, fish, dry beans, eggs, and nuts group. Select broiled, baked, steamed, or poached foods rather than fried foods. Use egg substitutes. Choose low-fat or fat-free foods from the milk, yogurt, and cheese group.

Watch eating habits and activity levels. Eat snacks between meals. Exercise to increase muscle mass. Continue to drink plenty of fluids, especially water. Ask for the support of family members and friends. It is helpful if you keep a journal of food and beverage intake and weight gain. Review the information in your journal with a physician or dietitian.

Reading Review

1. What is desirable weight?
2. What is body composition?

 Sensitive Issues

Being Underweight Being underweight or "skinny" can be just as traumatic as being overweight, maybe even more so because people are sometimes less sensitive or aware about comments made to those that are exceptionally thin. Many people struggle with gaining weight in the same way that others struggle with losing it. Recognize that there are many reasons for people being underweight, many of which they cannot control, such as heredity, digestive and metabolic problems, and hormone imbalance. Some have poor eating habits due to lack of appetite, which may be a side effect of being treated for certain illnesses. Exercise care when discussing this topic so as not to offend anyone who may be struggling to gain weight.

Losing Weight

A body weight that is 10 percent or more than desirable body weight is *overweight*. A body weight that is 20 percent or more than desirable body weight is *obesity*. Obesity is extremely harmful to health. Unfortunately, obesity is on the rise among U.S. children and teenagers. Follow the steps below to ensure that obesity does not harm your health.

How to Lose Weight

A physician can check for other causes of overweight, such as an underactive thyroid gland. People who are overweight and obese are at risk for developing cardiovascular diseases, diabetes, and certain cancers.

Steps to Lose Weight Healthfully

Before you begin your weight-loss program, have a physical examination by a physician. Then have a physician or dietitian determine the number of pounds you need to lose and help you design a plan for weight loss. Remember, the energy equvalent of 1 pound of body fat is equal to 3500 calories.

Decrease food intake. Suppose you want to lose 10 pounds. You may want to lose 2 pounds a week for five weeks. This means you need to use 1000 more calories each day than you take in. For example, you might reduce your caloric intake by 500 calories and engage in physical activity to burn 500 calories. Select low-calorie foods and beverages from each food group. Read food labels to determine serving sizes and calories.

Follow the Dietary Guidelines. Be especially careful to choose low-fat and fat-free foods that also are low-calorie. Trim fat from foods. Select broiled, baked, poached, and steamed foods rather than fried foods. Limit sugars and salt. Keep available ready-to-eat, low-calorie snacks with you to eat between classes. Drink plenty of fluids. Your body needs plenty of water to burn fat.

Stay active. Participate in regular physical activity. Physical activity increases BMR. Try to engage in physical activity early in the morning and again later in the day. Physical activity tones muscle. When you engage in vigorous physical activity, your body secretes beta-endorphins. These hormones improve mood. They keep you from feeling down when you are dieting.

Keep a journal. Keep a journal of food and beverage intake and weight loss. Your physician or dietitian will recommend a way of keeping a record of your food and beverage intake and weight loss. Review this information with the physician or dietitian. Ask for the support of family and friends.

Did You Know?

Combo Meal
You can "up-size" a combo meal, soda pop, pastry, and other foods for only a few extra cents, but doing so can double the calories you will eat. Eating much larger portion sizes is one reason for the current epidemic of obesity in the United States.

Teacher FYI

Obesity in the United States
The American Obesity Association reports that 127 million Americans are overweight, 60 million are obese, and 9 million are severely obese. The association also found that 64.5 percent of all American adults over the age of 20 are overweight and 30.5 percent are obese. Obesity increases the risk of illness for many serious medical conditions.

Class Activity

Food Diary Have students record everything they eat and drink for five days. They should write down every bite or sip, no matter how small or inconsequential it may seem. They should review their diary after the five days. Ask if they realized how much they were actually eating. Remind students that even a small bite of cake or just a few chips can add up over the course of a week or a month.
L1 **ELL**

Differentiated Instruction

Physical Challenges If appropriate for your class, have students who have physical challenges share with the class different activities they are involved in to help them stay physically fit. These may be students who are physically challenged due to accident, illness, or who have been physically challenged since birth. Maybe they are permanently challenged and have learned to play basketball in a wheelchair or they have run in a marathon wearing a prosthesis. All students should participate in the discussion and offer other examples of how friends and/or family members who are physically challenged maintain a healthful weight and remain physically fit. **L2**

National Health Education Standards
Pages 328–329: 1.1, 1.5, 1.7, 7.1, 7.2

Weight-Loss Strategies

There are healthful ways to lose weight gradually. A person should attempt gradual weight loss after checking with a physician and/or dietitian. This procedure allows a person to develop healthful eating habits. After reaching desirable weight, a person gradually adds more calories to his or her diet to maintain weight. Some people try other strategies for losing weight.

What to Know About Weight-Loss Strategies

Liquid diets A diet in which beverages are substituted for some or all meals is a *liquid diet.* Some liquid diets are obtained only at a diet center, hospital, or physician's office and must be followed under medical supervision. Before beginning a medically supervised liquid diet, a person has a physical examination and extensive blood tests. An electrocardiogram is required to check the condition of the heart.

While on the liquid diet, a person has medical supervision with blood tests at set intervals. Because more fluids are taken in, urination will occur more frequently.

An over-the-counter product may be taken to help with bowel movements. The person may attend classes to learn more about eating habits. When the weight-loss goal is reached, a maintenance plan must be followed. The plan is designed to help the person practice healthful eating habits.

Some liquid diets are sold in supermarkets and drugstores and do not require medical supervision. Using these liquid diets can be dangerous. These diets usually contain few calories. People who use them may have side effects. They often do not learn healthful eating habits and may regain the weight that was lost.

Fad diets A quick, weight-loss strategy that is popular for a short time is a *fad diet.* The grapefruit diet and the cabbage soup diet are examples of fad diets. Some people try so many different diets that they never develop healthful eating habits. They lose weight and gain it back when they resume their former eating habits. Some fad diets are dangerous. The only way to obtain a balanced diet is to get the correct number of servings from each food group in MyPyramid.

There are a variety of products from which to choose that claim to ▼ help you lose weight.

Prescription medications The Food and Drug Administration (FDA) has approved prescription drugs for the treatment of obesity. An *anorectic drug* is a drug that decreases appetite. Some anorectic drugs help increase serotonin levels in the brain. *Serotonin* is a chemical in the body that helps regulate primitive drives and emotions. People who take anorectic drugs for obesity require medical supervision. They need a physical examination, electrocardiogram, and regular blood tests. They usually follow a special diet and meet regularly with a dietitian. Long-term studies are being conducted on the safety and effectiveness of anorectic drugs.

Starvation diets A method of weight loss in which a person severely restricts calories is a *starvation diet.* Starvation diets are dangerous. When caloric consumption is very low, there is not enough blood glucose to provide energy. The body relies on stored fat for energy. A high amount of fat is released into the

blood. *Fat ketosis* (kee TOH suhs) is a condition in which excessive ketones are released into the blood. Symptoms include a "fruity-smelling" breath, loss of appetite, nausea, vomiting, and abdominal pain. Confusion, unconsciousness, and death can occur.

▲ Many diet pills may be purchased over the counter.

Over-the-counter diet pills Some diet pills can be purchased in drugstores, grocery stores, health food stores, and by mail order without a prescription. Some of the diet pills claim to suppress appetite. Others claim to fill the stomach and curb a person's hunger.

Diet pills can be dangerous, addictive, and ineffective. Side effects may include headaches, heart palpitations, dizziness, nervousness, drowsiness, rapid pulse rate, and sleeplessness. In addition, teens who use diet pills often do not get a balanced diet. They may suffer from malnutrition.

Laxatives and diuretics A drug that helps a person have a bowel movement is a *laxative.* A product that increases the amount of urine excreted is a *diuretic.* A person may take laxatives or use diuretics to rid the body of fluids. However, the weight loss from their use is temporary because it is only fluid loss. Ridding the body of fluids can be dangerous—it may decrease the amount of potassium in the blood. This can interfere with normal heart function and cause abdominal pain, nausea, diarrhea, bloating, and dehydration.

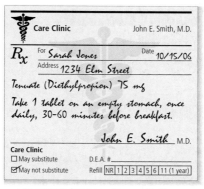

Care Clinic	John E. Smith, M.D.

R_x For Sarah Jones   Date 10/15/06
Address 1234 Elm Street

Tenuate (Diethylpropion) 75 mg

Take 1 tablet on an empty stomach, once daily, 30–60 minutes before breakfast.

John E. Smith M.D.

Care Clinic
☐ May substitute   D.E.A. #_____
☑ May not substitute   Refill NR 1 2 3 4 5 6 11 (1 year)

▲ An anorectic drug is sometimes used in the treatment of obesity.

Reading Review

1. What is a fad diet?
2. What is a starvation diet?
3. What is the purpose of a laxative?

LESSON 29 • Maintaining a Healthful Weight **331**

Eating Disorders

Class Activity

Collage Have students make a collage of pictures from old magazines that portray people with a positive body image. The collage should include people of all shapes, sizes, colors, and levels of attractiveness. **L1** **ELL**

Teacher FYI

Eating Disorders According to the National Institute of Health, eating disorders often coexist with other disorders such as depression, substance abuse, and anxiety. People who suffer from eating disorders can experience a wide range of physical health complications, including serious heart conditions and kidney failure, which could lead to death. Recognizing an eating disorder as a real, treatable disease is critically important.

INTERACTIVE CHALKBOARD
with Image Bank

Teaching Transparency

Page 61, **Unit 5 Fast File Resources**

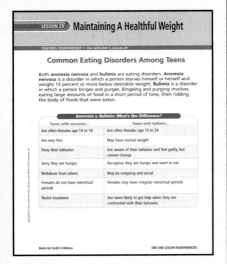

A condition in which a person has a compelling need to starve, to binge, or to binge and purge is an *eating disorder*. To eat large amounts of food over a short period of time is to *binge*. To rid the body of food by vomiting or by using laxatives and diuretics is to *purge*. Eating disorders are addictions. Teens with eating disorders feel compelled to starve, eat to excess, vomit, use laxatives and diuretics, and exercise to extremes to control their weight. As with other addictions, eating disorders are caused by misinformed attitudes and harmful ways of coping.

Did You Know?

Binge Eating Disorder As many as 2 percent of females in the United States may be affected by binge eating disorder.

Why Some Teens Are at Risk for Developing Eating Disorders

Emphasis on appearance Body image is the perception a person has of his or her body's appearance. Teens who have a positive body image look in the mirror and like what they see. They are not uncomfortable if they are shorter, taller, or less muscular than other teens. Teens who have a negative body image look in the mirror and are dissatisfied. They want to have a different appearance. They may develop a distorted body image. When they look in the mirror, they see themselves as fat when they are not. Television shows and magazine ads often portray teens who are excessively thin. Teens who lack self-confidence may begin to compare themselves to successful models and professional athletes.

Uncomfortable with secondary sex characteristics During puberty, the secondary sex characteristics develop. Some teens have difficulty when these changes occur. For example, some females are uncomfortable

TABLE 29.1 Anorexia versus Bulimia: What's the Difference?	
Teens with anorexia...	**Teens with bulimia...**
Are often females age 14 to 18	Are often females age 15 to 24
Are very thin	May have normal weight
Deny their behavior	Are aware of their behavior and feel guilty, but cannot change
Deny they are hungry	Recognize they are hungry and want to eat
Withdraw from others	May be outgoing and social
Females do not have menstrual periods	Females may have irregular menstrual periods
Resist treatment	Are more likely to get help when they are confronted with their behavior

Community Involvement

Treatment Centers Have students use the local phone book to locate nearby facilities that treat people with eating disorders. Ask students to answer the following questions: What types of facilities offer these services? Do they offer both inpatient and outpatient services? What type of health professional provides the treatment? Do they offer both individual and group services? How much does treatment cost? Do insurance companies usually pay for any of the expenses? Students can compile a list of these facilities and the services they offer and share the information with the school counselor to make available to students. They can also share it with the Parent Teacher Organization (PTO) at school to be available for parents and teachers who might encounter a student who has an eating disorder. **L2**

when their breasts begin to develop. They slouch and wear baggy clothes to hide their breasts. They feel anxious and uncomfortable about body changes. Some males may feel embarrassed about voice changes during puberty. They may have difficulty dealing with other hormonal changes, such as facial hair growth. These teens may choose harmful ways to cope with their feelings. They may starve or binge and purge rather than talk about their feelings.

Perfectionism A compelling need to be flawless is *perfectionism.* Teens who are perfectionists are overly critical of themselves. Perfectionism is the result of feeling inadequate and insecure. Some teens become perfectionists because adults had unrealistic expectations of them during their childhood. When teens who are perfectionists begin a diet, they may go overboard. This may result is an eating disorder.

The need to control Some teens feel compelled to control every situation. These teens may have had traumatic childhoods. Perhaps they were raised in families with alcoholism or abuse and were not able to rely on responsible adults to protect them. They might never know when a parent, guardian, or adult family member might be drinking or be physically or sexually abusive. As a result, these teens have difficulty trusting the unknown and feel more secure when they control situations. They diet or exercise to extremes as a way to show control.

Expression of emotions Some teens are not able to express their emotions. They have difficulty when they feel frustrated, lonely, depressed, or anxious. They substitute other behaviors

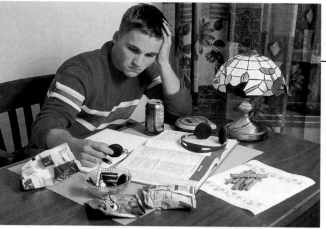

▲ Teens often express their emotions through their eating habits.

for the healthful expression of these emotions. For example, suppose a teen feels lonely and rejected. This teen may eat sweets or have other foods to comfort himself or herself. Suppose a teen is frustrated when doing algebra. This teen may turn to food for comfort. He or she relies on excessive eating as a way to satisfy his or her emotional needs. Other teens starve when they have emotional needs.

Behaviors of an Eating Disorder

Read each of the following statements. If one or more describe you, talk to your parents, guardian, or other responsible adult. These behaviors may indicate that you are at risk for developing an eating disorder.

- I constantly compare myself to others.
- I am unhappy with my physical appearance.
- I wear baggy clothes to hide my body changes, such as my breasts. (females)
- I think it is disgusting to have menstrual periods. (females)
- I am never satisfied with anything I do.
- My parent or guardian is never satisfied with anything I do.

- I felt unsafe during my childhood (from alcoholism, physical abuse, or sexual abuse in the family).
- I only feel secure when I can feel that I am in control of a situation.
- I do not know what to do when I feel lonely, frustrated, rejected, or depressed.
- I reach for food, starve, exercise, or rid myself of food when I am uncomfortable.

LESSON 29 • Maintaining a Healthful Weight **333**

Extension

Read a Biography Have students read a biography about someone with an eating disorder. They should write a brief essay about that person's life and his or her struggle with the eating disorder. **L2**

Class Activity

Ways to Cope Divide students into groups. Have groups list positive ways of coping with the pressures that can cause some teens to develop eating disorders. Each group's ideas should be shared with the rest of the class. *Some suggestions might include: Develop a positive self-image. Offer to tutor someone who is struggling in an area that is easy for you. Set realistic goals. Select friends who like you for who you are as a person, not the way you look. Focus on the things you do well and be proud of them.* **L2**

Class Discussion

A Responsible Friend Have students discuss what they should do if they suspect that a good friend might have, or is developing, an eating disorder. Discuss how they should handle that situation without destroying the trust in the relationship. Ask if they would be willing to break the trust of a good friend if it was a life-threatening situation. **L2**

🄳🄸 Differentiated Instruction

Gifted and Talented Have students who are gifted and talented prepare a video on the types of eating disorders. The video should include eating disorders, such as anorexia nervosa, bulimia, or binge eating disorder. The video should include the causes and factors that contribute to the disorders, as well as ways the disorders are diagnosed. Also included should be the types of treatment available for eating disorders. The video can be presented with factual information about the disorders followed by a skit or dramatization of a student who recognizes that she or he has the disorder. The video should include the importance of support from family and friends to a person suffering from an eating disorder. Students can show the completed video to the class for feedback and discussion. **L3**

National Health Education Standards

Pages 332–333: 1.1, 1.2, 1.5, 1.7, 2.1, 2.3, 2.5, 2.7, 4.4, 5.1

Anorexia Nervosa

Teacher FYI

Anorexia According to Anorexia Nervosa and Related Eating Disorders Inc., for every four females diagnosed with anorexia, there is one male. The risk factors for males developing anorexia are: they were fat or overweight as a child, recent dieting, participating in a sport that requires thinness, or having a job that demands thinness.

Class Activity

Thinness in the Media With their parents' permission, have students watch one hour of music videos. Have them record the number of men and women they see that they would consider as not well-built, physically fit, or attractive. Have them write a reaction paper about the type of people who are most often shown in music videos. **L2** **ELL**

NHES Assessment/SCASS

Selected Response Which of the following is not commonly associated with anorexia nervosa?

A. perfectionism

B. *vomiting*

C. obsession with weight

D depression

An eating disorder in which a person starves himself or herself and weighs 15 percent or more below desirable weight is ***anorexia nervosa***. The person also may exercise to extremes in order to lose weight. Anorexia nervosa, which is usually referred to as anorexia, is life-threatening.

What to Know About Anorexia

Did You Know?

Anorexia One-half of 1 percent to 3.7 percent of U.S. females suffer from anorexia in their lifetime. The mortality rate of people with anorexia is one-half of 1 percent per year, which is 12 times higher than the annual death rate due to all causes of death among females ages 15–24.

Obsessed with being thin People with anorexia do not recognize when they are dangerously thin. When they look at their bodies in the mirror, they see themselves as fat when they are very thin. The disease can affect males and females, teens and adults. Many people with anorexia, especially teens, are obsessed with exercise. Some abuse laxatives, enemas, and diuretics. Most are perfectionists—people who consider anything less than perfect as unacceptable.

Perfectionism Teens with anorexia often are good students and are obedient and respectful. They often set very high expectations for themselves. As a result, they feel inadequate if these expectations are not met on a consistent basis. To gain back control, they starve themselves.

When family members or others pressure them, they become even more committed to starving. Teens with anorexia deny their behavior.

Treatment for anorexia nervosa Treatment for anorexia involves a team of professionals—physicians, nurses, dietitians, and mental-health professionals. A treatment plan is developed that deals with physical, mental, and emotional health problems. A hospital stay may be necessary to treat for dehydration and malnutrition. Intravenous feedings may be required to supply nutrients. Tests are required to assess and treat damage to body organs. Mental-health professionals work with the teen who is anorexic and with his or her family.

Metropolis High School		Superintendent	Telephone				
		Terry Ellis	555-0788				
		Principal	Telephone				
		Phyllis White	555-0789				

Student name	I.D. No.	Sex	Grade	Home rm.	Counselor	GP	Year
Stephanie Gluck	0082	F	10	C273	Dean Smith	4	2005

Attendance	GP1	GP2	GP3	GP4	Total	
Days Absent	1.0	1.5	1.5	1.0	5.0	
Days Tardy	0.0	1.0	0.0	0.0	1.0	06/17/05

Course name	GP1	GP2	Exam	GP3	GP4	Exam	Final	Credit	Comments
English 2	A–	A	A	A–	A–	A	A	1.0	
Health	A+	A	A+				A+	0.5	
Physical Ed.				A	A+	A+	A	0.5	A pleasure to have in class
Spanish 3	A	A	A	A–	A	A–	A	1.0	Cooperative, attentive attitude
U.S. History	A	B+	A	A+	A	A	A	1.0	A pleasure to have in class
Algebra 2	A+	B+	A+	A–	A–	A+	A	1.0	
Science	A–	B+	A	A	A+	A	A	1.0	Responsible and dependable
Orchestra	A–	A–	B	A	A+	A+	A	1.0	A pleasure to have in class
								7.0	Total credits earned

▲ Teens who have anorexia are often obsessed with perfectionism.

How Anorexia Nervosa Harms Health

Teens with anorexia may have:

- dehydration and constipation,
- abdominal pain and nausea,
- hormonal changes,
- damage to body organs,
- decrease in heart rate and blood pressure,
- impaired immune system function,
- absence of menstruation in females,
- hair loss,
- malnutrition,
- negative self-confidence,
- a lack of self-respect,
- depression,
- an urge to withdraw.

🜚 Achieving Health Literacy

Effective Communicator Have students create a talk show that has a guest who has successfully recovered from anorexia. Students need to write a script that incorporates the guest's personal experience with the disease, how he or she developed it, how it affected every aspect of his or her life, and how he or she managed to recover. The script should include red flags that might have been evident to family, friends, and teachers, but were overlooked. Several students should be responsible for gathering the factual information, others for writing the script, and others for acting out the talk show. **L2**

Bulimia

An eating disorder in which a person binges and purges is ***bulimia***. Bingeing and purging involves eating large amounts of food in a short period of time, then ridding the body of the foods. Teens with bulimia may vomit or use laxatives or diuretics to purge. An estimated 1.1 to 4.2 percent of U.S. females have bulimia in their lifetime.

What to Know About Bulimia

Bulimia is far more common than anorexia nervosa. Most cases of bulimia occur in teen females who want to lose weight, but males also may suffer from the disorder.

Obsession People with bulimia are obsessed with their body shape and size. They try to follow a diet but are unsuccessful. So they turn to starvation to lose weight. Then they feel compelled to eat and go on a binge. After the binge, they feel guilty and worry about weight gain. Then they feel compelled to purge.

Negative body image Teens who have a negative body image are at risk for bulimia. Many try to emulate a thin body image portrayed in the media. Teens who were raised in families in which there was alcoholism or abuse also might be at risk. These teens often are insecure and depressed. Denying their feelings increases the likelihood that they will binge and purge.

Behaviors of teens with bulimia Unlike teens with anorexia, teens with bulimia usually know they have a problem. They feel guilty and ashamed, but are unable to change their behavior. Many teens try to conceal their bulimic behavior, often by hiding the containers and wrappers from food on which they just binged. They may frequently visit the bathroom directly after a meal.

How bulimia harms health Teens with bulimia may have dissolved tooth enamel, tooth decay, and sore gums. Other indications of bulimia are enlarged salivary glands and swollen cheeks. There is often severe water loss, which causes a depletion of potassium in the blood and an increase in blood pressure. The person may suffer damage to the colon, heart, and kidneys. Sometimes there is impaired bowel function.

Treatment for bulimia Teens with bulimia often have desirable weight and are successful at hiding their behavior. Treatment for bulimia involves a team of professionals who deal with physical and emotional health problems. Teens with bulimia must develop new ways of coping to gain self-respect and self-confidence.

Reading Review

1. What is anorexia nervosa?
2. What is bulimia?

Signs of Bulimia in Teens

Teens with bulimia may:

- binge in private, but eat regular amounts when with others,
- have one secret place in which to binge, such as a closet,
- steal food or hide it in a secret place,
- think about food constantly and plan each binge carefully,
- buy or steal special treats or elaborate dishes for a binge,
- gulp food quickly while bingeing so as not to be discovered,
- steal money to purchase food or steal food from the stores,
- exercise and diet excessively between binges.

LESSON 29 • Maintaining a Healthful Weight **335**

⚖️ Legal Issues

Confidentiality Counselors and other mental-health professionals are bound by law to keep confidential the information discussed in a counseling session. Teens should be encouraged to talk about their feelings with a counselor or mental-health professional without fear of ridicule or reprisal. However, students also should understand that, by law, even these individuals must report any behavior or action revealed that might threaten the health and safety of themselves or others.

336

Binge Eating and Obesity

An eating disorder in which a person cannot control eating and eats excessive amounts is *binge eating disorder*. The diagnosis is made when a person binges two or more times per week for six months. During binge episodes, a person often eats rapidly, eats until he or she is uncomfortably full, eats alone, and feels guilty about binging. Between 2 and 5 percent of Americans experience binge eating disorder in a six-month period.

What to Know About Binge Eating Disorder and Obesity

Binge eating disorder is more common in females. Teens with this disorder turn to food as a substitute for coping. After a time, they are addicted to food. Family and friends know they have a weight problem, but may not realize that the cause is an eating disorder.

Teens with binge eating disorder need medical and psychological help. Their attempts at weight loss are never successful. Binge eating disorder is more common in people who are severely obese.

How binge eating disorder and obesity harm health There are many physical problems associated with binge eating disorder and obesity. Teens who are overweight or obese may have skeletal difficulties due to the need for bones to support extra weight. There is an increase in the person's heart rate and blood pressure. There is an increased risk of developing cardiovascular diseases, high blood pressure, diabetes, and certain types of cancer.

Teens with binge eating disorder may lack self-respect, have negative self-esteem, have a negative body image, and have frequent bouts of depression. Many do not feel accepted by peers, and often turn to eating as a substitute for meaningful relationships.

Treatment for binge eating disorder and obesity Treatment for binge eating disorder and obesity involves a team of health-care professionals who deal with physical and emotional problems. A weight-loss plan is designed. The person on the diet has medical supervision with blood tests at set intervals. Obese people sometimes are placed on liquid diets under close physician supervision.

After weight loss, patients must learn new eating habits. They are supervised on a maintenance plan to prevent relapse. To change eating habits, patients need to examine the reasons why they developed binge eating disorder. Therapy, nutrition classes, and support groups are helpful.

---

anorexia nervosa
basal metabolic rate
(BMR)
binge eating disorder
body composition
bulimia
caloric expenditure
caloric intake
eating disorder
laxative
obesity
overweight
underweight

Key Terms Review

Match the definitions below with the lesson Key Terms on the left. Do not write in this book.

1. fat tissue and lean tissue in the body
2. calories the body uses at rest
3. the number of calories a person takes in from foods and beverages
4. the number of calories a person uses for BMR, digestion, and physical activity
5. a body weight that is 10 percent or more than desirable body weight
6. a body weight that is 20 percent or more than desirable body weight

7. a mental disorder in which a person has a compelling need to starve, to binge, or to binge and purge
8. a life-threatening eating disorder in which a person starves himself or herself and weighs 15 percent or more below desirable weight
9. an eating disorder in which a person binges and purges
10. an eating disorder in which a person cannot control eating and eats excessively

Recalling the Facts

11. What is basal metabolic rate (BMR)?
12. Distinguish between caloric intake and caloric expenditure.
13. What causes malnutrition?
14. When is a person considered overweight?
15. What two things should a person do before going on a liquid diet?

16. What type of prescription drug has been approved by the FDA in the treatment of obesity?
17. Describe the causes, symptoms, and treatment of eating disorders.
18. What are three characteristics of a person who has anorexia?

Critical Thinking

19. How can a person gain 1 pound every week for six weeks?
20. How can a person lose 1 pound every week for four weeks?
21. Many people feel they should weigh more or less than they actually weigh. Explain the factors that might contribute to this way of thinking.
22. Discuss how a person can determine if he or she has a small, medium, or large frame. Who can help you make this determination?

Real-Life Applications

23. How can you determine your desirable weight and body composition?
24. One of your classmates weighs 102 pounds, but she thinks she is fat. Explain why she might be in danger of developing anorexia.
25. Explain what you might say to a team member of yours who exercises excessively.
26. What would your advice be to a friend who decides to take a diuretic each day because she is afraid of gaining weight?

Activities

Responsible Decision Making

27. **Resistance** A friend suggests that you buy laxatives to use for quick weight loss. Write a response to your friend. Refer to the Responsible Decision-Making Model on page 61 for help.

Sharpen Your Life Skills

28. **Analyze Influences on Health** Write a news show report in which you evaluate a trendy fad diet. Use MyPyramid as the basis for your evaluation.

26. Offer more healthful ways to maintain weight, such as healthful foods and regular, moderate exercise.

Activities

Responsible Decision Making

27. Responses will vary. Students might explain to their friend that the use of laxatives is not a healthful way to lose weight.

Sharpen Your Life Skills

28. Evaluations will vary, but should indicate that most fad diets consist of large amounts of some foods and few of others. A balanced diet consists of foods from all food groups in the MyPyramid.

Key Terms Review

1. body composition
2. basal metabolism rate (BMR)
3. caloric intake
4. caloric expenditure
5. overweight
6. obesity
7. eating disorder
8. anorexia nervosa
9. bulimia
10. binge eating disorder

Recalling the Facts

11. Number of calories the body uses at rest
12. See page 326.
13. Inadequate dietary intake of vitamins and minerals.
14. when their body weight is 10 percent or more above desirable body weight
15. Have a physical examination and extensive blood tests.
16. an anorectic drug, one that decreases appetite
17. See pages 332–336.
18. obsessed with being thin; obsessed with exercise; most are perfectionists

Critical Thinking

19. See page 328.
20. See page 329.
21. They lack self-confidence and have a negative body image.
22. See page 325.

Real-Life Applications

23. This answer should include that a physician or dietitian would determine the desirable weight. Desirable weight factors include: age, height, gender, body frame, BMR, and activity level; body composition: calipers to measure thickness of skin-folds, underwater weighing, or simply pinch a fold of skin on upper arm—more than 1 inch may indicate excess body fat
24. Because people with anorexia do not recognize that they are very thin even when they are, they tend to starve themselves to become even thinner.
25. Answers will vary.

Key Terms Review

1. g	6. l
2. i	7. f
3. a	8. c
4. j	9. e
5. h	10. b

Recalling the Facts

11. combination of dietary cholesterol and cholesterol produced by body; can be lowered by eating fewer saturated fats
12. nutrition facts, serving size, servings per container, calories per serving, ingredients listing, percent daily value
13. Eating fiber-rich foods helps you have a daily bowel movement and reduces the risk of developing cancer of the colon and rectum.
14. meat and beans and fruit; need fewer servings daily from these foods
15. reduce risk of developing cancers of the colon, rectum, prostate, stomach, esophagus, and lung
16. eat carrots, sweet potatoes, and squash for vitamin A; eat citrus fruits for vitamin C; eat green vegetables, nuts, and whole-grain cereals and breads for vitamin E
17. energy to start the day, "jump start" metabolism, feel alert, and reduce likelihood of craving high-energy foods during snack attacks
18. cramps, nausea, diarrhea, vomiting, fever
19. developing cardiovascular disease, diabetes, certain cancers
20. below desirable weight, dehydration and constipation; abdominal pain and nausea; hair loss; hormonal changes; damage to heart, kidneys, other body organs; decrease in heart rate and blood pressure; impaired immune system function; absence of menstruation; malnutrition; negative self-confidence, lack self-respect; bouts with depression; withdraw; risk for suicide attempts

Key Terms Review

Match the following definitions with the correct Key Terms. Do not write in this book.

a. antioxidant *(p. 303)*
b. caloric expenditure *(p. 326)*
c. Dietary Guidelines *(p. 294)*
d. diuretic *(p. 331)*
e. eating disorder *(p. 332)*
f. food-borne illness *(p. 320)*
g. MyPyramid *(p. 296)*
h. food intolerance *(p. 308)*
i. herbal supplement *(p. 288)*
j. megadosing *(p. 314)*
k. metabolism *(p. 312)*
l. nutrient *(p. 282)*

1. shows how many servings a person should eat from each food group
2. contain extracts or ingredients from the roots, berries, seeds, and stems of plants
3. a substance that protects cells from being damaged by oxidation
4. taking vitamins in excessive amounts
5. an abnormal response to food that is not caused by the immune system
6. a substance in food that helps with body processes and repair of cells
7. an illness caused by consuming contaminated foods or beverages
8. recommendations for diet choices among healthy Americans who are two years of age or more
9. a condition in which a person has a compelling need to starve, to binge, or to binge and purge
10. the number of calories a person uses for BMR, digestion, and physical activity

Recalling the Facts

11. What determines your blood cholesterol level? *(Lesson 25)*
12. What information is included on a food label? *(Lesson 25)*
13. Why do you need a diet with plenty of grain products, vegetables, and fruits? *(Lesson 26)*
14. Which food groups are in the thinnest sections of MyPyramid? Why? *(Lesson 26)*
15. Why should you include cruciferous vegetables in your diet? *(Lesson 27)*
16. What are three ways to obtain antioxidants in your diet? *(Lesson 27)*
17. Why do you need to eat a healthful breakfast each morning? *(Lesson 28)*
18. What are signs you may have eaten contaminated food? *(Lesson 28)*
19. What are the health risks associated with having a high percentage of body fat? *(Lesson 29)*
20. What are ways that having anorexia nervosa may harm health? *(Lesson 29)*

Critical Thinking

21. How can you get the equivalent of six to eight glasses of water a day? *(Lesson 25)*
22. Why might a person choose to take vitamin supplements? *(Lesson 25)*
23. Why do you need to eat a variety of foods? *(Lesson 26)*
24. Why do people eat more fats and sugars than they need? *(Lesson 26)*
25. Why does eating a poor diet put a person at risk for so many diseases? *(Lesson 27)*
26. How would people know if they might be at risk for a diet-related disease? *(Lesson 27)*
27. Why do people eat even when they are not hungry? *(Lesson 28)*
28. What eating habits might a person change to have a more healthful diet? *(Lesson 28)*
29. How does regular physical activity help teens manage their weight? *(Lesson 29)*
30. What are healthful things teens can do to lose weight? *(Lesson 29)*

Use **Interactive Tutor** at **www.glencoe.com** for additional help.

Critical Thinking

21. juice, milk, soup, frozen juice pops, fruits and vegetables, water
22. on vegetarian diet, to ensure getting what is needed, unbalanced diet, illness
23. to get all the nutrients needed: vitamins, minerals, essential amino acids, complex carbohydrates, water, some fat
24. availability, taste, culture, inexpensive, marketing, television advertising
25. All body parts need nutrients to rebuild and function. Not supplying the right nutrients can result in many different health problems.
26. Answers might include: They might not eat vegetables or enough fiber; eat lots of fat; drink soda and not milk; overweight
27. it is time for a meal; emotions like stress, loneliness or boredom; others are eating; see or smell food

Health Literacy Activities

What Do You Know?
Self-Directed Learning Prepare to play "foodball" by writing a factual question relating to nutrition. Get into groups. Each group will take turns taping a nutrition question onto a small football and passing it to a member of the opposing team. If the person that catches the ball answers the question correctly, their team gets a point. If the person "fumbles" the question, the team who threw the pass will get a point.

Connection to Government
Effective Communication Write a letter to the Food and Drug Administration (FDA) requesting information about a nutritional issue in which you are interested. Share with classmates the information you receive.

Family Involvement
Critical Thinking Evaluate your family's eating habits, using the information you have learned in this unit. Does your family have healthful eating habits? What can your family do to improve its eating habits?

Investigating Health Careers
Problem Solving A dietitian is a nutrition expert who counsels patients, health-care providers, community members, and the food industry on nutrition. Dietitians advise people about what foods to eat to help maintain optimal health and wellness. Write a letter to a dietitian in your community asking for suggestions on how to eat healthfully. Ask questions about aspects of nutrition that interest you.

Group Project
Responsible Citizenship Investigate the laws that govern food safety. Include information on regulations that govern the storage and transportation of food, and restaurant cleanliness. Make a list of these regulations. Share the list with your family members and classmates. Visit **www.glencoe.com** for more information.

Standardized Test Practice

Reading & Writing

Read the following selection and answer the questions that follow.

The sight was unforgettable. A cow would begin to stumble crazily, collapse, and quickly fall to its death. The dying cows suffered from bovine spongiform encephalopathy, or BSE. It is better known as mad cow disease. The cows got the disease from eating food made of ground-up parts from diseased sheep. People became aware of a deadly new threat to the food supply and to their health. Several young people developed Creutzfeldt-Jakob disease, a rare but deadly nerve illness related to BSE. Officials suspected the affected people may have contracted the disease from eating BSE-contaminated beef. British beef sales plummeted and hundreds of thousands of British cows were slaughtered. The disease is now under control, but the horrible films of "mad cows" remain as a warning.

Multiple Choice

1 In this paragraph, the word *plummeted* means
   A fell sharply
   B rose
   C shocked
   D influenced

2 According to this paragraph, which of these statements is true?
   A Cows infected sheep with BSE.
   B Cows and sheep grazed together in the same pastures and the sheep infected the cows.
   C Cows ate food intended for sheep and got the disease.
   D Cows got BSE by eating parts of diseased sheep.

Open-Ended

3 In order to destroy BSE, the British government slaughtered many cows that did not have the disease. Was this right or not? Write a paragraph supporting your position.

www.glencoe.com

---

28. Answers might include: eat breakfast; eat when hungry, not for appetite; choose more healthful fast food; keep healthful snacks handy; drink more water and less pop
29. burns calories, increases BMR, and helps balance caloric intake with caloric expenditure
30. participate in regular physical activity, follow the Food Guide Pyramid and Dietary Guidelines, eat low-calorie snacks, drink lots of water, keep a food and beverage journal

Health Literacy Activities

What Do You Know?
Use this to help students engage in a fun activity that will help them recall information presented in this unit.

Connection to Government
Have students share their letters and responses with the class. Encourage class discussion on each nutritional issue.

Family Involvement
Ask students if they would like to share the results of evaluating their family's eating habits.

Investigating Health Careers
Students might want to share the information received from the dietitian on ways to eat healthfully.

Group Project
Set aside time for sharing the rules and laws that govern food safety.

Standardized Test Practice

Reading & Writing

1. A   2. D

Open-Ended
3. Students' paragraphs should support the writer's positions with reasons. Those who believe the slaughter was acceptable may claim that it was necessary for the health of the entire population of cattle and to protect consumers. Those opposed may argue that the slaughter was unnecessarily broad and could have been better targeted at infected herds. Paragraphs should contain correct spelling, capitalization, punctuation, grammar, usage, and sentence structure.

Personal Health and Physical Activity

STANDARDS AND FEATURES

Lesson	National Standards	State/Local Standards	Activities and Features
Lesson 30 *(2 sessions, 1 block)* Having Regular Physical Exams	1.1, 3.4, 3.5, 6.1		**Using Life Skills:** Accessing Valid Health Information, Products, and Services: Scheduling a Medical or Dental Exam, p. 350
Lesson 31 *(2 sessions, 1 block)* Being Well-Groomed	1.1, 1.5, 3.4, 7.1, 7.2		**Facts About:** Visiting a Dermatologist, p. 356
Lesson 32 *(1 session, 1 block)* Getting Adequate Rest and Sleep	1.1, 1.5		**Using Life Skills:** Using Goal-Setting and Decision-Making Skills: Keeping a Sleep Journal, p. 364
Lesson 33 *(3 sessions, 1 block)* Participating in Physical Activity	1.1, 6.1, 7.2		**Using Life Skills:** Using Goal-Setting and Decision-Making Skills: Creating a FITT-ness Plan, p. 372
Lesson 34 *(2 sessions, 1 block)* Practicing Fitness	1.1, 1.5, 7.1, 7.2		**Health News:** How Many Calories Does Exercise Burn?, p. 377 **Using Life Skills:** Practicing Healthful Behaviors: Health-Related Fitness Assessment, p. 383 **Just the Facts:** Ephedra, p. 389
Lesson 35 *(2 sessions, 1 block)* Exercising Safely	1.5, 7.3		**Speaking Out:** Being a Sports Trainer, p. 398

Key to Differentiated Instruction

L1 Level 1 activities should be appropriate for students with learning difficulties.

L2 Level 2 activities should be within the ability range of all students.

L3 Level 3 activities are designed for above-average students.

ELL ELL activities should be within the ability range of English language learners.

FAST FILE RESOURCES

INTRODUCING THE UNIT

Parent and Family Letter	p. 1	Health Behavior Contract	p. 3
Spanish Parent and Family Letter	p. 2	Unit Focus Transparency Master and Worksheet	p. 4

TEACHING THE UNIT LESSONS

Reproducible Student Pages	Lesson 30	Lesson 31	Lesson 32	Lesson 33	Lesson 34	Lesson 35
Reading Strategy	p. 7	p. 21	p. 33	p. 45	p. 59	p. 75
Vocabulary Practice	p. 8	p. 22	p. 34	p. 46	p. 60	p. 76
Transparency Master and Worksheet	p. 9	p. 23	p. 35	p. 47	p. 61	p. 77
Real-Life Health	p. 11	p. 25	p. 37	p. 49	p. 63	p. 79
5-Minute Check	p. 15	p. 29	p. 41	p. 53	p. 67	p. 83
Lesson Quiz	p. 18	p. 30	p. 42	p. 55	p. 71	p. 85

CLOSING THE UNIT

Family Involvement Activity	p. 89	Health in the News	p. 99
Community Involvement Activity	p. 91	Health Career Research Activity	p. 101
Health Lab	p. 93	Unit Test A	p. 103
Activity: Strengthening Health Skills	p. 97	Unit Test B	p. 107

Technology

- **Interactive Chalkboard CD-ROM**
- **TeacherWorks™ CD-ROM**
- **StudentWorks™ CD-ROM**
- **Reading Essentials CD-ROM**
- **Exam*View*® Assessment Suite**

Glencoe Exclusive!

TeacherWorks™
All-In-One Planner and Resource Center

www.glencoe.com
- **Vocabulary Puzzlemaker**
- **Interactive Tutor**
- **Your Health Checklist**
- **Web Links**
- **Student Web Activities**

TEST YOUR PERSONAL HEALTH IQ

Use the three statements on the student page to initiate a class discussion about personal health and physical activity. *Additional True/False statements are:*

4. **You have to belong to a fitness facility to stay in shape.**
   FALSE: You can jog or go for a walk in your neighborhood, take the stairs, or do calisthenics.

5. **You should see a physician only when you are not feeling well.**
   FALSE: You should get a checkup at least every 2 years regardless of how you're feeling. Physicians can detect problems before you experience any symptoms.

6. **It is important to warm up before performing any vigorous physical activity to help prevent injury.**
   TRUE: Warming up gets muscles prepared for the upcoming activity.

in the news Pilates

Physical Activity Ask students if they agree with Jennifer Lopez's statement about beauty. Discuss with students various types of exercise they could try, such as Pilates, to benefit all sides of the health triangle. According to the National Center for Chronic Disease Prevention and Health Promotion, moderate physical activity can be attained by walking briskly, mowing the lawn, dancing, swimming, or bicycling. Vigorous-intensity physical activity can be attained by jogging, doing heavy yard work, swimming laps, or bicycling uphill. **L2**

UNIT 6 Personal Health and Physical Activity

TEST YOUR PERSONAL HEALTH IQ
True or False?

1. **Teenagers need about 8 hours of sleep per night.**
   TRUE: Teenagers do need about 8 hours of sleep per night. Teenagers who get more sleep do better in school and are less likely to be depressed.

2. **Boys need more physical activity than girls to stay healthy.**
   FALSE: The body needs physical activity to stay healthy, regardless of gender. Physical activity increases heart rate, strengthens muscles, and reduces stress.

3. **All body piercings can become infected.**
   TRUE: Infection can occur anytime the skin is pierced. All body piercings must be carefully cleaned and protected to decrease the chance of infection.

> "Beauty is only skin deep. I think what is really important is finding a balance of mind, body, and spirit."
>
> —Jennifer Lopez, actress and musician

in the news Pilates

Research The Pilates method of exercise was developed by Joseph H. Pilates. Research the history of the Pilates method. How is Pilates different from other forms of exercise? What are the benefits of this form of exercise? Present the results of your research to your class.

LESSON 30	LESSON 31	LESSON 32
Having Regular Physical Exams	Being Well-Groomed	Getting Adequate Rest and Sleep

Two-Minute Unit Launcher

Activity Have students stand beside their desks or tables so they have room to move. Have students raise their arms above their heads, reaching as far as they can. Next, have them reach to one side, then the other. Then, have students clasp hands in front of their bodies and round their shoulders to stretch their upper backs. Finally, have students slowly bend the neck to the side and hold. Then repeat to the other side. Students should hold each stretch for 20 seconds. Have them discuss how they feel afterwards. Stretching lengthens muscles and increases blood flow. It might make students feel more alert. Before beginning this activity, ask students if any of them have restrictions on the physical activity they may perform. Any students who feel they should not perform these stretches should be excused from the activity and given a different activity to perform. **L2 ELL**

EVALUATING MEDIA MESSAGES

SONIC SOUND

You want quality music without the cost. So experience your next concert at home with **Sonic Sound,** headphones that give you crystal-clear sound and pumped-up volume. **Sonic Sound's** breakthrough technology allows you to double the volume, with bass you can feel and with no distortion.

It's *your* music—experience it.

WHAT'S YOUR VERDICT?
To evaluate this advertisement, use the criteria for analyzing and evaluating health messages delivered through media and technology that you learned in Unit 1.

Visit **www.glencoe.com** to find regularly updated statistics about physical activity. Using the information provided, determine the answer to this question: How many U.S. teens exercise regularly?

Visit **www.glencoe.com** to use *Your Health Checklist*, an interactive tool that helps you determine your health status.

LESSON 33	**LESSON 34**	**LESSON 35**
Participating in Physical Activity	Practicing Fitness	Exercising Safely

Health Online

Answers About half of people ages 12–21 regularly participate in vigorous physical activity. One-fourth report no vigorous physical activity. Of adults, approximately 25 percent report no physical activity; more than 60 percent are not active for the recommended 30 minutes a day, three to five days a week. The International Consensus Conference on Physical Activity Guidelines for Adolescents issued the following recommendations: "All adolescents should be physically active daily, or nearly every day, as part of play, games, sports, work, transportation, recreation, physical education, or planned exercise, in the context of family, school, and community activities. Adolescents should engage in three or more sessions per week of activities that last 20 minutes or more at a time and that require moderate to vigorous levels of exertion."

 What's Your Verdict?

What's Missing? Ask students what information this ad is leaving out. Have students discuss whether the stereo equipment could cause any negative health effects. Investigate the negative health effects of loud music heard through headphones and ask students if louder is better and if there is such a thing as too loud. Music from headphones can reach 110 decibels, which can be harmful after 30 minutes per day. Normal conversation is about 60 decibels. **L2**

Health Journal

Write an Essay Have students write an essay in their health journals about health examinations. Ask students to answer these questions: How often should a person have a health examination? What should a person take with them to a health examination? What can be expected during a health examination? **L2**

Unit Focus Transparency
Page 4, **Unit 6 Fast File Resources**

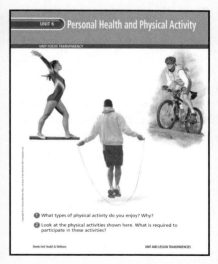

National Health Education Standards
Pages 340–341: 1.1, 2.5, 7.2

341

LESSON 30

Having Regular Physical Exams

⏱ Out of Time?

If time does not permit an in-depth study of this topic, use the following activities in this Teacher Wraparound Edition:

- Class Discussion, p. 343
- Teacher FYI, p. 346
- Class Activity, p. 347
- Quick Demo, p. 348

1 Focus

HEALTH GOALS **Regular Exams** Have students respond to the first Health Goal for this lesson by listing the benefits of getting regular physical exams. *Reasons may include improving and maintaining their health.* **L2**

Write ABOUT IT!

Research Ask students to further research cavities. Have them learn about the causes, and the short- and long-term effects of cavities. Students also should learn more about preventing and treating cavities. Ask students to make a visual presentation, such as a poster, a computer graphic, or a model of an aspect of cavities. **L2**

LESSON 30

Having Regular Physical Exams

HEALTH GOALS
- **I will have regular examinations.**
- **I will follow a dental health plan.**

The kind of health care available to you and the way you use it affects your health. For example, to improve and maintain your health, you need regular physical examinations. It also is important to have regular eye and ear screenings and regular dental checkups.

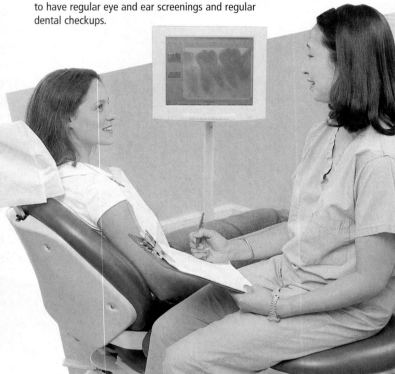

What You'll Learn

1. Identify what takes place during typical physical, eye, hearing, and dental examinations. *(pp. 343, 344, 346, 348)*
2. Identify symptoms that should prompt individuals to seek health care. *(p. 343)*
3. Identify ways to protect your eyes, and conditions and diseases that can affect the eye. *(p. 345)*
4. Identify symptoms that indicate a need for an ear exam, factors that can lead to hearing loss, and ways to protect against hearing loss. *(p. 347)*
5. Identify how to keep teeth and gums healthy. *(p. 350)*

Why It's Important

Unlike a car, you can't trade in your body for a newer model. To look and feel good you must take care of your body, including your eyes, ears, and teeth.

Key Terms

- myopia
- hyperopia
- astigmatism
- conjunctivitis
- glaucoma
- conductive hearing loss
- sensorineural hearing loss
- periodontal disease
- gingivitis
- fluoride

Write ABOUT IT!

Writing About Dental Care Suppose that lately your tooth has been hurting whenever you eat something that is cold or sweet. You have been putting off having a dental exam because you don't want to get a filling. After you read the information about dental care on page 348, write an entry in your health journal about what you should do in this situation.

342 UNIT 6 • Personal Health and Physical Activity

National Health Education Standards—Guide for Lesson 30		
1.1	Predict how healthy behaviors can impact health status.	pp. 342, 345–347, 350, 351
3.4	Determine when professional health services may be required.	pp. 343–349, 351
3.5	Access valid and reliable health products and services.	pp. 343–350
6.1	Assess personal health practices and overall health status.	pp. 342, 343, 344, 346, 348, 350, 351

Physical Exams

T eens need a physical examination at least every two years. A *physical examination* is a series of tests that measure health status. A physician performs physical examinations with assistance from other health-care professionals.

What to Know About Physical Examinations

During a physical examination, a health history is taken. A *health history* is a record of a person's health habits, past health conditions and medical care, allergies, food and drug sensitivities, and family health histories. Bring health-related information with you so you can accurately answer questions. This information becomes a part of your health record. A *health record* is a file that includes a health history and the results of physical examinations.

During a typical physical examination, your height, weight, body temperature, pulse rate, respiratory rate, blood pressure, general appearance, skin, eyes, ears, nose, mouth, neck, lungs, heart, lymph nodes, back, legs, feet, bones, joints, and reflexes are checked. Laboratory tests, such as a urinalysis and blood tests may be included. A *urinalysis* (yur uh NA luh suhs) is a series of tests of a person's urine that check normal kidney function and detect urinary tract infections. A *blood test* is an analysis of blood for blood components, chemicals, pathogens, and antibodies. Sometimes the physician will order an electrocardiogram. An *electrocardiogram (ECG)* (ih lek tro KAHR dee uh gram) is a record of the electrical impulses of the heart that is used to detect disorders of the heart.

Your physician will discuss the results of your examination with you and your parents or guardian. If any health problems are detected, a treatment plan will be discussed, or you may be referred to a specialist for further treatment. Ask questions if you do not understand something. You may be advised to change some of your health habits.

When to see your physician You may need to see your physician between regular examinations if you have symptoms that require medical attention. A *symptom* is a change in a body function. Your physician will review your symptoms and test results before making a diagnosis. A *diagnosis* is the determination of a health problem. Once a physician makes a diagnosis, he or she can prescribe the proper treatment.

Symptoms Alert

Contact your physician if you have any of these symptoms:

- shortness of breath
- loss of appetite
- blood in urine or feces
- blood in mucus or saliva
- constant cough
- fever of 100°F or higher for more than one day
- severe pain in any body part
- swelling, stiffness, or aching in the joints
- frequent or painful urination
- sudden weight gain or loss
- dizziness
- cancer warning signs
- heart attack warning signs
- stroke warning signs

LESSON 30 • Having Regular Physical Exams **343**

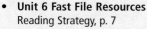

Lesson Resource Manager

- **Unit 6 Fast File Resources**
  Reading Strategy, p. 7
  Vocabulary Practice, p. 8
  Transparency Master and Worksheet, p. 9
  Real-Life Health, p. 11
  Real-Life Health, p. 13
  5-Minute Check, p. 15
  Lesson 30 Quiz, p. 18
- **Unit 6 Transparency**
- **Lesson 30 Transparency**

- **Reading Essentials**
- **Technology**
  TeacherWorks™ CD-ROM
  StudentWorks™ CD-ROM
  Reading Essentials CD-ROM
  Exam*View*® Assessment Suite
  Vocabulary Puzzlemaker

Physical Exams

2 Teach

NHES Assessment/SCASS

Performance Event Have students design a health history form that could be used in a doctor's office. Questions should cover all of the relevant information, including a person's specific health habits, past health conditions and medical care, allergies, food and drug sensitivities, and health information about family members. **L2**

Class Discussion

Prevention Have students discuss why it is recommended that they get a physical examination at least once every two years. Discuss the benefits of prevention over treatment. **L2**

PowerPoint® Presentations
This CD-ROM is an editable Microsoft® PowerPoint® presentation that includes:
- Lesson presentations
- Lesson checks
- Interactive graphics
- 5-Minute Checks
- Image Bank
- All transparencies

Vocabulary Refer to the Sentence Synthesis Strategy on page 16T, and ask students to brainstorm sentences using health concepts included in the Key Terms.

National Health Education Standards

Pages 342–343: 1.1, 1.5, 3.4, 6.1, 7.1, 7.2

343

Eye Care

Class Activity

Designer Eyeglasses Divide the class into groups. Have each group create a new style of eyeglasses that they think teens would enjoy wearing or being seen in. They can draw a picture, use a computer graphics program, or create a model out of wire, clay, cardboard, felt, or foam core. **L2** **ELL**

Explain the Concept

Blindness Cataracts, trachoma (an infection), and glaucoma together account for more than 70 percent of the world's blindness and visual disability. In the developing world, other leading causes of preventable blindness and visual disability include vitamin A deficiency, onchocerciasis (a parasitic worm), and leprosy. In the developed world, diabetic retinopathy is a leading cause of preventable blindness and visual disability. Eye injuries take their toll on sight in both groups of countries, as do degenerative and congenital/hereditary disorders.

Extension

Eye Care Careers Have students investigate the educational requirements that are needed to become either an ophthalmologist or an optometrist. Ask students to locate four colleges or universities that offer programs in these areas. **L3**

National Health Education Standards

Pages 344–345: 1.1, 3.4, 6.1, 7.1

Eye Care

Your vision is probably the most used sense for finding out about the world. Your sense of sight adds to the quality of your life. If you have your sight, you use it to acquire more than 80 percent of your knowledge.

What to Know About Eye Care

Eye examinations Ophthalmologists and optometrists perform eye examinations. An *ophthalmologist* (ahf thuh MAH luh jihst) is a physician who specializes in medical and surgical care and treatment of the eyes. Ophthalmologists can diagnose and treat eye conditions, test vision, perform surgery, and prescribe corrective lenses.

An *optometrist* is an eye-care professional who is specially trained in a school of optometry. Optometrists can test vision and prescribe corrective lenses. During an eye examination, an eye-care professional reviews your health history and examines your eyes for refractive errors, color blindness, lazy eye, crossed eyes, eye coordination, depth perception, eye disease, and general eye health. This helps determine if correction is necessary.

Visual acuity Sharpness of vision is called *visual acuity.* Refractive errors may interfere with visual acuity. A *refractive error* is a variation in the shape of the eye that affects the way images are focused on the retina and blurs vision. The *retina* is the inner lining of the eye.

Refractive errors include myopia, hyperopia, astigmatism, and presbyopia. With *myopia,* or nearsightedness, distant objects appear blurred and close objects appear clear. The nearsighted eye is longer than average and images are focused in front of the retina. With *hyperopia,* or farsightedness, close objects appear blurred and distant objects appear clear. The farsighted eye is shorter than average and images are focused behind the retina.

With *astigmatism* the irregularly shaped cornea causes blurred vision. The cornea is the transparent front part of the eye's outer shell. Astigmatism affects both distant and close vision. You can have astigmatism and either myopia or hyperopia. *Presbyopia* (prez bee OH pee uh) is age-related and is caused by weakening of eye muscles and hardening of the cornea. Older adults experience blurred vision of close objects.

Correcting visual acuity Refractive errors may be corrected with eyeglasses or contact lenses. Both help the eye focus images on the retina so that visual acuity is restored. People with presbyopia may wear bifocals. *Bifocals* are lenses that correct for both close and distant vision.

Eyeglasses usually are made of plastic or nonbreakable glass. A protective coating may be added to prevent glare and protect the eyes against ultraviolet radiation. Contact lenses can be hard or soft and are worn directly on the cornea. It is important to clean and store the lenses correctly to help prevent eye infection. *Radial keratotomy*

Make the Connection

Health Records For more information on how to keep personal and family health records, see page 23 in Lesson 2.

Family Involvement

Family History Have students ask older family members about their history of eye problems. Have students ask the following questions: Do any of them wear glasses or contacts? If so, when did they begin to have vision problems? Was it detected through a regular exam or because they were having vision trouble? If they do not wear glasses or contacts, when was the last time they had an eye exam? Ask students to write an entry in their health journals about their families' histories of eye problems. Have students include a plan for maintaining their own eye health. **L2**

(ker uh TAH tuh mee) is surgery that improves myopia by changing the curve of the cornea. ***Photorefractive keratectomy*** is laser surgery that reshapes the surface of the cornea to improve myopia, hyperopia, and astigmatism. ***Laser insitu keratomileusis (LASIK)*** is laser surgery in which a small flap in the cornea is made and some of the exposed tissue is removed to improve myopia and astigmatism. Some level of risk is involved in any eye surgery.

Eye Conditions and Diseases

Conjunctivitis An inflammation of the eye membranes that causes redness, discomfort, and discharge is called ***conjunctivitis,*** or pinkeye. Causes include bacterial infection, allergies, contact lenses, certain drugs, and secondhand smoke. Pinkeye that is caused by bacteria is highly contagious. Pinkeye usually is not serious unless the infection spreads to the deeper tissues in the eye. This may result in a permanent loss of vision.

Glaucoma A condition in which pressure of the fluid in the eye is high and may damage the optic nerve is called ***glaucoma.*** The ***optic nerve*** is the nerve fibers that transmit messages from the retina to the brain. Regular eye examinations are important for early detection. The increased pressure of glaucoma can be prevented with early treatment.

Cataract The clouding of the lens of the eye that obstructs vision is called a ***cataract.*** Images are hazy and out of focus. Cataract surgery involves removing the cloudy lens and implanting an artificial lens.

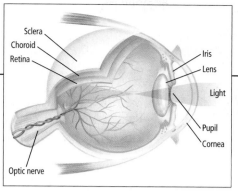

Sclera
Choroid
Retina
Optic nerve
Iris
Lens
Light
Pupil
Cornea

◀ Eyes are composed of over two million working parts. They can process 36,000 bits of information in one hour.

Macular degeneration An incurable eye disease is called ***macular degeneration.*** It is caused by the deterioration of the central portion of the retina, the inside back layer of the eye that records the images we see and sends them via the optic nerve from the eye to the brain.

How to Protect Your Eyes

Do not wear normal prescription eyeglasses or contact lenses in place of eye protectors. Normal prescription eyeglasses are not designed to withstand the force of a collision with objects, or to prevent liquid and debris from getting into your eyes. Contact lenses can trap chemicals and debris behind them. Wear eye protectors made of polycarbonate when playing sports that involve high-speed objects. Wear goggles when swimming to prevent chlorine and other substances in the water from irritating your eyes.

Wear safety goggles when working around dangerous chemicals that can splash into your eyes. Wear safety goggles when working with lawn and power tools to prevent dirt and debris from scratching your eyes. Wear a wide-brimmed hat and sunglasses with 99–100 percent ultraviolet (UV) protection to protect your eyes from exposure to UV radiation in sunlight. Avoid using BB guns, slingshots, or fireworks, which can lead to permanent eye damage and loss of vision.

Did You Know?

Eye Disease Macular degeneration is the leading cause of blindness for those aged 55 and older in the United States, affecting more than 10 million Americans.

Reading Review

1. What is macular degeneration?
2. Describe a cataract.

LESSON 30 • Having Regular Physical Exams **345**

Ear Care

Quick Demo

Hearing Loss Bring in two cotton balls for each student (or ask students to bring in cotton balls or earplugs from home). Instruct each student to place a cotton ball or earplug just inside each ear, being careful not to insert it too far. Once students have the cotton or earplug in place, have students read to each other from this textbook. Explain that this is a demonstration of hearing loss. Explain that over time, the ability to hear naturally diminishes, but exposure to excessive noise can exacerbate the problem. Ask students to remove the cotton and discuss the differences they experienced in their ability to hear with and without the cotton or earplug.

Teacher FYI

Tinnitus Overexposure to loud noises is frequently the cause of hearing loss and tinnitus, or ringing in the ears. The American Tinnitus Association estimates that nearly 50 million Americans have experienced tinnitus at one time in their lives and 12 million suffer constantly and severely.

Explain the Concept

Hearing Aids and Cochlear Implants Students might not understand the difference between hearing aids and cochlear implants. Explain that hearing aids rely on hair cells to amplify sound. People with severe and profound hearing loss may obtain limited benefit for speech perception. Cochlear implants bypass hair cells to directly stimulate the auditory nerve. Insertion of the cochlear implant results in total hair cell loss; therefore, a hearing aid cannot be used in the implanted ear.

Y our ears contain structures for both your sense of hearing and your sense of balance. Your sense of hearing adds to your quality of life. You should have regular ear examinations and hearing tests.

What to Know About Ear Care

Ear examinations Ear examinations are performed by audiologists or by otolaryngologists. An *audiologist* (ah dee AH luh jihst) is a specialist who diagnoses and treats hearing and speech-related problems. An *otolaryngologist (ENT)* (oh toh lar un GAH luh jihst) is a physician who specializes in medical and surgical care and treatment of the ears, nose, and throat. An ENT can diagnose and treat ear conditions, test hearing, recommend hearing devices, and perform surgery.

A common way to test for hearing loss is to use an audiometer. An *audiometer* is a machine used to measure the range of sounds a person hears. The results provide data on the type and extent of hearing loss. A *tympanogram* is a measure of the vibrations of the ear drum and air pressure in the Eustachian tube.

The *Eustachian tube* connects the middle ear and the back of the nose. It allows fluid to drain from the middle ear and regulates air pressure on both sides of the eardrum. Increased air pressure in the Eustachian tube may affect hearing.

Hearing loss Hearing loss ranges from mild to profound deafness. Causes of hearing loss include premature birth; respiratory distress at birth; a birth defect; exposure to drugs or infections such as rubella, herpes, or syphilis before birth; childhood illnesses, such as meningitis and chicken pox; middle ear infections; high fevers; injuries; and noise pollution.

Noise pollution is a loud or constant sound that causes hearing loss, stress, fatigue, irritability, and tension. Sound is measured in decibels. A *decibel* (dB) is a unit used to measure the loudness of sounds. Sounds of more than 85 decibels can cause discomfort and hearing loss.

Hearing loss is either conductive or sensorineural. *Conductive hearing loss* occurs when sound is not transported efficiently from the outer to the inner ear and is caused by excessive wax buildup, ear injury, birth defects, and middle ear infection.

Sensorineural (sen suh re NUR uhl) *hearing loss* occurs when there is damage to the inner ear or auditory nerve. The *auditory nerve* connects the inner ear to the brain.

Symptoms Alert

Contact your physician if you have any of these symptoms:

- pain in your ears
- drainage from your ears
- difficulty hearing conversation
- difficulty hearing on the telephone
- need to have the volume on the TV at a point that others complain is too loud
- difficulty determining from what direction sounds are coming
- difficulty understanding conversation in a noisy room
- difficulty hearing in social situations

 Legal Issues

The Americans with Disabilities Act President Bush signed the Americans with Disabilities Act (ADA) in 1990. The law states that people with disabilities are an essential part of society and should not be segregated, isolated, or subjected to discrimination. The ADA enables people with disabilities to take charge of their lives, build self-determination and self-reliance, and participate in and have full access to all aspects of society. The law requires that individuals with disabilities shall have equal access to jobs, public accommodations, government services, public transportation, and telecommunications.

Generally, sensorineural hearing loss is permanent. Some people with sensorineural hearing loss receive **cochlear** (KOH klee ur) **implants,** which are electronic devices that are implanted in the ear to restore partial hearing to the totally deaf.

Assistive hearing devices People who have hearing loss may use assistive hearing devices. An **assistive hearing device** is a device that helps a person with hearing loss communicate and hear. The most common assistive hearing device is the hearing aid. A **hearing aid** is an electronic device worn in or near the ear that improves hearing. Even with a hearing aid, certain situations, such as using the telephone, may pose problems for people with hearing loss.

A person with hearing loss may need a telephone amplifier that increases the volume on the telephone. A TTY (Text Telephone Yoke), also known as a TDD (Telecommunications Device for the Deaf), which consists of a keyboard, a display screen, and a modem, may be used. The letters that the TTY user types into the machine are turned into electrical signals that can travel over telephone lines. When the signals reach their destination, they are converted back into letters which appear on a display screen, are printed out on paper, or both.

Message Relay Centers (MRC) can be used between hearing and deaf callers. The caller simply calls the MRC and an operator will use a TTY to act as an interpreter, typing the hearing person's message into a TTY and reading the response to him as it returns.

Background noise also can cause problems for people with hearing

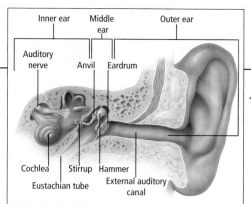

Inner ear · Middle ear · Outer ear

Auditory nerve · Anvil · Eardrum

Cochlea · Stirrup · Hammer

Eustachian tube · External auditory canal

◄ Common causes of hearing loss include birth defects, viral infections, and middle ear infections.

loss—especially when listening to the TV, radio, or stereo. Increasing the volume to overcome background noise may make the sound too loud for others. Headphones and other headsets can be connected directly to a TV, radio, or stereo. Television caption devices allow a person to read the audio portion of TV programs.

Signaling devices can be used to deal with special circumstances. Flashing lights indicate that the phone is ringing, someone is at the door, or the smoke detector has been activated.

Ways to protect against hearing loss Do not insert any objects, including cotton-tipped swabs, into your ears. Objects may puncture the eardrum. Clean the outer ear with a soft, clean washcloth to avoid wax buildup. Use the corner of a dry, clean towel to gently dry your ears after bathing or swimming.

Contact your physician if your ears become infected or you have signs of hearing loss. Keep the volume of radios, compact disc players, stereos, and TVs at safe levels. Avoid listening to music through headphones at unsafe levels. Wear protective earplugs when operating loud machinery, using power tools, or attending rock concerts.

Reading Review

1. What is a hearing aid?

2. What does a TTY consist of?

LESSON 30 • Having Regular Physical Exams **347**

Differentiated Instruction

Hearing Impairment Some hearing impaired students can lip-read or they might have a hearing aid, a cochlear implant, or an interpreter. Even with this assistance, they can still miss a lot of information presented in class. Ask qualified student volunteers to take turns taking notes for a student who has a hearing impairment. The student volunteers should be willing to take good notes on the lectures and discussions that occur during class time and be willing to share those notes with the student, explaining them if necessary. **L3**

347

Dental Care

Quick Demo

Brushing and Flossing Demonstrate proper brushing and flossing techniques. Use an American Dental Association-approved toothpaste and toothbrush. Tilt the toothbrush at a 45-degree angle toward the gums. Using small circular motions, brush fronts, backs, and chewing surfaces of all teeth. Brush your tongue. Rinse your mouth thoroughly. Hold floss tightly with both hands. Guide the floss between teeth using a gentle back-and-forth motion. At the gumline, curve floss around the tooth. Rub the floss against the tooth moving away from the gum. Repeat for each tooth. Rinse mouth thoroughly. Emphasize that proper technique ensures a more thorough cleaning and that being too rough can cause damage to the gumline. **ELL**

Class Discussion

Universal Precautions Have students discuss why dentists and dental hygienists wear gloves and masks even when performing seemingly simple procedures. **L2**

Class Activity

Sealants Have students locate several local dentists in the phone book to inquire about sealants. Ask students to call the offices to find out if each dentist performs this procedure. Have students ask: How much does the procedure cost? On average, how many teeth does a person have sealed? How much of a reduction in cavities could a person with sealants expect? Ask students to compile their information and create a bulletin board using graphs and tables. **L2**

Dental Care

F or good dental health, you need a dental examination every six months. Even if you are not aware of any dental problems, you should have a checkup. A dentist can find and correct problems before they become painful or obvious to you.

What to Know About Dental Care

Teeth cleaning A thorough cleaning by a dental hygienist is a part of a dental checkup. Dental plaque and calculus that have built up on your teeth will be removed. *Dental plaque* is an invisible, sticky film of bacteria on teeth, especially near the gum line. *Calculus* is hardened plaque. A fluoride treatment may be given to help strengthen your teeth and help prevent cavities. The dental hygienist also will give you instructions for brushing and flossing your teeth.

X rays In order to detect tooth decay or other dental problems that cannot be seen by examination, X rays of your teeth may be taken. X rays show the inside of the teeth, gums, and supporting bones. Cavities appear as a darker area in a tooth on an X ray.

Dental sealants A thin, plastic coating painted on the chewing surfaces of the back teeth to prevent tooth decay is *dental sealant.* The chewing surfaces of back teeth are rough, so food and germs can get stuck. Many dentists recommend that children get sealants on their permanent molars before any decay occurs.

Malocclusion The abnormal fitting of teeth when the jaws are closed is called *malocclusion* (ma luh KLOO zhuhn). Malocclusion can make it difficult for a person to bite and speak properly and to clean teeth thoroughly, which can lead to decay and gum disease. It also affects a person's appearance. Malocclusion can be corrected by removing teeth or by applying braces. A dentist will recommend which of these choices would work best for a patient.

▲ A dental X ray is taken to detect tooth decay or other dental problems.

▲ Malocclusion can be corrected by applying braces.

DI Differentiated Instruction

Learning Disabilities Provide students with two diagrams of a tooth—one with a cavity and one without. The diagrams should have blank spaces pointing to the parts of the tooth. Students could fill in the blank spaces with the correct tooth parts. Have students write a paragraph about the causes of cavities and how they can be prevented. Ask students to use their diagrams as reference and present their paragraphs about cavities to the class. **L1**

Large gaps can be corrected ▶ with dental veneers.

Cosmetic concerns Dentists can offer treatments to whiten teeth. As you age, your teeth will become more yellow, but this does not increase the risk of dental problems. The only reason to get whitening treatment is cosmetic. Whitening kits are available over-the-counter, but there are possible side effects, such as tooth sensitivity.

Dental veneers also can improve the appearance of the front teeth. A **dental veneer** is a thin shell of ceramic material used to cover teeth. They are used to treat broken or chipped teeth, large gaps between teeth, permanently stained or discolored teeth, and crooked teeth. They are resistant to stains and chipping. However, nail biting and chewing on hard objects, such as ice and hard candies, can damage them.

Tooth decay During a regular examination, a dentist will check for cavities and problems with the teeth and gums. The chief cause of dental decay is plaque. The bacteria found in plaque ingest sugars and starches. Then, the bacteria excrete an acid waste product that is corrosive to teeth. This acid causes tooth decay by dissolving the hard enamel and dentin of the teeth. Dentin is the hard tissue that forms the body of the tooth. A dentist may put a filling into a cavity.

Sometimes tooth decay progresses into the pulp of the tooth. The pulp is the living tissue within a tooth. If the pulp becomes irreversibly damaged or dies, a root canal must be performed. A root canal is a dental procedure in which the tooth is opened and dead tissue and bacteria are cleaned out

with very small files that go down to the end of the root. The pulp chamber and the canals are enlarged and flushed with a germicide until they are clean. The canals are then filled to totally block them out so the space cannot harbor bacteria again.

Periodontal disease When brushing and flossing are ignored, plaque and calculus buildup occurs. **Periodontal** (pehr ee oh DAHN tuhl) **disease** is a disease of the gums and other tissues supporting the teeth. Plaque formation and acid production by bacteria in the plaque can cause periodontal disease. This disease is the main cause of tooth loss in adults.

The early stage of periodontal disease is called gingivitis. **Gingivitis** (jin juh VY tuhs) is a condition in which the gums are red, swollen, tender, and bleed easily. The condition worsens if it is not treated. The gums pull away from the teeth. Pockets form between the teeth and gums, and these pockets fill with more bacteria, pus, plaque, and calculus, which causes bad breath and infection. Particles of food also become trapped in the pockets and begin to decay. The supporting bones and ligaments that connect the root to the tooth can be destroyed. The teeth may loosen and fall out.

SEM Magnification: 19x

▲ Plaque build up causes tooth decay.

Gingivitis is an early stage of ▼ periodontal disease.

LESSON 30 • Having Regular Physical Exams **349**

Accessing Valid Health Information, Products, and Services Using the local phone book, have students locate three different doctors and dentists in their area who are taking new patients. Ask students to compile a list of their names and phone numbers. Ask the principal to distribute the list to students who are new to the school. **L2**

3 Assess

Vocabulary Practice
Page 8, **Unit 6 Fast File Resources**

Activity: Using Life Skills

Accessing Valid Health Information, Products, and Services: Scheduling a Medical or Dental Exam

Your parent or guardian may schedule all of your medical appointments now, but it is a good idea to learn how to do this on your own. It is not difficult. Simply follow the steps below.

1 **Identify health information, products, and services you need.** Look at your time budget or calendar before you call. Decide which days and times would be good for an appointment. Have several days in mind.

2 **Find health information, products, and services.** Schedule the appointment. Call the doctor's or dentist's office and say, "I need to make an appointment with Dr. Smith to get my teeth cleaned (or my yearly physical)." The receptionist will work with you to find the right day and time to see the doctor.

3 Ask what you need to bring with you to your appointment. The office may need to see your insurance card or medical records.

4 Arrive at your appointment 15 minutes early. You may have to fill out some paperwork before the doctor can see you.

5 Cancel ahead of time if you can't make it. If an important event comes up that would prohibit you from keeping your doctor's or dentist's appointment, call at least 24 hours before the appointment to reschedule it. This way, the doctor can fit another patient into his or her schedule. Some offices will charge you if you do not cancel within a certain amount of time.

6 **Evaluate health information, products, and services, and take action when health information is misleading and/or health products and services are unsatisfactory.** If you are unsatisfied with the care and treatment you receive, it is your responsibility to find a different doctor.

▲ It is important to schedule regular medical and dental exams.

Keeping teeth and gums healthy

Brushing your teeth helps remove plaque from the exposed surfaces of the teeth. It also freshens your breath. Your toothbrush should be soft-bristled to prevent injury to the gums, and use toothpaste that contains fluoride. Take time to brush the outer, inner, and chewing surfaces of your teeth and your tongue with gentle and short strokes.

Flossing helps remove dental plaque and bits of food between teeth where brushing cannot reach. Flossing plays an important part in preventing gum disease. Wrap dental floss around one finger on each hand, and gently move the dental floss between your teeth up to the gum line.

Fluoride can help strengthen teeth and prevent tooth decay. *Fluoride* is a mineral that strengthens the enamel of teeth. Teeth with strong enamel are resistant to tooth decay because they are able to withstand acid in the mouth. Fluoride also helps repair areas of teeth that have begun to dissolve. Fluoride is present in some communities' water supplies. If you do not have fluoride in your water, you can get fluoride supplements from your dentist. Your dentist also can apply topical fluoride directly to the teeth.

Mouthguards should be worn at all times during athletic competition and practices to protect your teeth and face. Mouthguards need to be kept clean. Never allow anyone else to use your mouthguard.

350   UNIT 6 • Personal Health and Physical Activity

🏛 Community Involvement

Fluoridated Water Supply Have students research the history of fluoride. Students should answer the following questions: Who discovered it? When and how was it discovered that fluoride helps prevent tooth decay and cavities? When was fluoride added to the water supply? Is there any controversy about adding fluoride to the water supply? Why? Have students contact the local water and sewage agency to see if their community's water supply is fluoridated. If so, when did the fluoridation begin? Ask students to write an essay about their findings. **L3**

National Health Education Standards

Pages 350–351: 1.1, 1.5, 4.1, 4.2, 4.3, 6.1, 6.3, 7.1

astigmatism
cataract
conductive hearing loss
conjunctivitis
fluoride
gingivitis
glaucoma
hyperopia
myopia
periodontal disease
retina
sensorineural hearing loss

Key Terms Review

Complete these fill-in-the-blank statements with the lesson Key Terms on the left. Do not write in this book.

1. _____ is an inflammation of the eye membranes that causes redness, discomfort, and discharge.

2. _____, or nearsightedness, is where distant objects appear blurred and close objects are seen clearly.

3. _____ is a disease of the gums and other tissues supporting the teeth.

4. _____, the early stage of periodontal disease, is a condition in which the gums are red, swollen, tender, and bleed easily.

5. _____ is hearing loss that occurs when sound is not transported efficiently from the outer to the inner ear.

6. _____ is a condition in which pressure of the fluid in the eye is high and may damage the optic nerve.

7. _____ is hearing loss that occurs when there is damage to the inner ear or auditory nerve.

8. _____ is a refractive error in which an irregular shape of the cornea causes blurred vision.

9. _____ is a mineral that strengthens the enamel of teeth.

10. _____, or farsightedness, is a refractive error in which close objects appear blurred and distant objects are seen clearly.

Recalling the Facts

11. Describe what you should expect during a typical physical examination.

12. What is a urinalysis?

13. Explain television captioning.

14. How can visual acuity be corrected?

15. Identify ways to protect your eyes.

16. Describe noise pollution.

17. What symptoms indicate the need for an ear exam?

18. How does fluoride help prevent tooth decay?

Critical Thinking

19. Explain why a health history is such an important part of a physical examination.

20. Discuss why it is important to contact a physician if you have any of the symptoms outlined in this lesson.

21. Explain why it is important to wear a mouthguard when participating in athletic competitions and practices.

22. Discuss why prescription eyeglasses should not be worn in place of eye protectors.

Real-Life Applications

23. Your friend is hearing impaired. How can you call him about an assignment?

24. You cannot see the chalkboard clearly from your desk. What could the problem be and how can it be corrected?

25. You like listening to music and going to concerts. How can you protect your hearing?

26. Your dentist says you have malocclusion. Why is getting braces a good idea?

Activities

Responsible Decision Making

27. **Determine** When you arrive at a classmate's house, you discover that the teens gathered are lighting fireworks. Someone says, "Come on, join the party!" Write a response to this situation. Refer to the Responsible Decision-Making model on page 61 for help.

Sharpen Your Life Skills

28. **Analyze Influences on Health** Research how many decibels are produced by: a whisper, normal conversation, city traffic, a rock concert, a jackhammer, and a jet engine. Make a graph to illustrate your findings. Include the decibels that can cause hearing loss.

Visit **www.glencoe.com** for more *Health & Wellness* quizzes.

LESSON 30 • Study Guide 351

Key Terms Review

1. Conjunctivitis
2. Myopia
3. Periodontal disease
4. Gingivitis
5. Conductive hearing loss
6. Glaucoma
7. Sensorineural hearing loss
8. Astigmatism
9. Fluoride
10. Hyperopia

Recalling the Facts

11. See page 343.
12. a series of tests of a person's urine that check normal kidney function and detect urinary tract infection
13. Captioning allows a person to read the audio portion of TV programs.
14. See page 344.
15. See page 345.
16. loud or constant sound that causes hearing loss, stress, fatigue, irritability, and tension
17. See page 346.
18. It strengthens the enamel of teeth therefore making them more resistant to tooth decay.

Critical Thinking

19. Past personal medical information and family medical history will be in one place.
20. They can be symptoms of serious illness which should be treated quickly.
21. to protect teeth and mouth
22. Prescription glasses are not made to withstand impact.

Real-Life Applications

23. You can communicate if your friend has a TTY or MRC.
24. You might have myopia, and should visit an eye-care professional for a prescription for glasses or contacts.
25. wear protective ear plugs

26. Braces might improve a person's bite, speech, or appearance, and make it easier to clean teeth.

Activities

Responsible Decision Making

27. Answers will vary.

Sharpen Your Life Skills

28. a whisper = 20–30 dB, normal conversation = 60–70 dB, city traffic = 60–70 dB, a rock concert = 120–130 dB, a jackhammer = 120–130 dB, a jet engine = 130–140 dB

LESSON 31

Being Well-Groomed

Out of Time?

If time does not permit an in-depth study of this topic, use the following activities in this Teacher Wraparound Edition:
• Class Activity, p. 353
• Class Discussion, p. 355
• Class Activity, p. 357

1 Focus

HEALTH GOAL **Grooming** Have students respond to the Health Goal for this lesson by listing good grooming habits. *Habits may include bathing daily, using deodorant, and brushing teeth.* **L2**

Write ABOUT IT!

NHES Assessment/SCASS

Performance Task Have students research acne treatments commonly prescribed by dermatologists. Students should answer the following questions: How are the treatments used? What are the possible side effects? How long before results are seen? Ask students to choose the treatment they would recommend. Have students present their reasoning to the class. **L2**

LESSON 31

Being Well-Groomed

HEALTH GOAL • **I will be well-groomed.**

Keeping the body clean and having a neat appearance is *grooming*. Good grooming practices protect your health. When you keep your skin, hair, and nails clean, you help reduce the risk of infection from pathogens. Good grooming practices also improve the state of your social health. When you keep your body clean and have a neat appearance, other people find you more attractive.

What You'll Learn

1. Explain how you can prevent body odor and treat acne. *(p. 353)*
2. Discuss common foot problems, including athlete's foot, ingrown toenails, blisters, calluses, corns, and bunions. *(p. 354)*
3. Discuss the causes and treatments of warts, moles, and psoriasis. *(p. 354)*
4. Discuss the possible risks of tattoos, body piercings, artificial fingernails, and tanning beds. *(p. 355)*
5. Discuss how to keep hair clean, what to do about dandruff, products for hair care, and hair removal. *(p. 357)*

Why It's Important

Good grooming improves your physical and social health. How you present yourself demonstrates how you feel about yourself.

Key Terms

• dermatologist
• acne
• deodorant
• antiperspirant
• moles
• psoriasis
• athlete's foot
• warts
• dandruff
• lice

Write ABOUT IT!

Writing About Skin Care Suppose that like many of your friends, you have pimples, but yours seem to be worse. You have been diligent in keeping your face clean and have used over-the-counter acne products, but the acne does not seem to be clearing up. After you read the information about skin care on page 353, write your course of action in your health journal.

352 UNIT 6 • Personal Health and Physical Activity

National Health Education Standards—Guide for Lesson 31		
1.1	Predict how healthy behaviors can impact health status.	pp. 352, 353–355, 357, 359
1.5	Propose ways to reduce or prevent injuries and health problems.	pp. 352, 353–355, 359
3.4	Determine when professional health services may be required.	pp. 353–356, 359
7.1	Analyze the role of individual responsibility for enhancing health.	pp. 352, 353–355, 357, 359
7.2	Demonstrate a variety of healthy practices and behaviors that will maintain or improve the health of self and others.	pp. 353–355, 357

Caring for Skin and Nails

Clean your skin thoroughly before going to bed, so that your skin can breathe freely at night. Eat a well-balanced diet, with all food groups represented. Drink plenty of water to help flush toxins out of your body.

How to Care for Skin and Nails

What to do if you have smelly feet Foot odor is caused by bacteria. To prevent foot odor, wash your feet regularly with soap and scrub your toenails with a nail brush. Dry your feet well. Wear clean socks every day. Let your shoes air out after you wear them.

Why some grooming products make your skin red and itchy Some people have sensitive skin. If you have a reaction to a grooming product, such as a rash, stop using the product. If the rash does not clear up, contact a dermatologist or other physician. A *dermatologist* is a physician who specializes in skin care.

What is acne? A skin disorder in which pores are plugged with sebum, or oil, dead skin cells, and bacteria is called *acne.* One type of acne lesion is a *comedone.* When comedones are open, they commonly are called blackheads because the surfaces of the plugs have a blackish appearance. When comedones are closed, they commonly are called whiteheads—skin-colored or slightly inflamed bumps in the skin.

Acne usually appears first during puberty when oil glands produce and secrete more oil. Factors that cause acne include hormones, excess sebum, bacteria, and inflammation. Acne is not caused by foods, beverages, or by dirt. Acne is not contagious.

How to treat acne Wash your skin gently with a clean washcloth and rinse well. Ask a physician to recommend a cleanser or over-the-counter topical medication. Keep hair away from your face. Select water-based cosmetics. Limit time in the sun to reduce perspiration. Do not squeeze, pick, scrub, or pop acne which can cause infection and scars. Contact a dermatologist if you have severe acne, acne that does not clear up, or acne accompanied by signs of infection. Severe, untreated acne may result in permanent scarring.

How to prevent body odor Body odor occurs when perspiration combines with bacteria. Regular bathing and use of deodorant or an antiperspirant help prevent body odor. A *deodorant* reduces the amount of bacteria, may reduce the amount of perspiration, and contains fragrance to cover up odor. An *antiperspirant* reduces the amount of perspiration.

> **Make the Connection**
>
> **Integumentary System** For more information on the integumentary system, see page 222 in Lesson 19.

Caring for Skin and Nails

2 Teach

Class Activity

Comparison Shop Ask students to visit the personal care aisle of a supermarket or pharmacy. Have students list and describe ten different products that are designed to treat acne. Have students include the active ingredients. Ask students to make note of the claims each makes. Ask students to present their findings to the class. **L2**

INTERACTIVE CHALKBOARD with Image Bank

PowerPoint® Presentations

This CD-ROM is an editable Microsoft® PowerPoint® presentation that includes:
- Lesson presentations
- Lesson checks
- Interactive graphics
- 5-Minute Checks
- Image Bank
- All transparencies

CRISS Project

Journals Refer to the Pre- and Post- Reading Response Strategy on page 17T. Ask students to write in their health journals what they know about risks involved with tattoos, body piercings, and tanning beds both before and after reading the lesson.

Lesson Resource Manager

- **Unit 6 Fast File Resources**
  Reading Strategy, p. 21
  Vocabulary Practice, p. 22
  Transparency Master and Worksheet, p. 23
  Real-Life Health, p. 25
  Real-Life Health, p. 27
  5-Minute Check, p. 29
  Lesson 31 Quiz, p. 30
- **Unit 6 Transparency**
- **Lesson 31 Transparency**

- **Reading Essentials**
- **Technology**
  TeacherWorks™ CD-ROM
  StudentWorks™ CD-ROM
  Reading Essentials CD-ROM
  ExamView® Assessment Suite
  Vocabulary Puzzlemaker

> **National Health Education Standards**
> Pages 352–353: 1.1, 1.2, 1.5, 3.4, 7.1, 7.2

Explain the Concept

Warts There are different types of warts: common, plantar, and flat. Common warts typically are raised and occur on the hands. Plantar warts occur on the foot, and typically do not appear raised. Flat warts occur on the face or legs, and are typically smaller than the other two types of warts. Warts are spread from person to person.

Extension

Bunions Have students research the causes and treatment options of bunions. Ask students to determine the success rate for each treatment option. Have students write a report on their findings and how they can avoid developing bunions. **L3**

NHES Assessment/SCASS

Selected Response Which of the following skin-related conditions might be treated with sunlight?

A. psoriasis
B. wart
C. athlete's foot
D. blister

5-Minute Check

Page 29, **Unit 6 Fast File Resources**

1. How can good grooming protect your health? *It can reduce the risk of infection from pathogens.*
2. What type of light is emitted by tanning beds? *UVA*
3. What is the cause of foot odor? *bacteria*
4. How can you prevent body odor? *regular bathing and using an antiperspirant or deodorant*
5. What causes warts? *the human papillomavirus (HPV)*

▲ If a mole changes color, size, or shape, have it checked by a dermatologist.

HPV There are more than 60 types of human papillomavirus (HPV).

Psoriasis is not ▼ contagious.

What are moles? Smooth, raised areas on skin that can be lighter or darker than surrounding skin are called **moles.** Sun exposure increases the number of moles and may cause some moles to darken.

Some moles can develop into malignant melanoma, a serious form of cancer. Sunburns increase the risk of this type of cancer. Look for changes in color, size, or shape of your moles. If any moles look suspicious, see your physician, particularly if they become painful or bleed.

Most moles are not a threat to your health. There are other reasons, however, that moles may need to be removed. Some moles become irritated. Some moles are unattractive. Sometimes a mole that has been removed reappears. In this case, you should return to your dermatologist. You should never attempt to remove a mole by yourself.

What is psoriasis? An immune system disease that often produces inflamed skin covered with thick, white scales is called **psoriasis.** Psoriasis can be so mild that a person does not notice they have it. It also can be so severe that it covers large areas of skin. Psoriasis appears most often on the scalp, knees, elbows, and torso. It also can occur in the fingernails, toenails, and joints. It is not contagious. Treatments include sunlight, ultraviolet B light (UVB), lasers, and topical and oral medications.

Problems that can affect your feet A fungus that grows on feet is called **athlete's foot** and is treated by using foot powders or creams. An **ingrown toenail** grows into the skin causing swelling and infection. Clip toenails straight across to reduce the risk of ingrown toenails. A **blister** is a raised fluid-filled area that is caused by a burn or by an object rubbing against the skin. If a blister breaks, clean the area, treat it with an antiseptic, and cover it with a sterile bandage. A **callus** is a thick layer of skin caused by excess rubbing. Determine what causes the rubbing and make changes to stop it. A **corn** is a thick layer of skin, usually on or between toes, that results from excess rubbing of an ill-fitting shoe. Special pads can reduce pain caused by corns. A **bunion** is a deformity in the joint of the big toe that causes swelling and pain. Wearing low-heeled shoes with square or open toes helps prevent bunions. See a physician if a foot problem interferes with walking or lasts for a long period of time.

What are warts? Noncancerous growths on the skin that are caused by human papillomavirus (HPV) are called **warts.** Warts usually are the color of skin and rough to the touch, but they can be white, pink, or dark-colored and flat or smooth. Warts can occur wherever there is skin or mucous membranes.

Sometimes warts go away on their own, but warts that are painful, bothersome, or multiply should be removed. You should never attempt to remove warts on the face or genitals by using over-the-counter drugs or home remedies.

354 UNIT 6 • Personal Health and Physical Activity

Differentiated Instruction

Gifted and Talented Have students investigate cryotherapy. Ask students to answer the following questions: What is cryotherapy? Aside from treating warts, for what medicinal purposes can it be used? What are the possible complications of cryotherapy? What are the side effects? Ask students to write essays about one medicinal purpose of cryotherapy including the possible complications and side effects. Have students share their essays with the class. **L3**

◄ Warts can occur on skin and mucous membranes.

One method of removing warts is by applying over-the-counter salicylic acid. Your doctor may apply cantharidin to kill the wart, and the dead wart will later be removed. Another method is cryotherapy, which involves applying liquid nitrogen to freeze the wart. Other methods include burning warts and removing warts with a laser. Talk to your doctor about the risks and benefits of each method.

Risks involved with tattoos A permanent design made by inserting pigment into the dermal layer of skin is called a *tattoo.* Skill levels of tattoo artists vary, therefore, pigment can be inserted improperly. Tattoos may fade or blur. Unsterile tattoo equipment can transmit diseases, such as hepatitis C.

Tattoo and permanent makeup removal can be painful, expensive, and require several treatments. In some cases, complete removal without scarring is not possible. Allergic reactions to tattoo pigments are rare, but when they occur, they can be very troublesome.

Risks associated with body piercings There is a risk of infection any time the skin is pierced. For this reason, the equipment used to perform a body piercing must be sterile. The site of a body piercing needs to be kept clean. Any redness, swelling, or pus that appears at the piercing site should be reported to your doctor. Sometimes, allergic reactions to jewelry or over-the-counter antibiotic ointments develop. Other risks

include bleeding, scarring, and permanent holes in the body. Oral piercings can lead to chipped or broken teeth, choking, difficulty speaking, and a high risk of infection.

Risks of nail products Nail products need to be kept away from children because they could put these products in their mouths or eyes. Some products are flammable.

Bacterial and fungal infections frequently occur with artificial nails. Nail discoloration, pain, redness, itching, or pus in or around a nail area may indicate infection. If infection is present, artificial nails should be removed and hands should be cleaned thoroughly. The infection may need to be treated by a doctor. Allergic reactions to nail products sometimes occur.

The Centers for Disease Control and Prevention (CDC) recommends that salons follow practices to prevent diseases, such as HIV and hepatitis. These practices include properly sterilizing manicure implements, state inspections, and proper hand washing by employees.

Risks of tanning beds Light that is emitted by a tanning bed is mostly ultraviolet A (UVA) rays. While UVA rays are less likely to cause burning than UVB rays, they can still damage the skin and increase the risk of skin cancer and immune system damage. Tanning causes the skin to age faster.

Lotions and sprays that contain dihydroxyacetone (DHA) are effective in making the skin appear tanned without the risks of sun or tanning bed exposure. The tanned color usually lasts about five to seven days after the application.

▲ Infections can occur with artificial nails, so make sure that you choose a nail salon that has undergone a state inspection.

Did You Know?

Blood Donors The American Red Cross prohibits donors from donating blood for one year after getting tattooed. Tattooing exposes a person to diseases and infections, such as hepatitis B and C, tetanus, and HIV.

Reading Review

1. How can tattooing transmit hepatitis C?
2. What symptoms indicate an infection of the nails?

LESSON 31 • Being Well-Groomed **355**

FACTSABOUT

VISITING A DERMATOLOGIST

Investigating the Issue

- *Answers will vary, but might include information on fungal nails, ingrown nails, paronychia, or onycholysis.*
- *Answers will vary, but might include vitamin D generation, dry skin, wrinkles, age spots, severe photo-allergies and accelerated aging, reduced immunological defenses, resistance to infectious diseases, skin tumors, diminished effectiveness of vaccines, and comedones.*
- *Answers will vary but might include surgery, radiation, chemotherapy, carbon dioxide laser, and photodynamic therapy.*

FACTSABOUT
VISITING A DERMATOLOGIST

◄ Dermatologists can determine whether a mole is benign or cancerous.

Acne A dermatologist is a doctor that specializes in the treatment of skin disorders and diseases. Many people visit a dermatologist to seek treatment for acne. Acne occurs when pores in the skin become blocked with oil and dead cells. Bacteria that thrive in an environment without oxygen cause the skin tissues to become inflamed and a pimple is formed.

Treatments for acne include over-the-counter creams, soaps, or pads that contain small amounts of benzoyl peroxide or salicylic acid. A dermatologist may prescribe a stronger medication such as a topical or oral antibiotic or a topical medicine that contains higher amounts of benzoyl peroxide than over-the-counter products.

Skin cancer In recent years there has been increased awareness and concern about skin cancer. Skin cancer results from the DNA in skin cells being damaged by ultraviolet B (UVB) rays from the sun. There are three types of skin cancer: basal cell carcinoma, squamous cell carcinoma, and malignant melanoma.

If a dermatologist suspects that a person has a cancerous skin lesion, he or she will perform a biopsy. During a biopsy, part of the suspected tissue is removed. The tissue is later examined under a microscope in a laboratory. If the lesion is cancerous, the patient and doctor will discuss treatment options.

Early detection is an important part of treating skin cancer. Dermatologists recommend that people give themselves regular self-examinations. Being familiar with and monitoring the pattern of moles, freckles, and other pigmented areas on your skin for change is one of the most important things you can do to detect the early development of cancerous lesions.

Mole mapping For people who are at a high risk for developing skin cancer, such as those who have previously had a cancerous lesion, dermatologists recommend that these patients undergo a procedure called mole mapping.

During mole mapping, the entire surface of the patient's skin is digitally photographed. The photos of the moles are then magnified and used to monitor changes and irregularities in moles, such as changes in size, shape, or color. The photos are stored and used as a baseline to compare the appearance over time of moles during self-examination, as well as against future mole mapping sessions.

Mole mapping can be an important tool in the early detection of the most serious form of skin cancer, malignant melanoma. It also can help prevent unnecessary biopsies of benign moles.

Investigating the Issue

Visit www.glencoe.com to learn more information about the field of dermatology and skin disorders.

- Dermatologists treat disorders of the nails as well as skin. Research some common nail disorders and the treatments available.
- What other effects does exposure to ultraviolet rays have on the skin?
- What are the treatment options for the different types of skin cancer?

Use a software program to design a pamphlet that gives tips on how to reduce exposure to ultraviolet rays and protect your skin.

www.glencoe.com

Cross-Curricular Connections

History Have students research the history of tattooing or body piercing. Ask students to answer the following questions: When did these practices begin? Who were the first to engage in these practices? What were the motivations behind these practices? How have they changed over the course of time? How has the application process changed? How has the art changed? How has public opinion of these practices changed? Ask students to present their findings to the class. **L3**

Caring for Hair

Your hair makes a statement about your personal style. Caring for your hair is an important part of grooming. Healthy hair is shiny and flexible. Unhealthy hair is dull, limp, or oily.

What to Know About Caring for Hair

Wash Wet hair with warm water and work shampoo into a lather. *Shampoo* is a mild detergent for the hair. If you have oily hair, do not rub your scalp vigorously which can stimulate the oil glands. Rinse well. If you use a conditioner after the shampoo, rinse well to remove it. *Conditioner* is a product that coats hair, helps detangle hair, and gives hair a smooth and shiny appearance. Squeeze extra water from hair and pat dry with a towel.

Choose a shampoo that meets the needs of your hair. Acidic shampoo smoothes hair. Shampoos for oily hair have more detergent than shampoos for dry or normal hair. Some people use a shampoo to control dandruff. *Dandruff* is a condition in which dead skin is shed from the scalp, producing white flakes.

Style Comb wet hair gently. Brushing wet hair may cause it to break. Let hair dry naturally or use a hair dryer set on warm or cool. Hair dryers set on hot, curling irons, and hot rollers can cause hair to become dry and brittle and have split ends. There are hair products to help hair keep its style. *Styling gel* is a jellylike substance that gives hair body and keeps it in place. *Hairspray* is a spray that stiffens hair to keep it in place. *Mousse* is a foam that keeps hair in place.

Relaxer is a product that takes curl out of hair. Curl activator puts curl in hair. Hair products may cause skin reactions and harm eyes. Incorrect use of hair products can damage hair.

Head lice Insects that live and lay eggs in human hair are called *lice.* You can avoid infection with head lice by not sharing brushes, combs, or hats with other people.

Hair removal There are products available to remove hair. A *razor* is a device with sharp blades used to shave hair off at the skin's surface. *Shaving cream* is a foam placed on hair to make shaving easier. *Shaving gel* is a jellylike substance placed on hair to make shaving easier. *Depilatories* are chemicals that dissolve hair at the skin's surface. *Waxing* is the use of hot wax to pull hairs out. *Laser hair removal* is the use of a laser to damage hair follicles. *Tweezing,* or plucking, is the use of metal forceps to manually pull hairs out. *Electrolysis* is the use of electricity to damage hair follicles. Hair removal products can cause reactions. If they are not used correctly, skin or hair follicles may be damaged.

Reading Review

1. Describe how to wash your hair.
2. List the methods of hair removal.

Caring for Hair

Class Activity

Hair-Care Products Have students create their own fictitious line of hair-care products. They should design the labels for each of the products. The labels should explain to the consumer for whom the product is designed, for what hair type the product is designed, how to use the product, what results the consumer might expect to see, and precautions. Ask students to promote their product to the class. **L2**

Class Discussion

Hair Removal Have students discuss the pros and cons of each hair removal option. Ask students: Are there certain products that would work better for certain people? Are there specific products that might work better on the legs than on the face? If so, which products would work better? **L2**

Teacher FYI

Head Lice Head lice can survive on a human host for up to 30 days, but can only exist for about 24 hours off the human body.

Reading Review

1. *wet hair, lather, rinse, possibly condition, and rinse*
2. *shaving, depilatories, waxing, laser, tweezing, and electrolysis*

📋 Family Involvement

Hair-Care Advertisement Have students discuss hair-care products with their family members. Have students ask the following questions: What shampoos do family members use? What styling products do family members use? What products do family members use for hair removal? Why were the hair-care products chosen? Ask students to create an advertisement for a hair-care product that would meet the needs of the majority of their family members. They could create an ad for an all-purpose shampoo, a versatile styling product, or a hair removal product that is usable by both men and women. Have students present their ads to the class. **L2**

National Health Education Standards
Pages 356–357: 1.1, 7.1, 7.2

Class Discussion

Fragile Hair Have students discuss the care and attention needed in order to maintain healthy Asian, African and Caucasian hair. Ask students to answer these questions: Which type of hair is driest, and what care is appropriate for that hair? Which type of hair is most porous, and what care is appropriate for that hair? **L2**

3 Assess

Vocabulary Practice

Page 22, Unit 6 Fast File Resources

Caring for Different Types of Hair

You inherit your hair type from your parents, and therefore, the race, or mixture of races, from which you have descended. Scientists have identified three basic types of hair—Asian, African, and Caucasian. These three types of hair look different. Each type also responds differently to hair treatments and to elements such as heat and humidity.

Asian hair is usually black and very straight. ▼

Asian hair People with Asian ancestry usually have very straight, black hair. The hair shaft is usually thick and round. The angle of the follicles causes hair to grow straight and perpendicular to the scalp. The density of Asian hair on the scalp (follicles per unit area of skin) is less than that of Caucasian hair. Asian hair grows about 1.3 cm a month. Asian hair is on average the thickest and most coarse hair. Asian hair tends to be highly porous, absorbing, and retains moisture more quickly. Highly porous hair tends to color and perm faster. Use gentler solutions and customize the amount of recommended time for color and perm application.

African hair is usually black and tightly curled. ▼

African hair People with African ancestry usually have hair that is black and tightly curled. The hair shafts are oval in shape. African hair grows almost parallel to the scalp, twisting around itself as it grows. The density is about the same as Caucasian hair. African hair grows a little less than 0.9 cm a month. African hair follicles produce more oils than follicles in other races, but due to the coil in the hair fiber the oils are not evenly distributed. The hair fiber is typically very dry; therefore, African hair needs more oils to supplement its natural oil production and help keep the hair fiber flexible. Also, tightly coiled hair is difficult to comb, so using oils helps reduce friction and static from combing, making hair more manageable. African hair is easily damaged by heat and chemicals. It is vulnerable to the drying effects of products such as relaxers, perms, and hair colorings. African hair requires more intensive conditioning and moisturizing.

Caucasian hair The most varied of the three groups is Caucasian hair. Caucasian hair fibers grow at an oblique angle to the scalp, and may be curly, wavy, or straight. The shaft can be circular or oval and is, on average, thinner than Asian hair. The color ranges from pale blond to black and every shade in between. The diameter of the hair also varies widely. Caucasian hair grows about 1.2 cm a month. Hair follicle density varies and can be related to hair color. Red hair is the least dense, blond hair is the most dense, and brown hair is somewhere in the middle. Hair care varies depending on its characteristics.

Over thousands of years, the basic groups have intermingled. Their descendants display every imaginable hair type and color.

⚖ Sensitive Issues

Hair Types Use caution to avoid any indication of racism when discussing "Caring for Different Types of Hair" with the class. Racism is a prejudice against a group of people based on the belief that members of one's own race are superior genetically, physically, mentally, culturally, and morally to members of other races. Scientists have acknowledged individual differences among ethnic and racial groups. Among these differences is hair type. Approach this topic in a scientific manner, sharing factual information with the class while avoiding any opinions or preferences.

National Health Education Standards

Pages 358–359: 1.1, 1.5, 3.1, 3.4, 7.1, 7.2

acne
antiperspirant
athlete's foot
blister
callus
dandruff
deodorant
dermatologist
lice
moles
psoriasis
warts

Key Terms Review

Complete the fill-in-the-blank statements with the lesson Key Terms on the left. Do not write in this book.

1. _____ is a fungus that grows on feet.

2. _____ is a condition in which dead skin is shed from the scalp producing white flakes.

3. A(n) _____ is a product that reduces the amount of body odor, may reduce the amount of perspiration, and contains fragrance to cover up odor.

4. _____ is a skin disorder in which pores in the skin are clogged with oil.

5. _____ is an immune system disease that often produces inflamed skin that looks like raised red sores covered with thick, white scales.

6. A(n) _____ is a product used to reduce the amount of perspiration.

7. _____ are smooth raised areas on the skin that can be lighter or darker than the surrounding skin.

8. _____ are insects that live and lay eggs in human hair.

9. A(n) _____ is a physician who specializes in the care of the skin.

10. _____ are noncancerous growths on the skin that are caused by a viral infection in the top layer of the skin or tissue.

Recalling the Facts

11. Discuss keeping your hair clean and styled.

12. How can you prevent body odor?

13. Discuss why it is dangerous to go to tanning beds.

14. What can you do about athlete's foot?

15. Why do some people have warts, and how are they treated?

16. What can you do about ingrown toenails?

17. How can acne be treated?

18. Describe what you can do about foot odor.

Critical Thinking

19. Discuss the causes and treatments of blisters, calluses, corns, and bunions.

20. Describe how good grooming improves your physical and social health.

21. Analyze why some teens go tanning even though it damages their skin.

22. What should you do if you have a bad reaction to a grooming product?

Real-Life Applications

23. A mole on your neck sometimes becomes irritated by your shirt. What should you do?

24. Why should you evaluate your decision to get artificial nails before you get them?

25. Describe your hair type. How should you care for your hair?

26. Why should you evaluate your decision to get a body piercing before you get one?

Activities

Responsible Decision Making

27. **Evaluate** All of your friends have the same tattoo on their lower leg and say that it is really cool. They suggest you have the same kind of tattoo applied by a guy they know, who does them in his basement. Write a response to this situation. Refer to the Responsible Decision-Making Model on page 61 for help.

Sharpen Your Life Skills

28. **Access Health Products** Find an advertisement for a skin, nail, or hair product that is designed to appeal to teens. What does the advertisement say about the product? How do the advertisers try to convince teens to buy the product? Would you buy the product? Why or why not?

Visit **www.glencoe.com** for more *Health & Wellness* quizzes.

LESSON 31 • Study Guide **359**

Key Terms Review

1. Athlete's foot
2. Dandruff
3. deodorant
4. Acne
5. Psoriasis
6. antiperspirant
7. Moles
8. Lice
9. dermatologist
10. Warts

Recalling The Facts

11. See page 357.
12. regular bathing, using an antiperspirant or deodorant
13. Tanning beds damage skin, increase risk of skin cancer, and immune system damage.
14. Use foot powder or cream.
15. See page 354.
16. Clip toenails straight across to reduce risk.
17. See page 353.
18. Wash feet regularly, scrub toenails, dry feet well, wear clean socks, and let shoes air out after wearing them.

Critical Thinking

19. See page 354.
20. Good grooming helps reduce the risk of infection from pathogens and helps you have a neat appearance.
21. Answers will vary. Some teens may value short-term appearance over long-term health.
22. Stop using the product. If the rash doesn't clear up, see a dermatologist.

Real-Life Applications

23. See a doctor about having it removed.
24. Bacterial and fungal infections frequently occur with artificial nails.

25. Answers will vary, but should include information from page 358 appropriate for caring for hair type.

26. You should think about the risk of infection, allergic reaction, bleeding, scarring, permanent holes; and broken teeth, choking, and difficulty in speaking with oral piercings.

Activities

Responsible Decision Making

27. Answers will vary, but should include information on risks associated with tattoos.

Sharpen Your Life Skills

28. Answers will vary.

359

Out of Time?

If time does not permit an in-depth study of this topic, use the following activities in this Teacher Wraparound Edition:
- Class Activity, p. 362
- Using the Table, p. 363
- Differentiated Instruction, p. 364

1 Focus

HEALTH GOAL **Sleep Journal** Have students respond to the Health Goal for this lesson by keeping a journal for a week about how they feel throughout the day. Ask students to make note whether they feel well rested or run-down. They should keep an accurate record of how many hours of sleep they get each night. **L2** **ELL**

Write ABOUT IT!

Letter Writing Ask students to write letters to the play's director in their health journals. Have students explain their time constraints for this semester. Students also might suggest that they could participate in next semester's play, if one or more current school activities will end when the semester is over. **L2**

LESSON **32**

Getting Adequate Rest and Sleep

HEALTH GOAL • **I will get adequate rest and sleep.**

The alarm clock rings. You jump out of bed, quickly shower and dress, rush through breakfast, and set off for school. Sound familiar? Most teens rush from one activity to the next. It seems like days are not long enough to get everything done. If you skimp on sleep, you will have extra hours to pack everything into your day. You might even want to brag about how little sleep you get. But lack of rest and sleep will catch up with you.

What You'll Learn

1. Discuss the body changes that occur during the sleep cycle. *(p. 361)*
2. Explain why you need adequate rest and sleep to protect your health status. *(p. 362)*
3. Evaluate whether you are getting adequate sleep and rest. *(p. 362)*
4. List seven tips for getting a good night's sleep. *(p. 363)*

Why It's Important

When you don't get the rest you need you can feel sluggish, irritable, or stressed. You need to get adequate sleep to grow, concentrate, and stay physically and emotionally healthy.

Key Terms

- sleep
- rapid eye movement (REM) sleep
- nonrapid eye movement (NREM) sleep
- tryptophan
- insomnia
- sleep apnea
- restless legs syndrome (RLS)
- narcolepsy

Writing About Adequate Sleep You would like to try out for the school play, but you already have numerous time commitments this semester. Although it sounds like fun, you would have to give up lots of sleep to keep up with your other school activities, studies, and part-time job. After you read the information about getting adequate rest on page 362 write a response to this situation in your health journal.

National Health Education Standards—Guide for Lesson 32		
1.1	Predict how healthy behaviors can impact health status.	pp. 360, 362–364, 365
1.5	Propose ways to reduce or prevent injuries and health problems.	pp. 360, 362–363, 364, 365

The Sleep Cycle

A state of deep relaxation in which there is little movement or consciousness is called *sleep*. There are two kinds of sleep. *Rapid eye movement (REM) sleep* is the period of sleep characterized by rapid eye movements behind closed eyelids. Most dreaming occurs during REM sleep and is very vivid. *Nonrapid eye movement (NMREM) sleep* is the period of sleep in which the eyes are relaxed. NREM sleep can range from very light to very deep sleep.

What to Know About the Sleep Cycle

Sleep is an active state in which the brain continues to process information and the body continues to undergo changes. There are certain stages of sleep that you go through during each night.

The first stage is a transition between being awake and asleep. Each stage progresses to deeper sleep and unresponsiveness. Heart rate slows by about 10–15 beats per minute, blood pressure decreases, fewer breaths are taken per minute, muscles lose tension, and brain waves become much slower. It takes about one hour to get to the stage of deepest sleep.

When you are in the deepest stage of sleep, you begin REM sleep. Brain wave activity increases to the level of your brain when you are awake even though you are asleep. Muscles in your face, arms, legs, and torso remain relaxed, and your eyes dart back and forth in rapid motion. If you are awakened during REM sleep, you will recall a very vivid dream.

Adults spend about one-fourth of a night's sleep in REM sleep. Infants spend half of their sleep in REM sleep. It takes about 90 minutes to go through the stages of sleep. After REM sleep, you start the sequence again. Throughout the night, you repeat the stages of sleep.

Infants sleep about 16 hours a day. From age two until puberty, children need about ten hours of sleep per day. Teens need about eight hours per day, adults need about seven hours per day, and older adults need about six hours per day.

Did You Know?

Record Rockers The record for the longest period without sleep is 18 days, 21 hours, 40 minutes during a rocking chair marathon. The record holder reported hallucinations, paranoia, blurred vision, slurred speech, and memory and concentration lapses.

Amount of Sleep Needed by People of Different Ages (with percentage of time occupied by REM sleep)

Age	
Infants	1-15 days
	3-5 mo
	6-23 mo
Children	2-3 yr
	3-5 yr
	5-9 yr
	10-13 yr
	14-18 yr
Adults	19-30 yr
	33-45 yr
	50-70 yr
	70-85 yr

Time (hours): 0, 4, 8, 12, 16

= Sleep/day
= % REM sleep

Source: University of Southampton, Southampton, U.K.

The Sleep Cycle

2 Teach

Teacher FYI

Dreaming People who sleep eight hours per night spend one-third of their lives sleeping. Everyone dreams but many people don't remember their dreams.

PowerPoint® Presentations

This CD-ROM is an editable Microsoft® PowerPoint® presentation that includes:
- Lesson presentations
- Lesson checks
- Interactive graphics
- 5-Minute Checks
- Image Bank
- All transparencies

CRISS Project

Discussion Refer to the Seed Discussion Strategy on page 17T, and have students write down one important thing about sleep taken from their reading that they would like to use as a subject for class discussion.

Lesson Resource Manager

- **Unit 6 Fast File Resources**
  Reading Strategy, p. 33
  Vocabulary Practice, p. 34
  Transparency Master and Worksheet, p. 35
  Real-Life Health, p. 37
  Real-Life Health, p. 39
  5-Minute Check, p. 41
  Lesson 32 Quiz, p. 42
- **Unit 6 Transparency**
- **Lesson 32 Transparency**

- **Reading Essentials**
- **Technology**
  TeacherWorks™ CD-ROM
  StudentWorks™ CD-ROM
  Reading Essentials CD-ROM
  ExamView® Assessment Suite
  Vocabulary Puzzlemaker

National Health Education Standards
Pages 360–361: 1.1, 7.1, 7.2

Getting Adequate Rest

Getting Adequate Rest

Rest and sleep are essential to good health. You need adequate rest and sleep, or your ability to concentrate is affected. This influences your performance in school, in sports, and in other activities. Your immune system becomes weakened when you do not get enough sleep. People who lack sleep also become more accident-prone. Sleep is needed to restore your physical, emotional, and mental energy. Sleep is even critical to your growth. The growth hormone is released so that growth occurs during rest and sleep.

What to Know About Getting Adequate Rest

The amount of rest and sleep needed varies from person to person according to a person's level of physical activity and usually decreases with age. As a teenager, you often will require extra rest and sleep because of your rapid physical growth. Feeling rested and energetic during the day is a good sign that you have had enough sleep.

Ways to relax and rest Take time for enjoyable activities, such as hobbies, interests, and entertainment, which can energize you. These activities can take your mind off of your problems and worries, therefore reducing stress and promoting relaxation. Participating in physical activities promotes relaxation by providing an outlet for stress and tension. If you feel uptight, try going for a walk, shooting some hoops, or kicking around a soccer ball.

Your biological sleep clock Your body is programmed by your biological clock to feel sleepy during the nighttime hours and to be active during the daytime hours. People who work at night and sleep during the day must constantly fight their biological clock. The same is true for people who fly to other time zones. They get jet lag because they do not maintain a regular sleep/wake schedule. They feel tired and sluggish and may have difficulty falling asleep.

Signs That You Need More Rest and Sleep

You may need to get more rest and sleep if you answer yes to any of the following questions.

- Do you always have to have an alarm clock to wake up?
- Do you have trouble waking up in the morning?
- Do you feel tired and irritable most of the day?
- Do you think about and crave more sleep during the day?
- Do you rely on caffeine to stay awake during the day?

- Do you find yourself dozing off during class?
- Do you doze off while watching television in the evening?
- Do you get more sleep on weekends?
- Do you wake up during the night? If so, what is the cause (dreams, noise, trips to the bathroom)?

TABLE 32.1 Seven Tips for Getting a Good Night's Sleep

Sleep Tips	Encouraging Sleep
Establish a sleep schedule.	Encourage sleep by establishing a regular time to go to bed at night and to get up in the morning.
Engage in activities and nightly rituals that encourage sleep.	Read, take a warm bath, listen to relaxing music. Nightly rituals, such as brushing teeth, setting the alarm clock, and organizing materials for the next day, also encourage sleepiness.
Avoid napping too long.	Restrict naps during the day to 20 or 30 minutes. Avoid naps if you have difficulty falling asleep at night.
Create a comfortable place to sleep.	A medium-hard mattress that supports a person's back, carpets and rugs that muffle sounds, a dark room, and earplugs may make it easier to fall asleep and sleep restfully.
Avoid substances that can interrupt your sleep.	Limit liquid intake before bedtime in order to avoid needing to get up to empty the bladder. Avoid caffeine during the evening. Alcoholic beverages and some sleeping medications suppress REM sleep and cause restlessness. Nicotine in cigarettes is a stimulant.
Watch what you eat before you go to bed.	Do not eat large amounts of food just before going to bed. Hunger pangs can keep you awake if you go to bed hungry.
Get out of bed if you cannot sleep.	If you can't fall asleep after about 30 minutes, get out of bed and go into another room. Try reading, listening to relaxing music, doing a simple task, or having a glass of milk. Milk contains *tryptophan,* which is an amino acid that helps promote relaxation.

Sleep Disorders

According to the National Institute of Health, at least 40 million Americans each year suffer from long-lasting sleep disorders, and 20 million others have occasional sleeping problems. Sleep disorders interfere with a person's ability to work, drive a motor vehicle, and many other activities. There are more than 70 different sleep disorders.

Insomnia At times, not being able to fall asleep is normal. **Insomnia** is the prolonged inability to fall asleep, stay asleep, or get back to sleep once a person is awakened during the night. Insomnia becomes a pattern and can cause problems during the day, such as tiredness, a lack of energy, difficulty concentrating, and irritability. Insomnia affects people of all ages.

Sleep apnea A disorder of brief interruptions of breathing during sleep is called **sleep apnea.** Air cannot flow into or out of the person's nose or mouth at times while asleep, because the person's windpipe (trachea) collapses when muscles relax during sleep. These breathing pauses are usually accompanied with loud snoring and gasping for air. The risk of developing sleep apnea is higher for people who are overweight and increases with age. Sleep apnea is a dangerous medical condition because it deprives a person of oxygen. Sleep apnea can lead to headaches, a decline in mental functioning, breathing disorders, and irregular heartbeats. Sleep apnea is associated with increased risk of heart attacks, stroke, and automobile accidents.

Reading Review

1. Describe sleep apnea.
2. Who has a higher risk of developing sleep apnea?

LESSON 32 • Getting Adequate Rest and Sleep **363**

🛈 Family Involvement

Sleep Habits Have students share what they have learned about sleep and sleep disorders with their parents or guardian. Have students ask the following questions: Has either of their parents ever experienced any sleeping problems? Have they ever not been able to sleep for an extended period of time? Do they snore loudly? Do they wake up frequently during the night? How do they cope with lack of sleep? Have they ever considered or received treatment for their sleeping problem? Were they aware that help was available? Have students share tips from Table 32.1 with their families. **L2**

Using the Table

Tips for a Good Night's Sleep
Have students divide into seven groups. Have each group follow one of the tips for getting a good night's sleep for one week. Have each student keep a journal of how helpful the tip was to their sleeping patterns and how easy it was to accomplish. At the end of the week, have the groups meet to discuss each student's experiences. Have each group share with the class. **L2**

INTERACTIVE CHALKBOARD with Image Bank

5-Minute Check

Page 41, **Unit 6 Fast File Resources**
1. How much of an adult's night is spent in REM sleep? *about one-fourth*
2. What happens to a person's immune system when they do not get enough sleep? *it weakens*
3. How can participation in sports help with sleeping? *It promotes relaxation by providing an outlet for stress and tension.*
4. How many Americans suffer from long-lasting or occasional sleep problems? *60 million*
5. What is insomnia? *the prolonged inability to fall asleep, stay asleep, or get back to sleep once awakened*

Reading Review

1. *disorder of brief interruptions of breathing during sleep*
2. *people who are overweight and older adults*

National Health Education Standards
Pages 362–363: 1.1, 1.2, 1.5, 1.7, 6.1, 7.1, 7.2

Using Goal-Setting and Decision-Making Skills Have students create a sleep survey. They can have other interested students answer questions about their sleeping patterns. After students gather information, they can summarize their findings and present short reports to the class. **L2**

Class Discussion

Narcolepsy Have students discuss how narcolepsy might affect the life of a teenager. Ask students to answer the following questions: In what ways might their social, academic, and emotional life be affected? What could a teen with narcolepsy do to minimize problems in each of these areas? **L2**

3 Assess

Vocabulary Practice

Page 34, **Unit 6 Fast File Resources**

Name _____ Date _____ Class _____

LESSON 32   Getting Adequate Rest and Sleep

Vocabulary Practice

Read each statement below. If the statement is true, write *true*. If the statement is false, write *false*. Then replace the *italicized* word or words to make the statement true.

insomnia	rapid eye movement (REM) sleep	sleep apnea
narcolepsy	restless legs syndrome	tryptophan
nonrapid eye movement (NREM) sleep	sleep	

_____ 1. *Sleep* is an active state in which the brain continues to process information.

_____ 2. *Sleep apnea* is a pattern of sleeplessness that can cause problems such as tiredness, lack of energy, and irritability.

_____ 3. *Rapid eye movement sleep* can range from very light to very deep.

_____ 4. The deepest stage of sleep is *nonrapid eye movement sleep.*

_____ 5. *Insomnia* is a dangerous sleep disorder because it deprives a person of oxygen.

_____ 6. *Tryptophan* is an amino acid that helps promote relaxation.

_____ 7. The period of sleep in which most dreaming occurs is *nonrapid eye movement sleep.*

_____ 8. People with *restless legs syndrome* feel the need to move their lower limbs to relieve discomfort.

_____ 9. People who suffer from *insomnia* have difficulty in getting back to sleep once awakened.

_____ 10. A person with *narcolepsy* may have brain damage as a result of a head injury or disease.

34   LESSON 32 • Getting Adequate Rest and Sleep   UNIT 6

National Health Education Standards

Pages 364–365: 1.1, 1.2, 1.5, 1.7, 2.5, 3.1, 4.1, 6.1, 6.3, 6.4, 7.2

364

Activity: Using Life Skills

Using Goal-setting and Decision-Making Skills: Keeping a Sleep Journal

Healthy people make sure they get enough sleep to be well rested and alert each day. This activity will help you reach that goal.

1 Write your health goal and make an action plan to meet your health goal. Record the number of hours you sleep every night for two weeks. Draw a chart that displays the amount of sleep you got each night and any naps you took during the day.

2 Identify obstacles to your plan and set up a timeline to accomplish your health goal. Answer the questions on page 362.

3 Keep a chart or diary in which you record progress toward your health goal. Based on your answers, write a paragraph on how you can improve your sleeping habits. For example, you could write, "When I drink soda with dinner, I fall asleep later than I should. I will avoid caffeine after 3 p.m."

4 Build a support system. Enlist your family's help in achieving your health goal. For example, you could ask your parents not to buy soda so you will not be tempted to drink it at night.

5 Revise your action plan or timeline, if necessary, and reward yourself when you reach your health goal. Adjust your schedule if you are not getting adequate sleep.

▲ Sample sleep journal page.

Restless legs syndrome (RLS) A sleep disorder in which there are unpleasant sensations in the legs and feet and an urge to move them for relief is called *restless legs syndrome (RLS)*. People with this sleep disorder usually describe feeling a creeping or crawling feeling or sometimes a tingling, cramping, burning, or painful sensation in the legs and feet when trying to sleep.

They feel that they need to move their legs to relieve the discomfort. The moving might be stretching, bending, or rubbing the legs. It might cause a person to toss and turn in bed or get up and pace. RLS can occur at any age, but occurs most often among the elderly. The cause of this disorder is not known. It is sometimes the result of diabetes or pregnancy.

Narcolepsy People with narcolepsy are unable to resist falling asleep regardless of how much sleep they have had. *Narcolepsy* is a disabling condition in which a person experiences "sleep attacks" at inappropriate and various times of the day. "Sleep attacks" can last several seconds or for more than half an hour and include loss of muscle control, hallucinations, and temporary muscle paralysis upon waking. This sleep disorder makes activities like driving or using heavy machinery dangerous for people with the disorder. The sleep attacks also are very embarrassing for people suffering from the disorder. Narcolepsy is a neurological disorder of unknown origin. The symptoms of narcolepsy often begin during the teenage years. Drugs, such as stimulants and antidepressants, can be used to control the narcolepsy and prevent the embarrassing and dangerous effects of falling asleep at inappropriate times. Doctors also recommend taking naps at certain times of the day to reduce the excessive daytime sleepiness.

ⅅⅠ Differentiated Instruction

Visual Impairment Divide students into four groups. Assign each group a different sleep disorder. Students in each group should brainstorm a list of adjectives that describes their assigned disorder. Groups should choose the best five adjectives. Each group should take a turn reciting their list to the rest of the class. The class members could guess which sleep disorder is being described (without the benefit of visual cues). **L2**

insomnia
narcolepsy
nonrapid eye
    movement
    (NREM) sleep
rapid eye movement
    (REM) sleep
restless legs
    syndrome
sleep
sleep apnea
tryptophan

Key Terms Review

Match the definitions below with the lesson Key Terms on the left. Do not write in this book.

1. an amino acid that helps promote relaxation and is found in milk

2. a state of deep relaxation in which there is little movement or consciousness

3. the period of sleep in which the eyes are relaxed

4. a disabling condition in which a person experiences sleep attacks at inappropriate and various times of the day

5. the period of sleep characterized by rapid eye movements behind closed eyelids and when most dreaming occurs

6. prolonged inability to fall asleep

7. people with this sleep disorder usually describe feeling a creeping or crawling feeling or sometimes a tingling

8. a disorder in which there are brief interruptions of breathing during sleep

Recalling the Facts

9. Describe a "sleep attack."

10. How many hours of sleep do children, teens, and adults need?

11. List the tips for getting a good night's sleep.

12. How long should you stay in bed if you are having trouble falling asleep?

13. Explain why sleep apnea is a dangerous medical condition.

14. Why do people get jet lag?

15. How do people describe restless leg syndrome?

16. Discuss the body changes that occur during the sleep cycle.

17. What substances can interrupt your sleep?

18. What shouldn't you eat before trying to sleep?

Critical Thinking

19. List long-term health problems you could develop if you continually did not get adequate rest and sleep.

20. Why is it not helpful to take long naps when experiencing insomnia at night?

21. Explain how adequate sleep protects your health.

22. Describe the last vivid dream you remember having. Which sleep cycle were you in?

Real-Life Applications

23. What nightly rituals do you participate in that encourage sleep?

24. What symptoms do you experience when you do not get enough sleep?

25. How much sleep do you need to feel rested and energized during the day?

26. What time is your "biological clock" set for going to sleep and waking up?

Activities

Responsible Decision Making

27. **Decide** It has been a difficult week for you. You've been up late every night and feel drained. It is Friday, and your best friend has invited you to a party. You want to go, but know that you also need to catch up on your sleep and that you have to work all day Saturday and Sunday. Write a response to this situation. Refer to the Responsible Decision-Making Model on page 61 for help.

Sharpen Your Life Skills

28. **Analyze Influences on Health** Ask a pharmacist about advertisements in magazines and on television for over-the-counter medications to help you get a better night's sleep. How accurate are the claims? How effective are the medications? What risks do the medications pose? Explain why a person should or should not believe the advertisements.

Visit **www.glencoe.com** for more *Health & Wellness* quizzes.

LESSON 32 • Study Guide **365**

Key Terms Review

1. tryptophan
2. sleep
3. NREM
4. narcolepsy
5. REM
6. insomnia
7. restless legs syndrome
8. sleep apnea

Recalling the Facts

9. See page 364.
10. Children need about ten, teens need about eight, adults need about seven.
11. See page 363.
12. about 30 minutes
13. It is dangerous because it deprives a person of oxygen. It can lead to headaches, a decline in mental functioning, breathing disorders, irregular heartbeats, and increased risk of heart attacks, stroke, and motor vehicle accidents.
14. They cannot maintain a regular sleep/wake schedule.
15. creeping or crawling feeling, tingling, cramping, burning, painful sensation
16. See page 361.
17. caffeine, alcohol, some sleeping medications, and nicotine
18. large amounts of food

Critical Thinking

19. lack of energy, difficulty concentrating, irritability, headaches, decline in mental functioning, weakened immune system and impeded growth
20. Long naps could make it difficult to fall asleep later that night.
21. See page 362.
22. Answers will vary. REM

Real-Life Applications

23. Answers will vary, but may include ideas from Table 32.1, "Seven Tips for Getting a Good Night's Sleep," on page 363.

---

24. Answers will vary, but might include tiredness, lack of energy, difficulty concentrating or irritability.

25. Answers will vary, but should be about eight hours.

26. Answers will vary.

Activities

Responsible Decision Making

27. Answers will vary, but should include mentioning the need to catch up on sleep.

Sharpen Your Life Skills

28. Answers will vary, but may include ideas from lesson 4, "Analyzing Influences on Health."

365

Participating in Physical Activity

HEALTH GOALS Out of Time?

If time does not permit an in-depth study of this topic, use the following activities in this Teacher Wraparound Edition:
- Class Discussion, p. 368
- Using the Table, p. 370
- Teacher FYI, p. 371
- Using Life Skills, p. 372

1 Focus

HEALTH GOALS **Benefits of Physical Activity** Have students respond to the Health Goals for this lesson by listing benefits of physical activity. *Answers might include emotional and physical benefits.* **L2**

Write ABOUT IT!

Journaling Student responses should include the type of physical activity they will do, as well as a plan for how much they will do and how they will increase their workout time or intensity as their fitness improves. They may also indicate the types of benefits they will achieve, such as improved cardiorespiratory endurance from aerobic exercise, and the type and length of warm-up and cooldown they plan to do, and how they will implement strategies to avoid physical activity-related injuries and illnesses. **L2**

 LESSON 33

What You'll Learn

1. Outline 11 benefits of regular physical activity. *(p. 367)*
2. Analyze at least ten ways to obtain a moderate amount of physical activity. *(p. 370)*
3. Outline six steps to design an individualized plan for health-related fitness. *(p. 371)*
4. Analyze the four parts of the FITT formula. *(p. 371)*
5. Design a FITT-ness Plan to develop health-related fitness. *(p. 372)*

Why It's Important

Regular physical activity is a vital key to achieving these health goals: having energy, feeling happy and less stressed, controlling your weight, and being healthy now and for many years to come.

Key Terms

- type II diabetes
- life expectancy
- premature death
- cardiac output
- high-density lipoproteins (HDLs)
- low-density lipoproteins (LDLs)
- blood pressure
- dynamic blood pressure
- physical fitness
- FITT formula

Participating in Physical Activity

HEALTH GOALS
- I will participate in regular physical activity.
- I will follow a physical fitness plan.

Any bodily movement produced by skeletal muscles that results in energy expenditure is ***physical activity.*** Physical activity provides many emotional and physical benefits. There are many types of physical activity that will help you enjoy the benefits of being physically active. A physical fitness plan can help motivate and guide you in your physical activity.

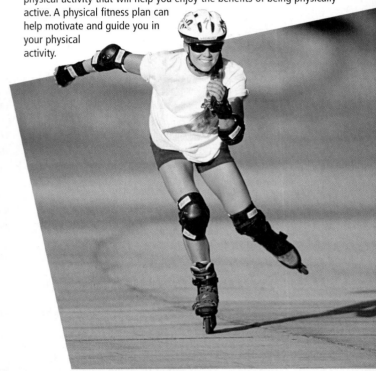

Write ABOUT IT!

Writing About Fitness Suppose a new 5-mile-long asphalt biking and walking path has opened near your home. How long and how hard should you run, walk, bike, or rollerblade to achieve your fitness goals? After you read the information about designing a plan for fitness, write a statement about the healthful behavior you plan to practice to reach your goal in your health journal.

National Health Education Standards—Guide for Lesson 33		
1.1	Predict how healthy behaviors can impact health status.	pp. 366, 367–369, 373
6.1	Assess personal health practices and overall health status.	pp. 366, 367, 372, 373
7.2	Demonstrate a variety of healthy practices and behaviors that will maintain or improve the health of self and others.	pp. 370–372, 373

Physical Activity and Health Status

P hysical activity that is performed on most days of the week is called *regular physical activity.* MyPyramid recommends that children and teenagers be physically active for 60 minutes each day. People who usually are inactive can improve their health and well-being by becoming even moderately active on a regular basis. Physical activity does not have to be strenuous to achieve health benefits.

What to Know About Physical Activity and Health Status

Reduces feelings of depression and anxiety Regular physical activity improves circulation to the brain. As a result, a person feels more alert. Regular physical activity causes the body to produce higher levels of norepinephrine and beta-endorphins. *Norepinephrine* (NOR eh puh neh fruhn) is a chemical that helps transmit brain messages along certain nerves. *Beta-endorphins* are chemicals produced in the brain that create a feeling of well-being. These two chemicals are helpful in reducing the risk of depression.

Regular physical activity counterbalances the bodily changes that occur in the first stage of stress by using up the adrenaline that is secreted. This relieves anxiety and helps the body return to its normal state.

Promotes psychological well-being Performing regular physical activity promotes psychological well-being. Improved appearance from muscle tone and reduced body fat may boost self-confidence. Regular physical activity increases self-discipline and self-respect. Completing a workout makes a person feel accomplished.

Helps control weight Inactivity is a major factor contributing to overweight and obesity. Regular physical activity increases metabolic rate, burns calories, and shrinks fat cells. It also helps regulate the hypothalmus in the brain and decreases appetite.

Regular physical activity also affects body composition. *Body composition* is the percentage of fat tissue and lean tissue in the body. Having too much fat tissue is a risk factor for cardiovascular diseases, diabetes, cancer, and arthritis.

Reduces the risk of developing type II diabetes A type of diabetes in which either the body does not produce enough insulin, or the body cannot properly use the insulin produced is *type II diabetes.*

Did You Know?

BMI Avoiding obesity can reduce the risk of developing chronic diseases. Body Mass Index (BMI) is calculated by the formula

$$BMI = \left(\frac{\text{Weight in pounds}}{\text{(Height in inches) x (Height in inches)}} \right)$$

x 703. A BMI below 18.5 is considered underweight, 18.5–24.9 is normal, 25.0–29.9 is overweight, and 30.0 and above is obese. BMI is one factor in developing chronic diseases. Other factors include blood pressure and family history.

Lesson Resource Manager

- **Unit 6 Fast File Resources**
  Reading Strategy, p. 45
  Vocabulary Practice, p. 46
  Transparency Master and Worksheet, p. 47
  Real-Life Health, p. 49
  Real-Life Health, p. 51
  5-Minute Check, p. 53
  Lesson 33 Quiz, p. 55
- **Unit 6 Transparency**
- **Lesson 33 Transparency**

- **Reading Essentials**
- **Technology**
  TeacherWorks™ CD-ROM
  StudentWorks™ CD-ROM
  Reading Essentials CD-ROM
  ExamView® Assessment Suite
  Vocabulary Puzzlemaker

Physical Activity and Health Status

2 Teach

Class Activity

Write a Letter Ask each student to write a hypothetical letter to a friend who is under a lot of stress or feeling down. The letter should express concern for the friend, and suggest exercise as a way to elevate the friend's mood and relieve stress. Students should explain the psychological benefits that come from physical activity. Advise students that if a friend is severely depressed, exercise may lighten his or her mood, but he or she should seek help. **L2**

INTERACTIVE CHALKBOARD with Image Bank

PowerPoint® Presentations

This CD-ROM is an editable Microsoft® PowerPoint® presentation that includes:
- Lesson presentations
- Lesson checks
- Interactive graphics
- 5-Minute Checks
- Image Bank
- All transparencies

CRISS Project

Discussion Refer to the Authentic Questions Strategy on page 17T, and, as the students read the lesson, ask them to write down questions about physical activity they would like to discuss.

National Health Education Standards

Pages 366–367: 1.1, 1.2, 1.5, 6.1, 7.2

Class Discussion

Stress Relief Have students discuss how regular physical activity can help relieve stress. Ask them to respond to the following questions: Is there a certain type of activity that may be more likely to reduce stress? Why? Can physical activity ever cause stress? When? **L2**

Teacher FYI

Osteoporosis The National Institute of Health states that osteoporosis is a major public health threat for an estimated 44 million Americans. Ten million currently suffer from osteoporosis, and another 34 million are said to have low bone mass which places them at increased risk for developing the condition. Of those diagnosed, 80 percent are women. Although this problem can strike in any ethnic group, it is more prevalent in Caucasians and Asians.

Explain the Concept

Type II Diabetes Students may have heard type II diabetes called either adult-onset diabetes or noninsulin-dependent diabetes. All of these terms refer to the same disease, and that may confuse students.

NHES Assessment/SCASS

Selected Response Regular physical activity can help reduce the swelling around the joints and increase the pain threshold and energy levels of people who have:

A. arthritis
B. osteoporosis
C. cardiovascular disease
D. type II diabetes

Did You Know?

Cardiovascular Disease Cardiovascular disease (heart attacks, strokes) is the number one killer of men and women in the United States. Physically inactive people are twice as likely to develop coronary heart disease as regularly active people.

Controlling weight is one benefit of regular physical activity. ▼

People who are overweight and who are physically inactive have the greatest risk of developing type II diabetes.

Builds and maintains healthy bones, muscles, and joints Weight-bearing physical activity is essential for normal skeletal development in children and teens and for maintaining peak bone mass as people age. A lifetime habit of activities, such as running, walking, or roller-blading, helps prevent osteoporosis. *Osteoporosis* is a disease characterized by low bone mass and deterioration of bone tissue.

Regular physical activity helps joints as well as bones. Stretching helps muscles lengthen. This allows the joints to move freely and easily through the full range of motion. People who have arthritis also benefit. *Arthritis* is a painful inflammation of the joints. Moderate physical activity reduces the swelling around the joints. It increases the pain threshold and energy levels of people who have arthritis.

Reduces the risk of premature death The number of years a person can expect to live is *life expectancy.* Death before a person reaches his or her predicted life expectancy is *premature death.* However, you should know that participating in regular physical activity early in life will affect the quality of your life in middle and late adulthood. Prepare now to live a long and healthful life.

Helps older adults become stronger and better able to avoid falling Regular physical activity may help prevent accidents by improving muscular strength, balance, and reaction time.

Reduces the risk of cardiovascular diseases A disease of the heart and blood vessels is a *cardiovascular disease*. During physical activity, cardiac output increases to provide muscle cells with oxygen. *Cardiac output* is the amount of blood pumped by the heart each minute. Regular physical activity makes the threadlike muscle fibers of the heart thicker and stronger. As a result, the heart does not have to beat as often to maintain the same cardiac output. Resting heart rate is lowered.

Regular physical activity helps control cholesterol levels in the body. *High-density lipoproteins (HDLs)* are substances in blood that carry cholesterol to the liver for breakdown and excretion. *Low-density lipoproteins (LDLs)* are substances in blood that deposit cholesterol in body cells. The cholesterol is not excreted. Physical activity increases the number of HDLs and reduces the risk of developing atherosclerosis. Atherosclerosis is a

---

🏛 Community Involvement

Physical Activity in the Elderly Older adults often need encouragement and support to participate in physical activity. Some older adults may be fearful of going for a walk by themselves. Encourage students to find a couple of friends and ask one or more older adults to take a walk or participate in some other physical activity with them. Perhaps they could organize a nature walk with a group of older adults from a local senior center. Be sure that students obtain permission from a parent or guardian first. **L2**

disease in which fat deposits collect on artery walls. This results in arteries becoming narrow and blood flow being reduced.

Regular physical activity decreases the clumping together of platelets to form a blood clot. The likelihood of developing coronary thrombosis is reduced. ***Coronary thrombosis*** is the narrowing of one of the coronary arteries by a blood clot. This causes a section of the heart muscle to die from lack of oxygen.

Regular physical activity improves coronary collateral circulation. ***Coronary collateral circulation*** is the development of additional arteries that can deliver oxygenated blood to the heart muscle. When you work out, your heart muscle needs more oxygen. Small arteries branch off existing arteries to provide the additional blood flow.

Reduces the risk of developing high blood pressure When your arteries remain elastic, they can dilate when your body needs more oxygenated blood. Resting blood pressure stays in normal range. ***Blood pressure*** is the force of blood against the artery walls. When your arteries are elastic, your dynamic blood pressure remains low.

Dynamic blood pressure is the measure of the changes in blood pressure during the day. Sudden changes in blood pressure can cause a stroke. A ***stroke*** is condition caused by a blocked or broken blood vessel in the brain.

Reduces blood pressure in people who already have high blood pressure People who already have high blood pressure must pay attention to the

▲ Lifetime habits of regular physical activity can be very rewarding.

risk factors over which they have control. Regular physical activity helps them maintain a desirable weight or lose weight if needed. Regular physical activity helps prevent plaque from collecting in artery walls. When arteries are clear, they remain elastic and can dilate when more oxygenated blood is needed. This helps prevent high blood pressure.

Reduces the risk of developing colon cancer Regular physical activity helps the movement of waste through the colon. As a result, a person is more likely to have daily bowel movements, which decreases the risk of colon cancer.

Reading Review

1. How does regular physical activity help control weight?

2. What is type II diabetes?

Prevent and Improve Illnesses Through Regular Physical Activity

Millions of Americans suffer from illnesses that can be prevented or improved through regular physical activity.

- About 64 percent of Americans age 20 years and older are overweight and more than 44 million are obese.
- 17 million people have diabetes.
- About 105,500 people are newly diagnosed with colon cancer each year.

- About 61 million people live with cardiovascular disease including high blood pressure, coronary heart disease, stroke, and congestive heart failure.
- About 950,000 people die of cardiovascular disease each year.

LESSON 33 • Participating in Physical Activity **369**

Extension

Life Expectancy Graph Have students research life expectancy. They should obtain information based on gender and race or ethnicity. They should also look for information about life expectancy for three other countries. All information should be graphed so that it may be easily presented to the class. **L3**

Reading Review

1. *increases metabolic rate, burns calories, shrinks fat cells, and decreases appetite*

2. *a type of diabetes in which the body produces insulin, but the insulin cannot be used by body cells*

5-Minute Check

Page 53, **Unit 6 Fast File Resources**

1. How does regular physical activity improve coronary collateral circulation? *Small arteries branch off of existing arteries to provide additional oxygenated blood to your heart muscle.*

2. What two chemicals that are released during exercise can help reduce the risk of depression? *norepinephrine and beta-endorphins*

3. What is the condition in which bones become thin and brittle? *osteoporosis*

4. How does regular physical activity benefit older adults? *may prevent accidents by improving muscular strength, balance, and reaction time*

5. Which type of cholesterol reduces the risk of atherosclerosis? *high density lipoproteins (HDL)*

⚖️ Legal Issues

Blood Pressure Guidelines In May 2003, the Joint National Committee on Prevention, Detection, Evaluation, and Treatment of High Blood Pressure, which includes representatives from the National Institutes of Health, issued new, stricter guidelines about blood pressure. A new category of prehypertension was introduced for people with systolic pressure—the top number, which occurs when the heart pumps—between 120 and 139 millimeters of mercury (mm Hg) or with diastolic pressure—the bottom number, which occurs when the heart rests—between 80 and 89 mm Hg. Only one of the two numbers needs to be elevated to be considered prehypertension. Normal blood pressure is below 120/80 mm Hg. Hypertension begins at 140/90 mm Hg.

National Health Education Standards

Pages 368–369: 1.1, 1.5

Healthful Physical Activities

Healthful Physical Activities

NHES Assessment/SCASS

Performance Event Have students list ideas of nontraditional ways they can achieve moderate physical activity. They should include activities that do not require access to exercise equipment and activities that can be performed during bad weather. **L2**

Teacher FYI

Rating of Perceived Exertion The Borg Rating Scale is a subjective measure of Perceived Exertion of effort while exercising and a gauge of how hard you are working. The scale is as follows: 6–nothing, 7.5–extremely light, 11–light, 13–somewhat hard, 15–hard, 17–very hard, 19–extremely hard, 20–maximal exertion. It is suggested that a level of 12–14 should be maintained to achieve cardio respiratory benefit.

Using the Table

Exercise Regimen Have students use the table and the information on "Ways to Get a Moderate Amount of Physical Activity" to plan a regimen of regular physical activity. If they are already physically active, have them modify the intensity or length of time they would perform the activity to reap even more benefits. If students want to implement their plan, caution them to get a physician's approval first. **L2**

Quick Demo

Equipment Show students equipment that is easy to obtain and that can be used to achieve moderate physical activity. Examples include a jump rope, snow shovel, walking or running shoes, a basketball, a swimsuit, or a rake. **ELL**

National Health Education Standards
Pages 370–371: 1.5, 7.2

S hort sessions of strenuous activity are not the only way to achieve physical activity. The same amount of activity can be obtained in longer sessions of moderately intense activities such as brisk walking. If you already participate in moderate physical activity, you can benefit even more by increasing the time or intensity of your activity.

Ways to Get a Moderate Amount of Physical Activity

> **Make the Connection**
>
> **Exercise** For more information on exercise and health-related fitness, see page 375 in Lesson 34.

A moderate amount of physical activity can be achieved in a variety of different ways. You might choose to jump rope, ride a bike, or shovel snow for 15 minutes. Or perhaps you can run 1.5 miles in 15 minutes. How about washing and waxing a car or washing windows or floors for 45 minutes? You might choose to play touch football for 30–40 minutes or a game of basketball for 15–20 minutes or volleyball for 45 minutes. You can accomplish the same results if you walk 1.75 miles in 35 minutes, swim laps for 20 minutes, do water aerobics for 30 minutes, or stair walk for 15 minutes. You can choose different activities at different times.

TABLE 33.1 Achieving a Moderate Amount of Physical Activity

	Activity	Time
	Dance: Any kind of dancing can provide health benefits. Consider tap dancing, ballet, ballroom dancing, square dancing, Irish dancing, swing dancing, or salsa, or visit a dance club.	60 minutes: You can break this up into three 20-minute periods of activity and still receive the same health benefits.
	Rake leaves: Many people consider raking a chore, but it can be one of the most healthful ways to enjoy autumn weather. Bundle up, grab a rake, and take in the sight of the multicolored leaves still on the trees or covering the grass.	60 minutes: You can break this up into three 20-minute periods of activity and still receive the same health benefits.
	Play wheelchair basketball: Some people mistakenly assume that people who are disabled cannot exercise or play sports. They are wrong. Basketball is a popular sport among people who have physical disabilities.	60 minutes: You can break this up into three 20-minute periods of activity and still receive the same health benefits.

(DI) Differentiated Instruction

Physical Challenges Have students discuss activities that can be performed by those with physical challenges. Some questions you could ask include: What modifications can be made for people with physical challenges who want to be physically active? What types of sports or activities are offered in your school for those who have physical challenges? What types of sports or activities are available in your community for people with physical challenges? **L2**

Physical Fitness Plans

T he ability to perform physical activities and to meet the demands of daily living while being energetic and alert is called *physical fitness*. To become physically fit, you must participate in physical activities that develop each of the components of health-related and skill-related fitness. A *physical fitness plan* is a written plan of physical activities to develop each of the components of fitness and a schedule for doing them.

What to Know About Physical Fitness Plans

Follow these steps to develop health-related and skill-related fitness.

Design a physical fitness plan. Include the goal or goals you want to reach and when you want to reach them.

Use the FITT formula. A formula in which each letter represents a factor for determining how to obtain fitness benefits from physical activity is the ***FITT formula:*** *F*-Frequency, *I*-Intensity, *T*-Time, and *T*-Type.

Physical Fitness Plan

Today's date:

My goal:

Date to reach goal:

Plan:
Warm-up, FITT formula

Include a warm-up and cooldown. Five to ten minutes of easy physical activity to prepare the muscles to do more work is a ***warm-up***. Five to ten minutes of reduced physical activity to help the body return to the nonexercising state is a ***cooldown***. A warm-up and cooldown reduce the risk of physical activity-related injuries.

Include aerobic exercises to develop cardiorespiratory endurance and a healthful body composition. Do aerobic exercises three to five days a week at your target heart rate. If you want to lose weight, figure 1.8 calories for each pound of your body weight to calculate how many calories you should burn per session.

Include resistance exercises to develop muscular strength and muscular endurance. Lift your own weight, lift free weights, or lift weights on a weight machine. Do resistance exercises two to four days a week with a day of rest between workouts. Increase resistance gradually.

> **Make the Connection**
>
> **FITT Formula** For more information about the FITT Formula, see page 378 in Lesson 34.

Did You Know?

Target Heart Rate Your target heart rate is the number of beats per minute that will be safe and will provide you with maximum cardiovascular benefits. Target heart rate depends upon your age and physical fitness level. Talk to your doctor to determine your target heart rate.

LESSON 33 • Participating in Physical Activity **371**

🔹 Achieving Health Literacy

Self-Directed Learner Have students follow the steps described on the student pages to develop their own physical fitness plans. They should make sure to clearly state their goals and when they want to reach them. They might want to include both short- and long-term fitness goals. Students should be as detailed as possible about how they will achieve fitness benefits by using the FITT formula. The FITT formula should be used for each type of exercise they will do. Have students make health behavior contracts to follow their physical fitness plans and try to meet their goals. Before beginning their physical fitness plans, students should consult their physicians. **L2**

Physical Fitness Plans

Class Activity

Warm-Up and Cooldown Have students work in groups to generate a list of activities that could be used to warm-up and cooldown before and after rigorous physical activities. If they need ideas, encourage them to ask a physical education teacher, coach, or a trainer. Students should list the activity, how long it should be performed, and whether it should be done to warm-up, cooldown, or both. **L2 ELL**

Teacher FYI

Staying Motivated Starting a fitness program is easy, while maintaining it can prove to be more difficult. Here are some suggestions for staying motivated: 1. Select a variety of physical activities. 2. Work out with a friend. 3. Work out with family members. 4. Reward yourself when you reach a goal. 5. Record your progress. 6. Listen to music. 7. Have a backup plan for bad weather. 8. Organize your day so it is easy to work out. 9. Join a sports club or team. 10. Take lessons to improve a fitness skill.

INTERACTIVE CHALKBOARD with Image Bank

5-Minute Check

Page 54, **Unit 6 Fast File Resources**

1. What is physical fitness? *the ability to perform physical activities and to meet the demands of daily living while being energetic and alert*
2. What do the letters in FITT stand for? *Frequency, Intensity, Time, Type*
3. Why are warm-ups and cooldowns important? *They reduce the risk of physical activity-related injuries.*
4. How often should aerobic exercises be performed? *three to five days per week*
5. How long should warm-up activities be performed? *five to ten minutes*

Using Life Skills

Using Goal-Setting and Decision-Making Skills People often get bored doing the same activities over and over. Have students include at least two different styles of aerobic, resistance, and stretching activities in their fitness plan. Have them ask a physical education teacher, coach, or personal trainer for a list of different types of activities. **L2**

3 Assess

Vocabulary Practice

Page 46, **Unit 6 Fast File Resources**

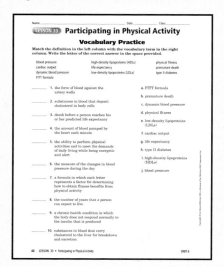

Activity: Using Life Skills

Using Goal-Setting and Decision-Making Skills: Creating a FITT-ness Plan

Follow these steps when you design your physical fitness plan to make sure you've included everything you need to stay healthy.

1 Write your health goal. Design a physical fitness plan. Decide which aerobic and strength-training exercises you want to do and how often you will do them.

2 Make an action plan to meet your health goal. Use the FITT formula. The FITT formula stands for F=Frequency, I=Intensity, T=Time, T=Type. This formula will make sure you are working out at the best pace to see results and prevent injury.

3 Identify obstacles to your plan. To reduce your chance of injury, you need to spend 5–10 minutes warming up your muscles before you do aerobic or strength training and 5–10 minutes cooling down after. Try a slow jog or do a less intense version of your workout to get your body prepared.

4 Set up a time line to accomplish your health goal. Do aerobic exercise three to five times a week. Determine your target heart rate with your doctor. Maintain continuous activity for a minimum of 15 minutes and continue for up to 60 minutes.

5 Keep a chart or diary in which you record progress toward your health goal. Do resistance training two to four days a week, working the upper and lower parts of your body and opposing muscle groups (like your abdominals and your back). Do three sets of 8–12 repetitions for each exercise and record your progress.

6 Build a support system. Enlist a friend or family member to work out with you. He or she can help you with stretching exercises, which you should do two to three times a week as part of your warm-up and cooldown. Hold each stretch for 15–30 seconds, then rest for 30–60 seconds. Perform each stretch three to five times. Do not bounce while you stretch.

7 Revise your action plan or timeline, if necessary, and reward yourself when you reach your health goal. Set a small goal at first and then set your sights a little higher. Keep track of your progress.

Running is an aerobic exercise that ▶ teens can incorporate into their physical fitness plans.

Perform three sets of 8–12 repetitions of each exercise with free weights or weight machines. Perform additional exercises when using your body for resistance.

Include static stretching exercises to develop flexibility. Perform various stretching exercises two to three days a week. Hold each stretch for 30 seconds, then rest for 30–60 seconds. Repeat each stretch three to five times. Your flexibility workout should last for 15–30 minutes. Also include stretching exercises as part of your warm-up and cooldown to reduce the risk of injuries, such as sprains, strains, and tendonitis.

372 UNIT 6 • Personal Health and Physical Activity

Cross-Curricular Connections

Music Have students record a compilation of songs that would be appropriate and motivational for a particular type of exercise. The music should last for as long as a typical exercise session, which could be 20–60 minutes, or more. Have them specify whether the music is for an aerobic workout, strength training session, or for a stretching or yoga class. Have them use their music compilation tapes while exercising according to their fitness plans. Ask students to answer the following questions: What did you like about the music? What didn't you like? What changes would you like to make in your music choices so that you will enjoy using the tapes for future exercise sessions? **L2**

LESSON

33 STUDY GUIDE

arthritis
blood pressure
cardiac output
coronary thrombosis
dynamic blood
  pressure
FITT formula
high-density
  lipoproteins
  (HDLs)
life expectancy
low-density
  lipoproteins (LDLs)
physical fitness
premature death
type II diabetes

Key Terms Review

Explain the relationship between the pairs of lesson Key Terms below. Do not write in this book.

1. cardiac output—FITT formula
2. life expectancy—premature death
3. blood pressure—dynamic blood pressure
4. physical fitness—type II diabetes
5. high-density lipoproteins (HDLs)—low-density lipoproteins (LDLs)

Recalling the Facts

6. List three benefits of regular physical exercise.
7. What is one of the greatest risk factors for developing type II diabetes?
8. List five illnesses that can be prevented or improved through regular physical activity.
9. List five examples of moderate physical activity.
10. What is the FITT formula?
11. How is regular physical activity related to osteoporosis and arthritis?
12. Why does regular physical activity reduce the risk of cardiovascular diseases?
13. What kind of exercise develops muscular strength and muscular endurance?
14. What is arthritis?
15. What is cardiac output?
16. Explain how changes in blood pressure can cause a stroke.
17. What is osteoporosis?
18. How does regular physical activity help control weight?

Critical Thinking

19. What steps would you take to help a friend who does not exercise to design an individualized health plan for fitness?
20. Explain the benefits of using the FITT formula.
21. Discuss how the collection of plaque on the walls of arteries is related to blood pressure.
22. Explain why it is important to keep a record of your progress when you set a health goal.

Real-Life Applications

23. What are five activities you like to participate in that provide a moderate amount of physical activity?
24. Which of the six steps to follow to design an individualized plan for health-related fitness do you have trouble doing and why?
25. What would you include in your personal FITT-ness plan?
26. Which benefit of regular physical activity is most meaningful to you? Explain.

Activities

Responsible Decision Making

27. **Write** You usually are busy with school and a part-time job. You get a moderate amount of physical activity by walking to school every day. Your friends ask you to ride to school with them. They do not understand why you choose to walk to school rather than hang out with them. Write a response to this situation. Refer to the Responsible Decision-Making Model on page 61 for help.

Sharpen Your Life Skills

28. **Advocate for Health** Your school district is changing its curriculum. Some of the people who live in your city suggest dropping physical education from the curriculum. They argue that time will be better spent on subjects that are more academic, such as math or science. Write a letter to the editor of your local paper. Explain the importance of having physical education in the curriculum.

Visit **www.glencoe.com** for more *Health & Wellness* quizzes.

Key Terms Review

1. Cardiac output is affected by fitness level and each of the four factors in the FITT formula.
2. Premature death occurs before a person reaches his or her predicted life expectancy.
3. Dynamic blood pressure is the measure of the changes in blood pressure during the day.
4. People who are physically fit are at lower risk of developing type II diabetes than physically inactive people.
5. HDLs carry the cholesterol to the liver for breakdown, LDLs deposit cholesterol in body cells.

Recalling the Facts

6. See pages 367–369.
7. being overweight and inactive
8. See pages 367–369.
9. See page 370.
10. Frequency, Intensity, Time, Type
11. See page 368.
12. See pages 368–369.
13. resistance exercise
14. painful inflammation of the joints
15. Amount of blood pumped by the heart each minute.
16. See page 369.
17. A condition in which bones become thin and brittle; see page 368.
18. See page 367.

Critical Thinking

19. Have your friend follow the steps in the Using Life Skills activity on page 372. Offer to work out with your friend.
20. The formula helps ensure that you are working out at the best pace to see results and prevent injury.
21. Plaque on the walls of arteries makes them less elastic, and less able to dilate when more oxygenated blood is needed. This increases blood pressure.
22. A record will show your progress toward your goal, and that will help you stay motivated.

Real-Life Applications

23. Answers may include: walking, shooting baskets, dancing, bicycling, and volleyball.

---

24. Answers should include at least one reason why it is difficult.
25. Answers should include all four factors in the FITT formula.
26. Answers will vary.

Activities

Responsible Decision Making

27. Possible answer: Walking to school is one way that I fit physical activity into my schedule. Why don't you walk to school with me? Then, we can spend time together and get some exercise at the same time.

Sharpen Your Life Skills

28. Students' letters will vary, but should include information about the importance of physical activity and its benefits.

Practicing Fitness

If time does not permit an in-depth study of this topic, use the following activities in this Teacher Wraparound Edition:

- Class Activity, p. 376
- Class Discussion, p. 379
- Explain the Concept, p. 380
- Quick Demo, p. 384

1 Focus

HEALTH GOALS **Benefits of Physical Fitness** Have students respond to the first Health Goal for this lesson by listing in their health journals the benefits of being physically fit. *Reasons might include being able to meet the demands of daily living while being energetic and alert.* **L2**

Write ABOUT IT!

Journaling Student answers may include stretches such as across-the-body, ankle flex, calf stretcher, lateral stretch, side lunge, sit and reach, spine twist, step stretch, towel stretch, and upper back stretch. **L2**

LESSON 34

What You'll Learn

1. Examine five kinds of exercise. *(p. 375)*
2. Using the FITT formula, examine how to develop cardiorespiratory endurance, flexibility, and muscular strength and endurance. *(pp. 378, 379, 380)*
3. Examine six fitness skills. *(p. 382)*
4. Examine the benefits of various lifetime sports and physical activities. *(p. 384)*
5. Examine the behaviors and characteristics of responsible sports spectators and participants. *(p. 390)*

Why It's Important

Developing lifetime fitness will increase the quality and length of your life.

Key Terms

- health-related fitness
- aerobic exercise
- anaerobic exercise
- isometric exercise
- isotonic exercise
- isokinetic exercise
- static stretching
- resistance exercise
- skill-related fitness
- agility

Practicing Fitness

HEALTH GOALS
- I will develop and maintain health- and skill-related fitness.
- I will be a responsible spectator and participant in sports.

The ability to perform physical activity and to meet the demands of daily living while being energetic and alert is *physical fitness*. The ability of the heart, lungs, muscles, and joints to function at optimal capacity is *health-related fitness*. Skill-related fitness is the capacity to perform well in sports and physical activities. This lesson discusses exercises that promote health-related fitness, the components of skill-related fitness, and how to be a responsible sports spectator and participant.

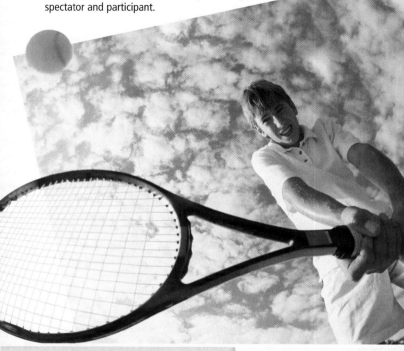

Write ABOUT IT!

Writing About Flexibility Suppose you want to become more physically fit. In a fitness assessment test, you scored low in flexibility. What physical activities could you engage in that would help you improve your flexibility? After you read the information on flexibility on page 379, write a summary in your health journal of the types of activities that would help you improve your flexibility.

National Health Education Standards—Guide for Lesson 34		
1.1	Predict how healthy behaviors can impact health status.	pp. 374, 379, 381, 383
1.5	Propose ways to reduce or prevent injuries and health problems.	pp. 374, 383, 391
7.1	Analyze the role of individual responsibility for enhancing health.	p. 374
7.2	Demonstrate a variety of healthy practices and behaviors that will maintain or improve the health of self and others.	pp. 374, 379–381, 384, 385

Exercise and Health-Related Fitness

T here are five components of health-related fitness: cardiorespiratory endurance, muscular strength, muscular endurance, flexibility, and healthful body composition.

What to Know About Exercise and Health-Related Fitness

Cardiorespiratory endurance is the ability of the circulatory and respiratory systems to supply oxygen during sustained physical activity. *Flexibility* is the ability to bend and move the joints through the full range of motion. *Muscular strength* is the maximum amount of force a muscle can produce in a single effort. *Muscular endurance* is the ability of the muscle to continue to perform without fatigue. *Healthful body composition* is the ratio of lean body mass to body fat.

Exercise is planned, structured, and repetitive bodily movement done to improve or maintain one or more components of physical fitness. There are five kinds of exercises: aerobic, anaerobic, isometric, isotonic, and isokinetic.

Aerobic exercise An exercise in which large amounts of oxygen are required continually for an extended period of time is an *aerobic exercise.* These exercises are vigorous, continuous, and rhythmic. They improve cardiorespiratory endurance and body composition, and help develop flexibility and muscular strength.

Anaerobic exercise An exercise in which the body's demand for oxygen is greater than what is available during exertion is an *anaerobic exercise.* Anaerobic exercises help improve muscular strength and endurance and flexibility.

Isometric exercise An exercise in which a muscle is tightened for about 5–8 seconds and there is no body movement is an *isometric exercise.* Isometric exercises strengthen muscles.

Isotonic exercise An exercise in which a muscle or muscles moves against a resistance weight and/or gravity 8–15 times is an *isotonic exercise.* Weight lifting, push-ups, squats, and curl-ups are isotonic exercises. Isotonic exercises improve muscular strength and endurance, and increase flexibility.

Isokinetic exercise An aexercise that uses special machines to provide weight resistance through the full range of motion is an *isokinetic exercise.* Isokinetic exercises promote muscular strength and endur-ance, and flexibility.

Did You Know?

Staying Active
The key to staying active is to select an exercise or activity that you like to do and that you want to do. No single exercise is the best. For example, jogging can be an excellent choice for some people, but it's not for everyone.

2 Teach

Class Discussion

Sport-Specific Training Have students discuss which type(s) of exercises would be most suitable and beneficial for specific sports. Ask them which exercises would be best for basketball, baseball, golf, tennis, or soccer. Have students give reasons for their examples. **L2**

PowerPoint® Presentations

This CD-ROM is an editable Microsoft® PowerPoint® presentation that includes:
- Lesson presentations
- Lesson checks
- Interactive graphics
- 5-Minute Checks
- Image Bank
- All transparencies

CRISS Project

Discussion Refer to the Read-and-Say Something Strategy on page 17T, and ask students in cooperative groups to silently read passages about different kinds of exercise and then take turns saying something about the topic until it has been thoroughly covered.

Lesson Resource Manager

- **Unit 6 Fast File Resources**
  Reading Strategy, p. 59
  Vocabulary Practice, p. 60
  Transparency Master and Worksheet, p. 61
  Real-Life Health, p. 63
  Real-Life Health, p. 65
  5-Minute Check, p. 67
  Lesson 34 Quiz, p. 71
- **Unit 6 Transparency**
- **Lesson 34 Transparency**

- **Reading Essentials**
- **Technology**
  TeacherWorks™ CD-ROM
  StudentWorks™ CD-ROM
  Reading Essentials CD-ROM
  ExamView® Assessment Suite
  Vocabulary Puzzlemaker

National Health Education Standards
Pages 374–375: 1.1, 1.5, 7.1, 7.2

Cardiorespiratory Endurance

Class Activity

Cardiorespiratory Activities Have students divide into several groups. Each group should generate a list of activities that will improve cardiorespiratory endurance. Each group should share its list with the class. **L2**

Explain the Concept

Diabetes Explain to the students that diabetes is a disease in which the body produces little or no insulin or cannot use the insulin it does produce. Insulin is a hormone that regulates the blood sugar level. If the pancreas does not produce enough insulin, a person develops diabetes. Diabetes disrupts a person's metabolism.

NHES Assessment/SCASS

Selected Response Which type of exercise is most effective at improving cardiorespiratory endurance?

A. isokinetic exercise
B anaerobic exercise
C. *aerobic exercise*
D. isometric exercise

Cardiorespiratory Endurance

The ability of the circulatory and respiratory systems to supply oxygen during sustained physical activity is cardiorespiratory endurance. This kind of endurance improves as you regularly participate in aerobic exercises, such as jogging or swimming.

Did You Know?

Physical Activity Only about one-half of U.S. young people (ages 12 to 21) regularly participate in physical activity. One-fourth reported no vigorous physical activity. About 14 percent reported no recent vigorous or light-to-moderate exercise.

What to Know About Cardiorespiratory Endurance

Heart and lung function and metabolic rate Cardiorespiratory endurance helps your heart and lungs function more efficiently and improves your metabolic rate. Physical activities that promote cardiorespiratory endurance burn calories. They raise the resting metabolic rate for up to 12 hours.

Healthful aging Healthful aging also is promoted because physical activities that promote cardiorespiratory endurance activate antioxidants. Antioxidants are substances that protect cells from being damaged by oxidation. Antioxidants also remove free radicals, which are highly reactive compounds that can damage body cells. Free radicals are believed to be one cause of aging.

Insulin sensitivity Cardiorespiratory endurance also improves insulin sensitivity, which helps with the metabolism of carbohydrates, fats, and proteins. The risk of developing diabetes is lowered.

Alarm stage of GAS General adaptation syndrome (GAS) is a series of body changes that result from stress. Cardiorespiratory endurance reduces the harmful effects of the alarm stage of the GAS. During the alarm stage of stress, two hormones are secreted. Epinephrine and cortisol put the body in a state of emergency. Too much of these two hormones increases the risk of developing cardiovascular diseases and also can suppress the immune system. This increases the risk of developing certain kinds of cancers. Physical activities help prevent too much of these two hormones in the bloodstream.

Ability of muscles Cardiorespiratory endurance improves the ability of muscles to avoid lactic acid buildup.

Physical activity has many benefits as people age. ▶

📅 Family Involvement

Diabetes Have students discuss diabetes with their adult family members. They should ask the following questions: Do any members of the family have a history of this condition? How are they dealing with it? Are they keeping it under control? Are they using exercise, medication, change in diet, or a combination of these things to control it? Are their methods of controlling diabetes successful? Students with a family history of diabetes should find out if other family members are making an effort to reduce their risk of developing this disease, and if so, what they are doing. Do not ask students to share family health information. **L2**

Lactic acid is produced by muscles during vigorous exercise and is one of the factors that causes cramps. Physical activities that promote cardiorespiratory endurance provide a training effect because they lengthen the time people can exercise without feeling fatigue or cramping.

HDLs Physical activities that promote cardiorespiratory endurance increase the number of high-density lipoproteins (HDLs) and decrease the number of low-density lipoproteins (LDLs). HDLs carry cholesterol to the liver for breakdown and excretion. This reduces the risk of developing cardiovascular diseases.

Immune system Cardiorespiratory endurance improves the function of the immune system. You may have fewer colds and upper respiratory infections. (Caution: Overly strenuous physical activity may depress the function of the immune system.)

Movement of food Physical activities that promote cardiorespiratory endurance speed the movement of food through the gastrointestinal tract. When people have daily bowel movements, their risk of developing colon cancer decreases.

Psychological well-being Psychological well-being is improved. Physical activity can help you manage stress more effectively, reduce anger and frustration, relax and sleep more restfully, and increase your self-esteem and confidence.

Benefits of warm-ups A period of 5–10 minutes of light physical activity to prepare the muscles to do more work is a *warm-up.*

 www.glencoe.com

How Many Calories Does Exercise Burn?

Walking slowly and stretching are examples of light-intensity activities. Walking briskly and weight lifting are moderate-intensity activities. Vigorous-intensity activities include swimming laps or jogging. The American Heart Association recommends that everyone participate in low-to-moderate intensity activities for at least 30 minutes at a time, a minimum of three times per week.

The numbers in the chart below are based on a person weighing 150 pounds. To convert these numbers to your own weight, use the following formula: Your weight divided by 150 equals W. W times the number of calories burned by the activity equals the number of calories you burn per hour of activity.

Health Online Visit www.glencoe.com for more information on exercise.

Activity and Calories Burned per Hour

Activity	Calories
Bicycling	240-410
Gymnastics	270
Baseball	282
Skating	300
Tennis	400
Swimming	275-500
Hiking and backpacking	408
Dancing	420
Walking (brisk)	440
Soccer	540
Football	540
Ice hockey	546
Field hockey	546
Basketball	564
Cross-country skiing	700
Racquetball	750
Jumping rope	750
Jogging	740-920
Running	650-1280

Source: *Physical Activity,* The National Heart, Lung, and Blood Institute, 2003

Analyzing the Chart
Study the chart above and answer these questions.

1. How many calories will a 170-pound person burn while playing basketball for 1 hour?

2. How many calories will a 125-pound person burn while walking briskly for 2 hours?

LESSON 34 • Practicing Fitness **377**

Analyzing Graphs
1. 639 calories
2. 733 calories

Project
Exercise Benefits Have students create a pamphlet or brochure that explains the health benefits of regular exercise. They should include a list of activities and the number of calories people can burn per hour by participating in each activity. **L2 ELL**

Class Discussion
A Runner's High Have students discuss the phrase "a runner's high" by responding to the following questions: Why might a runner experience this type of euphoria? *The explanation for a runner's high is not clearly known, but it probably involves both chemicals, such as endorphins, and psychological factors, such as self-esteem felt by people who are fit enough to perform strenuous exercise.* Have students who have experienced this sensation share their experience with the class. **L2**

Healthy People 2010

Objective 22-6 *Increase the proportion of adolescents who engaged in moderate physical activity for at least 30 minutes on five or more of the previous seven days.*

Twenty-seven percent of students in grades 9 through 12 engaged in moderate physical activity for at least 30 minutes on five or more of the previous seven days in 1999. The Healthy People 2010 target is 35 percent. Assuming that students in your school are at 27 percent, have students calculate the number of students in their school who would need to engage in moderate physical activity more frequently in order to meet the 35 percent target. Have your students consider whether they are meeting the activity goal themselves. Have them make lists of specific, realistic actions that can be taken to increase moderate physical activity among students in their school. **L3**

National Health Education Standards
Pages 376–377: 2.10

A thorough warm-up ▲ must always come before stretching exercises.

As you warm up, more blood flows to active muscles. Your muscles work better when their temperature is slightly above resting level. As you warm up, synovial fluid, which lubricates and provides nutrition to the cells on the surface of joints, spreads throughout the joints. These body changes enhance performance and decrease the chances of injury from physical activities.

Reading Review

1. List nine benefits of cardio-respiratory endurance.
2. Why is a cooldown important?

Benefits of cooldowns A period of five to ten minutes of reduced physical activity to help the body return to a nonexercising state is a *cooldown.* As you cool down, your heart rate, breathing, and circulation return to normal. You should include stretching exercises during a cooldown. If you do not cool down, your muscles will be sore and you will be more likely to experience a pulled muscle.

How do I maintain cardiorespiratory endurance? You will notice steady improvement for about four to six weeks when you begin a training program. During training sessions, you have to gradually increase intensity and time to become more fit. As you become more fit, it will be more difficult to make gains. When you reach an acceptable level of cardiorespiratory fitness, begin a maintenance program. Continue training at the same intensity on at least three non-consecutive days of the week.

What is a test to measure cardiorespiratory endurance? The one-mile walk test measures cardiorespiratory fitness based on the amount of time it takes a person to complete one mile of brisk walking and his or her heart rate at the end of the walk. Age, gender, and body weight also are considered. A fast time and a low heart rate are desirable. This test is included in the Using Life Skills feature on page 383.

The FITT Formula

The **FITT formula** is a formula in which each letter represents a factor for determining how to obtain fitness benefits from physical activity.

- **F**requency is how often you will perform physical activities. You should participate in physical activity three to five days a week. Less frequent activity will not produce fitness benefits, and more might stress your immune system and lead to injury.
- **I**ntensity is how hard you will perform physical activities.
- **T**ime is how long you will perform physical activities. The length of time you perform physical activity will depend on the intensity.
- **T**ype is the kind of physical activities you will perform to develop fitness.

378 **UNIT 6** • Personal Health and Physical Activity

◄ Timing is essential for the 1-mile walk test.

Flexibility

The ability to bend and move the joints through the full range of motion is *flexibility.* A measure of your flexibility is your ability to move your joints through their natural range of motion.

What to Know About Flexibility

What are the benefits of flexibility?
Flexibility helps improve quality of life. If you are flexible, you can bend and move easily and without pain. Flexibility decreases the likelihood of having accidents, such as falls, and it helps prevent lower back pain and injuries to muscles and joints. With flexibility, the symptoms associated with arthritis also may be prevented or relieved. Performance in such sports as golf and tennis, in which a range of motion is required, improves when you are flexible.

How does one develop flexibility?
Follow the FITT formula to improve flexibility. For **F**requency, perform stretching exercises two to three times a week and as part of your warm-up and cooldown.

For **I**ntensity, hold each stretch for 15–30 seconds. Rest for 30–60 seconds between each stretch. Repeat each stretching exercise three to five times.

For **T**ime, include exercises to stretch the muscles that work each of the major joints in the body. This will probably take you 15–30 minutes.

For **T**ype, you should understand that there are two techniques for stretching muscles that move joints: static stretching and ballistic stretching.

Static stretching is stretching the muscle to a point where a pull is felt and holding the stretch for 15–30 seconds. Static stretching is safe and effective. *Ballistic stretching* is rapidly stretching the muscle with a bouncing movement. Fitness experts warn against ballistic stretching because it may cause injuries. Stretching should be a slow and gentle movement. Begin each stretch gradually and hold it when you feel a comfortable pull.

Do stretching exercises, such as across-the-body, ankle flex, calf stretch, lateral stretch, side launch, sit and reach, spine twist, step stretch, towel stretch, and upper back stretch.

What test is used to measure flexibility? Several tests measure flexibility. The V-sit reach test assesses flexibility by measuring how far you can lean forward. This test is included in the Using Life Skills on page 383.

Do I need to warm up and cool down when I do stretching exercises? Warm up by walking or jogging slowly for 5–10 minutes. This increases blood flow to muscles to get them ready for more work. Begin gradually with slow stretches. Finish your workout with a cooldown. Walking and easy jogging improve circulation. Easy stretches keep you from being sore.

> **Make the Connection**
>
> **Preventing Injuries**
> For more information on preventing physical activity-related injuries and illnesses, see page 394 in Lesson 35.

Muscular Strength and Endurance

Quick Demo

Weight Training Show students some examples of exercises to build muscle strength and endurance. Bring in a light free weight or, if none is available, a food can. Show students a few exercises such as biceps curls, lateral raises, and front raises. You or a student volunteer could also demonstrate a push-up or sit-up. If you do not know how to properly execute these exercises, ask a physical education teacher at your school to demonstrate them. Warn students that they could injure themselves if they do too many repetitions. Have students ask a fitness trainer or a physical education teacher how many repetitions are safe for them to do. Tell students to perform exercises that build muscle strength and endurance only with their parents' or guardian's permission. **ELL**

Explain the Concept

Strength versus Endurance
Muscular strength is achieved by performing an exercise with a weight or enough resistance so that only a low number of repetitions may be performed—no more than 6–8. Muscular endurance can be obtained by performing more repetitions with less resistance or lighter weight, usually 12–30 repetitions.

Muscular Strength and Endurance

The maximum amount of force a muscle can produce in a single effort is called *muscular strength.* The ability of the muscle to continue to perform without fatigue is called *muscular endurance.*

What to Know About Muscular Strength and Muscular Endurance

What are the benefits of muscular strength and endurance? Muscular strength and endurance help you perform everyday tasks. You maintain correct posture and enjoy physical activities without tiring, and the risks of lower back pain and of being injured are reduced. Your body composition is improved by increasing muscle mass and decreasing fat tissue. Your self-image also is improved.

How do I develop a conditioning program for muscular strength and endurance? Your program should include *resistance exercises,* which are exercises in which a force acts against muscles. To obtain resistance, you can lift free weights, or work with weights on a weight machine. A *repetitions maximum* is the maximum number of repetitions one can perform of a given exercise at a given weight and intensity while using proper exercise form. *Repetitions* are the number of times an exercise is performed in one set. A set is a group of repetitions followed by a rest period. You build muscular strength by lifting more weight only a few times. You build muscular endurance with less resistance and more repetitions.

Weight training is a conditioning program in which free weights or weight machines provide resistance for muscles. You also can do isometric exercises, such as tightening abdominal muscles or using a wall to provide resistance. You can use your body to do isotonic or isokinetic exercises, such as push-ups or sit-ups. You can use a free weight to do isotonic and isokinetic exercises. A *free weight* is a barbell or dumbbell. A collar is a device that secures weights to a barbell or dumbbell. Weight machines also can be used for isotonic and isokinetic exercises. A *weight machine* is an apparatus that provides resistance to a muscle or group of muscles. Check with a coach or trainer when beginning to use free weights or a weight machine.

You can follow the FITT formula when you are developing a conditioning program for muscular strength and endurance.

For **F**requency, train with weights two to four days a week. Schedule a day of rest between workouts.

For **I**ntensity, keep a record of the amount of resistance and number of repetitions you do.

> **Make the Connection**
>
> **Setting Goals** For more information on setting health goals, see page 57 in Lesson 6.

Legal Issues

Professional Standards People who work in the fitness industry, including aerobics instructors and personal trainers, are required to undergo some form of professional training. Most fitness clubs and other health facilities require their employees to become certified in the area in which they are to instruct. Certification helps to ensure that the employees and staff are competent and that the company is protected from legal action in the case of injury to one of the clients or members. Some topics covered in training may include nutrition, supplements, weight training, aerobic training and safety.

Standards for the National Physical Fitness Awards

Age	1-Mile Run (min:sec)	Shuttle Run (sec)	V-Sit Reach (in)	Pull-Ups (#)	Curl-Ups (#/1 min)
Boys					
12	7:11	9.8	4.0	7	50
13	6:50	9.5	3.5	7	53
14	6:26	9.1	4.5	10	56
15	6:20	9.0	5.0	11	57
16	6:08	8.7	6.0	11	56
17	6:06	8.7	7.0	13	55
Girls					
12	8:23	10.4	7.0	2	45
13	8:13	10.2	7.0	2	46
14	7:59	10.1	8.0	2	47
15	8:08	10.0	8.0	2	48
16	8:23	10.1	9.0	1	45
17	8:15	10.0	8.0	1	44

Source: *The President's Challenge: Physical Activity and Fitness Awards Program 2001–2002*, The President's Council on Physical Fitness and Sports

Begin with a weight that you can move easily for 8–12 repetitions. Add more weight until you can do three sets of 10–12 repetitions. A heavy weight and a low number of repetitions (1–5) build muscular strength. A lighter weight and a high number of repetitions (20–25) build muscular endurance.

For **T**ime, perform 8–12 repetitions of each exercise to build muscular strength and endurance. Perform at least one set of each exercise. Perform three sets for maximum fitness benefits.

For **T**ype, choose exercises using your own body for resistance: abdominal crunches, bent arm hang, curl-up twists, pull-ups, push-ups, or side leg raises, for example. Choose exercises using free weights or weight machines: bench press, bicep curl, decline press, flies, half squats, or kickbacks, for example.

How do I maintain muscular strength and endurance? You will improve rapidly during the first four to six weeks of your conditioning program. After six weeks, you must evaluate

▲ Working out with weights increases muscle mass.

your goals. Maintain muscular strength and endurance by continuing to train two to three days a week.

What are tests to measure muscular strength and endurance? Muscular strength is tested by measuring the maximum amount of weight a person can lift at one time.

Muscular endurance is tested by counting the maximum amount of time a person can hold a muscular contraction. Muscular endurance also can be tested by the maximum number of repetitions of a muscular contraction a person can do.

Pull-ups also are used to measure muscular strength and endurance. Pull-ups are included in the Using Life Skills on page 383.

Do I need to warm up and cool down when I participate in a weight-conditioning program? Before a training session, warm up by walking or easy jogging for 3–5 minutes. Warm up different muscle groups before strength and endurance training. Cool down by walking or jogging slowly for 5–10 minutes. Follow the cooldown with stretching exercises to prevent muscle soreness.

▲ This chart shows the physical fitness goals set for teens by the President's Council on Physical Fitness and Sports.

Reading Review

1. List seven benefits of muscular strength and endurance.

2. How is muscular strength tested?

Skill-Related Fitness

The capacity to perform well in sports and physical activities is called ***skill-related fitness***. Skills that can be used in sports and physical activities are ***fitness skills***. There are six fitness skills: agility, balance, coordination, reaction time, speed, and power. Heredity is an important influence on these fitness skills. However, most fitness skills can be developed and improved.

What to Know About Skill-Related Fitness

Agility Physical activities in which you change directions quickly require agility. For example, you need agility to change directions to hit a tennis ball. ***Agility*** is the ability to rapidly change the position of the body.

Balance You need balance if you ski or if you ride a bicycle. You need balance if you in-line skate. ***Balance*** is the ability to keep from falling when a person is in a still position or moving.

Coordination The ability to use the senses together with body parts during movement is ***coordination.***

Volleyball improves
▼ hand-eye coordination.

The use of the hands together with the eyes during movement is ***hand-eye coordination.*** Suppose you are going to hit a tennis ball. You keep your eyes on the ball as you swing the racket with your hands. Without hand-eye coordination, you would have difficulty playing sports. Suppose you want to kick a soccer ball or a football. You would need foot-eye coordination. Your eyes must focus on the ball as you move your foot toward it to kick it.

Reaction time The time it takes a person to move after he or she hears, sees, feels, or touches a stimulus is ***reaction time.*** The less time that elapses, the quicker your reaction time. Suppose a person is throwing a ball to you. The time it takes you to get into position to catch the ball is your reaction time. Suppose you are in the starting block for a race. A starting signal sounds for the race to begin. The time it takes you to begin to push off out of the starting block after the starting signal sounds is your reaction time.

Speed The ability to move quickly is ***speed.*** Many sports and physical

Activity: Using Life Skills

Practicing Healthful Behaviors: Health-Related Fitness Assessment

Below are the five tests from the National Physical Fitness Award Program. After a 5-minute warm-up, perform each of these activities and record your score. Compare your results to the chart on page 381.

1 To make a health behavior contract to become more fit, do the following. Write your name and the date. Write the healthful behavior you want to practice as a health goal. Write specific statements that describe how this healthful behavior reduces health risk. Make a specific plan to record your progress. Complete an evaluation of how the plan helped you accomplish the health goal.

2 **One-mile walk/run** This test checks cardiorespiratory endurance. Do this test on a track (4 laps = 1 mile on most tracks). Time yourself as you run a mile. If you can't run the entire time, walk. If you feel dizzy or sick, stop. Record your time.

3 The shuttle run test measures speed. Mark two parallel lines 30 feet apart and place two blocks of wood or similar objects behind one of the lines. Start behind the opposite line. Your partner will say, "Ready? Go!" You will run to the blocks, pick up one, run back to the starting line, place the block behind the line, run back, pick up the second block, and run back across the starting line. The time it took is your score.

4 The V-sit reach test checks flexibility. Draw a line on the floor with chalk or masking tape. Sit with your heels directly behind the line and your feet 8–12 inches apart. Turn your palms down and hook your thumbs together. Have a partner keep your legs straight, and reach forward as far as you can. Have your partner measure the distance between the line and your fingertips to get your score.

5 The pull-ups test determines muscular strength and endurance. Use a horizontal bar that is high enough so you can hang from it without your feet touching the ground. Grab the bar with your palms facing away from your body. Lift your body until your chin goes above the bar. Lower your body. Do not kick or swing. Your score is the number of pull-ups you complete.

6 The curl-ups test determines abdominal strength. Lie on the floor with your knees bent and your feet about 12 inches apart. Have a partner hold your feet. Cross your arms and place each hand on the opposite shoulder. Using your abdominal muscles, raise your upper body, touch your elbows to your thighs, and lower your body until your shoulder blades touch the floor. Your partner will time you. The number of curl-ups you do in one minute is your score.

▼ A sample results page.

My Results

Test	Baseline	Four Months Later
One-mile run/walk test	_____ minutes/seconds	_____ minutes/seconds
Pull-up test	_____ pull-ups	_____ pull-ups
Curl-up test	_____ curl-ups	_____ curl-ups
V-sit reach test	_____ inches	_____ inches
Body composition	_____ pounds or % body fat	_____ pounds or % body fat

activities require speed. Suppose you are playing basketball and have just grabbed a rebound under your opponent's basket. You use speed to dribble the length of the court to your team's basket. Or, suppose you are playing tennis and your opponent hits a drop shot close to the net. You need speed to get to the ball before it bounces twice. You must run fast when you play soccer, football, lacrosse, and baseball.

Power The ability to combine strength and speed is ***power***. To throw a discus far requires power. If you are playing baseball, power is required to throw a fastball. If you make a high jump, you need power to lift your body high into the air.

Reading Review

1. Name and describe three examples of skill-related fitness.
2. How is speed related to power?

LESSON 34 • Practicing Fitness **383**

A Guide to Lifetime Sports

Class Activity

The Cost of Sports Equipment
Divide students into several groups. Assign each group a particular sport. Each group should research what equipment and what protective equipment is required or recommended for the particular sport. Students should also research the cost of the equipment and protective equipment that is required or recommended. **L2** **ELL**

NHES Assessment/SCASS

Constructed Response Have students write one or two paragraphs explaining the advantages of lifetime sports over skill-related sports. Have them also consider these questions: Are there any disadvantages to lifetime sports? If so, what are they? **L2**

Quick Demo

Protective Equipment Show students protective equipment appropriate for playing basketball. Examples include: a mouthguard, eye protection, elbow and knee pads, and proper footwear. Show them protective equipment for other sports, if you have access to it.

A Guide to Lifetime Sports

L ifetime sports and physical activities are sports and physical activities in which a person can participate throughout his or her life. There are many advantages to participating in lifetime sports and physical activities.

What to Know About a Guide to Lifetime Sports and Physical Activities

Lifetime sports and physical activities often become long-lasting habits that ensure you will be physically active throughout your life. Participating in a variety of lifetime sports and physical activities can help you improve different areas of physical fitness and different fitness skills.

Social interaction with friends and family members is another important benefit of lifetime sports and physical activities.

Basketball improves cardiorespiratory and muscular endurance, agility, balance, and ▼ coordination.

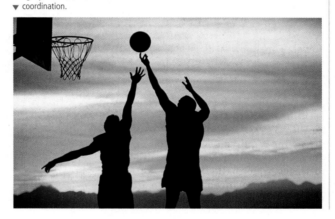

Basketball Basketball is a game that involves two teams of five players. Variations of basketball called "pick-up" games can be played with fewer players.

Playing basketball improves cardiorespiratory endurance and muscular endurance. Learning how to dribble, shoot, and pass the ball improves agility, balance, and coordination. When you play basketball, you burn between 400 and 800 calories per hour.

Common basketball injuries include sprained ankles, sprained knees, and eye injuries. Avoid basketball injuries by wearing protective equipment, such as a mouthguard, eye protection, and elbow and knee pads. Stretching while warming up before playing and during cooldown is another way to prevent injuries.

Cross-country skiing Cross-country skiing is gliding over snow using specialized cross-country skis, boots, and poles. The skier uses the poles and the skis to push forward and turn on the snow and to maintain balance.

384 UNIT 6 • Personal Health and Physical Activity

〚Ⅰ〛 Differentiated Instruction

Learning Disabilities Bring in tapes of professional, college, or local sporting events to use as a demonstration of skills such as agility, balance, coordination, reaction time, speed, and power. Point out the skills demonstrated as they occur throughout the video. Alternatively, you could have students who are athletes volunteer to demonstrate for the class. Explain a skill, then have the students show it. Then have the students show a different skill, and have other class members describe the skill involved. **L1** **ELL**

You can cross-country ski almost anywhere there is snow. Some golf courses and parks have walking or hiking trails that double as cross-country ski trails during the winter.

Cross-country skiing equipment includes skis, poles, boots, safety equipment, and the proper clothing. Your clothing depends on the climate and the difficulty of the terrain. In a cold and snowy climate, wear a hat, gloves, waterproof and windproof jacket and pants, thermal underwear, insulated socks, and goggles or sunglasses.

Cross-country skiing helps maintain and improve fitness. The leg and arm movements involved in cross-country skiing improve muscular endurance and cardiorespiratory endurance. On difficult terrain, cross-country skiing also improves balance, coordination, power, and reaction time.

When you cross-country ski, you burn between 500 and 700 calories per hour. This activity reduces your percentage of body fat. Safety is important when cross-country skiing. Be aware of natural dangers, such as avalanches, freezing temperatures, and UV radiation from the Sun. Know your physical abilities, skill level, and limitations. Know how to prevent and treat illnesses and injuries, such as hypothermia, frostbite, pulled muscles, sprains, dislocations, fractures, and broken bones.

Golf Golf is played on a course that has 9 or 18 holes. The distance to each hole may vary as well as the degree of difficulty. Golf is scored by keeping track of the number of strokes it takes to get the ball into each hole.

A handicap system allows players with different levels of skill to play with one another. To play golf, you need golf clubs, golf balls, and tees. Most public golf courses rent golf clubs for a small fee. Many courses also require that you wear special shoes.

When you play golf you have two options: you can walk or ride in a golf cart. Walking the length of a golf course improves cardiorespiratory endurance.

You burn between 200 and 350 calories when you walk an 18-hole round of golf. Riding in a cart is less strenuous and burns many fewer calories.

Hitting the ball also has fitness benefits. Learning how to hit the ball correctly can improve balance, coordination, and power. The repeated swinging motion you use when you play a round of golf also improves your muscular endurance. To avoid injuries, always stretch before playing golf.

Cross-country skiing is a ▼ rigorous sport.

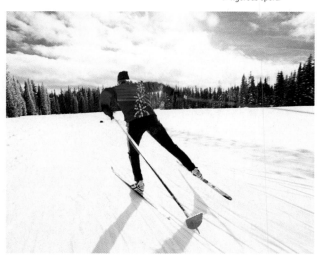

Martial Arts Have students discuss their thoughts on the media's effect on the popularity of martial arts. Ask students if they believe that popular actors such as Jackie Chan or Jet Li have increased the popularity of martial arts. Ask whether they feel that people may have an unrealistic perception of martial arts because of how they are often portrayed in the movies. **L2**

Extension

Comparing Martial Arts Have pairs or small groups of students choose at least three different martial arts. They should research the differences between the chosen styles, and include which country each style developed in. Students should create a table or chart that presents the differences they have discovered. **L3**

Class Activity

Wall Climbing Have students search the telephone book or other local or regional resource guides for the nearest wall climbing facility. They should contact the facility to ask questions about climbing. Have students ask the following questions: Do people have to have a certain fitness level to wall climb? Is the cost based on the number of trips up the wall or on time? Is there an age requirement? Do parents have to sign a consent form for minors? What are their hours of operation? With permission from their parents or guardian, students may climb the wall and write a reaction paper about their experience. **L2**

National Health
Education Standards

Pages 386–387: 1.1, 1.2

Did You Know?

Health Benefit Sedentary people who adopt an active lifestyle receive a significant health benefit even if they have been sedentary for most of their lives. Becoming active is as important as changing other risk factors for cardiovascular disease, such as quitting smoking and improving diet.

Mountain biking Mountain biking is riding an all-terrain bicycle, or mountain bike, on mountains or off-road trails. For mountain biking, you need a mountain bike and protective equipment. When you mountain bike you must wear a helmet. You also can wear special gloves to protect your hands during falls.

Buying mountain biking equipment can be an expensive investment. Rent and try out a bike before you commit to buying one.

The peddling motion of mountain biking promotes muscular endurance, muscular strength, and cardiorespiratory endurance. Balance, coordination, and reaction time are important as you face steep trails and obstacles.

Mountain biking requires great balance, swift reactions, and quick recovery times. To avoid injuries and accidents, you need to maintain control of your mountain bike, use proper equipment, and keep a watchful eye on other bikers.

Golf can improve balance, coordination, ▼ and power.

▲ Different martial arts promote different levels of fitness.

Martial arts Martial arts are any of several methods of self-defense and combat developed in eastern Asia. Martial arts include karate, tae kwon do, judo, tai chi, and sumo.

Training for martial arts includes physical, psychological, and emotional preparations. The physical preparations include stretching, running, practicing, and sparring. The psychological and emotional preparations vary with individuals.

Martial arts usually do not require much equipment. For example, most dojos (centers for studying karate) require students to wear a white jacket and pants known as a karate-gi. The students also must wear a colored belt that designates their skill level. Students often wear padded gloves and mouthguards for protection. Some students also wear chest and abdominal guards.

✦ Cross-Curricular Connections

Art Have each student find photographs or art related to his or her favorite lifetime sport. They could cut photographs or art out of magazines or old calendars, or they could use real photographs if they are available. For example, for mountain biking, the pictures may depict people riding bikes, safety equipment, places people would go mountain biking, words related to mountain biking, or the health benefits of mountain biking. Students should glue the pictures on a posterboard to make a collage. Their collages should be displayed in the classroom. **L2 ELL**

Different martial arts promote different levels of physical fitness and fitness skills. Karate training combines vigorous cardiorespiratory workouts with skill training.

The different movements involved in karate training improve agility, coordination, and reaction time. Most martial arts involve substantial physical contact resulting in frequent shoulder, elbow, and wrist injuries. Broken toes and fingers also are common.

To avoid serious injuries while engaging in martial arts training, wear protective equipment and follow the instructor's safety guidelines. Also follow the instructor's directions about how to execute martial arts moves as closely as you can, because doing so will cut down on injuries.

Rock climbing and wall climbing Rock climbing is scaling rocks or cliffs. Wall climbing is scaling indoor or outdoor walls that are made to resemble rocks and cliffs. To rock climb and wall climb, you need proper equipment, such as ropes, harnesses, protective equipment, and other specialized devices. Wear a safety helmet designed for these sports to prevent serious injuries.

When you climb a wall or rock, you use your arms to pull yourself up and to maintain your position. This improves muscular strength and muscular endurance.

Agility, coordination, and reaction time are important in rock climbing and wall climbing because each move requires viewing the terrain, analyzing it, and using your abilities to climb it. When you rock climb and wall climb, you can burn 600–950 calories per hour, depending on your weight.

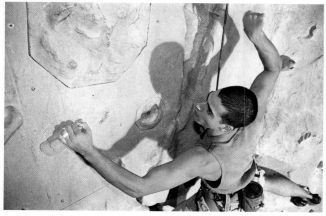

▲ Rock and wall climbing require safety equipment, including ropes and harnesses.

Safety is always a concern when rock or wall climbing. To avoid injuries and accidents, receive proper instruction and know the safety rules.

In-line skating In-line skating uses a motion similar to skiing and ice skating. Bending your knees gives your legs a harder workout.

The most common cause of falls by in-line skaters are loss of balance, debris or an irregular skating surface, collisions with other skaters, and running into a stationary object like a fence or tree. Safety equipment for in-line skating includes skates, helmet, knee and elbow pads, and wrist guards. Carry a water bottle to avoid dehydration and heat exhaustion.

In-line skating provides a fast-paced, vigorous cardiorespiratory workout in which you burn between 300 and 600 calories per hour.

The wide range of movements improve muscular strength and muscular endurance and promote agility, balance, coordination, and power.

Reading Review

1. What are two benefits of lifetime sports and physical activities?

2. Name three benefits of karate training.

LESSON 34 • Practicing Fitness **387**

Lifetime Sports

Class Activity

Shoe Shopping Students should compare ten shoe styles that are designed for running. They should present their findings in a magazine article that compares cost, product features, and appearance. A photo or drawing of each shoe style may be included. They could present the comparisons in a table or in text descriptions, but it should be organized to help someone who wants to choose the best shoe for his or her needs. **L2**

Extension

Water Safety Classes Have students contact an organization that offers water safety classes in your area. Have students find out what skills are taught in the classes; usually skills taught include CPR, basic first aid, and water safety guidelines. Encourage students to take one of these classes and report back to the class about their experiences. **L2**

Lifetime Sports

The following lifetime sports require little equipment. A person on a budget might choose one of these sports to work on a fitness plan and reach his or her goals of improving or maintaining health-related fitness.

What to Know About Other Lifetime Sports

Swimming The only equipment you need for swimming is a bathing suit and a towel. The area in which you swim should be supervised by a responsible adult. The various swimming styles, called strokes, require different levels of health-related fitness and different fitness skills.

For example, the crawl is a common stroke. The crawl helps improve coordination, power, and speed. The crawl also promotes cardiorespiratory endurance, muscular endurance, and muscular strength. Other strokes involve other fitness skills and different levels of health-related fitness.

Depending on their speed and which stroke they use, swimmers can burn 275–500 calories per hour. The most common swimming injuries are tendonitis and pulled muscles that result from overuse of muscles.

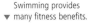

Swimming provides
▼ many fitness benefits.

To avoid injuries, it is important to warm up and stretch before swimming. Learn CPR and basic first aid and follow water safety guidelines.

Running and jogging When you begin running or jogging, do not overexert yourself. Start at a slow or conversational pace. As you improve, your speed and distance will improve.

Shoes are the most important piece of equipment for runners and joggers. When you buy new running or jogging shoes, consider your body size, your running style, and your skill level. Remember that the comfort and shock absorption of the shoes are most important.

Running and jogging improve health-related fitness. They improve cardiorespiratory endurance and also help reduce body fat and cholesterol levels.

When you run you can burn between 650 and 1280 calories per hour. When you jog at a moderate pace, you burn between 500 and 700 calories per hour. Running on hills or other inclines can triple the calories you burn depending on the incline. Watch out for injuries such as pulled muscles, tendonitis, and shin splints that result from overuse of muscles. Carry a water bottle when you run or jog to avoid dehydration and heat exhaustion.

388 UNIT 6 • Personal Health and Physical Activity

 Family Involvement

Fun Day at the Pool Have students contact their local YMCA or swimming facility. They should inquire about open swim times and the cost per person or family. Depending on the ages and interests of family members and friends, students could consider a group swim, lap swim, or even water aerobics classes that the whole group could participate in together. Each student could invite his or her parents or guardian, siblings, and/or friends to the pool for some healthful fun. The invitation should include the health benefits of swimming and the promise of a good time. **L1**

Just the FACTS: EPHEDRA

the FACTS Ephedra, an herbal supplement that comes from the Asiatic shrub ma huang, is a stimulant and is a cousin to the drug called speed. Its principal active ingredient is ephedrine. The Food and Drug Administration (FDA) moved to ban ephedra from distribution in the U.S. in December 2003, saying that ephedrine alkaloids "present an unreasonable risk to the public health"; and at the same time, the FDA urged consumers to stop buying and using ephedra products immediately, before the ban took effect in early 2004. The ban covers all dietary supplements that contain a source of ephedra alkaloids, such as ephedra, ma huang, Sida cordifolia, and pinellia. The ban does not cover traditional Chinese herbal remedies or herbal tea. Serious health risks for ephedra users include seizure, heart attack, stroke, and death. Baltimore Orioles pitcher Steve Bechler died of heatstroke in 2003 after taking three tablets containing ephedra every morning. Milder effects from ephedra include irregular heartbeat, anxiety, digestive problems, tremors, and insomnia. The risk increases if ephedra is combined with strenuous exercise or other stimulants, including caffeine.

"If ephedra is 'all natural,' isn't it safe to use?"

the FACTS A 2003 study by the RAND Corporation showed that the benefits of using ephedra for weight loss are "unknown." This substance may result in a short-term weight loss of perhaps two pounds a month, but so far, no studies show weight loss for longer than six months. More importantly, the risk of long-term, serious health problems is real. The FDA's ban on ephedra is in effect now, and teens should be aware that if they come across any old containers of dietary supplements containing ephedra, they should not use them.

"Doesn't ephedra help people lose weight?"

the FACTS The RAND study found no studies measuring the long-term effects of ephedra on athletic performance. In other words, there is no proof that ephedra builds muscles. Even before the FDA ban went into effect in 2004, the use of ephedra had been banned by the International Olympic Committee, the NCAA, and the NFL.

"Doesn't ephedra build muscles?"

Walking Many shopping malls open their doors before shopping hours to let people walk for exercise. You can walk by yourself or with a group. To make your walk more challenging, carry small hand weights. Walking up steps and walking on step machines are other ways to make walking more vigorous.

Walking provides a moderate cardiorespiratory workout. When you walk briskly, you burn 150–350 calories per hour, depending on the intensity of your walk. Many physicians and health professionals recommend walking as an easy way to maintain physical fitness as you grow older.

Safety is an important aspect of walking, especially when you are walking on the street. Most injuries to walkers are caused by traffic accidents. Be familiar with traffic laws and traffic patterns. Walk facing the traffic.

Remember to stretch before and after you walk to avoid minor injuries. Also, carry a water bottle to avoid dehydration and heat exhaustion.

Reading Review

1. What health-related fitness components are improved by swimming?

2. What are five factors to consider when buying running or jogging shoes?

LESSON 34 • Practicing Fitness **389**

Sports Participants and Spectators

Class Discussion

Unruly Sports Fans Have students discuss their thoughts on how unruly sports fans should be handled. Ask them what should be done when a spectator becomes irresponsible and irate. The students can discuss what penalties should be invoked when a sports fan becomes a fanatic. **L2**

---

3 Assess

Vocabulary Practice

Page 60, **Unit 6 Fast File Resources**

Name_____ Date_____ Class_____

LESSON 34 Practicing Fitness

Vocabulary Practice

Answer the questions below. Include a definition of each vocabulary term as part of your answer.

aerobic exercise	isokinetic exercise	resistance exercise
agility	isometric exercise	skill-related fitness
anaerobic exercise	isotonic exercise	static stretching
health-related fitness		

1. What is *health-related fitness?*

2. What is the relationship between *static stretching* and *health-related fitness?*

3. Contrast the terms *aerobic exercise* and *anaerobic exercise.*

4. Compare and contrast the following types of exercise: *isometric, isotonic, and isokinetic.*

5. What are the relationships between *isotonic exercise, isokinetic exercise, and resistance exercise?*

6. How is *agility* an important part of *skill-related fitness?*

60 LESSON 34 • Practicing Fitness UNIT 6

Sports Participants and Spectators

Sports can be an enjoyable part of your life. You can attend or participate in sports events at your school or in your community. Remember that it is important that you be a responsible sports participant and spectator.

What to Know About Sports Participants and Spectators

A *sports participant* is a person who plays sports. A responsible participant gives maximum effort and has realistic expectations. He or she manages time well, keeps grades a priority and cooperates with teammates. A participant has a healthful attitude toward winning and losing and shows respect for officials, coaches, and other players. He or she does not start or participate in fights and avoids the use of alcohol and other drugs. A *sports spectator* or *fan* is a person who watches and supports sports without actively participating in them. Be responsible when you are a spectator or fan.

Show respect. Learn the rules for the sports events. Don't boo or yell critical comments to officials, players, coaches, or other fans; don't make unkind remarks about any member of the opposing team; and don't throw any materials onto the field or court.

Show support. Applaud the good play and sportsmanship of both teams. Cheer and encourage players when they lose or do not play well. Be loyal and supportive during a losing as well as a winning season.

Express appropriate disapproval. Rough play and poor sportsmanship by either team are unacceptable. Cheering for displays of poor sportsmanship will encourage the offending players to repeat their wrong actions.

Stay in control of your emotions. If you are a spectator, don't instigate or participate in any confrontations or fights, don't damage property, and don't run onto the court or field before or immediately after the play.

Practice healthful behaviors. Don't attend sports events under the influence of alcohol or other drugs. Don't bet or gamble on sports events.

▲ Fans of both teams show their support.

390 UNIT 6 • Personal Health and Physical Activity

(DI) Differentiated Instruction

Behavioral Disorders Research indicates that the strategies that are effective with students who have behavioral disorders are provided in environments where appropriate behavior is valued and rewarded. Engage your student who has a behavioral disorder in a short, private discussion regarding unruly sports fans. Ask him or her to identify the unruly behavior and the reasons why it is not considered acceptable. Reward or praise the student if he or she uses control during the discussion. **L2**

National Health Education Standards

Pages 390–391: 1.1, 1.2, 1.5, 2.3, 4.4

Key Terms Review

Match the definitions below with the lesson Key Terms on the left. Do not write in this book.

aerobic exercise
agility
anaerobic exercise
health-related fitness
isokinetic exercise
isometric exercise
isotonic exercise
resistance exercise
skill-related fitness
static stretching
warm-up

1. an exercise in which a muscle is tightened and there is no body movement
2. an exercise in which oxygen is needed continually for an extended period of time
3. ability to function at optimal capacity
4. force acts against muscles in this exceraise
5. an exercise in which the body's demand for oxygen is greater than what is available

6. an exercise that uses special machines to provide weight resistance
7. capacity to perform well in sports
8. holding a stretch for 15–30 seconds
9. an exercise in which a muscle or muscles moves against a resistance weight and/or gravity 8–15 times
10. allows you to change direction quickly

Recalling the Facts

11. What kind of exercises would you do to increase cardiorespiratory endurance?
12. What kind of exercises would you do to increase muscular strength and why?
13. What are the health-related and skill-related fitness benefits for two different lifetime sports you enjoy?
14. Describe a responsible sports spectator.

15. Why is it important to be a responsible sports spectator?
16. What are two benefits of lifetime sports and physical activity?
17. How do aerobic and anaerobic exercises differ?
18. What is the FITT formula? Describe and give examples of its components.

Critical Thinking

19. Explain why cardiorespiratory endurance improves as you regularly participate in aerobic activity. How does cardiorespiratory endurance benefit your body?
20. Explain the ways in which agility and balance differ.
21. Explain the ways in which speed and power differ.
22. Explain the ways in which a warm-up is similar to a cooldown.

Real-Life Applications

23. How would you develop cardiorespiratory endurance using the FITT formula?
24. How would you develop muscular strength and endurance using the FITT formula?
25. How would you develop flexibility using the FITT formula?
26. Which characteristics of a responsible sports participant do you possess and which do you need to work on?

Activities

Responsible Decision Making

27. **Write** A friend invites you to a health club where he has been using weight machines for a year. You have never used weight machines before. Your friend says you can lift the same weight that he does because you are the same gender and body weight. Write a response to this situation. Refer to the Responsible Decision-Making Model on page 61 for help.

Sharpen Your Life Skills

28. **Set Health Goals** The President's Council on Physical Fitness and Sports provides badges that can be earned for participation in different physical activities. Write to the council to obtain more information. Select a physical activity that you can participate in to earn a badge. Set a health goal for yourself to earn the badge, making sure to write an action plan.

Visit www.glencoe.com for more *Health & Wellness* quizzes.

Activities

Responsible Decision Making

27. Despite the fact that you are about the same size as your friend, you should not use the same weight. Your friend has spent a year developing muscle strength and endurance that you do not yet have. You need to start with less weight and build your muscle strength and endurance up slowly to avoid injury.

Sharpen Your Life Skills

28. Students' letters should have a specific request for information. Each student should choose one of the listed activities for earning a badge.

Key Terms Review

1. isometric exercise
2. aerobic exercise
3. health-related fitness
4. resistance exercise
5. anaerobic exercise
6. isokinetic exercise
7. skill-related fitness
8. static stretching
9. isotonic exercise
10. agility

Recalling the Facts

11. aerobic exercises
12. See page 380.
13. See pages 384–389.
14. See page 390.
15. See page 390.
16. See page 384.
17. See page 375.
18. See page 378.

Critical Thinking

19. The heart and lungs become more efficient at supplying large amounts of oxygen for an extended period of time. See pages 376–378 for benefits.
20. Agility is the ability to rapidly change position and balance is the ability to keep from falling; agility helps maintain balance.
21. Speed is the ability to move quickly. Power is the ability to combine strength and speed, so speed is a part of power.
22. Both involve several minutes of easy physical activity to prepare the body to begin or end a workout.

Real-Life Applications

23. Possible answer: jog for 25 minutes at target heart rate three times a week
24. Possible answer: lift weights for an hour doing exercises to build leg, arm, back, and stomach muscles doing 10–12 repetitions, three times a week—on days when not jogging.
25. Possible answer: Stretch three times a week for fifteen minutes after jogging, holding each stretch for 15–30 seconds.
26. Answers will vary.

Exercising Safely

Out of Time?

If time does not permit an in-depth study of this topic, use the following activities in this Teacher Wraparound Edition:
- Class Activity, p. 393
- Teacher FYI, p. 394
- Explain the Concept, p. 395
- Class Discussion, p. 396

1 Focus

HEALTH GOAL **Injury Prevention** Have students respond to the Health Goal for this lesson by listing in their health journals reasons why they would want to avoid activity-related injuries and illnesses. *Reasons may include that an injury can permanently affect performance.* **L2**

 ABOUT IT!

Journaling Student answers should include the RICE treatment: rest, ice, compression, and elevation. Student answers also may include not playing basketball or engaging in other vigorous exercise until the ankle has fully healed. **L2**

INTERACTIVE CHALKBOARD
with Image Bank

Teaching Transparency
Page 77, **Unit 6 Fast File Resources**

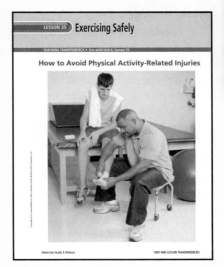
LESSON 35 Exercising Safely
TEACHING TRANSPARENCY • Use with Unit 6, Lesson 35
How to Avoid Physical Activity-Related Injuries

What You'll Learn

1. Describe six training principles for physical activities. *(p. 393)*
2. Explain the Fitness Training Zone. *(p. 394)*
3. Discuss how to prevent, recognize, and treat physical activity-related injuries. *(pp. 394, 395)*
4. Discuss precautions to take in physical activity during extreme weather conditions, at high altitudes, or in polluted air. *(pp. 396, 397)*

Why It's Important

Understanding training principles, how to prevent, recognize, and treat physical activity-related injuries, and how to train in extreme weather conditions will greatly reduce your risk of injury or illness.

Key Terms

- principle of warm-up
- principle of cooldown
- principle of specificity
- principle of overload
- principle of progression
- principle of fitness reversibility
- training zone
- cold temperature-related illnesses
- heat-related illnesses
- Air Quality Index (AQI)

Exercising Safely

HEALTH GOAL **• I will try to prevent physical activity-related injuries and illnesses.**

Physical activity stresses and strains the muscles and joints and may result in some muscle soreness or minor aches after you exercise. This discomfort is temporary and not a sign of injury or illness. However, you do need to know about physical activity-related injuries and illnesses. This lesson discusses how to prevent, recognize, and treat physical activity-related injuries and illnesses.

 ABOUT IT!

Writing About Recovery Suppose you rolled your ankle while playing basketball. After you read the information on treating activity-related injuries on page 394, write an entry in your health journal about what you can do to minimize damage from swelling and to hasten your recovery.

National Health Education Standards—Guide for Lesson 35		
1.5	Propose ways to reduce or prevent injuries and health problems.	pp. 392, 394–395, 400
7.3	Demonstrate a variety of behaviors to avoid or reduce health risks to self and others.	pp. 392, 394–397, 400

Training Principles

For good health, you need a plan to exercise on a regular basis. Training principles are guidelines to follow to obtain maximum fitness benefits and reduce the risk of injuries and illnesses.

What to Know About Training Principles

The principle of warm-up A workout should begin with 5–10 minutes of light exercise to increase blood flow and raise the temperature in muscles, according to the **principle of warm-up.** Begin your warm-up by walking or by jogging slowly. As you warm up, blood flow increases to the muscles being used. This raises their temperature and gets them ready to do more work. Your heart rate increases gradually. Synovial fluid lubricates the surfaces of your joints. Once your muscles are warmed, do some static stretching.

The principle of cooldown A workout should end with 5–10 minutes of reduced exercise to help the heart rate, breathing rate, body temperature, and circulation return to the nonexercising state according to the **principle of cooldown.** Your cooldown should include walking or slow jogging and static stretching.

The principle of specificity A workout should include a specific type of exercise to obtain the desired fitness benefits according to the **principle of specificity.**

Suppose you want to improve cardiorespiratory endurance. You might choose an aerobic exercise such as running for your workout. Aerobic exercises provide the specific fitness benefit you desire.

The principle of overload A workout must include exercise beyond what a person usually does to gain additional fitness benefits, according to the **principle of overload.** Suppose you want to develop strength in your arm muscles. Then you must work the arm muscles longer or harder than usual.

The principle of progression The amount and intensity of exercise during workouts must be increased gradually, according to the **principle of progression.** The Fitness Training Zone diagram on the next page helps explain this principle.

The principle of fitness reversibility Fitness benefits are lost when training stops according to the **principle of fitness reversibility.** How fast a person loses fitness benefits depends on fitness level and the number of years the person has been training.

Did You Know?

Sports Injuries Most organized sports-related injuries occur during practice rather than games. Despite this fact, many teens do not often take the same safety precautions during practices as they would for a game.

Reading Review

1. What is the principle of warm-up?
2. Why is a cooldown important?

Training Principles

2 Teach

Class Activity

Principle of Specificity Have students choose a sport in which they are interested. Have them research exercises or activities that would improve their skills for that particular sport. Each student should create a workout program that would enhance performance in his or her chosen sport. **L2**

Reading Review

1. *A workout should begin with 5–10 minutes of light exercise.*
2. *helps the heart rate, breathing rate, body temperature, and circulation return to the nonexercising state*

PowerPoint® Presentations

This CD-ROM is an editable Microsoft® PowerPoint® presentation that includes:

- Lesson presentations
- Lesson checks
- Interactive graphics
- 5-Minute Checks
- Image Bank
- All transparencies

Discussion Refer to the Sticky-Note Discussions Strategy on page 17T. Give students sticky notes to mark information in the lesson that they find interesting or that raises questions that can be used in class discussions.

National Health Education Standards
Pages 392–393: 1.1, 1.5, 4.1, 7.3, 8.4

Lesson Resource Manager

- **Unit 6 Fast File Resources**
  Reading Strategy, p. 75
  Vocabulary Practice, p. 76
  Transparency Master and Worksheet, p. 77
  Real-Life Health, p. 79
  Real-Life Health, p. 81
  5-Minute Check, p. 83
  Lesson 35 Quiz, p. 85
- **Unit 6 Transparency**
- **Lesson 35 Transparency**

- **Reading Essentials**
- **Technology**
  TeacherWorks™ CD-ROM
  StudentWorks™ CD-ROM
  Reading Essentials CD-ROM
  ExamView® Assessment Suite
  Vocabulary Puzzlemaker

Sports Injuries

Sports Injuries

Sports Injuries

If you put unusual demands on your bones and muscles, you increase your risk of being injured. Injuries are more apt to happen if you take part in sudden and unfamiliar kinds of exercise, especially if you do not warm up and stretch beforehand.

What to Know About Sports Injuries

What are guidelines I can follow to prevent physical activity-related injuries? First, have a medical examination before you begin vigorous physical activity or participate in a sport. Participate in physical activities and sports with appropriate adult supervision and obtain appropriate instruction. Develop and maintain proper conditioning.

The diagram of the Fitness Training Zone illustrates the importance of overload and proper progression. Know and follow safety guidelines and review basic first aid procedures and CPR.

Practice precautions to prevent the spread of blood-borne pathogens and wear protective clothing and select equipment carefully.

Wear footwear appropriate for the activity. Wear acrylic rather than cotton socks. Wear a safety helmet, face mask, mouth guard, and protective pads when needed. Wear reflective clothing for walking, running, and bicycling. Wear an athletic supporter and cup when appropriate. Wear an athletic bra when appropriate.

Do not participate in physical activities or sports when you have unhealed injuries. Follow precautions for exercising in extreme weather conditions.

What is the PRICE treatment? A technique for treating musculoskeletal injuries that involves rest, ice, compression, and elevation is the ***PRICE treatment.*** Lesson 69 includes more information about the PRICE treatment.

What Are Ten Physical Activity-Related Injuries I Can Avoid?

A side stitch A dull, sometimes sharp pain in the side of the lower abdomen is a side stitch. To prevent a side stitch, warm up and follow the FITT formula. Plan your workout with appropriate frequency, intensity, and time. To relieve a side stitch, bend forward while pressing your hand firmly at the point of the pain.

Make the Connection

CPR For more information on CPR, see page 734 in Lesson 70.

The ***training threshold*** is the ▶ minimum amount of overload required to obtain fitness benefits. Workouts below the training threshold provide health benefits—such as keeping one's body systems in good working order—but they do not improve fitness (such as expanding respiratory capacity, lowering one's resting heart rate, etc.). The ***training zone*** is the range of overload required to improve fitness. The ***training ceiling*** is the upper limit of overload required to obtain fitness benefits without risking injury or illness. Workouts that go beyond the training ceiling are dangerous to health.

Too Much Activity

Training Ceiling

Training Zone

Builds Fitness

Training Threshold

Too Little Activity

⚖ Legal Issues

Good Samaritan Laws Have students research the Good Samaritan law as it applies to providing first aid to someone who has been injured while participating in sports. They should try to find out the specifics of the law in your state, since the laws vary from state to state. Discuss students' findings in class. They should search for answers to the following questions: When was this law enacted? What is the purpose of this law? Who does the law protect? Under what circumstances or conditions does the law apply, and are there situations in which it does not? Does it seem that the law's protection is needed frequently or rarely? Ask students if they found any specific cases involving sports injuries in which the law was involved. If so, ask them what the case was about and what the outcome was. **L2**

A sprain The partial or complete tearing of a ligament is a sprain. A ligament is a tough fiber that connects bones. Sprains occur when the tissue around a joint is twisted. To prevent sprains, select shoes carefully. High-top athletic shoes support ankles. Talk to a trainer about taping weak ankles or wearing an ankle or knee brace for extra support. Use the RICE treatment if a sprain occurs.

A stress fracture A hairline break that results from repetitive jarring of a bone is a stress fracture. A stress fracture usually is an overuse injury. A stress fracture may not be detected on an X-ray or during superficial examination. To prevent stress fractures, pay attention to the FITT formula and do not overdo. The treatment for stress fractures depends on the severity and the area that is affected. Rest is important.

Tendonitis An inflammation of a tendon is tendonitis. A tendon is tough tissue fiber that attaches muscles to bones. Tendonitis causes pain and swelling in joints. Tendonitis in an elbow is called tennis elbow. Other joints affected by tendonitis are the knees, shoulders, and backs of ankles. To prevent tendonitis, warm up with static stretching. Choose exercises to develop muscle strength. When tendonitis occurs, use the RICE treatment. Tendonitis is slow to heal. Check with a physician before taking aspirin or other drugs to relieve pain and inflammation.

Overuse injury An injury that occurs from repeated use or excessive overload is an overuse injury. If you do too much, too fast, you may develop an overuse injury.

Microtrauma An injury that is not recognized as a person continues to work out is a microtrauma. If you do not rest a muscle or other body part before exercising again, the microtrauma will worsen.

Bruise A discoloration of the skin caused by bleeding under the skin is a bruise. Apply ice to reduce bleeding and swelling.

Muscle cramp The sudden tightening of a muscle is a muscle cramp. Sharp pains may signal muscle cramps. They often are caused by fatigue and dehydration. Taking precautions when exercising in hot weather and static stretching help prevent muscle cramps. Should they occur, drink plenty of fluids and gently massage the muscles that cramp.

Muscle strain The overstretching of a muscle that may result in tearing of a muscle or tendon is a muscle strain. A warm-up of walking, easy jogging, and static stretching help prevent muscle strain. Use the RICE treatment if muscle strain occurs.

Shin splint An overuse injury that results in pain in the front and sides of the lower leg is a shin splint. There may be tenderness over the shin and some swelling. To prevent shin splints, wear proper footwear. Run on even surfaces. Begin and end your workout with static stretching of the muscles of the shin and calf. Ice can be applied four times a day for 20 minutes. Check with a physician before taking aspirin or other drugs to reduce pain and inflammation.

▲ Static stretching helps prevent many sports injuries.

Did You Know?

Concussions Concussion, an injury to the brain caused by a blow to the head, is the mildest form of brain injury. About 30,000 concussions occur in the U.S. each year. Second impact syndrome (SIS), which can involve brain swelling or even death, can occur if a person has a second concussion before the first one is fully healed.

Reading Review

1. What is the training threshold?
2. What do the letters PRICE mean?

LESSON 35 • Exercising Safely **395**

Quick Demo

Side Stitch Demonstrate to the students the proper technique to relieve a side stitch. The information is at the bottom right of page 394. **ELL**

Explain the Concept

Strain versus Sprain Sometimes students confuse sprains and strains. Explain that a strain is the overstretching of a muscle that may result in tearing of a muscle or tendon, whereas a sprain is the partial or complete tearing of a ligament.

INTERACTIVE CHALKBOARD with Image Bank

5-Minute Check

Page 83, **Unit 6 Fast File Resources**

1. Which training principle states that fitness benefits are lost when training stops? *the principle of fitness reversibility*
2. What is the first thing you should do before starting an exercise program? *have a medical examination*
3. What is the PRICE treatment used to treat? *musculoskeletal injuries*
4. What is an overuse injury? *an injury that occurs from repeated use or excessive overload*
5. What causes a bruise? *a discoloration of the skin caused by bleeding under the skin*

Reading Review

1. *the minimum amount of overload required to obtain fitness benefits*
2. *protect, rest, ice, compression, elevation*

Community Involvement

Sports Medicine Have students interview a physical therapist at a local sports medicine center. Students should inquire about his or her educational background, the types of injuries he or she treats most often, and the most serious injury he or she has encountered or treated. They should also ask for the therapist's recommendations on injury prevention. Have students create a comic strip or other kind of drawing showing at least one way to prevent an injury. Discuss what students learned from their interviews in class. **L3**

National Health Education Standards
Pages 394–395: 1.5, 6.1

NHES Assessment/SCASS

Performance Event Have students write the dialogue for a talk show in which the host of the show interviews a hypothermia survivor. The dialogue should include interview questions about what happened and how the person survived. The show should close with recommendations for preventing hypothermia. **L2**

Class Discussion

Dressing Properly for the Weather Have students discuss proper dress for cold weather. Ask why dressing too warmly in cold weather could be problematic. *People who are exercising in cold weather should wear several layers of lightweight clothing. Dressing too warmly can cause sweating that leads to chilling.* **L2**

Explain the Concept

Heat Exhaustion versus Heatstroke The major difference between the two illnesses is body temperature. A low body temperature may be an indication of heat exhaustion, whereas a high body temperature may be a sign of heatstroke.

Exercising in Severe Weather

Different kinds of weather can cause safety and comfort concerns. However, it is possible to exercise in a variety of environmental conditions as long as you take certain precautions.

If You Participate in Physical Activity During Extreme Weather Conditions

What precautions should I take if I work out in cold weather? Conditions that result from exposure to low temperatures are *cold temperature-related illnesses.* The freezing of body parts, often the tissues of the extremities is *frostbite.*

Signs of frostbite include numbness in the affected area, waxy appearance of skin, and skin that is discolored and cold to the touch.

> **Make the Connection**
>
> **Taking Responsibility** For more information on taking responsibility for your health, see page 11 in Lesson 1.

Windchill Temperatures

Wind speed MPH	40	35	30	25	20	15	10	5	0	-5	-10	-15	-20	-25	-30	-35	-40	-45
5	36	31	25	19	13	7	1	-5	-11	-16	-22	-28	-34	-40	-46	-52	-57	-63
10	34	27	21	15	9	3	-4	-10	-16	-22	-28	-35	-41	-47	-53	-59	-66	-72
15	32	25	19	13	6	0	-7	-13	-19	-26	-32	-39	-45	-51	-58	-64	-71	-77
20	30	24	17	11	4	-2	-9	-15	-22	-29	-35	-42	-48	-55	-61	-68	-74	-81
25	29	23	16	9	3	-4	-11	-17	-24	-31	-37	-44	-51	-58	-64	-71	-78	-84
30	28	22	15	8	1	-5	-12	-19	-26	-33	-39	-46	-53	-60	-67	-73	-80	-87
35	28	21	14	7	0	-7	-14	-21	-27	-34	-41	-48	-55	-62	-69	-76	-82	-89
40	27	20	13	6	-1	-8	-15	-22	-29	-36	-43	-50	-57	-64	-71	-78	-84	-91
45	26	19	12	5	-2	-9	-16	-23	-30	-37	-44	-51	-58	-65	-72	-79	-86	-93
50	26	19	12	4	-3	-10	-17	-24	-31	-38	-45	-52	-60	-67	-74	-81	-88	-95
55	25	18	11	4	-3	-11	-18	-25	-32	-39	-46	-54	-61	-68	-75	-82	-89	97
60	25	17	10	3	-4	-11	-19	-26	-33	-40	-48	-55	-62	-69	-76	-84	-91	-98

Temperature (°F)

Frostbite times: More than 30 minutes | 30 minutes | 10 minutes | 5 minutes

Source: National Weather Service, 2003

▲ To determine windchill, find the outside air temperature on the top row. Then read down the left-hand column to the measured wind speed. This is measured in MPH (miles per hour). The windchill is the number in the box where these meet.

Hypothermia is a reduction in the body temperature so that it is lower than normal. Hypothermia results from overexposure to cool temperatures, cold water, moisture, and wind. People with hypothermia will shiver and feel cold. The pulse rate slows and becomes irregular. A person can become unconscious and die without treatment.

There are some steps you can take to prevent cold temperature-related illnesses. Check the windchill before exercising in cold weather and postpone exercise if the windchill puts health status at risk.

Postpone exercise if it is icy and wet. Wear gloves, a hat, and a ski mask to protect the fingers, ears, and nose. Wear two pairs of socks or thermal socks to protect the toes.

Wear several layers of lightweight clothing. Dressing too warmly causes sweating that can cause chilling. The first layer of clothing should be made of polypropylene, which takes moisture away from the skin. Over this layer, wear a layer of fleeced polyester, which serves as a good insulator.

DI Differentiated Instruction

Gifted and Talented Have students investigate new fabrics that were created to enhance athletic performance. These fabrics are designed to take moisture away from the body. Students should look at different types of fabrics and their properties. They should compare their level of breathability and how waterproof each is. If possible, have students try to get a sample of each fabric. Students should create a table or chart that compares the fabrics. **L3**

Heat Index — Temperature (°F) V. Relative Humidity (%)									
F	90%	80%	70%	60%	50%	40%	30%	20%	10%
65	65.6	64.7	63.8	62.8	61.9	60.9	60.0	59.1	58.1
70	71.6	70.7	69.8	68.8	67.9	66.9	66.0	65.1	64.1
75	79.7	76.7	75.8	74.8	73.9	72.9	72.0	71.1	70.1
80	88.2	85.9	84.2	82.8	81.6	80.4	79.0	77.4	76.4
85	101.4	97.0	93.3	90.3	87.7	85.5	83.5	81.6	79.6
90	119.3	112.0	105.8	100.5	96.1	92.3	89.2	86.5	84.2
95	141.8	131.1	121.7	113.6	106.7	100.9	96.1	92.2	89.2
100	168.7	154.0	140.9	129.5	119.6	111.2	104.2	98.7	94.4
105	200.0	180.7	163.4	148.1	134.7	123.2	113.6	105.8	100.0
110	235.0	211.2	189.1	169.4	151.9	136.8	124.1	113.7	105.8
115	275.3	245.4	218.0	193.3	171.3	152.1	135.8	122.3	111.9
120	319.1	283.1	250.0	219.9	192.9	169.1	148.7	131.6	118.2

High Temperature	Possible Heat Disorder
80F–90F	Fatigue possible with prolonged exposure and physical activity
90F–105F	Sunstroke, heat cramps, and heat exhaustion possible
105F–130F	Sunstroke, heat cramps, and heat exhaustion likely, and heatstroke possible
130F or Greater	Heatstroke highly likely with continued exposure

Source: The National Weather Service, 2003

The top layer should be a windbreaker of waterproof material that keeps out moisture but allows perspiration to filter out. Remember that even in cold weather you need to drink water.

What precautions should I take if I work out in hot weather? Conditions that result from exposure to temperatures higher than normal are *heat-related illnesses.*

Heat cramps are painful muscle spasms in the legs and arms due to excessive fluid loss through sweating. *Heat exhaustion* is extreme tiredness due to the body's inability to regulate its temperature. Signs of heat exhaustion include a very low body temperature; cool moist, pale, or red skin; nausea and headache; dizziness and weakness; and fast pulse.

An overheating of the body that is life-threatening is called *heatstroke.* Sweating ceases so that the body cannot regulate its temperature.

Signs of heatstroke include very high body temperature; rapid pulse; rapid respiration; hot, wet, or dry skin; feelings of weakness or dizziness; and headache.

There are steps to take to prevent heat-related illnesses. Check the heat index before exercising in hot weather. Postpone exercise if the heat index puts health status at risk. Plan your workout at the time of day when the temperature is lowest. Drink fluids before and during your workout. Avoid vigorous workouts on extremely hot and humid days.

Wear porous clothing that allows air to pass through it. Wear light colored clothing that reflects the Sun's rays.

Avoid wearing rubberized and plastic clothing. These kinds of clothing trap heat and perspiration and cause fluid loss and increased body temperature. Wear a hat, sunglasses, and sunscreen.

How does air pollution affect my workouts? Air pollution influences the safety and effectiveness of workouts. When air is polluted, you have to breathe more often to deliver oxygen to body cells. Air pollution can cause shortness of breath.

The media issue warnings when the PSI is high. The *Air Quality Index (AQI)* is a measure of air quality based on the sum of the levels of five different pollutants. It is best not to work out outdoors when the AQI is high.

How will being in a high altitude affect my workouts? Being in a high altitude places extra demands on the body. Think of the extra demands of the high altitude as being a form of overload. Your body must adjust to these extra demands.

Shorten the length of your workouts at first. People who work out too much at first may develop altitude sickness. Signs of altitude sickness are shortness of breath, chest pain, and nausea.

▲ The heat index is the temperature the body feels when heat and humidity are combined. The chart shows the heat index that corresponds to the actual air temperature and relative humidity.

Did You Know?

Water Overload
Drinking too much water—while exercising or at other times—can lead to a condition called hyponatremia. With this condition, too much water in a person's body can lower sodium content and lead to headache, confusion, and muscle aches. In extreme cases, hyponatremia can cause brain swelling, coma, and death.

Reading Review

1. What is hypothermia?
2. What is PSI?

LESSON 35 • Exercising Safely **397**

Achieving Health Literacy

Effective Communicator Have students write a public service announcement (PSA) issuing warnings about outdoor exercise. The PSA should provide information about windchill, the Air Quality Index, and the heat index. It may also include warnings about conditions that can result from exercising in cold weather and in warm weather and how they can be prevented. The announcements should be read aloud in class. Students should vote for the most catchy and creative PSA, and ask for permission to read it over the school's PA system. **L2**

National Health Education Standards
Pages 396–397: 1.1, 1.3

Analyzing the Feature

Use the following questions to help students uncover the main points of this feature.

1. Aside from preventing injuries, what does Chase's coach say proper training methods do? *They lead to better performance.*

2. What can happen if you overcompensate for an injury? *You could cause a different injury.*

3. What is Chase's advice? *Never skip stretching, conditioning, or cooldowns, and drink plenty of water.*

Journaling Activity

Interview a Top Athlete Ask students to interview a school athlete about his or her training practices. **L2**

3 Assess

Vocabulary Practice

Page 76, **Unit 6 Fast File Resources**

National Health Education Standards

Pages 398–399: 1.1, 1.3, 1.5, 4.1, 7.3, 8.4

**Chase Turnquest
Being a Sports Trainer**

> 66 Our coach says that if you're not out there stretching, running, and training, you're more likely to get hurt. 99

If you asked Chase Turnquest the secret to being an all-city tennis player, he might tell you it's the stretching. Having a killer serve and a wicked forehand also might help. But he's convinced of the importance of proper training methods.

"Our coach says that if you're not out there stretching, running, and training, you're much more likely to get hurt," Chase said. "And I've seen it happen too many times. The captain of our team tore his hamstring muscle because he didn't stretch. He just started playing," added Chase. "Another player twisted his ankle, without stretching. He went out and started running."

Each sport is different. In Chase's sport, like in any other, there are recommended training methods. "We do lots of running to build up endurance," he explained. The matches can last two hours or more under a hot spring sun. "Tennis players also do light weight training. We don't lift really heavy weights because we'd risk getting too bulky and losing flexibility."

Then there's the stretching before a match. "It's about the most important thing you can do to avoid getting hurt," Chase emphasized. Chase's coach puts together a training program for team members. "Another thing we're really serious about is cooling down after a training session or a match," Chase explained. His coach emphasizes that proper training methods not only help prevent injuries, but they also lead to better performance on the court.

Knock on wood. So far, Chase has been able to avoid serious injuries. However, like most athletes, he's had some minor ones. He cut his leg on a piece of glass while playing basketball and pulls muscles every now and then.

Rehabilitating from injuries is a special challenge for many young athletes. "When you're recovering from injury," explained Chase, "your body's not going to be in as good a shape as when you're playing. You're not going to be at the top of your game, so it can lead to trouble. You can overcompensate for an injury and get hurt in a different way all over again."

Word to the wise "Athletes I know could be more aware of good training practices," Chase said. "A lot of people I know just go out and play, without thinking about stretching and especially conditioning. They can get hurt really quickly out there." Then he put his finger on another way athletes hurt their own performance. "A lot of athletes smoke. You can tell really easily which ones are smokers. They get winded really quickly. If a match goes to three sets, they have more trouble hanging in there."

Chase advised other athletes to never skip stretching, conditioning, or cooldowns, and to drink lots of water.

Journaling Activity

Think of a sport or other physical activity you enjoy doing. Make a list of five questions you would like to ask a high school coach or a professional trainer about that activity.

398 UNIT 6 • Personal Health and Physical Activity

Family Involvement

Family Exercise If appropriate, students could invite family members to begin a walking program. They should share what they have learned in class about warming up, stretching, and cooling down with their family members. Students should be encouraging and supportive so that family members will stick with their program. Walking together may be more fun than walking or doing other exercise alone, so it may be easier for the whole family to continue the program. Perhaps the whole family can walk to a park, or to run errands, so that walking will fit naturally into family activities. **L2**

Air Quality Index
(AQI)
cold temperature-
related illnesses
heat-related illnesses
hypothermia
principle of
cooldown
principle of fitness
reversibility
principle of overload
principle of
progression
principle of
specificity
principle of warm-up
PRICE treatment
training zone

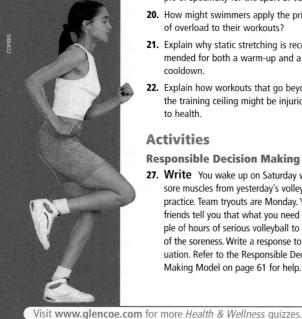

CORBIS

Key Terms Review

Explain the relationship between the pairs of lesson Key Terms below. Do not write in this book.

1. principle of warm-up—principle of cooldown
2. principle of specificity—principle of progression
3. principle of overload—training zone
4. Air Quality Index (AQI)—principle of fitness reversibility
5. cold temperature-related illnesses—heat-related illnesses

Recalling the Facts

6. What are ten guidelines you should follow to prevent sports injuries?
7. What training principle refers to losing fitness benefits? Why are they lost?
8. Why is heatstroke dangerous?
9. What is the PRICE treatment?
10. What is an overuse injury?
11. Why are warm-ups and cooldowns important?
12. What is the training ceiling?
13. How would you prevent getting a muscle cramp or strain?
14. How would you prevent getting a shin splint or side stitch?
15. How would you prevent getting a sprain or tendonitis?
16. How would you recognize and treat a side stitch, sprain, or tendonitis?
17. How would you recognize and treat a muscle cramp, strain, or shin splint?
18. Why is hypothermia a serious condition?

Critical Thinking

19. Give an example workout using the principle of specificity for the sport of volleyball.
20. How might swimmers apply the principle of overload to their workouts?
21. Explain why static stretching is recommended for both a warm-up and a cooldown.
22. Explain how workouts that go beyond the training ceiling might be injurious to health.

Real-Life Applications

23. What activities do you participate in that put you in the training zone?
24. How many times a week are you in the training zone?
25. Choose a sport you would like to be proficient in and list the skills you would need to have to become proficient.
26. Explain how you could determine what your personal training threshold would be.

Activities

Responsible Decision Making

27. **Write** You wake up on Saturday with very sore muscles from yesterday's volleyball practice. Team tryouts are Monday. Your friends tell you that what you need is a couple of hours of serious volleyball to get rid of the soreness. Write a response to this situation. Refer to the Responsible Decision-Making Model on page 61 for help.

Sharpen Your Life Skills

28. **Use Communication Skills** Select one lifetime sport or physical activity. Prepare a 2–3 minute talk in which you encourage classmates to participate in the lifetime sport or physical activity you selected. Talk about techniques that help people avoid illnesses or injuries that can be caused by this sport.

Visit **www.glencoe.com** for more *Health & Wellness* quizzes.

LESSON 35
STUDY GUIDE

Key Terms Review

1. They are related because they both refer to light exercise to prepare the body to begin or end a workout.
2. Both the type of exercise and intensity and amount of exercise must be chosen based on the desired benefit.
3. The training zone is the range of overload required to obtain fitness benefits.
4. If the AQI is high for a period of time and you cannot exercise outdoors, it will be necessary to find a way to exercise indoors to avoid losing fitness benefits.
5. Both refer to problems with exercising in extreme weather conditions.

Recalling the Facts

6. See pages 394–395.
7. the principle of fitness reversibility; because training stops
8. Heatstroke is life threatening; sweating ceases so the body cannot regulate its temperature.
9. See page 394.
10. an injury that occurs from repeated use or excessive overload
11. See page 393.
12. See page 394.
13. See page 395.
14. See pages 394–395.
15. See page 395.
16. See pages 394–395.
17. See page 395.
18. a person who has hypothermia can die without treatment

Critical Thinking

19. Include exercises to strengthen your legs for jumping and your arms for hitting the ball hard.
20. Swim longer and harder than in previous workouts.
21. muscles need to be stretched to prepare for working them and also afterwards to prevent soreness
22. Surpassing the training ceiling might lead to overuse injuries or exacerbate other injuries. Exhausting yourself may also make you more susceptible to illness.

Real-Life Applications

23. Answers will vary.
24. Answers will vary.
25. Answers will vary, but should include specific skills for the chosen sport.
26. First, have a medical exam. A physician or physical trainer can help you determine your training threshold. See page 394.

Activities

Responsible Decision Making

27. If your muscles are sore, you should rest them before tryouts. Some stretching also might help with soreness.

Sharpen Your Life Skills

28. Student talks should include specific ways to avoid injuries and illnesses that may occur with the activity they selected.

UNIT

6

STUDY GUIDE

Key Terms Review

1. e
2. c
3. d
4. h
5. b
6. i
7. l
8. g
9. a
10. j

Recalling the Facts

11. health habits, past health conditions and medical care, allergies, food and drug sensitivities, and family health histories

12. premature birth, respiratory distress at birth, a birth defect, exposure to drugs or infection before birth, viral infections, middle ear infections, high fevers, injuries, and noise pollution

13. to maintain good dental health and to possibly correct problems before they become painful or obvious

14. wash skin gently and rinse well, use a physician-recommended cleanser or topical medication, keep hair away from face, use water-based cosmetics, limit time in the sun, do not squeeze or pick acne

15. rapid eye movements, dreaming, brain wave activity similar to awake state

16. reduces depression and anxiety; promotes psychological well-being; helps control weight; reduces risk of type II diabetes; builds and maintains healthy bones, muscles, and joints; reduces risk of premature death; helps prevent falls; reduces risk of cardiovascular diseases; reduces risk of high blood pressure; reduces existing high blood pressure; reduces risk of colon cancer

17. to develop cardiorespiratory endurance and a healthful body composition

18. helps you perform everyday tasks, maintain correct posture and enjoy physical activities without tiring; reduces risk of lower back pain and of being injured; improves body composition and self-image

19. Benefits include improvement in different areas of physical fitness and fitness skills and social interactions.

20. Fitness benefits are lost; how fast they are lost depends on a person's fitness level and the number of years a person has been training.

Key Terms Review

Match the following definitions with the correct Key Terms. Do not write in this book.

a. aerobic exercise *(p. 375)*
b. athlete's foot *(p. 354)*
c. cardiac output *(p. 368)*
d. conjunctivitis *(p. 345)*
e. gingivitis *(p. 349)*
f. health-related fitness *(p. 374)*
g. insomnia *(p. 363)*
h. lice *(p. 357)*
i. physical fitness *(p. 371)*
j. principle of progression *(p. 393)*
k. psoriasis *(p. 354)*
l. skill-related fitness *(p. 382)*

1. a condition in which the gums are red, swollen, tender and bleed easily
2. the amount of blood pumped by the heart each minute
3. an inflammation of the eye membranes that causes redness, discomfort, and discharge
4. insects that live and lay eggs in human hair
5. a fungus that grows on feet
6. the ability to perform physical activity while being energetic and alert
7. the capacity to perform well in sports and physical activities
8. the prolonged inability to fall asleep, stay asleep, or get back to sleep
9. one in which large amounts of oxygen are required continually for an extended period
10. states that the amount and intensity of exercise during workouts must be increased gradually

Recalling the Facts

11. What information is included in a health history? *(Lesson 30)*
12. What are nine causes of hearing loss? *(Lesson 30)*
13. Why are regular dental examinations important? *(Lesson 30)*
14. What are six ways to treat acne? *(Lesson 31)*
15. Describe three actions that occur during REM sleep. *(Lesson 32)*
16. What are 11 benefits of regular physical activity? *(Lesson 33)*
17. Why should aerobic exercises be included in a physical fitness plan? *(Lesson 33)*
18. What are seven benefits of muscular strength and endurance? *(Lesson 34)*
19. What are two advantages of participating in lifetime sports? *(Lesson 34)*
20. What happens to fitness benefits if you stop working out? *(Lesson 35)*

Critical Thinking

21. Explain the relationship between visual acuity and refractive errors. *(Lesson 30)*
22. How might you overcome the dangers of sunbathing? *(Lesson 31)*
23. How are tattoos and body piercing related? *(Lesson 31)*
24. How might an inadequate amount of sleep affect your health? *(Lesson 32)*
25. Explain the link between getting adequate sleep and participating in regular physical activity. *(Lessons 32, 33)*
26. How are the level of your physical activity and your diet related? *(Lesson 33)*
27. How are cardiorespiratory endurance and muscular strength and endurance related? *(Lesson 34)*
28. How does the FITT formula relate to your level of physical fitness? *(Lesson 34)*
29. Why is it important to develop skill-related fitness even if you do not play sports? *(Lesson 34)*
30. Explain the relationship between the principles of warm-up and cooldown. *(Lesson 35)*

(Use **Interactive Tutor** at www.glencoe.com for additional help.)

Critical Thinking

21. Refractive errors may interfere with visual acuity.
22. Limit exposure to sun during the middle of the day and use sunscreen. Use lotions and sprays with DHA to make skin appear tanned.
23. Both are permanent changes to the body, both need to be done with sterile equipment and both can potentially lead to allergic reactions or other health problems.
24. Concentration, growth, and emotional health are affected; a weakened immune system may lead to more illness, and an increased risk of accidents may lead to injury.
25. Inadequate sleep inhibits your ability to concentrate and perform well in physical activity.
26. Regular physical activity increases metabolic rate and burns calories, so you can lose or maintain weight by exercising more while keeping diet constant or eating slightly more.

Health Literacy Activities

What Do You Know?
Self-Directed Learning Compose two factual questions relating to personal health or physical activity. Make one more difficult than the other. Place a * by this question. Collect questions from your classmates and put them in a bag. Play a form of basketball with your classmates. The easy question is worth 2 points and the other one is worth 3 points.

Connection to World Cultures
Critical Thinking The Olympic rings were developed as symbols of the Olympic spirit. Find out what the Olympic rings mean. Why is this symbol embraced by people of different cultures?

Family Involvement
Effective Communication Review with your family A Guide to Lifetime Sports and Physical Activities. Select one sport or activity in which your family can participate together. Plan a time to enjoy this sport or activity.

Investigating Health Careers
Responsible Citizenship Obtain permission from your parent or guardian. Interview a professional in the field of personal health or physical activity (for example, dental hygienist, athletic trainer, or sports nutritionist). Ask about the credentials needed for the career; where to get training; and job responsibilities. Write an article about the interview for your school newspaper or a teen magazine.

Group Project
Problem Solving A sedentary lifestyle is a lifestyle in which a person does not engage in much activity. For example, a person may take an elevator rather than climb stairs. What are five other examples of a sedentary lifestyle? How might a person change from being sedentary to being active? Compare your ideas with those in your group. How might you become a more active person? Visit **www.glencoe.com** for more information.

Standardized Test Practice

Read the following selection and answer the questions that follow.

One of the most common complaints that doctors hear from teenagers is "feeling tired all the time." One leading authority on teenagers' health believes that teens need at least as much sleep as adults. That means eight hours. But that may be a minimum. Why? The authority points out that teens can be growing as much as four inches a year during growth spurts, which is almost twice the rate before puberty. All that growing is hard work, and teens need their rest. Throw in studying, working, playing sports, and just having fun, and it's no wonder many teens feel tired much of the time. Experts recommend cutting back on some activities in order to leave enough time for rest. Many teens, however, would rather look for a way to add several hours to the 24 in each day.

 www.glencoe.com

Multiple Choice

1 According to this paragraph, which statement is true?
  A Growth spurts are one of the reasons teens may need more sleep than adults.
  B Scientists agree that teens need eight hours of sleep.
  C Young people grow faster before puberty than during it.
  D Spending too much time working or at sports is wrong.

2 Which statement best describes the author's theme?
  A Teens need more sleep to avoid serious health problems.
  B Doctors help teens learn about the importance of sleep.
  C Puberty is a difficult time in a young person's life.
  D Getting enough rest is important, but many teens may have trouble reducing their busy schedules.

Open-Ended

3 What time-management skills do you use to balance your need for rest against your other activities?

---

27. Both are components of health-related fitness.
28. The FITT formula represents factors for determining how to obtain fitness benefits from physical activity based on your current level of physical fitness.
29. Skill-related fitness will help you to participate in any physical activity and will reduce the chance of falls or injuries.
30. Both involve preparing your body for the start or end of exercise.

Health Literacy Activities

What Do You Know?
Questions will vary. Listen to the game to be sure that students are giving correct answers.

Connection to World Cultures
According to the International Olympic Committee, "The five rings represent the five continents. They are interlaced to show the universality of Olympism and the meeting of the athletes of the whole world during the Olympic games." This symbol is embraced by people of different cultures because it includes all cultures when their athletes compete.

Family Involvement
Answers will vary, but should include a specific activity and a specific time.

Investigating Health Careers
Student articles will vary, but should include information about credentials, training and job responsibilities.

Group Project
Student responses will vary, but some examples of a sedentary lifestyle may include driving rather than walking to a nearby destination, watching TV or playing video games rather than participating in physical activity, and always parking close to an entrance.

Standardized Test Practice

1. A   2. D

Open-Ended
3. Students' paragraphs should describe and explain how they manage their time, including making decisions about activities and finding time for sleep. Paragraphs should contain correct spelling, capitalization, punctuation, grammar, usage, and sentence structure.

Alcohol, Tobacco, and Other Drugs

STANDARDS AND FEATURES

Lesson	National Standards	State/Local Standards	Activities and Features
Lesson 36 *(3 sessions, 1 block)* Using Prescription and OTC Drugs Safely	2.10		
Lesson 37 *(4 sessions, 2 blocks)* Choosing an Alcohol-Free Lifestyle	1.2, 1.5, 1.8, 1.9, 2.9		**Health News:** U.S. Alcohol Laws, p. 415 **Using Life Skills:** Analyzing Influences on Health: Analyzing Alcohol Advertising, p. 417
Lesson 38 *(4 sessions, 2 blocks)* Choosing a Tobacco-Free Lifestyle	1.7, 2.9, 6.1		**Using Life Skills:** Advocating for Health: Advocating Quitting Smoking, p. 431
Lesson 39 *(4 sessions, 2 blocks)* Avoiding Illegal Drug Use	1.8, 1.9, 2.9		**Just the Facts:** Marijuana, p. 439 **Facts About:** Club Drugs, p. 441 **Speaking Out:** Participating in a Drug-Free Club, p. 443
Lesson 40 *(3 sessions, 2 blocks)* Avoiding Drug Dependence	1.1, 1.7, 2.1, 2.3		
Lesson 41 *(2 sessions, 1 block)* Resisting Pressure to Abuse Drugs	1.5, 2.1, 2.3		**Using Life Skills:** Resistance Skills: Ways to Say "No" When Pressured to Use Drugs, p. 465
Lesson 42 *(2 sessions, 1 block)* Reducing Risk by Being Drug Free	2.9, 6.3		**Using Life Skills:** Using Goal-Setting and Decision-Making Skills: Making a Responsible Decision, p. 470
Lesson 43 *(1 session, 1 block)* Assessing Treatment Options	3.1, 3.4, 3.5		

Key to Differentiated Instruction

L1 Level 1 activities should be appropriate for students with learning difficulties.

L2 Level 2 activities should be within the ability range of all students.

L3 Level 3 activities are designed for above-average students.

ELL ELL activities should be within the ability range of English language learners.

FAST FILE RESOURCES

INTRODUCING THE UNIT

Parent and Family Letter	p. 1	Health Behavior Contract	p. 3
Spanish Parent and Family Letter	p. 2	Unit Focus Transparency Master and Worksheet	p. 4

TEACHING THE UNIT LESSONS

Reproducible Student Pages	Lesson 36	Lesson 37	Lesson 38	Lesson 39	Lesson 40	Lesson 41	Lesson 42	Lesson 43
Reading Strategy	p. 7	p. 19	p. 33	p. 47	p. 61	p. 73	p. 85	p. 97
Vocabulary Practice	p. 8	p. 20	p. 34	p. 48	p. 62	p. 74	p. 86	p. 98
Transparency Master and Worksheet	p. 9	p. 21	p. 35	p. 49	p. 63	p. 75	p. 87	p. 99
Real-Life Health	p. 11	p. 23	p. 37	p. 51	p. 65	p. 77	p. 89	p. 101
5-Minute Check	p. 15	p. 27	p. 41	p. 55	p. 69	p. 81	p. 93	p. 105
Lesson Quiz	p. 16	p. 30	p. 43	p. 58	p. 70	p. 82	p. 94	p. 106

CLOSING THE UNIT

Family Involvement Activity	p. 109	Health in the News	p. 119
Community Involvement Activity	p. 111	Health Career Research Activity	p. 121
Health Lab	p. 113	Unit Test A	p. 123
Activity: Strengthening Health Skills	p. 117	Unit Test B	p. 127

Glencoe Exclusive!

TeacherWorks™
All-In-One Planner and Resource Center

Technology

- **Interactive Chalkboard CD-ROM**
- **TeacherWorks™ CD-ROM**
- **StudentWorks™ CD-ROM**
- **Reading Essentials CD-ROM**
- **Exam*View*® Assessment Suite**

www.glencoe.com
- **Vocabulary Puzzlemaker**
- **Interactive Tutor**
- **Your Health Checklist**
- **Web Links**
- **Student Web Activities**

UNIT 7

Alcohol, Tobacco, and Other Drugs

TEST YOUR DRUG IQ

Use the three statements on the student page to initiate a class discussion about the consequences of using drugs. *Additional True/False statements are:*

4. **Marijuana is a harmless drug that hurts no one.**
   FALSE: Marijuana can harm the lungs and cause short-term memory loss. Marijuana contains more tar than cigarettes do.

5. **LSD is a drug that will cause you to experience only pleasant, enjoyable visual and auditory effects.**
   FALSE: LSD can cause terrifying hallucinations that can recur for years.

6. **Ecstasy is a fun party drug that has no side effects.**
   FALSE: Ecstasy, a club drug, does have side effects. It can trigger depression, anxiety, and other psychological problems, and cause brain and liver damage.

 Celebrity Drug Abuse

Role Models Ask students if Denzel Washington's statement has affected how they think about using alcohol and drugs. According to the Entertainment Industries Council, young people view drug use in entertainment as a kind of role modeling. Discuss with students how powerful an influence that might be. **L2**

UNIT 7 — Alcohol, Tobacco, and Other Drugs

TEST YOUR DRUG IQ
True or False?

1. **You cannot become addicted to heroin if you use it only once.**
   FALSE: Many people die or become addicted after one use of certain substances, such as heroin.

2. **Drinking alcohol is safer than using other drugs.**
   FALSE: Alcohol, which many teens think is relatively harmless, can cause death by alcohol poisoning or from accidents related to alcohol, such as drinking and driving.

3. **If you smoke once in a while, you won't get hooked.**
   FALSE: Tobacco is highly addictive, and it's an addiction that is hard to shake. According to the Surgeon General, the probability of becoming addicted to nicotine after one exposure is higher than for other addictive substances.

> "I made a commitment to completely cut out drinking and anything that might hamper me from getting my mind and body together. And the floodgates of goodness have opened upon me—spiritually and financially."
>
> —Denzel Washington, Academy Award-winning actor and director

 Celebrity Drug Abuse

Research Certain musicians and other well-known personalities have had highly publicized bouts with drug abuse. Research the experience of one such celebrity. Why do you think this person may have turned to drugs? What other options do you think he or she may have had? Has this person tried to recover from drug addiction? How? Present a multimedia report on the results of your research to your class, using video clips or other technology, if possible.

LESSON 36	LESSON 37	LESSON 38	LESSON 39
Using Prescription and OTC Drugs Safely	Choosing an Alcohol-Free Lifestyle	Choosing a Tobacco-Free Lifestyle	Avoiding Illegal Drug Use

402   UNIT 7 • Alcohol, Tobacco, and Other Drugs

Two-Minute Unit Launcher

Demo Set up three glasses of water—one with 12 oz, one with 5 oz, and one with 1.5 oz. Add a few drops of food coloring to each glass of water to make the water visible. The first glass of water represents a serving of beer, the second a serving of wine, and the third a serving of whiskey. Explain that, in spite of the differences in volume, each contains about the same amount of alcohol (beer: 0.4 oz of alcohol; wine and whiskey: 0.5 oz of alcohol each).

EVALUATING MEDIA MESSAGES

Try Enitocin

It's the new wonder drug that has been scientifically shown to calm your nerves after a stressful day. 9 out of 10 people who try Enitocin like it so much that they use it almost every day. Check your local drugstore for this revolutionary new stress-reliever.

 WHAT'S YOUR VERDICT?

To evaluate this advertisement, use the criteria for analyzing and evaluating health messages delivered through media and technology that you learned in Unit 1.

 Health Online

Visit www.glencoe.com to find regularly updated statistics about teen drug use. Using the information provided, determine the answer to this question: How many teens died from drug abuse last year?

Visit www.glencoe.com to use *Your Health Checklist* ✔, an interactive tool that helps you determine your health status.

LESSON 40	**LESSON 41**	**LESSON 42**	**LESSON 43**
Avoiding Drug Dependence	Resisting Pressure to Abuse Drugs	Reducing Risk by Being Drug Free	Assessing Treatment Options

Health Online

Answers In 2001, 21,683 Americans died from drug-induced causes (see healthmh.com for specific information on teen mortality statistics). Drugs such as prescription medications, inhalants, and over-the-counter cough, sleep, and diet medications can be abused if not used correctly. Drugs used illegally are alcohol, tobacco, marijuana, stimulants, LSD, PCP, heroin, and other opiates. Teens give a variety of reasons for trying drugs, including curiosity, increasing self-esteem, relieving stress, and feeling grown-up. Peer pressure is often a reported reason for engaging in drug use. Teenagers have external pressure to conform to the behavior of friends. Fitting in and belonging to a group is important to most teens.

 What's Your Verdict?

Ads Prescription drugs are advertised in magazines and on television. Have each student bring in a magazine ad or a description of the parts of a TV ad for a prescription drug. Working in groups, students can analyze the ads and predict how people might react to what is said. Have students answer these questions: How are people depicted in the ads? What is the purpose of having these ads if they are for prescription drugs? Have students create a poster board or a paper illustrating common themes found in the ads. **L2**

Health Journal

Write an Essay Have students identify three long-term goals, such as going to college or becoming a responsible parent. Have them write an essay in their health journal about how using drugs might interfere with reaching these goals. Have students share their essays with the class. Ask the students what they can do to ensure a drug-free lifestyle throughout the course of their lives. **L2**

 INTERACTIVE CHALKBOARD with Image Bank

Unit Focus Transparency

Page 4, **Unit 7 Fast File Resources**

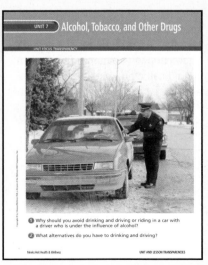

> UNIT 7 Alcohol, Tobacco, and Other Drugs
>
> ❶ Why should you avoid drinking and driving or riding in a car with a driver who is under the influence of alcohol?
>
> ❷ What alternatives do you have to drinking and driving?

National Health Education Standards

Pages 402–403: 1.1, 1.7, 2.5, 2.6, 3.1

LESSON 36

Using Prescription and OTC Drugs Safely

Out of Time?

If time does not permit an in-depth study of this topic, use the following activities in this Teacher Wraparound Edition:
- Class Activity, p. 406
- Quick Demo, p. 407
- Legal Issues, p. 407

1 Focus

HEALTH GOAL **Follow Guidelines for the Safe Use of Prescription and OTC Drugs** Have students respond to the Health Goal for this lesson by listing reasons that guidelines should be placed on drug use. *Answers may vary, but should include: unsafe use can harm a person's health or cause the drug not to help the problem he or she is experiencing.* **L2**

 ABOUT IT!

Journaling The student should not take the OTC drug due to the possible interaction with asthma. The student should call a pharmacist or a doctor and ask for advice. **L2**

LESSON

36

What You'll Learn

1. List and explain factors that influence the effects a drug will have on a person. *(p. 405)*
2. Discuss the ways that drugs are administered to the body. *(p. 405)*
3. Identify the difference between drug misuse and drug abuse. *(p. 405)*
4. Identify information that appears on a prescription and OTC drug labels. *(pp. 406, 407)*
5. List guidelines for the safe use of prescription and OTC drugs. *(pp. 406–407)*
6. Discuss the role of the FDA in regulating OTC drugs, prescription drugs, and herbal supplements. *(p. 407)*

Why It's Important

Prescription and OTC drugs can be helpful if used properly. This lesson will help you learn to use prescription and OTC drugs safely.

Key Terms

- drug
- drug misuse
- drug abuse
- dose
- prescription drug
- brand-name drug
- generic-name drug
- over-the-counter (OTC) drug
- tamper-resistant package
- side effect

Using Prescription and OTC Drugs Safely

HEALTH GOAL • **I will follow guidelines for the safe use of prescription and over-the-counter drugs.**

A substance other than food that changes the way the body or mind functions is a *drug.* Some drugs, such as tobacco, cocaine, and marijuana, harm health. Other drugs, such as prescription drugs and over-the-counter (OTC) drugs, promote health. Drugs intended to promote health can harm your health if you do not follow guidelines for their safe use. In this lesson you will learn guidelines for the safe use of prescription drugs and OTC drugs.

 ABOUT IT!

Writing About Using OTC Drugs Safely Suppose that you have a cold and you visit a drugstore to find an OTC drug that will relieve your congestion. You find one that seems perfect for your symptoms, but the label says that people who have asthma should not use it. You have asthma. After you read the information on using OTC drugs safely on page 407, write a response to this situation in your health journal.

National Health Education Standards—Guide for Lesson 36		
2.10	Analyze how public health policies and government regulations can influence health promotion and disease prevention.	pp. 404, 406–408, 409

Drugs

People use drugs in responsible and irresponsible ways. **Responsible drug use** is the correct use of legal drugs to promote health and well-being. An example of responsible drug use is taking a prescription drug for its intended purpose according to a physician's instructions. However, drugs also may be misused and abused.

What to Know About Drugs

Drug misuse is the incorrect use of a prescription or OTC drug. Examples of drug misuse include using another person's prescription drug. The intentional use of a drug without medical or health reasons is **drug abuse.** Both legal and illegal drugs can be abused. Drug misuse and abuse can destroy both health and relationships.

Ways Drugs Enter the Body

By mouth The most common way of taking a drug is by swallowing it. A drug in the form of a pill, capsule, or liquid may be swallowed. After being swallowed, a drug travels to the stomach and small intestine and is absorbed into the bloodstream.

By injection Some drugs are injected using a syringe and a needle. A drug that is injected must be dissolved in liquid. The drug goes directly under the skin into a muscle or blood vessel, causing immediate results.

By inhalation Some drugs are inhaled through the nose or mouth. Drugs that are inhaled produce effects very quickly by entering the bloodstream through the lungs. Sniffing drugs through the nose so that they can be absorbed through the mucous membranes of the nasal passages is **snorting.** Snorting drugs may cause damage to the nose and nasal passages.

By absorption A drug that is absorbed enters the bloodstream through the skin or mucous membranes. A patch worn on the body that contains a drug that is absorbed through the skin is a **skin patch.**

A wax-coated form of a drug that is inserted into the rectum is a **suppository.** The absorption of a drug between the cheek and gum is **buccal absorption.** The absorption of a drug when it is placed under the tongue is **sublingual absorption.**

By implantation Some drugs are implanted, or placed, under the skin where they can be released into the bloodstream. Other factors, besides the ways a drug enters the body, also determine the effects of a drug. The **dose** is the amount of a drug that is taken at one time. The larger the dose, the greater the effect of the drug on the user.

Weight, age, feelings and health also influence the effects a drug will have on the user.

> **Make the Connection**
>
> **Substance Absorption** For more information on how substances are absorbed into the body, see page 220, in Lesson 19.

>
> **Reading Review**
>
> 1. What is the name of a patch, worn on the body, that contains a drug that is absorbed through the skin?
> 2. Describe buccal absorption.

LESSON 36 • Using Prescription and OTC Drugs Safely **405**

405

Prescription Drugs

Class Activity

Locating Prescription and OTC Drugs
Placement of prescription and OTC medications can be different for each home. Ask students to investigate, with permission from a parent or guardian, the location of prescription and OTC medications in their home and see if they meet the requirements under the Guidelines for Safe Use of Prescription Drugs. Storage (are they still in the original box) and expiration dates should be listed in their assignment. **L2**

Quick Demo

Prescription Label Provide examples of what a prescription may look like, showing students all of the information contained on the label. Copy a label from a prescription bottle and pass out copies so students can identify all the parts of the label. **ELL**

5-Minute Check

Page 15, **Unit 7 Fast File Resources**

1. Name the five ways drugs can be taken. *by mouth, injection, absorption, inhalation, and implantation*

2. What method is most common? *by mouth*

3. What is the difference between buccal and sublingual absorption? *Buccal is between the cheek and gum, and sublingual is under the tongue.*

4. What things may factor into the effects of a drug? *the dose, how a person feels, weight, age, and health*

5. What is the difference between drug misuse and abuse? *Misuse is incorrect use of a prescription or OTC drug, and abuse is intentional use of a drug without medical or health reasons.*

A drug that is used to treat, prevent, or diagnose illness is a medicine. A medicine that fights specific illnesses and infections and can be obtained only with a ***prescription,*** a written order from a licensed health professional, is a ***prescription drug.***

What to Know About Prescription Drugs

Did You Know?

FDA Ingredients in legal drugs must be listed as safe and effective by the Food and Drug Administration (FDA). The FDA approves any new ingredient, prescription drug, or OTC drug before it is distributed.

A prescription contains a patient's name; the name of the drug; the form of the drug, such as pills or liquid; the dosage level; directions for use; the physician's name, address, phone number, and signature; the Drug Enforcement Agency registration; and the refill instructions.

Legal matters Obtaining or using prescription drugs without a prescription is illegal. By law, prescription drugs must be prepared and sold by licensed ***pharmacists*** who are allied health professionals who dispense medications that are prescribed by physicians. Prescription drugs are obtained from a pharmacy. A ***pharmacy*** is a place where prescription drugs are legally dispensed.

Brand-name versus generic Pharmacists fill prescriptions with either brand-name or generic-name drugs. A drug with a registered name or trademark given to a drug by a pharmacetical company is a ***brand-name drug.*** A drug that contains the same active ingredients as a brand-name drug is a ***generic-name drug.***

Generic-name drugs usually are less expensive than brand-name drugs. Generic and brand names of a particular drug usually have ***therapeutical equivalence,*** which means two drugs are chemically the same and produce the same medical effects.

Guidelines for the safe use of prescription drugs It is important to follow guidelines when using a prescription drug. Contact your physician if the drug does not seem to be producing the desired effects. If you are experiencing new or unexpected symptoms, report these to your physician. Often people will begin to feel better after a couple of days. However, do not stop taking the drug if you start feeling better. It is also important to carefully follow the instructions on the label. Follow instructions for storing the prescription drug. Keep all prescription drugs out of the reach of children. Since you do not know the effect a drug will have on your body, never take prescription drugs that have been prescribed for another person. Keep prescription drugs in their original containers. And finally, never take prescription drugs that appear to have been tampered with, are discolored, or have a suspicious odor.

406   UNIT 7 • Alcohol, Tobacco, and Other Drugs

Teacher to Teacher

Write an Essay Ask students to write a one-page essay about a medication they have taken. Have students answer the following questions: What are generic and brand names of the drug? What is it primarily prescribed for? Why were you taking the drug? How does it work? What does it actually do? What is the recommended dosage? What was your dosage? What are the possible side effects? Did you experience any? What are the contraindications? What are the cautions during use? Students should include a bibliography of at least two sources of information. **L3**
Joseph Varga
Burlington County Alternative High School, Pemberton, NJ

OTC Drugs

T hink about the last time you went shopping. Perhaps you were in a supermarket and saw the drug section. You noticed many kinds of drugs on the shelves: aspirin, vitamins, and cold medicines. You saw many different kinds of over-the-counter drugs.

What to Know About Over-the-Counter Drugs

A drug that can be purchased without a prescription in stores such as grocery stores or drugstores is an *over-the-counter drug (OTC).* OTC drugs are medicines that are available without a prescription or a doctor's direction. OTC drugs usually are taken to relieve signs and symptoms of an illness. Some drugs that were once only available by prescription are now OTC drugs. The Food and Drug Administration (FDA) requires that OTC drugs have labels with detailed information.

Indication for use A symptom or condition for which the OTC drug should be used is an *indication for use.* A symptom or condition for which the OTC drug should not be used is a *contraindication for use.*

Guidelines for the Safe Use of OTC Drugs

There are ways to be safe when taking an OTC drug. First, obtain permission from your parents or guardian to take an OTC drug.

Do not purchase an OTC drug if the tamper-resistant packaging is broken. A package that is sealed to assure the buyer that the package has not been opened previously is a *tamper-resistant package.* The FDA requires that all OTC drugs be placed in tamper-resistant packages.

Carefully follow the directions for use. Ask a pharmacist or physician if you have questions about the use of an OTC drug. Do not take more than the recommended dose, and do not take an OTC drug if you have a condition listed under the contraindications.

Stop using the OTC drug and notify a physician if you have unwanted side effects. A *side effect* is an unwanted body change that is not related to the main purpose of a drug. Do not take more than one OTC drug at a time without telling a pharmacist or physician.

Do not take an OTC drug after the expiration date. The effectiveness of a drug may change with time.

Do not participate in activities that put you at risk if you are taking an OTC drug that may cause drowsiness. For example, do not drive a motor vehicle, ride a bicycle, play a contact sport, or operate machinery while taking an OTC drug that may cause drowsiness.

Make the Connection

Healthful Behaviors For more information about practicing healthful behaviors, see page 27 in Lesson 3.

 Reading Review

1. Describe an indication for use for OTC drugs and a contraindication for OTC drug use.
2. If an OTC drug causes drowsiness, describe what activities you should not engage in and why.

LESSON 36 • Using Prescription and OTC Drugs Safely   **407**

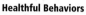
407

Herbal Supplements

NHES Assessment/SCASS

Performance Task Supplements often are used by people to improve their health. Have students visit a natural food or herbal store and choose a specific herbal supplement to investigate. Ask students to determine if there is any scientific evidence behind its claim. Have students create a poster discussing the chosen herbal supplement, including a critical analysis of its potential benefits and dangers. **L2**

Teacher FYI

Ephedra The FDA's ban on ephedra includes all dietary supplements that contain a source of ephedrine alkaloids, such as ephedra, ma huang, Sida cordifolia, and pinellia. The rule does not apply to traditional Chinese herbal remedies.

3 Assess

Vocabulary Practice
Page 8, **Unit 7 Fast File Resources**

Name _____ Date _____ Class _____

LESSON 36 Using Prescription and OTC Drugs Safely

Vocabulary Practice

Explain the relationship between the pairs of words given below. Include a definition of each vocabulary term as part of your answer.

brand-name drug	drug misuse	prescription drug
dose	generic-name drug	side effect
drug	over-the-counter (OTC) drug	tamper-resistant package
drug abuse		

1. prescription drug—drug misuse

2. drug—side effect

3. over-the-counter drug—tamper-resistant package

4. brand-name drug—generic-name drug

5. dose—drug abuse

8 LESSON 36 • Using Prescription and OTC Drugs Safely   UNIT 7

Herbal Supplements

You have probably heard or read a great deal on the news about dietary supplements. *Dietary supplements* are nutrients that are not a part of food and that may come in the form of pills, capsules, liquids, or powders. You may have seen stories that claim many benefits from using these substances, such as make you stronger or relieve stress. When prescribed by a health professional, dietary supplements may be helpful, especially if the body cannot get a certain nutrient from a daily diet. But sometimes, dietary supplements can be dangerous.

The Risks of Herbal Supplements

Chemicals from plants that contain nutrients and are taken in addition to or in place of foods in one's diet are called *herbal supplements.* These supplements now have crossed from health food stores to supermarket drugstores.

Safety issues While many herbal supplements can be healthful, by no means are they safe for everyone. Suppose you buy a prescription or an OTC drug. You have learned that these products have been tested by the government. You can be fairly certain that they are safe to take, provided they are used responsibly.

This is not the case with herbal supplements. Manufacturers of herbal supplements, including vitamins and minerals, do not have to provide tests that show they are safe and effective before their products are sold to consumers. Manufacturers of supplements are responsible for providing accurate "supplement facts" labels and ingredients lists. The FDA steps in if there are health problems associated with supplements, or if they

include a new ingredient that has not been shown to be safe. As a result, the use of herbals has come under much criticism.

Ephedra The herbal supplement *ephedra* is known for its stimulating effect. It provides energy and increased metabolism, with subsequent weight loss. But ephedra also is considered dangerous. The effects of ephedra, as reported to the FDA, include changes in blood pressure, headaches, chest pain, heart attack, stroke, and death. In December 2003, the FDA moved to ban ephedra from being distributed in the U.S. The ban went into effect in early 2004.

Kava Another herbal supplement receiving much attention is kava. *Kava* is an ingredient in plants from South Pacific islands. Kava, which is promoted for relaxation, is sold as a product that is supposed to relieve stress, anxiety, and tension. There appears to be evidence that kava causes liver diseases, such as hepatitis, cirrhosis, and liver failure.

Did You Know?

Dietary Supplements Makers of dietary supplements do not have to seek FDA approval before placing a supplement on the market.

408   UNIT 7 • Alcohol, Tobacco, and Other Drugs

 Healthy People 2010

Objective 26-17 *Increase the proportion of adolescents who perceive great risk associated with substance abuse.*

The Healthy People 2010 target is to have 80 percent of adolescents perceiving great risk in substance abuse. Ask students if they believe that over-the-counter and prescription drug abuse is as harmful as using alcohol, marijuana, or cocaine. Have groups research drug abuse, including mortality and morbidity rates of OTC drugs, prescription drugs, alcohol, marijuana, and cocaine. Ask students to create a graph representing this information. Have each group create a public service announcement containing information obtained in their research. **L2**

brand-name drug
dose
drug
drug abuse
drug misuse
generic-name drug
herbal supplements
over-the-counter
(OTC) drug
prescription drug
responsible drug use
side effect
tamper-resistant
package

Key Terms Review

Complete these fill-in-the-blank statements with the lesson Key Terms on the left. Do not write in this book.

1. _____ is the incorrect use of a prescription or OTC drug.
2. A drug purchased without a prescription is called a(n) _____.
3. An unwanted body change from a drug is called a(n) _____.
4. A drug with a trademark manufactured by a drug company is a(n) _____.
5. The general name for a substance other than food that changes the way the body works is a(n) _____.
6. A written order by a health professional for a drug is a(n) _____.
7. A drug that has the same ingredients as a brand-name drug is a(n) _____.
8. The amount of a drug taken at one time is a(n) _____.
9. A package that is sealed, which assures the user it has not been opened, is in a(n) _____.
10. _____ is the intentional use of a drug without medical or health reasons.

Recalling the Facts

11. What are the five ways in which drugs can enter the body?
12. Of the five ways drugs can enter the body, which one allows the drug to be absorbed most quickly?
13. Name at least eight types of information that can be found on a prescription.
14. Describe the difference between indication of use and contraindication of use.
15. Why does a drug taken by mouth take longer to have an effect on the body than a drug that is injected?
16. What is buccal absorption?
17. There are ten guidelines for the safe use of OTC drugs. List five of them.
18. There are ten guidelines for the safe use of prescription drugs. List five of the guidelines.

Critical Thinking

19. Why might a health professional prescribe a dietary supplement to one of his or her patients?
20. Why do you think some drugs require a prescription while other drugs are sold over the counter?
21. What is the difference between drug misuse and drug abuse?
22. Why might a person request a generic-name drug from a physician rather than a brand-name drug?

Real-Life Applications

23. If a peer offered you use of his or her prescription drug, what would you do?
24. What are some things to consider if you decide to take an herbal supplement?
25. Your parent has a prescription for headaches. You have a headache. Why do you think it would not be wise to take the prescription medicine?
26. What do you think are common illnesses for which people take OTC drugs?

Activities

Responsible Decision Making

27. **Determine** You have followed the directions on the label of an OTC cold medicine but feel no relief. You could double the dose. What should you do? Refer to the Responsible Decision-Making Model on page 61 for help.

Sharpen Your Life Skills

28. **Access Health Information** Working with a parent at home, read the labels of several OTC drugs, including the ingredients, the indications for use, and the contraindications for use. Ask your parents for help in understandiing the labels

---

Key Terms Review

1. Drug misuse
2. over-the-counter drug
3. side effect
4. brand-name drug
5. drug
6. prescription
7. generic-name drug
8. dose
9. tamper-resistant package
10. Drug abuse

Recalling the Facts

11. by mouth, by injection, by inhalation, by absorption, and by implantation
12. injection
13. See page 406 for information found on a prescription.
14. An indication for use is a symptom or condition for which the OTC drug should be used. A contraindication for use is a symptom or condition for which the OTC drug should not be used.
15. It must first travel to the stomach and small intestine before getting into the bloodstream.
16. the absorption of a drug between the cheek and gum
17. See page 407 for guidelines.
18. See page 406 for guidelines.

Critical Thinking

19. to provide nutrients to the body
20. A drug may be available only by prescription because of its harmful effects if not taken correctly.
21. Drug misuse is the incorrect use of prescription or OTC drugs. Drug abuse is intentional use of a drug without medical or health reasons.
22. A generic-name drug will be less expensive than a brand-name drug.

Real-Life Applications

23. Tell him or her that the prescription drug is not prescribed for you and refuse the drug.
24. Do I know the effects of the herbal supplement? Are the claims supported by research? Will the effects of this supplement interact with any other prescriptions or OTC drugs I am taking?

---

25. The prescription is made for your parent. The dose might be too strong for a teenager.
26. flu, cough, mild fever, sore throat, upset stomach, and heartburn

Activities

Responsible Decision Making

27. Do not take a double dose. It's possible that you may have a more serious condition than a cold, and the OTC medication is not what is needed. First, a double dose can be harmful. Second, you may be delaying treatment of the real problem.

Sharpen Your Life Skills

28. Answers will vary, but may include ideas from "OTC Drugs" on page 407.

If time does not permit an in-depth study of this topic, use the following activities in this Teacher Wraparound Edition:

- 5-Minute Check, p. 412
- Cross-Curricular Connections, p. 415
- Teacher to Teacher, p. 422

1 Focus

HEALTH GOAL **Alcohol Use** Have students respond to the Health Goal for this lesson by discussing reasons why teens might feel pressure to drink alcohol. *Reasons might include friends who drink alcohol, or believe there is no harm in drinking.* **L2**

Write ABOUT IT!

Journaling The student's journal entries should tell their friend that they do not want to drink alcohol. Drinking might cause the student to do things that he or she may regret. **L1**

What You'll Learn

1. Discuss BAC and the effects of alcohol on the body systems. *(p. 411)*
2. Explain ways alcohol affects decision making and increases the risk of violence and illegal behavior. *(p. 416)*
3. Discuss the effects of alcohol on a developing fetus. *(p. 415)*
4. Discuss causes, health problems, and treatment of alcoholism. *(p. 419)*
5. Discuss how advertisements may encourage drinking. *(p. 421)*
6. Practice resistance skills to resist peer pressure to drink. *(p. 422)*

Why It's Important

More than 18 million people in the United States abuse alcohol. You can take steps now to reduce your risk of having problems with alcohol.

Key Terms

- proof
- blood alcohol concentration (BAC)
- toxin
- hazing activity
- binge drinking
- cirrhosis
- blackout
- alcoholism
- denial
- delirium tremens syndrome

Choosing an Alcohol-Free Lifestyle

HEALTH GOAL • **I will not drink alcohol.**

Self-control is the degree to which a person regulates his or her own behavior. You must have self-control to have a healthy mind, body, and relationships. Drinking alcohol influences your self-control and causes harmful changes in your mind, body, and relationships. In this lesson, you will learn how drinking affects the body, thinking, and decision making and increases the risk of violence and illegal behavior.

Write ABOUT IT!

Writing About Self-Control Suppose you are at a party and one of your classmates tells you that he has some beer in his car. He asks you to have a few drinks. After you read the information on how alcohol can affect thinking and decision making on page 416, and how alcohol increases the risk of illegal behavior on page 418, write an entry in your health journal about how you would respond to this situation.

National Health Education Standards—Guide for Lesson 37		
1.2	Describe the interrelationships of emotional, intellectual, physical, and social health.	pp. 410, 412, 413, 417–420, 421
1.5	Propose ways to reduce or prevent injuries and health problems.	pp. 410, 414–415, 420, 422, 423
1.8	Analyze personal susceptibility to injury, illness, or death if engaging in unhealthy behaviors.	pp. 412–413, 416–419, 423
1.9	Analyze the potential severity of injury or illness if engaging in unhealthy behaviors.	pp. 416–419
2.9	Analyze how some health risk behaviors can influence the likelihood of engaging in unhealthy behaviors.	pp. 413, 416–417, 418, 423

Alcohol and the Body

A drug that depresses the brain and nervous system is *alcohol*. Alcohol is made by fermentation. *Fermentation* is a process in which yeast, sugar, and water are combined to produce alcohol and carbon dioxide. The most common alcoholic beverages are beer, wine, and liquor.

What to Know About Alcohol and the Body

Beer An alcoholic beverage that is made by fermenting barley, corn, or rye is beer. Most beers are about 4 percent alcohol. Malt liquor is beer that has a higher alcohol content than regular beer. Light beer is beer that has fewer calories than regular beer, but about the same alcohol content.

Wine An alcoholic beverage made by fermenting grapes or other fruits is wine. Most wines are about 12 to 14 percent alcohol. A wine cooler is a carbonated, fruit-flavored alcoholic beverage that is 1.5 to 6 percent alcohol.

Liquor An alcoholic beverage that is made by distillation is liquor. *Distillation* is a process that uses a fermented mixture to obtain an alcoholic beverage with a high alcohol content. Whiskey, bourbon, rye, rum, gin, vodka, tequila, and brandy are types of liquor. Most liquors are about 40 percent alcohol. A measure of the amount of alcohol in a beverage is the *proof* of the liquor. The proof of a beverage is double the percent of alcohol in the beverage. For example, a beverage with 20 percent alcohol is 40 proof.

How Alcohol Enters the Body

Alcohol enters the bloodstream within minutes. About 20 percent of the alcohol that a person drinks is absorbed into the bloodstream through the walls of the stomach. A majority of the rest of the alcohol is absorbed through the walls of the intestine. After it is absorbed, alcohol moves quickly into the bloodstream. The remaining alcohol is excreted through urine, perspiration, or breath.

Alcohol affects every cell in the body. Most of the alcohol is changed to harmless waste by the liver, and all of the alcohol is eventually excreted, but the liver can process only about one drink per hour. If people have more than one drink, the excess alcohol builds up in the body. The alcohol in a drink goes to the body tissues before being excreted. The effects of alcohol intensify as the concentration of alcohol in the blood increases. The amount of alcohol in a person's blood is the *blood alcohol concentration (BAC)*. BAC is given as a percentage. The higher the BAC, the greater the effects of alcohol on the body.

Reading Review

1. Describe fermentation.

2. What percentage of alcohol is absorbed into the bloodstream through the walls of the stomach?

3. If a beverage has 50 percent alcohol, what is the proof of the beverage?

Lesson Resource Manager

- **Unit 7 Fast File Resources**
  Reading Strategy, p. 19
  Vocabulary Practice, p. 20
  Transparency Master and Worksheet, p. 21
  Real-Life Health, p. 23
  Real-Life Health, p. 25
  5-Minute Check, p. 27
  Lesson 37 Quiz, p. 30
- **Unit 7 Transparency**
- **Lesson 37 Transparency**

- **Reading Essentials**
- **Technology**
  TeacherWorks™ CD-ROM
  StudentWorks™ CD-ROM
  Reading Essentials CD-ROM
  Exam*View*® Assessment Suite
  Vocabulary Puzzlemaker

2 Teach

Class Activity

Effects of Alcohol After students read pages 411–415, ask them to list on pieces of scrap paper both long-term and short-term effects of drinking alcohol. Put the papers in a box. Draw them out one at a time and ask students to say whether the effect is short- or long-term, what body part(s) can be affected, and a possible consequence.

Reading Review

1. *a process in which yeast, sugar, and water are combined to produce alcohol and carbon dioxide*
2. *20 percent*
3. *100 proof*

INTERACTIVE CHALKBOARD with Image Bank

PowerPoint® Presentations

This CD-ROM is an editable Microsoft® PowerPoint® presentation that includes:
- Lesson presentations
- Lesson checks
- Interactive graphics
- 5-Minute Checks
- Image Bank
- All transparencies

Discussion Use the Think-Pair-Share Strategy on page 17T to involve all students actively in a discussion about alcohol use.

National Health Education Standards

Pages 410–411: 1.2, 1.5, 2.1, 2.3, 2.5, 4.3, 6.1, 6.3, 7.2, 8.1

▲ Others may pressure you to have "just one drink," but remember that all alcoholic beverages are toxins.

One-half ounce is one drink. An alcoholic beverage that contains about one-half ounce of alcohol is considered one drink of alcohol. One-half ounce of alcohol is about the amount of alcohol in one can of beer, 4 to 5 ounces of wine, or one mixed drink. Drinking more than this causes BAC to rise. Alcohol is a toxin. A ***toxin*** is a substance that is poisonous. If too large an amount is swallowed, the stomach will reject it. This causes a person to vomit. The body attempts to break down alcohol as quickly as possible to remove it from the body. However, a large amount of alcohol in the body takes a long time to be excreted. This is why people who drink alcohol at night may still feel its effects the next morning. These people may still be "drunk" the next day. There is no way to speed alcohol through the body. Coffee, showers, and fresh air do not break down alcohol.

Factors That Affect BAC

Amount of alcohol consumed The number of drinks people have affects their BAC. The alcohol content of each drink determines the effects of the alcohol.

Speed at which alcohol is consumed Drinking at a faster rate increases

BAC. Drinking alcohol quickly is dangerous and can be fatal. When people consume several alcoholic beverages in a short period of time, the liver does not have time to break down the alcohol.

Body weight People with a higher body weight have a higher volume of blood than people with less body weight. The same amount of alcohol produces a greater effect on people with less body weight.

Percentage of body fat Body fat does not absorb as much alcohol as lean body tissue. A person with the higher percentage of body fat will have a higher BAC after one drink than a person with a lower percentage of body fat.

Gender BAC rises faster in females than in males. Females usually have a higher percentage of body fat than males. Certain hormones make females more sensitive to the effects of alcohol than males. Females also have less of a certain stomach enzyme that breaks down alcohol before it enters the bloodstream.

Feelings Feelings, such as stress, anger, and fear, can affect BAC by speeding up the time it takes alcohol to enter the bloodstream.

Amount of food eaten Alcohol passes more quickly into the bloodstream when the stomach is empty than when it is full.

Presence of other drugs in the bloodstream The presence of certain drugs in the bloodstream increases the effects of alcohol. For example, tranquilizers and painkillers increase the depressant effects of alcohol.

Did You Know?

Alcohol Expenses
The total cost of alcohol use by youth (including car crashes, crime, alcohol poisonings, fetal alcohol syndrome, etc.) is more than $58 billion per year.

 Healthy People 2010

Objective 26-5 *Reduce alcohol-related hospital emergency department visits.*
The Healthy People 2010 document notes that alcohol consumption is associated with a wide range of events that can result in visits to a hospital emergency department—motor vehicle crashes, violence, alcohol poisoning, etc. In 1996, alcohol-related hospital ED visits (2.2 million) accounted for 2.4 percent of all ED visits. Have students discuss the negative consequences of drinking, especially binge drinking. Have students make a list of specific, realistic actions they could take to help decrease the amount of alcohol-related hospital emergency department visits that take place in their community.

Age Elderly people are more sensitive to the effects of alcohol than are younger people. The bodies of elderly people contain a lower volume of blood than the bodies of younger people.

Drinking carbonated alcoholic beverages The alcohol in carbonated beverages passes into the bloodstream more quickly than the alcohol in noncarbonated drinks.

Drinking Games and Hazing

Drinking can be a hazing activity. An activity in which a person is forced to participate in a dangerous or demeaning act to become a member of a club or group is a *hazing activity*. Some teens have died from these hazing activities. Hazing activities are against the law in most states, and these hazing activities violate the rules of most schools.

Drinking games can be life-threatening. Drinking alcohol quickly—chugging, doing shots, or funneling—is especially dangerous. Binge drinking also is extremely dangerous. Consuming large amounts of alcohol in a short amount of time is called *binge drinking*. People may become unconscious or dangerously drunk. Drinking games are dangerous and are considered binge drinking.

What Happens as BAC Increases

BAC .02 People feel relaxed. They may have increased social confidence and become talkative. Thinking and decision-making abilities may be impaired.

◀ Alcohol-related auto accidents are high among teens.

BAC .05 Areas of the brain that control reasoning and judgment are impaired. People feel warm, relaxed, and confident. Speech may be slurred. People may say or do things they usually would not say or do. There is a decrease in muscular coordination, and reaction time is slowed.

BAC .08–.10 Reasoning, judgment, self-control, muscular coordination, and reaction time are seriously impaired. People no longer can make responsible decisions. However, they may claim not to be affected by the alcohol. They have slurred speech and walk with a stagger. In most states, they are considered legally drunk.

BAC .12 People usually become confused and disoriented. People may have loss of control of coordination and balance. People become nauseous and vomit.

BAC .20 Emotions are unpredictable and may change rapidly. For example, people may quickly switch from crying to laughing. They may pass out.

BAC .30 People will have little or no control over their minds and bodies. Most people cannot stay awake to reach this BAC.

BAC .40 People are likely to be unconscious. Breathing and heartbeat slow down. Death can occur.

BAC .50 People may enter a deep coma and die.

LESSON 37 • Choosing an Alcohol-Free Lifestyle **413**

Reading Review

1. Why are elderly people more sensitive to the effects of alcohol than younger people?

2. What effect does food in the stomach have on absorption of alcohol?

3. What effect does carbonation have on the absorption of alcohol?

5-Minute Check

Page 28, **Unit 7 Fast File Resources**

1. What is the definition of malnutrition? *a condition in which the body does not get the nutrients required for optimal health*

2. What is cirrhosis? *a disease of the liver caused by chronic damage to the liver cells due to alcohol*

3. Why is heavy drinking associated with malnutrition? *Heavy drinking interferes with the digestion and absorption of nutrients.*

4. Describe how alcohol is harmful to the digestive system. *Alcohol increases the risk of mouth, esophagus, and stomach cancers. Alcohol also increases the secretion of stomach acids, which injure the inner lining of the stomach.*

5. Describe the three stages of liver disease due to alcohol use. *The first stage occurs when the liver becomes enlarged with fatty tissue. The second stage is alcohol hepatitis, in which the liver swells due to alcohol. Yellowing of the skin and eyes, abdominal pain, and fever may occur. The third stage is cirrhosis. Cirrhosis can cause liver failure and death.*

Make the Connection

Body Systems For more information on how body systems work, see page 208 in Lesson 19.

How Alcohol Affects the Body

Alcohol is a leading cause of death. Almost every part of the body is harmed when people drink large quantities of alcohol.

Nervous system Drinking impairs the brain and other parts of the nervous system, such as nerve cells. Drinking alcohol can cause blackouts and seizures, and dementia, which is a general decline in all areas of mental functioning.

Digestive system Drinking increases the risk of developing cancers of the mouth, esophagus, and stomach. Drinking alcohol also stimulates the secretion of stomach acids and injures the inner lining of the stomach and causes ulcers. An ***ulcer*** is an open sore on the skin or on a mucous membrane.

Drinking also increases the risk of developing liver disease. When the liver is poisoned by alcohol it goes through three stages of disease. The first stage occurs when the liver becomes enlarged with fatty tissue. People with a fatty liver usually do not feel sick. In the second stage, they develop alcoholic hepatitis. A condition in which the liver swells due to alcohol is ***alcoholic hepatitis.*** People with this condition may have yellowing of the skin and eyes, abdominal pain, and fever. Alcoholic hepatitis can cause serious illness or death.

The third stage is cirrhosis. A disease of the liver caused by chronic damage to liver cells is called ***cirrhosis.*** Cirrhosis can cause liver

To have a healthful pregnancy, pregnant women should drink plenty of water and should avoid alcohol. ▼

failure and death. A liver transplant is the only effective treatment for people with advanced cirrhosis.

Heavy drinking also can cause malnutrition. A condition in which the body does not get the nutrients required for optimal health is called ***malnutrition.*** Drinking interferes with the digestion and absorption of nutrients.

Immune system Drinking depresses the function of the immune system. This increases the risk of developing certain illnesses, such as respiratory infections, tuberculosis, and certain cancers. Long-term drinking lowers the number of infection-fighting cells in the body.

Cardiovascular system Drinking can damage the organs of the cardiovascular system. People who drink are at increased risk for developing cardiovascular diseases, high blood pressure, and stroke.

Skeletal system Drinking causes the body to lose calcium. Calcium is necessary for proper development of the skeletal system and bones. Frequent, long-term use of alcohol is a risk factor for developing osteoporosis, a condition in which the bones become thin and brittle.

Urinary system Alcohol increases urine flow. Long-term, heavy drinking can cause kidney failure.

Reproductive system Drinking can have significant effects on the reproductive system during puberty. In females, it can delay the first menstrual cycle and cause irregular periods. In males, drinking can affect the size of the testes and the development of muscle mass.

414 UNIT 7 • Alcohol, Tobacco, and Other Drugs

🎓 **Differentiated Instruction**

Visual Impairment Ask a student to work with a visually impaired student to research the effects within a family when one parent is an alcoholic. They should find out about the gamut of emotions felt by family members, as well as the lasting psychological damage incurred by the children. Ask the student with normal vision to conduct the research and share the findings with his or her partner. Have the visually impaired student give the oral report to the class. **L2**

Warning: Drinking Alcohol During Pregnancy Can Cause FAS

Early pregnancy Drinking alcohol at any time during pregnancy is harmful to a developing baby. When a pregnant female drinks, the alcohol quickly reaches the developing baby through the bloodstream.

Miscarriages and still births Drinking alcohol during pregnancy can cause miscarriage and stillbirth. A *miscarriage* is the natural ending of a pregnancy before a baby is developed enough to survive on its own. A *stillbirth* is a baby that is born dead.

Low birth weight Pregnant females who have been drinking heavily during the last three months of pregnancy are more likely to have an infant with a low birth weight.

Newborns Newborn babies with mothers who drink alcohol during the latter part of pregnancy, or are alcohol-dependent, may have symptoms of alcohol withdrawal shortly after they are born, such as sleeping problems, abnormal muscle tension, shakes, and abnormal reflexes.

Fetal alcohol syndrome Babies of mothers who drink alcohol during pregnancy may be born with fetal alcohol syndrome. The presence of severe birth defects in babies born to mothers who drink alcohol during pregnancy is *fetal alcohol syndrome (FAS).* Babies with FAS may have small eye slits, a small head, and delayed physical and mental growth. FAS is a leading cause of mental disability.

www.glencoe.com

HEALTH NEWS

U.S. Alcohol Laws

The manufacture, transport, and sale of alcohol were, at one time, illegal in the United States. The 18th Amendment of the Constitution was ratified in 1919, thus beginning Prohibition. Alcohol was illegal, but it remained available through bootlegging, the illegal distribution or production of liquor. Prohibition ended in 1933 when Congress passed the 21st Amendment.

During the early 1970s, 29 states lowered their minimum drinking age from 21 to ages ranging from 18 to 20. Studies done shortly after these changes in the minimum drinking age showed that the occurrence of motor vehicle accidents involving teens increased when the minimum drinking age was lowered to 18. In 1984, Congress passed the Uniform Drinking Age Act. This bill required all states to raise the minimum drinking age to 21. Since then, numerous studies have shown that the higher minimum drinking age has resulted in fewer alcohol-related problems among young people.

Visit www.glencoe.com for more information about minimum drinking age laws in the United States.

Percent of Fatally Injured Drivers with BAC > .08

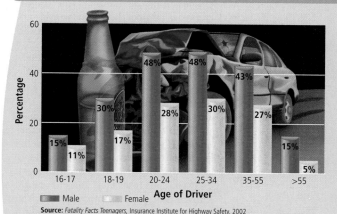

Source: *Fatality Facts Teenagers,* Insurance Institute for Highway Safety, 2002

Analyzing Graphs

1. Across all age groups, which gender is more likely to have a fatal injury due to alcohol?

2. Which age groups have the highest rates of fatal injuries?

LESSON 37 • Choosing an Alcohol-Free Lifestyle **415**

HEALTH NEWS

Analyzing Graphs

1. males
2. 20–24 year olds and 25–34 year olds

Project

BAC for States Split the students into groups. Assign a region to each group (such as Midwest: Ohio, Michigan, Indiana, Illinois, etc.). Have students research when each state in their assigned area adopted the minimum drinking age and current laws regarding legal BAC limits in each state. **L2**

Class Discussion

FAS Discuss the consequences of drinking alcohol during pregnancy. Show students an example of the Surgeon General's warning found on alcohol packaging and advertisements. Ask students the following questions: What risks does it highlight? Are there other risks that it does not mention? Do you think such warnings are effective in preventing alcohol use by pregnant women? **L2**

Class Activity

Alcohol Impairment Give students glasses that distort their vision and have them complete a simple task such as putting various shaped blocks into the correspondingly shaped holes. Ask students to discuss how they felt during the activity and how difficult it was to complete the task. Students should note that simple tasks become difficult when your body is impaired. **L1 ELL**

Cross-Curricular Connections

Social Studies Have the students research social, religious, and cultural reasons people drink alcohol. How do social, religious, and cultural beliefs impact attitudes toward alcohol use? For example, in western Europe, alcohol is often consumed at lunch and dinner. In many religions people drink wine during communion and other religions forbid the consumption of alcohol. Have students choose a religion, a nation, or a particular culture and research its attitude toward alcohol. Have students create a poster, a brochure, or a booklet explaining their findings. **L2**

National Health Education Standards
Pages 414–415: 1.5, 1.7

Thinking and Decision Making

Think about all of the decisions you make each day. Some of these decisions may be very simple, such as deciding what to wear. Certain decisions may be more complex. You may need to make a decision to study for an exam or to complete a job application for a part-time job. While the tasks involved in these decisions have many aspects, drinking alcohol can interfere with the simplest of tasks. Alcohol can cause you to take actions that can be harmful to yourself and others.

How Drinking Affects Thinking and Decision Making

It can cause you to make wrong decisions. If you drink alcohol, you may not use the guidelines for making responsible decisions. You might make a choice that you would not make if you were not under the influence of alcohol. The choice may risk your health and safety or cause you to break the law and family guidelines.

It can give you a false sense of self-confidence in social situations and interfere with your judgment. Teens should never use a drink to be more social. If you do, you are using alcohol as a crutch. Because alcohol affects communication and reasoning, you may find out later that you did or said things that were not appropriate. You may insult someone or share a secret you were supposed to keep. The next day you may find out that you lost a friend because of your actions.

It can make you feel invincible. You may do something daring or dangerous. You might injure yourself or someone else. For example, teens who have been drinking alcohol have been known to jump from rooftop to rooftop. Several teens have misjudged the distance and were seriously injured.

It can increase the likelihood that you will give in to negative peer pressure. If you have been drinking, you are more likely to be persuaded by peers to do things you would not normally do. Suppose you drink too much alcohol and are talked into experimenting with marijuana. You have engaged in two risk behaviors that are harmful and illegal.

It can intensify your sexual feelings and dull your reasoning. If you drink, your sexual feelings may be difficult to control. Many teens who have been sexually active were drinking before they had sex. The consequences of unprotected sex include unplanned pregnancy, sexually transmitted diseases (STDs), HIV, and emotional trauma.

 Achieving Health Literacy

Effective Communicator Have students research effective methods for developing written material. Students can work in small groups to design an informational pamphlet educating their peers on how drinking can affect thinking and decision making. When developing the pamphlet, have students consider: Who is the target population? What is the population's reading level? What is the purpose of the pamphlet? What pictures would be appropriate? Have students share and explain the pamphlets that were created. **L2**

Activity: Using Life Skills

Analyzing Influences on Health: Analyzing Alcohol Advertising

The alcohol industry spends more than 1 billion dollars each year advertising their products. Some of the world's top advertisers work hard to influence the consumers' opinion. This section will help you to analyze an alcohol advertisement so you can see what techniques advertisers use to try to influence consumers.

1 Identify people and things that might influence you. Choose an alcohol ad and obtain a copy of it, if possible, from a newspaper or magazine. If it is a TV ad, tape it. If it is a billboard, take a photo of it. Who is the target audience for the ad (men, women, certain ages)?

2 Evaluate how the influence might affect your health behaviors and decisions. Explain what type of ad it is (billboard, commercial, magazine ad) and why the advertiser may have chosen that form of advertising. Show the ad to your class. What method does the ad use to sell its product (humor, sex appeal, scientific evidence)?

3 Choose positive influences on health. Check to see if the messages the ad is sending are positive and healthful. Explain what happens in the ad. How are women treated in the ad? How are men treated in the ad? What advertising appeals (page 421) are used in the ad?

4 Protect yourself from negative influences on health. Answer these questions: What does the advertiser want you to believe? What do you really believe?

▲ The alcohol industry often targets teens in its magazine ads.

It slows your reaction time and affects your coordination. If you drink, you cannot respond as quickly as usual. For example, you may be a responsible pedestrian. After a few drinks, you might step onto a street without looking both ways. You may be struck by a car.

It can cause you to have aggressive behavior. If you drink, you are more likely to become violent and to commit physical abuse or murder. For example, a teen male who has been drinking alcohol at a party may have a drink spilled on him accidentally by another teen. He usually would resolve conflict without violence. However, because he has been drinking alcohol, he becomes angry and beats up the other teen.

It intensifies your emotions. If you drink, you will have more intense feelings than usual. You may feel extremely sad, depressed, desperate, jealous, or angry. Drinking to numb depressed feelings is very dangerous. Many teen suicide attempts involve alcohol or other drugs.

Hangover An aftereffect of using alcohol and other drugs is called a *hangover.* A hangover may involve a headache, increased sensitivity to sounds, nausea, vomiting, tiredness, and irritability. Some teens think that it is not dangerous for people in high school and college to get drunk occasionally. Drinking alcohol one time can have serious consequences. Some experts claim that teens who drink are more at risk for developing alcoholism than adults who drink.

Blackouts People who drink alcohol may have blackouts. A *blackout* is a period in which a person cannot remember what has happened. People who have been drinking may do something risky, embarrassing, or violent, engage in sex, or find themselves in an unfamiliar place and not remember anything.

LESSON 37 • Choosing an Alcohol-Free Lifestyle **417**

Using Life Skills

Analyzing Influences on Health
Companies spend millions of dollars on alcohol-related advertisements. Have students keep track of the number of alcohol advertisements that they see in one day. Have students create a report that contains the time of day they saw the advertisement, where the advertisement was located, the message of the advertisement and their response to the advertisement. **L2**

Class Activity

Alcohol Effects Reaction time and coordination are slowed after drinking alcohol. Bring in gloves and ask students to perform tasks wearing the gloves, such as screw nuts onto bolts, write a sentence, put together a puzzle. The gloves in this activity simulate the effects of intoxication. **L1 ELL**

Class Discussion

Behavior Have students discuss possible behaviors of a person at each stage of BAC. What might they do, and what might be consequences of those actions? *Examples could include, embarrass one's self, get into a fight, date rape.* **L2**

National Health Education Standards

Pages 416–417: 1.2, 1.8, 1.9, 2.1, 2.3, 2.5, 2.9, 5.1, 5.2, 5.7

Violence and Illegal Behavior

Class Activity

Alcohol-Related Behavior Ask students to find a newspaper or magazine article relating to one of the violent or illegal behaviors listed on the student page. Have students write essays commenting on the role alcohol played in the story and whether they think the outcome would have been different if alcohol were not involved. **L2**

Teacher FYI

Alcohol and Abuse According to the U.S. Department of Health and Human Services, alcohol is involved in more than 50 percent of reported cases of domestic abuse.

Reading Review

1. *no*
2. *domestic violence*
3. *People who have been drinking are more likely to commit rape or to be a victim of rape.*

National Health Education Standards

Pages 418–419: 1.2, 1.8, 1.9, 2.1, 2.9, 2.10, 5.7

Violence and Illegal Behavior

A high percentage of crimes are related to the use and abuse of alcohol. Any kind of crime is considered illegal behavior. Some of these crimes include committing acts of violence and driving while under the influence. You need to know that alcohol use and violence and illegal behavior often go hand-in-hand. Understanding this connection can help keep you and others safe.

How Drinking Increases the Risk of Violence and Illegal Behavior

Make the Connection

Rape Laws For more information on laws that concern rape, see page 687 in Lesson 66.

Reading Review

1. Is drunkenness or being high on drugs a legal defense in court?
2. What is the leading cause of divorce and broken families?
3. How is alcohol related to rape?

Alcohol and violence Alcohol, more than any other drug, has been linked with violence. People who drink, often have little regard for feelings and safety of others. This may lead to violence and illegal behaviors.

Alcohol and domestic violence A leading cause of divorce and broken families is domestic violence. Violence that occurs within a family is ***domestic violence***. Many acts of domestic violence occur after a family member has been drinking alcohol.

Alcohol and suicide Drinking can intensify feelings of sadness and depression. Alcohol is a factor in many teen suicide attempts.

Alcohol and rape Drinking alcohol is a risk factor for rape. The threatened or actual use of physical force to get someone to have sex without giving consent is called ***rape.*** Rape in which the person who is raped knows the rapist is ***acquaintance rape,*** or date rape. People who have been drinking are more likely to commit rape. Drunkenness or being high on drugs is not a legal defense against rape. Also, a female who is under the influence of alcohol or other drugs cannot give legally binding consent to have sex.

Alcohol and the law In all states, people must be 21 years old to purchase or possess alcohol. A minor is a person who is under the legal age. Minors who drink or purchase alcohol risk being arrested, fined, and jailed.

Alcohol and school policies Teens who drink alcohol during school hours or bring alcohol to school are breaking school policies. Most schools suspend or expel students who break school alcohol policies.

Alcohol and driving People who drink and drive may injure or kill themselves or other people. Alcohol-related motor vehicle accidents are a leading cause of death and spinal injury in young people.

418 UNIT 7 • Alcohol, Tobacco, and Other Drugs

Sensitive Issues

Violence Be sensitive to the fact that students may have been directly involved in these violent situations and their privacy should be respected. Provide students with resources in the school to get help if faced with these situations. Invite the school counselor to discuss violent situations with the class. Ask the counselor to talk about what one should do if confronted with a violent situation or if one becomes a victim of violence. Have the school counselor give students information about where to get help. Ask each student to write a short paper illustrating his or her reaction to the school counselor's presentation. **L2**

Alcoholism

A disease in which there is physical and psychological dependence on alcohol is **alcoholism.** Alcohol dependence is another term for alcoholism. Alcohol dependence can destroy the life of an individual and the lives of those around him or her. Alcoholism is a factor in automobile accidents, injuries, suicide, violence, job loss, divorce, serious illness, and death. Alcoholism often causes family dysfunction and relationship difficulties.

What to Know About Alcoholism

Difficulty controlling behavior People with alcoholism have difficulty controlling their drinking. They often feel overwhelmed by the desire for another drink. Some people with alcoholism do not drink often, but they have out-of-control binges when they do drink. Alcoholism causes people's personalities to change. Moods and emotions change rapidly and behavior becomes unpredictable and irresponsible. Feelings of anger, paranoia, and depression can increase.

Denial People with alcoholism continue to drink alcohol even though it causes many problems. They are in denial. Refusing to admit a problem is **denial.** Many people deny that there is a connection between their problems and their drinking.

Withdrawal People with alcoholism may try to stop drinking. This often occurs after they do something they regret, such as abuse a family member. They promise to quit drinking, but they usually do not. If they do quit, they may suffer from alcohol withdrawal syndrome. The reaction of the body to the sudden stop of alcohol consumption is **alcohol withdrawal syndrome.** People with alcohol withdrawal syndrome feel nauseous, anxious, and agitated. They may vomit, have tremors ("the shakes"), have trouble sleeping, and have delirium tremens. A severe form of alcohol withdrawal syndrome in which there are hallucinations and muscle convulsions is **delirium tremens syndrome.**

The family connection Alcoholism affects entire families. Children whose parents abuse alcohol are more likely to have problems with alcohol. Alcohol abuse is lower in families in which parents or guardians clearly disapprove of drinking. People with alcoholism often have difficulties with relationships. They experience problems with money and jobs. They may neglect or injure family members.

◄ In families in which parents tell their children that they disapprove of drinking alcohol, there is a lower rate of alcohol abuse.

LESSON 37 • Choosing an Alcohol-Free Lifestyle **419**

Alcoholism

Class Discussion

Alcoholism Ask the class to examine how each factor (difficulty controlling behavior, denial, withdrawal, and family connection) can affect the treatment of alcoholism. **L2**

INTERACTIVE CHALKBOARD with Image Bank

5-Minute Check

Page 29, **Unit 7 Fast File Resources**

1. Does a person have to drink every day to be considered to have alcoholism? *No, a person with alcoholism may not drink often, but has out-of-control binges when he or she does drink.*

2. What is the definition of denial? *Denial is refusing to admit a problem.*

3. Why is denial a barrier for seeking treatment? *People cannot be helped until they admit they have a problem.*

4. Why is alcohol withdrawal syndrome a barrier for people to quit drinking alcohol? *The symptoms of alcohol withdrawal syndrome are unpleasant, so a person might try to quit, but might begin again to avoid these consequences.*

5. Describe how the family influences alcoholism. *Children whose parents have problems with alcohol are more likely to have problems with alcohol. Parents who have alcoholism may neglect their job and children.*

🏛 Community Involvement

Alcoholism Treatment Ask students to identify and create a list of the different resources and organizations available to help people within the community deal with alcoholism. Have each student research one organization. Ask students to determine the purpose of the organization, and the service provided by the organization. Have students create a pamphlet describing the organization. The pamphlet should illustrate various departments and discuss various services provided. **L3**

Getting Help

Class Discussion

Drinking Have students read the information in "Did You Know?" and discuss why the initiation of drinking at an early age is a risk factor for developing alcoholism as an adult. **L2**

NHES Assessment/SCASS

Performance Task Give students the following scenario. They have a friend who has alcoholism and they want to encourage their friend to get help. Divide the class into groups and have each group write and perform a skit to demonstrate how they would encourage their friend. Ask each student to write a paragraph describing the strategy that was employed in their skit, why that strategy was chosen, and if it demonstrated good communication and decision-making skills. **L2**

Extension

Factors Have students research alcoholism. Ask students to write a paper on hereditary, social, or environmental factors that are associated with increased use of alcohol. Have students present their findings to the class. **L3**

Getting Help

Alcoholism is a disease. Like many other diseases, alcoholism can be treated. The kind of treatment that is best may depend on many different factors. A family's financial situation may be the deciding factor in the type of treatment program that is selected. Private counseling, admittance to a special hospital, or group meetings are some choices for treatment.

Treatment for Alcoholism

People with alcoholism need treatment. This involves treatment for people with the disease, as well as counseling for family members and friends. Treatment usually involves short- or long-term stays at a recovery facility and may involve recovery programs.

Alcoholics Anonymous (AA) is one recovery program for people who have alcoholism. Al-Anon is a recovery program for people who have friends or family members with alcoholism.

Alateen is a recovery program for teens who have a family member or friend with alcoholism. Adult Children of Alcoholics (ACOA) is a recovery program for children who have one or more parents, a guardian, or a caregiver with alcoholism.

After completing a recovery program, people with alcoholism need support, such as individual or group counseling. Medications may be prescribed to help prevent a return to drinking during recovery.

Are You at Risk for Alcoholism?

Genetics Studies have shown that there is a relationship between a person's vulnerability to alcoholism and family history of the disease. A child of a parent who has alcoholism is more likely to develop alcohol problems than a child of a parent who does not have alcoholism. Some people may have a genetic predisposition for alcoholism.

Childhood behavior Some research has shown that children who are easily distracted and restless at a young age are more likely to develop alcoholism later in life than children who are well-adjusted.

Psychiatric disorders There appears to be a relationship between conduct problems in school, depression, and the development of alcoholism later in life. People with alcoholism also have higher rates of suicide.

Self-esteem Children who feel good about themselves are shown to have a reduced risk of developing alcoholism.

Social factors There have been many studies that examine relationships and drinking behavior. For example, parents who drink a great deal and hold favorable attitudes about drinking have children with an increased risk of developing drinking problems. Children who come from families in which they feel rejection or are disciplined harshly or inconsistently are at increased risk to develop alcohol-related problems.

Did You Know?

Alcoholism People who begin drinking alcohol before age 15 are four times more likely to develop alcoholism than those who begin after age 21.

 Health Project

Alcohol and the Brain Ask students to research the effects of alcohol on the brain. Have each student create a diagram of the brain. Students should use colors and captions to indicate which areas and functions of the brain, such as memory, emotions, and judgment, are affected and how. Ask students to indicate how alcohol will affect an adolescent brain differently than an adult brain, and whether the effects are short-term or long-term. Have each student present his or her diagram to the class. **L3**

Alcohol Advertising

Advertising is big business. Companies spend millions of dollars each year to get their products in front of consumers. These advertisements can be seen in newspapers and magazines and on radio and television. The alcohol beverage industry is one of the leading industries spending money to advertise its products. People of all ages see these advertisements, whose purpose is to convince people to buy a specific product.

What to Know About Alcohol Advertising and Teens

Disposable income Young people see thousands of advertisements for alcohol before their 16th birthday. These ads mostly are for beer. Many teens have disposable income. Disposable income is money that is not needed to live on for everyday needs. Advertisers would want this income spent on their products.

Loyalty Also, many advertisers want to develop brand loyalty in young people. They may believe that the earlier you see ads for a product, the more likely you are to use the product in the future.

Timing of ads Young people can be influenced by TV ads because of the time that these ads are shown. For example, many young people watch football, basketball, and baseball games that may be on during the daytime on weekends. In addition, many companies place advertisements in popular magazines that young people read. This is another way to get the attention of young people.

Neighborhood Alcohol companies spend a great deal of money on billboard advertising in neighborhoods. Billboards and other public alcohol signage put people in those neighborhoods at increased risk of developing irresponsible drinking habits.

Internet The Internet is another area where alcohol ads appear in large numbers. There are numerous Web sites that people of all ages can access that promote alcohol use. Some of these Web sites will use specific ways to attract young people to its products. For this reason, you need to be responsible when using the Internet. Parents need to be aware of what their children are viewing on computers.

Attractive people Alcohol advertisements tend to show attractive people drinking and having fun. Teens may think that drinking is "cool" and that they need to drink to have fun like the people in the ads.

> **Make the Connection**
>
> **Brand Loyalty** For more information about brand loyalty, see page 37 in Lesson 4.

Reading Review

1. How does genetics relate to alcoholism?
2. Describe the relationship between self-esteem and alcoholism.
3. Where do alcohol ads appear?

LESSON 37 • Choosing an Alcohol-Free Lifestyle **421**

Advertisements Ask students to bring alcohol ads from magazines to class. Have each student present an ad to the class, and explain the message he or she thinks the ad sends. **L2**

Advertisements Ask students to think about how they might react to an alcohol ad if the word *drug* were used when referring to alcohol. Ask students whether alcohol ads should have disclaimers listing possible risks and side effects like prescription drug advertisements. Have students propose what might be listed in a similar disclaimer for alcohol products. Ask students whether they think providing that information would influence people's choices about alcohol use. **L2**

1. *People who have a parent who has alcoholism or a family history of alcoholism are more likely to develop alcohol problems.*
2. *Children who feel good about themselves are less likely to develop alcoholism.*
3. *newspapers, magazines, radio, television, billboards, and the Internet*

TV Talk Have each student choose one half-hour during a weekend with a parent or guardian to observe the alcohol advertising that is shown on television. Ask each student to keep a log of the company placing the ad, the product being advertised, and how the advertisement made him or her feel. Have students record the differences and similarities in the types of ads seen, and discuss with family members what messages each person received from the ads. Have each student bring his or her information to compare with classmates for a class discussion. **L2**

> **National Health Education Standards**
>
> Pages 420–421: 1.2, 1.4, 1.5, 1.7, 2.1, 2.5, 2.6, 2.7, 3.4

Performance Event In groups, have students list five situations in which a student may need to refuse a ride. Ask groups to exchange their lists and write suggestions for the five situations, describing how a student can refuse a ride. Their suggestions should demonstrate effective use of resistance and refusal skills. **L2**

Class Discussion

Peer Pressure Ask students whether the choice not to drink alcohol is a difficult one to make and to stick with. Have students explain their reasoning. Ask students to discuss the barriers, such as peer pressure, that affect decisions not to drink. **L2**

3 Assess

Vocabulary Practice
Page 20, **Unit 7 Fast File Resources**

Name _____ Date _____ Class _____

LESSON 37 **Choosing an Alcohol-Free Lifestyle**

Vocabulary Practice

Use the vocabulary terms to solve the puzzle. Write the word or phrase that matches each clue listed below. Write one letter of each answer in the space provided. Copy the boxed letters in order to complete the sentence at the bottom of the page.

alcoholism	cirrhosis	hazing activity
binge drinking	delirium tremens syndrome	proof
blackout	denial	toxin
blood alcohol concentration (BAC)		

1. People with this disease have difficulty controlling their consumption of alcohol.
2. not admitting a connection between problems and alcohol dependence
3. This is double the percent of alcohol in a beverage.
4. A liver transplant is the only effective treatment for people with an advanced stage of this disease.
5. Involvement in this is against the law in most states.
6. Playing a drinking game is an example of this type of behavior.
7. This measurement, given as a percentage, is affected by the number of drinks a person consumes.

1. _ _ _ _ _ _ _ _ _
2. _ □ _ _ _ □ _ _
3. _ _ _ □ _ _
4. _ _ □ _ _ _ _ _
5. _ _ _ _ _ _ □ _ _
6. _ _ _ _ □ _ _ _ _ _ _ □ _
7. _ _ □ _ _ _ _ _ □ _ _ _ _

You can strengthen your commitment to _ _ _ _ _ _ _ _ _ _ _ _ _ _ _ _ _ by choosing an alcohol-free lifestyle.

20 LESSON 37 • Choosing an Alcohol Free Lifestyle UNIT 7

National Health
Education Standards

Pages 422–423: 1.1, 1.5, 1.9, 2.1, 2.3, 2.5, 2.6, 2.9, 2.10, 3.2, 4.2, 5.1, 6.3, 7.2, 8.1, 8.2

Resisting Peer Pressure

Peer pressure is the most important factor identified by teens who drink alcohol. Despite the fact that drinking is illegal for teens, most teens can obtain alcoholic beverages. You may be pressured to drink and buy alcohol. Use resistance skills to avoid drinking and buying alcohol.

1. Use assertive behavior. Stand tall and look directly at the person. Say "no" in a firm and confident voice.

2. Give reasons for saying "no" to alcohol. Explain that drinking is harmful, unsafe, and illegal for teens. Drinking does not show respect for yourself and others. Drinking is against the law for minors and against family guidelines.

3. Use nonverbal behavior to match verbal behavior.
   - Do not pretend to drink alcoholic beverages.
   - Do not agree to buy alcohol.
   - Do not behave in ways that indicate that you approve of drinking.

4. Avoid being in situations in which there will be pressure to drink alcohol.
   - If there will be alcohol in a situation, do not go.
   - Attend only alcohol-free activities and do not go into bars.

5. Avoid being with people who drink alcohol.
   - Choose friends who do not drink alcohol.

- Stay away from gang members.
- Stay away from people over the legal age who buy alcohol or give alcohol to minors.
- Stay away from minors who use fake IDs to buy alcohol and get into bars.

6. Resist pressure to engage in illegal behavior.
   - Stay away from people who break laws.
   - Stay away from parties where minors are drinking alcohol.

7. Influence others to choose responsible behavior.
   - Encourage those who pressure you to use alcohol to change their behavior.
   - Encourage people who drink alcohol to stop by suggesting alcohol-free activities.
   - Know signs that indicate the presence of a drinking problem. Ask a responsible adult or trained counselor how you might help the person.

8. Avoid being influenced by advertisements for alcohol.
   - Realize that advertisements may incorrectly portray the use of alcohol as sexy, sophisticated, adventurous, healthful, or fun.
   - Realize that advertisements may incorrectly imply that drinking will result in success, relaxation, or romance.
   - Be aware that alcohol companies pay enormous amounts of money to advertise during major sporting events.
   - Be aware that alcohol companies use the Internet to advertise their products to young people.
   - Do not wear clothing that displays beer logos or logos of other alcoholic beverages.

ALCOHOL in the Media **Writing Activity** Movies, TV programs, and music often portray drinking alcohol as a fun, harmless activity without showing the consequences of alcohol use. Choose one movie, one TV program, or one song and write a newspaper article analyzing the negative consequences of alcohol use that are not portrayed in the type of media you have chosen. Present your article to the class. If possible, play a part of the movie, TV program, or song to the class before you present your article.

422 **UNIT 7** • Alcohol, Tobacco, and Other Drugs

🍎 Teacher to Teacher

Saying "No" Have students list the resistance skills from the student page. Write the list on the chalkboard. Ask students to give examples for each resistance skill. Divide students into groups and have each group create a scenario in which they would use resistance skills. Have each group role-play their scenario for the class, practicing the resistance skills. **L2**

Nancy Facello
Iaeger High School, Iaeger, WV

LESSON 37
STUDY GUIDE

Key Terms Review

Complete these fill-in-the-blank statements with the lesson Key Terms on the left. Do not write in this book.

1. The amount of alcohol in a person's blood is _____.

2. A person who drinks and cannot remember what happened has had a(n) _____.

3. The general name for a disease in which a person has a dependence on alcohol is called _____.

4. The measured amount of alcohol in a drink is called _____.

5. A disease caused by alcohol that causes chronic damage to liver cells is _____.

6. Consuming large amounts of alcohol in a short amount of time is called _____.

7. A person who refuses to acknowledge he or she has a problem with alcohol is said to be in _____.

8. A poisonous substance is known as a(n) _____.

9. An activity in which a person is forced to participate in dangerous or demeaning activities is called _____.

10. Hallucinations caused by withdrawal from alcohol is called _____.

Recalling the Facts

11. Name four factors that affect blood alcohol concentration (BAC).

12. What are the legal consequences of consuming alcohol underage?

13. What is alcohol hepatitis?

14. Name three organizations that assist people who are affected by alcoholism.

15. What is binge drinking?

16. Analyze the harmful effects of alcohol on fetuses.

17. Why do people who drink at night, still feel the effects in the morning?

18. Why can drinking alcohol be considered a hazing activity?

Critical Thinking

19. How is drinking alcohol a risk-taking activity, and what physical, legal, emotional, and social consequences might occur if a teen drinks alcohol?

20. Describe the reasons behind the law that sets the legal age for drinking alcohol.

21. Why would a person who weighs 200 lbs. not be impacted as rapidly as a person who weighs 150 lbs. if they both had one drink?

22. Explain the relationship between alcohol and the role it plays in unsafe situations.

Real-Life Applications

23. Why do you think teenagers start to drink alcohol?

24. What could you do to make your school an alcohol-free school?

25. What are the best ways to resist peer pressure to drink?

26. If a friend offered you alcohol, what would you do?

Activities

Responsible Decision Making

27. **Responsible Decisions** A friend is trying to decide whether he or she should attend a party where there will be alcohol. Write an email to your friend explaining what the responsible decision would be. Refer to the Responsible Decision-Making Model on page 61 for help.

Sharpen Your Life Skills

28. **Analyze Influences of Health** In groups of three, make a video that shows at least three consequences of alcohol abuse. If you do not have access to a video camera, write the script for a "true" alcohol commercial.

Key terms (left column):

alcoholism
binge drinking
blackout
blood alcohol
   concentration
   (BAC)
cirrhosis
delirium tremens
   syndrome
denial
distillation
hangover
hazing activity
proof
toxin

Key Terms Review

1. blood alcohol concentration
2. blackout
3. alcoholism
4. proof
5. cirrhosis
6. binge drinking
7. denial
8. toxin
9. hazing activity
10. delirium tremens syndrome

Recalling the Facts

11. amount of alcohol consumed, speed at which alcohol is consumed, body weight, percentage of body fat, gender, feelings, amount of food eaten, presence of other drugs in the blood stream, age, drinking carbonated alcoholic beverages

12. Minors who purchase or drink alcohol risk being arrested, fined, and jailed.

13. a condition where the liver swells due to alcohol

14. AA, Alateen, Al-Anon, ACOA

15. consumption of large amounts of alcohol in a short amount of time

16. See page 415, for information on effects of alcohol on fetuses.

17. the people could still have elevated BAC levels or could be having a hangover

18. People could be forced to drink alcohol by peers.

Critical Thinking

19. See pages 414, 416, 418 and 419.
20. See Health News on page 415.
21. People who weigh more can drink more alcohol because they have more blood volume.
22. See page 418, for information on how drinking increases the risk of violence and illegal behavior.

Real-Life Applications

23. peer pressure, curious about effects
24. try to change social norms, organize non-alcoholic groups

---

25. not to surround yourself with friends who engage in alcoholic events. See page 422.
26. Tell the friend "no."

Activities

Responsible Decision Making

27. Answers will vary, but may include ideas from "Resisting Peer Pressure" on page 422.

Sharpen Your Life Skills

28. Answers will vary, but may include ideas from "Thinking and Decision Making" on page 416 or "Violence and Illegal Behavior" on page 418.

LESSON **38**
Choosing a Tobacco-Free Lifestyle

Out of Time?

If time does not permit an in-depth study of this topic, use the following activities in this Teacher Wraparound Edition:
• Class Activity, p. 426
• Community Involvement, p. 428
• Teacher to Teacher, p. 430

1 Focus

HEALTH GOAL **Avoiding Tobacco Use and Secondhand Smoke** Have students respond to the Health Goal for this lesson by listing the things they don't like about smoke and smoking. *Dislikes could include the smell, discoloration of teeth, and health risks involved.* **L2**

ABOUT IT!

Journaling The student should tell his or her friend that he or she doesn't want to smoke. Smoking is harmful to health. **L1**

LESSON **38**
Choosing a Tobacco-Free Lifestyle

What You'll Learn

1. Discuss the harmful physical and mental effects of nicotine. *(p. 425)*
2. Understand the negative effects smoking has on a fetus. *(p. 427)*
3. Explain the harmful effects of secondhand smoke. *(p. 428)*
4. Discuss laws regarding the sale and use of tobacco. *(p. 430)*
5. Discuss how tobacco companies try to convince minors to use tobacco products. *(p. 430)*
6. Outline steps to stop using tobacco products. *(p. 432)*
7. Outline eight ways to resist pressure to use tobacco products. *(p. 434)*

Why It's Important

Smoking is a major public health problem. Each year, smoking contributes to more deaths than AIDS, alcohol, homicide, drugs, car accidents, and suicide combined.

Key Terms

• nicotine
• tobacco
• carcinogen
• tar
• carbon monoxide
• emphysema
• secondhand smoke
• snuff
• leukoplakia
• nicotine patch

HEALTH GOAL • **I will avoid tobacco use and secondhand smoke.**

Tobacco products contain a drug called nicotine. You are more likely to become addicted to nicotine after using a tobacco product once than you are to become addicted to heroin after using it once. This lesson explains why you must avoid tobacco use and secondhand smoke. You will learn about techniques used to convince people to use tobacco products, skills to resist pressure to use them, and suggestions for teens who use tobacco products and want to quit.

ABOUT IT!

Writing About Resisting Pressure to Smoke Suppose that you are really stressed out. You are feeling overwhelmed by the demands of school, swim team practice, and your job. A friend tells you that smoking cigarettes is a good way to relax, and urges you to try it. What should you do? After you read the information on the dangers of smoking on page 426, write a response to this situation in your health journal.

National Health Education Standards—Guide for Lesson 38		
1.7	Compare and contrast the benefits of and barriers to practicing a variety of healthy behaviors.	pp. 430–431
2.9	Analyze how some health risk behaviors can influence the likelihood of engaging in unhealthy behaviors.	pp. 425, 426–427, 435
6.1	Assess personal health practices and overall health status.	pp. 426–427

Nicotine

A stimulant drug found in tobacco products—including cigarettes, clove cigarettes, cigars, chewing tobacco, pipe tobacco, and snuff—is called ***nicotine***. Nicotine stimulates the nervous system and is highly addictive. It dulls the taste buds, constricts the blood vessels, and increases heart rate and blood pressure. When tobacco smoke is inhaled into the lungs, nicotine is absorbed into the bloodstream and quickly reaches the brain. Nicotine also can be absorbed into the bloodstream from smokeless tobacco that is placed in the mouth. When the "pick-me-up" effect of nicotine wears off, a user is motivated to use more tobacco.

What to Know About Nicotine

Nicotine dependence Many health experts and health organizations have declared that nicotine is as addictive as heroin, cocaine, and alcohol. Nicotine dependence causes more premature death and disease than all other forms of drug dependence combined. People who regularly use tobacco develop a tolerance to nicotine. They need more and more to produce the desired effect. At first, the desired effect is to feel the stimulation that nicotine causes. Later, it is to lessen the craving for nicotine. People develop a physical dependence on nicotine when the body becomes used to its effects. Psychological dependence develops when people feel the need to smoke or chew tobacco at certain times or for specific reasons.

Nicotine withdrawal syndrome People who try to quit using tobacco often have nicotine withdrawal syndrome. ***Nicotine withdrawal syndrome*** is the body's reaction to quitting the use of tobacco products. People with nicotine withdrawal syndrome feel a craving for tobacco; may be anxious, irritable, restless, have a headache, and have difficulty concentrating; can become frustrated and angry; and have heart palpitations and an increased appetite.

Why experimenting with tobacco is risky Experimenting with tobacco puts you at risk for nicotine dependence. According to the Surgeon General, the probability of becoming addicted to nicotine after one exposure is higher than for other addictive substances, such as heroin, cocaine, and alcohol. Teens have a more difficult time quitting smoking than people who start smoking when they are older. A majority of adult smokers started before the age of 18. They also are more likely to become heavy smokers and to die of a disease caused by smoking.

What is tobacco? An herbal plant that is grown for its leaves and that contains nicotine is ***tobacco.*** It can be smoked in different forms, such as cigarettes, cigars and pipes. ***Smokeless tobacco*** is tobacco that is chewed or snorted, but not smoked. Chewing tobacco and snuff are forms of smokeless tobacco.

Did You Know?

Smoking Every day, almost 3000 teens in the United States— 1 million a year— become smokers. One-third of these teens will eventually die from smoking.

Lesson Resource Manager

- **Unit 7 Fast File Resources**
  Reading Strategy, p. 33
  Vocabulary Practice, p. 34
  Transparency Master and Worksheet, p. 35
  Real-Life Health, p. 37
  Real-Life Health, p. 39
  5-Minute Check, p. 41
  Lesson 38 Quiz, p. 43
- **Unit 7 Transparency**
- **Lesson 38 Transparency**

- **Reading Essentials**
- **Technology**
  TeacherWorks™ CD-ROM
  StudentWorks™ CD-ROM
  Reading Essentials CD-ROM
  ExamView® Assessment Suite
  Vocabulary Puzzlemaker

Nicotine

2 Teach

Class Activity

Types of Tobacco Products Have students research types of tobacco products, such as cigars, pipes, smokeless tobacco, and cigarettes. Ask students to determine which tobacco products contain the most tar, the most nicotine, the most carbon monoxide. **L2**

Class Discussion

Tobacco is a Drug Ask students to discuss how people would view using tobacco if the advertising stated it contained a drug. Have students discuss the effects nicotine has on the body. **L2**

PowerPoint® Presentations

This CD-ROM is an editable Microsoft® PowerPoint® presentation that includes:
- Lesson presentations
- Lesson checks
- Interactive graphics
- 5-Minute Checks
- Image Bank
- All transparencies

Discussion Refer to the KWL Strategy on page 17T to clarify misconceptions regarding the deadly habit of tobacco use.

National Health Education Standards

Pages 424–425: 1.2, 1.5, 2.5, 2.6, 2.9, 2.10, 3.4, 7.2

425

Smoking

Extension

Researching Chemicals Tobacco contains many chemicals. Ask students to research the chemicals found in tobacco and make a list of other places where that chemical can be found, where it comes from, and what it may be used for. For example, tobacco smoke contains carbon monoxide, which can also be found in car exhaust. Cigarettes also contain acetycolonine, which is found in nail polish remover. Have students describe the effect each chemical has on the body. **L3**

Quick Demo

Experience Smoking-Related Illnesses Have students perform an activity in the room, such as walking, jumping jacks, or stand up/sit down, while breathing through a straw with their nose pinched. Ask students to describe any difficulty they might have had. This would represent what a person with a smoking-related breathing condition may experience each day. **L2** **ELL**

Class Activity

Smoking Affects the Body Have students create a picture of the human body and label the parts of the body that are affected by tobacco and how the parts are affected by tobacco. **L2** **ELL**

Reading Review

1. *the body's reaction to quitting the use of tobacco products*
2. *lung, throat, mouth, esophagus, pancreas, and bladder*

Smoking

obacco smoke contains many harmful chemicals in addition to nicotine. Scientists estimate there are more than 4,000 different chemicals in tobacco smoke, at least 43 of which are carcinogens. A *carcinogen* is a chemical that is known to cause cancer. Most carcinogens in tobacco smoke are found in tar. *Tar* is a sticky, thick fluid that is formed when tobacco is burned. Tar irritates respiratory tissues and is a major cause of lung cancer. Another dangerous substance that forms when tobacco is burned is carbon monoxide. *Carbon monoxide* is an odorless, tasteless gas. It interferes with the ability of blood to carry oxygen.

How Smoking Harms Health

Make the Connection

Health Concerns For more information about the nation's major health concerns, see page 58 in Lesson 6.

Smoking causes cancer. Smoking causes lung cancer and increases the risk of many other types of cancer. Lung cancer kills more people than any other cancer. It is rare for someone who has never smoked to develop lung cancer. Lung cancer almost always causes death. Most people with lung cancer die within five years of learning that they have cancer.

Smoking also is a major risk factor for cancer of the throat, mouth, esophagus, pancreas, and bladder. The American Cancer Society reports that one-third of all cancer deaths are due to tobacco use. They also report that nine out of every ten lung cancer cases are caused by smoking cigarettes.

Reading Review

1. What is nicotine withdrawal syndrome?
2. Name three cancers that are associated with smoking.

Smoking harms the respiratory system. Smoking prevents the lungs from working effectively. When a person smokes, tar lines the lungs and air passages. Tobacco also harms the cilia in the nose, throat, and bronchial tubes. Cilia are hair-like structures that remove dust and other particles from the air and prevent harmful substances from reaching the lungs. This increases the risk of respiratory infection. Smoking also aggravates asthma.

Smoking is a risk factor for *chronic obstructive pulmonary disease (COPD)*, a disease that interferes with breathing. Examples of COPDs are chronic bronchitis and emphysema. Chronic bronchitis is a recurring inflammation of the bronchial tubes that causes mucus to line the bronchial tubes. This increases risk of lung infection and interferes with the ability to breathe.

A condition in which the alveoli lose most of their ability to function is

The blackened lung tissue on the left is diseased with pulmonary emphysema, while the lung tissue on the right is healthy.

 Cross-Curricular Connections

History Ask students to research the history of the Surgeon General reports to the public about the use of tobacco products. For example, in 1964, the federal government released its first document that stated smoking caused lung cancer. In 1971, the federal government banned tobacco advertisements on TV and radio. In 1972, secondhand smoke was described as a health risk. In 1975, states began limiting smoking in public places. In 1989, smoking was banned on domestic airline flights. In 1993, the EPA classified secondhand smoke as a Group A carcinogen. Have each student create a poster explaining one of the events. Display the posters as a timeline. **L3**

emphysema. The lungs lose their ability to properly inflate and hold air. As a result, it is difficult for oxygen to be absorbed into the bloodstream. Some people with emphysema must remain in bed and use special equipment to receive an adequate amount of oxygen. Emphysema cannot be cured.

Smoking causes cardiovascular diseases. Smoking is a major cause of death from heart and blood vessel diseases and stroke. Smoking speeds up the development of fat deposits in the arteries and damages the inner lining of arteries. Fat deposits reduce the space in the artery through which blood can flow. The risk of developing blood clots increases.

A clot in an artery in the heart can cause a *heart attack*. A clot in the brain can result in a stroke. Smoking also is a risk factor for aortic aneurysm. An *aortic aneurysm* is a bulging in the aorta. The aorta is the main artery in the body. An aneurysm is the result of a weakening in an artery wall. The nicotine

in tobacco smoke raises a person's resting heart rate approximately 20 beats per minute. This change in heart rate and inhaled carbon monoxide places extra strain on the heart.

▲ Many people with emphysema need breathing assistance.

Smoking causes accidents. Cigarette smoking is a leading cause of fires. Cigarette smoking also is a factor in many motor vehicle accidents. Accidents have happened when a driver was distracted trying to light a cigarette or by dropping a lit cigarette.

Smoking causes other health problems. Smokers are more likely to develop gum disease and to lose teeth and supporting gum tissues. Smoking may cause or worsen ulcers in the stomach and small intestine. Smoking during pregnancy harms the developing baby. Studies show that if a female quits smoking during pregnancy, the risk of infant death, having a low birthweight baby, and delivering prema-

TABLE 38.1   Myths and Facts About Smoking

Teens Who Smoke May Convince Themselves...	The Truth
"I look cool when I smoke."	People who smoke have yellow teeth and dirty and stained fingernails. Their clothes stink of smoke.
"It is 'in' to smoke."	In 2002, only 22.9 percent of high school students were current smokers. Many people will not hang out with people who smoke. They will not date a person who smokes.
"My smoking doesn't bother anyone."	Many people do not want to be around people who smoke. Many people do not want people to smoke around their children.
"My favorite TV and movie stars use tobacco products."	Many celebrities and athletes do not use tobacco products. The celebrities and athletes who do use tobacco products face the same risks from tobacco use as others do. Many have died of cancer.

LESSON 38 • Choosing a Tobacco-Free Lifestyle   **427**

Secondhand Smoke

Class Discussion

Should People Be Allowed to Smoke? Ask students the following questions: Should smoking be banned in public places? Where should people be allowed to smoke? Do smokers have the right to smoke? Discuss how secondhand smoke affects a nonsmoker. Have students debate for or against current smoking laws. **L2**

Class Activity

Tobacco Ads Provide examples of tobacco ads and have students recreate the ads with all of the information about the harmful effects of tobacco products. Ask students to present their new ads to the class. **L2**

NHES Assessment/SCASS

Selected Response Which of the following is not secondhand smoke?
A. sidestream
B. *mainstream*
C. exhaled smoke
D. environmental smoke

Secondhand Smoke

I f you are in a room in which other people are smoking, you will be exposed to over 4000 chemicals. Of these chemicals, 200 are poisonous and many are carcinogens. The smoke from other people's cigarettes is responsible for 3000 lung cancer deaths and 35,000 deaths from heart disease per year in the United States. In addition, the smoke from other people's cigarettes is responsible for causing between 150,000 and 300,000 lower respiratory tract infections in infants and children under 18 months of age.

What to Know About Secondhand Smoke

A lit cigarette burns for about 10 minutes. During those 10 minutes, people who are near the smoker will breathe in secondhand smoke. Exhaled mainstream smoke and sidestream smoke are types of *secondhand smoke,* or *environmental tobacco smoke.* Passive smoking and involuntary smoking are other terms used to describe breathing in secondhand smoke. Smoke that enters the air from a burning cigarette, cigar, or pipe is *sidestream smoke,* Sidestream smoke has more tar, nicotine, carbon monoxide, ammonia, and benzene than mainstream smoke.

Mainstream smoke, is smoke that is directly inhaled into the smoker's mouth and lungs.

Major health risk Secondhand smoke is more than just an annoyance. The Environmental Protection Agency (EPA) has classified secondhand smoke as a *Group A carcinogen*, which is a substance that causes cancer in humans. Secondhand smoke is the most hazardous form of indoor air pollution. It can cause lung cancer in nonsmokers and increase their risk of developing heart disease and respiratory problems. People who already have heart disease or respiratory problems are especially affected. Secondhand smoke is a major health risk for children with parents who smoke. The children are at increased risk for ear infection, bronchitis, and pneumonia. The lungs of children exposed to secondhand smoke may not develop properly.

Protecting nonsmokers Laws are being passed to prevent smoking inside public buildings and schools and in the workplace. Airlines have restricted smoking during flights. Many businesses no longer allow smoking in their office buildings or factories.

How You Can Avoid Secondhand Smoke

The following are suggestions on how to avoid secondhand smoke:

- Speak up to the person who is smoking, but be polite. Let people know that you are concerned about your health.
- Ask smokers not to smoke in indoor areas that you share.
- Encourage your family to have a nonsmoking policy for your home.
- Encourage family members who smoke to quit smoking and to go outside if they must smoke.
- Request seating in nonsmoking sections of restaurants or in public areas.

428 UNIT 7 • Alcohol, Tobacco, and Other Drugs

🏛 Community Involvement

Antismoking Ads Divide students into groups. Have each group develop an antismoking flyer and find one place in the community that is willing to display the antismoking flyer. Have students develop questions and interview people as to why they are willing to display the antismoking flyer. Ask each student to write a report describing their experience of creating and distributing their antismoking flyer. **L2**

Smokeless Tobacco

Smokeless tobacco is manufactured and sold in two forms. Chewing tobacco is a tobacco product made from chopped tobacco leaves that is placed between the gums and cheek. *Snuff* is a tobacco product made from powdered tobacco leaves and stems that is snorted or placed between the gums and cheek. Smokeless tobacco has most of the same harmful ingredients as other tobacco products.

What to Know About Smokeless Tobacco

Smokeless tobacco causes nicotine dependence. Every time people use smokeless tobacco they feel the stimulating "pick-me-up" effects of nicotine. The body becomes used to these effects, and tolerance is the result. Cravings and tolerance are both signs of nicotine dependence. Nicotine dependence makes it difficult for people to quit.

Smokeless tobacco contains many chemicals that harm health. Smokeless tobacco contains formaldehyde, lead, nitrosamines, cadmium, and polonium. All forms of smokeless tobacco contain carcinogens.

Smokeless tobacco increases the risk of developing cancer. When people use smokeless tobacco, the tobacco and its irritating juices are in contact with the gums, cheeks, and lips for long periods of time.

This causes a change in the cells of the mouth. Abnormal cells in the mouth that appear as white patches of tissue are *leukoplakia.* The abnormal cells can develop into cancer. Using smokeless tobacco also increases the risk of cancer of the larynx, the pharynx, and the esophagus.

Smokeless tobacco causes problems with the gums and teeth. Smokeless tobacco permanently stains teeth and causes bad breath. Chewing tobacco includes particles that scratch and wear away teeth, and the sugar in smokeless tobacco mixes with dental plaque to form acids that cause tooth decay. Smokeless tobacco also can cause the gums to pull away from the teeth, exposing the roots and making them more likely to fall out.

What to do If you use smokeless tobacco, quit now. (See page 432 for quitting strategies.) Check your gums and teeth for signs of oral cancer: a persistent sore, lump, or white patch in the mouth; a persistent sore throat; and/or difficulty chewing and moving the tongue or jaw. Contact a physician or dentist immediately and have an oral examination. Have your mouth checked by a dentist every three months.

Leukoplakia, abnormal cells, is often a result of using smokeless
▼ tobacco.

Smokeless Tobacco

Class Activity

Negative Effects Have students research the negative effects of smokeless tobacco. Ask students to specify any different effects between chewing tobacco and snuff. Have students create their own versions of packaging for smokeless tobacco products that emphasize the negative effects they cause to health. **L3**

Class Activity

Smokeless Tobacco Statistics Ask students to research current statistics about smokeless tobacco use and health problems. Have students estimate, based on the statistics, how many students in your school building use smokeless tobacco products. **L3**

Class Discussion

Smokeless Tobacco Have students discuss whether they believe smokeless tobacco is less harmful than cigarettes. *People often believe smokeless tobacco to be less harmful because there is no smoke. However, people who use smokeless tobacco have a greater risk of mouth cancer.* **L2**

🟥 Health Project

Bulletin Board Contest Provide students with magazines, construction paper, scissors, markers and glue. Assign students to groups. Have the groups create a bulletin board or a collage that lists reasons to quit using tobacco products, healthy substitutes, and facts about negative effects. A reason to quit could be that smoking causes yellow teeth and bad breath. A healthy alternative to smoking would be to exercise. Have students write an essay describing their experiences. Ask other classes to vote, and then allow the winners to display their bulletin board in the school. **L2 ELL**

National Health Education Standards

Pages 428–429: 1.3, 2.1, 2.3, 2.10, 3.4, 7.2

Tobacco Advertising

Class Discussion

Messages Divide the class into groups. Using advertisements from a magazine, ask students to list the techniques the advertisers are using to portray their message. Rotate the ads around to different groups. Compare responses each group had for each of the ads. **L2**

Teacher FYI

Adolescents and Advertisements A study published in the *Journal of the American Medical Association (JAMA)* in 1996 reported that six-year-olds could identify a cartoon animal associated with cigarettes more than they could identify animals in cartoons specifically made for children.

Class Activity

Creating a Nonsmoking School Norm Have students create and hang antismoking posters around the building or in the school bathrooms. Ask students to discuss the impact of the posters on themselves and their peers. **L2**

Explain the Concept

Carcinogen A carcinogen is a cancer-causing agent. Tar contains thousands of substances, many of which are carcinogens. Tar is the sticky substance that remains after water vapor and nicotine are removed from smoke. Smoking causes 87 percent of lung cancer deaths.

Tobacco Advertising

A paid announcement about a product or service is an *advertisement*. Tobacco manufacturers are not allowed by law to put tobacco ads on TV or radio. Advertising in stores and on billboards and signs on the inside and outside of buses no longer can have photos or artwork and cannot be in color. The same rule applies to advertising in publications read by a significant number of people under the age of 18.

Be Happy

Make the Connection

Evaluating Ads For more information about evaluating advertisements, see page 37 in Lesson 4.

What to Know About Tobacco Advertising

Influencing young people Tobacco manufacturers have promoted their products in many ways. One way was by distributing clothing and other items that displayed their logos and symbols. People wearing or using these items were a "walking ad" for the tobacco company. In 1997 the FDA prohibited the sale or giveaway of products such as caps or gym bags that carry tobacco product brand names or logos. In 2000, the FDA lost its power to control tobacco products. Much of this power is now local and state controlled. The Federal Trade Commission (FTC) also has control over tobacco products.

Tobacco companies also promote their products by offering merchandise in exchange for coupons found on cigarette packs or smokeless tobacco containers. They may have promoted their products by sponsoring sporting events and rock concerts, wanting people to associate their product and their logo with excitement and glamour. This was a way to advertise their products on TV, as advertising tobacco products on TV was banned. Now brand-name sponsorship of these events can be done in the corporate name only. Only the automobile industry spends more money than tobacco companies on advertising.

Required warnings on tobacco products Tobacco manufacturers include warnings on their packages and in their ads to educate people about the dangers of using tobacco products.

Tobacco companies have different warnings on their cigarette packages. (See page 431 for a photo of one of the warnings.)

Smokeless tobacco Smokeless tobacco manufacturers place different warnings on their packages and in their ads, such as: "This product is not a safe alternative to cigarettes," "this product may cause gum disease and tooth loss," and "this product may cause mouth cancer."

FTC The FTC regulates tobacco advertising, including health warning labels. The FTC provides data on the tar, nicotine, and carbon monoxide levels of domestic tobacco products.

What tobacco ads do not tell you Tobacco companies spend billions of dollars each year to influence people

🕐 Teacher to Teacher

Make an Ad Reveal how much media influences choices. Ask students to keep a one week log of all smoking ads they see in magazines, movies, TV, and billboards. Have students get into groups of four. Using video and audio equipment, make a 1-minute antismoking public service announcement. Have students vote on the best PSA. The winners can present their ad to a middle school. **L2**

Tim Delmore
Red River High School, Grand Forks, ND

Activity: Using Life Skills

Advocating for Health: Advocating quitting smoking

If someone you know smokes, you can try to convince them to stop. It will take a lot of work, but the results will be worth your efforts. Remember, though, that even if you try hard, you cannot force someone to stop smoking. It's ultimately up to the smoker to quit.

To advocate for health, follow these four steps: 1) select a health-related concern; 2) gather reliable information; 3) identify your purpose and target audience; and 4) develop a convincing and appropriate message.

1 Explain how the person's smoking makes you feel. It could be as simple as saying that you don't like the way the smoke smells on his or her clothes, or you could say you're afraid this habit could shorten your loved one's life.

2 Be patient and supportive. Nagging will just annoy the smoker or make him or her defensive. Show that you understand that giving up cigarettes is difficult. Try not to be judgmental. Smoking has become a part of this person's life.

3 Get involved. Encourage your loved one to be active instead of smoking, then join him or her in a walk, a bike ride, or seeing a movie. Offer him or her gum or hard candy to replace cigarettes.

4 Suggest boundaries. Agree to make certain places off-limits for smoking, such as the car, the kitchen, or maybe the whole house.

5 Add up how much money could be saved every month if your loved one didn't smoke. Encourage him or her to set aside that money for something special as a reward for quitting.

SURGEON GENERAL'S WARNING: Smoking Causes Lung Cancer, Heart Disease, Emphysema, And May Complicate Pregnancy.

UNDERAGE SALE PROHIBITED

Using Life Skills

Advocating for Health Ask students to respond to each step listed for trying to help someone to quit smoking. Ask students: Which ones would be easy to do and which ones might be more difficult? Do you have any other suggestions that were not listed? Have you tried any of these activities before? If so, were they successful? Challenge students to share this information with a smoker they know and would like to help quit. **L2**

Class Activity

Harmful Effects Divide students into groups of three or four people. Have the groups discuss the harmful effects of smoking on the human body. Have students create a poster illustrating the harmful effects of smoking. For example, smoking causes yellow teeth. **L1**

Reading Review

1. *the FTC*
2. *See photo on page 431.*

---

to use tobacco. They want you to think tobacco use is "in" and to take your attention away from the warnings. Many tobacco ads are designed to appeal to teens. People in the ads are models who are attractive, healthy looking, and well-dressed. They are having fun and are very appealing to members of the opposite sex.

Don't be fooled by these ads. What they fail to tell you is that smoking cigarettes does not help you to look attractive, healthy, or well-dressed. People are likely to be turned off by your behavior, your breath, and your stained teeth. Tobacco ads also do not tell you that more than 400,000 people die each year from smoking. They do not show people dying of lung disease or restricted to bed because of emphysema. They do not show family members grieving the death of loved ones who used tobacco.

How tobacco companies hook young children Tobacco companies claim they do not design ads that target children. On the Internet, tobacco companies appeal to children by using interactive games, giveaways, and chats to promote their products. They promote the idea that using tobacco products makes a person seem more grown-up and "cool."

In the past cigarette companies hooked children by placing "kiddy packs" and "loosies" in stores. A kiddy pack is a package of cigarettes containing fewer than the standard 20 cigarettes in a pack. A loosie is a single cigarette that is available for purchase. However, many cities and states have laws banning the sale of kiddy packs and loosies. There are also laws that ban free samples of tobacco products.

▲ Tobacco companies are required to display warnings on their products.

Reading Review

1. Who has regulatory control over tobacco products?

2. Give examples of warning labels on tobacco products.

👥 Healthy People 2010

Objective 27-17 *Increase the number of adolescents that disapprove of smoking.*

In 1998, a survey was taken of eighth, tenth, and twelfth graders about smoking. Eighty percent of eighth graders disapproved of smoking, while only 75 percent of tenth graders and 69 percent of twelfth graders disapproved of smoking. The goal of Healthy People 2010 is to raise the percentage for each of those grade levels to 95 percent. Ask students to come up with ideas that may help more adolescents begin to disapprove of smoking. Ask students why they think that the percentages recorded in 1998 show that there was a decrease in the percentage of students who disapproved as the grade levels increased. **L2**

National Health Education Standards

Pages 430–431: 1.5, 1.7, 2.5, 2.6, 2.10, 4.4, 5.1, 8.2

Quitting Tobacco Use

Class Discussion

Quitting Smoking Ask students: Are there advantages or disadvantages to different methods of quitting smoking? Have students list the different methods a person can use when trying to quit (cold turkey, gradually, with OTC products, or programs) and discuss what advantages or disadvantages each may have. **L2**

Class Activity

Smoking Drawbacks Have a large sheet of paper available on the wall for students from each class to add to over a period of a few days. Ask students to list the negative things they have to say about tobacco use. Compare the lists at the end of a few days to share the comments made by the students. Have each student anonymously write on a piece of paper how many people they know who have died from smoking-related illnesses. Tally up the total numbers. **L2**

NHES Assessment/SCASS

Performance Task Ask each student to interview at least five people that have smoked or currently do smoke and ask the following questions: Have you attempted to quit? How many times? Using what methods? Have you been successful? Then ask students to compare results with the other students in their class. Based on their combined results, have students write an essay about the success rates of smokers who try to quit. **L2**

Quitting Tobacco Use

There are many reasons to quit using tobacco. People who quit using tobacco live longer than those who continue to use tobacco. They reduce their risk of heart disease, stroke, emphysema, chronic bronchitis, and some forms of cancer. There are even more immediate rewards to quitting smoking. Within a day after people stop smoking, the body begins to heal itself from the damages caused by tobacco. Breathing is easier, and a smoker's cough is not as frequent. The senses of taste and smell improve.

How to Quit Using Tobacco

Did You Know?

Smoking Expenses Smoking costs the nation over $150 billion per year in health-related economic costs.

List the reasons why you want to quit. Focus on all the things that you do not like about using tobacco. For example, you might think about the mess, the inconvenience, wasting money, and the way it makes you smell. Ask family members and friends to contribute to reasons.

Decide when you want to quit. Set a target date to quit. Know what to expect. Understand that nicotine withdrawal symptoms are temporary. Understand that quitting is not easy, but it is possible. Expect to experience pressures to use tobacco when you feel stress.

Make a health behavior contract. Make a health behavior contract with the life skill "I will stop using smokeless tobacco" or "I will stop smoking." Design a plan to quit using tobacco.

Consider situations in which you usually have a cigarette or use smokeless tobacco. Change your daily routines to avoid situations in which you previously used tobacco. Stay busy and active.

Join a tobacco cessation program. A tobacco cessation program is a program to help a person stop smoking or using smokeless tobacco. Tobacco cessation programs are offered by local chapters of the American Cancer Society, the American Lung Society, the American Heart Association, health departments, schools, and hospitals.

Get help from others. Tell family members and friends that you are quitting. Ask for encouragement and support.

Throw away all tobacco products. Get rid of items associated with tobacco use, such as ashtrays, lighters, and matches.

Be prepared for temptation. For the first few weeks or longer after quitting, you may have the urge to use tobacco. Try to stay away from people and places that might trigger a craving.

 Teacher to Teacher

Cost of Tobacco Over Time Give students a list of brand-name and generic types of cigarettes and smokeless tobacco. Have them determine the cost of using these products for different periods of time (one day, one week, one month, one year, five years, ten years, etc.). Base it on one pack of cigarettes a day, or one tin of smokeless tobacco a day. Ask students to consider what a person could do with the money if it is not spent on cigarettes or smokeless tobacco. **L2 ELL**
Ryan Sweeney
Clarke Community High School, Osceola, IA

TABLE 38.2 Methods to Help Quit Smoking

Type	Description	Side Effects
Nicotine patch	A *nicotine patch* is worn on the skin of the upper body or arms. It releases nicotine into the bloodstream at a slow rate; it does not contain cancer-causing chemicals	Can cause redness, itching, swelling, nervousness, dry mouth, and inability to sleep
Nicotine chewing gum	Chewing gum that releases nicotine when chewed; does not contain cancer-causing chemicals	Can result in sore jaws, upset stomach, nausea, heartburn, loosened dental fillings, and problems with dentures
Nicotine nasal spray	Spray nicotine in each nostril. Recommended dosage is 1–2 sprays/hour, not to exceed 40 sprays in a day	Nasal and sinus irritation
Nicotine inhaler	Mouthpiece the size and shape of a cigarette, which puts out vaporized nicotine when you puff on it; simulates the hand-to-mouth ritual; good for beginners trying to quit	Mild throat and mouth irritation; coughing; or upset stomach; should not be used for more than 6 months
Non-nicotine pill	Antidepressant that helps reduce cravings and withdrawals; take two pills/day 1–2 weeks before quitting and maintain up to six months	Most common side effects are shakiness and skin rash. More severe side effects include: increased blood pressure, seizures, kidney and liver failure

Participate in activities that keep your mind off of using tobacco. Try vigorous exercise to release beta-endorphins. Beta-endorphins may help relieve tension caused by quitting. Participating in other activities, such as working on a hobby or going to a movie, also may help.

Get help from a health-care professional. Make an appointment with a school nurse or a physician to help you with your plan. A physician may prescribe a nicotine patch, nicotine chewing gum, nicotine nasal sprays, a nicotine inhaler, or a pill that cuts cravings to use nicotine.

Avoid weight gain. Eat a healthful diet with the proper amount of protein, carbohydrates, and fat. Eat plenty of fruits and vegetables. Have low-fat and low-calorie snacks.

Keep your guard up. The urge to use tobacco often comes at predictable times. Continue to plan ahead for these situations.

If you slip up and use tobacco, keep trying to quit. Slipping up does not have to mean failure. Figure out why you slipped up and how to avoid it the next time. Remember that quitting smoking takes perseverance.

LESSON 38 • Choosing a Tobacco-Free Lifestyle   **433**

Resisting Peer Pressure

NHES Assessment/SCASS

Constructed Response Ask students to come up with reasons people may give to why they smoke. Have students write one to two paragraphs that would advocate nonsmoking in response to each of the reasons for smoking. **L2**

Class Activity

Who Should Avoid Smoking? Read the following statements aloud and ask students to stand if the statement read applies to them. Stand if you are an athlete, if you currently suffer a breathing condition, if someone in your family has allergies or a breathing problem, if you play a wind or brass instrument, if you want to live a full healthy life. At this point all students should be standing up, so everyone should have special reasons to avoid smoking. **L2**

3 Assess

Vocabulary Practice
Page 34, Unit 7 Fast File Resources

National Health Education Standards
Pages 434–435: 1.1, 1.5, 2.5, 2.6, 2.9, 2.10, 4.2, 5.1, 6.3, 7.2, 8.1, 8.2

Resisting Peer Pressure

Even though an increasing number of teens use tobacco, the majority of teens do not. Think of ways you might be pressured to use tobacco, and be ready to use resistance skills if someone pressures you to use tobacco products.

1. Use assertive behavior.
   - Stand tall and look directly at the person with whom you are speaking. Say "no" in a firm and confident voice.

2. Give reasons for saying "no" to tobacco.
   - Explain that tobacco use is harmful and illegal for minors. Using tobacco does not show respect for yourself and others.
   - Using tobacco is against the guidelines of your family and school.

3. Use nonverbal behavior to match verbal behavior.
   - Do not hold a cigarette or pretend to smoke.
   - Do not use or carry candy cigarettes or shredded gum that is designed to look like smokeless tobacco.
   - Do not agree to get tobacco for a minor.
   - Do not keep tobacco products in your possession for someone else.
   - Do not behave in ways that indicate that you approve of tobacco use.

4. Avoid being in situations in which there will be pressure to use tobacco.
   - Think ahead about what to say or do if your peers are using tobacco.

5. Avoid being with people who use tobacco.
   - Choose friends who do not use tobacco.
   - Stay away from secondhand smoke.

6. Resist pressure to engage in illegal behavior.
   - Learn the laws that apply to tobacco use in your community and state.
   - Do not lie about your age to buy tobacco products.
   - Do not purchase tobacco products from vending machines.

7. Influence others to choose responsible behavior.
   - Encourage people who pressure you to use tobacco to change their behavior.
   - Suggest tobacco cessation programs to people who smoke or use smokeless tobacco.
   - Be a role model for a tobacco-free lifestyle.
   - Tell others who smoke not to light up around you.

8. Avoid being influenced by tobacco ads.
   - Recognize that ads are designed to convince people to use a product and make profit for the company.
   - Recognize that tobacco use is not sexy, sophisticated, adventurous, healthful, fun, or the "in" thing to do.
   - Do not attend or view sporting events or concerts sponsored by tobacco companies.
   - Pay attention to the warnings on tobacco ads.
   - Make complaints to city officials if billboards for tobacco are placed in your neighborhood or near your school.

434   UNIT 7 • Alcohol, Tobacco, and Other Drugs

Achieving Health Literacy

Effective Communicator Divide the class into two groups. One group will be the group who argues that there should not be restriction of tobacco. The other group will be the group who argues for tobacco restriction. Have tobacco debate groups prepare to argue about the restriction of tobacco product sales to people under 18. Have the students research the topic to find information to support both age requirements and conduct a debate in class. **L3**

carbon monoxide
carcinogen
emphysema
leukoplakia
mainstream smoke
nicotine
nicotine patch
secondhand smoke
sidestream smoke
snuff
tar
tobacco

Key Terms Review

Complete these fill-in-the-blank statements with the lesson Key Terms on the left. Do not write in this book.

1. The stimulant drug found in tobacco products is _____.
2. The inability of alveoli to function is called _____.
3. A product that is placed on the skin of the arm to release nicotine in the body is called a(n) _____.
4. Powdered tobacco leaves and stems form a product called _____.
5. White patches of abnormal cells in the mouth are called _____.
6. A(n) herbal plant that contains nicotine and is grown for its leaves is called _____.
7. Any chemical known to cause cancer is a(n) _____.
8. A gas that interferes with the ability of the blood to carry oxygen is _____.
9. The sticky, thick liquid formed when tobacco burns is called _____.
10. Exhaled and sidestream smoke also is called _____.

Recalling the Facts

11. What are the effects of nicotine on the body?
12. Name three types of tobacco products.
13. What are the three types of tobacco smoke?
14. Name two methods people use to quit smoking.
15. Why is nicotine considered a stimulant?
16. How does smoking harm the respiratory system?
17. How is smoking related to heart disease?
18. What is the relationship between smoking and automobile accidents?

Critical Thinking

19. Analyze the physical, mental, social, and legal consequences of tobacco use.
20. Discuss the laws and policies regarding the sale and use of cigarettes.
21. Why do you think people who began smoking as teens have a more difficult time quitting than people who began smoking as adults?
22. Why do you think advertisers target minors?

Real-Life Applications

23. Why do you think teenagers start smoking?
24. What tip to resist peer pressure do you think is the most useful and why?
25. If you saw a friend or sibling smoking, what would you say to him or her?
26. Why do you think teenagers are influenced by television or magazine ads?

Activities

Responsible Decision Making

27. **Resist Peer Pressure** Suppose your friend offers you a cigarette. You have never smoked before. Your friend tells you that trying one cigarette will not harm you. Write a paragraph about what you should do. Refer to the Responsible Decision-Making Model on page 61 to see the steps involved in making responsible decisions.

Sharpen Your Life Skills

28. **Make Responsible Decisions** Find two different ads for tobacco products. Identify how each ad is designed to make tobacco more appealing to teens. Write a story about the scene in each ad that tells the truth about using tobacco products. Attach each story to the appropriate ad. Share the stories with your classmates.

Visit **www.glencoe.com** for more *Health & Wellness* quizzes.

Key Terms Review

1. nicotine
2. emphysema
3. nicotine patch
4. snuff
5. leukoplakia
6. tobacco
7. carcinogen
8. carbon monoxide
9. tar
10. secondhand smoke

Recalling the Facts

11. stimulates nervous system, dulls taste buds, increases heart rate and blood pressure, constricts blood vessels
12. cigarettes, clove cigarettes, cigars, chewing tobacco, pipe tobacco, and snuff
13. mainstream, secondhand, and sidestream
14. cold turkey, nicotine gum, nicotine patch, nicotine nasal spray, nicotine inhaler, non-nicotine pill
15. increases heart rate
16. See page 426 for information on how smoking harms the respiratory system.
17. See page 427 for information on how smoking is related to heart disease.
18. smokers could be distracted by trying to light the cigarette or by dropping a lit cigarette

Critical Thinking

19. See pages 425–429.
20. See pages 430–431 for information on the laws and policies regarding the sale and use of cigarettes.
21. Answers will vary.
22. Minors are more susceptible to advertisements; teens have a more difficult time quitting smoking than people who start smoking when they are older.

Real-Life Applications

23. peer pressure, do not believe they will become addicted; curious; want to be like an adult
24. student's opinion
25. quit smoking, tell them of the consequences of smoking, tell them methods to quit
26. Teenagers want to appear to be cool.

Activities

Responsible Decision Making

27. Answers will vary, but should include strategies from "Resisting Peer Pressure" on page 434.

Sharpen Your Life Skills

28. Answers will vary, but may include ideas from "Tobacco Advertising" on page 430.

LESSON 39

Avoiding Illegal Drug Use

Out of Time?

If time does not permit an in-depth study of this topic, use the following activities in this Teacher Wraparound Edition:
- Just the Facts, p. 439
- Class Activity, p. 440
- Class Discussion, p. 442
- Legal Issues, p. 448

1 Focus

HEALTH GOALS **Controlled Prescription Drugs** Have students respond to the Health Goal for this lesson by having them discuss what controlled drugs are, as well as their intended uses. List some examples on the board, such as morphine which is used by doctors and hospitals as a pain-reliever. Other examples could include mood-altering drugs, such as valium, which is used to treat anxiety. Discuss what makes these drugs useful in medicine, yet dangerous for people to use recreationally without a doctor's advice. **L2**

Write ABOUT IT!

Journaling Steroids can cause low sperm count, sterility, and baldness. Steroids also may cause people to become more aggressive. The brother should tell his teammates that he does not want to harm his health by taking steroids. **L2**

LESSON 39

Avoiding Illegal Drug Use

HEALTH GOAL • **I will not be involved in illegal drug use.**

A controlled drug is a drug whose possession, manufacture, distribution, and sale are controlled by law. A prescription is needed to obtain controlled drugs. Illegal drug use is the use of a controlled drug without a prescription. It is illegal to buy or sell controlled drugs on the street. You will learn the powerful effects that controlled drugs have on the mind and body. You also will learn how to resist pressure to be involved in illegal drug use.

What You'll Learn

1. Explain the harmful effects of inhalants. *(p. 437)*
2. Describe the physical and emotional effects of marijuana. *(p. 438)*
3. Determine how the illegal use of hallucinogens, stimulants, narcotics, and sedative-hypnotics harm health. *(pp. 442, 444, 446, 448)*
4. Determine how the illegal use of anabolic-androgenic steroids harms health. *(p. 449)*
5. Practice resistance skills that can be used to resist peer pressure to use illegal drugs. *(p. 450)*

Why It's Important

There are many different types of illegal drugs. Knowing how these illegal drugs can harm you and others will help you avoid them.

Key Terms

- inhalants
- marijuana
- Ecstasy
- club drugs
- LSD
- stimulants
- cocaine
- narcotics
- codeine
- steroids

Write ABOUT IT!

Writing About Avoiding Illegal Drug Use Suppose your younger brother tells you that two soccer teammates are taking steroids. They say the steroids improve their performance, and they tell your brother that if he takes them he will make first string. After reading about steroids on page 449, write an entry in your health journal about the dangers of steroid use and how you would tell your brother to handle the situation.

National Health Education Standards—Guide for Lesson 39		
1.8	Analyze personal susceptibility to injury, illness, or death if engaging in unhealthy behaviors.	pp. 437–442, 444–449
1.9	Analyze the potential severity of injury or illness if engaging in unhealthy behaviors.	pp. 437–442, 444–449
2.9	Analyze how some health risk behaviors can influence the likelihood of engaging in unhealthy behaviors.	pp. 437, 439, 440, 442, 444, 446–447, 448, 449, 451

Inhalants

◀ Scan of an oxygen-deprived brain.

◀ Scan of an oxygen-rich brain.

▲ Inhalants deprive the brain of oxygen. They can cause permanent brain damage. The color yellow shows the presence of oxygen.

C hemicals that affect mood and behavior when inhaled are *inhalants*. Most inhalants are not controlled drugs. Most inhalants are chemicals that are not produced to be inhaled or used as drugs. Inhalants often are the first drug that a young person uses because inhalants are easily accessible. Inhalants produce a very quick high because they are inhaled. However, the high usually lasts only a few minutes. Inhaling fumes to get high is called *huffing* or *sniffing*. *Bagging* is inhaling fumes from a bag to get high. Inhalants also are inhaled from balloons, aerosol cans, and other containers.

How the Illegal Use of Inhalants Can Harm Health

By causing immediate death Inhalants can cause heart failure and instant death. They also cause the central nervous system to slow down. This interferes with breathing and may cause suffocation. People who use inhalants may become unconscious and have seizures. They could choke on their own vomit if they get sick.

By harming the body People who use inhalants may experience euphoria, nausea, vomiting, headache, dizziness, and uncontrollable laughter. Inhalants reduce the flow of oxygen to the brain and can cause permanent brain damage. People who use inhalants may have an irregular heartbeat, difficulty breathing, and headaches. Inhalants damage the immune system, heart, kidneys, blood, and bone marrow. Some inhalants can cause leukemia and lead poisoning.

By harming the mind People who use inhalants cannot make responsible decisions because reasoning and judgment are impaired. They can have hallucinations that may cause them to harm themselves or others.

By causing dependence People who use inhalants can develop psychological or physical dependence. They need to take more and more of the inhalant to get the desired effects.

By increasing the risk of accidents, violence, and crime Inhalants affect reasoning and judgment, coordination, vision, and reaction time. Inhalants can cause disorientation and confusion. People who use inhalants do not have the skills needed to drive and make responsible decisions. They might do things they would not normally do, such as get into a physical fight with someone.

Did You Know?

Inhalant Damage Inhaling the fumes from paint sprays, glues, dewaxers, cleaning fluids, and correction fluids can cause permanent hearing loss.

Examples of Inhalants

There are many kinds of inhalants. The following are some of them:

- amyl nitrite and butyl nitrite
- nail polish remover
- furniture polish
- gasoline
- glue
- hairspray
- laughing gas (nitrous oxide)
- lighter fluid
- marker fluid
- paint thinner
- paper correction fluid
- rubber cement
- spray paint
- transmission fluid

LESSON 39 • Avoiding Illegal Drug Use **437**

Lesson Resource Manager

- **Unit 7 Fast File Resources**
  Reading Strategy, p. 47
  Vocabulary Practice, p. 48
  Transparency Master and Worksheet, p. 49
  Real-Life Health, p. 51
  Real-Life Health, p. 53
  5-Minute Check, p. 55
  Lesson 39 Quiz, p. 58
- **Unit 7 Transparency**
- **Lesson 39 Transparency**

- **Reading Essentials**
- **Technology**
  TeacherWorks™ CD-ROM
  StudentWorks™ CD-ROM
  Reading Essentials CD-ROM
  ExamView® Assessment Suite
  Vocabulary Puzzlemaker

Inhalants

2 Teach

Teacher FYI

Other Dangers Although students may be familiar with the dangers to their bodies when they use inhalants, they may not realize the other dangers caused by these drugs. Many people are harmed or killed each year by using inhalants, such as gasoline, hairspray, lighter fluid, paint thinner and others that ignite and catch the participants on fire. Due to the extreme flammability of many of these inhalants and the impaired judgment of the users, people who are involved with flammable inhalants are often consumed very quickly by the flames.

INTERACTIVE CHALKBOARD with Image Bank

PowerPoint® Presentations

This CD-ROM is an editable Microsoft® PowerPoint® presentation that includes:

- Lesson presentations
- Lesson checks
- Interactive graphics
- 5-Minute Checks
- Image Bank
- All transparencies

Vocabulary Strategies Refer to the Mapping Complete Definitions Strategy on page 16T. Have the students create definition maps of each Key Term, including the harmful effects of each drug.

National Health Education Standards

Pages 436–437: 1.2, 1.5, 1.8, 1.9, 2.9, 5.5, 8.1, 8.2

437

Marijuana

Marijuana

The dried leaves and tops of the cannabis plant is *marijuana*. It is the most commonly used illegal drug in the United States. It can harm the different systems of the body, including the immune system, making the body unable to fight off communicable diseases, such as the common cold, and noncommunicable diseases, such as cancer. *THC* is a drug found in the cannabis plant that produces psychoactive effects. THC is a fat-soluble drug that builds up in the fatty parts of the body, including the brain, heart, and liver. The effects of smoking or eating marijuana depend on the amount of THC. In the past, marijuana contained between 1 and 5 percent THC. Today's marijuana is much more potent. It usually contains between 8 and 15 percent THC.

How the Illegal Use of Marijuana Can Harm Health

> **Make the Connection**
>
> **Respiratory System** For more information on the respiratory system, see page 215 in Lesson 19.

Marijuana and hashish can harm health. **Hashish** is one of the drugs that is made from marijuana. **Hashish oil** is the liquid resin from the cannabis plant. Marijuana, hashish, and hashish oil are considered gateway drugs. A *gateway drug* is a drug that increases the likelihood that a person who uses it will use other harmful drugs. Marijuana is associated with flashbacks, similar to ones experienced by people who use hallucinogens.

By harming the body People who use marijuana may feel relaxed, euphoric, drowsy, and have an increased appetite. Smoking marijuana damages the lungs and respiratory system. Marijuana smoke contains many of the same carcinogens that tobacco smoke contains.

Long-term use of marijuana can affect the reproductive system. A pregnant female who uses marijuana runs the risk of harming the developing baby.

TABLE 39.1	Types of Marijuana	
Drug/Also Known As	**How Ingested/Legality**	**Effects**
Marijuana: Chronic, herb, reefer, ganja, tea, Mary Jane, grass, pot, weed, joint (marijuana cigarette)	Smoked or eaten/illegal without a prescription	Users become relaxed, euphoric, drowsy, and hungry
Hashish (hashish oil)	Smoked, mixed with tobacco, or eaten in candies or cookies/illegal	Similar to marijuana, but stronger

438 UNIT 7 • Alcohol, Tobacco, and Other Drugs

Cross-Curricular Connections

Science Since THC adheres to the fatty tissues of the body, it takes a long time for traces of the drug to disappear. Just one dose of THC from a single marijuana cigarette is commonly detectable for up to 30 days from the time it was smoked. The most common tests for THC are urine, and hair sample tests. Have students research the health risks of THC use. *People who use marijuana take more sick days than non-users. Marijuana has some of the same cancer-causing components as tobacco. Marijuana causes people to have more chest colds, and be susceptible to bronchitis and other lung diseases. Marijuana also suppresses the immune system.* **L2**

Just the FACTS: MARIJUANA

❝Doesn't everyone use marijuana?❞

the FACTS The number of 8th and 12th graders who have used marijuana in the last year is dropping. In a recent study the percentage of 8th graders who had used marijuana in the past year dropped from 18.3 percent in 1996 to 15.4 percent in 2001. In the same study, more than half (57.4 percent) of 12th graders believed that smoking marijuana was harmful. Nearly 80 percent of them disapproved of regular marijuana use.

❝But using marijuana makes you feel good, right?❞

the FACTS Marijuana may have a relaxing effect on the brain. This same effect also makes it harder to concentrate, remember, and solve problems. The National Household Survey on Drug Abuse found that teenagers with a grade average of D or lower were four times as likely to have used marijuana than those with an A average. Using marijuana also interferes with decision making. Teens who have used marijuana are four times more likely than nonusers to have been pregnant or to have gotten someone pregnant. According to the American Psychiatric Association, teens who use marijuana because they feel anxious or depressed are likely to experience panic attacks, paranoia, and even psychoses.

❝My friend says marijuana is harmless. Is that true?❞

the FACTS Marijuana smoke contains the same cancer-causing substances as tobacco smoke, but at higher concentrations. Users usually inhale more deeply and hold their breath longer than cigarette smokers. This exposes their lungs to these carcinogens for longer periods of time. Because of this increased concentration and increased exposure, smoking marijuana may increase the risk of cancer more than smoking tobacco. In addition, poor thinking and decision making often cause marijuana users to be involved in accidents, including car crashes. Although the use of marijuana is dropping, the number of emergency room visits linked to this drug is rising. For example, between 1994 and 2001, the rate of visits related to marijuana for patients ages 12 to 17 rose 126 percent.

By harming the mind Marijuana causes short-term memory loss and impairs concentration. People who smoke marijuana often lose their train of thought and do things they later regret. They may take unnecessary risks that harm health.

Marijuana can cause ***amotivational syndrome,*** a persistent loss of ambition and motivation. Marijuana can cause drowsiness and loss of interest in daily activities.

By causing dependence People who use marijuana develop tolerance after high doses and long-term use. They can develop psychological dependence. They may feel they have to use marijuana to enjoy other activ-

ities. It is not clear if marijuana causes physical dependence and withdrawal symptoms.

By increasing the risk of becoming infected with HIV and hepatitis B People who use marijuana cannot make responsible decisions. A person who has smoked marijuana may have sex with a person who is infected with HIV or hepatitis B, and become infected.

By increasing the risk of accidents, violence, and crime Marijuana impairs people's ability to judge distances and slows their reaction time, making them more likely to cause a motor vehicle accident or to have an accident operating machinery.

Did You Know?

Cancerous Effects Marijuana smoke contains 50 to 70 more carcinogenic hydrocarbons than does cigarette smoke.

Just the FACTS:

Marijuana Ironically, because marijuana is illegal, less information is available on how dangerous its use can be. Ask students about their perceptions on drinking and driving. Then ask about their perceptions about marijuana use and driving. Although using marijuana while driving is extremely dangerous, most students may not perceive such behavior as negatively as they perceive drinking and driving. *Marijuana causes loss of coordination, slows reaction time, and impairs ability to judge speed and distance.* **L2**

5-Minute Check

Page 55, **Unit 7 Fast File Resources**

1. What is an inhalant? *a chemical that affects mood and behavior when inhaled*
2. Name three ways inhalants can harm the body. *causing nausea, vomiting, an irregular heartbeat, and reducing the flow of oxygen to the brain*
3. How does marijuana increase the risk of accidents? *It impairs people's ability to judge distance and slows reaction time.*
4. What is the active ingredient in marijuana? *THC*
5. What is the most commonly used illegal drug in the United States? *marijuana*

🛡 Sensitive Issues

Student Privacy According to the National Survey on Drug Use and Health, 7.9 percent of Americans (19.1 million) 12 years and older used a drug illicitly sometime in the month prior to the survey in 2004. This is a decrease from 2003, when 19.5 million Americans reported current use. These statistics make it evident that you may have a student or several students experimenting with drugs, or students who know someone who is abusing drugs. When discussing drugs in class, care needs to be taken to avoid personal questions. Have a list of trusted counselors and resources ready that students can utilize if they ask for help.

National Health Education Standards
Pages 438–439: 1.2, 1.8, 1.9, 2.9

Ecstasy (MDMA)

An illegal psychoactive drug that has a stimulating effect and the ability to cause hallucinations is called *Ecstasy,* also known as *MDMA.* Some other names given to Ecstasy are Adam, XTC, hug, beans, roll, Y2K, and 007. Ecstasy is a drug that is synthetic, meaning it is made in a laboratory. The chemical makeup of Ecstasy is similar to that of drugs such as methamphetamine and mescaline. These drugs are known to cause brain damage. While Ecstasy is generally taken in pill form, it also can be snorted or injected.

How the Illegal Use of Ecstasy Can Harm Health

Harmful psychological effects The harmful effects caused by Ecstasy are similar to those found in amphetamines and cocaine. Among the psychological effects are: confusion, depression, insomnia, severe anxiety, and paranoia or extreme fear.

Physical problems Use of Ecstasy can result in different kinds of physical problems. Among these are muscle tension, involuntary teeth clenching, nausea, blurred vision, faintness, chills, and sweating. Ecstasy also causes an increase in heartbeat rate and blood pressure. Research also shows that Ecstasy can have long-term effects on the brain. It can harm the memory and pleasure centers of the brain. The effects of Ecstasy last between three and six hours. Ecstasy allows users to dance for long periods of time, increasing the risk of dehydration, heart, or kidney failure.

Ecstasy is becoming more dangerous. Because Ecstasy is illegal, there is no regulation of the contents of the pills. Therefore, other substances might be added to the pills that can cause severe side effects. People might think they are taking Ecstasy, but instead are taking other substances. As a result, there have been deaths associated with the use of Ecstasy.

Warning signs Be alert to signs of Ecstasy use around you. Pacifiers and suckers control teeth-grinding, a common side effect of Ecstasy. Strobe lights enhance the hallucinogenic effects. Candy dispensers are used to hide Ecstasy tablets.

▲ Possession of some types of objects might indicate use of Ecstasy.

Reading Review

1. Name two street names for Ecstasy.
2. How long does the effect of Ecstasy last?
3. Name two warning signs of Ecstasy use.

⚖️ Legal Issues

Synthetic Drugs Ecstasy is a synthetic drug. Ask students if they understand that a synthetic drug is one which is made in a laboratory. Ask questions to prod students about the ramifications of this fact. Questions can include: What materials are used to make the drug? What testing measurements and guidelines must be met? Are synthetic drugs subject to regulation and standards? It should be apparent to students that synthetic drugs can cover a range of quality and safety. These drugs are not made with any of the quality and safety assurances that pharmaceutical drug manufacturers must follow. The people making them probably do not meet the education and training required of makers of legal drugs. If some needed materials are not available, some synthetic drugs may even be made with toxic materials in their place. **L2**

FACTSABOUT
CLUB DRUGS

The collective term *club drugs* is used to describe the drugs that often are available at raves, which are large, all-night dance parties attended by teens and young adults. Club drugs include Ecstasy, GHB, roofies, ketamine, LSD, and nitrous oxide. Many users of club drugs mistakenly believe that these drugs are safe and legal. These drugs produce dangerous side effects that can leave the user with permanent physical and/or mental damage, and leave people vulnerable to sexual assault.

GHB, roofies, and ketamine are drugs that have been named in cases of date rape. All three are tasteless and can be easily dissolved in a drink. The sedative and anesthetic effects of these drugs often leave the user incapable of resisting a sexual assault.

GHB People began using *GHB* in the early 1990s for its intoxicating, sedative, or euphoriant effects. Body builders purchased GHB to help in fat reduction and muscle building. Among the street names of GHB are soap and liquid Ecstasy. People who use GHB can have seizures or go into a coma. When GHB is combined with alcohol, nausea and difficulty breathing can result. Withdrawal symptoms include insomnia, anxiety, shaking, and sweating.

Flunitrazepam A drug that belongs to a class of drugs called benzodiazepines is called *flunitrazepam* and is also known as "roofies," "roach," and "rope." When mixed with alcohol, it can cause people to lose their ability to resist sexual assault. It also can produce a type of amnesia, which means that people may not be able to remember events they have experienced while under the influence of this drug. Roofies can cause death.

Ketamine A drug that has been used medically as an anesthetic for both human and animal use is called *ketamine*. It is most often used by veterinarians. Known as "Special K" or "Vitamin K," ketamine can cause dream-like states and hallucinations. This drug also is common in club and rave scenes and has been used as a date-rape drug.

GHB, which ▶ can be produced in clear liquid, white powder, tablet, and capsule form, is often abused in combination with alcohol, making it even more dangerous.

LSD Known on the street as acid or yellow sunshines, *LSD* is a hallucinogen. The physiological effects of LSD include increased heart rate and blood pressure, increased body temperature, sleeplessness, and loss of appetite. The user may experience visual hallucinations.

Nitrous oxide The inhalant *nitrous oxide* also is called laughing gas. It enters the body through the respiratory system, usually by being inhaled from a balloon or a bag. Nitrous oxide produces a quick head rush. It also acts as a depressant on the central nervous system and can cause permanent brain damage.

Investigating the Issue

Visit www.glencoe.com to research more about the dangers of club drugs.

- What additional health dangers exist due to the fact that many of these club drugs are produced illegally?
- Is Ecstasy addictive?
- What side effects can result from repeated use of LSD?

Produce a video about the dangers of club drugs. Include information about how to avoid their use. Share the video with your class.

FACTSABOUT
CLUB DRUGS

Teacher FYI

Heatstroke When someone takes ecstasy or any other stimulant, his or her body temperature rises. If someone takes ecstasy while they are exercising, such as when they are dancing at a club, the body can overheat and lose fluids rapidly. Some users can lose several pints of body fluids in only a few hours, increasing the risk of heatstroke. These cases are not ecstasy overdoses. Heatstroke can happen even if a user takes only one tablet.

Investigating the Issue

- *Additional dangers include not knowing what other substances/drugs may be mixed in, and not knowing the dosage.*
- *Evidence suggests that ecstasy may have the potential to be physically addictive. Studies show that ecstasy affects the "reward pathway" within the brain—the same pathway that is affected by addictive drugs such as cocaine and heroin.*
- *flashbacks (hallucinogen persisting perception disorder) and persistent psychosis, such as schizophrenia or depression*

🍎 Teacher to Teacher

Lyrics in Popular Songs Use cooperative learning to help students organize information to avoid the negative effects of drug use. Break students into small groups and have them research the effects of a particular drug. Groups should then change the lyrics of popular songs to reflect an anti-drug message. They can also design a CD case and title which promote anti-drug messages. Song lyrics must include factual information about the effects of the drug researched by the group. Each group can perform its song "in concert" for the class. **L2**
Greg Varnade
Slidell High School, Slidell, LA

National Health Education Standards
Pages 440–441: 1.2, 1.8, 1.9, 2.9, 8.2

Hallucinogens

NHES Assessment/SCASS

Performance Event Have students take turns role-playing a student who is contemplating using drugs. Have another student play someone using positive peer pressure and another using negative peer pressure. Ask students to write a response in their health journals evaluating whether the first student in the role-play used responsible decision-making skills. **L2**

Using the Table

Synthetic Drugs Ask the students to examine the table and determine which drug is also known as "tabs." *LSD* Ask students which drug is most likely to produce aggressive behavior. *PCP* **L2**

Class Discussion

Dangers of Mushrooms Students may think mushrooms are a safer alternative to synthetic drugs. Have students find pictures of poisonous mushrooms, such as Amanita, that often are mistaken for edible mushrooms. The toxins released by Amanita phalloides cause fatal kidney and liver damage. Psilocybin is also dangerous. Students also may find some recent news items about people who have mistakenly eaten poisonous mushrooms and died. Have students share these with the class and discuss the dangers of eating misidentified mushrooms. **L2**

A group of drugs that interfere with the senses and cause hallucinations is called *hallucinogens,* also known as psychedelic drugs. A hallucination is an imagined experience that seems real. The effects of hallucinogens may last for several days.

How the Illegal Use of Hallucinogens Can Harm Health

By harming the body Hallucinogens can cause increased heart rate and blood pressure, tremors, and nausea.

By harming the mind Hallucinogens can alter perception of reality, time and environment, intensify mood, and cause rapid mood swings. They also can cause flashbacks. A *flashback* is a vivid memory of a hallucination.

By causing dependence People who regularly use hallucinogens may develop a tolerance.

By increasing the risk of accidents, violence, and crime Hallucinogens impair reasoning and judgment, and slow reaction time. Hallucinogens can increase anger and aggression and can lead to violence.

TABLE 39.2 Types of Hallucinogens

	Drug/Also Known As	How Ingested/Legality	Effects
	LSD: Acid, doses, beast, Lucy, diamond, tabs, trips	Swallowed, sniffed, or placed on tongue to dissolve/illegal	Pupils dilate, skin becomes flushed, heart rate and temperature increase, "bad trips"
	PCP: Angel dust, dust	Smoked, swallowed, or sniffed/illegal	Restlessness, disorientation, anxiousness, anger, aggression, feelings of invincibility
	Psilocybin: Mushrooms, shrooms	Eaten/illegal	Increased blood pressure and heart rate, dizziness, anxiety, "bad trips"
	MDMA: Ecstasy, XTC	Swallowed, sniffed, or injected/illegal	Also acts as a stimulant, can cause brain damage, similar to LSD

⟨⊟⟩ Cross-Curricular Connections

History LSD is made from synthesized lysergic acid. Lysergic acid was first discovered in ergot, which is a fungal disease of grain. The hallucinogenic effects of ergot have been thought to be responsible for the behavior of the female accusers in the Salem witch trials of 1692. The afflicted women behaved erratically and claimed to see visions. This led people to believe they were witches. Many were prosecuted and burned at the stake. Have students research the effects that LSD has on the body and research the Salem witch trials. From their findings, have students discuss if they think it is possible that LSD was responsible for the behavior of the women accused of being witches. **L3**

SPEAKING OUT

Teens Talk About Health

Gabrielle Gantos
Participating in a Drug-Free Club

> **❝** Having a strong group of friends who feel the way you do is really important. **❞**

For Gabrielle Gantos, being drug free is about a lot of different things. It's about finding the right group of friends. It's about being a role model to family, friends, and community. It's about knowing how to handle pressure to experiment with drugs, and it's about knowing who you are and what you want.

Getting organized For Gabrielle, being drug free is easier because of a group she joined at school. She became involved with this group through a friend. Being around people who feel the way she does about drugs is a big help. "Our group usually gets together once a week. We actually send around flyers that say something like 'We're going to a movie on Saturday night, or there's a party at this person's house, or we're going to have a picnic.' It's basically a whole bunch of people getting together to do something so you don't have to turn to drugs just to have fun." The get-togethers aren't about drug education. They're just a way for people who have decided to be drug free to support each other.

Helping the community Gabrielle's group also organizes activities for other members of the community. "Sometimes we do fund-raisers for different things," she explained. "We also go to elementary schools to meet with younger kids and talk to them about the dangers of drugs, alcohol, and tobacco. It's a lot of fun."

What about the pressure? Gabrielle doesn't have her head in the clouds when it comes to pressure to use drugs. "I know there's a lot of pressure to use drugs," she said. "It's not easy. Kids at my school who don't take drugs are called things like 'prude.' It's like people who

use drugs think drug-free people don't want to have fun." Plus, there's the pressure to be cool. "It's the whole popularity thing," said Gabrielle. "If you want to be popular it seems like you get high or drunk and go to wild parties. That's what you do."

What does Gabrielle tell herself in response to this pressure? She explained, "I'm OK with the pressure because I know I'll be better off in the long run. I have friends who don't pressure me to do that stuff. Having a strong group of friends who feel the way you do is really important." She also uses the resistance skills she's learned in health class. Gabrielle reported that she finds them easy to use and effective.

Top priority For Gabrielle, it's very important to be a role model. "I'm my brothers' older sister," she said, "and what I do affects them. If they see me do something, they'll think it's OK. And I don't want them doing this kind of stuff and taking a chance on wrecking their lives."

Gabrielle's advice is that there are a lot of other things high-school students can do to have fun. "If you like the people you're around and like who you are there are so many things you can do without drugs."

LESSON 39 • Avoiding Illegal Drug Use **443**

Journaling Activity

Jot down five ways you could encourage other people to be drug free. Choose one and a write a proposal about how you could put this plan into action.

SPEAKING OUT

Analyzing the Feature

Use the following questions to help students uncover the main point of this feature.

1. What kinds of activities does Gabrielle's group participate in? *movies, picnics, and other recreational activities, as well as community projects*

2. How does Gabrielle deal with peer pressure to use drugs? *She uses resistance skills and the support of friends to resist peer pressure.*

3. Why does Gabrielle take her responsibility as a role model seriously? *She knows that her younger brothers look to her to determine acceptable actions.* **L2**

Class Discussion

Peer Support Studies show that the best way to be successful at something is to surround yourself with others who are successful at that particular activity. For instance, people who surround themselves with others who are physically fit are more likely to be fit themselves. Have students discuss the things that attract them to other people as friends. Ask students whether being drug free is one of the things that can be made easier by having friends who feel the same way. **L2**

Journaling Activity

Ask students to share ideas for staying drug-free that they listed in their health journals. **L2**

🚶 Healthy People 2010

Objective 26-17 Increase the proportion of adolescents who perceive great risk associated with substance abuse.

In the 1998 Healthy People survey of teens aged 12–17, 47 percent perceived great risk associated with consuming five or more alcoholic drinks at a single occasion once or twice a week. Thirty-one percent perceived great risk associated with smoking marijuana once per month, and 54 percent perceived great risk associated with using cocaine once per month. The Healthy People 2010 target for all three is 80 percent. Have students brainstorm ways to raise awareness among teens of the risks associated with substance abuse. **L2**

National Health Education Standards
Pages 442–443: 1.2, 2.7, 2.9, 5.6, 5.7, 8.2

Stimulants

A group of drugs that speed up the activities of the central nervous system are *stimulants*. Stimulants sometimes are called "uppers" because they make people feel alert, awake, and active. They increase blood pressure, heart rate, and breathing rate. Some teens use legal and illegal stimulants to get a high, stay awake, and to lose weight. The use of stimulants always is followed by a crash, or the intense down period that follows a stimulant high. People who crash feel fatigued, weak, sleepy, and depressed. People who use stimulants often take larger amounts of stimulants to avoid the crash. They develop physical and psychological dependence.

How the Illegal Use of Stimulants Can Harm Health

By causing immediate death Within minutes, people who have taken a stimulant may have a heart attack or seizure, stop breathing, and die. Some people lack a chemical in the liver needed to break down *cocaine,* a white powder extracted from the leaves of a cocoa plant. They can have an immediate fatal reaction. Mixing other drugs with stimulants increases the risk of overdose and death.

By harming the body People who use stimulants may experience body tremors, vomiting, increased alertness, quickened movements, a racing heart, and increased blood pressure. Some of these changes can cause a stroke. Snorting stimulants causes sores and burns in and around the nose. People who snort large amounts may develop holes between their nostrils and have a runny nose, sore throat, and hoarse voice.

By harming the mind People who use stimulants can become confused, anxious, aggressive, and paranoid.

They may have hallucinations. An imagined sight, sound, or feeling is a *hallucination.*

By causing dependence The body builds up tolerance to stimulants very quickly. Some people who use stimulants increase their doses rapidly. Physical dependence can occur after one use.

By increasing the risk of becoming infected with HIV and hepatitis B People infected with HIV or hepatitis B may leave infected blood on a needle after injecting themselves with stimulants. If the needle is used by other people, the infected blood may enter their bodies and infect them.

By increasing the risk of accidents, violence, and crime Stimulants impair reasoning and judgment, causing accidents. They increase feelings of anger and aggressiveness and can lead to violence. Selling and buying cocaine and other stimulants often is associated with gangs and violence.

Did You Know?

Methamphetamine Repeated use of methamphetamine can cause paranoia, psychotic behavior, hallucinations, violent behavior, and even strokes.

Health Project

Diet Pills Many people are not aware of the role and types of stimulants used in various diet pills and products. Have students form small groups, and assign each group one or more popular diet products. Have students search for the product in grocery stores, department stores, and in magazines. Have each group investigate the product to find the ingredients. The groups should identify any stimulants used in the products, as well as any dangers or side effects of these stimulants. Have students answer these questions: How accessible is the product? How much does it cost? Where is the product advertised? What claims does the product make? **L2**

TABLE 39.3 Types of Stimulants

Drug/Also Known As	How Ingested/Legality	Effects
Cocaine: Coke, blow, gold dust, white lady, snow, Charlie	Snorted, injected, or smoked/illegal	Highly addictive; can cause stroke, heart attack, or seizure; can be fatal with one use
Crack (freebase cocaine): Rock	Smoked/illegal	Effects ten times greater than cocaine, can be fatal with one use, extremely addictive
Amphetamines: Diet pills (no longer sold for this purpose)	Swallowed/illegal without prescription	Can cause multiple health problems, highly addictive
Methamphetamines: Meth, crank, crystal meth, crystal tea, crystal, ice, speed, chalk, glass	Swallowed, snorted, injected, or smoked/illegal without prescription	Addictive, effects similar to cocaine, can be fatal with one use
Methcathinone: Cat, bathtub speed, wildcat, goob	Swallowed, snorted, injected, or smoked/illegal	Similar to methamphetamines
Ephedrine: Effies, white cross	Swallowed or inhaled/illegal without prescription	Prescribed to relieve asthma, can be used to make methamphetamines, has same effects as methamphetamines
Methylphenidate: Vitamin R, West Coast	Swallowed, snorted, injected/illegal without prescription	Prescribed to control attention deficit hyperactivity disorder (ADHD); suppresses appetite; increases focus, attentiveness, wakefulness; can cause euphoria

A drug manufactured to resemble another drug or mimic its effects is a *look-alike drug.* Look-alike amphetamines contain large amounts of legal, non-prescription stimulants such as *caffeine,* a stimulant found in chocolate, coffee, tea, and some soda pops. It is the most widely used stimulant. However, it increases the likelihood of having irregular heartbeats, irritates the stomach, and increases urine production. Some people develop *caffeinism,* which is poisoning due to heavy caffeine intake. Symptoms include nervousness and irritability as well as the symptoms listed above.

Extension

Herbal Drugs Many drugs, especially diet drugs, are marketed as herbal. Discuss with the class what the term herbal means. Discuss whether herbal necessarily means that the drug is safe. Ask students: What other drugs could be called herbal? Could tobacco or marijuana be termed herbal drugs? What would be the result of labeling tobacco or marijuana as herbal? Have students research the regulations for labeling a drug as herbal. Ask students what kinds of stimulants are marketed as herbal. **L2**

Using the Table

Stimulants Have students form small groups. Assign each group one of the drugs presented in Table 39.3. Ask students to research the history of the drug. For example, cocaine was once an ingredient in cola. Groups should present their findings in a poster or multimedia format. **L2**

Explain the Concept

Combination Drugs Tell students that some users compound the dangers of drug use by combining several drugs. Combining one stimulant with another can actually multiply the effects of both drugs, which can have serious consequences. **L2**

🏛 Community Involvement

Community Drug Abuse Programs Have students explore the drug-abuse prevention or intervention programs that are currently underway in your community. Set up a display in your classroom with the information and brochures, and other educational material that was obtained from the drug-abuse prevention or intervention programs. Discuss as a class the focus and effectiveness of the programs and campaigns. Make information available to students on counseling as well as volunteer opportunities for those who may be interested. **L2**

National Health Education Standards
Pages 444–445: 1.1, 1.2, 1.8, 2.9, 5.7

Narcotics

Explain the Concept

Medicinal Narcotics Although narcotics are a widely abused class of drugs, they are often legitimately prescribed by doctors to control pain. This legitimate use leads many people to become unwittingly dependent on narcotics. Some people have been treated with narcotic pain killers to battle pain from injuries, only to find themselves unable to give up the drugs. Warn students that they might need to use narcotics under a doctor's supervision at some point in their lives and that these drugs should be respected and used very cautiously. **L2**

5-Minute Check

Page 56, **Unit 7 Fast File Resources**

1. What is a stimulant? *a drug that speeds up the activities of the central nervous system*

2. Name three body functions affected by stimulants. *heart rate, blood pressure, breathing rate*

3. What are hallucinogens? *drugs that interfere with the senses and cause imagined experiences that seem real*

4. Explain the crash that follows stimulant use. *down period; feelings of fatigue, weakness, sleepiness, and depression*

5. How can narcotics cause death? *they depress the central nervous system, slow breathing, and can induce coma*

Narcotics

A group of drugs that slow down, or depress, the central nervous system and relieve pain are **narcotics**. They slow down body functions, such as breathing and heart rate. Narcotics often are prescribed by physicians as analgesics. A drug that relieves pain is an **analgesic**. Narcotics also are used to suppress coughs and control diarrhea. Narcotics should be used only with the supervision of a physician. Narcotics include **opium**, a white, milky fluid from the seedpod of the poppy plant; **morphine**, a naturally occurring substance extracted from the poppy plant; **codeine**, a painkiller produced from morphine; and **heroin**, a narcotic processed from morphine.

How the Illegal Use of Narcotics Can Harm Health

By causing immediate death Narcotic drugs depress the central nervous system. Large doses of narcotic drugs slow down breathing and can cause coma and even death.

By harming the body People who use narcotics may experience euphoria, drowsiness, nausea, rapid heartbeat, and clammy skin. Large doses can induce sleep and may cause vomiting. Narcotics can be especially dangerous to people who have respiratory problems because narcotics interfere with breathing and coughing. People who are allergic to narcotics may develop a skin rash.

By harming the mind People who use narcotics cannot use reasoning and judgment to make responsible decisions. They may become depressed and lazy. Their emotions may change and they may have mood swings.

By causing dependence Repeated use of narcotics results in increased tolerance. This leads to physical dependence. People who are physically dependent on narcotics have withdrawal if they stop taking the drug. They may become deeply depressed, have mood swings, and be very sensitive to pain. Narcotics also cause psychological dependence. People who use narcotics become preoccupied with taking and obtaining the drug. They often lack energy and motivation and neglect themselves and their responsibilities. They may suffer from malnutrition, infection, illness, or injury. They may rob or steal to get narcotics.

▲ People who abuse narcotics may suffer from depression and become obsessed with taking and obtaining the drug.

 Teacher to Teacher

Bridge the Gap To help teens develop open communication lines with a parent or guardian about drug use, provide students with a questionnaire to use as they interview a parent or guardian. Include questions about drugs that are familiar to both generations. Questions about Ecstacy, GHB, and other popular modern drugs also educate parents on what is abused by teens today. Have students record responses and use them in making wise decisions about drug use. **L1**
Mark Tallant
Westside High School, Macon, GA

By increasing the risk of becoming infected with HIV and hepatitis B People who are infected with HIV or hepatitis B may leave blood on a needle after injecting themselves with narcotics. If the needle is used by another person, the infected blood may enter his or her body and infect him or her. Heroin and morphine are narcotics that usually are injected. People who use narcotics might engage in risky sexual behaviors, which also increase their risk of infection.

By increasing the risk of accidents, violence, and crime People who use narcotics may fall in and out of sleep. This is called "nodding out." Nodding out can cause an accident if a person is driving a car, riding a bicycle, or operating machinery. When people who smoke nod out, they can suffer burns or start a fire. A person who is addicted to narcotics might steal money or become violent in order to support their habit.

Reading Review

1. How do stimulants harm the mind?
2. How do narcotics harm the body?
3. What are the withdrawal symptoms of narcotic use?

TABLE 39.4	Types of Narcotics	
Drug/Also Known As	**How Ingested/Legality**	**Effect**
Opium: O	Smoked/illegal	Extremely addictive
Morphine: Morph, Miss Emma	Injected, snorted, smoked, or swallowed/illegal without prescription	One of the strongest pain relievers used in medicine, causes addiction and severe withdrawal symptoms, can cause respiratory arrest and death
Codeine	Swallowed/illegal without prescription, available in very small amounts in OTC drugs	Painkiller; cough suppressant, sleep aid
Heroin: Smack, junk, brother, garbage	Injected, snorted, smoked/illegal	Extremely addictive, can cause respiratory arrest and death, severe withdrawal symptoms. Heroin injection heightens the risk for infection with HIV and hepatitis B

Teacher FYI

Hidden Dangers Morphine, a derivative of opium, was originally used by doctors as a painkiller and a cure for opium addiction until its own addictive properties were discovered. Heroin was also originally believed to be non-addictive and was used as a cure for respiratory illness and morphine addiction. Heroin is more potent than morphine, making it the most dominant illegal narcotic.

Using the Table

Illicit Narcotics Have students examine Table 39.4 and determine which drugs have a legitimate, medicinal value. *Morphine and codeine are both prescribed medicinally; heroin and opium are illegal.* **L2**

Explain the Concept

Toxic Chemicals Explain and reinforce the idea to students that narcotics are especially powerful drugs. Incorrect use of narcotics can cause death.

Reading Review

1. *A person can become confused, anxious, aggressive, and paranoid, and can have hallucinations.*
2. *euphoria, drowsiness, nausea, vomiting, and rapid heartbeat*
3. *deep depression, mood swings, sensitive to pain*

DI Differentiated Instruction

Learning Disabilities Pair each student who has a learning disability with a non-challenged student. Have the pairs research and then make posters that summarize the effects of using a specific narcotic substance on the body or find out about treatments for narcotics addiction and the success rates of these treatments. Combine all of the posters into a storyboard to help the whole class review this topic. Have students discuss their posters and their reactions to other posters. **L2**

National Health Education Standards

Pages 446–447: 1.2, 1.8, 2.9, 5.7

Sedative-Hypnotics

Teacher FYI

Most Commonly Abused In 2002, the Substance Abuse and Mental Health Service Administration conducted a survey that showed that more than 6.2 million people over age 12 reported current use of a psychotherapeutic drug for a nonmedical purpose. According to the survey, the most commonly misused drugs were pain relievers, tranquilizers, and stimulants. Psychotherapeutic drugs are abused because of their effect on the brain and central nervous system.

INTERACTIVE CHALKBOARD
with Image Bank

5-Minute Check

Page 57, Unit 7 Fast File Resources

1. What is the definition of a narcotic? *a group of drugs that slow down, or depress, the central nervous system and relieve pain*

2. Name two types of narcotics. *morphine, heroin, opium, codeine*

3. How can repeated use of narcotics cause dependence? *the body can become tolerant, creating a physical dependence, and a user also can become psychologically dependent by focusing on his or her need for the drug*

4. What is a sedative-hypnotic? *a drug that depresses the activities of the central nervous system*

5. How can a sedative-hypnotic cause death? *Mixing alcohol with sedative-hypnotics multiplies the effect on the central nervous system, causing slowed respiration, coma, and death.*

A group of drugs that depress the activities of the central nervous system are **sedative-hypnotics**. A sedative is a drug that has a calming effect on a person's behavior. A hypnotic is a drug that produces drowsiness and sleep. Sedative-hypnotics include tranquilizers and sleeping pills. They are highly addictive and are illegal when used without a prescription.

How the Illegal Use of Sedative-Hypnotics Can Harm Health

By causing death Combining sedative-hypnotics with alcohol is extremely risky and can be fatal. Alcohol multiplies the depressive effects of sedative-hypnotics on the central nervous system, causing slowed respiration, coma, and death.

By harming the body This group of drugs slows body functions, causing slurred speech, lack of coordination, clammy skin, dilated pupils, and an inability to stay awake.

By harming the mind People who take sedative-hypnotics cannot use reasoning and judgment to make responsible decisions. They may be lazy, feel constantly tired, and might develop depression.

By causing dependence The use of barbiturates and benzodiazepines can lead to physical dependence. People who are physically dependent have withdrawal if they stop taking the drug. Withdrawal symptoms include anxiety, sweating, restlessness, agitation, and hallucinations.

By increasing the risk of becoming infected with HIV and hepatitis B People who use sedative-hypnotics may have sex with a person who is infected with HIV or hepatitis B and become infected themselves.

By increasing the risk of accidents, violence, and crime Sedative-hypnotics impair reasoning and judgment, cause confusion, reduce muscular coordination, and slow reaction time.

TABLE 39.5	Types of Sedative-Hypnotics		
	Drug/Also Known As	**How Ingested/Legality**	**Effects**
	Barbiturates: Barbs, bank bandits, reds, blockbusters	Swallowed/illegal without prescription	Highly addictive, sleep aid, ease tension
	Benzodiazepines: Tranquilizers	Swallowed or injected/illegal without prescription	Ease anxiety, relax muscles, anticonvulsant

---

⚖️ Legal Issues

Schedules of Controlled Substances Controlled substances are classified by the Attorney General of the United States into five categories: Schedules I, II, III, IV, and V. Students should look up the differences among the five schedules and create a table showing what drugs are classified in each schedule. In summary, the range is:
- Schedule I: drugs with the highest potential for abuse, with no currently accepted medical use in treatment, and a lack of safety for use under medical supervision.
- Schedule V: drugs with low potential for abuse, have a current accepted medical use, and abuse may lead to limited physical or psychological dependence. **L2**

Anabolic-Androgenic Steroids

A group of synthetic drugs that are related to hormones are **steroids**. One type of steroid is an **anabolic-androgenic steroid**, which is related to male sex hormones. Physicians prescribe anabolic-androgenic steroids to treat medical conditions. Some people illegally use steroids to build muscles and improve strength, athletic performance, and appearance. Steroid use is banned in sports.

How the Illegal Use of Steroids Can Harm Health

By harming the body Steroids can cause undesired effects. In males, steroids cause reduced sperm count, sterility, baldness, and painful urination. In females, steroids cause missed menstrual periods, hair growth on the face and body, and smaller breasts. Using steroids might also affect bone growth in teens.

By harming the mind People who use steroids may become aggressive and have violent **roid rages** which are outbursts of anger and hostility caused by steroid use.

By causing dependence People who regularly use steroids may develop physical or psychological dependence. Withdrawal symptoms include depression, headaches, and nausea.

By increasing the risk of becoming infected with HIV and hepatitis B People may leave infected blood on a needle after injecting themselves with steroids. Anyone using the needle also could become infected.

By increasing the risk of accidents, violence, and crime People who illegally buy and sell steroids break the law and may spend time in jail.

Did You Know?

Dangerous Steroid In October 2003, the FDA designated tetrahydrogestrinone (THG), which was being marketed as a dietary supplement, as a dangerous, illegal anabolic steroid. Some athletes used THG, which was then undetectable in drug tests, to try to sidestep rules against steroid use.

TABLE 39.6	Types of Anabolic-Androgenic Steroids	
Drug	**How Ingested/Legality**	**Effects**
Anabolic-androgenic steroids	Injected or swallowed/illegal without prescription	Voice deepens, increases facial and/or body hair, increases muscle size, may increase aggressiveness
Corticosteroids	Injected or swallowed/illegal without prescription	Anti-inflammatory used to treat asthma, eczema, and arthritis; increases weight; mood swings; headaches

LESSON 39 • Avoiding Illegal Drug Use **449**

Anabolic-Androgenic Steroids

Class Discussion

Obtaining Steroids Students should be aware that, although anabolic-androgenic steroids are not illegally manufactured drugs, obtaining steroids or providing steroids to someone without a valid medical prescription is illegal and punishable by law. Have the class discuss what they think the laws are concerning steroid use. Ask students what they think about athletes who obtain steroids. Ask students to research regulations that high school, college, or professional athletic organizations have regarding steroid use. **L2**

Extension

Effects of Steroids Have students examine the effects that steroids can have on: blood pressure *raises blood pressure*, cholesterol *can raise bad cholesterol*, and reproductive function *can cause infertility or impotence in men and women* **L2**

Explain the Concept

Role of Hormones Define the term hormone for the class: a chemical messenger released into the bloodstream. Explain that specific hormones are made in glands throughout the body and cause changes in tissue or organs in another part of the body. Emphasize to students that steroids are made from the hormone testosterone.

(DI) Differentiated Instruction

Gifted and Talented Performance-enhancing drugs, such as steroids, are controversial in the world of sports. Many sports figures admit to using steroids and human growth hormone to build up their bodies and increase their strength. Adding to the confusion is the variety of regulations and enforcement (or lack of enforcement) of drug policies in different sports. Have students research the drug policies in their favorite sports. Then the students should choose a sports figure who is known to have used steroids, and track his or her performance over time before, during, and after steroid use. Students should find that many sports figures who take steroids have dramatic performance slides after prolonged drug use, with their bodies quickly breaking down, shortening their careers. **L3**

National Health Education Standards
Pages 448–449: 1.2, 1.8, 2.9, 5.7

449

How to Resist Pressure to Use Illegal Drugs

Class Activity

Resisting Pressure Have students reinforce their understanding of the importance of resisting the use of illegal substances by creating a mock documentary. Have students play the roles of news anchor, law enforcement representative, parent, students, an addicted individual, physician, and treatment facility coordinator. The narrator of the mock documentary should interview each participant about his or her experiences and opinions regarding substance abuse. **L2**

3 Assess

Vocabulary Practice

Page 48, **Unit 7 Fast File Resources**

How to Resist Pressure to Use Illegal Drugs

NO!

Many teens may not recognize that using illegal drugs can have serious physical, mental, social, and legal consequences. Peers may try to influence you to try an illegal drug. You can resist pressure to use illegal drugs. Resistance skills are skills that help a person say "no" to an action or to leave a situation.

1. Use assertive behavior. Stand tall and look directly at the person with whom you are speaking. Say "no" in a firm and confident voice. Be confident because you are being responsible. Be proud because you are obeying laws and following the guidelines of your parents or guardian.

2. Give reasons for saying "no" to drug use. Explain that you could be arrested for using, selling, carrying, or buying illegal drugs. There is no way of knowing what a drug actually contains. You could overdose on illegal drugs. Illegal drugs lead to violence and accidents.

3. Use nonverbal behavior to match verbal behavior.
   - Do not try to fit in by using illegal drugs.
   - Do not buy or carry materials or objects associated with drug use.
   - Do not listen to music that promotes illegal drug use.
   - Do not keep illegal drugs in your possession for someone else.

4. Avoid being in situations in which there will be pressure to use illegal drugs.
   - Do not attend parties where illegal drugs are being used.
   - Always tell your parents or guardian where you will be.

5. Avoid being with people who use illegal drugs.
   - Choose friends who are drug free.
   - Stay away from people who buy and sell illegal drugs.

6. Resist pressure to engage in illegal drug use.
   - Learn the laws that apply to illegal drug use in your community and state.
   - Do not buy or sell drugs.
   - Do not attempt to grow or make illegal drugs.

7. Influence others to choose responsible behavior.
   - Encourage people who pressure you to use illegal drugs to change their behavior.
   - Encourage people who use illegal drugs to talk to their parents, guardian, or other responsible adults about their drug use.
   - Encourage people who use illegal drugs to seek treatment for drug dependency.
   - Be a role model for a drug-free lifestyle.
   - Volunteer to participate in a drug prevention program as a peer leader.

DRUGS in the Media **Writing Activity** Some movies, TV programs, videos and music CDs promote illegal drug use. They may portray people using drugs and living a glamorous life, but still staying safe and healthy. Choose one movie, TV program, video, or music CD, and write a newspaper article about the falsehoods of drugs. Present your findings to your class. If possible, play the relevant parts of the movie, TV program, video, or music CD to the class before you read your article to them.

450   UNIT 7 • Alcohol, Tobacco, and Other Drugs

Family Involvement

Drug Prevention After completing this lesson, encourage students to discuss what they've learned with their families. Students who involve their families and communicate with them about drug use are significantly more successful in avoiding drug abuse. Families are a great resource for students to ask questions, and parents will appreciate even brief communications initiated by the student. With their parents, have students create a book that the family can use as a future source of drug and alcohol information. **L2**

National Health Education Standards

Pages 450–451: 1.1, 1.2, 1.5, 2.5, 2.9, 4.2, 4.4, 6.3, 7.1, 7.2, 8.1, 8.2

Key Terms Review

Complete these fill-in-the-blank statements with the lesson Key Terms on the left. Do not write in this book.

club drugs
cocaine
codeine
Ecstasy
inhalants
ketamine
LSD
marijuana
narcotics
roid rage
stimulants
steroids

1. A painkiller produced from morphine is___.
2. The collective term used to describe drugs such as GHB and roofies is called _____.
3. _____ is a hallucinogen.
4. A group of drugs that slow down the central nervous system and relieve pain are known as _____.
5. A psychoactive drug that can act as a hallucinogen or stimulant is _____.

6. Chemicals that are inhaled and affect mood are _____.
7. THC is found in _____.
8. A stimulant derived from the cocoa bush is _____.
9. _____ are drugs made from hormones.
10. A group of drugs that speed up the central nervous system are known as _____.

Recalling the Facts

11. What is the most commonly used illegal drug?
12. What percentage of THC does marijuana usually contain?
13. Name three slang terms given to Ecstasy.
14. What are some psychological effects of Ecstasy?

15. Name three club drugs and explain the dangers of each.
16. What is a sudden hallucination a person has long after having used a drug?
17. Name three warning signs of Ecstasy use.
18. What is the outburst of anger and hostility caused by the use of steroids?

Critical Thinking

19. Why might a person who wants to lose weight take amphetamines?
20. Why might a person who has taken LSD do something like jump out a window or off a roof?
21. How can a person test positive for marijuana, even if they haven't used it in a few days?
22. Analyze the physical, emotional, legal, and social consequences of using illegal drugs.

Real-Life Applications

23. What do you think is the best way to resist peer pressure to use illegal drugs?
24. What can you do to spread the message that using illegal drugs is a bad idea?
25. How is drug use portrayed in music and movies?
26. What would you tell a younger sibling about avoiding drugs?

Activities

Responsible Decision Making

27. **Role-Play** Suppose you are tired in class one day. Your friend Susan tells you she has been using over-the-counter caffeine pills to stay awake at night. She says the pills have the same effect as drinking a soda pop. Role-play your response. Refer to the Responsible Decision-Making Model on page 61 for help.

Sharpen Your Life Skills

28. **Use Resistance Skills** Imagine you are writing an advice column and explain how you would respond to a letter from a teen who mistakenly believes that smoking marijuana will ease her depression. Include examples of resistance strategies and where the writer might go for help.

Visit www.glencoe.com for more *Health & Wellness* quizzes.

LESSON 39 • Study Guide **451**

Key Terms Review

1. codeine
2. club drugs
3. LSD
4. narcotics
5. ecstasy
6. inhalants
7. marijuana
8. cocaine
9. steroids
10. stimulants

Recalling the Facts

11. marijuana
12. today's 8–15 percent
13. Adam, XTC, hug, beans, roll, Y2K, 007
14. confusion, depression, insomnia, severe anxiety, paranoia or extreme fear
15. ecstasy, GHB, roofies, ketamine, LSD, nitrous oxide; See page 441 for the dangers of each.
16. flashback
17. pacifier use, suckers, candy dispensers, strobe lights
18. roid rage

Critical Thinking

19. to speed up metabolism
20. They might be having hallucinations.
21. THC, the chemical in marijuana, is stored in fat cells.
22. See pages 437–442, 444–449.

Real-Life Applications

23. Do not associate with people who use drugs; avoid situations in which there will be pressure to use drugs.
24. Create a non-drug group; hang posters; volunteer to participate in a drug prevention program as a peer leader.
25. The stars are attractive and you rarely see the stars having negative consequences.
26. See page 450. Explain to your younger sibling that drugs are harmful to the body.

Activities

Responsible Decision Making

27. Answers will vary, but should include the risks of abusing OTC drugs.

Sharpen Your Life Skills

28. Answers will vary, but should include the risks of marijuana use and suggest resistance skills from page 450. The teen should be advised to seek help from a responsible adult.

Avoiding Drug Dependence

 Out of Time?

If time does not permit an in-depth study of this topic, use the following activities in this Teacher Wraparound Edition:
- Health Goal, p. 452
- Class Activity, p. 453
- Family Involvement, p. 456
- Class Discussion, p. 460

1 Focus

HEALTH GOAL **Risk Factors** Have students respond to the Health Goal for this lesson by listing examples of risk factors and protective factors for drug misuse and abuse. *risk factors: friends or family members that use drugs, easy access to drugs due to environment, lack of self-respect; protective factors: friends and family members that do not use drugs, practicing resistance skills, being resilient* Have students compare their lists to the lists on pages 454–457 of this lesson. How many of the items match? **L2**

Write ABOUT IT!

Journaling Students' journal entries should discuss that it is important to have friends who do not misuse or abuse drugs. If they go to the pottery class, they will not face temptation to engage in risky behavior. Engaging in extracurricular activities, such as pottery, prevents boredom and reduces free time, making it less likely that teens will use harmful drugs. **L2**

LESSON 40

Avoiding Drug Dependence

HEALTH GOAL • I will avoid risk factors and practice protective factors for drug misuse and abuse.

Something that increases the likelihood of a negative outcome is a *risk factor*. Something that increases the likelihood of a positive outcome is a *protective factor*. In this lesson, you will learn the risk factors for drug abuse and skills to resist drug use and abuse.

What You'll Learn

1. Explain reasons why drug use is risky. *(p. 453)*
2. List risk factors and protective factors for drug use. *(pp. 454, 456)*
3. Discuss drug dependence, including physical and psychological dependence. *(p. 458)*
4. Outline the five stages of drug use that can progress to drug dependence. *(p. 459)*
5. Discuss roles played by family members who are codependent: chief enabler, family hero, scapegoat, mascot, and lost child. *(p. 460)*

Why It's Important

When you know the risk factors of drug abuse, you can take action to avoid them. In turn, you will decrease your risk of drug misuse and abuse.

Key Terms

- risk factor
- protective factor
- instant gratification
- mentor
- physical dependence
- tolerance
- withdrawal symptoms
- psychological dependence
- codependent
- enabler

Write ABOUT IT!

Writing About Avoiding Drug Dependence Suppose that one of your classmates asks you to smoke marijuana. A friend of yours overhears him and warns you not to. After you read the information about protective factors on page 456, write an entry in your health journal about what you will tell your friend.

National Health Education Standards—Guide for Lesson 40		
1.1	Predict how healthy behaviors can impact health status.	pp. 456–457, 461
1.7	Compare and contrast the benefits of and barriers to practicing a variety of healthy behaviors.	pp. 454–455, 456–467
2.1	Analyze how family influences the health of individuals.	pp. 452, 454–457, 459, 461
2.3	Analyze how peers influence healthy and unhealthy behaviors.	pp. 452, 454–457, 459, 460, 461

Why Drug Use Is Risky

The continued use of a drug even though it harms the body, mind, and relationships is *drug dependence*. Terms for drug dependence are ***chemical dependence*** and chemical addiction. Drug dependence affects judgment and common sense. Using drugs becomes more important than school, work, family, and relationships. People who are drug dependent often try to quit using drugs, but they usually are not successful.

What to Know About the Risks of Drug Use

Both legal and illegal drugs can be detrimental to health. There are many risks involved in using drugs such as alcohol, marijuana, narcotics, and amphetamines. Even experi- menting with a drug "just once" can cause serious consequences, even death. It is important that you understand the risks of using drugs.

TABLE 40.1 The Risks of Drug Use

Using Drugs Can:		Description
	lead to drug dependence and overdose	A drug overdose can cause serious injury or death. An overdose can happen the first time or the fiftieth time a person takes a drug. Using drugs may stimulate the pleasure center of the brain, which is why people repeatedly use drugs.
	cause accidents and lead to violence and illegal behavior	Drugs slow reaction time, impair coordination, and affect judgment. Most homicides, suicides, and episodes of abuse occur when people are using drugs. Many deaths caused by motor vehicle accidents involve a person under the influence of alcohol.
	increase the risk of HIV infection, sexually transmitted diseases (STDs), and unplanned pregnancy	Drugs affect people's ability to make responsible decisions. Teens who have been sexually active often were under the influence of drugs. This increases the likelihood of unplanned pregnancy and of having intimate sexual contact with a person infected with HIV or another STD.
	prevent people from developing social skills and harm relationships	People under the influence of drugs may say and do things that they later regret. Shy people may use drugs to relax, which prevents them from improving social skills.

LESSON 40 • Avoiding Drug Dependence **453**

Why Drug Use Is Risky

2 Teach

Class Activity

Myth or Fact Have students list state- ments that they think are true or not true about the risks of drug use, such as "You can't get addicted from doing a drug just once." Have students investi- gate the statements to determine whether they are myth or fact. **L2**

PowerPoint® Presentations

This CD-ROM is an editable Microsoft® PowerPoint® presentation that includes:
- Lesson presentations
- Lesson checks
- Interactive graphics
- 5-Minute Checks
- Image Bank
- All transparencies

 Discussion Refer to the Seed Discussions Strategy on page 17T. Ask students to write one important point from the lesson to use as a dis- cussion topic.

Lesson Resource Manager

- **Unit 7 Fast File Resources**
  Reading Strategy, p. 61
  Vocabulary Practice, p. 62
  Transparency Master and Worksheet, p. 63
  Real-Life Health, p. 65
  Real-Life Health, p. 67
  5-Minute Check, p. 69
  Lesson 40 Quiz, p. 70
- **Unit 7 Transparency**
- **Lesson 40 Transparency**

- **Reading Essentials**
- **Technology**
  TeacherWorks™ CD-ROM
  StudentWorks™ CD-ROM
  Reading Essentials CD-ROM
  Exam*View*® Assessment Suite
  Vocabulary Puzzlemaker

National Health Education Standards

Pages 452–453: 1.1, 1.2, 1.5, 1.8, 1.9, 2.1, 2.3, 5.7, 7.1, 8.1

Risk Factors

NHES Assessment/SCASS

Performance Event Have students review healthful ways to express emotions from Lesson 10, and recall strategies they learned to cope with anger, stress, or depression. Ask students to write a short essay explaining how these strategies can be adapted to help them to avoid drug dependence. *use anger-management skills; exercise; time-management; talk to a close friend, family member, or doctor about feelings of depression* **L2**

Class Discussion

Gratification Provide or ask students to list examples of real-life instances of instant gratification versus delayed gratification. *Examples may include getting paid at the end of every work day versus receiving a paycheck every two weeks; using a microwave versus a conventional oven; using email versus postal service for letters; or using a credit card versus waiting to pay cash for an expensive purchase.* Have students discuss advantages and disadvantages for each example they list. **L2 ELL**

Risk Factors

Research has identified risk factors that increase a teen's risk of drug misuse and abuse. Some of these risk factors may describe your behavior or the environment in which you live. If so, you are at risk for using harmful drugs and need to recognize this risk. You have varying degrees of control over the risk factors for drug misuse and abuse. For example, you do not have control over living in a neighborhood in which drugs are easy to buy. But you do have control over whom you choose as friends. Risk factors refer only to the statistical likelihood that you might use harmful drugs. Having certain risk factors for drug use does not mean you have an excuse to use harmful drugs. You have control.

Thirteen Risk Factors for Drug Use

> **Make the Connection**
>
> **Drug Risks** For more information on the risks of drug use, see page 45 in Lesson 5.

Lacking self-respect Teens who lack *self-respect* believe they are unworthy of love and respect. They are at risk because they believe drugs will numb the negative feelings they have about themselves. They may not have enough confidence to say "no" to negative peer pressure.

Being unable to express emotions in healthful ways Teens who have difficulty expressing emotions are more likely than other teens to use harmful drugs. Teens who cannot cope with stress, anger, and depression may think that drugs will help numb these feelings. They may use drugs instead of expressing feelings openly and honestly.

Having friends who use drugs One of the strongest risk factors for drug use is having friends who use drugs. They may pressure you to use drugs with them. They want you to support their unsafe and illegal habits. They may continue to pressure you when you say "no."

Being unable to delay gratification Voluntarily postponing an immediate reward in order to complete a task before enjoying a reward is *delayed gratification*. Drug use is a form of instant gratification. ***Instant gratification*** is choosing an immediate reward regardless of potential harmful effects. Immediate pleasure is more important to people who use drugs than maintaining good health and staying safe.

Having access to drugs The temptation to use drugs is greater when drugs are easily available. Having access to drugs includes living in a neighborhood where drugs are sold, going to a school where people sell drugs, and knowing people who sell drugs.

Being rejected by peers Teens who feel rejected by peers may use drugs to try to numb feelings of loneliness or to fit in. They are friends with any teen who can supply them with drugs or will use drugs with them.

454 UNIT 7 • Alcohol, Tobacco, and Other Drugs

 Sensitive Issues

Drug Abuse Some teens may be struggling personally with drug misuse or abuse, or they may have close friends or family members who have addictions. If this is the case, teens may be dealing with enormous physical and emotional stress. Some teens may find themselves in adult roles, such as housekeeper or caretaker. Be sure to remind students that drug addiction is a serious problem that can happen to anyone who uses drugs, no matter what his or her educational background or socioeconomic status. Have a list of resources available for any students who need assistance dealing with drug misuse or abuse by themselves, their family members, or their friends.

454

Having a biological family member(s) who is drug-dependent Certain individuals may inherit a genetic predisposition to addiction. A *genetic predisposition* is the inheritance of genes that increase the likelihood of developing a condition. Children born to parents who are addicted to drugs or alcohol are more likely to become addicted than children born to parents without addictions.

Having difficult family relationships Teens who live in families that do not have good communication and conflict resolution skills often have difficult family relationships. These teens have an increased risk of drug use. They may not have consistent and clear family guidelines. They may not have a responsible adult with whom they can share feelings. Difficult family relationships often create a stressful atmosphere. These teens may turn to drugs to cope with stress and numb their feelings.

Having role models who use drugs A role model may be someone a teen knows, such as a friend or family member. Or a role model may be a celebrity, such as a sports star or entertainer. Some teens have role models who use drugs and act like it is sexy, macho, or cool. Teens who admire role models who use drugs may use drugs to be like their role models.

Using drugs early in life The use of drugs during early childhood and adolescence is a risk factor for harmful drug use. Teens who begin drug use at an early age are more likely to become drug dependent when they are adults.

Doing poorly in school and/or having a learning disability Teens who get poor grades in school are more at risk for drug use than their peers who have better grades. Teens who have learning disabilities are at special risk. They may become frustrated and feel inadequate if they compare themselves to peers who do not have learning disabilities. They may use drugs to numb these feelings.

Being uninvolved in school activities and athletics Teens who do not participate in school activities and athletics are more likely to use harmful drugs. They are more likely to be bored and to have more free time.

Lacking respect for authority and laws Teens who lack respect for authority and laws are more at risk for drug use. They disregard the guidelines of parents or guardians and other responsible adults. They disregard community laws and may not care that using drugs is against the law.

Reading Review

1. Describe how having low self-respect is a risk factor for drug use.

2. How is instant gratification related to drug use?

Warning Signs

Recognize these warning signs of drug use in peers:

- slurred speech
- red eyes and frequent use of eyedrops
- glassy eyes and a blank stare
- sloppy appearance
- frequent use of breath fresheners
- long-term runny nose and sniffing
- giving up friends who do not use drugs
- joining a gang
- skipping school
- doing poorly in school
- missing money or objects of value
- changing eating habits
- having mood swings and hostility
- lacking energy and motivation
- friends who use drugs

Protective Factors

Class Activity

Journaling Have students evaluate the protective factors listed in the text as they relate to their own lives. Ask students to consider the following questions: Which of the protective factors may be the most difficult to incorporate into their lives, and why? What steps can they take to strengthen protective factors in their lives? Have students record their answers in their health journals. **L2**

Class Discussion

Resistance Skills Review with students resistance skills from Lesson 5 and ask the following questions: Have you recently practiced resistance skills? What situations required you to use resistance skills? What skill did you use during the situation? Were your resistance skills effective in the situation? **L2**

NHES Assessment/SCASS

Constructed Response Discuss the importance of personal responsibility when it comes to making decisions about drug use. Have students write one to two paragraphs explaining the statement, "You are responsible for your own health" and how it relates to the refusal or use of drugs. Ask students to discuss the excuses people may give rather than take responsibility for their actions in regard to drug use. **L2**

The more protective factors you practice, the less risk there is that you will abuse drugs. Examine the protective factors listed on this page and the next one. Do they describe your behavior and the environment in which you live? If so, you already have some protection against harmful drug use. However, lacking protective factors does not give you an excuse to use drugs. You have control over whether or not you use harmful drugs.

Thirteen Protective Factors That Reduce the Risk of Drug Use

Having self-respect Teens who have self-respect feel confident about themselves. They want to take care of their health and to stay safe. They know that using drugs harms health. Teens who have self-respect make responsible decisions. They are less likely to give in to negative peer pressure than other teens.

Practicing resistance skills Teens who practice *resistance skills* do not give in to pressure to use drugs. They are able to say "no." They stand up to peers who want them to use drugs. They know that peers who pressure them are not concerned about their health and safety.

Having friends who do not misuse and abuse drugs Teens who have friends who are drug free have less temptation than other teens to experiment with drugs. Drug-free friends do not pressure you to use drugs. They encourage you to participate in drug-free activities.

Being able to delay gratification When you are able to delay gratification, you use self-control. You recognize that using drugs interferes with long-term goals. You know that using drugs, in an attempt to "feel good now," will have negative consequences later.

Being resilient, even when living in an adverse environment An adverse environment is an environment that interferes with a person's growth, development, and success. A teen may be exposed to drugs in his or her neighborhood or at home. A teen may have a parent or guardian who is drug dependent.

However, a teen who is resilient knows that drugs only lead to more problems. You can be resilient if you live in an adverse environment and recognize that you can control your own behavior and decisions.

Having social skills Using social skills reduces the risk of harmful drug use. Teens who lack social skills often have difficulty relating to others and may feel rejected by peers. Having social skills helps teens make and keep friends. They develop close bonds with others and have a sense of belonging. Teens who engage in sports and other extra-curricular activities have a reduced chance of engaging in drug use.

 Family Involvement

Healthful Family Relationships The National Institute on Drug Abuse lists several aspects of family relationships as being protective factors against drug abuse. These include having a strong and positive bond within the family, parental monitoring, the establishment of clear rules of conduct that are consistently reinforced within the family, and the involvement of parents in their children's lives. Students can review the components of a healthful relationship by rereading Lesson 13. Have students consider ways they can improve or strengthen the relationships with their parents or guardian. **L2**

Having a set of goals and plans to reach these goals Teens who have goals are more likely to evaluate the consequences of their actions. They recognize that using drugs now may affect their entire future. For instance, students who wish to go to college know good grades are important. If they abuse drugs, they will have a hard time getting good grades, and they might not be accepted to the college they would like to attend. Also, if they do not have good grades, they are less likely to receive scholarships and grants, which would help them be financially able to go to college.

Having healthful family relationships Teens who are close to family members are less likely than other teens to use harmful drugs. Having a supportive relationship with your parents or guardian is especially important. It motivates you to behave in responsible ways. You want to follow family guidelines and remain drug free. You do not want to lose the respect and trust of your family. A teen who does not have a supportive adult family member can find a mentor. A **mentor** is a responsible person who guides another person. A mentor will encourage you to stay drug free.

Having a positive role model Teens often choose to copy the behavior of their role models. Having a *role model* who does not use drugs shows teens they can be successful and worthy of admiration without using drugs.

Having good stress-management skills Teens who are able to manage stress in healthful ways do not use drugs to cope with stress. They recognize that using drugs can cause more stress.

Having anger-management skills Teens who are able to manage anger in healthful ways do not use drugs to cope with anger. They recognize that drugs may make them violent and cause them to lose control.

Being involved in school activities and athletics Teens who are involved in school activities and play on athletic teams are less likely than other teens to use harmful drugs. Participating in such activities leaves teens with less free time. These teens are less likely to be bored. Schools usually have eligibility requirements for participation in school activities. For example, teens who use drugs often are ineligible to participate in school activities. Teens who enjoy these activities do not want to lose the privilege of participation.

Having respect for authority and laws Teens who have respect for authority and laws are less likely to use harmful drugs. They follow guidelines of parents or guardians and other responsible adults. They respect the laws of the community and know that drug use is against the law.

Did You Know?

Drug Treatment Drug addiction is a treatable disorder. Through treatment that is tailored to individual needs, patients can learn to control their condition and live productive lives.

Teens who are close to their family are less likely ▼ to use drugs.

LESSON 40 • Avoiding Drug Dependence **457**

5-Minute Check

Page 69, **Unit 7 Fast File Resources**

1. List three risks involved in using drugs. *drug dependence, overdose, accidents, violence, illegal behavior, HIV, STDs, unplanned pregnancy, prevent development of social skills, harm to relationships*

2. Why is being uninvolved in school activities and athletics a risk factor for drug use? *Uninvolved people are more likely to be bored and have a lot of free time.*

3. Explain the relationship between genetics and possible drug dependence. *Some people may inherit a genetic predisposition to addiction that increases the likelihood of developing drug dependence.*

4. Why is having strong social skills considered to be a protective factor against drug use? *Having social skills helps teens make and keep friends, so they develop close bonds with others and have a sense of belonging.*

5. What is a mentor? *a responsible person who guides another person*

Extension

School Drug Policies Have students find out how the school drug policy relates to extracurricular activities. Give students the following questions: Does the school do random drug testing of athletes? What are the consequences of testing positive for drugs while participating in school sports or other activities? Have students interview the school principal and report their findings to the class. **L2**

 Community Involvement

Exposure to Drugs Have students evaluate their community to determine whether their environment is a risk factor or a protective factor. They should consider the following questions: Are drugs easily accessible in their neighborhoods? Why or why not? What steps can be taken to change a risk factor into a protective factor in their community environment? Have students write newspaper articles about the accessibility of drugs in their environment, and how it can be reduced. Have students share their articles and discuss how the environment is a risk factor for drug use. **L3**

National Health Education Standards

Pages 456–457: 1.1, 1.5, 1.7, 2.1, 2.3, 2.7, 7.1

Teacher FYI

DSM The *Diagnostic and Statistical Manual of Mental Disorders (DSM)* is published by the American Psychiatric Association. The manual provides doctors with definitions and guidelines for diagnosing mental disorders or illnesses, including drug dependence. There is usually a checklist of symptoms for each disorder. If a patient exhibits the majority of the symptoms for a defined period of time then a preliminary diagnosis can be made.

Explain the Concept

Dependence The difference between physical dependence and psychological dependence may be difficult for students to understand. Spend time explaining these concepts to students. Physical dependence does not necessarily imply addiction. Some substances, such as blood pressure medication, do not cause addiction but do cause physical dependence. Other drugs, such as cocaine, cause addiction but may not cause the classic physical symptoms of withdrawal. Withdrawal from cocaine may manifest as depression rather than physical illness.

Drug Dependence

When a person is dependent on someone or something, that person has a need. Some people become dependent on drugs. They have a need for a drug. This need comes in different forms. Some people may become dependent because they believe they need a drug. Other people may need a drug because their body has a strong craving for it. This section describes the different kinds of drug needs or dependence.

What to Know About Drug Dependence

Physical dependence A condition in which a person develops tolerance to a drug, the drug becomes necessary for the person to function, or the person has withdrawal symptoms is called *physical dependence.* A condition in which the body becomes used to a substance is *tolerance.* People with a high tolerance to a drug need a greater amount of the drug to produce the same effect as people with a low tolerance.

For example, people may feel certain effects from drinking one can of beer. After repeated drinking, they may need to drink two cans of beer to achieve the same effect. Later on, they may need three cans of beer.

With some drugs, such as heroin, a tolerance to the drug develops quickly. A user continually needs to take more of the drug, increasing his or her chances of overdose and death.

Withdrawal symptoms Unpleasant reactions that occur when a person who is physically dependent on a drug no longer takes the drug are called *withdrawal symptoms.* Withdrawal symptoms include chills, fever, muscular twitching, nausea, cramps, and vomiting.

People who are physically dependent on a drug must continue taking the drug in order to avoid withdrawal symptoms.

With many groups of drugs, withdrawal symptoms can be severe, but not necessarily life-threatening. However, withdrawal from depressants can cause seizures, and can potentially be life-threatening.

Psychological dependence A very strong desire to continue using a drug for emotional reasons is called a *psychological dependence.* People

Symptoms of Drug Dependence

According to the Diagnostic and Statistical Manual of Mental Disorders, people are drug dependent if they have had three or more of the following symptoms in the past year:

- experiencing withdrawal symptoms when stopping the use of a drug
- taking large amounts of a drug or taking a drug for a long period of time
- trying to quit taking a drug with no success
- spending lots of time obtaining a drug, using a drug, or
- recovering from the effects of drug use
- giving up important activities, such as work or school, because of drug use
- continuing to use a drug even though it is causing problems, such as physical illness and injury
- developing tolerance to a drug

458 UNIT 7 • Alcohol, Tobacco, and Other Drugs

DI Differentiated Instruction

Physical Challenges Pair a student who has a physical disability with another student in the class. Have the students contact a drug rehabilitation clinic near them and ask a doctor or director about the types of addictions treated at their facility, the treatment given for withdrawal symptoms, and the average length of a client's stay. Have the students present their findings to the class. **L2**

TABLE 40.2 Progression to Drug Dependency	
Stages of Progression	**Examples**
STAGE 1: Experimentation "I'll just try it." A person is tempted to experiment with a drug. He or she tries the drug.	A teen is with friends. The friends are drinking beer. They are having fun. The teen does not want to feel left out. He or she decides to drink just this once to see what it is like.
STAGE 2: Desired effect "I like the feeling." A person enjoys the feeling he or she gets from trying the drug. He or she continues to use the drug.	The teen drinks the beer. He or she feels "cool" and relaxed. The friends comment on how great it is that he or she is drinking with them. The teen feels like he or she fits in. The next time the teen is with these friends, he or she drinks.
STAGE 3: Tolerance "I need more of the drug to feel good." A person develops a tolerance to the drug. The drug may no longer have the same pleasurable effects. The person may suffer from withdrawal symptoms when he or she stops using the drug.	The teen has been drinking with friends several times. He or she needs several beers to feel any effect and is able to drink large amounts at one time. He or she is proud of winning drinking games. The teen has a headache, throws up, and has body tremors the morning after drinking.
STAGE 4: Denial "I don't have a drug problem." A person is in denial. He or she does not admit that drug use is causing problems. The person claims that he or she can stop using the drug at any time.	The teen does not think the drinking is a big deal since his or her friends drink. The teen misses classes due to hangovers, gets into fights with friends and forgets what he or she said and did. The teen is sexually active when drunk. The teen gets into trouble with his or her parents or guardian because he or she breaks curfew or steals beer from his or her parents or guardian.
STAGE 5: Drug dependence "I have to have the drug." A person has become drug dependent.	The teen drinks at every social event. He or she drinks a lot of beer at one time. The teens brings his or her own alcohol to events and sneaks drinks. The teen decides to quit drinking, but cannot stick with the decision.

with psychological dependence may or may not be physically dependent. Psychological dependence is sometimes described as a strong craving for drugs.

For example, the pleasurable feelings that a drug produces may be desired again and again. Or, people may rely on a particular drug that they believe helps reduce stress or anxiety.

People who have a psychological dependence on drugs may have taken the drug only for a short time and they begin to crave the drug, but do not go through physical withdrawal if they stop taking it. Psychological dependence can become so severe that people become obsessed with the drug and may center their lives around buying and taking it.

Reading Review

1. Describe the relationship between physical dependence, tolerance, and withdrawal.

2. Describe how psychological dependence prohibits people from stopping drug use.

LESSON 40 • Avoiding Drug Dependence **459**

Class Discussion

Progression to Drug Dependency
Hold a class discussion about the stages of progression to drug dependency. Have students consider the following questions: How might the length of each stage vary depending on the drug used? How might the length of each stage depend on each individual's body chemistry or genes? How might the environment in which an individual is using drugs affect the progression of drug dependency? **L2**

Teacher FYI

Treating Drug Addiction Treatment for drug addiction includes behavioral therapies such as counseling, psychotherapy, support groups, and family therapy. It also may include medications, such as methadone, that help reduce withdrawal symptoms and cravings. Different types of treatment programs include outpatient services and therapeutic communities in which a patient remains in a residential treatment program for six to twelve months.

Reading Review

1. *A person who has a physical dependence needs a drug to function. Physically dependent people have likely developed a tolerance to the drug and experience withdrawal symptoms when they stop taking it.*

2. *Psychological dependence can become so severe that people become obsessed with drugs and may center their lives around buying them and taking them.*

❤ Health Project

Resources Have students research trends in drug use among teens today. Have them address questions such as: What drugs are more likely to be used by teenagers? What are the risks associated with their use? What should you do if you suspect a friend or family member is using drugs? What resources are available through your school or community to help someone who is struggling with drug addiction? Have students create a pamphlet with the information or produce a public service announcement on video. Share the pamphlets or PSAs with younger students. **L2**

National Health Education Standards
Pages 458–459: 2.1, 2.3

Drugs and Codependency

NHES Assessment/SCASS

Performance Task Break students into groups. Have them create skits that depict the different types of code-pendent behavior listed on the student page. Have each group act out their skits for the rest of the class. Ask the class to respond to the skits by writing in their health journals about what behaviors helped them to identify the roles being depicted. **L2** **ELL**

Class Discussion

Positive Reinforcement Have students discuss ways they can use positive reinforcement to help their friends and family make responsible decisions about drug use and exhibit self-respect. **L2**

3 Assess

Vocabulary Practice

Page 62, **Unit 7 Fast File Resources**

Name_____ Date_____ Class_____
LESSON 40 **Avoiding Drug Dependence**
Vocabulary Practice
Explain the relationship between the pairs of words given below. Include a definition
of each vocabulary term as part of your answer.

codependent   physical dependence   risk factor
enabler   protective factor   tolerance
instant gratification psychological dependence   withdrawal symptoms
mentor

1. risk factor—instant gratification

2. protective factor—mentor

3. tolerance—withdrawal symptoms

4. codependent—enabler

5. psychological dependence—physical dependence

62 LESSON 40 • Avoiding Drug Dependence   UNIT 7

National Health Education Standards

Pages 460–461: 1.1, 1.2, 1.5, 2.1, 2.3, 4.2, 4.5, 6.3

Codependency is a problem in which a person neglects himself or herself to care for, control, or try to "fix" someone else. A family member or close friend of people who are drug dependent may be a codependent. A ***codependent*** is a person who wants to rescue and control the person with addictive behavior and who is controlled by the drug user's addictive behavior. People who are codependent usually respond to drug-dependent people by playing one of the roles below.

How Family Members With Codependence Respond

Make the Connection

Codependency For more information on codependent relationships see page 143 in Lesson 13.

Chief enabler A person who supports the harmful behavior of others is called an ***enabler.*** There usually is a chief enabler. The chief enabler is the family member who tries to "smooth over" the problems caused by the drug-dependent person. The chief enabler usually is the spouse or parent of the drug-dependent person.

Scapegoat A person who is blamed as the cause of problems in the family is called the ***scapegoat.*** The blaming takes attention away from the drug-dependent family member. Scapegoats are labeled as not being able to do anything right. They often become rebellious and use drugs. They may have little self-respect and feel resentment and anger toward family members.

Family hero A family member who tries to do everything right is called the ***family hero.*** Family members know they can count on this person to be responsible for housekeeping and childcare. The family hero often is the oldest child. The family hero may believe that if he or she were a better child, the parent or guardian who is drug dependent would stop using drugs.

Mascot A family member who relieves tension by acting in a funny or entertaining way is called the ***mascot.*** This person makes the family laugh and feel good. The mascot usually is one of the younger children in the family. A mascot sometimes has a hard time growing out of this role and acting like an adult. The mascot often feels lonely, insecure, and inadequate.

Lost child A child who helps the family maintain balance by not causing problems is called the ***lost child.*** This child requires little attention in the family and often withdraws from others and is shy or quiet.

460 UNIT 7 • Alcohol, Tobacco, and Other Drugs

🕐 Teacher to Teacher

Refusal Skills Give students the following steps for resisting a peer who pressures them to engage in risky behavior, and ask them to demonstrate a statement or action that illustrates each step. Step one: Say "no" calmly; Step two: Explain why you are refusing; Step three: Suggest other things to do; Step four: Back up words with body language; Step five: Leave if necessary. In groups, have students create scenarios and practice each of the refusal skills. **L2**
Nancy Facello
Iaeger High School, Iaeger, WV

codependent
drug dependence
enabler
instant gratification
mentor
physical dependence
protective factor
psychological
  dependence
resistance skills
risk factor
tolerance
withdrawal
  symptoms

Key Terms Review

Complete these fill-in-the-blank statements with the lesson Key Terms on the left. Do not write in this book.

1. Something that increases the likelihood of a negative outcome is a(n) _____.

2. When the body becomes used to a certain drug, a person is said to have built up a(n) _____ to that drug.

3. A strong desire to continue using a drug for emotional reasons is called a(n) _____.

4. A person who supports the harmful behavior of others is a(n) _____.

5. A physical need for a drug is called _____.

6. Something that increases the chances of a positive outcome is a(n) _____.

7. A responsible person who helps another is a(n) _____.

8. A person who wants to rescue a person with addictive behavior is a(n) _____.

9. Wanting _____ means wanting something immediately.

10. Unpleasant reactions when a person stops using a drug are called _____.

Recalling the Facts

11. Why might a person who is driving a car and is on a drug take longer to hit the brakes in an emergency situation?

12. Why do some people find a need to increase the amount of a drug they are taking?

13. Name five of the thirteen protective factors that reduce the risk of drug use.

14. Describe the role of the mascot.

15. Describe some of the symptoms of withdrawal.

16. Discuss two risks of drug use.

17. Explain how needing instant gratification is a problem for drug abusers.

18. Describe the five roles of codependency.

Critical Thinking

19. Why might a person who does not feel good about him- or herself be at risk for using drugs?

20. Why is it important to have self-control?

21. Why would having a role model, such as a strict but fair teacher, be more advantageous than having a role model, such as a person who drops out of school?

22. How is drug dependence related to overdose?

Real-Life Applications

23. Why are positive role models important?

24. Why do you think that being involved in school activities and athletics reduces the chances of using drugs?

25. Why do you think having a healthful family relationship is protective against the use of drugs?

26. Why do you think it is not wise to use drugs to improve social skills?

Activities

Responsible Decision Making

27. **Evaluate** Your best friend has started using drugs. Lately, he has been hanging around with people who also use drugs, and invites you to their party. Write a response to this situation. Refer to the Decision-Making Model on page 61 for help.

Sharpen Your Life Skills

28. **Use Resistance Skills** Work with a partner and think of at least five pressure statements teens use to try to convince other teens to use drugs. Role-play responses for the statements.

Visit **www.glencoe.com** for more *Health & Wellness* quizzes.

Key Terms Review

1. risk factor
2. tolerance
3. psychological dependence
4. enabler
5. physical dependence
6. protective factor
7. mentor
8. codependent
9. instant gratification
10. withdrawal symptoms

Recalling the Facts

11. drugs slow reaction time
12. People with a high tolerance to a drug need a greater amount of the drug to produce an effect.
13. See pages 456–457.
14. relieves tension by acting in a funny or entertaining way
15. chills, fever, muscular twitching, nausea, cramps, and vomiting
16. See page 453.
17. Immediate pleasure is more important to drug users than their health or safety.
18. See page 460.

Critical Thinking

19. may want to numb negative feelings or have difficulty saying "no" to negative peer pressure
20. Self-control enables a person to make responsible decisions through delayed gratification.
21. The teacher would demonstrate responsible, positive behavior rather than poor decision-making skills.
22. Drug dependence means the person has a physical dependency on a drug. The person develops tolerance for the drug and therefore needs more of the drug to get the same effect. The person may take more of the drug to get a better high and may overdose on the drug.

Real-Life Applications

23. Having a role model who does not use drugs shows teens they can be successful and worthy of admiration without using drugs.

24. Teens are less likely to be bored.
25. Healthful family relationships motivate teens to behave responsibly so they don't lose the respect and trust of their families.
26. You will not develop the social skills needed for healthful relationships.

Activities

Responsible Decision Making

27. Answers will vary, but should mention that having friends who use drugs is a risk factor for drug misuse and abuse.

Sharpen Your Life Skills

28. Answers will vary.

Resisting Pressure to Abuse Drugs

Out of Time?

If time does not permit an in-depth study of this topic, use the following activities in this Teacher Wraparound Edition:

- Health Goals, p. 462
- Class Activity, p. 463
- Healthy People 2010, p. 464
- Health Project, p. 465

1 Focus

HEALTH GOALS **Resistance Skills** Have students respond to the second Health Goal for this lesson by reviewing the resistance skills in Lesson 5 and then journaling about how they might use these skills if they feel pressured to misuse or abuse drugs. **L2**

Write ABOUT IT!

Answers Students might respond by accepting the responsibility. They would agree to choose a drug-free lifestyle and encourage classmates to do the same. **L2**

Resisting Pressure to Abuse Drugs

 HEALTH GOALS
- I will not misuse or abuse drugs.
- I will use resistance skills if I am pressured to misuse or abuse drugs.

Influence that people of similar age or status place on others to behave in a certain way is *peer pressure*. Influence from peers to behave in a responsible way is *positive peer pressure*. Influence from peers to behave in a way that is not responsible is *negative pressure*. In this lesson you will learn how to recognize peer pressure to use drugs and resist this pressure.

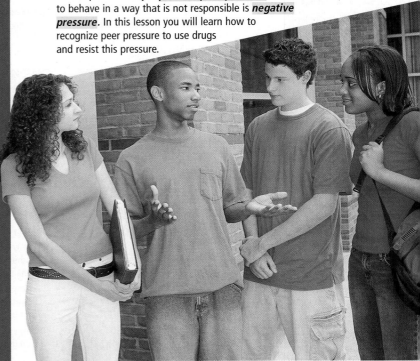

What You'll Learn

1. Explain why teens who use drugs pressure their peers to use drugs. *(p. 463)*
2. Give examples of direct and indirect pressure to use drugs. *(p. 463)*
3. Outline resistance skills that can be used to resist pressure to use drugs. *(p. 464)*
4. List reasons to say "no" when pressured by peers to use drugs. *(p. 465)*
5. List ways to be a drug-free role model. *(p. 466)*

Why It's Important

There are many skills you need to grow up healthy. This lesson will give you skills that you can use to avoid the misuse and abuse of drugs. These skills are resistance skills.

Key Terms

- positive peer pressure
- negative peer pressure
- drug-free role model
- drug-free lifestyle
- peer leader
- genuine
- positive reinforcement

 ABOUT IT!

Writing About Being a Drug-Free Role Model Suppose that you are very popular with your classmates. They respect you, and look up to you. One of your teachers tells you that you can be a drug-free role model and exert positive peer pressure on your classmates to be drug free. After reading the information about drug-free role models on page 466, write an entry in your health journal about how you would respond to this situation.

National Health Education Standards—Guide for Lesson 41		
1.5	Propose ways to reduce or prevent injuries and health problems.	pp. 462, 464–465, 466, 467
2.1	Analyze how family influences the health of individuals.	pp. 462, 463–466, 467
2.3	Analyze how peers influence healthy and unhealthy behaviors.	pp. 462, 463–466, 467

Recognizing Peer Pressure

A person who uses self-control to act on responsible values has *good character*. To maintain self-respect, you need to have good character. It also is important to choose friends who have good character.

How to Recognize Peer Pressure to Use Drugs

Why teens who use drugs pressure their peers to use drugs Have you ever wondered why there is so much peer pressure to use drugs? Think about it. Why should another person care if you use drugs? Does a teen who tells you that drugs will make you feel good really care about how you feel?

Support for wrong behavior Teens who use drugs often say they will not hang out with teens who do not use drugs. They pressure peers to use drugs. They do this because they want support for their wrong behavior.

Embarrassment of another teen Some teens who use drugs pressure a peer to use drugs because they want to embarrass the other teen. Some teens who use drugs get their peers to use drugs without knowing it. They might trick a person into taking a drug by saying it is a piece of candy, or by slipping a drug into his or her drink.

No concern that their behavior is disrespectful and illegal Some teens who use drugs pressure peers to use drugs because they know drugs impair judgment. For example, a teen male may want a teen female to have sex with him. The female may have said "no" when she was sober. The male knows that a female teenager is more likely to agree to have sex with him after drinking alcohol. He does not realize or care that having sex with someone who does not give consent is rape.

What Teens Who Use Drugs Might Say to Their Peers

- "You're not afraid, are you?"
- "Everybody is doing it."
- "Don't mess up the fun for everyone else."
- "Don't be a nerd."
- "Nobody will know but me and you."
- "It can't hurt just this one time."
- "If you won't do it, don't bother to come."
- "It really is safe."
- "Don't worry, we've been doing this for a long time."
- "It will be fun."
- "You will feel better than you ever have before."

LESSON 41 • Resisting Pressure to Abuse Drugs **463**

Recognizing Peer Pressure

2 Teach

Class Discussion

Peer Pressure Engage students in discussing the list of ways a peer might pressure them into using drugs. Encourage students to come up with other statements that peers might use to pressure a teen into using drugs. **L2**

Class Activity

Journaling Have students write in their health journals about situations in which they might be pressured by their peers to use drugs. Ask students to include the following: How might they feel about being pressured? How would they react? Is the action a good decision? **L2**

INTERACTIVE CHALKBOARD with Image Bank

PowerPoint® Presentations

This CD-ROM is an editable Microsoft® PowerPoint® presentation that includes:
- Lesson presentations
- Lesson checks
- Interactive graphics
- 5-Minute Checks
- Image Bank
- All transparencies

Journals Refer to the Pre- and Post-Reading Response Strategy on page 17T and instruct students to record what they know about peer pressure and drug abuse in their health journals both before and after they read the lesson.

Lesson Resource Manager

- **Unit 7 Fast File Resources**
  Reading Strategy, p. 73
  Vocabulary Practice, p. 74
  Transparency Master and Worksheet, p. 75
  Real-Life Health, p. 77
  Real-Life Health, p. 79
  5-Minute Check, p. 81
  Lesson 41 Quiz, p. 82
- **Unit 7 Transparency**
- **Lesson 41 Transparency**

- **Reading Essentials**
- **Technology**
  TeacherWorks™ CD-ROM
  StudentWorks™ CD-ROM
  Reading Essentials CD-ROM
  ExamView® Assessment Suite
  Vocabulary Puzzlemaker

NHES Assessment/SCASS

Constructed Response Have students discuss the list of reasons to say "no" to someone pressuring them to use drugs. After the discussion, ask students to write one or two paragraphs offering additional reasons for saying "no." **L2**

Class Activity

Peer Pressure Role-Playing Assign students to groups. Have each group choose a scenario of peer pressure from the student text on the previous page to role-play. Some students will fulfill the role of the peers pressuring a friend into using drugs. Each group also will have one student who plays the role of the person being pressured. This student should respond with appropriate "no" responses to the pressure situation. **L2**

Teacher FYI

Dangers of Drug Use Resisting peer pressure to drink alcohol or take drugs is important for all teens. The link between alcohol and drug use and suicide makes use of these substances even more dangerous. According to the National Survey on Drug Use and Health, teens that use alcohol or drugs are more likely to attempt suicide. The survey showed that teens using any illicit drug other than marijuana were almost three times more likely to be at risk for suicide.

Resistance Skills

Some teens have a difficult time resisting peer pressure. They lack self-confidence. They may plan to say "no," but they give in when they are pressured. Negative peer pressure takes many forms. Sometimes it is direct. Teens who use drugs make persuasive statements. Sometimes it is indirect. Teens may not be pressured directly, but they choose to go along with the crowd.

How to Resist Peer Pressure

You may face peer pressure to smoke cigarettes, chew tobacco, drink alcohol, sniff inhalants, smoke marijuana, use cocaine, or take other drugs. You must always resist the pressure to use drugs. ***Resistance skills*** are skills that help a person say "no" to an action or to leave a situation. Use resistance skills when you are pressured to use drugs.

Say "no" to drug use with self-confidence. Look directly at the person to whom you are speaking. Say "no" in a firm voice. Be confident because you are being responsible. Be proud because you are obeying laws and respecting family guidelines.

Give reasons for saying "no" to drug use. Explain that drug use is harmful, unsafe, and illegal.

Reasons for Saying "No" When Pressured by Peers to Use Drugs

If peers pressure you to use drugs, tell them why you won't:

- I don't want to betray the trust of my parents or guardian.
- I don't want to break the law and get arrested.
- I don't want to become violent and harm others.
- I don't want to say something I will regret later.
- I don't want to experience blackouts.
- I don't want to hallucinate.
- I don't want to spend time in jail.

- I don't want to become depressed and consider suicide.
- I don't want to become addicted.
- I don't want to risk overdosing.
- I don't want to be suspended from school.
- I don't want to increase my risk of developing cirrhosis of the liver, cancer, or cardiorespiratory diseases.
- I don't want to get kicked off my athletic team.

- I don't want to waste money.
- I want to think clearly.
- I want to stay in control and stick to my decision to choose abstinence.
- I want others to respect me.
- I want to be a role model for my younger siblings.
- I want to have social skills without relying on drugs.
- I want to be able to react quickly to prevent accidents.

464 UNIT 7 • Alcohol, Tobacco, and Other Drugs

👥 Healthy People 2010

Objective 26–16 *Increase the proportion of adolescents who disapprove of substance abuse.*

According to the Healthy People 2010 report, between 69 percent and 77 percent of 8th through 12th graders disapproved of having one or two alcoholic drinks almost every day. Trends show that increased disapproval of substance use among teens typically coincides with a drop in use of substances. The 2010 goal for disapproval of substance use is 83 percent. Have students construct a survey that measures disapproval for alcohol, tobacco, and other drug use. Obtain permission from the school to administer the survey. Students can create a bulletin board containing the results and reasons for teens to remain drug free. **L3**

Activity: Using Life Skills

Resistance Skills: Ways to Say "No" When Pressured to Use Drugs

Resisting peer pressure can be difficult. However, using resistance skills can be helpful. The steps for resisting peer pressure are 1) say "no" with self-confidence 2) give reasons for saying "no" 3) repeat your "no" response several times 4) use nonverbal behavior to match verbal behavior 5) avoid situations in which there will be pressure to make wrong decisions 6) avoid people who make wrong decisions 7) resist pressure to engage in illegal behavior and 8) influence others to make responsible decisions.

1 Below are ways someone may pressure you to take drugs. Write a response that you could use for each point.
1. "It will make you feel like you can do anything."
2. "It will make all your problems melt away."
3. "Come on, everyone else does it."
4. "One time won't hurt you. Just try it."

2 Avoid being in situations in which there will be pressure to use harmful drugs.
• Think ahead about what peers will be doing when they invite you to join them.
• Ask if there will be drug use before you put yourself in a situation. Do not go anywhere you know there will be drug use.
• Attend only drug-free activities.

3 Avoid being with people who use harmful drugs.
• Choose friends who do not use drugs.
• Stay away from people who use or sell drugs.

▲ It is important to firmly resist peer pressure to abuse drugs.

Use the broken-record technique. Repeat the same response several times to convince the person pressuring you that you will not change your mind.

Use nonverbal behavior to match verbal behavior. What you do and say should be consistant. Do not pretend to use a drug or sip a beer. Do not hold or pass a cigarette or marijuana joint. Do not touch a syringe or needle used to inject drugs. Do not agree to buy a drug for someone else or keep drugs for someone else. Do not do or say anything that indicates that you approve of harmful drug use.

Being high is never an excuse for wrong behavior. Some teens use alcohol and other drugs as an excuse for something they say or do. Suppose a teen has been drinking and does something embarrassing. The teen thinks he or she can laugh it off. He or she thinks that it will not affect his or her reputation because he or she was drinking. Or suppose a teen uses drugs. The teen then has sex. Later, the teen says, "I only had sex with the person because I was on drugs and couldn't help it." Suppose a teen does something illegal. Being high cannot be used as a defense for breaking the law. This is faulty thinking. You are responsible for what you say and do at all times.

Using Life Skills

Resistance Skills Have students discuss why it is important to avoid being in situations in which there will be pressure to use harmful drugs. Also ask students why avoiding people who use or sell drugs is important. Students can write their responses in their health journals. **L2**

INTERACTIVE CHALKBOARD with Image Bank

5-Minute Check

Page 81, **Unit 7 Fast File Resources**

1. What is peer pressure? *the influence that people of similar age or status place on others to behave in a particular way*

2. Explain the difference between positive and negative peer pressure. *Positive peer pressure is influence from peers to behave in a responsible way. Negative peer pressure is influence to behave in an irresponsible way.*

3. What are four steps to resisting peer pressure? *Say "no" with self-confidence and a firm voice, give reasons for saying "no," use the broken record technique of repeating the same response, and use nonverbal behavior to match your verbal behavior.*

4. Why is being high never an excuse for wrong behavior? *You are always responsible for your actions, regardless of whether you are high or not.*

5. How can you make your nonverbal behavior match your verbal behavior when you are resisting pressure to abuse drugs? *Do not do anything that indicates that you approve of harmful drug use.*

⚡ Health Project

Drug-Free Activities Have students discuss what drug-free social activities their school currently offers to help students avoid situations where peers may pressure them to use drugs. Encourage students to give examples of additional social activities the school could offer. Students should choose two or three activities from the list to present to the school administration for approval. Before presenting the ideas to the school administration, students should outline the benefits that will result from each activity, as well as a budget outline to describe costs of the program. **L2**

Drug-Free Role Models

Reading Review

1. *A drug-free role model can teach how to live a productive, drug-free lifestyle.*
2. *A peer leader is a student who teaches another student about how to resist drugs.*

3 Assess

Vocabulary Practice
Page 74, **Unit 7 Fast File Resources**

Drug-Free Role Models

A person who chooses a drug-free lifestyle knows and follows laws and policies regarding drugs, and educates others about the risks of using drugs is a *drug-free role model*. A drug-free role model is able to analyze the difference between achieving goals when drug-free and how using drugs prevents one from reaching goals.

Steps to Becoming a Drug-Free Role Model

Make the Connection

Healthful Behaviors For more information on promoting a healthy mind, see page 92 in Lesson 9.

Choose a drug-free lifestyle. A lifestyle in which a person does not misuse or abuse drugs is a *drug-free lifestyle*. When you choose a drug-free lifestyle, you have more control over your life. You take responsibility for your behavior and decisions.

Know and follow policies regarding drug use. Know and follow the laws and school policies regarding legal and illegal drugs and drug use. Encourage others to follow these policies. Some peer programs offer special training to become a peer leader or counselor. A *peer leader* is a student who teaches another student about drugs and how to resist pressure to use them.

Show you care about others. Part of being a role model is to be genuine. To be *genuine* is to be sincere. People who are genuine have a way of showing others that what they say and do is real. The way you interact with your friend will show if you care and are genuine.

Discuss responsible rules with others. Sometimes, people do not know what is expected of them. For example, you are on a team at school and your friend is thinking of trying a cigarette. But your friend is not aware of a team and school rule that says that if a person is caught smoking, that person can be suspended from the team. You can make your friend aware of the rules.

Be encouraging to others. A role model pushes others to take responsible actions by providing positive reinforcement. *Positive reinforcement* is rewarding others when they take actions that help them reach a goal. There are many different ways of giving positive reinforcement, including praise, writing a note, being present at a special occasion. People who receive positive reinforcement feel positive about themselves and are less likely to become involved with drug misuse and abuse.

Reading Review

1. Describe the importance of a drug-free role model.
2. Describe a peer leader.

466   UNIT 7 • Alcohol, Tobacco, and Other Drugs

National Health Education Standards

Pages 466–467: 1.1, 1.5, 2.1, 2.3, 3.2, 7.1, 8.1, 8.2, 8.3

Key Terms Review

Complete these fill-in-the-blank statements with the lesson Key Terms on the left. Do not write in this book.

drug-free lifestyle
drug-free role model
genuine
good character
negative peer
    pressure
peer leader
peer pressure
positive peer
    pressure
positive
    reinforcement
resistance skills

1. People who are_____, or sincere, show others that what they say is real.

2. A person who influences others to act in responsible ways uses _____.

3. To reward others when they do something responsible is to give _____.

4. Leading a life in which drugs are not abused or misused is to lead a _____.

5. A student who teaches another student about drugs and how to resist pressure to use them is a _____.

6. Influencing peers to act in irresponsible ways is using _____.

7. A person who chooses a drug-free lifestyle and educates others about a drug-free lifestyle is a _____.

Recalling the Facts

8. Name the eight resistance skills for peer pressure.

9. Name four reasons that one can state for saying "no" when pressured by peers to use drugs.

10. What is a peer leader?

11. Discuss ways in which you can show a friend you are genuine.

12. What are two reasons why teens may try to pressure others to use drugs?

13. Why should you choose a drug-free lifestyle?

14. Why is good character important in avoiding drug misuse and abuse?

15. Define the two types of peer pressure.

16. What is positive reinforcement?

17. How can you show you care about others?

Critical Thinking

18. Why might a person who has a lack of confidence have difficulty resisting the temptation to use drugs?

19. What could a person say if a peer says, "Try this drug. You'll feel good."?

20. Why is it important for you to stay away from people who break laws?

21. Why do you have a good deal of control over your life if you follow a drug-free lifestyle?

22. How can you say "no" with self-confidence?

Real-Life Applications

23. Why is someone who wants you to misuse or abuse drugs showing disrespect to you?

24. Why would it be dangerous for you to do something for someone else that is illegal?

25. Why are you less at risk for using drugs if you receive positive reinforcement?

26. As a drug-free role model, what alternatives could you suggest to a lifestyle of substance abuse?

Activities

Responsible Decision Making

27. **Decide** You and your teammate are at a party. Your teammate wants to drink alcohol. He says that it's no big deal. Write a response to what you would do in this situation. Refer to the Responsible Decision-Making Model on page 61 for help.

Sharpen Your Life Skills

28. **Advocate for Health** Identify a drug prevention peer program in your school or community. Obtain information about the responsibilities and contributions of a volunteer to the organization. Share this information with your class.

Visit www.glencoe.com for more *Health & Wellness* quizzes.

LESSON 41 • Study Guide **467**

Key Terms Review

1. genuine
2. positive peer pressure
3. positive reinforcement
4. drug-free lifestyle
5. peer leader
6. negative peer pressure
7. drug-free role model

Recalling the Facts

8. See page 465.
9. See page 464.
10. a student who teaches another student about drugs and how to resist pressure to use them
11. by looking at them when they are talking to you; nod in acknowledgement; listen to them
12. want support for their wrong behavior; want to embarrass another teen
13. you have more control over your life; you take responsibility for your behavior and decisions
14. Having good character means you make responsible decisions, and it helps you feel good about yourself. This discourages drug misuse and abuse.
15. positive: influence from peers to behave in a responsible way; negative: influence from peers to behave irresponsibly
16. rewarding others when they take actions that help them reach a goal
17. be genuine

Critical Thinking

18. A person who lacks self-confidence might want to be accepted by others. This might influence them to use drugs to gain acceptance.
19. Give a reason for saying "no" such as "It is illegal."
20. By being with others who break the law, you are at risk of also breaking the law.
21. People who follow a drug-free lifestyle make responsible decisions that allow them to have control over their lives.

Real-Life Applications

22. See page 464.
23. The person is not concerned with your health or well-being.
24. You could go to jail.
25. Positive reinforcement enables people to feel good about themselves, which decreases the need to become involved in drug use.
26. watch movies, listen to music

Activities

Responsible Decision Making

27. You can leave the party. You can encourage your friend not to take a drink. You can encourage your friend to leave the party with you.

Sharpen Your Life Skills

28. Answers will vary.

467

Reducing Risk by Being Drug Free

If time does not permit an in-depth study of this topic, use the following activities in this Teacher Wraparound Edition:
• Health Goals, p. 468
• Achieving Health Literacy, p. 470
• Health Project, p. 471

1 Focus

HEALTH GOALS **Journaling** Have students respond to the Health Goals for this lesson by writing in their health journals how they feel drug use is affecting the levels of violence, HIV infection, and unplanned pregnancy in their school and community. **L2**

 ABOUT IT!

Journaling Journal entries should include actions, such as telling a teacher, principal, or another responsible adult about the classmate's actions and not socializing with the classmate. **L2**

Reducing Risk by Being Drug Free

What You'll Learn

1. Discuss ways drugs alter mood and behavior and increase the risk of violent behavior. *(p. 469)*
2. List ways to protect yourself from violence associated with drug use. *(p. 469)*
3. Explain how a safe and drug-free school zone decreases the risk of drug trafficking. *(p. 469)*
4. Explain reasons why teens who use drugs increase their risk of HIV infection and unplanned pregnancy and accidents. *(pp. 471, 472)*

Why It's Important

You can make responsible decisions when you can think clearly. People who use drugs place themselves at risk for harmful behaviors that result from not thinking clearly.

Key Terms

• drug trafficking
• safe and drug-free school zone
• human immunodeficiency virus (HIV)
• acquired immunodeficiency syndrome (AIDS)
• prostitution
• injection drug use

HEALTH GOALS

• I will choose a drug-free lifestyle to reduce the risk of violence and accidents.
• I will choose a drug-free lifestyle to reduce the risk of HIV infection and unplanned pregnancy.

A lifestyle in which a person does not misuse or abuse drugs is a *drug-free lifestyle*. When you choose a drug-free lifestyle, you help protect yourself from the harmful effects of drugs, injuries, violence and accidents.

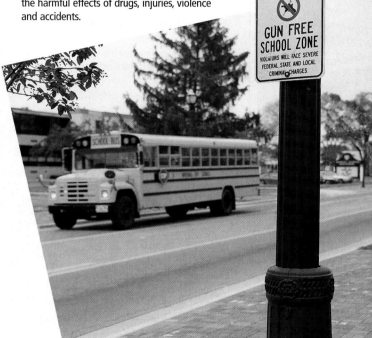

DRUG FREE
GUN FREE SCHOOL ZONE
VIOLATORS WILL FACE SEVERE FEDERAL, STATE AND LOCAL CRIMINAL CHARGES

 ABOUT IT!

Writing About a Safe and Drug-Free School Zone Suppose that you know that one of your classmates is selling drugs at school. After reading the information about the importance of a safe and drug-free school zone on page 469, write an entry in your health journal about how you could help keep your school free from drug trafficking by telling a teacher or your principal about your classmate's illegal actions.

National Health Education Standards—Guide for Lesson 42		
2.9	Analyze how some health risk behaviors can influence the likelihood of engaging in unhealthy behaviors.	pp. 469, 470, 472, 473
6.3	Implement strategies and monitor progress in achieving a personal health goal.	pp. 470, 473

Drug Use, Violence, and Accidents

D rugs alter the way people think and feel. The way people think and feel affects the way they behave. The following drugs may increase the risk that people will behave in violent ways or be involved in an accident.

Why Drug Use Increases the Risk of Violence and Accidents

Alcohol Alcohol depresses the nervous system and changes mood and behavior. Alcohol intensifies feelings, sometimes causing people to harm themselves or others.

Stimulants Stimulants may cause people to become impulsive and experience feelings of paranoia. They may become irrational when they believe other people are going to harm them.

Marijuana and hallucinogens People who use marijuana or hallucinogens may experience hallucinations and feel threatened. They may resort to violent actions.

PCP People who use PCP can become angry, aggressive, and irritable. They may have hallucinations and experience severe depression. They are difficult to control.

Anabolic-androgenic steroids People who use anabolic-androgenic steroids may have mood swings and outbursts of anger called "roid rages."

Sedative-hypnotics People who take high doses of sedative-hypnotics can become angry and aggressive.

How Drug Trafficking Increases the Risk of Violence

The illegal production, distribution, transportation, selling, or purchasing of drugs is called ***drug trafficking.*** All people involved in drug trafficking are criminals. Drug trafficking is dangerous because people associated with drug trafficking usually own and use weapons to protect their territory, or "turf." Many drive-by shootings are related to drug trafficking.

> **Make the Connection**
>
> **Self-Defense** For more information on protecting yourself from violence, see page 671 in Lesson 65.

Protect Yourself from Violence Associated with Drug Trafficking

These actions will help protect you from violence associated with drug trafficking:

- Do not associate with anyone who produces, distributes, transports, sells, or purchases drugs.
- Do not associate with gang members or people who associate with gangs.
- Stay away from people who own weapons.
- Stay away from areas in which there is drug trafficking.

- Stay away from gang turf.
- Help your school enforce a ***safe and drug-free school zone,*** which is a defined area around a school for the purpose of sheltering young people from the sale of drugs and use of weapons. There are increased penalties for using and selling drugs and having weapons in this zone.

LESSON 42 • Reducing Risk by Being Drug Free **469**

Drug Use, Violence, and Accidents

2 Teach

Extension

Drug-Free School Zone Have students research whether or not their school has a drug-free school zone. If it does, students should write a report on the specifics of their school's policies. If the school does not have a drug-free school zone, students should research other schools' policies and come up with a presentation for their school's administration to adopt a drug-free school zone. **L2**

INTERACTIVE CHALKBOARD with Image Bank

PowerPoint® Presentations

This CD-ROM is an editable Microsoft® PowerPoint® presentation that includes:
- Lesson presentations
- Lesson checks
- Interactive graphics
- 5-Minute Checks
- Image Bank
- All transparencies

Discussion Use the Sticky-Note Discussions Strategy on page 17T to stimulate discussion about the advantages of a drug-free lifestyle.

Lesson Resource Manager

- **Unit 7 Fast File Resources**
  Reading Strategy, p. 85
  Vocabulary Practice, p. 86
  Transparency Master and Worksheet, p. 87
  Real-Life Health, p. 89
  Real-Life Health, p. 91
  5-Minute Check, p. 93
  Lesson 42 Quiz, p. 94
- **Unit 7 Transparency**
- **Lesson 42 Transparency**

- **Reading Essentials**
- **Technology**
  TeacherWorks™ CD-ROM
  StudentWorks™ CD-ROM
  Reading Essentials CD-ROM
  ExamView® Assessment Suite
  Vocabulary Puzzlemaker

> **National Health Education Standards**
> Pages 468–469: 1.1, 1.5, 2.9, 4.3, 7.2

Using Life Skills

Using Goal-Setting and Decision-Making Skills Have the class discuss possible decisions that could be made about the scenario provided in the student activity. Students also should provide consequences for each possible decision. Write both the possible decisions and the consequences on the chalkboard. **L2**

Teacher FYI

Prescription Drug Abuse According to the Substance Abuse and Mental Health Services Administration, the lifetime use of prescription drugs for non-medical purposes increased from 9.6 percent in 2001 to 11.2 percent in 2002 among teens ages 12 to 17. The most commonly abused prescription drugs are pain killers, CNS depressants (used to treat anxiety and sleep disorders), and stimulants (used to treat ADHD and narcolepsy).

INTERACTIVE CHALKBOARD with Image Bank

5-Minute Check

Page 93, **Unit 7 Fast File Resources**

1. How are cigarettes related to automobile accidents and house fires? *A driver who is smoking may drop the cigarette and become distracted. Smokers may fall asleep and ash from their cigarettes may start a fire in a house.*

2. What is a safe and drug-free school zone? *an area around a school that shelters young people from the sale of drugs and the use of weapons*

3. What is a drug-free lifestyle? *a lifestyle in which a person does not misuse or abuse drugs*

4. Explain drug trafficking. *the illegal production, distribution, transportation, sale or purchase of drugs*

5. How might prescription drugs cause accidents? *by causing drowsiness or dizziness*

Activity: Using Life Skills

Using Goal-Setting and Decision-Making Skills: Making a Responsible Decision

Suppose you had a bad day at school and an argument with your parents, but it's Friday and your best friend has invited you to a party. The music at the party is great, and all your friends are there. Your best friend pulls you aside and asks if you want to try Ecstasy. She says, "I just took a hit, and I am flying. Come on, do this with me. You'll forget about all your problems." You were supposed to be staying at your friend's house tonight, and you don't have a ride home. What should you do?

1 Describe the situation that requires a decision, list possible decisions you might make, and share the list of possible decisions with a parent, guardian, or other trusted adult. Think about what that responsible adult would do in your situation. List the results of each possible decision.

2 Use six questions to evaluate the consequences of the decision. Is it a healthful thing to do? Is it safe? Is it legal? Does it show respect for me and others? Does it follow the guidelines of my parent or guardian? Does it demonstrate good character?

3 Decide which decision is most responsible and appropriate. Imagine what the results would be. Write a one-page paper on at least two results you can imagine.

4 Act on your decision and evaluate the results. Write another one-page paper evaluating the two results that you imagined.

▲ It is important to remember that a "friend" who tries to pressure you into abusing drugs is not really your friend at all.

Make the Connection

Responsible Decisions For more information about responsible decisions, see page 61 in Lesson 6.

Drug Use and Accidents

Both legal and illegal drugs increase the risk of having an accident.

Prescription drugs Some prescription drugs can act as stimulants while others can act as depressants. Prescription drugs are responsible for many kinds of accidents by causing drowsiness or dizziness.

Illegal drugs Many accidents are a result of illegal drug use. For example, a person who uses hallucinogens may not be aware of surrounding circumstances. A person who uses barbiturates may be too slow to react to different situations.

Alcohol You have read a great deal about alcohol and automobile accidents, but alcohol also is involved in many other kinds of accidents. People who drink and use tools can harm themselves and others. People who drink alcohol and swim increase the risk of drowning.

Tobacco Many fires are started by people who smoke cigarettes. Smokers may dispose of a cigarette in a trash can or fall asleep while smoking. Many automobile accidents are caused by drivers who drop lighted cigarettes. The driver, while looking for the cigarette, becomes distracted and causes an accident.

470 **UNIT 7** • Alcohol, Tobacco, and Other Drugs

🖋 Achieving Health Literacy

Responsible Citizen Responsible citizens realize their obligation to their family and community. They avoid making decisions that are health or safety threats to themselves and others. Have students describe a time in which they chose the most responsible decision for a scenario like the one given in the text. Have students list on the chalkboard ways the decision affected their family and their community. Have students discuss the situations. Students can create a hypothetical situation if they do not have a real situation to share. **L2**

Drug Use and HIV

A pathogen that destroys infection-fighting T cells in the body is the *human immunodeficiency virus (HIV)*. People who are infected with HIV develop AIDS. *Acquired immunodeficiency syndrome (AIDS)* is a condition that results in a breakdown of the body's ability to fight infection.

How a Drug-Free Lifestyle Reduces the Risk of HIV Infection

Abstinence from sex Teens who use drugs may not stick to their decision to practice abstinence from sex. *Abstinence from sex* is voluntarily choosing not to be sexually active. HIV is transmitted from one person to another during intimate sexual contact. Teens who drink alcohol or use marijuana or other drugs that change reasoning and judgment do not think clearly. During drug use, they are not clear as to the consequences of their behavior. Most teens who have been sexually active were under the influence of alcohol during their first sexual experience. One occurrence of sexual contact can cause HIV infection and change your life.

Avoidance of rape Teens who use drugs increase their risk for being in situations in which rape occurs. *Rape* is the threatened or actual use of physical force to get someone to have sex without giving consent. When teens use drugs, they are less likely to think about the consequences of their behaviors. Females under the influence of drugs may take risks they usually would not take. For example, they might leave a party with a male they do not know well. Males under the influence of drugs may struggle to control their sexual feelings. They may disregard a female's disapproval of sexual advances. Rape is illegal and increases the risk of HIV infection.

No need to support drug habit Teens who are drug dependent may have sex as a way of getting drugs. Suppose teens who are drug dependent are not able to support their drug habit. They may engage in prostitution to get money to buy drugs. *Prostitution* is sexual activity for pay. Prostitution and the exchange of sex for drugs is illegal and increases the risk of HIV infection.

Avoidance of infected needles Teens who are involved in injection of illegal drugs may share a needle with infected blood on it. *Injection drug use* is drug use that involves injecting drugs into the body. When people inject drugs, the needle or syringe they use will have droplets of their blood on it. Suppose a teen uses a needle or syringe that has been used by a person infected with HIV. The droplets of blood infected with HIV will enter the teen's body and he or she may be infected with HIV. Injection of illegal drugs increases the risk of HIV infection.

Reading Review

1. How is prostitution related to drug dependence and risks for HIV?
2. Why are injection drugs so dangerous?

 Health Project

Local AIDS Resources Split the class into groups. Have each group research different aspects of AIDS in their community. One group should research local trends in HIV infection; another group can investigate local resources for individuals infected with HIV; a third group can investigate nonprofit organizations in their area that help individuals with AIDS. Each group should compile their information and present it to the class. The class, as a whole, should work to create a presentation on the status of HIV and AIDS in their community. This presentation can be used to teach other students how to avoid HIV infection. The presentation also can be used to encourage students and adults to volunteer for one of the organizations that help HIV-infected individuals. **L2**

Drug Use and HIV

Explain the Concept

HIV and AIDS AIDS first was recognized in the United States in 1981. AIDS is caused by HIV, which progressively destroys the body's ability to fight infection by destroying or impairing the cells of the immune system (specifically T cells).

Teacher FYI

HIV and AIDS According to a report from the Centers for Disease Control and Prevention, there were an estimated 5653 young persons between the ages of 15 and 24 living with AIDS in the United States at the end of 2002. Of all new cases of HIV infection, almost half of the people are under the age of 25. HIV is the sixth leading cause of death for the 13- to 19-year-old age group.

NHES Assessment/SCASS

Performance Task Have students work in groups to research HIV infection statistics and trends locally, nationally, and internationally. Students also should research what is being done at the local, national, and international levels to combat HIV infection and AIDS. Students should write a report or multimedia presentation to share with the class. **L2**

Reading Review

1. *Teens who are drug dependent may turn to prostitution to support their drug habit, which puts them at high risk for HIV infection.*
2. *Needles used to inject drugs might contain infected blood. HIV can be spread through contact with this blood.*

Communicable and Chronic Diseases

STANDARDS AND FEATURES

Lesson	National Standards	State/Local Standards	Activities and Features
Lesson 44 *(1 session, 1 block)* Avoiding Communicable Diseases	6.4, 7.2		**Facts About:** Viruses, p. 486 **Using Life Skills:** Practicing Healthful Behaviors: Avoiding Spreading Pathogens, p. 488
Lesson 45 *(1 session, 1 block)* Dealing with Respiratory Diseases, Asthma, and Allergies	2.3, 2.4, 3.4, 7.2		**Using Life Skills:** Accessing Valid Health Information, Products, and Services: Managing Asthma, p. 495
Lesson 46 *(4 sessions, 2 blocks)* Reducing the Risk of STDs and HIV	1.1, 1.5, 1.7, 1.9, 3.4, 5.7		**Just the Facts:** STDs and HIV, p. 509 **Health News:** Global Health Initiative, p. 511
Lesson 47 *(3 sessions, 1 block)* Reducing the Risk of Cardiovascular Diseases	1.5, 6.1		**Using Life Skills:** Using Goal-Setting and Decision-Making Skills: Being Heart Healthy, p. 517
Lesson 48 *(2 sessions, 1 block)* Managing Chronic Health Conditions	1.1		**Using Life Skills:** Being a Health Advocate: Reducing the Risk of Diabetes, p. 524 **Speaking Out:** Living with Diabetes, p. 525
Lesson 49 *(3 sessions, 1 block)* Reducing the Risk of Cancer	1.1, 1.5, 3.4, 6.1		

Key to Differentiated Instruction

L1 Level 1 activities should be appropriate for students with learning difficulties.

L2 Level 2 activities should be within the ability range of all students.

L3 Level 3 activities are designed for above-average students.

ELL ELL activities should be within the ability range of English language learners.

FAST FILE RESOURCES

INTRODUCING THE UNIT

Parent and Family Letter	p. 1	Health Behavior Contract	p. 3
Spanish Parent and Family Letter	p. 2	Unit Focus Transparency Master and Worksheet	p. 4

TEACHING THE UNIT LESSONS

Reproducible Student Pages	Lesson 44	Lesson 45	Lesson 46	Lesson 47	Lesson 48	Lesson 49
Reading Strategy	p. 7	p. 19	p. 31	p. 47	p. 59	p. 73
Vocabulary Practice	p. 8	p. 20	p. 32	p. 48	p. 60	p. 74
Transparency Master and Worksheet	p. 9	p. 21	p. 33	p. 49	p. 61	p. 75
Real-Life Health	p. 11	p. 23	p. 35	p. 51	p. 63	p. 77
5-Minute Check	p. 15	p. 27	p. 39	p. 55	p. 67	p. 81
Lesson Quiz	p. 16	p. 28	p. 43	p. 56	p. 69	p. 82

CLOSING THE UNIT

Family Involvement Activity	p. 85	Health in the News	p. 95
Community Involvement Activity	p. 87	Health Career Research Activity	p. 97
Health Lab	p. 89	Unit Test A	p. 99
Activity: Strengthening Health Skills	p. 93	Unit Test B	p. 103

Technology

Glencoe Exclusive!

TeacherWorks™
All-In-One Planner and Resource Center

- **Interactive Chalkboard CD-ROM**
- **TeacherWorks™ CD-ROM**
- **StudentWorks™ CD-ROM**
- **Reading Essentials CD-ROM**
- **Exam***View*® **Assessment Suite**

www.glencoe.com
- **Vocabulary Puzzlemaker**
- **Interactive Tutor**
- **Your Health Checklist**
- **Web Links**
- **Student Web Activities**

UNIT 8

Communicable and Chronic Diseases

TEST YOUR DISEASE IQ

Use the three statements on the student page to initiate a class discussion about family and social health issues. *Additional True/False statements are:*

4. **You can contract an STD only by having sexual contact with another person.**
   FALSE: A person who comes in contact with infected blood, through unclean needles or external contact, is at risk for contracting an STD.

5. **Secondhand smoke is not very dangerous.**
   FALSE: The Environmental Protection Agency (EPA) estimates that secondhand smoke causes approximately 3000 lung cancer deaths and 35,000 heart disease deaths in nonsmokers each year.

6. **If there is a history of cardiovascular disease in your family, you are at greater risk even if you maintain a healthy diet and exercise regularly.**
   TRUE: The risk of heart disease may be as much as five times greater for children of parents who died from cardiovascular disease, particularly if a parent developed the problem before age 55.

 Smoking and Health

Trends in Teen Smoking Have students create graphs that show trends in teen smoking from the 1990s until now. Hang these graphs in the classroom and refer to them when discussing the relationship between smoking and disease. Point out that people who start smoking when they are teenagers have an especially hard time quitting. **L2**

TEST YOUR DISEASE IQ
True or False?

1. **Allergies are contagious.**
   FALSE: Unlike the common cold, you cannot catch allergies from another person. However, the symptoms are quite similar to those of the common cold.

2. **Cardiovascular disease kills more people than cancer each year.**
   TRUE: Cardiovascular diseases (CVD), such as heart disease and stroke, are the number one and number three leading causes of death in the United States.

3. **Diabetes is an "old person's" disease.**
   FALSE: Type II diabetes, which used to be considered an adult disease, now affects many teenagers. A sedentary lifestyle, along with a high-fat diet, are considered the main reasons why teenagers are more at risk for developing diabetes.

"We need real people from the community to get out there and say, 'You know, I was able to conquer this. I was able to do something about it, and so can you.'"

—Dr. Amelie G. Ramirez, a behavioral research expert and a member of the Susan G. Komen Breast Cancer Foundation's National Hispanic/Latino Advisory Council, speaking about breast cancer

in the news Smoking and Health

Research In 1964, the Surgeon General released the first report on the health consequences of smoking. Since then, other reports have included information about specific groups of people and smoking. Research Surgeon General reports on child and teen smoking, and present the results of your research to the class.

LESSON 44	LESSON 45	LESSON 46
Avoiding Communicable Diseases	Dealing with Respiratory Diseases, Asthma, and Allergies	Reducing the Risk of STDs and HIV

 Two-Minute Unit Launcher

Activity Provide each student with a 2-inch straw. Have the students attempt to breathe only through the straw while they rest for a minute to get used to it. Then have the students do some type of simple physical activity for at least 1 minute to increase their breathing rate. Have the students try to breathe through the straw again. Discuss the experience as a class. The purpose of this activity is to simulate the feeling of having emphysema, lung cancer, or asthma. Ask students to describe how they felt as they tried to get more air through the straw. Explain that Lesson 45 will discuss respiratory diseases. Students with medical conditions should not participate in this activity. If necessary, this activity could be completed in groups. **L2 ELL**

EVALUATING MEDIA MESSAGES

Gives you a perfect tan

Pull up a lounge chair and enjoy the sunny day. *bronze bliss* tanning lotion ensures that even, bronze glow you want, so you can focus on everything else—or nothing at all. Do what you want to make your day perfect.

Perfect tan with *bronze bliss*

 WHAT'S YOUR VERDICT?
To evaluate this advertisement, use the criteria for analyzing and evaluating health messages delivered through media and technology that you learned in Unit 1.

Visit **www.glencoe.com** to find regularly updated statistics on the flu. Using the information provided, research the answer to this question: How many Americans contracted the flu last year?

Visit **www.glencoe.com** to use *Your Health Checklist* ✔, an interactive tool that helps you determine your health status.

LESSON 47	**LESSON 48**	**LESSON 49**
Reducing the Risk of Cardiovascular Diseases	Managing Chronic Health Conditions	Reducing the Risk of Cancer

UNIT 8 • Communicable and Chronic Diseases **483**

Health Online

Answers According to the Centers for Disease Control and Prevention, between 10 and 20 percent of people in the United States will get the flu each year. The elderly are particularly susceptible. It is recommended that elderly people and others with increased risk, such as people with weakened immune systems, get a flu shot. You also might ask students to locate information on the strains of the flu that are responsible for causing flu outbreaks. Influenza A and B cause the majority of cases of influenza in the United States.

 What's Your Verdict?

Read the Label Have the students read the Bronze Bliss advertisement and discuss their first impressions. Ask students what claims are made about the product. Ask students to answer the following questions: Does the ad discuss skin cancer and the damage sun can do to the skin? Why doesn't it? What are realistic factors that must be considered before purchasing such a product? What are some consequences of making a purchase without investigating the product first? **L2**

Health Journal

Write an Essay Have students create a list in their health journals of ways they know to avoid diseases. Have students write an essay comparing and contrasting ways to avoid diseases. Students' essays should include their current practices and an evaluation of how effective their practices are. **L2**

Unit Focus Transparency
Page 4, **Unit 8 Fast File Resources**

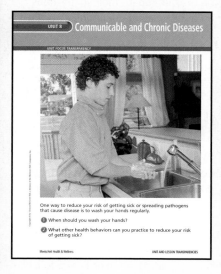

National Health Education Standards
Pages 482–483: 1.8, 1.9, 2.5, 3.2, 5.5, 5.7, 7.1, 8.4

Avoiding Communicable Diseases

Out of Time?

If time does not permit an in-depth study of this topic, use the following activities in this Teacher Wraparound Edition:

• Health Goals, p. 484
• Investigating the Issue, p. 486
• Health Project, p. 487
• Cross-Curricular Connections, p. 488

1 Focus

HEALTH GOALS **Spreading Disease** Have students respond to the first Health Goal for this lesson individually by listing in their health journals ways in which diseases can be spread. Then have them come together as a class and discuss what they wrote. Write on the blackboard their suggestions on how to avoid infection with communicable diseases. *Answers will vary, but may include contact with infected materials, contact with infected blood, or through the air.* **L2**

Write ABOUT IT!

NHES Assessment/SCASS

Performance Event Have students draw a diagram in their health journals that shows how they can become infected with a pathogen. Have volunteers draw their diagrams on the blackboard. Ask students to answer these questions in their health journals: What might be in the dirt from the garden that could harm their health? How would it get into their bodies? **L2** **ELL**

Avoiding Communicable Diseases

HEALTH GOALS
• I will choose behaviors that reduce my risk of infection with communicable diseases.
• I will be aware of immunizations that protect health.

Most teens have a few colds a year. Colds are caused by a virus, one of several pathogens that can cause disease. In this lesson, you will learn about communicable diseases.

What You'll Learn

1. Explain how the immune system responds when a pathogen enters the body. *(p. 485)*
2. Discuss ways to develop active and passive immunity. *(p. 485)*
3. Identify types of pathogens that cause disease, and give examples of the types of diseases caused by the types of pathogens. *(p. 487)*
4. Discuss ways pathogens are spread. *(p. 488)*
5. Analyze strategies to prevent infection with communicable diseases. *(p. 488)*

Why It's Important

Diseases affect people of all ages, races, and genders. Many of these diseases can be prevented when the facts about these diseases are known.

Key Terms

• lymphocytes
• B cell
• antibody
• helper T cell
• macrophage
• vaccine
• pathogen
• bacteria
• fungi
• protozoa

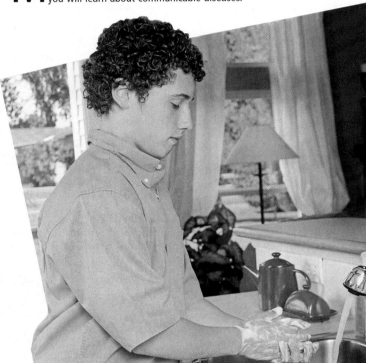

Write ABOUT IT!

Writing About Containing Pathogens Suppose you are working outdoors in a garden. You come into your home for lunch, and a sandwich is waiting for you. You are hungry and want to eat it immediately. After reading the information on containing pathogens on page 488, write an entry in your health journal about how you could avoid becoming infected with pathogens.

National Health Education Standards—Guide for Lesson 44		
6.4	Formulate an effective long-term personal health plan.	p. 488
7.2	Demonstrate a variety of healthy practices and behaviors that will maintain or improve the health of self and others.	pp. 484, 488

The Immune System

The system that removes harmful organisms from the blood and combats pathogens is the *immune system.* The immune system is composed of body organs, tissues, cells, and chemicals. Unbroken skin acts as a barrier to prevent pathogens from entering the body. Tears, perspiration, saliva, and oils on skin kill many pathogens. Mucus and hairs that line the inside of the nose also trap and destroy pathogens. Other pathogens that are swallowed are destroyed by stomach acids.

Protection Inside the Body

The immune system White blood cells that help the body fight pathogens are *lymphocytes.* When a pathogen enters the body, lymphocytes multiply in lymph tissue to fight infection. Two types of lymphocytes are B cells and helper T cells. A *B cell* is a white blood cell that produces antibodies. An *antibody* is a special protein that helps fight infection. A *helper T cell* is a white blood cell that signals B cells to produce antibodies.

Soon after a pathogen invades the body, helper T cells send signals to B cells to produce antibodies. B cells enter the lymph nodes and other lymph tissues. Antibodies then travel through the blood to destroy the pathogen. Antibodies can make pathogens ineffective and sensitive to macrophages. A *macrophage* (MA kruh fahzh) is a white blood cell that surrounds and destroys pathogens. Antibodies attach to pathogens and make them easier for macrophages to destroy. Destroyed pathogens enter lymph, are filtered in lymph nodes, and removed by the spleen.

Immunity The immune system helps people develop immunity. *Immunity* is defined as the body's resistance to disease-causing agents. Resistance to disease due to the presence of antibodies is called *Active immunity.* For example, after a person recovers from the chicken pox virus, the chicken pox antibody remains in the body and protects him or her from developing chicken pox again.

Active immunity also can result from being given a vaccine. A *vaccine* is a substance containing dead or weakened pathogens that is introduced into the body to give immunity. Vaccines are either given by injection or orally.

Vaccines cause the body to make antibodies for a specific pathogen. If these pathogens enter the body again, the antibodies destroy them. People should be immunized against diphtheria, pertussis (whooping cough), tetanus, measles, mumps, rubella (German measles), polio, hepatitis A, hepatitis B, and chicken pox.

Passive immunity is immunity that results from introducing antibodies into a person's bloodstream. The antibodies may be from another person's blood. This type of immunity is short-term and is used when the risk of developing a disease is immediate.

Did You Know?

White Blood Cells A normal white blood cell count is 4,000 to 10,000 white blood cells per cubic millimeter of blood.

INTERACTIVE CHALKBOARD with Image Bank

PowerPoint® Presentations
This CD-ROM is an editable Microsoft® PowerPoint® presentation that includes:
- Lesson presentations
- Lesson checks
- Interactive graphics
- 5-Minute Checks
- Image Bank
- All transparencies

CRISS Project

Note-Taking Refer to the Two-Column Notes: Main Idea-Detail Strategy on page 16T. Have students list the pathogens and diseases they cause in the left-hand column and how those diseases are spread in the right-hand column.

Lesson Resource Manager

- **Unit 8 Fast File Resources**
  Reading Strategy, p. 7
  Vocabulary Practice, p. 8
  Transparency Master and Worksheet, p. 9
  Real-Life Health, p.11
  Real-Life Health, p. 13
  5-Minute Check, p. 15
  Lesson 44 Quiz, p. 16
- **Unit 8 Transparency**
- **Lesson 44 Transparency**

- **Reading Essentials**
- **Technology**
  TeacherWorks™ CD-ROM
  StudentWorks™ CD-ROM
  Reading Essentials CD-ROM
  Exam*View*® Assessment Suite
  Vocabulary Puzzlemaker

National Health Education Standards
Pages 484–485: 1.5, 1.7, 7.2

FACTSABOUT
VIRUSES

Teacher FYI

Lytic Cycle The life cycle of a virus is referred to as the lytic cycle. The steps in the cycle are: attachment or absorption, virus penetrates the cell, replication of viral DNA, and release of the replicated virus from the cell. Sometimes the host cell is destroyed once the viruses are released.

Investigating the Issue

- *The word* prion *means proteinaceous infectious particle. It is an infectious disease that affects the central nervous system. Mad cow disease, kuru, and spongiform encephalopathy are caused by prions.*
- *There are currently major studies being conducted for HIV/AIDS and genital herpes. The antiviral medication for HIV/AIDS primarily focuses on controlling the spread of HIV in the body. The genital herpes antiviral medication treats the outbreaks caused by the virus and not the virus directly.*

INTERACTIVE CHALKBOARD with Image Bank

Teaching Transparency
Page 9, **Unit 8 Fast File Resources**

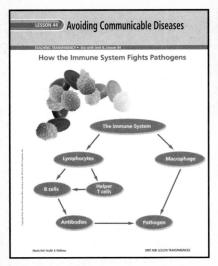

LESSON 44 Avoiding Communicable Diseases

TEACHING TRANSPARENCY • Use with Unit 8, Lesson 44

How the Immune System Fights Pathogens

The Immune System
Lymphocytes — Macrophage
B cells — Helper T cells
Antibodies — Pathogen

Meeks Heit Health & Wellness   UNIT AND LESSON TRANSPARENCIES

FACTSABOUT
VIRUSES

Color-enhanced TEM Magnification: 250 000x

▲ This magnification of an influenza virus shows the pink protein coat that allows the virus to attach to and infect the cells that line the respiratory tract.

What do a cold, the chicken pox, and rabies have in common? They are all caused by viruses. A virus is a structure that consists of genetic material enclosed in a protein coat. Viruses are not considered to be living organisms because they cannot reproduce independently. Viruses can only reproduce by invading another cell and taking over that cell's organelles. In the process of viral replication, the host cell is destroyed.

Diseases caused by viruses Viruses, such as the Ebola virus, polio virus, and the human immunodeficiency virus (HIV), are responsible for some of the most serious diseases known to humans. Viruses are spread in the same way as bacteria and other pathogens—through the air and water, through handling contaminated objects, and through carriers such as mosquitoes and ticks. Viruses can affect the gastrointestinal systems, the respiratory systems, and the nervous systems of humans and other animals. Antibiotics, which are used to fight bacterial infections, are not effective against viruses.

History of viruses Viruses, which are microscopic, were first defined by scientists in the 1930s. Early work on viruses was done using a virus that affects plants, the tobacco mosaic virus. Viruses are grouped together in families and classified based on characteristics, such as the type of genetic material they have (DNA or RNA), the method by which they reproduce, and their shape. Today, much of the research on viruses focuses on trying to develop medications that will be effective against viruses such as HIV and the common cold.

New viruses Emerging viruses, those that are new or changing, also are cause for concern in the scientific and medical communities. Diseases, such as AIDS, hantavirus pulmonary syndrome, and severe acute respiratory syndrome (SARS) are examples of diseases caused by viruses that were previously unrecognized until the outbreaks occurred in 1981, 1993, and 2003, respectively.

Sometimes, as in the case of HIV, it takes several years of research to be able to identify and describe an unknown virus. Learning information about a virus's structure, how it is transmitted, and what body systems it affects can all help in the development of possible vaccines or medications that fight the virus.

Some viruses have been linked to certain types of cancer. There is strong evidence that the hepatitis B virus plays a role in the development of liver cancer. Several viruses that affect the human immune system's T cells are known to cause leukemia and lymphoma. It is estimated that up to 10 percent of cancers are induced by viruses.

Investigating the Issue

Visit **www.glencoe.com** to research more information about viruses.

- What is a prion? What diseases are caused by prions?
- Describe research currently being done in the development of antiviral medications.

Choose one virus and research its history. When was it first identified? What disease does it cause in humans, and what are the symptoms? In what area of the world is it most prevalent? Write a report about the virus and present it to your class.

 www.glencoe.com

Differentiated Instruction

Learning Disabilities Give students two stacks of notecards. Students should write a Key Term and its definition on one notecard from each stack. Have students write the Key Terms on the front of the two notecards, and the definitions on the back of the two notecards. Students will repeat this step until they have two notecards for each Key Term in the lesson. Separate the notecards into two stacks and mix them up. Have students place one stack of notecards with the Key Terms face-up on their desk. Then, have students place the second stack definition-side face-up. Students can study the terms by either finding the definition that matches a Key Term, or by finding a Key Term that matches a definition. **L1 ELL**

Containing Pathogens

A germ that causes disease is a *pathogen*. An illness caused by pathogens that can be spread from one living thing to another is a *communicable disease,* or *infectious disease.* Some pathogens are spread more readily than others. There are many types of pathogens that cause disease.

What to Know About Types of Pathogens

Bacteria There are many types of *bacteria,* or single-celled microorganisms. Most bacteria are beneficial, but some are known to cause disease. Bacteria cause disease by releasing *toxins,* or poisonous substances. Some diseases caused by bacteria are strep throat, tuberculosis, tetanus, diphtheria, Lyme disease, syphilis, and gonorrhea. *Rickettsia* (rih KET see uh) are intracellular parasites that are classified as bacteria. Two diseases caused by rickettsia are typhus and Rocky Mountain spotted fever.

Fungi Another category of pathogen includes single- or multi-celled parasitic organisms called fungi. *Fungi* obtain their food from organic

Color-enhanced TEM Magnification: 4 000x   Color-enhanced TEM Magnification: 5 700x

▲ Streptococcus faeciuum bacteria   ▲ Malaria parasite

materials, such as plant, animal, or human tissue. Fungi can live on the skin, mucous membranes, and lungs and cause disease in the process. Some diseases caused by fungi are athlete's foot, ringworm, jock itch, nail infections, and thrush.

Viruses One of the smallest known pathogens is a *virus.* When a virus enters a cell, it takes over the cell and causes it to make more viruses. Newly produced viruses are released and take over other cells. In this way, viruses spread rapidly. Some viral diseases are the common cold, mumps, hepatitis, mononucleosis, chicken pox, and influenza.

Protozoa Tiny, single-celled organisms that produce toxins that cause disease are called *protozoa.* Malaria, African sleeping sickness, and dysentery are diseases caused by protozoa. A *helminth* is a parasitic worm. People can become infected with helminthes when they eat undercooked pork or fish or practice poor hygiene. Some helminthes, such as tapeworms, pinworms, and hookworms, can infect the human digestive tract. Other helminthes can infect muscle tissue and blood.

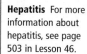

Make the Connection

Hepatitis For more information about hepatitis, see page 503 in Lesson 46.

Reading Review

1. How do vaccines prevent disease?
2. What are the different types of pathogens that cause diseases?

LESSON 44 • Avoiding Communicable Diseases   487

Practicing Healthful Behaviors

Have students assess how they practice each of the tips stated using this three-point scale:

1 – need improvement
2 – sometimes practice it
3 – practice the majority of the time

After they assess themselves, have students list ways they can improve on those that need improvement. For the tips they practice the majority of the time, have students list how they implement them. **L2**

3 Assess

Vocabulary Practice

Page 8, **Unit 8 Fast File Resources**

| **LESSON 44** Avoiding Communicable Diseases |
| **Vocabulary Practice** |

Explain the relationship between the pairs of words given below. Include a definition of each vocabulary term as part of your answer.

antibody	helper T cell	pathogen
B cell	lymphocytes	protozoa
bacteria	macrophage	vaccine
fungi		

1. B cell—antibody

2. helper T cell—lymphocytes

3. vaccine—pathogen

4. fungi—protozoa

5. macrophage—bacteria

LESSON 44 • Avoiding Communicable Diseases   UNIT 8

National Health Education Standards

Pages 488–489: 1.1, 1.5, 2.5, 7.1, 7.2

Activity: Using Life Skills

Practicing Healthful Behaviors: Avoiding Spreading Pathogens

Follow the tips below to avoid spreading pathogens to keep yourself and your community healthy.

1 If you are going to make a health behavior contract, write your name and the date. Writing the date will help you keep track of your start date.

2 Write the healthful behaviors you want to practice as health goals. Always wash your hands for 10–20 seconds with soap and water after you use the restroom; blow your nose; handle raw meat, poultry, or fish; take out the garbage; or tend to someone who is sick.

3 Only drink water that you know is safe, such as tap water and bottled water. This is especially important while traveling or out in nature. Get appropriate vaccinations.

4 Write specific statements that describe how this healthful behavior reduces health risks. Avoid crowded places, such as work, school, or sports events, if you are not feeling well and encourage others who are ill to do the same. Cover your mouth when you cough or sneeze.

5 Keep hot foods hot and cold foods cold to avoid bacteria growth, and wash fruits and vegetables before serving them.

6 Do not eat raw eggs, even in cookie dough.

7 Make a specific plan for recording your progress and complete an evaluation of how the plan helped you accomplish the health goal. The evaluation will help you determine if you need to alter your plan to fully meet your health goal.

Make the Connection

Respiratory Diseases For more information on respiratory diseases, see page 491 in Lesson 45.

How pathogens are spread Pathogens may be spread from person to person through direct contact, shaking hands, intimate kissing, sexual intercourse, receiving a transfusion of the person's blood, touching ulcers or sores, or handling bodily fluids, such as blood or urine. They may be spread through the air by coughing or sneezing. Contact with contaminated objects can spread pathogens. This includes sharing a needle with an infected person to inject drugs or get a tattoo and using objects such as combs, toothbrushes, razors, or eating utensils touched by an infected person. Handling or being bitten by an infected insect or animal also spreads pathogens. Other ways pathogens are spread include contact with contaminated food and water by drinking infected water, eating infected food, undercooking meats and other foods, improperly canning or preparing foods, and not washing hands after using the restroom.

▲ Drinking water that you know is safe will help keep you healthy.

🜛 Cross-Curricular Connections

History Have students look up an infection or disease that has plagued the world in the past, or one that is an epidemic now. Examples are the bubonic plague, malaria, and AIDS/HIV. Have students create a multimedia presentation that includes the following facts:

• where the disease is believed to have originated,
• where the disease was or is prevalent,
• how it affects the body,
• how it was or is spread,
• how scientists, physicians, and governments have tried to control the disease, and
• how it was or is cured or controlled. **L3**

44 STUDY GUIDE

Key Terms Review

Complete these fill-in-the-blank statements with the lesson Key Terms on the left. Do not write in this book.

active immunity
antibody
B cell
bacteria
fungi
helper T cell
lymphocytes
macrophage
pathogen
protozoa
vaccine
virus

1. A special protein in the body that helps fight infection is a(n) _____.
2. Single- or multi-celled parasites are called _____.
3. The general term for a germ that causes disease is a(n) _____.
4. A white blood cell that produces antibodies is a(n) _____.
5. A white blood cell that helps the body fight pathogens is a(n) _____.

6. _____ are single-celled organisms that produce toxins.
7. Single-celled microorganisms, most of which are beneficial, are _____.
8. A(n) _____ is made up of dead or weakened viruses injected into the body.
9. A white blood cell that signals B cells to produce antibodies is a(n) _____.
10. A white blood cell that surrounds and destroys pathogens is a(n) _____.

Recalling the Facts

11. How is the risk of catching a cold reduced when someone covers his or her mouth when coughing?
12. Why are viruses so hard to control?
13. Why is cooking food thoroughly a good way to reduce the risk of disease caused by eating certain foods?
14. How can a person become ill just by shaking another person's hand?

15. Why is sharing a needle to inject drugs or get a tattoo a risk factor for HIV infection?
16. Why can perspiration be helpful in preventing disease?
17. Why is the spleen an important part of the immune system?
18. How does the immune system fight infection?

Critical Thinking

19. What can happen to a person who has a low helper T cell count?
20. Analyze how strategies can be used in different settings to prevent the spread of disease.
21. If a person had a raised white blood cell count, what would that signify? Explain your answer.
22. When might passive immunity occur naturally?

Real-Life Applications

23. Why do you think diseases spread so quickly in developing countries?
24. Why might drinking water in another country make you sick, but not make the people who live there sick?
25. Why do you think antibiotics are not effective in fighting viruses?
26. Why do you think some vaccinations are required for children to begin school?

Activities

Responsible Decision Making

27. **Inform** Suppose you have a cold or the flu. Your friend had planned to come to your home to study with you. You really need her help. What should you do? Refer to the Responsible Decision-Making Model on page 61 to review the steps involved in making responsible decisions.

Sharpen Your Life Skills

28. **Advocate for Health** Prepare an advertisement for a TV show in which you promote reducing the risk of the flu spreading. Describe what students in your school can do to reduce the risk. Analyze how these strategies can be effective. Show the advertisement to your classmates.

Visit www.glencoe.com for more *Health & Wellness* quizzes.

LESSON 44 • Study Guide 489

LESSON 44

STUDY GUIDE

Key Terms Review

1. antibody
2. fungi
3. pathogen
4. B cell
5. lymphocyte
6. Protozoa
7. bacteria
8. vaccine
9. helper T cell
10. macrophage

Recalling the Facts

11. Pathogens do not become airborne.
12. Viruses enter a cell, take over the cell, and replicate. They cannot be controlled by antibiotics.
13. Cooking food thoroughly decreases the chance that microorganisms will survive.
14. Germs from an infected person's hand can enter the body when touching the mouth, nose, or eyes.
15. Contaminated blood on the needle can infect another person.
16. It kills germs that get on the skin.
17. The spleen removes destroyed pathogens from the body.
18. When a pathogen enters the body, lymphocytes multiply to fight infection. Antibodies then travel through the blood to destroy the pathogen, which eventually is removed by the spleen.

Critical Thinking

19. They are at greater risk of becoming infected by a pathogen.
20. Wash hands with soap and water or use an antibacterial hand gel; handle and cook foods properly; avoid contact with people who are sick.
21. It would signify that there is a pathogen in the body. When a pathogen enters the body, lymphocytes multiply to attack the pathogen.
22. from a mother to her baby

Real-Life Applications

23. improper sewage and waste control, lack of resources, contamination of food and water

24. Your immune system may not have developed antibodies to fight a pathogen in the water. A native person likely developed those antibodies earlier in life.
25. Viruses are smaller and take over cells in the body. Antibodies kill bacteria, not cells.
26. If students are vaccinated before they enter school, they are not likely to contract or spread certain diseases.

Activities

Responsible Decision Making

27. Your friend should not come to your home as you can spread your infection. You can study together by talking on the telephone or scheduling another time to study together.

Sharpen Your Life Skills

28. Answers will vary.

489

Dealing with Respiratory Diseases, Asthma, and Allergies

If time does not permit an in-depth study of this topic, use the following activities in this Teacher Wraparound Edition:

- Health Goals, p. 490
- Extension, p. 491
- Using the Table, p. 493
- Class Discussion, p. 495

1 Focus

HEALTH GOALS **Common Cold** Have students respond to the first Health Goal for this lesson by writing in their health journals what they dislike about having a cold, how they usually catch one, and how they cope with having a cold. *Dislikes may include a runny nose or an overall drained feeling. Catching a cold may include being around someone with a cold. A response to dealing with a cold may include taking cold medicine and resting.* **L2**

Write ABOUT IT!

Answers Ask students to respond to the "What Would You Do?" scenario in their health journals. *Students' answers may include: They could tell their friend that they are allergic to dog dander and that they cannot stay. Their friend could understand and agree to meet them again without her dog. They could not mention their allergies and stay with their friend. This may cause them to have an allergic reaction.* **L2**

LESSON 45

Dealing with Respiratory Diseases, Asthma, and Allergies

What You'll Learn

1. Analyze the causes, symptoms, diagnoses, and treatments of communicable respiratory diseases. *(p. 491)*
2. Analyze ways to prevent infection with communicable respiratory diseases. *(p. 491)*
3. Discuss asthma and ways to prevent and manage asthma attacks. *(p. 494)*
4. Describe common causes of allergies. *(p. 496)*
5. Describe ways to prevent or treat allergies. *(p. 496)*

Why It's Important

At some time, almost everyone will be affected by a respiratory illness. In addition, millions of people are affected by asthma or allergies.

Key Terms

- common cold
- influenza
- pneumonia
- strep throat
- rheumatic fever
- asthma
- allergy
- allergen
- pollen
- hay fever

 HEALTH GOALS
- **I will choose behaviors to reduce my risk of infection with respiratory diseases.**
- **I will recognize ways to manage asthma and allergies.**

Some diseases are spread from person to person while others are not. You will learn ways to prevent and manage these diseases.

Write ABOUT IT!

Writing About Allergies Suppose that you are meeting your friend in the park. You notice she has her dog with her, and you are allergic to dog dander. After reading the information on page 496, write an entry in your health journal about two different ways you could handle this situation, and the possible outcomes of each.

National Health Education Standards—Guide for Lesson 45		
2.3	Analyze how peers influence healthy and unhealthy behaviors.	pp. 490, 491
2.4	Evaluate how the school and community can impact personal health practice and behaviors.	p. 491
3.4	Determine when professional health services may be required.	pp. 492, 496
7.2	Demonstrate a variety of healthy practices and behaviors that will maintain or improve the health of self and others.	pp. 495, 496, 497

A Guide to Communicable Respiratory Diseases

This part of the lesson includes a Guide to Communicable Respiratory Diseases. *Communicable diseases* can be spread from person to person. The guide includes six communicable respiratory diseases: the common cold, influenza, pneumonia, strep throat, tuberculosis, and SARS. You will learn the causes, methods of transmission, symptoms, diagnoses and treatments, and prevention for each disease.

What to Know About Communicable Respiratory Diseases

The common cold A respiratory infection caused by more than 100 different viruses is the *common cold.* One-third of all colds are caused by rhinoviruses. A *rhinovirus* is a virus that infects the nose. High levels of stress can increase a person's chances of catching a cold. Being exposed to cold weather or getting chilled does not cause a cold. A cold can last from 2 to 14 days.

OTC medicines may help relieve some symptoms, but they will not cure or shorten the length of a cold. Gargling with warm salt water may bring relief to a sore throat. Applying petroleum jelly to the nose may help an irritated nose.

Influenza A highly contagious viral infection of the respiratory tract is *influenza,* or the flu. Most people recover within a week or two, but it can be life-threatening for elderly people, newborn babies, and people with chronic diseases. The flu can lead to pneumonia. Flu viruses are constantly changing, making it difficult for the immune system to form antibodies to new variations of the flu virus. Flu can spread rapidly in crowded places. The infected person who spreads it often does not show symptoms, yet can still spread the disease. An infected person is particularly contagious during the first three days of infection.

A physician usually determines if people have the flu by their symptoms and by whether the flu is present in the community. Aspirin or acetaminophen may relieve fever and discomfort.

Children and teens should not take aspirin to relieve symptoms as it may increase the chances of developing Reye's syndrome.

Make the Connection

Diseases in the United States For more information on the nation's health concerns, see page 59 in Lesson 6.

Lesson Resource Manager

- **Unit 8 Fast File Resources**
  Reading Strategy, p. 19
  Vocabulary Practice, p. 20
  Transparency Master and Worksheet, p. 21
  Real-Life Health, p. 23
  Real-Life Health, p. 25
  5-Minute Check, p. 27
  Lesson 45 Quiz, p. 28
- **Unit 8 Transparency**
- **Lesson 45 Transparency**

- **Reading Essentials**
- **Technology**
  TeacherWorks™ CD-ROM
  StudentWorks™ CD-ROM
  Reading Essentials CD-ROM
  ExamView® Assessment Suite
  Vocabulary Puzzlemaker

A Guide to Communicable Respiratory Diseases

2 Teach

Extension

Diseases in the U.S. Have students look up the history and statistics on each communicable respiratory disease in the United States. Information can include who discovered the disease and in what year, how many people are affected each year, what age group is affected the most, and whether any of these diseases can be fatal and how. Students can work in groups and give 3-minute presentations on their findings.
L2 **ELL**

PowerPoint® Presentations

This CD-ROM is an editable Microsoft® PowerPoint® presentation that includes:
- Lesson presentations
- Lesson checks
- Interactive graphics
- 5-Minute Checks
- Image Bank
- All transparencies

Discussion Refer to the KWL Strategy on page 17T to pinpoint misconceptions the students might have regarding asthma and allergies.

National Health Education Standards

Pages 490–491: 1.1, 1.5, 2.1, 2.3, 4.4, 7.1

Teacher FYI

Tuberculosis TB has been found in Egyptian mummies' spinal column fragments dating back to 2400 B.C. The World Health Organization estimates that 8 million people contract TB each year and an estimated 3 million die as a result. The majority of TB cases are found in sub-Saharan Africa, southeast Asia, and eastern Europe, where economic conditions are the poorest. A great influence in the rising number of TB cases is HIV infection. People with HIV infection have weakened immune systems and are at increased risk of developing active TB. In fact, a person who is infected with both HIV and TB is much more likely to develop active TB than a person who is infected only with TB.

Explain the Concept

Avian Influenza Ask students how many of them have heard reports of avian influenza (bird flu) in the news. Have students explain what they would do or how they would feel if they heard that a case of avian flu occurred in their hometown. *Answers may vary. Responses may include leaving town or staying indoors or not worrying at all.* Point out that according to the CDC in 2006, the H5N1 virus in birds poses two main risks to humans: more than half of those infected (by birds with the virus) die, and the virus could change form so that it spreads easily from person to person. **L2**

Make the Connection

Communicable Diseases For more information on accessing health information, see page 17 in Lesson 2.

Reye's syndrome is a disease that causes swelling of the brain and deterioration of liver function. Antibiotics are not effective against flu viruses, but may help prevent the pneumonia that sometimes follows it.

Flu shots are available. Since flu viruses change often, flu vaccines are updated each year. They are highly recommended for people under age 2 and/or over age 65; people with chronic illnesses, and/or a history of respiratory infections; pregnant women who are in their second or third trimester during flu season; and health-care workers.

Pneumonia An infection in the lungs caused by bacteria, viruses, or other pathogens is ***pneumonia.*** Pneumonia bacteria and viruses can be spread by direct contact with an infected person or with contaminated objects. Laboratory tests, chest X rays, and physical examinations are used to diagnose pneumonia. Prompt treatment is critical. Antibiotics are used to treat bacterial pneumonia, but viral pneumonia is much more difficult to treat. Severe cases may require hospital care. A vaccine is available to prevent pneumococcal pneumonia, a type which kills more people than all other vaccine-preventable diseases.

▲ A chest X ray can confirm a tuberculosis diagnosis.

▲ Healthy lungs will appear clear in a chest X ray.

Strep throat A bacterial infection of the throat is ***strep throat.*** If it is not treated promptly, rheumatic fever can occur. ***Rheumatic fever*** is an autoimmune disease in the heart that can cause fever, weakness, and damage to heart valves. When someone has strep throat, the throat may appear very red and small patches of pus may be visible. A throat culture is needed to diagnose strep throat. Antibiotics are prescribed to kill the bacteria and to prevent spread of the infection. Rest and fluids help the body fight the infection.

Tuberculosis A bacterial infection of the lungs is ***tuberculosis.*** People with a weakened immune system, such as those with HIV and the elderly, are highly susceptible to tuberculosis. Those who are homeless, malnourished, or inject drugs are at increased risk for tuberculosis.

Tuberculosis bacteria become airborne through coughing and sneezing by an infected person. Only people with active tuberculosis are contagious. Tuberculosis is not likely to be spread through items or objects that have been touched by a person with the disease.

A tuberculin skin test is the injection of a protein substance under the skin in the forearm. If within two days a red welt forms around where the protein was injected, the person has been exposed to tuberculosis. This does not confirm that a person has tuberculosis. Chest X rays and sputum samples are used to confirm a diagnosis. Although antibiotics are used to treat tuberculosis, some tuberculosis pathogens have become resistant to them. Drugs are available to prevent tuberculosis in people

Achieving Health Literacy

Effective Communicator Have students create an FYI Respiratory Disease bulletin board for the school. Break the class into six groups and assign each one a type of respiratory disease to research. Information they can gather for their disease can include:

- a description of the disease,
- a close-up picture of a common virus or bacteria that causes their assigned disease,
- common signs and symptoms,
- how the disease is spread,
- world statistics,
- common remedies, treatments, or cures, and
- ways to avoid the disease. **L2**

TABLE 45.1 Communicable Respiratory Disease Facts

Disease and Symptoms	Transmission	Treatment	Prevention
Cold runny nose, watery eyes, difficulty breathing, sneezing, sore throat, cough, and headache	air, contact with an infected person, or by touching contaminated objects	rest and drink plenty of fluids	wash hands frequently and do not touch the nose or eyes, sneeze or cough into a facial tissue, avoid close contact with anyone who has a cold
Influenza headache, chills, sneezing, stuffy nose, sore throat, and dry cough, followed by body aches and fever	air, enters the body through the mucous membranes of the eyes, nose, or mouth	rest and drink plenty of fluids	wash hands often, avoid direct contact with infected person, get a flu vaccination
Pneumonia shortness of breath, difficulty breathing, coughing, chest pain, weakness, fever, and chills	direct contact with a contaminated person or object, untreated respiratory diseases	antibiotics	avoid direct contact with infected person, get treatment for respiratory diseases, get a pneumococcal pneumonia vaccination
Strep throat fever and severe sore throat	coughing, sneezing, and close contact with an infected person	antibiotics, rest, and drink plenty of fluids	avoid contact with infected person, wash hands often
Tuberculosis extreme tiredness, coughing, night sweats, loss of appetite, weight loss, low-grade fever, chills, bloody sputum, shortness of breath, and chest pain	air, through coughing and sneezing of an infected person	antibiotics, supportive care	avoid contact with infected person
SARS fever higher than 100.4°F and symptoms of other respiratory illnesses, including cough, shortness of breath, difficulty breathing, low oxygen in the blood, or X-ray findings of pneumonia	air, enters the body through mucous membranes	good supportive care, rest	wash hands often, avoid close contact with infected person

who are in close contact with infected people. Rooms with good ventilation and air flow reduce the risk of the spread of tuberculosis.

Severe acute respiratory syndrome (SARS) A contagious respiratory illness caused by a new type of coronavirus is *SARS*. SARS surfaced in early 2003 in some Asian countries and then caused outbreaks in other countries. It is important to understand that the symptoms of SARS are typical for many other respiratory illnesses, including a fever, cough, or shortness of breath. With this illness, another criterion for diagnosis is travel to specific Asian countries where SARS exists and/or close contact with a person infected with SARS. Since the initial outbreak, SARS is now under control.

LESSON 45 • Dealing with Respiratory Diseases, Asthma, and Allergies **493**

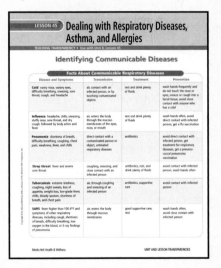

Asthma

Class Discussion

Asthma in Teens Have a guest speaker discuss his or her experiences with asthma with the class. Ask the speaker to share the answers to these questions with the class: When did the speaker first find out he or she had asthma? How is it treated? Did the speaker outgrow his or her asthma? How has it inhibited his or her activities? What management techniques does he or she use to prevent an asthma attack? **L2**

INTERACTIVE CHALKBOARD
with Image Bank

5-Minute Check

Page 27, Unit 8 Fast File Resources

1. What is influenza? *a highly contagious viral infection of the respiratory tract*

2. How is pneumonia diagnosed? *with lab tests, chest X rays, and physical exams*

3. What types of people are more susceptible to tuberculosis? *senior citizens; people with weak immune systems due to disease; those who are homeless, malnourished, or who inject drugs*

4. What are some types of asthma triggers? *tree pollen, grasses, weeds, air pollution, stress, animal dander, cigarette smoke, dust and mold*

5. What is EIA? *Exercise-induced asthma is a condition in which a person has difficulty breathing during and shortly after strenuous physical activity.*

Asthma

A condition in which the bronchial tubes become inflamed and constrict, making breathing difficult for many people, is *asthma*. Asthma is an example of a noncommunicable disease. *Noncommunicable diseases* are not spread from person to person. No type of condition results in as much absenteeism in school as asthma.

What to Know About Asthma

Did You Know?

Asthma and Children Asthma is the most common long-term disease in school-age children.

Asthma Asthma is a chronic disease that cannot be cured. Symptoms of asthma include coughing, wheezing, and shortness of breath. People with asthma have sensitive lungs that react to certain asthma triggers. *Asthma triggers* are substances that cause the airways to tighten, swell, and fill with mucus. The airways become narrow and blocked, and it is difficult to breathe.

Asthma triggers include pollen from trees; grasses and weeds; dust and mold; dog, cat, or other animal dander; cigarette smoke; air pollution; having a cold or the flu; aspirin or other OTC drugs; perfumes and fragrances; odors from sprays and paints; insecticides; certain foods; and smoke from burning wood, paper, or other items.

Asthma also can be triggered by emotional stress, especially during childhood and adolescence. Asthma attacks can be very serious.

An *asthma attack* is an episode of coughing, wheezing, shortness of breath and tightness in the chest experienced by a person who has asthma. Some people may become extremely sick from asthma attacks and need to be hospitalized, and some people have died from them.

Most children who suffer from asthma continue to have asthma as adults. However, for about one-fourth of children with asthma, the symptoms decrease significantly as they get older. Sometimes, however, asthma does not develop until a person is an adult.

Exercise-induced asthma A condition in which a person has difficulty breathing during or shortly after strenuous physical activity is called *exercise-induced asthma (EIA).* The symptoms of EIA can be mild or severe and include coughing, wheezing, shortness of breath, and tightness in the chest.

Some people with EIA suffer an asthma attack only with exercise. A high percentage of people with EIA suffer asthma from allergies to airborne substances, such as air pollutants, dust, and animal dander. Exposure to cold, dry air during physical activity is a major trigger.

Six Warning Signs and Symptoms of Asthma

The following are warning signs of an asthma attack:

- coughing
- wheezing
- shortness of breath
- tightness in the chest
- rapid breathing
- itchy or sore throat

494 UNIT 8 • Communicable and Chronic Diseases

 Differentiated Instruction

Learning Disabilities Create a "guided notes" page for the lesson. The notes page should outline the major topics in the lesson, leaving blanks for students to fill in information. Students who need extra help can use the notes pages to help them organize the information in the lesson. For example, for the information on this page, you might list "asthma," then offer a blank for students to fill in with the definition. You may also include "asthma triggers," and leave a blank for students to list the triggers. **L1 ELL**

Activity: Using Life Skills

Accessing Valid Health Information, Products, and Services: Managing Asthma

Asthma must be taken seriously, but it doesn't have to keep you from having fun. You can control asthma symptoms and have fewer, less severe asthma attacks by following these tips.

1 Identify health information, products, and services you need. Develop a daily management plan and an emergency plan with your health-care provider.

2 Find health information, products, and services. Find out what triggers your asthma attacks, and then stay away from those triggers.

3 Use your peak flow meter every day if it is part of your management plan.

4 Take your medications regularly, and keep them with you for emergencies.

5 Evaluate health information, products, and services. Learn how you feel right before an asthma attack. If you know your warning signs or symptoms, you can get the help you need.

6 Take action when health information is misleading and/or health products and services are unsatisfactory. Don't let asthma keep you from enjoying a sport or activity you love. Consult your health-care provider about how to manage your symptoms so you can participate.

▲ Some asthma medicines help prevent asthma attacks.

Since regular physical activity improves health status, learning to manage EIA is important. Proper medication allows most people who have EIA to participate in regular physical activity. People with EIA frequently breathe in puffs of medication from an inhaler before they exercise to prevent an EIA attack.

EIA often can be reduced and prevented by improving physical fitness. Breathing warm, moist air usually helps the condition. Swimming and other indoor water sports provide an ideal environment for people who have EIA.

Ways to prevent asthma attacks People who have asthma can prevent asthma attacks by avoiding asthma triggers. For instance, they may avoid smoky restaurants, refrain from wearing perfumes and fragrances, or trade household chores with siblings so that they don't have to do yard work that could aggravate their asthma. Other ways of avoiding asthma attacks include recognizing warning signs and taking certain medication. If they fail to recognize these signs, their symptoms may get worse.

If you have asthma, make a plan with your parents or guardian and your physician about what to do when you notice warning signs and symptoms of asthma. People with asthma should always carry their medications with them in case of an attack.

Reading Review

1. What are some common communicable respiratory diseases?

2. What is the difference between a cold and asthma?

LESSON 45 • Dealing with Respiratory Diseases, Asthma, and Allergies **495**

🖊 Achieving Health Literacy

Responsible Citizen Have students survey their home and evaluate how "asthma-friendly" their home is. Have students answer these questions: Are there any plants in the house? Are there any pets? Does anyone smoke? These are a few considerations they can use in their home evaluations. Ask students what other asthma triggers might be present in a home. After evaluating their home, have teens discuss with their parents ways to reduce asthma triggers in the home. Teens should make a list of three things they could do to reduce the risk of a visitor having an asthma attack in their home. **L2**

Using Life Skills

Accessing Valid Health Information, Products, and Services Give each student an index card. Have each student create a unique logo focusing on managing asthma. On the back of their cards, have students paraphrase the six tips on how to manage asthma. **L2**

Class Discussion

Fewer Attacks Ask students how people who have asthma can decrease their chances of having an asthma attack. *Point out that physical fitness can improve asthma. Specifically, being physically fit reduces the risk of triggering an attack.* Students may ask you if exercise can trigger asthma attacks. *Yes, it can. This is the reason breathing needs to be monitored carefully during exercise.* Use this opportunity to emphasize the benefits of physical fitness. **L2**

NHES Assessment/SCASS

Selected Response Ask students to imagine they have been diagnosed with exercise-induced asthma. They have established a treatment plan with their doctors. Ask students which of the following lifestyle changes is not appropriate.

A. Learn to recognize the warning signs and symptoms of an attack.

B. Avoid exposure to triggers.

C. *Stop all physical activity.*

D. Keep your medications with you for emergencies.

Reading Review

1. *common cold, influenza, pneumonia, strep throat, tuberculosis*

2. *A cold is communicable; asthma is not.*

National Health Education Standards
Pages 494–495: 1.3, 1.5, 7.2

Allergies

Preventing an Allergic Reaction
Describe the following situation to students: you are planning to have some friends over. You have a family pet and many blooming plants in the house. You just found out that a few of your friends are allergic to animal dander and pollen. Ask students how they might handle this situation. *dust and vacuum, have a neighbor watch the pet, place plants outside* **L2**

3 Assess

Vocabulary Practice

Page 20, **Unit 8 Fast File Resources**

An overreaction of the body to a substance, that in most people causes no response, is an *allergy*. A substance that produces an allergic response is called an *allergen*. Most allergens are harmless substances. They come into contact with the skin, respiratory airways, the surface of the eyes, and the stomach.

What to Know About Allergies

Make the Connection

Food Allergies For more information on food allergies and intolerances, see page 308 in Lesson 27.

Airborne allergens The most common airborne allergens are animal dander, feathers, pollens, and mites. *Animal dander* is flakes of dead skin from an animal. People who have symptoms, such as dizziness, nausea, skin rash, itchy or watery eyes, drops in blood pressure, or difficulty in breathing when they are near cats, dogs, or other animals, are allergic to animal dander.

Pollen is a yellowish powder produced by flowers, trees, and grass. Pollen may become airborne and trigger an allergic response. The most common response is hay fever. *Hay fever* is a common term for seasonal respiratory allergies that typically occur in the spring and fall. Symptoms include coughing, sneezing, and inflammation of the nasal mucous membranes. People who have hay fever may take medicine or receive shots regularly to lessen their response to pollen.

Some people are allergic to house dust because it usually contains small fragments of mites and their feces. Mites are tiny, eight-legged animals that resemble spiders.

Other allergens Not all allergies are airborne. A person can be allergic to medication, latex, insect stings, or foods. One medication to which many people are allergic is penicillin, an antibiotic. A person who is allergic to penicillin may experience breathing difficulties, rapid pulse, and a sudden drop in blood pressure. Other types of antibiotics can be used to treat disease if a person is allergic to penicillin.

People also can have an allergic reaction to latex or an insect sting. Symptoms include skin rash, respiratory irritation, and in some cases, shock. To avoid a reaction to latex, a person could use plastic or vinyl gloves.

Many people are allergic to certain types of food. Peanuts, eggs, milk, and shellfish are some common food allergens. People with food allergies should avoid foods that contain their allergy trigger.

Allergy tests Skin tests can be used to identify allergens that produce allergic reactions. A *skin patch test* involves putting allergens on a patch, taping the patch to the skin, and observing the reaction. Another test involves using a needle to place allergens under the skin and observing the reaction. A *wheal,* or a round skin lump, indicates sensitivity to a particular allergen.

Treating allergies Medications can help reduce or eliminate the severity of certain reactions. People may need to receive medication on a regular basis.

Health Project

Pollen Count Have students watch the news or research information about pollen count. Many radio and television stations issue information about the current pollen count for that day. Ask students to research the answers to these questions for their local area: When are the warnings issued? Where and when is the pollen count the highest? When is it the lowest? Have students track the pollen count for two weeks along with the weather. Students should graph the pollen count throughout the project. Ask students to record if they saw any correlation between the weather and the pollen count. **L3**

National Health Education Standards

Pages 496–497: 1.1, 1.3, 1.5, 3.2, 3.4, 6.1, 7.1, 7.2

Key Terms Review

Complete these fill-in-the-blank statements with the lesson Key Terms on the left. Do not write in this book.

allergen
allergy
asthma
common cold
communicable
    disease
hay fever
influenza
pneumonia
pollen
rheumatic fever
strep throat
wheal

1. A person with constricted bronchial tubes may have a condition called _____.

2. A respiratory infection that can be caused by one of more than 100 viruses is called the _____.

3. A powder made in flowers that is associated with allergies is _____.

4. A viral infection of the respiratory tract that is very contagious is _____.

5. Seasonal respiratory allergies are commonly known as _____.

6. An infection in the throat caused by bacteria is _____.

7. The general name for a substance, which is usually harmless, that produces an allergic response is a(n)_____.

8. A disease that can damage heart valves is _____.

9. An infection of the lungs caused by any number of pathogens is _____.

10. An overreaction of the body to a substance is called a(n) _____.

Recalling the Facts

11. Why is proper hand washing important in preventing the common cold?

12. How is the flu spread?

13. Why is viral pneumonia more problematic than bacterial pneumonia?

14. What should a person do to reduce the risk of having an asthma attack?

15. Why should a person always know what the warning signs and symptoms of an asthma attack are?

16. Why should family members not smoke if another family member has asthma?

17. Why should you know if you are allergic to certain medications?

18. How do allergy tests show that you have an allergy?

Critical Thinking

19. Why are being exposed to cold weather or getting chilled not causes of a cold?

20. How is it possible that a person who gets a flu shot can still get the flu?

21. Why do people with hay fever have symptoms such as coughing, sneezing, and inflammation of the nasal mucous membranes?

22. Why are allergies not contagious?

Real-Life Applications

23. What do you think is the best thing you can do to avoid communicable diseases?

24. Why do you think all people are not vaccinated for the flu?

25. Why do you think people might confuse a cold with allergies?

26. Is it a good idea to use leftover antibiotics for a cold? Why or why not?

Activities

Responsible Decision Making

27. **Discuss** You are at home recovering from strep throat. Your friends invite you to a party and you want to go. Discuss with your classmates what would be a responsible decision in this situation. Refer to the Responsible Decision-Making Model on page 61 to review the steps involved in making responsible decisions.

Sharpen Your Life Skills

28. **Access Health Information** There are several different ways to treat allergies. Contact your physician or a local allergist to research allergy treatments. Write a one-page paper on the advantages and disadvantages of these treatments. Could any of them help your own allergies, if you have any?

Key Terms Review

1. asthma
2. common cold
3. pollen
4. influenza
5. hay fever
6. strep throat
7. allergen
8. rheumatic fever
9. pneumonia
10. allergy

Recalling the Facts

11. it rids the hands of germs.
12. through the air; enters the body through mucus membranes
13. Bacterial pneumonia can be cured with antibiotics, while viral pneumonia cannot.
14. avoid triggers of an asthma attack
15. Knowing the signs and symptoms will help a person take action sooner, which will result in a reduced chance of serious harm.
16. Secondhand smoke can trigger an asthma attack.
17. You can avoid an allergic reaction to a medication by letting your physician know about your allergy.
18. If a needle is used to place an allergen under the skin, a wheal will appear to indicate sensitivity to a particular agent. A skin patch may also be performed.

Critical Thinking

19. Colds are caused by viruses that are spread from person to person. They are not caused by cold air.
20. There are different strains of the flu. A flu shot for one strain may not affect another strain.
21. A person's body overacts to a substance, and thinks that it is a pathogen. The person's body may react by coughing or sneezing, to try to rid the body of the pathogen.
22. Allergies are not caused by a pathogen.

Real-Life Applications

23. Answers will vary, but may include washing hands.

---

24. The flu is more serious in certain groups, such as the elderly. Though it makes people sick, it is less likely to cause death in people who are otherwise healthy.

25. A cold and allergies can cause the same type of symptoms, such as sneezing, a runny nose, or coughing.

26. No. Leftover antibiotics may not be the correct treatment for the illness.

Activities

Responsible Decision Making

27. If you go to the party, you can infect others. In addition, you can worsen your condition if you do not rest. Untreated strep throat can lead to rheumatic fever. It is best not to go to the party but instead to rest at home.

Sharpen Your Life Skills

28. Answers will vary.

LESSON 46

Reducing the Risk of STDs and HIV

Out of Time?

If time does not permit an in-depth study of this topic, use the following activities in this Teacher Wraparound Edition:

- Health Goals, p. 498
- Quick Demo, p. 500
- Health Project, p. 502
- Explain the Concept, p. 507

1 Focus

HEALTH GOALS **Risky Behaviors** Have students respond to the Health Goals for this lesson by creating a list of behaviors they know can spread sexually transmitted diseases. Then have them expand on ways to reduce risks based on the behaviors they wrote down. Ask them to identify bodily fluids that can spread sexually transmitted diseases. *blood, vaginal fluids, and semen* What are some ways these fluids can be avoided? *Use the universal precautions and abstain from intimate sexual contact.* **L2**

Write ABOUT IT!

PSA Ask students to respond to the "What Would You Do?" scenario by creating a public service announcement regarding the misconceptions surrounding the spread of HIV. **L2**

LESSON 46

Reducing the Risk of STDs and HIV

HEALTH GOALS
- I will choose behaviors to reduce my risk of infection with sexually transmitted diseases.
- I will choose behaviors to reduce my risk of HIV infection.

People your age who are abstinent from sexual activity will not become infected with a ***sexually transmitted disease (STD)***, a disease caused by pathogens that are transmitted from an infected person to an uninfected person during intimate sexual contact. Sexually transmitted diseases are also known as sexually transmitted infections (STIs).

What You'll Learn

1. Discuss the causes and methods of transmission of common STDs. *(p. 499)*
2. Discuss the symptoms, diagnoses, and treatments of common STDs. *(p. 499)*
3. Analyze the complications of common STDs. *(p. 499)*
4. Analyze ways to prevent infection from STDs. *(p. 502)*
5. Discuss the progression of HIV infection to AIDS. *(p. 504)*
6. Identify treatment and prevention strategies for HIV and AIDS. *(p. 508)*
7. List tests used to determine the presence of HIV. *(p. 512)*

Why It's Important

You can avoid becoming infected with an STD or HIV. The information in this lesson will help reduce your risk of being infected.

Key Terms

- sexually transmitted disease (STD)
- chlamydia
- gonorrhea
- herpes
- genital warts
- pubic lice
- thrush
- Kaposi's sarcoma (KS)
- Western blot
- HIV negative

Write ABOUT IT!

Writing About AIDS The AIDS quilt above represents people who have died of AIDS. After reading about AIDS on page 504, write an entry in your health journal about the ways HIV is spread, and the ways it is not spread. Then make an HIV awareness brochure, using what you wrote in your journal.

National Health Education Standards—Guide for Lesson 46		
1.1	Predict how healthy behaviors can impact health status.	pp. 499–503, 506–509
1.5	Propose ways to reduce or prevent injuries and health problems.	pp. 498, 508–509, 512, 513
1.7	Compare and contrast the benefits of and barriers to practicing a variety of healthy behaviors.	pp. 508–509
1.9	Analyze the potential severity of injury or illness if engaging in unhealthy behaviors.	pp. 498, 499–505, 509
3.4	Determine when professional health services may be required.	pp. 499–503, 510–512
5.7	Evaluate the effectiveness of health-related decisions.	pp. 498, 499–505, 509

Bacterial STDs

Some STDs are caused by types of bacteria. These STDs can be cured through the use of antibiotics. However, antibiotics will not provide lifelong protection against reexposure, and a person can be reinfected with the disease. In this section, you will learn the causes, methods of transmission, symptoms, and treatments of these types of STDs.

What to Know About Bacterial STDs

Chlamydia

Cause The most common bacterial STD in the U.S. is *chlamydia* (kluh MIH dee uh), an STD that is caused by the bacterium *Chlamydia trachomatis* that produces inflammation of the reproductive organs.

Methods of transmission Chlamydia is spread by sexual contact with an infected partner. A pregnant female may pass the infection to her newborn baby during delivery. During delivery, the chlamydia bacteria can enter the baby's eyes or lungs. If not treated, the baby can become blind or develop pneumonia.

Symptoms Symptoms usually appear one to three weeks after exposure. One-half of infected males have no symptoms, but still can infect a sexual partner. Chlamydia bacteria can continue to multiply in a male who does not know he is infected. Males with symptoms may have painful urination, a discharge from the penis, and pain or swelling in the scrotum.

Roughly three-quarters of infected females have no symptoms. A female may not know she has chlamydia until complications develop. Symptoms include a burning sensation during urination and an unusual discharge from the vagina.

Diagnosis and treatment A physician uses a cotton swab to collect a sample of the discharge, which is examined in a laboratory for the presence of the chlamydia bacteria. Antibiotics are used to treat chlamydia. Infected persons must take all the prescribed antibiotics, even after the symptoms disappear. A follow-up visit with a physician is necessary to be sure that the infection is cured. All sex partners of persons infected with chlamydia should be checked and treated.

Complications A serious infection of the internal female reproductive organs is called *pelvic inflammatory disease (PID).* Many cases occur in females infected with chlamydia who had no symptoms. PID can cause a scarring of the Fallopian tubes, or oviducts, which can block the tubes and cause sterility. To be sterile means that a person is unable to produce children. If left untreated, chlamydia also can cause sterility in males.

Ectopic pregnancy also is linked to PID. An *ectopic pregnancy,* or *tubal pregnancy,* occurs when a fertilized egg implants in a Fallopian tube instead of in the uterus. This condition results in the death of the fetus and can be fatal for the pregnant female. Early and continuous prenatal care are important in the detection and treatment of any disease.

Did You Know?

STDs The incurable STDs are viral, and begin with the letter "H."

Bacterial STDs

2 Teach

Class Discussion

Which Is More Vulnerable? Ask students if they believe males or females are more prone to contracting an STD from an infected partner. Tell students that females are actually more prone to contracting an STD than males. Ask them why they think that females are more prone to contracting an STD from an infected partner than males. *When females have intercourse, micro-tears might occur inside the vagina which increases the risk of bodily fluid exchange; whereas in a male, there would have to be a lesion or open wound on the penis for there to be bodily fluid exchange.* **L2**

INTERACTIVE CHALKBOARD with Image Bank

PowerPoint® Presentations

This CD-ROM is an editable Microsoft® PowerPoint® presentation that includes:
- Lesson presentations
- Lesson checks
- Interactive graphics
- 5-Minute Checks
- Image Bank
- All transparencies

CRISS
Project

Discussion Use the Authentic Question Strategy on page 17T to initiate discussion on the sensitive issues of STDs and HIV.

Lesson Resource Manager

- **Unit 8 Fast File Resources**
  Reading Strategy, p. 31
  Vocabulary Practice, p. 32
  Transparency Master and Worksheet, p. 33
  Real-Life Health, p. 35
  Real-Life Health, p. 37
  5-Minute Check, p. 39
  Lesson 46 Quiz, p. 43
- **Unit 8 Transparency**
- **Lesson 46 Transparency**

- **Reading Essentials**
- **Technology**
  TeacherWorks™ CD-ROM
  StudentWorks™ CD-ROM
  Reading Essentials CD-ROM
  Exam*View*® Assessment Suite
  Vocabulary Puzzlemaker

National Health Education Standards

Pages 498–499: 1.1, 1.3, 1.5, 1.8, 1.9, 3.4, 4.1, 7.1, 7.4

Extension

Syphilis in the Past Have students research the history of syphilis. Student reports should answer the following questions: When was it discovered? How do scientists believe it originated? When was it a major problem? How did the public battle it? What were the views on STDs at that time? How do these views relate to today's societal views of STDs? **L3**

Quick Demo

Spreading the STD Have one index card for each student available prior to the demo. Have three of them labeled with an STD, three labeled with *abstinent,* and the rest labeled *blank,* representing unprotected intercourse. Have the index cards folded in half and be sure none of the students look at their contents until told to do so. Tell the students to shake five other students' hands, and write their names on the outside of the card.

After everyone has done so, have them look at their cards. Have the five students that have an STD stand up, then have those that shook their hands stand up, unless they have an *abstinent* card. Then have those who shook the hand of anyone standing up, stand up as well. Continue this until all those who have shaken hands are standing. The majority of the class should be standing except those with the *abstinent* cards. Explain that shaking hands represented some type of sexual contact and point out how easily the diseases were spread. **L2 ELL**

Teacher FYI

STIs Some health resources use the term *STI* instead of *STD*. Both terms refer to the same thing. *STI* refers to sexually transmitted infections, while *STD* refers to sexually transmitted diseases.

Did You Know?

Terminology In this textbook, the term *sexually transmitted diseases* (STDs) is used. In some health resources, the term *sexually transmitted infections* (STIs) is used. These terms can be used interchangeably.

Syphilis

Cause An STD caused by the bacterium *Treponema pallidum* is **syphilis.** The bacterium enters the body through tiny breaks in the mucous membranes and then burrows its way into the bloodstream.

Methods of transmission Syphilis is spread by intimate sexual contact with an infected person. The bacteria also can be transmitted from a pregnant female to her fetus.

Symptoms The first stage of syphilis is *primary syphilis.* The first symptom of syphilis is a chancre. A *chancre* (SHAN ker) is a painless, open sore that appears at the site where the bacteria entered the body, such as the genitals or the mouth. Chancres appear within ten days to three months after exposure to syphilis, but may go unnoticed if inside the body. Though painless, chancres are contagious. The chancre will disappear within a few weeks whether or not an infected person is treated; however, the pathogens for syphilis remain in the body and the disease progresses to secondary syphilis.

Secondary syphilis is characterized by a skin rash and begins anywhere from weeks to months after the chancre appears. Other symptoms, such as fever, tiredness, headache, sore throat, swollen lymph glands, and loss of weight and hair, may occur. The symptoms will disappear without treatment and may come and go during the next few years. People are still contagious during secondary syphilis.

Diagnosis and treatment People with a suspicious skin rash or sore in the genital area should be checked by a physician. A blood test will detect the presence of the bacteria that cause syphilis in any stage of the disease. Syphilis is treated with antibiotic drugs, though treatment in the later stages cannot reverse the damage done to body organs in earlier stages.

Complications If secondary syphilis is not treated, it may become latent syphilis. *Latent syphilis* is a stage of syphilis in which there are no symptoms, but the bacteria are still present. Latent syphilis can last for years and even for decades. Eventually, people who are infected will develop late syphilis. *Late syphilis,* or *tertiary syphilis,* is the final stage of syphilis in which bacteria irreversibly damage body organs. Mental incapacity, blindness, paralysis, heart disease, liver damage, and death may occur.

If a pregnant female has syphilis, the fetus is at risk. The pregnancy may result in a miscarriage, stillbirth, or fetal death. If a baby is born to a mother with syphilis, it has a high risk of becoming infected with syphilis. Babies with syphilis may have birth defects, skin sores, rashes, fever, a swollen liver and spleen, yellowish skin, anemia, and are at high risk for developing mental retardation.

A symptom of ▶ secondary syphilis is a skin rash that can appear on any part of the body, such as the foot.

500 UNIT 8 • Communicable and Chronic Diseases

Sensitive Issues

Sexually Transmitted Diseases in Teenagers According to the Centers for Disease Control and Prevention, over one-fourth of newly reported sexually transmitted diseases are found in teenagers. That is nearly 4 million a year. These statistics make it evident that you may have students who are sexually active or who know someone who is sexually active. Also, you may have students who have been or are infected with a type of sexually transmitted disease. When discussing STDs in class, care needs to be taken to avoid personal questions. Let students know that if they need to speak to someone, their privacy is important and will be respected by you. Encourage students to talk to a parent or guardian. Also have ready a list of trusted counselors and resources that students can utilize.

Gonorrhea

Cause A highly contagious STD caused by the bacterium *Neisseria gonorrhoeae* is **gonorrhea.** Gonorrhea infects the linings of the genital and urinary tracts of males and females.

Methods of transmission Gonorrhea is spread by sexual contact with an infected person. A baby born to an infected female can become infected during childbirth if the bacteria enter the baby's eyes.

Symptoms Males usually have a white, milky discharge from the penis and a burning sensation during urination. They usually experience pain and increased urination within two to five days after infection, or they may not have any symptoms. Whether or not symptoms are present, an infected person may still be contagious.

Many infected females have no symptoms. If symptoms appear, they include a burning sensation during urination and a yellow discharge from the vagina that usually appear within ten days after sexual contact with an infected partner.

Severe symptoms, such as abdominal pain, bleeding between menstrual periods, vomiting, or fever, can occur if gonorrhea is not treated.

Diagnosis and treatment Diagnosis of gonorrhea is made by a microscopic examination of the discharge or analysis of the urine. The gram stain is a test that involves placing a smear of the discharge on a slide stained with a dye. The test is accurate for males but not for females. The preferred method for females is the culture test, which involves

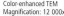

Color-enhanced TEM
Magnification: 12 000x

◄ This magnification shows the bacteria *Neisseria gonorrhoeae*, which cause gonorrhea.

placing a sample of the discharge on a culture plate and letting it grow for 24–72 hours.

Another type of test, a nucleic acid amplification test, can be done on urine or discharge. This test is highly accurate, but not all health-care providers offer it.

Antibiotics are used to treat gonorrhea. Some strains are resistant to certain antibiotics, making treatment difficult. People with gonorrhea should take the full course of prescribed medication. A follow-up visit to a physician is necessary. All sex partners of infected people should be tested even if they have no symptoms.

Most states require that the eyes of newborn babies be treated with antibiotics or silver nitrate immediately after birth to prevent gonococcal infection of the eyes in case the mother was infected.

Complications The *Neisseria gonorrhoeae* bacteria can spread into the bloodstream and infect the joints, heart valves, and the brain. Gonorrhea in both males and females can cause permanent sterility, and is a major cause of pelvic inflammatory disease (PID) in females.

In newborns, gonococcal infection can lead to blindness.

LESSON 46 • Reducing the Risk of STDs and HIV **501**

5-Minute Check

Page 39, **Unit 8 Fast File Resources**

1. How are bacterial STDs cured? *through the use of antibiotics*
2. What can occur if chlamydia is left untreated? *People can become sterile. Females can develop PID or have an ectopic pregnancy.*
3. How many stages of syphilis are there? *four*
4. Why should syphilis be treated as soon as possible? *It can cause permanent organ damage and even death after many years.*
5. Why should someone being treated for gonorrhea have a follow-up visit? *They may not be cured because there are many strains of gonorrhea that are resistant to certain antibiotics.*

Achieving Health Literacy

Self-Directed Learner Have students create an STD FYI bulletin board. They can post statistics on teen STDs, information about each common STD, common signs and symptoms, and how abstinence is the most effective means of preventing the spread of STDs. Encourage students to be creative and think of catchy phrases they could use to grab other students' attention. Have them do more extensive research on each STD so that the bulletin board contains up-to-date information. Set aside space for the bulletin board in your classroom. **L3**

National Health Education Standards

Pages 500–501: 1.1, 5.7

Viral STDs

S everal STDs are caused by viruses. Treatment for symptoms of these STDs is available, but there are no cures for them. In this section, you will learn about the causes, methods of transmission, symptoms, and treatments of viral STDs.

What to Know About Viral STDs

Did You Know?

HPV in the U.S. It is estimated that 500,000 to 1,000,000 people in the United States are infected with HPV each year.

Herpes

Cause and complications An STD caused by the herpes simplex virus (HSV) that produces cold sores or fever blisters in the genital area or mouth is *herpes.* A virus that causes cold sores or fever blisters in the mouth or on the lips is *herpes simplex virus type 1 (HSV-1).* HSV-1 also may cause genital sores. *Herpes simplex virus type 2 (HSV-2)* is a virus that causes genital sores, but also may cause sores in the mouth. Both viruses remain in the body for life. People with genital herpes fear recurrences and are at greater risk of HIV infection.

Methods of transmission Genital herpes is spread by sexual contact with an infected person. An infected pregnant female can infect her baby during vaginal delivery.

Symptoms Symptoms of genital herpes occur within two weeks after contact with an infected partner. Symptoms can include an itching or burning sensation; pain in the legs, buttocks, or genital area; vaginal discharge; or a feeling of pressure in the abdominal area. Clusters of small, painful blisters that may develop into open sores appear in the genital area. The symptoms disappear after a few weeks. Outbreaks may recur throughout an infected person's life.

Diagnosis and treatment Diagnosis is made by growing the virus from a swab taken from the ulcers. Blood tests can be given to detect the presence of antibodies to HSV in the blood. Antiviral drugs have been approved to relieve symptoms and prevent recurrences, but they do not cure genital herpes.

HPV

Cause and complications The most common type of viral STD in the United States is *HPV,* or *human papillomavirus.* There are more than 70 known types of HPV. Some of these types of HPV cause *genital warts,* or wartlike growths on the genitals. Other types of HPV have been linked to cervical cancer.

Methods of transmission Genital warts are contagious and are spread during sexual contact. They also can be spread from a pregnant female to her baby during vaginal delivery of the baby.

Symptoms Genital warts may appear after a few weeks or even years after infection. They can be soft or hard, are usually flesh-colored or white, and resemble a cauliflower. These warts are usually painless.

Diagnosis and treatment A physician inspects the warts to make a diagnosis.

A Pap smear is used to collect cells from the cervix to be tested for cervical cancer. No treatment completely eradicates the virus causing genital warts. Though warts can be frozen, burned, or cut off, they may reappear.

Viral Hepatitis

Cause and complications A viral infection of the liver is ***viral hepatitis.*** Several different viruses cause hepatitis, including hepatitis A (HAV), hepatitis B (HBV), hepatitis C (HCV), delta hepatitis (HDV), and hepatitis E (HEV). Many cases of hepatitis are not a serious threat to health. Others are long-lasting and can lead to liver failure, liver cancer, and death.

Methods of transmission Viral hepatitis, except infection by HEV, is known to be spread through sexual contact. HBV, HCV, and HDV also are spread through sharing contaminated needles. HAV is most commonly spread fecal-orally by contaminated food and water. HEV is spread mainly through contaminated water. HBV and HCV can be spread from a pregnant female to her baby.

Symptoms Many infected people have no symptoms. The most common early symptoms are flu-like. Later symptoms may include dark urine, abdominal pain, and jaundice. ***Jaundice*** is yellowing of the skin and whites of the eyes.

Diagnosis and treatment Blood tests confirm viral hepatitis. Treatment consists of bed rest, a healthful diet, and avoidance of alcoholic beverages. Drugs may be prescribed to improve liver function. Vaccines are now available for lifelong immunity to hepatitis A and hepatitis B.

Other STDs

Parasitic STDs are caused by organisms that feed off a person's body. Pediculosis and trichomoniasis are STDs that are caused by parasites and spread through sexual contact.

Pediculosis An infestation of crab lice, or ***pubic lice,*** is called pediculosis. The lice pierce the skin to feed on human blood. The bites and waste matter cause itching. These parasites can contaminate bedding, towels, and toilet seats because they can live for about 24 hours without feeding.

To diagnose an infestation of lice, a physician examines the body to find the lice and their nits, or eggs, which are visible by the naked eye or through a magnifying glass. Prescription or OTC medicated creams or shampoos are used to kill the lice.

Trichomoniasis A parasite, *Trichomonas vaginalis,* causes the STD ***trichomoniasis*** (trih kuh muh NI uh suhs). The parasite is spread through intimate sexual contact.

Although most males do not experience any symptoms, symptoms can include a thin, whitish discharge from the penis and painful or difficult urination. About half of all infected females have no symptoms. There may be a yellow-green or gray vaginal discharge that has an unpleasant odor, painful urination, or irritation and itching in the genital area.

To diagnose trichomoniasis, a smear of the discharge is examined under a microscope. Drug treatment is used to treat both infected partners.

Reading Review

1. Which STDs are bacterial?
2. Which STDs are viral?
3. What is the difference between the two types?

1. What are the most common signs of genital herpes? *cold sores and blisters in the mouth or genital area*
2. What is the treatment for genital herpes? *Antiviral drugs help relieve the symptoms.*
3. What bodily organ can hepatitis affect? *the liver*
4. Other than sexual contact, what are other ways that viral hepatitis can be spread? *sharing contaminated needles, contaminated food and water, and from infected mother to child*
5. What are the complications of having pubic lice? *itching and irritation in the genital area*

Class Activity

Word Search Have students create a word search using the Key Terms and other vocabulary words in this lesson. Include the names of the STDs and their symptoms. **L2** **ELL**

Reading Review

1. *chlamydia, syphilis, gonorrhea*
2. *herpes, HPV, hepatitis*
3. *Bacterial STDs can be cured with antibiotics. Viral STDs have no cure.*

🏛 **Community Involvement**

STDs in the Community Have students contact their local health department and find out how many cases of various STDs occur in the community and state where they live. Have students ask these questions: Which STDs are the most common? Are the STDs more or less prevalent in their community than in the state? Are those STDs bacterial, viral, or parasitic? Can the STDs that are prevalent in their community be cured? Why do they think this is occurring? Where can someone obtain help? After they have obtained the information, have the students present their findings to the class in a multimedia report. **L2**

National Health Education Standards
Pages 502–503: 1.1, 3.4, 5.7

HIV Infection and AIDS

Extension

Current Statistics Have students research the most current statistics about HIV and AIDS. Have them find out how many people have died each year from AIDS since the AIDS epidemic began in the early 1980s and how many new cases of AIDS have been diagnosed this year. Have students create a news report of their findings and present it to the class. **L3**

Teacher FYI

International Statistics According to the Joint United Nations Program on HIV/AIDS, there were 5 million new HIV infections in 2001 worldwide, of which 800,000 were children. Also, in 2002, an estimated 3.1 million people died of AIDS worldwide. Women are becoming increasingly affected by HIV. About 50 percent of the people living with HIV worldwide are women. **L2**

NHES Assessment/SCASS

Selected Response Which of the following is a protein that helps fight infection?

A. B cell
B. antibody
C. lymphocyte
D. helper T cell

You may have heard, at some time or another, someone say "You can catch AIDS." This statement is false. AIDS (aquired immunodeficiency syndrome) is a condition that results after a person becomes infected with HIV. You cannot "catch" AIDS, but you can develop AIDS after HIV has inflicted enough destruction of the body cells. The information in this lesson will describe what happens when HIV enters the body and develops into AIDS.

The Body's Response to HIV

Recall that **lymphocytes** are white blood cells that help the body fight pathogens. When a pathogen enters the body, lymphocytes multiply in lymph tissue to fight infection. A **B cell** is a white blood cell that produces antibodies. A **helper T cell** is a white blood cell that signals B cells to produce antibodies. An **antibody** is a special protein that helps fight infection.

HIV A pathogen that destroys infection-fighting T cells in the body is the **human immunodeficiency virus (HIV).** When HIV enters the body, it attaches to a molecule called CD4 on helper T cells. HIV then takes control of the helper T cells and reproduces more HIV. As HIV reproduces, it attacks the other helper T cells and takes control of them.

Some signs of HIV infection may include flu-like symptoms, such as fever, sore throat, skin rash, diarrhea, swollen glands, loss of appetite, and night sweats. These signs may come and go as the helper T cell count fluctuates. Many people will not develop severe symptoms for years. As their helper T cell count drops, however, they become more susceptible to many opportunistic infections when they are infected with HIV.

Opportunistic infections An infection that develops in a person with a weak immune system is an **opportunistic infection.** The pathogens that cause opportunistic infections already are present in the bodies of most people, but usually are harmless unless a person has HIV or another disease that weakens the immune system.

There are many types of opportunistic infections. **Thrush** is a fungal infection of the mucous membranes of the tongue and mouth. White spots and ulcers cover the infected area. Infections of the skin and mucous membranes also appear. There may be sores around the anus, genital area, and mouth.

Oral hairy leukoplakia is an infection causing fuzzy white patches on the tongue. **Pneumocystis carinii pneumonia (PCP)** is a form

Make the Connection

Immune System To learn more about the immune system, see page 485 in Lesson 44.

Cross-Curricular Connections

History Have students research the history of HIV and AIDS and create a timeline. Questions students can consider when creating a timeline include: When did HIV/AIDS first appear? Where was the first case reported? When did it first appear in the United States? When was it labeled as an epidemic? When was the first treatment for HIV/AIDS discovered? Who was the first doctor to do major research on HIV/AIDS, and when did his or her research begin? Have students use illustrations and create a title for their timelines. **L3**

of pneumonia that may affect people infected with HIV. Luckily, PCP can be prevented or treated with medication. People who are infected with HIV are also at risk for developing tuberculosis.

People who are infected with HIV also are at risk for developing rare types of cancers. *Kaposi's sarcoma (KC)* is a type of cancer that affects people who are infected with HIV. KS causes purplish lesions and tumors on the skin and in the linings of the internal organs. These lesions spread to most of the linings of the body.

HIV also destroys brain and nerve cells. *AIDS dementia complex* is a loss of brain function caused by HIV infection. There is gradual loss of a person's ability to think and move, a personality change, and a loss of coordination. As AIDS dementia complex

progresses, confusion increases and memory loss becomes severe.

People who have AIDS may develop HIV wasting syndrome. *HIV wasting syndrome* is a substantial loss in body weight that is accompanied by high fevers, sweating, and diarrhea.

Roughly 40,000 people in the United States become infected with HIV each year, though one-quarter to one-third do not know they are infected. People with or without symptoms can pass the virus to others.

Many people do not show symptoms for many years after infection, so they may pass the disease onto others unknowingly. According to the Centers for Disease Control and Prevention (CDC), a person infected with HIV who has 200 or fewer helper T cells per microliter of blood or an opportunistic infection is diagnosed with AIDS.

When HIV Enters the Body

❶ HIV enters the body.

❷ HIV attaches to and takes control of helper T cells.

❸ HIV reproduces itself and destroys helper T cells.

❹ HIV continues to attack, reproduce, and destroy other helper T cells. This weakens the body's ability to fight infection.

According to the Centers for Disease Control and Prevention, a person infected with HIV has AIDS when (s)he has 200 or fewer helper T cells per microliter of blood or an opportunistic infection.

LESSON 46 • Reducing the Risk of STDs and HIV   **505**

NHES Assessment/SCASS

Performance Event Have students create a chart on different types of opportunistic infections. The chart should include the following information: Are the infections protozoan, viral, mycobacterial, fungal, or cancerous? What are some important points about each opportunistic infection? What are the signs and symptoms? **L3 ELL**

Class Activity

Misconceptions Have students get in groups of three or four. Have each group come up with and write down as many "facts" about HIV and AIDS that they can think of. Then come together as a class and have each group share their "facts." Discuss as a class which ones truly are facts and which ones are misconceptions. **L2 ELL**

Class Discussion

Tattoos and HIV Ask students if they think someone could obtain HIV from getting a tattoo. *yes* Have students explain how it can be transmitted. *if an infected needle is used to tattoo* Ask students how spreading HIV from obtaining tattoos can be prevented. *Do not get a tattoo.* **L2**

(DI) Differentiated Instruction

Physical Challenges Pair a physically challenged student with another student. Together, student pairs should decide upon the main points of the lesson, including the types of STDs, how they are spread, symptoms, diagnosis, and treatment. Students can help the student with a physical impairment create flash cards with the main points of the lesson. The student with the physical impairment can categorize the diseases into types, such as viral, bacterial, and parasitic. The students can quiz each other using the flash cards. **L2**

National Health Education Standards
Pages 504–505: 5.7

HIV Transmission

Quick Demo

Mixing Colors Bring to class three containers with three different colors of paint and two paintbrushes. Line up the three containers of paint next to each other. Explain to the students that each color is a person. Take one brush and dip it into one color. Tell the class that the brush is another person. Take the same brush and dip it into the next color and then the third color. Explain that the demonstration shows that one person having sexual contact with another is also passing infections to others. Point out that the colors are not mixed if there is no contact. **ELL**

NHES Assessment/SCASS

Constructed Response Present students with the following situation: They are coming home from school and find a person unconscious on the sidewalk. There is blood coming from a wound on the person's head, and it appears that he or she has bitten his or her lip as well. There is no pulse or breathing. Ask students to write one or two paragraphs answering the following questions: What do you do? *Call for help and start CPR.* How do you protect yourself from exposure to the blood? *Use a face mask and use universal precautions or wash the area off.* **L2**

HIV Transmission

People who are infected with HIV may have HIV in most of their bodily fluids. HIV is spread from infected persons to others by contact with certain bodily fluids. These bodily fluids are blood, semen, vaginal secretions, and in a few cases, breast milk. Minute traces of HIV have been found in saliva and tears. To date, there have been no documented cases of HIV transmission through saliva and tears. However, if these bodily fluids contain infected blood, the virus could be transmitted through these fluids. HIV is transmitted when a person engages in specific risk behaviors or is involved in risk situations.

What to Know About HIV Transmission

Sexual contact During sexual contact, HIV from an infected person may enter the body of an uninfected partner through exposed blood vessels in small cuts or tiny cracks in mucous membranes. HIV transmission can occur if the male ejaculates or if he withdraws before ejaculation. This is because HIV is present in the pre-ejaculatory fluid. A person that comes in contact with this fluid can become infected with HIV.

Increased risks from sexual contact include having multiple sex partners, having sex with someone involved in risky behaviors, such as prostitution or injection drug use, or having other sexually transmitted diseases. The greater the number of sex partners people have, the more likely they will have sex with someone who is infected with HIV. STDs that produce sores or lead to bleeding or discharge provide ways for HIV to spread more easily. Genital sores provide an exit point for infected people and an entry point for uninfected people for transmission of HIV in blood, semen, and vaginal secretions.

Open-mouth kissing The Centers for Disease Control and Prevention warns against open-mouth kissing with a person infected with HIV because of the possibility of contact with infected blood. However, the risk of transmission of HIV in this manner is low.

Sharing needles or syringes for injectable drugs An intravenous drug user is a person who injects illegal drugs into the body with syringes, needles, and other injection equipment. When an infected person injects drugs, droplets of HIV-infected blood remain on the needle, syringe, or other injection equipment. If another person uses a needle, syringe, or other drug equipment that is contaminated with blood from an HIV-infected person, that person may become infected with HIV.

Sharing needles for tattoos or piercings Droplets of HIV-infected blood remain on the needle when an infected person uses a needle to make a tattoo or to pierce ears or other body parts. A second person who shares the needle could become infected with HIV.

👥 Healthy People 2010

Objective 13-5 *Reduce the number of cases of HIV infection among adolescents and adults.*
 Ask students what the most effective way of reducing the number of cases of HIV infection among adults and adolescents is. *Abstain from sexual activity* Have students create an abstinence contract. Have students sign their contracts to remind them of their pledge. Ask students to list ways that teens can resist pressure to engage in sexual activity. Tell students to read more about abstinence in Lesson 16 for help in completing the assignment. **L2**

Contact with the blood, other bodily fluids, or mucous membranes People who handle the body fluids of a person who is infected with HIV risk having HIV enter the body through small cuts or tears on the skin or through a splash in the eyes. Touching the mucous membranes or broken skin of an HIV-infected person may result in contact with exposed blood vessels. Sharing a personal item, such as the razor of an infected person, increases the risk of having HIV enter the body.

Having a blood transfusion with infected blood or blood products In the United States, the FDA controls blood donations, blood donor centers, and blood labs. All donors are screened. After donation, blood is tested for HIV, hepatitis B, syphilis, and other diseases, so the risk of HIV infection is extremely rare. People traveling to countries other than the United States should inquire about the safety of the blood supply, so that if they become injured and in need of a blood transfusion, they will know if a blood transfusion in that country will be safe. You cannot become infected with HIV from donating blood or receiving a blood transfusion within the United States.

Having a tissue transplant (organ donation) In the United States, screening and testing procedures have reduced the risk of being infected as a result of human tissue transplants. Potential donors for all human tissues must be tested for HIV, hepatitis B, hepatitis C and other diseases. They also must be screened for risk behaviors and symptoms of AIDS and hepatitis. Imported tissues must be accompanied by records showing that the tissues were screened and tested. If no records are available, tissues are shipped under quarantine to the United States. People having tissue transplants outside the United States should check screening and testing procedures.

Being born to a mother infected with HIV A pregnant female infected with HIV can transmit HIV through the umbilical cord to her developing embryo or fetus. A baby also can be infected while passing through the mother's vagina at birth. Although not as common, a nursing baby can become infected with HIV through the breast milk of an infected mother. From 15 to 30 percent of all pregnant females infected with HIV infect their babies with HIV through perinatal transmission. Perinatal transmission is the transfer of an infection to a baby during pregnancy, during delivery, or after birth through breast milk.

▲ When people donate blood in the United States, it is screened for HIV and other diseases.

Ways HIV Is Not Transmitted

To date, there have been no documented cases of HIV transmission through saliva or tears. According to the Centers for Disease Control and Prevention, HIV is not spread through casual contact, such as

- closed-mouth kissing;
- hugging;
- touching, holding, or shaking hands;
- coughing or sneezing;
- sharing food or eating utensils, such as soda or silverware;
- having casual contact with friends;
- sharing bathroom facilities or water fountains;

- sharing a pen or pencil;
- being bitten by insects;
- sharing towels or combs;
- eating food prepared or served by someone else;
- attending school;
- using a telephone or computer used by someone else;
- swimming in a pool;
- using sports and gym equipment.

LESSON 46 • Reducing the Risk of STDs and HIV **507**

INTERACTIVE CHALKBOARD with Image Bank

5-Minute Check

Page 41, **Unit 8 Fast File Resources**

1. What does AIDS stand for? *acquired immunodeficiency syndrome*
2. Name several opportunistic infections. *oral hairy leukoplakia, pneumocystis carinii pneumonia, thrush*
3. What is HIV wasting syndrome? *a substantial loss in body weight that is accompanied by high fevers, sweating, and diarrhea*
4. What bodily fluids can spread HIV? *blood, semen, vaginal fluids, and breast milk*
5. What are some behaviors through which HIV can be spread? *sexual contact, sharing infected needles, tissue transplants*

Explain the Concept

Not Transmitted Have the students go through the list of ways in which HIV is not transmitted. Ask them why some of these ways were originally suspected of spreading AIDS. *Students may reply that so little was known about HIV when the epidemic started that some people believed that AIDS could be spread in these ways.* Explain that even though saliva, sweat, and tears can contain a minuscule amount of HIV, the other person would have to consume an extremely large amount of the fluids to become infected. **L2**

Health Project

Simulated AIDS Quilt Give a sheet of poster board to each student. Before completing this activity, students should research a person who has died from AIDS. This person might have been someone they knew or a public figure who died from AIDS. Have them list, on their poster boards, qualities, accomplishments, interests, and any other unique characteristics about their chosen person. Make sure students focus on the positive qualities of the person. After everyone is finished, have them connect each of their poster boards together like a quilt and read through each student's poster board. **L2**

National Health Education Standards

Pages 506–507: 1.1, 5.7

Avoiding STDs and HIV

Avoiding STDs and HIV

A person's use of self-control to act on responsible values is *character.* If you value your health and that of others, your relationships, and your family's guidelines, you must use self-control to prevent the spread of STDs. The following section gives you guidelines on how to protect yourself and others from STDs.

What to Know About Avoiding STDs and HIV

> **Make the Connection**
>
> **Choosing Abstinence** For more information on making responsible decisions, see page 61 in Lesson 6.

▲ Abstinence from sexual activity until marriage is the only method that is 100 percent effective in preventing STDs and the sexual transmission of HIV.

Abstain from sex until you are married. The only method that is 100 percent effective in preventing the spread of STDs and HIV is abstinence. No form of contraception or barrier protection is 100 percent effective in preventing the spread of STDs. When you practice abstinence from sex, you avoid risk behaviors in which STDs are transmitted.

Change your behavior and be tested for STDs and HIV if you have been sexually active. People who are sexually active now can begin to practice abstinence, and should see a physician or go to a clinic to be tested for STDs. If a person is infected, he or she needs prompt treatment. Remember, it is possible to be infected and not have symptoms. If a person plans to marry in the future, he or she must tell a potential partner that he or she is infected with HIV, genital herpes, or genital warts because there is no cure. Discuss your past behavior with your parents, guardian, or other responsible adult and ask for their help and support.

Have a monogamous marriage if you choose to marry in the future. A monogamous marriage is a marriage in which partners have sex only with each other. It provides security and protects partners from infection with STDs and HIV.

Choose a drug-free lifestyle. Drugs dull your reasoning. You might not think clearly and thus violate your decision to practice abstinence until marriage. You might become infected with STDs.

Avoid use of injectable drugs. Sharing injection equipment for drug use, including steroids, is a risk behavior for STDs and HIV.

Change your behavior if you use drugs. If a person misuses or abuses drugs, he or she should talk to a parent or guardian, and see a physician or be tested for STDs at a clinic.

508 UNIT 8 • Communicable and Chronic Diseases

Just the FACTS: STDS AND HIV

❝Is it correct that few teenagers get STDs?❞

❝If I get an STD, can I get rid of it with a shot or some pills?❞

❝Can you get HIV if you've only had sex with one person? Anyway, can't you tell if someone has HIV or an STD?❞

the FACTS According to the U.S. Centers for Disease Control and Prevention, teenagers are at high risk for getting most STDs. Approximately one out of every four new STD infections occurs in a teenager every year. Why? Teenagers are more likely than adults to have more than one sex partner and to have unprotected sex. Young women also are biologically more susceptible to chlamydia, gonorrhea, and HIV than are young men. In fact, it is estimated that 5 percent of young men and 5–10 percent of young women are infected with chlamydia.

the FACTS Viral STDs, such as genital herpes and hepatitis B, cannot be cured. The herpes virus remains in your body for life, and open sores may reappear from time to time. Also, bacterial STDs, such as chlamydia, can have no symptoms, especially in women. They can go untreated and can be spread unknowingly. You also can be re-infected with STDs. Women experience more severe health problems because of STDs than men, including pelvic inflammatory disease (PID) and cervical cancer.

the FACTS If a person has sex with one partner, he or she is essentially having sex with every person who has had sex with that partner, plus every person who has had sex with the partner's former partners. A person is at risk of getting any STD that these people have, as well as HIV. It can be difficult and often impossible to tell if a person has an STD by just observing the person. In fact, many people who have STDs do not know it. They may find out, eventually, when the symptoms finally appear. For HIV, this can mean years from the time they are infected. About 5 million people worldwide became infected with HIV in 2002. They include 2 million women and 800,000 children under the age of 15.

If he or she is infected, he or she needs prompt treatment. If you are dependent on drugs, you need treatment in order to stop. Ask your parents, guardian, or other responsible adult for their help and support.

Avoid sharing a needle to make tattoos or to pierce ears and other body parts. Sharing a needle to make a tattoo or pierce ears and other body parts is a risk behavior.

Follow universal precautions. Universal precautions are steps taken to prevent the spread of disease by treating all human blood and certain bodily fluids as if they contained HIV, HBV, and other pathogens. Always follow universal precautions when you have contact with a person's blood and other bodily fluids. Wear disposable latex or vinyl gloves and wash your hands with soap and water or waterless antiseptic hand cleanser after removing the gloves. Use a face mask or shield with a one-way valve if you perform first aid for breathing emergencies. Avoid touching objects that have had contact with a person's blood. Do not eat or drink anything or touch your mouth, eyes, or nose while performing first aid.

Take other precautions to prevent STDs. Do not engage in open-mouth kissing with someone who has blisters, lesions, ulcers, or chancres in his or her mouth. Avoid contact with an infected person's objects, linens, clothing, and damp towels.

Just the FACTS:

STDs and HIV According to the American School Health Association, roughly 15 million new cases of STDs occur each year. Have the students read each question in Just the Facts and tell whether they agree or disagree with the answer. The discussion may uncover misconceptions students may have about STDs, HIV, and sexual choices. **L2**

Class Activity

Universal Precaution List Have students list the universal precautions. (See page 711 in Lesson 69 for more information on the universal precautions.) Have them rate themselves by each step if they would always, sometimes, or rarely follow these precautions. Then have them write down how they could improve in those that they would rarely or sometimes follow. How does abstinence help them practice universal precautions? **L2**

Extension

Abstinence Advocate Have students investigate the social activities in which teens in their community can participate when dating. Have them develop a list of healthful activities in which teens can participate instead of being sexually active. Students also should include information about STDs and HIV. Encourage them to be creative when making the list and to make copies for students who would be interested. **L2**

🧭 Achieving Health Literacy

Effective Communicator Have students pretend that they are advice columnists for a teen magazine. Tell them that a sexually active teen has written in and wants to change his or her behavior and practice abstinence. However, he or she is afraid of losing his or her significant other. Have students write a letter to the teen. Ask them to address these issues in the letter: What are the possible consequences the teen will face if he or she continues his or her behavior? What might happen if the teen decides to practice abstinence? Which is the healthy decision? The letters should reflect healthful decision-making skills. **L2**

National Health Education Standards

Pages 508–509: 1.1, 1.5, 1.7, 1.8, 1.9, 5.7, 7.1, 7.2

HIV and AIDS Treatments

There is no cure for HIV infection or AIDS. Treatment focuses on slowing the progression of the virus by taking drugs and practicing healthful habits. Early treatment is critical in slowing the rate at which HIV multiplies. This, in turn, delays the progression of HIV to AIDS. Though the rate of progression of HIV to AIDS varies greatly from person to person, it is estimated that the average time between HIV infection and AIDS related symptom onset is typically 8–11 years.

What to Know About HIV Treatments

Did You Know?

Treatment Regimens Depending on the treatment regimen and stage of the disease, a person infected with HIV may need to take between 2 and 20 pills per day.

Reading Review

1. How does HIV harm the body?
2. What is the criteria for diagnosing AIDS?
3. How can HIV be transmitted?

HIV treatments are complex issues. Many critical elements must be taken into consideration before beginning any treatment regimen. A comprehensive medical evaluation must be performed, including a physical examination and blood work. Blood work is done to look at the baseline of the patient's viral load, or the amount of HIV particles that are in the blood, and CD4 counts. Both of these numbers help physicians track the progression of the disease.

Drugs are used to treat HIV infection to slow the progression of the disease. However, there are serious side effects to some of these drugs. The drug regimen to slow HIV progression can be difficult to adhere to. Patients can also develop a tolerance to the drug regimen.

Antiretroviral drugs Protease inhibitors, or drugs that decrease the amount of HIV in the blood and increase helper T cell counts, and strong combination therapies were first introduced in 1995. More and more antiretroviral drugs, or drugs that suppress the action of HIV, are being approved each year, including reverse transcriptase inhibitors, which decrease the amount of HIV in the blood by interfering with enzymes HIV uses to replicate itself. Currently, there are 19 approved antiretroviral drugs to use for designing regimens, which involve three or more drug combinations.

In addition, there are therapies available to help prevent and fight the many opportunistic infections. Opportunistic infections lead to the death of most people with HIV.

Side effects of antiretroviral drugs People who are infected with HIV may take several combinations of drugs per day. They may forget to take their medication, or may forget which drugs must be taken with food. Some people have difficulty adhering to the food restrictions and drug regimens. Antiretroviral drugs can have some dangerous side effects. These drugs can cause metabolic changes, such as changing cholesterol levels or glucose

510 UNIT 8 • Communicable and Chronic Diseases

Cross-Curricular Connections

Science Have a group of students research how HIV treatment is used to fight off the infection. Have the students answer the following questions: What are the different types of treatments that are currently being used? What do the treatments consist of? How do they specifically block HIV from cells? How do they affect a person's T cell count? Do they help battle against opportunistic infections as well? Are there new treatments that are being tested? How do these treatments fight the infection? Have the group present a multimedia presentation to the class. **L3**

levels. Damage to mitochondria also may occur with antiretroviral drug use. This can lead to muscle wasting, heart failure, or swelling.

People who are infected with HIV must work closely with their doctor to discover the best combination of medications to slow the progress of HIV, but produce the least severe symptoms. The best combination of medications will vary from person to person.

Other ways to stay healthy People who are infected with HIV or who have developed AIDS should practice healthful habits. They should eat healthful foods, get enough rest and sleep, exercise, and avoid alcohol, tobacco, and other drugs. Their weakened immune systems leave them vulnerable to illnesses that are spread through contaminated food. They should avoid eating nonpasteurized dairy products, raw eggs, and raw seafood. Food should be cooked thoroughly. They should wash their hands and eating utensils well with soap and water.

Scientists have made progress in the treatment of HIV and AIDS. They continue to test vaccines and research ways to keep people with HIV and AIDS healthy for as long as possible. Some people may import unapproved, but promising, drugs for HIV and life-threatening AIDS-related diseases. Because there are many scams, the FDA initiated an AIDS Health Fraud Task Force to explain how to identify phony health products and to distribute general information about HIV infection.

www.glencoe.com

Global Health Initiative

At the end of 2002, an estimated 42 million people worldwide were living with HIV/AIDS, and during 2002, approximately 5 million new HIV infections occurred worldwide. In the face of such staggering statistics, the Global Health Initiative (GHI) is working to coordinate resources to reduce these numbers.

The GHI is a collaboration between companies that are members of the World Economic Forum, the World Health Organization (WHO), and the Joint United Nations Programme for HIV/AIDS (UNAIDS). One of the goals of the GHI is to increase the awareness and involvement of businesses in the health of their employees.

To date, the GHI has founded the Global Fund to Fight AIDS, tuberculosis, and malaria and has taken other actions. According to the World Economic Forum, the overall goal of the GHI is to "help reduce the disease burden . . . of HIV by 25 percent [by the year] 2010."

Health Online   Visit www.glencoe.com for more information on HIV.

HIV Incidence and Prevalence Around the World

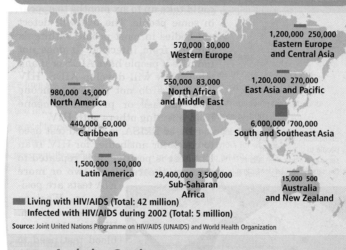

570,000 30,000
Western Europe

1,200,000 250,000
Eastern Europe and Central Asia

550,000 83,000
North Africa and Middle East

1,200,000 270,000
East Asia and Pacific

980,000 45,000
North America

440,000 60,000
Caribbean

6,000,000 700,000
South and Southeast Asia

1,500,000 150,000
Latin America

29,400,000 3,500,000
Sub-Saharan Africa

15,000 500
Australia and New Zealand

■ Living with HIV/AIDS (Total: 42 million)
■ Infected with HIV/AIDS during 2002 (Total: 5 million)

Source: Joint United Nations Programme on HIV/AIDS (UNAIDS) and World Health Organization

Analyzing Graphs

Study the graph above and answer these questions:

1. Which area has the most people living with HIV/AIDS?

2. Are more people newly infected with HIV in Africa or in Europe and Asia combined?

LESSON 46 • Reducing the Risk of STDs and HIV   **511**

Analyzing Graphs

1. Sub-Saharan Africa
2. Africa

Project

Newscast Have the students read the Health News and research the incidence of HIV around the world. Then have them create a 1–2-minute newscast using the information they have obtained from all their sources. **L3**

Extension

Treatment Details Have students choose a specific type of HIV and AIDS treatment. Then have them research the treatment answering the following questions: What does the treatment entail? When should treatment begin? What are the side effects? What are ways to deal with the side effects? How can people decrease their chances of contracting an opportunistic infection? Students should find a creative way to present their findings in class. **L3**

Class Discussion

Is Having HIV the End? Ask students how they would feel if they found out that either they or someone close to them had HIV. Ask them if they would be able to live a "normal" life again. *Over time, treatment has increased the life expectancy of people infected with HIV and many of them live "normal" lives, but with modifications.* What kind of lifestyle changes do HIV patients have to make in order to enjoy life longer? *They have to have treatment, plan their diets, and be careful around people with communicable diseases since their immune systems are weaker.* **L2**

🏛 Community Involvement

Speaker on AIDS Have a speaker from a local AIDS organization visit the class. The speaker can be a nurse or other health professional, or he or she can be a speaker who is infected with HIV. Students should prepare at least one question to ask the speaker. Prior to the speaker's arrival, review students' questions to be sure they are appropriate and that they are not duplicates. After the students listen to the speaker's remarks, have them write a paper on what they learned. Ask them to write about whether this experience caused them to rethink any of their opinions on HIV/AIDS. **L2**

LESSON 47

Reducing the Risk of Cardiovascular Diseases

Out of Time?

If time does not permit an in-depth study of this topic, use the following activities in this Teacher Wraparound Edition:

- Health Goal, p. 514
- Health Project, p. 516
- Using Life Skills, p. 517
- 5-Minute Check, p. 517

1 Focus

HEALTH GOAL **Risky Behaviors** Have students respond to the Health Goal for this lesson by discussing what types of behaviors can increase one's chances of developing cardiovascular disease. Write two categories on the board: *controllable and not controllable,* and write responses in the correct category. Ask students whether there are more factors that are controllable or more that are not controllable. *There should be more ways to control car-diovascular disease.* Emphasize that cardiovascular disease is one of the most preventable diseases people face today. **L2**

Discuss Have students read the scenario, and then discuss it as a class. Students might have difficulty responding now, but will be better able to respond after reading the lesson. **L2**

LESSON 47

What You'll Learn

1. Identify characteristics of different cardiovascular diseases. *(p. 515)*
2. Identify cardiovascular disease risk factors that cannot be controlled. *(p. 518)*
3. Identify cardiovascular risk factors that can be controlled. *(p. 518)*
4. Describe medical diagnoses and treatments for heart disease. *(p. 520)*

Why It's Important

Heart disease, a type of cardiovascular disease, is the leading cause of death in the United States. You can take steps to reduce your risk of developing heart disease. This lesson will describe what you can do to keep your heart healthy.

Key Terms

- cardiovascular disease
- angina pectoris
- plaque
- arteriosclerosis
- arrhythmia
- pacemaker
- stroke
- aneurysm
- prehypertension
- antihypertensives

Reducing the Risk of Cardiovascular Diseases

HEALTH GOAL • I will choose behaviors to reduce my risk of cardiovascular diseases.

A disease of the heart and blood vessels is a ***cardiovascular disease***. In this lesson you will learn about the risk factors you can and cannot control.

Writing About Reducing Risk Suppose that since several members of your family suffer from cardiovascular diseases, you know that you have a higher risk of developing a cardiovascular disease. What can you do to lower your risk? After reading about reducing your risk on page 518, make a list in your health journal of ways you can reduce your risk of developing cardiovascular disease.

National Health Education Standards—Guide for Lesson 47		
1.5	Propose ways to reduce or prevent injuries and health problems.	pp. 518–519, 521
6.1	Assess personal health practices and overall health status.	pp. 518–519, 521

T here are many different kinds of cardiovascular diseases. They have signs and symptoms that are unique to each. In this section you will learn about the characteristics of eight different kinds of cardiovascular diseases.

What to Know About Cardiovascular Diseases

Angina pectoris Chest pain that results from narrowed coronary arteries is ***angina pectoris*** (an JY nuh•PEK tuh ruhs). The pain occurs because the heart is not getting an adequate amount of oxygen. Sudden physical exertion, vigorous exercise, or excessive stress can cause angina pectoris in people with coronary heart disease. Many people with coronary heart disease take nitroglycerin pills to relieve chest pains. ***Nitroglycerin*** is a drug that widens the coronary arteries, allowing more oxygen to get to the cardiac muscle. A heart attack may occur if the narrowing that causes angina pectoris is very severe.

▲ This artery contains plaque buildup.

Congestive heart failure A condition that occurs when the heart's pumping ability is below normal capacity and fluid accumulates in the lungs and other areas of the body is ***congestive heart failure.*** Causes of congestive heart failure are heart attack, atherosclerosis, birth defects, high blood pressure, and rheumatic fever. Drugs that improve the heart's pumping ability and get rid of excess fluids are used to treat congestive heart failure. Reducing the amount of sodium in the diet is helpful.

Coronary heart disease A disease in which the coronary arteries are narrowed or blocked is ***coronary heart disease*** (CHD). A ***coronary artery*** is a blood vessel that carries blood to the heart muscles. The coronary arteries encircle the heart and continuously nourish it with blood. Plaque buildup in the coronary arteries causes coronary heart disease, which can cause a heart attack. ***Plaque*** is hardened deposits of fat and other materials in the walls of arteries throughout the body.

Did You Know?

Fish Oils Omega-3 fatty acids, found in fish oils, are good for the heart. Studies are underway to determine their effect on the health of the brain.

LESSON 47 • Reducing the Risk of Cardiovascular Diseases **515**

2 Teach

Quick Demo

Fatty Deposits Bring in a small sample of vegetable oil and bacon fat, or any other type of animal fat. Explain to the class that both are fats and that both can clog your cardiovascular system if you consume too much. Ask the class which type of fat they think would collect onto the walls of your system faster. *the animal fat* Which one is harder to get rid of? *The animal fat since it solidifies more easily than the vegetable fat.* Reinforce the idea that exercise can burn away fat. Emphasize that fats are essential to a healthful diet. Moderation is the key. **ELL**

INTERACTIVE CHALKBOARD with Image Bank

PowerPoint® Presentations

This CD-ROM is an editable Microsoft® PowerPoint® presentation that includes:
- Lesson presentations
- Lesson checks
- Interactive graphics
- 5-Minute Checks
- Image Bank
- All transparencies

CRISS Project

Vocabulary Refer to the Sentence Synthesis Strategy on page 16T, and after reading the lesson, ask students to brainstorm sentences using the medical terms found in the lesson.

National Health Education Standards
Pages 514–515: 1.1, 1.5

Lesson Resource Manager

- **Unit 8 Fast File Resources**
  Reading Strategy, p. 47
  Vocabulary Practice, p. 48
  Transparency Master and Worksheet, p. 49
  Real-Life Health, p. 51
  Real-Life Health, p. 53
  5-Minute Check, p. 55
  Lesson 47 Quiz, p. 56
- **Unit 8 Transparency**
- **Lesson 47 Transparency**

- **Reading Essentials**
- **Technology**
  TeacherWorks™ CD-ROM
  StudentWorks™ CD-ROM
  Reading Essentials CD-ROM
  Exam*View*® Assessment Suite
  Vocabulary Puzzlemaker

Deadly Arrhythmias According to the American Heart Association, over 40,000 individuals die each year from a primary heart rhythm problem. They are also a contributing cause in about 25 percent of all deaths each year. Plus, over four million people are admitted to hospitals each year with a heart rhythm problem as part or all of their initial symptoms.

Class Activity

Heart Rate (Pulse can be found by the carotid artery on the inner part of the wrist. Students should use their fingertips.) Have each student find his or her pulse and take it for about 15 seconds. Have them multiply the number they counted by four. Explain that each student's number is an estimate of his or her resting heart rate. Ask the class the following question: Could everyone feel a constant rhythm in their pulse? *Everyone should respond with a yes.* Explain that the rhythm is their blood flowing through their body. Ask the class the following: Did anyone have a resting heart rate lower than 60? Tell the class that 60–80 beats per minute is within the normal range. Anything lower signifies a stronger heart. Point out that someone with a heart rhythm abnormality can have an irregular pulse. **L2 ELL**

◄ A pacemaker is used to treat arrhythmia.

Did You Know?

Stroke Stroke is the third leading cause of death in the United States.

Arteriosclerosis and atherosclerosis A term used to describe hardening and thickening of the arteries is **arteriosclerosis** (ahr tee ree oh skluh ROH sis). Arteriosclerosis tends to occur naturally as people age. **Atherosclerosis** is a disease in which fat deposits collect on artery walls. The fatty deposits may harden and form plaque. Medical scientists believe that high blood cholesterol levels, a high-fat diet, high blood pressure, and smoking can cause injury to the lining of arteries and contribute to plaque buildup. The buildup of plaque in artery walls does not develop suddenly later in life, but may begin as early as age two. Both arteriosclerosis and atherosclerosis are types of coronary heart disease.

◄ A physician can determine if a person's heartbeat is normal.

Heart rhythm abnormalities The heart must beat in rhythm to effectively pump blood throughout the body. A heart condition in which the heart may beat very slowly or very fast for no obvious reason is **arrhythmia** (ay RIHTH mee uh). The heart may skip beats or beat irregularly. Various drugs are available to treat arrhythmia. People who do not improve after taking drugs may need to have surgery to implant a pacemaker. A **pacemaker** is a device that is implanted in the heart to stimulate normal heart contractions.

Rheumatic fever An autoimmune action in the heart that can cause fever, weakness, and damage to the valves in the heart is **rheumatic fever**. The symptoms of rheumatic fever are painful, swollen joints, and skin rashes. Rheumatic fever is most common in children and teens. Prevention of rheumatic fever involves getting prompt treatment for strep throat. Permanent heart damage that results from rheumatic fever is called **rheumatic heart disease.**

Stroke A condition caused by a blocked or broken blood vessel in the brain is a **stroke,** or **cerebrovascular** (suh ree broh VAS kyuh luhr) **accident.** Brain cells in the area of the blocked or broken blood vessel are deprived of the oxygen they need. The brain cells die within minutes and the affected area of the brain and the parts of the body controlled by those brain cells cannot function. One of the most common causes of a stroke is a blood clot in an artery in the brain. Strokes also can be caused if an aneurysm in the brain bursts. An **aneurysm** (AN yuh rih zuhm) is a weakened area of a blood vessel.

516 **UNIT 8** • Communicable and Chronic Diseases

ⓥ Health Project

Cardiovascular Disease Have students work in groups to find out specific information on one of the eight cardiovascular diseases listed in the guide to cardiovascular diseases. Have them research current statistics on deaths and survival rates of their assigned disease. They also should look up statistics among different ethnic groups and for both males and females. Students also should include in their research the incidence of cardiovascular disease in other countries compared to the incidence of the disease in the United States. Have students present their information in the form of a chart or graph. **L2**

Activity: Using Life Skills

Using Goal-Setting and Decision-Making Skills: Being Heart Healthy

One of the best things you can do to keep your heart healthy is to keep moving. Regular moderate to vigorous exercise strengthens your heart. It also helps control blood cholesterol and blood pressure and reduces stress. Remember that exercise that is good for your heart is aerobic. It makes your muscles use oxygen and causes your heart to pump harder to deliver oxygen to the muscles. Recognize that aerobic exercise is vigorous, repetitive, and sustained—lasting 20 minutes or more at a time. Here are some tips to help you fit more heart-healthy exercise into your weekly routine.

1 Write your health goal. For one week, keep a daily chart of your aerobic activities and the number of minutes spent on each one. Try to include a variety of aerobic exercises.

2 Make an action plan to meet your health goal. Review your chart. Rate your level of aerobic activity as low, medium, or high. A high level is three or more sessions per week of moderate to vigorous exertion lasting 20 minutes or more at a time.

3 Identify obstacles to your plan. If your rating is low or medium, set one or more goals for increasing your level of aerobic activity. For example, if you spend an hour or more each day playing video games, you could replace 20 minutes of that time with an aerobic activity.

4 Set up a timeline to accomplish your health goal and keep a chart or diary in which you record progress towards your health goal. As you set your goals, consider your schedule. Do you prefer to be active in the morning or evening? How can you make more time for exercise? Think about location. Will you exercise at home, at school, or somewhere else? Do you prefer exercising alone or with others?

5 Build a support system. Have fun while exercising. Choose activities that you will enjoy. This will make it easier for exercise to become a habit.

6 Revise your action plan or timeline if necessary and reward yourself when you reach your health goal. Lastly, be realistic. If you haven't exercised much, start with a low level of activity. As you adjust, you can increase the length or intensity of the exercise.

Strokes also can be caused by a head injury. A stroke may result in paralysis, disability, or death. High blood pressure, cigarette smoking, high blood cholesterol, and having heart disease or diabetes are major risk factors for having a stroke.

Heart attack The death of cardiac muscle caused by a lack of blood flow to the heart is a *heart attack.* The medical term for heart attack is myocardial infarction (my uh KAR dee uhl•in FARK shun) (MI). A coronary artery that is narrowed by plaque might become clogged by a blood clot, preventing blood flow to the heart muscle. A heart attack may result in disability or death. The warning signs include uncomfortable pressure or pain in the center of the chest that lasts for more than a few minutes; pain that spreads to the shoulders, neck, jaw, back, or stomach; lightheadedness; fainting; sweating; nausea; and shortness of breath.

Most heart attacks start with mild pain or discomfort and progress slowly. Others are sudden and intense. The American Heart Association (AHA) warns that not all of these signs occur in every heart attack. The AHA advises that a person should get medical help immediately when some of these symptoms occur.

▲ Keep a daily log of your aerobic activities.

Using Life Skills

Using Goal-Setting and Decision-Making Skills Have students write down three realistic goals to improve their cardiovascular fitness. Ask them also to write down ways in which they can achieve these goals. Finally, have them write down ways they can reward themselves for achieving their goals. Encourage students to follow through with their three fitness goals using the six steps given in the text. **L2**

INTERACTIVE CHALKBOARD with Image Bank

5-Minute Check

Page 55, **Unit 8 Fast File Resources**

1. How can rheumatic fever be prevented? *prompt treatment of strep throat*
2. How is nitroglycerin used to treat angina pectoris? *It widens the coronary arteries, allowing more oxygen to get to the heart.*
3. What can cause a stroke? *a blood clot in an artery in the brain, or a burst aneurysm in the brain, or a head injury*
4. What is the medical term for a heart attack? *myocardial infarction*
5. What are some warning signs for a heart attack? *uncomfortable pressure or pain in the chest that lasts for more than a few minutes; pain that spreads to the shoulders, jaw, neck, stomach or back; lightheadedness, fainting, sweating, nausea, and shortness of breath*

🚶 Healthy People 2010

Objective 7-11 *Increase the proportion of local health departments that have established culturally appropriate and linguistically competent community health promotion and disease prevention programs.*

Obtain permission to form a group of students, parents, and teachers to work with the local health department or local hospital to set up a display of materials in your school that promotes healthful lifestyle choices and disease prevention. Encourage your English as a Second Language (ESL) parents and students to participate by volunteering to assist with translating the materials for others. **L2**

Reducing Your Risk

Reducing Your Risk

Teacher FYI

Why Care? According to the American Heart Association, almost one in every four Americans has one or more types of cardiovascular disease. Strokes and heart disease cause more than one of every two deaths, which is more than all other diseases combined. An individual is more than ten times as likely to die of cardiovascular disease than to die as the result of an accident. It is also the leading cause of death in both men and women and in all ethnic and racial groups in the United States. Finally, the yearly estimated cost of cardiovascular disease in the United States is $351 billion.

Extension

Healthful Menu Have students look up breakfast, lunch, dinner and dessert recipes that meet the standards for a heart-healthy diet on this page. Students should be able to explain why each recipe is healthful. Ask students to answer: Does it seem like something you would eat? Why or why not? Divide the class into groups of four. Have the groups create a cookbook with their recipes. Have them organize the recipes by meal categories such as breakfast, lunch, dinner, and desserts. **L2**

Reading Review

1. *Cardiovascular disease is a disease of the heart and blood vessels.*
2. *A heart attack is a lack of blood flow in the heart, while a stroke is the blockage of blood flow or break in a blood vessel in the brain.*
3. *Maintain a healthy blood cholesterol level. Choose a heart-healthy diet. Avoid tobacco products and secondhand smoke. Maintain a healthful blood pressure. Maintain a healthful body weight. Participate in regular physical activity. Manage stress.*

Characteristics of people and ways they might behave that increase the possibility of cardiovascular disease are ***cardiovascular disease risk factors.*** The greater the number of cardiovascular disease risk factors people have, the greater their risk of cardiovascular disease. The severity of a risk factor also determines its importance.

What to Know About Reducing Your Risk

Risk Factors You Cannot Control

Age, gender, race, and having blood relatives with cardiovascular disease are risk factors you cannot control. The risk of cardiovascular disease increases with age. Males generally have a higher incidence of cardiovascular disease than females.

Risk Factors You Can Control

Maintain a healthy blood cholesterol level. The risk of a heart attack rises as blood cholesterol level increases. ***Cholesterol*** is a fat-like substance made by the body and found in certain foods. People can check their blood cholesterol level by having a small amount of their blood analyzed and, if cholesterol is high, a lipoprotein analysis. A ***lipoprotein analysis*** is a measure of two main types of lipoproteins in the blood. ***Low-density lipoproteins*** (LDLs) are substances in the blood that carry cholesterol to body cells. ***High-density lipoproteins*** (HDLs) are substances in the blood that carry cholesterol to the liver for breakdown and excretion. The higher the HDL level in the blood, the lower the risk

of developing heart disease. Reducing the amount of saturated fat in the diet can help lower blood cholesterol level. ***Saturated fat*** is a type of fat from dairy products, solid vegetable fat, and meat and poultry. Saturated fat raises LDL blood cholesterol level. Physical activity and quitting smoking help increase the level of HDLs.

Choose a heart-healthy diet. A low-fat diet rich in fruits, vegetables, whole grains, nonfat and low-fat milk products, lean meats, poultry, and fish is a heart-healthy diet. Choosing a heart-healthy diet can help control factors that influence the risk of cardiovascular disease. A heart-healthy diet includes foods that contain antioxidants. An ***antioxidant*** is a substance that protects cells from being damaged by oxidation.

Avoid tobacco products and secondhand smoke. Nicotine in tobacco products causes an increase in heart rate and blood pressure, which results in wear and tear on the heart and blood vessels. Smokers are about three times more likely than nonsmokers to die from coronary heart disease. Exposure to secondhand smoke also increases the risk of cardiovascular disease.

Make the Connection

Smoking Risks For more information on the dangers of secondhand smoke, see page 428 in Lesson 38.

Reading Review

1. What is a cardiovascular disease?
2. What is the difference between a heart attack and a stroke?
3. What are risk factors for cardiovascular disease that you can control?

 Family Involvement

Reducing the Risk in the Family Have students talk to their parents about their family history of cardiovascular disease. Have students answer the following questions: Are there any relatives who died from or reportedly suffered from some type of cardiovascular disease? What can family members do to improve their diets? Does anyone smoke? Is there a history of high blood pressure in the family? What kinds of physical activities can the family do together to maintain or improve cardiovascular health? Ask each student to target his or her family's number one risk factor for cardiovascular disease and create an action plan to reduce that risk. **L2**

Maintain healthful blood pressure. *Prehypertension* is a blood pressure range that places people at higher risk for heart disease and stroke. People with prehypertension have a blood pressure of between 120–139 over 80–89. Previously, this pressure reading was considered normal. High blood pressure remains at 140 over 90.

Two stages of high blood pressure High blood pressure ranging between 140–159 over 90–99 is *stage-one hypertension.* Blood pressure of more than 160 over 100 is *stage-two hypertension.* Both stage-one and stage-two hypertension require medical treatment. When a person has high blood pressure, the heart has to work extra hard to pump enough blood and oxygen to the body. This often contributes to scarred, hardened, and less elastic artery walls.

Symptoms of high blood pressure There usually are no symptoms of high blood pressure. The only way people can tell if they have high blood pressure is to have it checked. High blood pressure that is left untreated can contribute to heart attack, stroke, kidney failure, or vision problems.

Treatment of high blood pressure People can keep blood pressure low, or lower high blood pressure, by making lifestyle choices. They can lose weight if they are overweight; participate regularly in physical activity; avoid tobacco products and secondhand smoke; get an adequate amount of potassium, calcium, and magnesium in their diets; and choose foods low in saturated fat, cholesterol, and sodium. A physician may prescribe *antihypertensives* (an ty hy pur TEN sivhz), drugs that lower hypertension or high blood pressure.

Maintain a healthful body weight. Excess body weight increases the risk of cardiovascular disease. When overweight people lose weight, they lower levels of LDLs, increase levels of HDLs, and lower blood pressure.

Participate in regular physical activity. Physical activity helps control blood cholesterol, blood pressure, body weight, and diabetes. The Centers for Disease Control and Prevention (CDC) estimates that fewer people would die each year if half of all inactive people began to participate in moderate physical activity at least three times a week. Regular physical activity decreases the tendency to form blood clots, helps reduce stress, and contributes to a stronger cardiovascular system.

Manage stress. Stress causes the heart to work harder and increases resting blood pressure and blood cholesterol levels in some people. *Stress-management skills* are techniques to prevent and deal with stressors.

Make the Connection

Managing Stress For more information on managing stress, see page 98 in Lesson 10.

It is important to have your blood pressure checked by a health-care ▼ professional.

519

Teacher FYI

Good News for the Heart Individuals who get regular physical activity cut their risk of cardiovascular disease in half. Smokers who quit can return their risk of cardiovascular disease to almost normal levels within five years after quitting. Overweight individuals who lose as little as 5–10 percent of their body weight can substantially lower their risk of cardiovascular disease. Finally, deaths from cardiovascular disease have declined 20 percent in the last decade, largely due to lifestyle changes.

NHES Assessment/SCASS

Performance Event Have students create a top-ten list of ways they manage stress. Have them also write down three consequences of suffering from stress and five benefits of managing stress. Have students share their stress-management strategies with the class. Ask students: Have you learned any new strategies from your peers? Emphasize that stress management skills also include responsible decision-making skills, keeping a time-management plan, having a support network of friends, and getting plenty of rest and sleep. **L2**

🏛 **Community Involvement**

American Heart Association Have students interview an administrative employee at the local American Heart Association on ways he or she promotes healthful living to the public. Students can ask: What are the organization's objectives? What types of media are used in promoting healthful behaviors? Does he or she use statistics, scare tactics, positive reinforcement, or a combination of methods? After the interview, have students volunteer their time to help the American Heart Association by helping to educate others about prevention of heart disease. **L3**

National Health Education Standards
Pages 518–519: 1.1, 1.4, 6.1

Using the Table

The Price of Heart Disease Have students talk to a health insurance agency or a doctor about the estimated price of each procedure for diagnosis and treatment of heart disease listed in Table 47.1. Also, have them research the price for drugs used to treat heart disease. Ask students to create a sample budget for the diagnosis and one year's worth of treatment for heart disease. Have students present their findings to the class. **L3**

3 Assess

Vocabulary Practice

Page 48, **Unit 8 Fast File Resources**

Diagnosis and Treatment

Heart disease can have many different characteristics. In some people, heart disease may be present but there are no signs and symptoms. In others, there may be indications of heart disease and yet, a person may not be aware of the warning signs.

What to Know About Diagnosing and Treating Heart Disease

Many different procedures are used to diagnose heart disease. Treatments include diet and exercise, drugs, procedures, and surgery.

TABLE 47.1 Diagnosing and Treating Heart Disease	
Procedure	**Description**
Electro-cardiogram	In this test, electrodes that record the electrical activity of the heart are attached to the chest, arms, and legs to determine heart function.
Cardiac catheterization	A procedure in which a thin, plastic tube is inserted into a blood vessel in the groin. A hollow tube called a catheter is then inserted through the plastic tube to the arteries in the heart. Material is injected through the catheter to allow the physician to see if there is blockage in the blood vessels in the heart.
Exercise stress test	A stress test, also called a treadmill test, usually involves walking or running on a treadmill at increasing levels of difficulty. Heart action is monitored while this takes place.
Echocardiogram	A test that uses ultrasound to visualize the heart's walls and pumping action.
Thallium or nuclear stress test	A test that shows which parts of the heart function normally and which function abnormally. A radioactive substance is injected into the bloodstream and sends a signal that produces clear pictures on a monitor. The pictures show the health of the heart muscle.
Balloon angioplasty	A procedure in which a special catheter with a small balloon tip is guided to a narrowing artery in the heart. When the balloon is in place, it is inflated to compress the plaque in the artery wall. This stretches the artery open to increase blood flow to the heart. This procedure can reduce the risk of having a heart attack.
Stent	A procedure in which a small, stainless steel, mesh tube is placed through a catheter into an artery in the heart. A small balloon is inflated; it pushes the stent open inside the wall of the artery. When the balloon is deflated, the stent stays open to keep the artery expanded so that blood flow is strong.

Cross-Curricular Connections

History Have students use the library to research the biography of a famous figure in history who suffered from a type of cardiovascular disease. Ask students to answer: What kind of lifestyle did the person live that could have increased his or her chances of cardiovascular disease? Did the person smoke, lack physical activity, have unhealthful eating habits or high blood pressure? What types of treatment did he or she receive? Did the person die from the heart disease? If not, how did he or she recuperate from the disease? Have students turn in a paper on the famous figure they chose. **L2**

47 STUDY GUIDE

aneurysm
angina pectoris
antihypertensives
arrhythmia
arteriosclerosis
cardiovascular
   disease
pacemaker
plaque
prehypertension
rheumatic fever
stroke

Key Terms Review

Match the definitions below with the lesson Key Terms on the left. Do not write in this book.

1. deposits around an artery wall
2. drugs that lower blood pressure
3. a device placed into the heart to regulate heartbeat
4. chest pain caused by narrowed coronary arteries
5. a weakened area of a blood vessel
6. hardening of the arteries

7. a blocked blood vessel in the brain
8. a heart condition in which the heart may beat very slowly or very fast for no obvious reason
9. a blood pressure between 120–139 over 80–89
10. the general name for a disease of the heart and blood vessels

Recalling the Facts

11. What is cardiovascular disease?
12. Explain the cause of angina pectoris.
13. Explain what causes a stroke.
14. Describe four warning signs of a heart attack.
15. List three risk factors for cardiovascular disease that you can control.

16. What is the purpose of cardiac catheterization?
17. What are two methods of treating heart disease?
18. Distinguish between stage-one hypertension and stage-two hypertension.

Critical Thinking

19. How would a person know if there is a lack of oxygen to the heart?
20. Why would a person who has arteriosclerosis have trouble exercising for long periods of time?
21. What would happen if a heart could not beat regularly?
22. Why should a person with heart disease avoid eating fatty foods?

Real-Life Applications

23. What behaviors would you practice if you were at risk for hypertension?
24. What actions would you take if you suspect you might be at risk for heart disease?
25. What are some healthful things you might do to relieve stress?
26. Explain why having a physical exam before engaging in a sport is important.

Activities

Responsible Decision Making

27. **Write** Suppose you decide to follow a heart-healthy diet. You have lunch with some of your classmates. They suggest that you have pizza, soda, and cake instead of your grilled chicken salad, skim milk, and apple. What should you do? What should you say to your friends? Write a response to this situation. Refer to the Responsible Decision-Making Model on page 61 for help.

Sharpen Your Life Skills

28. **Access Health Services** The American Heart Association (AHA) has information on heart-healthy diets. Write or call the American Heart Association for suggestions on how to plan and eat a heart-healthy diet. Using their suggestions, plan a heart-healthy lunch diet for one week. Share your diet suggestions with your classmates.

Visit **www.glencoe.com** for more *Health & Wellness* quizzes.

LESSON 47 • Study Guide **521**

STUDY GUIDE

Key Terms Review

1. plaque
2. antihypertensives
3. pacemaker
4. angina pectoris
5. aneurysm
6. arteriosclerosis
7. stroke
8. arrhythmia
9. prehypertension
10. cardiovascular disease

Recalling the Facts

11. a disease of the heart and blood vessels
12. narrowed coronary arteries, therefore the heart does not get an adequate amount of oxygen
13. a blocked or broken blood vessel in the brain
14. See page 517 for warning signs.
15. See page 518 for risk factors.
16. to see if there is blockage in the blood vessels in the heart
17. balloon angioplasty and the use of a stent
18. Stage-one hypertension is high blood pressure ranging between 140–159 over 90–99 and stage two hypertension is high blood pressure of more than 160 over 100.

Critical Thinking

19. A person may have pain in the chest area.
20. Hardening and thickening of the arteries prevents adequate blood flow to the heart.
21. Adequate blood could not be pumped through the heart.
22. Scientists believe that fatty foods cause plaque to build up in the arteries and increase the risk of a heart attack.

Real-Life Applications

23. control weight; stay physically active; avoid tobacco products; select foods low in saturated fat, cholesterol, and sodium

---

24. regular exercise, check blood cholesterol, choose a heart-healthy diet, avoid tobacco products and secondhand smoke
25. Answers will vary, but may include: develop a time-management plan, engage in regular physical activity, plenty of rest and sleep, support of friends.
26. It would show evidence of diseases that would require monitoring during exercise.

Activities

Responsible Decision Making

27. Answers will vary, but should explain that the salad, milk, and apple are more heart healthy

Sharpen Your Life Skills

28. Answers will vary, but might include foods that are low-fat, plenty of fruits and vegetables, and poultry, fish, and lean meats.

521

Managing Chronic Health Conditions

 Out of Time?

If time does not permit an in-depth study of this topic, use the following activities in this Teacher Wraparound Edition:

- Health Goals, p. 522
- Using Life Skills, p. 524
- Speaking Out, p. 525
- 5-Minute Check, p. 527

1 Focus

HEALTH GOALS **Risky Behaviors** Have the class respond to the first Health Goal for this lesson by discussing what types of behaviors can increase a person's risk of developing diabetes. Then discuss specific ways in which these behaviors can be modified. *For example, lack of physical activity increases your chance of developing diabetes. Running, walking, and taking the stairs instead of the elevator are specific ways someone can increase their physical activity.* **L2**

Write ABOUT IT!

Discuss Have students read the scenario provided. Then discuss it as a class. After reading the lesson, students should recognize the friend's symptoms as warning signs for diabetes. They should also recognize that the friend should see a physician immediately. **L2**

LESSON 48

Managing Chronic Health Conditions

HEALTH GOALS
- I will choose behaviors to reduce my risk of diabetes.
- I will recognize ways to manage chronic health conditions.

Over 17 million people in the United States have diabetes, which is a *chronic health condition*, or a recurring and persistent condition that affects a person's health. More than 90 million people in the United States live with a chronic health condition.

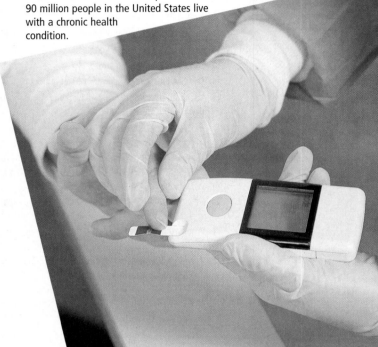

What You'll Learn

1. Distinguish between the different types of diabetes. *(p. 523)*
2. Identify the risk factors for diabetes and how to manage having diabetes. *(p. 524)*
3. Discuss ways to reduce the risk of diabetes. *(p. 524)*
4. Identify chronic health conditions and their characteristics. *(p. 526)*
5. Identify adjustments to make for different chronic health conditions. *(p. 526)*

Why It's Important

Chronic health conditions can cause great suffering and, in some cases, death. People who have chronic health conditions have to cope with changes in their health status over long periods of time. This lesson will provide many important facts about these conditions.

Key Terms

- chronic health condition
- insulin
- glucose
- autoimmune disease
- osteoarthritis
- cystic fibrosis
- hemophilia
- multiple sclerosis (MS)
- narcolepsy
- sickle-cell anemia

Write ABOUT IT!

Writing About Managing Diabetes Suppose your friend is always hungry yet is losing weight. He or she is unusually thirsty and frequently uses the restroom. Your friend is often tired. He or she also sometimes complains of blurred vision. After reading the information on diabetes on page 523, write an entry in your health journal about what you would encourage your friend to do.

National Health Education Standards—Guide for Lesson 48		
1.1	Predict how healthy behaviors can impact health status.	pp. 523, 524, 526–528, 529

Diabetes

M any people who have diabetes are not being treated. In this part of the lesson, you will learn how people who have diabetes manage their condition, and how you can reduce your risk of diabetes.

What to Know About Diabetes

A person develops diabetes when the pancreas fails to produce enough insulin. *Insulin* is a hormone that regulates the blood sugar level. Diabetes disrupts metabolism, the rate at which food is converted into energy in body cells. *Glucose* is a simple sugar that is the main source of energy for the body. If there is not enough insulin, or if the body does not use the insulin, glucose levels build up in the blood. The excess glucose overflows into urine and passes out of the body. Because glucose is the main source of energy, the body loses its source of fuel even though the blood contains large amounts of glucose.

There are three types of diabetes: insulin-dependent, non-insulin dependent, and gestational diabetes.

Insulin-dependent diabetes mellitus (IDDM) Diabetes in which the body does not produce insulin is *insulin-dependent diabetes mellitus (IDDM),* or type I diabetes. It is considered to be an autoimmune disease. An *autoimmune disease* is a disease that results when the immune system produces antibodies that turn against the body's own cells. In IDDM, the immune system attacks and destroys cells that produce insulin. IDDM occurs most often in children, appears suddenly, and progresses quickly.

The buildup of sugar in the blood and the loss of sugar in the urine cause the following symptons: increased thirst, frequent urination, constant hunger, weight loss, blurred vision, and extreme tiredness. People with IDDM may need daily injections of insulin and a special diet.

Non–insulin-dependent diabetes mellitus (NIDDM) A type of diabetes in which either the body does not produce enough insulin, or the body cannot properly use insulin that is produced is called *non–insulin-dependent diabetes mellitus (NIDDM),* or type II diabetes. NIDDM appears most often in adults over age 40.

Symptoms include feeling tired, frequent urination, unusual thirst, weight loss, blurred vision, frequent infections, and slow healing of sores. NIDDM often can be treated through weight loss, diet, physical activity, and oral medications.

Gestational diabetes Diabetes that occurs in some females during pregnancy is *gestational diabetes.* As in NIDDM, insulin might be produced, but the body does not respond normally to it. Gestational diabetes usually is treated with diet and usually disappears after the birth of the baby.

Reading Review

1. What is diabetes?
2. What is the difference between IDDM and NIDDM?

LESSON 48 • Managing Chronic Health Conditions **523**

Reading Review

1. *Diabetes is a disease in which the body fails to produce enough insulin or does not respond normally to insulin.*
2. *IDDM patients produce little or no insulin while NIDDM patients produce insulin, but the body cells do not respond normally to it.*

INTERACTIVE CHALKBOARD
with Image Bank

PowerPoint® Presentations

This CD-ROM is an editable Microsoft® PowerPoint® presentation that includes:
- Lesson presentations
- Lesson checks
- Interactive graphics
- 5-Minute Checks
- Image Bank
- All transparencies

CRISS Project

Discussion Refer to the Read-and-Say Something Strategy on page 17T, and ask students in cooperative groups to read silently about each chronic health condition, and then take turns saying one thing about each condition until the subject has been thoroughly covered.

Lesson Resource Manager

- **Unit 8 Fast File Resources**
  Reading Strategy, p. 59
  Vocabulary Practice, p. 60
  Transparency Master and Worksheet, p. 61
  Real-Life Health, p. 63
  Real-Life Health, p. 65
  5-Minute Check, p. 67
  Lesson 48 Quiz, p. 69
- **Unit 8 Transparency**
- **Lesson 48 Transparency**

- **Reading Essentials**
- **Technology**
  TeacherWorks™ CD-ROM
  StudentWorks™ CD-ROM
  Reading Essentials CD-ROM
  ExamView® Assessment Suite
  Vocabulary Puzzlemaker

National Health Education Standards
Pages 522–523: 1.1, 4.1, 8.1

Activity: Using Life Skills

Being a Health Advocate: Reducing the Risk of Diabetes

Diabetes is not a contagious disease. You cannot catch it from someone else who has it, and you cannot get it from eating too much sugar. People who are most at risk for diabetes are females who are over 40, overweight, and have a family history of the disease. If you are trying to convince a friend or family member to reduce his or her risk of diabetes, 1) select a health-related concern, 2) gather reliable information, 3) identify your purpose and target audience, 4) develop a convincing and appropriate message. Anyone can lower his or her risk for diabetes by following two simple rules: eat nutritiously and exercise.

1 To eat nutritiously, students need to follow the Food Guide Pyramid. If you are not a healthy eater, start making simple changes in your diet today to become healthier. Cut down on the amount of soda you drink and drink more water instead. Eat a banana instead of a bag of potato chips the next time you're hungry. Eat a salad with your meal.

2 Portion size can be a big factor in obesity. When you are eating out, realize that restaurant portions usually include enough food for two or three meals. Share or take your leftovers home. Paying attention to how much you consume each day will help keep you from overeating.

3 Exercise decreases blood glucose levels and helps your body respond to insulin better. The Centers for Disease Control and Prevention (CDC) says that you can walk 30 minutes a day, five times a week to make a big difference in your health. For some students, that simply means walking to school instead of driving.

4 Being active doesn't have to be a chore. Think of all the fun you had playing with your friends when you were younger. Even though you're a teenager now, you can still have fun and exercise at the same time: try in-line skating, dancing, or riding your bike. Talk to your best friend while the two of you go on a walk. You will set the foundation for a lifetime of good health.

▲ A bowl of fresh fruit is a healthy snack.

Managing Diabetes

People who have diabetes must manage their disease by controlling their blood glucose levels with diet, exercise, and/or medication.

Monitoring blood glucose levels Blood testing kits are available that allow diabetics to test their own blood glucose levels. People who have diabetes may test their glucose level several times a day. In this way, they can see how their body responds to meals, exercise, and insulin shots or oral medication. Research shows that people who manage their blood sugar levels have a reduced risk of developing complications from diabetes.

Methods of treatment People who have IDDM need daily injections of insulin to keep their blood glucose levels safe. Insulin injections must be balanced with meals and daily activities. Many people who have NIDDM are able to control their diabetes with diet and exercise exclusively. Some people who have NIDDM may need oral medication or insulin injections to lower blood glucose levels. People who have diabetes should have a physician monitor the disease and check for complications. Diabetes can lead to blindness, heart disease, stroke, kidney failure, nerve damage, and premature death.

🏠 Family Involvement

Avoiding NIDDM in the Family Have students talk to their families about type II diabetes. Each family member should individually assess their risk of developing the disease. As a part of the assessment, they should consider the following questions: Are you overweight? Are you physically active? Is there a family history of NIDDM? Family members should think about ways they can modify their behavior in order to reduce the risks of developing diabetes. Finally, the family should discuss ways they can work as a group to reduce risks. Plan a class discussion where students can share ways they plan to avoid NIDDM in their families. **L2**

SPEAKING OUT
Teens Talk About Health

Brandon Walker
Living With Diabetes

> 66 There is nothing I can't do now that I could do before I was diagnosed. . . I'm the same person I always was. 99

Considering his grandmother had just been diagnosed with diabetes, Brandon Walker's own diagnosis took his family by surprise. "Diabetes runs in families," Brandon said. "But the first couple of times I got sick, the doctors thought it was either the flu or a stomach virus."

Football practice Brandon's discovery that he had diabetes is fairly typical. "I probably had it for a while," he explained, "but because I was playing football, the symptoms weren't there. When you're really active, you can keep your blood sugar levels down to normal. It was when I stopped playing football for a year that the symptoms began to show up. I was still pretty active—using a treadmill and stuff like that—but that's just not the same level of physical activity as two-a-day football practices in August!"

Learning the truth While working one day at his job, Brandon felt sick. He had a stomachache and a headache. "I just didn't feel right," he said. "I went to the hospital, and that's when I found out I was a diabetic. I was really thirsty and dehydrated. I just couldn't drink enough. My breath smelled like nail polish, a sure sign of diabetes."

Diagnosis and treatment Brandon's doctors explained that Brandon has characteristics of both type I and type II diabetes. It's taken a while to get his dosage of insulin at the right levels. He now watches what he eats, and tries to stay as active as he can. "I've had a couple of incidents

that really scared me," he explained. "One time I was at the barber shop and I was shaking from low-blood sugar. I hadn't even noticed, but the barber did."

Battling human nature "Now, I've gotten a better idea of what I can and can't eat, so I sometimes go off my diet every now and then," said Brandon. "I guess it's human nature, but I still sometimes eat stuff I'm not supposed to have, like a little bit of candy. I only drink regular pop when I have to raise my blood sugar." Brandon's friends are generally helpful. Most of them are aware of what he shouldn't eat. As for activities, Brandon said, "There's nothing I can't do now that I could do before I was diagnosed. I can still play football. I'm the same person I always was."

Brandon's advice to other young people with diabetes is simple: "Know the type of medicine you're using, and know when you're supposed to take your meds. It's just like with anything else—know what you're supposed to be doing and try to do it." There's one more thing, too: "Don't be a couch potato."

Journaling Activity

Brandon says in this interview that, in spite of his diabetes, he's the same person he always was. Do you think students with illnesses or disabilities at your school are treated differently from other students? Should they be? Why or why not? Write an entry in your journal expressing your opinion on this topic.

LESSON 48 • Managing Chronic Health Conditions **525**

🛡 Sensitive Issues

Sharing Information There may be students in your class who have diabetes. They may be having a difficult time adjusting to the disease and may not want to share information on a personal level with their classmates. Some students may have parents, siblings, or other relatives who have become disabled or lost their lives as a result of the disease. Always use sensitivity when dealing with issues involving any disease or illness. Never force students to share when they are reluctant or feel uncomfortable sharing information in a classroom setting. Also, be sensitive when presenting role-play situations and/or demonstrations in the classroom.

Analyzing the Feature

Use the following questions to help students uncover the main points of this feature.

1. **How did football diminish the signs that Brandon had diabetes?** *Since he was very active, it kept his blood sugar levels down.*
2. **What were some of the signs that Brandon experienced indicating that he had diabetes?** *He had a stomachache, headache, and could not drink enough to hydrate himself.*
3. **How does Brandon treat his diabetes?** *He takes insulin, manages his diet, and tries to stay physically active.*

📓 Journaling Activity

Discuss Ask students to share ideas from their journal entries and discuss if they think students with disabilities or illnesses sometimes feel different, and what other students can do to make them feel included. **L2**

5-Minute Check

Page 67, **Unit 8 Fast File Resources**

1. **How does a person develop diabetes?** *The pancreas fails to produce enough insulin or, body cells do not respond normally to insulin that is produced.*
2. **What causes the symptoms of IDDM to occur?** *the buildup of sugar in the blood and the loss of sugar in the urine*
3. **When can gestational diabetes occur?** *during pregnancy*
4. **What must a person with diabetes do to manage their condition?** *They must control their blood glucose levels with diet, exercise, and/or medication.*
5. **How are people with NIDDM able to control their diabetes?** *through weight loss, diet, exercise, and oral medications*

A Guide to Chronic Health Conditions

Class Activity

Create a Table Have students read through the chronic health conditions. Then have them create a table with the name of the chronic health condition in one column, description and characteristics in another, and management and treatment in the last column. Be sure the information is accurate. For English language learners, provide slips of paper with the names, descriptions, and characteristics and have students put them into the correct columns on a blank table. **L2** **ELL**

Class Discussion

Dealing with Epilepsy Have students imagine that they have a family member with epilepsy. Have the students answer: What special challenges would your family member face? *They would probably have to use medication. Also, they would have to be sure that people with whom they associate were informed of their condition.* Also ask students: How would epilepsy affect your life and the lives of other family members? *They would need to be prepared to deal with an epileptic episode and be involved with ongoing treatment of the disease.* **L2**

Reading Review

1. *Arthritis is painful inflammation of the joints.*
2. *Chronic fatigue syndrome is a condition in which recurring tiredness makes it difficult for people to function in normal ways.*

A Guide to Chronic Health Conditions

A Guide to Chronic Health Conditions

This part of the lesson focuses on chronic health conditions. You will learn about the description, characteristics, and ways to manage and treat other chronic health conditions. Having knowledge of these conditions can greatly improve a person's quality of life.

What to Know About Chronic Health Conditions

> **Make the Connection**
>
> **The Immune System** For more information on how the immune system functions, see page 214 in Lesson 19.

Reading Review

1. What is arthritis?
2. What is chronic fatigue syndrome?

Arthritis The painful inflammation of the joints is called ***arthritis.*** Arthritis affects the muscles, tendons, and ligaments that surround joints. ***Osteoarthritis*** is the wearing down of the moving parts of joints. ***Rheumatoid arthritis*** is a condition in which joints become deformed and may lose function. Arthritis may be treated with medications, physical therapy and physical activity, or surgery.

Cerebral palsy A disorder of the nervous system that interferes with muscle coordination is ***cerebral palsy.*** Too much pressure on the head during childbirth, head injury, lead poisoning, accidental injury, and certain illnesses are possible causes. Treatments include physical therapy and physical activity, speech therapy, special devices to assist with motion, medications, or surgery.

Chronic fatigue syndrome A condition in which recurring tiredness makes it difficult for a person to function in normal ways is ***chronic fatigue syndrome (CFS).*** Symptoms include headache, sore throat, low-grade fever, fatigue, and weakness. Treatment for CFS may include a balanced diet, adequate rest and sleep, regular physical activity, stress management, or the use of medications.

Cystic fibrosis A condition in which large amounts of thick mucus are produced, affecting the lungs and pancreas, is ***cystic fibrosis.*** It is caused by an abnormal gene in the body. Signs and symptoms of cystic fibrosis include coughing, wheezing, difficulty breathing, vomiting, and constipation. Treatments may include physical therapy, dietary changes, vitamins, medications, and the use of oxygen to help with breathing.

Down syndrome A genetic disorder in which a child is born with an extra chromosome in each cell is called ***Down syndrome.*** Children born with Down syndrome have a mental disability and a slightly flattened face with upward, slanting eyes. Surgery is sometimes used to correct heart defects and other problems.

526 UNIT 8 • Communicable and Chronic Diseases

 Achieving Health Literacy

Effective Communicator Have students form groups to distribute information that describes two or three chronic health conditions. The information should be presented in the form of a pamphlet, a video, a skit, an article in the school newspaper, or a morning announcement on the school's public address system. Information presented should contain symptoms of the conditions and ways they can be managed and treated. Students should include some information beyond that presented in this lesson. **L2**

Epilepsy A disorder in which abnormal electrical activity in the brain causes a temporary loss of control of the mind and body is *epilepsy.* A person with epilepsy may have a seizure. *Petit mal* is a small seizure in which a person loses consciousness for a few seconds. *Grand mal* is a major seizure in which a person may have convulsions. During a convulsion, the body stiffens and twitching may occur. People who are having major seizures can be helped by removal of objects that may injure them. Do not place anything in the mouth.

Although people of any age can get epilepsy, it primarily affects children, teens, and young adults. Epilepsy can be caused by a head injury, a brain tumor, stroke, poisoning, or an infection. Heredity also plays a role in some cases of epilepsy. Medication is used to control seizures. Adequate rest and sleep are important, along with regular physical activity. Surgery in the treatment for epilepsy is often a last resort.

Hemophilia An inherited condition in which blood does not clot normally is *hemophilia.* A minor injury to a person with hemophilia can lead to uncontrolled bleeding. Spontaneous bleeding also occurs. Hemophilia occurs almost exclusively in males. Treatment for a person with hemophilia includes maintaining good physical and dental health status, avoiding injuries that can cause bleeding, learning how to manage bleeding when cut or scraped, learning how to recognize emergency situations, and blood transfusions, if necessary.

Migraine headache Severe head pain that is caused by the dilation of blood vessels in the brain is a *migraine headache.* The symptoms may include severe throbbing, blurred vision, nausea, and vomiting.

Treatments for migraines include medications to reduce pain, rest and relaxation, stress management, and management of conditions that may lead to headaches.

Multiple sclerosis A disease in which the protective covering of nerve fibers in the brain and spinal cord are destroyed is *multiple sclerosis (MS).* People who have MS experience tingling and numbness in the body and may feel tired and dizzy. There is no cure for MS. MS is more common in young adults. Treatment for MS includes physical therapy to strengthen muscles, medications, avoidance of stress and extreme temperatures, psychological counseling, and support from family and friends.

Muscular dystrophy A genetic disease in which the muscles progressively deteriorate is *muscular dystrophy.* There is no cure. Treatment includes physical therapy and physical activity, weight management, surgery in some cases, and canes and wheelchairs to improve mobility.

▲ Proper treatment of a chronic health condition—in this case, Down syndrome—can improve a person's quality of life.

LESSON 48 • Managing Chronic Health Conditions **527**

Chronic Health Conditions Billboard
Divide the class into seven groups. Assign each group two chronic health conditions to research for a billboard. Have students locate current statistics on their assigned chronic health conditions. Ask students to include descriptions and characteristics, as well as management and treatment options, for their assigned chronic health conditions. Encourage students to add illustrations and colors to their billboard. After everyone is finished, display their billboards in the school hallway for everyone to see. **L2**

3 Assess

Vocabulary Practice
Page 60, **Unit 8 Fast File Resources**

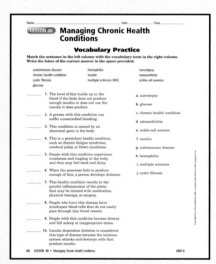

Make the Connection

The Digestive System
For more information on health of the digestive system, see page 220 in Lesson 19.

Narcolepsy A chronic sleep disorder in which people are excessively sleepy, even after adequate nighttime sleep, is called *narcolepsy.* People who have narcolepsy often become drowsy and fall asleep in inappropriate situations. The cause of narcolepsy is unknown. Although there is no cure, there is treatment. Medication is used to control sleepiness. A person who has narcolepsy needs adequate rest and sleep and the support of family members and friends.

Parkinson's disease A brain disorder that causes muscle tremors, stiffness, and weakness is *Parkinson's disease.* Signs and symptoms include rigid posture, slow movement, fixed facial expression, and a shuffling walk. The intellect is not affected until late in the disease, although speech is slow. Treatment includes medications, physical therapy, surgery, and the support of family members and friends.

Peptic ulcer An open sore on the lining of the esophagus, stomach, or first part of the small intestine is a *peptic ulcer.* The most common symptom is a burning pain in the abdomen. There may be upset stomach, back pain, and bleeding. A peptic ulcer is caused by a bacterial infection, which is treated with an antibiotic. Bleeding ulcers require emergency treatment. It is recommended

▲ An ulcer in the stomach is also called a gastric ulcer.

that a person with an ulcer avoid cigarettes, alcohol, aspirin, and caffeinated beverages.

Sickle-cell anemia An inherited blood disease in which the red blood cells carry less oxygen is *sickle-cell anemia.* Sickle-cell anemia occurs primarily in African-Americans.

normal red blood cell ▼   ▼ sickle cell

The red blood cells of people who have sickle-cell anemia are sickle-shaped and are fragile and easily destroyed. The sickle-shaped cells do not easily pass through tiny blood vessels. Symptoms include fatigue, headache, and shortness of breath. Children who have sickle-cell anemia are at increased risk for developing pneumonia and other infections. There is no cure. Treatment includes immunization against communicable diseases, oxygen therapy, antibiotics, medications, and fluids to prevent dehydration during physical activity, sickness, and hot weather.

Systemic lupus erythematosus (SLE) A condition in which connective tissue becomes inflamed is *systemic lupus erythematosus (SLE).* SLE affects the skin, kidneys, joints, muscles, and central nervous system. Symptoms include fatigue, fever, loss of appetite, nausea, joint pain, and weight loss. Treatment includes medications to reduce inflammation and fever and to relieve skin rashes.

Cross-Curricular Connections

Language Have students who are presently studying a language other than the one spoken at home, or who are fluent in a language other than English, take turns repeating the names of chronic health conditions in that language. Have the class repeat the names, and use each name in a sentence that explains each condition. Also, have students taking sign language name each chronic health condition for the class using sign. Then ask for student volunteers to try to repeat the name of the chronic health condition in a different language. **L2**

National Health Education Standards
Pages 528–529: 1.1, 1.5, 1.8, 1.9, 5.5, 5.7, 8.1

autoimmune disease
chronic health
condition
cystic fibrosis
epilepsy
glucose
hemophilia
insulin
multiple sclerosis
narcolepsy
osteoarthritis
peptic ulcer
sickle-cell anemia

Key Terms Review

Complete these fill-in-the-blank statements with the lesson Key Terms on the left. Do not write in this book.

1. Thick mucus that forms on the lungs is indicative of _____.
2. An inherited blood disease in which the red blood cells are fragile is called _____.
3. An inherited condition in which blood does not clot normally is _____.
4. A chronic sleep disorder in which people are excessively sleepy although they get enough sleep is _____.
5. The moving parts of joints wear down in a condition called _____.
6. A hormone that regulates blood sugar is _____.
7. The term for a disease in which antibodies in the immune system turn against the body's own cells is _____.
8. A disease in which the protective covering of nerve fibers is destroyed is _____.
9. A sugar that is the main source of energy in the body is _____.
10. A recurring and persistent condition that affects a person's health is a(n) _____.

Recalling the Facts

11. What is diabetes?
12. What is a chronic health condition?
13. Distinguish between insulin-dependent diabetes and non-insulin dependent diabetes.
14. List two behaviors that can lower a person's risk for diabetes.
15. What body parts surrounding joints are affected by arthritis?
16. Describe physical characteristics of a person with Down syndrome.
17. What is hemophilia?
18. What is sickle-cell anemia?

Critical Thinking

19. Explain why diabetes can be detected in a person's urine.
20. Why should a person know if a close family member has diabetes?
21. Discuss why a person who exercises and has diabetes should monitor his or her blood glucose level.
22. Why is exercise important for a person who has arthritis?

Real-Life Applications

23. If you had chronic fatigue syndrome, how could you protect your health?
24. Why should your basketball coach be informed if you have hemophilia?
25. Why is it important to be aware if you are in a car with a driver who has narcolepsy?
26. Why is it important that you know if your close friend has sickle-cell anemia?

Activities

Responsible Decision Making

27. **Write** Suppose you suffer from sickle-cell anemia. Today you forgot your water bottle. Your team has a big game tomorrow. Your teammates try to convince you that it will be OK to practice without it for just this one day. Write a response to this situation. Refer to the Responsible Decision-Making Model on page 61 for help.

Sharpen Your Life Skills

28. **Use Communication Skills** Design a pamphlet that describes a chronic health condition. Include information about the symptoms of the condition and ways that it can be managed and treated. Obtain permission from your teacher to make copies of the pamphlet to distribute to your classmates.

Visit www.glencoe.com for more *Health & Wellness* quizzes.

LESSON 48 • Study Guide **529**

STUDY GUIDE

Key Terms Review

1. cystic fibrosis
2. sickle-cell anemia
3. hemophilia
4. narcolepsy
5. osteoarthritis
6. insulin
7. autoimmune disease
8. multiple sclerosis
9. glucose
10. chronic health condition

Recalling the Facts

11. See page 523.
12. a recurring and persistent condition that affects a person's health
13. See page 523.
14. medication, diet, and exercise
15. muscles, tendons, and ligaments
16. a slightly flattened face with upward slanting eyes
17. an inherited condition in which blood does not clot normally
18. a disease in which red blood cells carry less oxygen to body cells; they are sickle-shaped, fragile, and easily destroyed

Critical Thinking

19. If the body does not use insulin, glucose builds up and passes into the urine where it can be detected.
20. Type I diabetes is related to genetic factors, so when a person has checkups, this person should be tested for diabetes.
21. Blood sugar levels can be lowered by exercise.
22. Exercise prevents loss of joint function.

Real-Life Applications

23. eat a balanced diet, get adequate rest and sleep, exercise regularly, practice stress management
24. because contact sports can cause injury leading to bleeding
25. They can fall asleep while driving so it is important to keep an eye on them and help them stay awake.
26. The person might often feel tired due to the illness. Your offer of assistance and support during this time will show your concern.

Activities

Responsible Decision Making

27. Refer to the Responsible Decision-Making Model on page 61. Explain to students that they should know their limits better than anyone else. Ask students: Would participating without water be healthy for you? Would it be a safe thing to do if participating in a strenuous sport? Have a class discussion on what is the responsible thing to do.

Sharpen Your Life Skills

28. Have students share their pamphlets with the class. This may be used as a review of the different chronic health conditions and reinforce the symptoms and ways the conditions may be managed and treated.

1 Focus

HEALTH GOAL **Risky Behaviors** Have the class respond to the Health Goal for this lesson by discussing what types of behaviors can increase one's chances of developing cancer. Then discuss specific ways in which these behaviors can be modified. *For example, use a high SPF lotion when out in the sun for a long period of time to prevent skin cancer; stay away from secondhand smoke to decrease the chance of developing lung cancer.* **L2**

Write ABOUT IT!

Discuss Have students read the scenario provided and then discuss it as a class. Many students may have volunteered to participate in a run for cancer. Others may have offered their services in other ways. Try to encourage active class discussion regarding efforts to find a cure for cancer and ways students can participate in this effort. **L2**

LESSON 49

Reducing the Risk of Cancer

HEALTH GOAL • **I will choose behaviors to reduce my risk of cancer.**

Cancer is a disease that affects people of all ages, races, and nationalities. Next to cardiovascular disease, cancer is the most common cause of death in the United States. Some types of cancer cannot be prevented, but some can if people take preventative measures. If a person does get cancer, early treatment can increase the chances for a cure. This lesson will provide information about different aspects of cancer.

What You'll Learn

1. Describe how cancerous cells grow and spread. *(p. 531)*
2. Describe the basic facts about common types of cancers. *(p. 533)*
3. Practice ways to reduce the risk of cancer. *(p. 534)*
4. Discuss different treatment procedures for cancer. *(p. 536)*

Why It's Important

To some degree, cancer is an illness that results from lifestyle choices. For example, overexposure to the sun increases the risk of developing skin cancer. You can make lifestyle choices that reduce your risk of developing cancer.

Key Terms

- cancer
- tumor
- benign tumor
- malignant tumor
- metastasis
- ultraviolet (UV) radiation
- malignant melanoma
- radon
- basal cell carcinoma
- chemotherapy

Write ABOUT IT!

Writing About Reducing Risk Suppose that your aunt has breast cancer. You decide to run in an annual national event that raises money for breast cancer research. Running is beneficial to you because exercising and controlling your weight helps reduce your risk of developing cancer. After reading about reducing your risk on page 534, write an entry in your health journal about other ways you can reduce your risk.

National Health Education Standards—Guide for Lesson 49		
1.1	Predict how healthy behaviors can impact health status.	pp. 530, 531, 533–535, 537–539
1.5	Propose ways to reduce or prevent injuries and health problems.	pp. 530, 534–535, 538
3.4	Determine when professional health services may be required.	pp. 531, 536
6.1	Assess personal health practices and overall health status.	pp. 534–535

Cancer

A ll cells in a person's body usually divide in an orderly pattern to produce more cells. This enables the body to grow and repair itself. Normal cell division is under precise control. Sometimes there are problems and cells do not divide in the usual way. *Cancer* is a group of diseases in which cells divide in an uncontrolled manner.

What to Know About Cancer

How cancer forms When cells divide in an uncontrolled manner, they can form a tumor. A *tumor* is an abnormal growth of tissue. Tumors can be benign or malignant. A *benign tumor* is a tumor that is not cancerous and does not spread to other parts of the body. Benign tumors rarely are life-threatening. They usually can be removed and do not grow back.

A *malignant tumor* is a tumor that is cancerous and may spread to other parts of the body. *Metastasis* (muh TAS tuh suhs) is the spread of cancer. Cancer cells can break away from a malignant tumor and enter the bloodstream or lymphatic system. They can form new tumors in other parts of the body.

Causes of cancer Cancer is not contagious. You cannot get cancer from another person. Cancer also is not caused by an injury, such as a bump or bruise. Although the causes of cancer are not completely understood, many risk factors for cancer have been identified. These risk factors can increase a person's chances of getting cancer.

How cancer is detected Some people are fearful of cancer. They do not realize that many types of cancer can be prevented or successfully treated when detected early.

They can improve the chance that cancer will be detected early if they have regular physical examinations, perform certain self-examinations, and are aware of risk factors for, and signs and symptoms of cancer.

Great strides have been made in the early detection and treatment of cancer due to improved technology. In many cases a needle-sharp probe replaces a scalpel in the detection and treatment of breast cancer. The survival rate for all types of cancers greatly improves with early detection.

A Guide to Common Cancers (on page 533) contains information on risk factors, signs and symptoms, and early detection of several types of cancer.

◀ A change in a mole or other change in the skin should be checked by a physician.

Did You Know?

Risk Factors You can control many factors that can put you at risk for cancer.

Reading Review

1. What is cancer?
2. What is metastasis?

LESSON 49 • Reducing the Risk of Cancer 531

Lesson Resource Manager

- **Unit 8 Fast File Resources**
  Reading Strategy, p. 73
  Vocabulary Practice, p. 74
  Transparency Master and Worksheet, p. 75
  Real-Life Health, p. 77
  Real-Life Health, p. 79
  5-Minute Check, p. 81
  Lesson 49 Quiz, p. 82
- **Unit 8 Transparency**
- **Lesson 49 Transparency**

- **Reading Essentials**
- **Technology**
  TeacherWorks™ CD-ROM
  StudentWorks™ CD-ROM
  Reading Essentials CD-ROM
  Exam*View*® Assessment Suite
  Vocabulary Puzzlemaker

---

2 Teach

Explain the Concept

Normal Cells versus Cancer Cells
The human body is made up of trillions of cells. Normal cells are quite uniform in size and almost identical in shape. In the precancerous state, many cells lose their uniformity and develop irregular nuclei. When the cells become cancerous, distortion is more pronounced and the abnormal cells begin spreading to surrounding tissues.

Reading Review

1. *Cancer is a group of diseases in which cells divide in an uncontrolled manner.*
2. *Metastasis is the spread of cancer.*

PowerPoint® Presentations

This CD-ROM is an editable Microsoft® PowerPoint® presentation that includes:
- Lesson presentations
- Lesson checks
- Interactive graphics
- 5-Minute Checks
- Image Bank
- All transparencies

Discussion Refer to the KWL Strategy on page 17T. Before reading, ask students to write what they know about reducing the risks of cancer and what they want to learn. After the lesson is finished, have them list what they have learned.

National Health Education Standards
Pages 530–531: 1.1, 1.5, 3.4

A Guide to Common Cancers

There are many different types of cancer. This section includes A Guide to Common Cancers, which makes each type of cancer easy to understand. Cancers are categorized by their risk factors, signs and symptoms, and early detection.

Early Detection of Cancer

Many kinds of cancer can be treated and cured if detected early. Get to know your body.

Early prevention of cancer Examination of the bladder by a physician can aid in early detection for **bladder cancer,** while regular dental and physical checkups plus watching for symptoms can help detect **oral cancer.** People can reduce their risk of **skin cancer** by doing a monthly skin self-examination and by noticing when there are changes in their skin and moles.

Women can reduce their risk of **breast cancer** by controlling their weight through diet and exercise, doing monthly breast self exams, having a physical exam every three years for women 20 to 40 and by having a mammogram every 1–2 years after the age of 40.

Women can reduce their risk of **cervical cancer** by having

A regular physical examination is important in the early detection and treatment of cancer. ▼

regular pelvic examinations and annual Pap smears. **Endometrial cancer** can be detected early if women age 40 and up have an annual pelvic exam by a physician.

People can help reduce their risk of **prostate cancer** (for men) and **colon** and **rectal cancer** (for men and women) by having an annual rectal examination after age 40 and having an annual blood test after age 50 (for colon and rectal cancer, an annual stool blood test).

For some types of cancer, including **Hodgkin's disease** and **non-Hodgkin's lymphoma,** there are no early detection tests available. For other types, early detection is difficult. One example is **leukemia,** because symptoms often appear late in the disease. The same is true for **lung cancer;** it can be detected late in the disease with chest X rays and an examination of bronchial tubes and mucus.

Ovarian cancer also is difficult to detect early because symptoms are often attributed to other conditions. **Pancreatic cancer** can be detected late in the disease with ultrasound imaging and CT scans.

🖤 Health Project

Cancer Bulletin Board Divide the class into groups of three or four. Assign each group two types of cancer to work on for their part of the bulletin board. Have them create an illustrative fact sheet about their cancers. The information on the fact sheet should include risk factors, signs and symptoms, and current statistics on their assigned cancers. Ask the students to include ways to reduce the risk of getting the cancers. Explain to students that some diseases have no noticeable signs and symptoms until the disease has progressed beyond treatment. Also, emphasize that the most recent statistics they are able to find in their research may not be correct, since statistics are constantly changing. After each group has finished their fact sheets, have the whole class post their information on a bulletin board. **L2**

TABLE 49.1   A Guide to Common Cancers

Type of Cancer/Risk Factors	Signs and Symptoms
Bladder Cigarette smoking, air pollution, exposure to industrial chemicals	Increased frequency of urination, weight loss and loss of appetite, blood in urine
Breast Family history of breast cancer, early start of menstruation, late menopause, never having children, late age when first having children	Breast tenderness, lumps or thickenings in the breast, changes in a nipple, discharge from a nipple, dimpling or puckering of the skin on a breast
Cervical Early age at first sexual intercourse, having multiple sexual partners, cigarette smoking, infection with human papilloma virus (HPV)	Pain, abnormal vaginal discharge, abnormal bleeding from the uterus or spotting
Colon and rectal Family history of colorectal cancer, polyps in the colon or rectum, inflammatory bowel disease, high-fat and low-fiber diet, physical inactivity	Changes in bowel habits (such as constipation or diarrhea), bleeding in the rectum, blood in the stool, unexplained weight loss
Endometrial Obesity, early start of menstruation, late menopause, family history of infertility, failure to ovulate, use of estrogen drugs	Pain, weight loss, irregular menstrual cycles, abnormal vaginal bleeding after menopause
Lymphoma: Hodgkin's disease Largely unknown, reduced immune function, exposure to certain infectious agents	Enlarged lymph nodes, unexplained fever, unexplained weight loss, itching, fatigue, night sweats
Leukemia Exposure to radiation, exposure to certain chemicals, infection with human T-lymphotropic virus: Type I, cigarette smoking	Fever, weight loss, fatigue, easy bleeding, repeated infections, enlarged lymph nodes, swelling of liver and spleen
Lung Cigarette smoking, exposure to secondhand smoke, air pollution, exposure to asbestos, exposure to radon, family history of lung cancer, exposure to industrial chemicals, exposure to radiation	Chronic coughing, blood in mucus, wheezing, chest pain, weight loss, hoarseness, shortness of breath, recurring pneumonia or bronchitis
Oral Chewing tobacco use, heavy alcohol use, smoking and using drugs multiplies the risk	Lump or thickening in the mouth, leukoplakia, bad breath, loose teeth, pain, a sore that bleeds easily and doesn't heal in the mouth, difficulty chewing and swallowing
Ovarian Never having children, family history of ovarian cancer, increased risk with age	Enlarged abdomen, abdominal pain and discomfort, abnormal vaginal bleeding
Pancreatic Cigarette smoking, chronic pancreatitis, diabetes, cirrhosis of the liver, high-fat diet	Weight loss, pain, change in bowel habits
Prostate Risk increases with age, high-fat diet, family history of prostate cancer, highest incidence among African-Americans	Frequent urination, painful or burning urination, weak or interrupted urine flow, bloody urine, persistent pain in the back, hips, or pelvis
Skin Exposure to UV radiation from the sun, tanning booths, and sunlamps, repeated sunburn, fair complexion, family history of skin cancer, exposure to coal, tar, pitch, creosote, arsenic, or radium	Changes in skin pigmentation, skin sores that do not heal, pain, tenderness, or itchiness of the skin, changes in the size, shape, color, thickness, or number of moles

LESSON 49 • Reducing the Risk of Cancer 533

5-Minute Check
Page 81, Unit 8 Fast File Resources

1. What is the difference between a benign and a malignant tumor? *A benign tumor is not cancerous and does not spread to other parts of the body, while a malignant tumor is cancerous and can spread to other parts of the body.*

2. How can a woman detect breast cancer early? *by doing a monthly self-exam, having a physical exam by a physician every three years for women aged 20–40 and every 1–2 years for women over 40, and having an annual mammogram beginning at age 40*

3. How can people reduce their risk of developing prostate, colon, and rectal cancer? *by having an annual rectal exam after age 40 and by having an annual blood test after age 50*

4. Why is ovarian cancer difficult to detect early? *because symptoms are often attributed to other conditions*

5. How is pancreatic cancer detected? *through ultrasound imaging and CT scans*

Teaching Transparency
Page 75, Unit 8 Fast File Resources

🏛 Community Involvement

Communication Have students contact organizations in the community that offer support groups for individuals who have cancer and their families. Ask students to compile a list of these organizations, the types of support groups offered, a list of fees if any, and the meeting dates and times. Students might also include typical reactions or emotions that people must deal with if they or a loved one is diagnosed with cancer. They should also indicate if emotional support has any impact on the effectiveness of the treatment. Students may then form groups to prepare flyers or pamphlets advertising these services. **L2**

Reducing Your Risk

Quick Demo

Reading the Label Bring in bottles and labels from different types of sunscreen lotions. Demonstrate for students how to evaluate a sunscreen by pointing out where on the labels they can find answers to the following questions: What is the SPF? What are the directions for use? How often does it need to be applied? Is it waterproof? What are the main ingredients? What is the expiration date? **ELL**

NHES Assessment/SCASS

Performance Task Have students work in pairs to create a 30–60 second radio commercial informing people about ways to reduce their risk of developing cancer. Encourage students to be creative by making a song, rap, or poem that catches people's attention. After they have finished, ask for volunteers to perform their commercials for the class. **L2**

Teacher FYI

Smoked to Death According to the Centers for Disease Control and Prevention, smoking kills more people than alcohol, AIDS, car crashes, illegal drugs, murders, and suicides combined. Tobacco kills more than 400,000 people each year, which is 1200 people each day. Also, tobacco causes about one in every five deaths in the United States. Secondhand smoke is the third leading preventable cause of death, after active smoking and alcohol abuse.

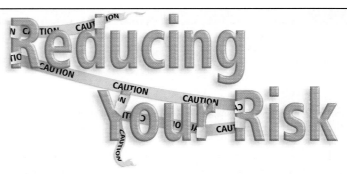

Reducing Your Risk

Some risk factors for cancer cannot be controlled. For example, people cannot control their heredity. However, almost all cancers are associated with choices over which people do have control.

What You Can Do to Reduce Your Risk

> **Make the Connection**
>
> **Weight** For more information on the importance of weight management, see page 324 in Lesson 29.

Reducing exposure to secondhand smoke will reduce risk of lung cancer. ▼

Know the warning signs of cancer. There are common warning signs that may indicate cancer.

- **C**hange in bowel or bladder habits
- **A** sore that does not heal
- **U**nusual bleeding or discharge
- **T**hickening or lump in a breast or elsewhere
- **I**ndigestion or difficulty swallowing
- **O**bvious change in a wart or mole
- **N**agging cough or hoarseness

These also may be symptoms of less serious conditions, so see a doctor if you have any of these signs.

Choose a tobacco-free lifestyle. Tobacco use is the most preventable cause of cancer death. Tobacco products contain many carcinogens. A carcinogen is a chemical that is known to cause cancer. Using tobacco products and being exposed to secondhand smoke are leading causes of cancer death. Cases of lung cancer would be greatly reduced if people never began to smoke and reduced their exposure to secondhand smoke. The use of smokeless, or chewing tobacco increases the risk of cancers of the mouth, gums, and throat.

Protect yourself from UV radiation. A type of radiation that comes from the sun and also is emitted by sunlamps and tanning booths is ***ultraviolet (UV) radiation.*** Repeated exposure to UV radiation increases the risk of skin cancer, including malignant melanoma. ***Malignant melanoma*** is the form of skin cancer that is most often fatal. Avoid exposure to the sun between 10 a.m. and 3 p.m. If you are in the sun, wear protective clothing. Use sunscreen lotions that have a sun protective factor (SPF) of at least 15. Never use a tanning booth or sunlamp. Check your skin regularly. If you notice any abnormal growths, consult your physician.

Follow dietary guidelines. Eat a variety of foods so that your body has a combination of nutrients. Follow the recommended number of servings of each food on the Food Guide Pyramid.

Maintain desirable weight. People who are overweight and have a high percentage of body fat are more at risk for developing cancer. Exercise regularly and manage your weight.

⚖️ Legal Issues

Laws Governing Education In 2002, President George W. Bush signed a massive federal law called the No Child Left Behind Act (NCLB). The law addresses major subgroups within a school's environment—racial and ethnic minorities, limited English-proficient learners, low-income, and special education students. Some students might do very well learning about and expressing understanding of cancer and its risks through the visual and performing arts, while others may not. Encourage the artistic student to display a visual aid while encouraging others to sing, write a poem, or simply learn just by listening. For students having difficulty, you may want to create a poster or give them a handout that lists the main ideas you wish to convey. In compliance with federal law, plan your teaching strategies and activities to meet the needs of all your students.

▲ Frequent sun exposure can cause skin cancer.

Avoid drinking alcohol. Drinking alcohol may cause changes in body cells. Alcohol also takes vitamins needed for optimal health away from your body. Drinking alcohol increases the risk of cancer of the liver, throat, mouth, breast, and stomach. Chances of developing cancer are multiplied further if you drink alcohol and use tobacco products.

Avoid exposure to dangerous chemicals and airborne fibers. The following have been found to increase risk of cancer: benzene, benzidene, vinyl chloride, uranium, radon, nickel, cadmium, asbestos, and pesticides. Wear rubber gloves and a mask when exposed to dangerous chemicals. Wear protective clothing if you will be exposed to airborne fibers.

Avoid air pollution. Polluted air contains many carcinogens. Avoid the exhaust from cars, buses, and trucks. Have your home tested for radon. **Radon** is an odorless, colorless radioactive gas that is released by rocks and soil. It can collect and be trapped in basements and crawl spaces. Inhaling radon can increase the risk of lung cancer.

Avoid infection with HIV and sexually transmitted diseases (STDs). Many people who are infected with HIV develop Kaposi's sarcoma and other cancers. People who have genital warts are at increased risk for cervical cancer. Choose abstinence to reduce your risk of cancer. Do not inject drugs, such as steroids and heroin. Discuss any procedure that involves piercing the skin with a parent or guardian beforehand. Avoid contact with blood and bodily fluids.

Know your family's cancer history. Some cancers, such as breast, colon, and ovarian cancers, occur more frequently in certain families. If a family member or other relative has had cancer, have regular cancer checkups and keep your physician informed.

Reducing the Risk of the Most Common Cancer: Skin Cancer

Skin cancer often begins to develop in young people who are overexposed to the sun for many years. Skin cancer is most easily detected because it is plainly visible to the eye. There are three types of skin cancer.

Basal cell carcinoma is the most common form of skin cancer. It develops on sun-exposed areas of the body in the form of a small, round, raised red spot. It is almost always cured if discovered early. *Squamous cell carcinoma,* the second most common skin cancer, also occurs on the parts of the body exposed to the sun. It is a slower growing cancer with a tendency to spread to other parts of the body. Malignant melanoma is the most dangerous skin cancer. It appears as a mole that changes its appearance and attacks other body parts. Most skin cancers can be prevented by avoiding the sun and wearing a sunscreen with a sun protection factor of at least 15.

The use of tanning beds significantly increases the risk of squamous cell carcinoma. The younger people are when they first start using tanning beds, the greater the risk of developing skin cancer.

Make the Connection

Air Pollution For more information on air pollution, see page 603 in Lesson 57.

Reading Review

1. What is ultraviolet (UV) radiation?
2. What is the most dangerous skin cancer?

LESSON 49 • Reducing the Risk of Cancer **535**

NHES Assessment/SCASS

Selected Response Which of the following types of cancers is related to sun-exposure and not likely to spread?
A. Kaposi's sarcoma
B. malignant melanoma
C. *basal cell carcinoma*
D. squamous cell carcinoma

Teacher FYI

Rays of Cancer According to the American Cancer Society, about 45 percent of Americans who live to age 65 will have had skin cancer at least once in their lives. Most skin cancer occurs after age 50, but it is from sun damage that occurred as a child and teen. Seventy-eight percent of skin cancer could have been prevented if people under the age of 18 had used sunscreen daily.

Extension

Shadowing Have several students volunteer for one day to shadow a representative from the American Cancer Society who works with community involvement. Have them write a report to share their experiences with the class. **L3**

Reading Review

1. *Ultraviolet radiation is a type of radiation that comes from the sun and also is emitted by sunlamps and tanning booths.*
2. *Malignant melanoma is the most dangerous skin cancer.*

Health Project

Sun Protection Online Have students create a PowerPoint® presentation promoting ways to keep safe in the sun and information on skin cancer. Encourage students to be creative, making use of audio and visual aids, such as photos, art, charts, and graphs. Have the students add animation for specific effects. The presentation can include: statistics on skin cancer, a description of ultraviolet rays, tips on how to protect yourself from UV rays, how to select sunscreen and apply it, and types of skin cancer. **L3**

National Health Education Standards

Pages 534–535: 1.1, 1.3, 1.4, 1.5, 6.1

3 Assess

Vocabulary Practice

Page 74, **Unit 8 Fast File Resources**

Treatment for cancer depends upon a number of factors. These factors include the type of cancer, how much the cancer has spread, the location of the cancer, and the patient's choice of treatment. Common treatment approaches for cancer include surgery, radiation therapy, chemotherapy, and immunotherapy.

What to Know About Treatment Approaches

Radiation therapy is used to treat some types of cancer. ▼

Surgery The most common treatment for cancer is surgery. If tumors are confined to a particular site, physicians may remove the cancerous tissue from the body. If tumors are spread out, surgery is more difficult to perform.

Radiation therapy Treatment of cancer with high-energy radiation to kill or damage cancer cells is *radiation therapy*. Radiation therapy is performed using a machine that generates radiation. It also is performed by placing radioactive materials in or near the cancer site. Radiation therapy may produce side effects, such as fatigue, nausea, and vomiting.

The skin also may become red and blistered in the areas that are treated with radiation.

Chemotherapy The treatment of cancer with anti-cancer drugs is *chemotherapy*. These drugs kill cancer inside the body. Chemotherapy works mainly on cancer cells. However, healthy cells can be harmed as well. Side effects may include nausea, vomiting, hair loss, and fatigue. Most of these side effects do not last long and will gradually go away. Fatigue may last several months.

Immunotherapy A process in which the immune system is stimulated to fight cancer cells is *immunotherapy*. Immunotherapy involves injecting patients with cancer cells that have been made harmless by radiation or injecting patients with other substances that stimulate the immune system.

536 UNIT 8 • Communicable and Chronic Diseases

Cross-Curricular Connections

Careers Have students research different careers that might involve either the diagnosis or treatment of cancer. Focus on the types of careers and the technology used to treat and diagnose the different types of cancer. Some careers they might consider when researching are: physician, genetic researcher, endocrinologist, organic chemist, oncologist, radiologist, pharmacist, pharmacologist, dietitian, laboratory technician, nurse practitoner, nurse's aide, nurse, therapist, etc. Have students share this information with the class and discuss the many health-care careers that are available today due to research and technology. **L3**

basal cell carcinoma
benign tumor
cancer
chemotherapy
immunotherapy
malignant melanoma
malignant tumor
metastasis
radiation therapy
radon
tumor
ultraviolet (UV)
  radiation

No Smoking

Key Terms Review

Complete these fill-in-the-blank statements with the lesson Key Terms on the left. Do not write in this book.

1. A noncancerous tumor is a(n) _____.

2. An odorless, colorless gas associated with cancer is _____.

3. The spread of cancer to other body parts is _____.

4. Being treated with anti-cancer drugs is called _____.

5. The general name for a disease in which there is uncontrollable growth of cells is _____.

6. The most dangerous type of skin cancer is _____.

7. The most common form of skin cancer is _____.

8. An abnormal growth of tissue forms a(n) _____.

9. Sunlamps emit a dangerous ray called _____.

10. A cancerous tumor also is called a(n) _____.

Recalling the Facts

11. Distinguish between a benign tumor and a malignant tumor.

12. What are three risk factors for developing lung cancer?

13. What are three treatments for cancer?

14. What are the seven early warning signs of cancer?

15. What methods are used for early detection of breast cancer?

16. Why is early detection for leukemia difficult?

17. What are three risk factors that might contribute to oral cancer?

18. Describe signs that might indicate skin cancer.

Critical Thinking

19. Discuss why a benign tumor is considered less harmful than a malignant tumor.

20. Why is cancer not considered a contagious disease?

21. Why should a woman infected with HPV have cervical examinations on a regular basis?

22. Explain why a person who has swollen lymph nodes, fever, weight loss, and fatigue should seek medical attention? List the types of cancer that these symptoms are signs of.

Real-Life Applications

23. How could you be supportive toward a friend who is feeling sick from receiving chemotherapy?

24. Why should you know the warning signs of cancer?

25. You notice that a classmate who smokes has a chronic cough and often complains of chest pains. What would you say to your classmate?

26. Describe why the use of tanning beds by people your age is particularly risky.

Activities

Responsible Decision Making

27. **Discuss** One of your friends works at a tanning salon and offers you three free sessions in the tanning booth. Your friend says you will look great. Write a response to this situation. Refer to the Responsible Decision-Making Model on page 61 for help.

Sharpen Your Life Skills

28. **Practice Healthful Behaviors** Plan a three-day menu of foods known to prevent cancer. Choose foods that are high in fiber. Include several fruits and vegetables each day. Avoid fatty foods. Avoid foods that are smoked, salted, or nitrate-cured.

Visit **www.glencoe.com** for more *Health & Wellness* quizzes.

LESSON 49 • Study Guide **537**

LESSON

49
STUDY GUIDE

Key Terms Review

1. benign tumor
2. radon
3. metastasis
4. chemotherapy
5. cancer
6. malignant melanoma
7. basal cell carcinoma
8. tumor
9. ultraviolet radiation
10. malignant tumor

Recalling the Facts

11. A benign tumor is not cancerous and does not spread to other parts of the body. A malignant tumor is cancerous and may spread to other parts of the body.

12. See page 533.

13. Treatments for cancer include surgery, radiation therapy, chemotherapy, and immunotherapy.

14. See page 534.

15. monthly breast self-examination, physical exams, mammograms

16. Symptoms often appear late in the disease.

17. tobacco use, heavy alcohol use, and drug use

18. See page 533.

Critical Thinking

19. A benign tumor, unlike a malignant tumor, is not cancerous and does not spread.

20. You cannot "catch" cancer from another person.

21. HPV is associated with the development of cervical cancer.

22. These symptoms indicate a serious medical problem and require medical attention. They could indicate Hodgkin's disease or leukemia.

Real-Life Applications

23. You could assist your friend with physical tasks such as carrying books to class or you could explain classwork if your friend has been absent from school.

24. If you know the warning signs, you can get early treatment, which increases the chances of a cure.

---

25. Suggest that they see a physician. The symptoms may indicate a serious illness.

26. Studies show that the earlier a person uses a tanning bed, the greater the risk of developing skin cancer.

Activities

Responsible Decision Making

27. You have learned that the use of tanning beds increases the risk of getting skin cancer. People should avoid using tanning beds and keep their skin healthy into adulthood.

Sharpen Your Life Skills

28. Answers will vary. Discuss the importance of choosing healthful foods in the prevention of cancer.

537

Key Terms Review

1. h
2. j
3. k
4. e
5. a
6. b
7. g
8. i
9. f
10. c

Recalling the Facts

11. Answers could include three of the following: syphilis, gonorrhea, strep throat, tuberculosis, tetanus, diphtheria, and Lyme disease.
12. Answers should include three of the following: coughing, wheezing, shortness of breath, tightness in the chest, rapid breathing, and itchy or sore throat.
13. A fertilized egg implants in a Fallopian tube instead of in the uterus. This condition results in the death of the fetus and can be fatal for a pregnant female.
14. A discharge is microscopically examined, or urine is analyzed.
15. It widens the coronary arteries, thereby allowing more oxygen to get to the cardiac muscle.
16. An antioxidant is a substance that protects cells from being damaged by oxidation.
17. Metabolism is the rate at which food is converted to energy in body cells.
18. Osteoarthritis and rheumatoid arthritis are the two main types of arthritis.
19. A benign tumor is a tumor that is not cancerous and does not spread to other parts of the body.
20. The more people who choose not to smoke, the more the number of lung cancer cases will be reduced.

Critical Thinking

21. If there were no vaccines, more people would have more viral diseases because they would have no protection against the diseases.
22. White blood cells, including B cells and helper T cells, fight pathogens.
23. Antibiotics are not effective against viruses that cause flu.

Influenza virus

Color-enhanced TEM
Magnification: 250,000x

Malaria parasite

Color-enhanced TEM
Magnification: 5 700x

ification: 5 700x

Key Terms Review

Match the following definitions with the correct Key Terms. Do not write in this book.

a. aneurysm *(p. 516)*
b. antibody *(p. 485)*
c. asthma *(p. 494)*
d. hemophilia *(p. 527)*
e. immune system *(p. 485)*
f. Kaposi's sarcoma *(p. 505)*
g. metastasis *(p. 531)*
h. plaque *(p. 515)*
i. pubic lice *(p. 503)*
j. strep throat *(p. 492)*
k. stroke *(p. 516)*
l. tumor *(p. 531)*

1. hardened deposits in the blood vessels
2. bacterial infection of the throat
3. a blocked or broken blood vessel in the brain
4. removes harmful organisms from the blood and combats pathogens
5. a weakened area of a blood vessel
6. a protein that helps fight infection
7. the spreading of cancer cells to other body parts
8. crab lice that pierce the skin and feed on human blood
9. a type of cancer that affects people who are infected with HIV
10. bronchial tubes become inflamed and constrict

Recalling the Facts

11. What are three diseases caused by bacteria? *(Lesson 44)*
12. Identify three signs of an asthma attack. *(Lesson 45)*
13. What takes place in an ectopic pregnancy? *(Lesson 46)*
14. How is gonorrhea diagnosed? *(Lesson 46)*
15. How does nitroglycerin work? *(Lesson 47)*
16. What is an antioxidant? *(Lesson 47)*
17. What is metabolism? *(Lesson 48)*
18. What are the two major types of arthritis? *(Lesson 48)*
19. What is a benign tumor? *(Lesson 49)*
20. How could the number of cases of lung cancer be greatly reduced? *(Lesson 49)*

Critical Thinking

21. Describe the quality of life today if there were no vaccines. *(Lesson 44)*
22. You have been exposed to the flu and your white blood cell count is high. How can this be a benefit to you? *(Lesson 44)*
23. Why would a physician not necessarily provide an antibiotic for flu? *(Lesson 45)*
24. Why might a female have PID and yet not know she has chlamydia? *(Lesson 46)*
25. Explain how pubic lice could become a public health problem among teens. *(Lesson 46)*
26. Why should a person with high blood pressure avoid too many salty foods? *(Lesson 47)*
27. Why are oral medications often avoided for a woman if she has gestational diabetes? *(Lesson 48)*
28. Why might a person with narcolepsy seek a support group? *(Lesson 48)*
29. What probably happened if a person had colon cancer, which was treated, but now has liver cancer? *(Lesson 49)*
30. Why should people who are overweight reduce their percentage of body fat? *(Lesson 49)*

538   UNIT 8 • Communicable and Chronic Diseases

Use **Interactive Tutor** at www.glencoe.com for additional help.

---

24. Often chlamydia has no symptoms.
25. Pubic lice can live outside the body for as long as a day. They can spread from person to person on towels, bedding, or toilet seats.
26. Salty foods are high in sodium, which tends to raise blood pressure.
27. The medications can pass through the placenta to the developing baby.

28. A person may feel depressed or upset about having this condition, and group support can help a person cope with this condition.
29. The treatment most likely failed to destroy all of the cancer cells, and they spread to the liver.
30. People who are overweight and have a high percentage of body fat are more at risk for developing cancer.

a blood platelet and
a white blood cell

white blood cells

cancer cells

Color-enhanced SEM
Magnification: 3,750x

Color-enhanced SEM
Magnification: unknown

Health Literacy Activities

What Do You Know?
Self-Directed Learning Write questions about common types of diseases—including respiratory, cardiovascular, and chronic diseases, as well as cancer, STDs, and HIV— that are factual, but difficult or challenging to answer. You might research information beyond what you learned in this unit. Form teams with classmates and compete by answering the other teams' questions. Keep score and declare a winner.

Connection to World Cultures
Effective Communication People of certain cultures and countries are more at risk than others for certain diseases and health conditions because of differences in diet, climate, and other factors. Find an article in a medical journal or other periodical that discusses a disease or health condition that is common in a certain culture or country. Write a summary of this article and share the information with your classmates.

Family Involvement
Responsible Citizenship Write a health plan with family members in which each member will play a role in reducing the risk of heart disease in the family. For example, you may recommend a family exercise night.

Investigating Health Careers
Problem Solving Interview a family physician or a dermatologist to obtain information about the effects of sunbathing or using a tanning booth on the skin. Prepare a poster to share with the class.

Group Project
Critical Thinking Prepare a 30-second public service announcement explaining ten ways to reduce the risk of certain types of cancer. Record your announcement and send the tape to a local radio station, or get permission to play it over your school's PA system. Visit **www.glencoe.com** for more information.

Standardized Test Practice

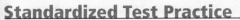

Reading & Writing

Read the following selection and answer the questions that follow.

Scientists have been reporting for many years about the healthful qualities of drinking black or green tea. Substances called antioxidants, found in many kinds of hot or cold tea, may reduce the risk of heart disease and cancer, strengthen bones, improve allergies, and even help prevent cavities. A 2003 National Academy of Sciences study shows that drinking five cups of tea a day may boost the body's ability to fight diseases. Researchers found that the T-cells in the blood of tea drinkers released up to five times the normal amount of a chemical called interferon. Interferon fights infection and can even shrink some kinds of tumors. Scientists are hopeful that the new discovery will lead to important breakthroughs in the ongoing battle against disease.

www.glencoe.com

Multiple Choice

1 In this paragraph, the word *breakthroughs* means
  A experiments
  B failures
  C successes
  D reports

2 Which statement best describes the author's attitude toward the new findings about tea?
  A Everyone should start drinking tea.
  B The findings are opinion, not fact.
  C More research is needed in order to apply research findings about tea to treatments for diseases.
  D Scientists are exaggerating the healthful qualities of tea.

Open-Ended

3 Write a letter to a friend summarizing this paragraph and making a recommendation about drinking tea.

Health Literacy Activities

What Do You Know?
This type of activity can be very interesting, but it will require monitoring. Instruct students on the types of questions they are allowed to ask. Caution students that questions should never be offensive to others.

Connection to World Cultures
Choose several diseases from among those researched to allow students to share with the class. Discuss reasons why diet, climate, and other factors contribute to conditions that might make a person more at risk for developing certain kinds of diseases.

Family Involvement
Encourage students to share their health plans with the class. Some families may have plans that can be easily used by other families who wish to reduce the risk of heart disease in their family.

Investigating Health Careers
Have students share their posters with the class. Inform students that they may want to contact their school counselor for more information on careers in a health-related field.

Group Project
This project may be coordinated with other activities occurring in your building. If students aren't allowed to make the announcement, they should write the announcement for someone at the school to announce or someone at a radio station to announce.

Standardized Test Practice

Reading & Writing

Multiple Choice
1. C   2. C

Open-Ended
3. Students' letters should accurately summarize the important points of the paragraph, while stressing that the findings are from one study only and need to be further examined. Most letters will end with a recommendation that the reader should think about drinking tea, perhaps instead of sugary soft drinks, and stay current on the latest research. Letters should contain correct spelling, capitalization, punctuation, grammar, usage, and sentence structure.

539

Use the three statements on the student page to initiate a class discussion about consumer and community health. *Additional True/False statements are:*

4. **Watching educational TV is the only good entertainment choice.**
   FALSE: Entertainment choices can include social activities, physical activities, hobbies, reading, and going to museums, concerts, and the theater, as well as TV.

5. **Movies that are rated PG-13 are suitable for all teenagers.**
   FALSE: PG-13 movies may contain moderate violence, sexual situations, coarse language, or suggestive dialogue, which may be unsuitable for some teens.

6. **Making a budget is a good way for teens to effectively manage their money.**
   TRUE: Making a budget helps a person keep track of his or her spending habits.

 Teen Volunteers

Role Models Many celebrities endorse charities. Have students investigate which charities celebrities support with their time, money, and status, and why they do so. **L2**

UNIT 9

Consumer and Community Health

> **"If you are motivated to excel in one area, you are usually motivated to excel in others."**
>
> —Ellen Ochoa, NASA astronaut and the first Hispanic woman in space, speaking about time management

TEST YOUR CONSUMER IQ

True or False?

1. **Advertisements can affect your health status.**
   TRUE: Advertisements try to make you feel dissatisfied with what you have. They try to convince you that you need to buy a product or service, even if it sounds too good to be true or you cannot afford it.

2. **Health fraud is easy to detect.**
   FALSE: Many health fraud promotions use scientific language in order to fool people.

3. **Only government officials work in public health.**
   FALSE: Anyone who is involved in bettering the health of the public works in public health, including researchers, doctors, nurses, nutritionists, and even those who work with hazardous materials.

 Teen Volunteers

Interview Through volunteer work, teenagers make valuable contributions to their community. Interview a teenager who volunteers. Ask what he or she likes about volunteering and what he or she has learned from the experience. Present your findings to your class.

LESSON 50	**LESSON 51**	**LESSON 52**
Acquiring Knowledge of Health Laws	Managing Time and Money	Analyzing Media Messages

 Two-Minute Unit Launcher

Demo Students may not think of some health problems as being public health issues. Play a public service announcement (PSA) for a public health issue. Examples include AIDS, cancer, heart disease, obesity, smoking, hunger, and childhood immunizations. Have students discuss how the problem is a public health issue. List questions on the chalkboard that students have about the various public health issues, and as you cover them in the unit, refer to the list and answer the students' questions. **L2**

EVALUATING MEDIA MESSAGES

Pure Azure

Take matters into your own hands. Don't hide your face. Just apply Pure Azure cream once a day, and your acne will disappear before your eyes. There are no side effects, and 8 out of 10 doctors recommend Pure Azure for their worst acne cases. Liberate yourself! Get Pure Azure today!

 WHAT'S YOUR VERDICT?
To evaluate this advertisement, use the criteria for analyzing and evaluating health messages delivered through media and technology that you learned in Unit 1.

Visit **www.glencoe.com** to find regularly updated statistics on health careers. Using the information provided, determine the answer to this question: Which health career is in need of professionals?

Visit **www.glencoe.com** to use *Your Health Checklist* ✔, an interactive tool that helps you determine your health status.

LESSON 53
Accessing Reliable Health Care

LESSON 54
Investigating Health Careers

LESSON 55
Learning About Public Health

Answers According to the Bureau of Labor Statistics, which is part of the U.S. Department of Labor, health services is one of the largest industries in the country, with more than 11 million jobs. About 13 percent of all wage and salary jobs created between 2000 and 2010 will be in health services. Students can check www.glencoe.com to find out which health career showed the largest growth in the last 10 years and which health career is in need of professionals. Many parts of the country need nurses, pharmacists, radiological technicians, and laboratory technicians.

 What's Your Verdict?
Analyzing Ads Skin-care products are advertised in magazines and on television. Ask each student to bring in a skin-care ad from a newspaper or magazine or a written description of an ad they have seen on TV. Working in groups, have students analyze the ads and answer the following questions: What advertising strategies are being used to sell the products? Who are the target audiences? Are the claims the ads make realistic or unrealistic? **L2**

Health Journal
Write an Essay Have students write an essay in their health journals about an experience with a health-care product they have tried and liked and one that did not live up to its claims. Ask students to discuss whether they feel advertisements for the products were accurate or misleading. Have students write about the satisfaction they may have felt after using a product they liked and the disappointment and frustration they might have felt after using the product they did not like. **L2**

Unit Focus Transparency
Page 4, **Unit 9 Fast File Resources**

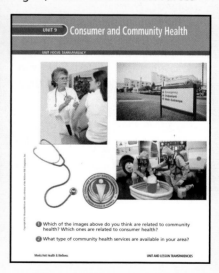

National Health Education Standards
Pages 540–541: 2.3, 2.5, 2.6, 2.10, 3.1

541

Out of Time?

If time does not permit an in-depth study of this topic, use the following activities in this Teacher Wraparound Edition:

• Legal Issues, p. 544
• Class Activity, p. 545
• Family Involvement, p. 545
• Using the Table, p. 547

1 Focus

HEALTH GOALS **Protect Yourself** Have students respond to the Health Goals for this lesson by listing reasons to protect themselves from health fraud. *Reasons may include not wasting money on products and services that don't work.* **L1**

Write ABOUT IT!

Role-Play Have students role-play a scenario in which they are trying to return a health product that did not work as advertised. They should try to convince the salesclerk to refund their money. **L2**

LESSON

50

What You'll Learn

1. Explain the hierarchy of federal, state, county, and city laws. *(p. 543)*
2. Discuss consumer rights. *(p. 544)*
3. List ways to be a successful consumer. *(p. 544)*
4. Explain the right to be informed. *(p. 544)*
5. List steps to take if health fraud is suspected. *(p. 545)*
6. Discuss agencies and organizations that play a role in consumer protection. *(p. 547)*
7. Outline actions that can be taken when consumer rights have been violated. *(p. 548)*

Why It's Important

It is important to learn how to protect yourself against being taken advantage of.

Key Terms

• law
• Food and Drug Administration (FDA)
• ordinances
• consumer rights
• health fraud
• Consumer Product Safety Commission (CPSC)
• recall
• Federal Trade Commission (FTC)
• National Health Information Center (NHIC)
• Council of Better Business Bureaus (BBB)

542 **UNIT 9** • Consumer and Community Health

Acquiring Knowledge of Health Laws

HEALTH GOALS
• I will acquire knowledge of laws to protect health.
• I will recognize my rights as a consumer.
• I will take action if my consumer rights are violated.

A person who uses products and services is called a ***consumer***. The promotion and protection of consumers' interests is ***consumerism***. If you purchase a defective product or hire a service that does not provide what you expected, you have the right to take action.

Write ABOUT IT!

Writing About Consumer Rights Suppose you bought an inexpensive radio through the mail last month. It hasn't worked correctly since you received it. Your friend says, "It was cheap. Just throw it away and buy another one." After reading the information about the Consumer Bill of Rights on page 544, write an entry in your health journal about how you would deal with this situation.

National Health Education Standards—Guide for Lesson 50		
2.4	Evaluate how the school and community can impact personal health practice and behaviors.	pp. 543, 547
2.10	Analyze how public health policies and government regulations can influence health promotion and disease prevention.	pp. 543, 544, 547, 549
3.1	Evaluate the validity of health information, products, and services.	pp. 542, 544–546, 549

Health Laws

There are many laws that protect health and aim to prevent disease and injury. A **law** is a rule of conduct, established and enforced by a controlling authority, to bring about and maintain an orderly coexistence. There are different types of laws that govern people's actions. In the United States, individuals are subject to the laws made by their federal, state, county, and city governments. It is best to think of laws as a hierarchy with federal laws at the top, local laws at the bottom, and state laws in between.

The Hierarchy of Health Laws

Federal laws Federal laws are enacted by the United States Congress and apply to every state in the country. If a state law contradicts a federal law, the federal law preempts the state law, and the state will be required to abide by the federal law.

Examples of federal laws that protect health are the Occupational Safety and Health Act and the Clean Water Act. The Occupational Safety and Health Act requires workplaces to be free from serious, recognized hazards and to comply with occupational safety and health standards. The Clean Water Act sets standards for water quality.

Various federal agencies have the responsibility of enforcing federal laws. For example, the ***Food and Drug Administration (FDA)*** has (or shares) the responsibility of enforcing several federal laws that protect health, such as the Food Quality Protection Act; the Federal Food, Drug, and Cosmetic Act; and the Controlled Substances Act.

State laws Federal laws do not cover all areas of the law, and in those instances, state or local laws can help to protect the public. State laws are enacted by state legislatures and apply to everyone within the state. They cannot violate the state constitution, federal constitution, or federal law. An example of state laws that protect health by preventing disease is school-entry immunization laws. All states require vaccinations before children enter school. The requirements of these laws vary from state to state. All states will exempt children from vaccinations for medical reasons, and some will exempt children for religious and philosophical reasons.

Ordinances County and municipal governments also enact laws called ***ordinances*** through the authority granted to them by the state. Ordinances apply to everyone within the county or municipality limits. These ordinances may not violate state or federal laws. An example of an ordinance that protects health is the requirement to use bicycle helmets. There is no federal law, and less than half of all states have laws requiring the use of bicycle helmets.

> **Make the Connection**
> **Clean Water Act** For more information on the Clean Water Act, see page 609 in Lesson 57.

LESSON 50 • Acquiring Knowledge of Health Laws 543

Consumer Rights

Consumer Rights

Privileges that a consumer is guaranteed are called ***consumer rights***. As consumers select products and services, they should not have to be concerned about safety, or have to contend with false and misleading advertising.

What to Know About Consumer Rights

Consumer rights known as The Consumer Bill of Rights are privileges. Those privileges come with responsibilities. It is your responsibility to become informed about a product or service. You are responsible for using products as they are intended. It is your responsibility to choose products and services at affordable prices. You also are responsible for notifying consumer protection agencies if products and services do not meet your expectations.

Successful consumerism In order to be a successful consumer, compare quality and price before making a purchase. Check the company's reputation before doing business with it. Get a written estimate. Never accept verbal guarantees. Understand contracts before signing. Never sign incomplete contracts. Keep contracts, warranties, guarantees and receipts. Use caution when giving out bank account numbers. Never pay in order to collect a "prize."

TABLE 50.1	The Consumer Bill of Rights
Consumer Right	**Privilege**
The right to choose	The ability to choose quality products and services at competitive prices
The right to be heard	The ability to have consumer well-being advocated when making and implementing government policy, and when developing products and services
The right to safety	The protection from products, services, and production methods that are unhealthy
The right to be informed	The ability to obtain information needed to make educated choices, and the protection from false or misleading advertising and labeling
The right to satisfaction of basic needs	The ability to obtain vital products and services
The right to redress or remedy	The ability to reach an acceptable solution for a complaint, including compensation for misrepresentation, poor quality products, and unsatisfactory service
The right to consumer education	The ability to be aware of consumer rights and responsibilities, and to act on them
The right to environmental health	The ability of present and future generations to exist in a healthy environment

544 UNIT 9 • Consumer and Community Health

 Legal Issues

Approved Claims The Food and Drug Administration approves some claims that can be made on food and dietary supplement labels. The claims can state that the product reduces the risk of certain health conditions or that the product can maintain the body's normal structure or function. The claims cannot state that the product is a treatment or a cure. Examples of approved claims are: "The vitamin folic acid may reduce the risk of neural tube defect-affected pregnancies," "Calcium may reduce the risk of the bone disease osteoporosis," and ". . . promotes healthy joints and bones." The claims must be accompanied with the disclaimer, "This statement has not been evaluated by the Food and Drug Administration. This product is not intended to diagnose, treat, cure or prevent disease."

Health Fraud

F alse advertisement and sale of products and services described as safe and effective to diagnose, treat, or cure a condition or benefit health, that have not been scientifically proven to be safe and effective, is *health fraud*. A quack is someone who is involved in fraudulent health activities.

What to Know About Health Fraud

The FDA identified categories in which health fraud is most frequent. The categories include: instant weight-loss schemes, AIDS cures, arthritis products, cancer treatments, baldness treatments, and nutritional supplements.

Health fraud is often targeted at teens and older adults. Teens who are overly concerned about their looks are vulnerable. They may buy products that claim to clear up acne, build muscles, or cause quick weight loss. Older adults with chronic health problems and life-threatening diseases are also vulnerable. They may buy products that claim to provide quick cures or to enable them to recapture their youth.

Protect against health fraud There are several reasons to protect yourself from health fraud. Health fraud leads to wasting money on products or services that do not do what has been claimed. Fraudulent products or services may cause harmful reactions or injuries, or delay valuable medical treatment.

Uncovering health fraud There are several things that may indicate health fraud, including a promise of a cure for a condition for which medical scientists do not have a cure. A product that promises quick and/or painless results or a claim that a product or treatment works by a secret formula or in a mysterious way is an indication of health fraud. The product or treatment may be sold over the telephone, on the Internet, door-to-door, or by mail order. The product or service may be promoted on the back pages of magazines or in newspaper ads that look like articles. Infomercials are used to sell products and they frequently rely on celebrity endorsements.

The seller may claim that the medical profession does not recognize the product or service. There may be claims that the product or service is effective for many unrelated disorders or that it is "all-natural." The product may lack labels that provide directions for use or cautions about use.

If health fraud is suspected Before buying a product that you suspect may be fraudulent, take any of the following steps. Contact a consumer protection agency to check for complaints against the company. Ask about the refund or exchange policy. Read the warranty if available to find out what must be done if there is a problem.

Did You Know?

Fraud If a product or service sounds too good to be true, it probably is.

Reading Review

1. Why are teens vulnerable to health fraud?

2. Why should you protect yourself from health fraud?

Health Fraud

Quick Demo

Evaluating Advertisements Find an ad in a magazine for a well-known health or weight-loss product. Make a copy for each student. Have students read the fine print and discuss why they think this information is written in such small print. **L2** **ELL**

Class Discussion

Easy Targets Have students discuss why they think health fraud is most frequent in the categories of weight loss, cures for AIDS, arthritis products, cancer treatments, nutritional supplements, and treatments for baldness. *Answers may include: AIDS, arthritis, cancer and baldness are health problems for which medical science has no known cures. Fast and effortless weight-loss can be tempting to people who are overweight.* **L2**

Class Activity

Find It in the Phone Book Have students use their local telephone book to locate a consumer protection agency in their area. Ask students whether it is a local, state, or federal organization. Students should list the name of the agency, the address, the phone number, and the Web address if one is provided. Have the class compile a list of all of the agencies serving your area. **L2** **ELL**

Reading Review

1. *Teens are often overly concerned with their appearance.*

2. *It wastes money, may cause harmful reactions or injuries, or delay medical treatment.*

Family Involvement

Family Shopping Trip Have students go to the store with the adult who does the shopping for the household. As they are shopping, have students make a list of five health-care products. The list should include the name of the product, the product's intended use, and any specific health claims that are made for each product. Ask students if the claims are realistic, and if they are backed by scientific research. Have students discuss the claims with their parents and share, in class, what they've learned about health fraud. **L2** **ELL**

> **National Health Education Standards**
> Pages 544–545: 2.5, 2.10, 3.1

FACTSABOUT
THE MOST COMMON HEALTH FRAUDS

Class Activity

Red Flags Divide the class into six groups. Assign each group one health claim, such as "dissolves fat instantly," that should send up a "red flag" to alert their attention to potential health fraud. Have students look through magazines (if available) or think of products they've seen advertised using that particular health claim. Share ideas and products with the class. **L2**

NHES Assessment/SCASS

Performance Task Ask students to develop a list of questions they could ask the manufacturer of a health-care product to uncover potential fraud. Have students identify a product(s) that they have heard advertised on the radio, seen in TV or Web ads, or read about in a magazine. Ask students to contact the company, ask the questions, and record their responses. **L3**

Investigating the Issue

- *Answers will vary, but may include products claiming to cure AIDS, arthritis, cancer, or baldness; weight-loss schemes; or nutritional supplements.*
- *Answers will vary, but may include claims that are too good to be true.*

FACTSABOUT
THE MOST COMMON HEALTH FRAUDS

The Food and Drug Administration (FDA) gives tips on how to identify possible health fraud through advertising. According to the FDA, health fraud is the promotion of drugs, devices, foods, or cosmetics of unproven effectiveness to enhance health, well-being, or appearance. When reading or listening to the promotion of a health product, the FDA recommends that you carefully review the claims while looking for the following "red flags."

Quick fixes Be wary of claims that a product can cure a serious disease, such as cancer, quickly.

Miracle cure Question products that are described as "magical" or a "miracle cure."

Satisfaction guaranteed Promises of money-back guarantees with no questions asked are often difficult to redeem in reality.

Rapid weight loss without dieting Weight is lost when the number of calories used by the body is greater than the number of calories consumed. This is usually achieved through some combination of dietary changes and increased physical activity.

One product cures all Treatments for serious diseases usually involve a combination of drugs and other therapies as well as dietary and lifestyle changes. One product cannot cure several ailments.

Nonsensical medical jargon The use of what seems like impressive medical terms may be just a ploy to disguise a lack of scientific evidence that would support a proven product.

Personal testimonials Be suspicious if the product being sold is accompanied by undocumented case histories or personal testimonials. (Example: "I tried this product for just two weeks, and I lost 30 pounds!"—Sarah M.)

▶ Weight-loss products are commonly fraudulent.

A good rule of thumb to use when deciding whether a new product may be right for you is that if the promotions sound too good to be true, the product may need to be further researched.

Before trying a product with which you are unfamiliar, talk to your parents or guardian, your doctor, or another health-care professional. Use resources such as the BBB, the FDA, or other health-advocate groups, such as the American Heart Association or the American Diabetes Association, to further research the product. These organizations can tell you whether there have been consumer complaints about the product, whether there are any adverse side effects that could result from using the product, or whether the product has been approved for use by the FDA. Your health-care professional can discuss other treatment options with you, as well as monitor the progress of your treatment.

Investigating the Issue

Visit www.glencoe.com for more information about health fraud.

- What products are currently under investigation by the FDA?
- Pick one product that is a suspected health fraud. Compare the promotional claims with information from the FDA. What assertions are made by the claims that may not be true?

Create a multimedia presentation that summarizes your research and present it to your class.

 www.glencoe.com

🛡 Sensitive Issues

Teens as Targets Teenagers are easy victims of health fraud. Many teens are overly concerned with their appearance. Teenagers are likely to experiment with products that promise to speed up and increase development, eliminate acne, build muscles, increase energy, and reduce weight. Studies on teenage spending reveal that teenagers spend an average of $95 a month on personal items. Be aware that some students may have fallen victim to health fraud gimmicks and may be embarrassed about their gullibility.

Consumer Protection

Federal, state, and local government agencies play important roles in consumer protection. Professional associations help consumers by monitoring the credentials and actions of their members. Private organizations provide additional assistance to consumers.

What to Know About Consumer Protection

State health departments People living within a state and visitors to the state receive health services from the state health department. *State health departments* set public health policy and provide administrative and technical assistance to local health departments.

Local health departments People living within a community receive health services from the local health department. *Local health departments* provide organized community programs with the goals of preventing disease, protecting people from hazards, and promoting healthy living.

TABLE 50.2 Consumer Protection Agencies

Agencies	Responsibilities
Consumer Product Safety Commission (CPSC)	Establishes and enforces product safety standards, receives consumer complaints, distributes product safety information, and *recalls* products—or takes products off the market due to safety concerns
Federal Trade Commission (FTC)	Enforces consumer protection laws and monitors trade practices and the advertising of foods, drugs, and cosmetics
National Health Information Center (NHIC)	Refers consumers to organizations that can provide health-related information
United States Department of Agriculture (USDA)	Enforces standards to ensure the safe processing of food, and publishes and distributes consumer pamphlets on nutrition and food safety topics
Council of Better Business Bureaus (BBB)	Monitors and publishes a listing of consumer complaints and advertising and selling practices
National Council Against Health Fraud (NCAHF)	Provides legal counsel and assistance to victims of health fraud, and provides many educational materials to consumers on the topic of health fraud

LESSON 50 • Acquiring Knowledge of Health Laws **547**

 Community Involvement

Local Health Department Ask students to contact their local health department. Have students determine five services that are provided by the health department and the cost of each service. Ask students to design a brochure or pamphlet describing the services offered and the cost of these services. Students should be sure to include the health department's address, phone number, Web address, hours of operation, and perhaps a map. Have students display their brochures or pamphlets on a bulletin board in the classroom. **L3**

Consumer Rights Violations

3 Assess

Vocabulary Practice

Page 8, **Unit 9 Fast File Resources**

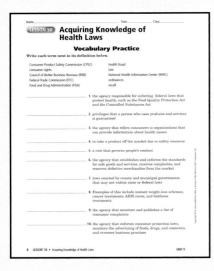

Consumer Rights Violations

Even informed consumers may purchase a product or use a service that does not meet their expectations. You, as a consumer, can report your complaint to one of the agencies or organizations identified in this lesson. If you do not know where or how to make a complaint, you can contact your local health department for advice. There are ten actions to take when your consumer rights have been violated.

> **Make the Connection**
>
> **Advocacy** For more information on advocating for personal, family, and community health, see page 65 in Lesson 7.

1. Talk to your parents or guardian and agree on a plan of action.

2. Save all paperwork related to the purchase in a file.

3. Contact the business that sold you the item or performed the service. Describe the problem and the action you want taken. For example, do you want your money back or the product exchanged?

4. Keep a record of your actions. Write down the name of the person with whom you spoke and a summary of the conversation.

5. Allow time for the person you contacted to resolve the problem.

6. Write a letter to the company headquarters if you are not satisfied with the actions taken to resolve the problem. Address your letter to the consumer office or the company president. Include the following information: date and place of purchase, a description of the product or service, what the problem is, and what you want done. Include copies of all documents, such as receipts or warranties. Do not send the originals. Keep a copy of the letter in your file.

7. Send a copy of the letter to a consumer group, your state's attorney general, or the local Better Business Bureau if the company does not respond in an adequate amount of time. Contact your local or state consumer protection agency right away if you think a law has been broken.

8. Advise the company that you have notified groups responsible for consumer protection.

9. Inform the news media when you believe an ad for a product or service is deceptive or inaccurate.

10. Consider the legal actions your family might take.

CONSUMER RIGHTS VIOLATIONS in the Media

Writing Activity Compare TV commercials and internet and magazine advertisements that promote items that may violate your consumer rights. Compare promotions for a potentially fraudulent product from each media type. Make a chart showing frequency of "red flags" in the promotions.

548   UNIT 9 • Consumer and Community Health

DI Differentiated Instruction

Hearing Impairment In order to be certain that a student with a hearing impairment has all of the information presented in class, regarding laws that protect our health, make duplicate copies of your lecture notes to give to the student. If you do not teach from notes, make copies of the notes from a conscientious student. This will help the student with a hearing impairment to understand the laws for his or her own protection and will provide a good source from which to prepare for tests. **L2 ELL**

Consumer Product
  Safety Commission
  (CPSC)
consumer rights
Council of Better
  Business Bureaus
  (BBB)
Federal Trade
  Commission (FTC)
Food and Drug
  Administration
  (FDA)
health fraud
law
local health
  department
National Health
  Information
  Center (NHIC)
ordinances
recall
state health
  department

Key Terms Review

Use what you know about the Key Terms to answer questions 1–5. Explain the purpose of and give an example of one problem that each of the agencies in questions 6–10 could help solve. Do not write in this book.

1. Compare ordinances with state laws.
2. What does it mean to recall a product?
3. Define consumer rights.
4. Describe health fraud.
5. What is a law?

6. Consumer Product Safety Commission (CPSC)
7. Federal Trade Commission (FTC)
8. Food and Drug Administration (FDA)
9. National Health Information Center (NHIC)
10. Council of Better Business Bureaus (BBB)

Recalling the Facts

11. List categories in which health fraud is most common.
12. Outline the hierarchy of health laws.
13. What are three things that may indicate health fraud?
14. What responsibilities go along with consumer rights?

15. How do federal laws protect health?
16. Who is most often targeted for health fraud?
17. What "red flags" do the FDA suggest consumers watch for when reviewing products?
18. What is the role of consumer protection agencies?

Critical Thinking

19. Why are state and local health laws needed in addition to federal health laws?
20. Explain how a fraudulent health product violates people's consumer rights. What actions should be taken?
21. How do the print and electronic media promote health fraud?
22. What changes would we see in our society if more people followed the steps to be a more successful consumer on page 548?

Real-Life Applications

23. Should you complain if your trash can broke while you stood on it? Why?
24. What would you do if you purchased a defective product?
25. Would you sign a service contract if the cost estimate was not filled in? Why?
26. A letter says "You won," but in order to claim your prize you must send $100. How would you respond?

Activities

Responsible Decision Making

27. **Writing** Your friend is excited about a new "natural, herbal, energy-boosting product" she bought. She enthusiastically tells you how she studied late into the night without getting tired. She hands you the product and tells you to try it. Write a paragraph about how you would respond. Refer to the Responsible Decision-Making Model on page 61 for help.

Sharpen Your Life Skills

28. **Comprehend Health Concepts** Create an advertisement for a product or service that would be considered fraudulent. Include the methods identified on page 545. Share your advertisement with a classmate. Have the classmate identify the methods you used in the advertisement.

Visit www.glencoe.com for more *Health & Wellness* quizzes.

Key Terms Review

1. State laws are enacted by state legislatures and apply to everyone in the state. Ordinances are enacted by county or municipal governments and apply to everyone within the county or municipality.
2. A recalled product is taken off the market due to safety concerns.
3. privileges that a consumer is guaranteed
4. false advertising and sale of products and services described, yet not scientifically proven, to be safe and effective to benefit health
5. a rule of conduct, established and enforced by a controlling authority, to bring about and maintain an orderly coexistence
6. establishes and enforces product safety standards; recalls dangerous products
7. enforces consumer protection laws; monitor advertising of food, drugs, and cosmetics
8. enforces laws that protect health; regulate labeling of food, drugs, and cosmetics
9. a health information referral service; refer consumers to organizations that provide health related information
10. monitors business advertising and selling practices; publishes a list of consumer complaints

Recalling the Facts

11. weight-loss, AIDS cures, arthritis products, cancer treatments, baldness treatments, and nutritional supplements
12. federal, state, county, and municipal
13. See page 545.
14. be informed, use products as they are intended, choose affordable products, and notify consumer protection agencies if products do not meet expectations.
15. See page 543.
16. teens and older adults
17. See page 546.
18. See page 547.

Critical Thinking

19. because federal laws do not cover all areas of the law
20. See pages 544 and 548.
21. advertisements and infomercials
22. fewer false advertising claims

Real-Life Applications

23. No, it was not used as it was intended.
24. See page 548.
25. No, the contract is incomplete.
26. Answers may include: Contact a consumer protection agency. Throw the letter away.

Activities

Responsible Decision Making

27. Answers will vary, but the student should not try the product.

Sharpen Your Life Skills

28. Answers will vary.

LESSON 51

Managing Time and Money

Out of Time?

If time does not permit an in-depth study of this topic, use the following activities in this Teacher Wraparound Edition:
• Family Involvement, p. 552
• Explain the Concept, p. 552
• Achieving Health Literacy, p. 554

1 Focus

HEALTH GOAL **Time Management** Have students respond to the Health Goal for this lesson by listing reasons to manage their time and money. *Reasons might include feeling happier and less stressed.* **L2**

Write ABOUT IT!

Managing Money Some students may decide to put a portion of the money in savings and use the rest for the concert. Others may decide that it was a birthday gift, so they spend the entire amount on the concert, the gift they want. Encourage students to discuss the reasons behind their decisions. **L2**

What You'll Learn

1. Identify 12 priorities for which a person needs to make time. *(p. 551)*
2. Identify five criteria to use for comparison shopping. *(p. 553)*
3. Explain how to make a budget. *(p. 554)*
4. Discuss reasons why a person must be careful when using credit cards. *(p. 554)*

Why It's Important

Managing your time effectively allows you time for the most important activities in your life. Setting up and following a budget allows you to have better control of your spending, which may allow you to save money to buy things you really want.

Key Terms

• time management
• credit card
• interest
• debt
• expenses
• savings
• income
• balanced budget

Managing Time and Money

HEALTH GOAL • **I will make a plan to manage my time and money.**

Most people wish they had more time and more money. Do you wish you had more time to finish homework? Do you wish you had more money to buy the things you want? Do you know how much money you spent in the past month? Although your time and money may be limited, effectively managing the time and money you do have will help you feel happier and less stressed.

Writing About Managing Money Suppose you receive $100 for your birthday. Your parents encourage you to put it into your savings account, but there is a concert you would like to attend. After reading the information about managing money on page 553, write an entry in your health journal about how you would deal with this situation.

National Health Education Standards—Guide for Lesson 51		
5.7	Evaluate the effectiveness of health-related decisions.	p. 553
6.2	Develop a plan to attain a personal health goal that addresses strengths, needs, and risks.	pp. 552, 554
6.3	Implement strategies and monitor progress in achieving a personal health goal.	pp. 552, 554

Managing Time

There are only so many hours in the day, so you must consider your priorities. **Time management** is organizing time to accomplish priorities. Priorities for Achieving Optimal Health appear in the chart below. If you organize your time to include these priorities, your life will be balanced and you will not feel rushed. People who manage time and set priorities are less likely to develop illnesses that are caused by mental and emotional stress.

What to Know About Managing Time

Scheduling your time may be easier than you think since several hours are already full due to sleep, meals, hygiene, work or school, and other essentials. You only have to schedule the available hours.

Time-management tips Set specific, realistic, and achievable goals. Set priorities and concentrate on important activities first. Use a calendar or date-book to keep track of important activities and large projects. Organize your calendar in a way that makes sense to you. Use a daily to-do list—make a list of things you need to do, then cross them off as they are complete. Allow time for sudden, yet important activities that sometimes come up. Have a place for everything and everything in its place, so you won't have to search. Work on large projects for short periods of time, or divide them into small tasks to complete. Take time to do it right the first time. Refer to your schedule. If you don't have time for an unimportant activity, say "no." If you have trouble managing your time, ask your parent or guardian for their ideas about adjusting your schedule.

Study-time management There are tips that may help you manage your study time. Determine your best study time. Do you concentrate better in the morning, afternoon, or evening? If possible, study when your concentration is better. Study difficult subjects first. Information is easier to learn when you are fresh. Study in short time blocks and take breaks periodically. Short breaks will keep you from becoming tired and losing your concentration. Study where there are few distractions. Distractions break your concentration and waste time. Combine activities if possible. If you have a long commute, have to wait for a ride, for practice to begin, or for an appointment, use that time to read or study.

> **Make the Connection**
>
> **Stress** For more information about stress, see page 100 in Lesson 10.

Priorities for Achieving Optimal Health

Organizing your time to include these priorities will keep your life balanced.

- family
- friends
- oneself
- chores and job responsibilities
- schoolwork
- school activities
- physical activities
- mental activities, such as reading and learning
- hobbies and entertainment
- rest and sleep
- healthful eating
- helping others

LESSON 51 • Managing Time and Money **551**

Managing Time

2 Teach

NHES Assessment/SCASS

Performance Task Divide the class into groups. Have each group write and perform a skit in which they must say "no" to an activity they do not have time to attend. Possible scenarios include: a ball game the night before a big test, or a friend invites you to the beach, but you are committed to a volunteer activity. Have students assess the effectiveness of the refusal skills demonstrated in the skits. **L2** **ELL**

PowerPoint® Presentations

This CD-ROM is an editable Microsoft® PowerPoint® presentation that includes:

- Lesson presentations
- Lesson checks
- Interactive graphics
- 5-Minute Checks
- Image Bank
- All transparencies

CRISS Project

Discussion Use the Sticky-Note Discussion Strategy on page 17T for students to mark places in the text where they find interesting facts or have unanswered questions on time and money management to be discussed in class.

Lesson Resource Manager

- **Unit 9 Fast File Resources**
  Reading Strategy, p. 19
  Vocabulary Practice, p. 20
  Transparency Master and Worksheet, p. 21
  Real-Life Health, p. 23
  Real-Life Health, p. 25
  5-Minute Check, p. 27
  Lesson 51 Quiz, p. 28
- **Unit 9 Transparency**
- **Lesson 51 Transparency**

- **Reading Essentials**
- **Technology**
  TeacherWorks™ CD-ROM
  StudentWorks™ CD-ROM
  Reading Essentials CD-ROM
  ExamView® Assessment Suite
  Vocabulary Puzzlemaker

> **National Health Education Standards**
> Pages 550–551: 1.2, 4.1, 4.2, 4.4

Activity: Using Life Skills

Using Goal-Setting and Decision-Making Skills: How to Create a Schedule

You may be wondering what a lesson about managing time is doing in a health textbook, but the connection between them is pretty simple. If you effectively manage your time, your stress level will stay low. You already know that stress can cause health problems, from headaches to more severe problems, such as heart attacks and cancer. Being able to manage time contributes to your health and well-being.

1 **Write your health goal and make an action plan to meet your health goal.** Create a schedule that will help you manage your time. Concentrate on important activities first.

2 **Identify obstacles to your plan and set up a timeline to accomplish your health goal.** Organize your schedule in a way that makes sense to you. Schedule your activities for one week.

3 **Keep a chart or diary in which you record progress toward your health goal.** Design a chart on a separate sheet of paper that includes the hours you are awake. Fill in the hours that are already full due to meals, hygiene, work and school, and other essentials. Use the available hours to plan your other activities. Use the sample chart as a guide. Determine which Priority for Achieving Optimal Health each falls under. Some may fall under more than one priority.

4 **Build a support system.** Make a copy of your schedule and post it on the refrigerator at home. Ask your family to help you keep to your schedule. Refer to your schedule and make a to-do list each morning.

5 **Revise your action plan or timeline, if necessary, and reward yourself when you reach your health goal.** At the end of the week evaluate how well you managed your time. Count the number of each priority. Determine if you spent too much, or too little, time on any of the priorities. Revise your weekly schedule as needed. Refer to the time-management tips on page 551 for help.

Make the Connection

Health Goals For more information on setting health goals, see page 57 in Lesson 6.

January

5 Wednesday	6 Thursday	7 Friday	8 Saturday
AM school	AM school	AM school	AM
8	8	8	8
9	9	9	9
10	10	10	10 Chores
11	11	11	11
12PM lunch	12PM lunch	12PM lunch	12PM Volunteer activity
1	1 school	1 school	1
2	2 English paper due	2	2 Free time
3 Sports practice	3 Sports practice	3 Chores	3
4	4	4 Free time	4
5 Chores	5 Chores	5	5
6 Dinner	6 Dinner	6 Dinner	6 Dinner
EVENING Homework, TV with family, video games	EVENING Homework, family night	EVENING Go to game	EVENING Mall with friends

▲ A written schedule will help you manage your time.

Benefits of Effective Time Management

As a high-school student, you can be involved in more activities than you could when you were younger. You can participate in sports and clubs, you can get an after-school job, and you definitely have more homework. You probably already know how stressful it is when you feel like you don't have enough time to get everything done.

There are many benefits of effective time management. Managing time effectively enables you to feel more in control of your daily activities, and reduces inner conflicts. It helps you gain self-direction and self-motivation. Your productivity increases. Studying becomes less stressful and more enjoyable. It helps you get started on what needs to be done, and keeps you from getting behind and missing deadlines. Your self-confidence improves. You have more time to enjoy yourself.

Effective time management helps you make sure you spend your time in a healthy, balanced way. An added health bonus: people who effectively manage their time to include the Priorities for Achieving Optimal Health, on page 551, are less likely to develop illnesses caused by mental and emotional stress.

Managing Money

Y ou may not have considered money management a health topic, but it is an important one. If you manage money wisely, you experience less stress. You are not anxious and worried about paying bills or overspending. You are less likely to develop stress-related illness. If you manage money wisely, you will have the money you need for health care. An important step in effective money management is making a budget.

What to Know About Managing Money

Base your spending decisions upon your budget. If something costs more than your budget will allow, wait until you have saved enough money to purchase it.

Using credit Use caution when purchasing on a credit card. A *credit card* is used to purchase items, for which the card holder agrees to pay later. Each month a statement of the charges placed on the credit card is sent to the card holder. The bill is either paid in full or in part. If only part of the bill is paid, interest is charged on the balance. *Interest* is a fee, charged by the credit card company, to the card holder, for the use of money.

Credit cards are convenient, but they should be used with caution. It is effective money management to not charge more than can be paid off in one month. Serious debt problems may arise if charging more than can be paid each month becomes a habit. *Debt* is the condition of owing.

Borrowing money from friends and family can be risky. This practice may cause disagreements between you if they want their money, but you can not repay it.

Guidelines for comparison shopping
Comparison shopping is evaluating products and services using the following criteria: Does the product cost less than a comparable product? Will the product save time or effort? Does the product have outstanding characteristics? Is the product made of better materials or with better craftsmanship than a comparable product? Is there written assurance that the product will be repaired or replaced if a problem occurs?

Ask yourself these questions before you buy a product: Is this something I need? Can I afford to buy this? Will I still enjoy this a month from now? Can I buy this for less money at a different store? Am I only buying this because of its name brand? Would a different brand be less expensive and just as good? Is the quality a good value for the price?

Investing money A savings account may earn a little interest every month. Once you have a fair amount of money built up in your savings account, you may want to consider investing it in a certificate of deposit (CD) or in the stock market.

Did You Know?

Credit Card Debt
If your credit card balance was $10,000 and you made the minimum monthly payment of $175 at 18 percent interest, and never charged another thing on the card, it would take you 11 years to pay off the debt. You would pay more than $13,000 in interest charges, which would bring your total of original debt plus interest to more than $23,000.

Teacher FYI

Credit Card Use The number of credit cards held by college undergraduates is steadily increasing. According to the National Center for Educational Statistics (NCES), 39.1 percent have one or two cards and 53.2 percent have three or more. More than 44 percent carry a balance, with the average balance over $3000.

NHES Assessment/SCASS

Performance Event Ask students to imagine they are in college. They plan to work hard over the summer so they can concentrate on their studies when classes start. Have students write an essay explaining how they will manage their money during the summer to save enough for the school year. **L2**

INTERACTIVE CHALKBOARD with Image Bank

5-Minute Check
Page 27, **Unit 9 Fast File Resources**
1. What is time management? *organizing time to accomplish priorities*
2. Why it is important to include the priorities for achieving optimal health when managing time? *life will be balanced and you will not feel rushed; you will be less likely to develop stress-related illnesses*
3. Why is it risky to borrow money from friends? *It may cause disagreements between you and your friends*
4. Why should you be a comparison shopper? *so you can evaluate products and services before you buy or use them*
5. What are options for investing money? *a savings account, CD, stocks*

Differentiated Instruction

Gifted and Talented Have students contact three local banks or savings institutions and research the current rates for certificates of deposit accounts (CDs). Ask students to graph the rates of interest based on the amount of the investment and the period of time the money was invested. Also, have students compare the rates of interest from each of the three banks, using a graph. Students should determine the relation between the amount of interest offered and the length of the investment. Ask students to present their findings to the class. **L3**

National Health Education Standards
Pages 552–553: 1.1, 1.2, 5.7, 6.2, 6.3, 7.1

Using Life Skills

Using Goal-Setting and Decision-Making Skills Have students list ways in which they can lower their expenses and limit their spending so that they can increase the amount of money they have to save or invest. **L2**

Reading Review

1. experience less stress and less likely to develop stress related illnesses
2. save first, think before spending, remember goals, use credit with caution, invest

---

Activity: Using Life Skills

Using Goal-Setting and Decision-Making Skills: Managing Your Money

Stress resulting from worrying about money can lead to a variety of health problems. Knowing how to effectively manage your money now is an important step to a healthy way of life.

1 Write your health goal and make an action plan to meet your health goal. Create a budget. Subtract your total expenses from your total income. *Expenses* are money you pay for products and services, and money you contribute to your family and your *savings*—money set aside for future use. *Income* is money you receive, such as allowance, pay you earn at your job, and gifts.

2 Identify obstacles to your plan and set up a timeline to accomplish your health goal. Keep a balanced budget. A *balanced budget* is a plan in which your income is greater than, or equal to, your expenses. If your expenses are greater than your income, it may lead to debt.

3 Keep a chart or diary in which you record progress toward your health goal. List and total your weekly income. Subtract your weekly expenses.

4 Build a support system. Evaluate your budget with your parent or guardian.

5 Revise your action plan or timeline, if necessary, and reward yourself when you reach your health goal. Determine if your weekly budget is balanced. If not, to avoid debt you can reduce your expenses or increase your income.

A budget is a useful tool ▼ for managing your money.

Monthly Income	
Job (10 hours a week)	$200
Allowance ($15 a week)	$60
TOTAL	**$260**

Monthly Expenses	
College fund	$50
Car fund	$25
Savings account/investments	$35
Money for entertainment/ food/clothes/music, etc.	$150
TOTAL	**$260**

Be Smart With Your Money

Balance is the key to money management. Follow these tips to save money and spend wisely.

Save first. Save a percentage of all the money you receive. It could be 10 or even 25 percent. Any time you receive money, deposit that percentage into your savings account.

Think before you spend. Making an impulse purchase, like buying a pair of shoes you really don't need, can keep your budget from staying balanced. Use the list in the Guidelines for Comparison Shopping section on page 553 to help you make good decisions.

Don't forget your goals. If you're saving money to buy a car and your friends want you to go to a concert with them, you need to decide if you want to spend $50 on a concert ticket or save $50 toward your car.

Use credit cards with caution. By using a credit card, you can get what you want now and pay for it later. But, if you do not pay the card off every month, you will be charged interest on the balance. That means you pay more than if you had paid cash.

Let your money work for you. Did you know you can earn money without even working? Investing in certificates of deposits (CDs) or in the stock market may help your money grow.

Reading Review

1. How does knowing how to manage your money affect your health?
2. How can you save money and spend wisely?

Achieving Health Literacy

Effective Communicator Credit card offers are widely available to teens, and some teens create financial problems for themselves because they do not understand how credit cards work. Have students create a public service announcement (PSA) about credit cards. The PSAs should be directed at first-time credit card holders. Ask students to include warnings about irresponsible spending along with tips on how to use credit cards wisely in their PSAs. Information on interest rates, grace periods, late fees, missed payments, credit history, and credit card scams also should be included in their PSAs. Ask the students to present their PSAs to the class. **L3**

National Health Education Standards

Pages 554–555: 1.2, 4.1, 4.3, 6.2, 6.3

balanced budget
credit card
debt
expenses
income
interest
savings
time management

Key Terms Review

Complete these fill-in-the-blank statements with the lesson Key Terms on the left. Do not write in this book.

1. A(n) _____ is a plan in which a person's income is equal to or more than their expenses.

2. _____ is the condition of owing.

3. _____ is additional money that is paid for the use of a larger sum of money.

4. _____ is money received.

5. A(n) _____ is used for payment when you agree to pay later.

6. _____ is the process of organizing time to accomplish priorities.

7. _____ is money set aside for future use.

8. _____ are money needed to purchase or do something.

Recalling the Facts

9. Identify ways to avoid debt.

10. Explain how to make a budget.

11. How is prioritizing beneficial when making a schedule?

12. Identify and explain the criteria used for comparison shopping.

13. Why should you save before you spend?

14. Explain the importance of being organized.

15. Explain why it is important to be flexible when making a schedule.

16. How can you let your money work for you?

17. List the priorities for achieving optimal health.

18. Why should you think before you spend?

Critical Thinking

19. What are the advantages of a savings account and investing money?

20. What are the benefits of effective time management?

21. Explain how effective money management can lead to optimal health.

22. Why should a person use credit cards with caution?

Real-Life Applications

23. Will you make changes in your time management? Why?

24. Should you ask a friend to lend you the money to buy a CD? Why?

25. Do you need to revise your money management? Why?

26. A friend asks you to go to a basketball game but you have a paper due tomorrow. How would you respond? Why?

Activities

Responsible Decision Making

27. **Determine** Suppose you are at the mall with friends. You see a new sequel to one of your favorite video games. You don't have any money, but your friend offers to lend you some money so you can purchase the game. You won't be able to pay him back until next month. Write a response to this situation. Refer to the Responsible Decision-Making Model on page 61 for help.

Sharpen Your Life Skills

28. **Practice Healthful Behaviors** Prepare a personal budget or spending plan for one month. Use the steps on page 554 as a guide. Review your budget with your parents or guardian. For one month, subtract from your income everything you buy. Write a summary of what you learned from this experience, including difficulties you may have had keeping your budget balanced.

Visit **www.glencoe.com** for more *Health & Wellness* quizzes.

Study Guide

Key Terms Review

1. balanced budget
2. debt
3. interest
4. income
5. credit card
6. time management
7. savings
8. expenses

Recalling the Facts

9. Use caution when using credit cards. Do not charge more than can be paid off in one month.

10. List income, list expenses, total each category, subtract expenses from income, keep income equal to or greater than expenses.

11. Prioritizing will help you achieve important activities first.

12. See page 553.

13. Saving first ensures that a portion of all money will be saved.

14. Organization saves time and effort when locating things.

15. Flexibility allows time for unexpected, yet important, activities.

16. Invest money and earn interest from savings accounts, CDs, and stocks.

17. See page 551.

18. Impulse purchases can cause an unbalanced budget.

Critical Thinking

19. Savings accounts allow you to put money away for future use, and investing in stocks and CDs can make money grow faster.

20. less stress, less illness caused by mental and emotional stress

21. less stress, less stress-related illness, will have money for health care

22. If you do not pay the balance each month, interest is charged on the remainder; therefore, you pay more than if you paid cash.

Real-Life Applications

23. Answers will vary, but should mention the priorities for achieving optimal health.

24. Answers will vary, but should include that borrowing money can cause disagreements.

25. Answers will vary, but should mention a balanced budget.

26. Answers will vary, but should include saying "no" and explain setting priorities.

Activities

Responsible Decision Making

27. Answers will vary.

Sharpen Your Life Skills

28. Answers will vary.

LESSON 52
Analyzing Media Messages

If time does not permit an in-depth study of this topic, use the following activities in this Teacher Wraparound Edition:
- Class Discussion, p. 557
- Using the Table, p. 559
- Class Activity, p. 562

1 Focus

HEALTH GOALS **Healthful Entertainment** Have students respond to the first Health Goal for this lesson by writing in their health journals about how the right amount of entertainment (at the right times) can be beneficial. *It can be a healthy outlet for stress, and it can lift your spirits and elevate your mood.* **L2**

Write ABOUT IT!

NHES Assessment/SCASS

Performance Event Students could explain to their friends why they object to the film. They also could offer suggestions for other movies they would like to see. **L2**

LESSON

52

What You'll Learn

1. Explain why adults are concerned with the amount of time teens spend on entertainment. *(p. 557)*
2. List guidelines to follow when choosing entertainment. *(p. 558)*
3. List 10 questions for evaluating entertainment media. *(p. 558)*
4. Discuss how to use television ratings and V-chips. *(p. 559)*
5. List seven ways health can be harmed by inappropriate entertainment choices. *(p. 561)*
6. Give evidence for the link between media violence and violent behavior. *(p. 561)*
7. Explain why entertainment addiction is risky. *(p. 562)*

Why It's Important

Media messages are everywhere. By learning how media messages can influence your attitudes you can make healthy choices.

Key Terms

- entertainment
- V-chip
- desensitization
- entertainment addiction
- promiscuous behavior

Analyzing Media Messages

HEALTH GOALS
- • **I will choose healthful entertainment.**
- • **I will analyze ways messages delivered through technology might affect my health status.**

When you eat nutritious foods, your body is well-nourished. Likewise, when you choose healthful entertainment, your mind is well-nourished. Entertainment also can have a negative affect on your health status. This lesson focuses on how to evaluate entertainment and how technology can affect your health status.

Write ABOUT IT!

Writing About Evaluating Entertainment Suppose some friends ask you to see a movie that has been heavily promoted on television. You think the movie commercials portray disrespectful attitudes toward women and ethnic groups. You do not want to see it. After reading the information about evaluating entertainment on page 558, write an entry in your health journal about how you would handle this situation.

National Health Education Standards—Guide for Lesson 52		
2.6	Evaluate the impact of technology on personal, family, and community health.	pp. 556, 557–562, 563
6.1	Assess personal health practices and overall health status.	pp. 558, 561, 563

Entertainment

S omething that is designed to hold people's interest is
entertainment. Entertainment can include a variety
of activities. You might play sports, participate in a
hobby, shop, or go to museums or concerts for entertainment.
One thing that has had a major impact on our choices of
entertainment is technology. Technology has brought many different
opportunities into our lives, not only for learning, but also for entertainment.

What to Know About Entertainment

Many forms of entertainment are available through media and technology. For example, the average American household has 2.7 televisions. Renting and going to the movies also are entertaining. People who enjoy musical entertainment often listen to the radio, CDs, and portable audio players, as well as attend live concerts. Others also enjoy video or computer games. An increasing number of teens use computers for many reasons, including entertainment.

Concerns about media entertainment
Many adults are concerned that media entertainment often takes away from activities that might serve as better uses of time, such as doing homework, participating in sports and physical activities, working, social activities or reading. They are concerned about the use of profanity, sexual content, and violence found in media entertainment. Popular movies and prime-time shows commonly depict sexual situations and include nudity, yet they rarely discuss the risks and responsibilities associated with sex. Profanity has increased on TV, in movies, and in popular music. Inappropriate material readily available on the Internet is a concern.

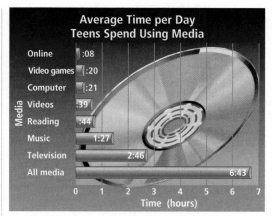

Average Time per Day Teens Spend Using Media

Media	Time (hours)
Online	:08
Video games	:20
Computer	:21
Videos	:39
Reading	:44
Music	1:27
Television	2:46
All media	6:43

◄ On average, teens spend nearly 7 hours a day using media.

Source: Kaiser Family Foundation *"Kids & Media @ The New Millennium: A Comprehensive National Analysis of Children's Media Use"*, 1999

Statistics: Teens' Media Entertainment Use

These statistics show the popularity of media entertainment among young people.

- Young people between ages 8 and 18 spend an average of 6 hours and 43 minutes a day using media outside of school.
- American teens listen to an estimated 10,500 hours of rock music between grades 7 and 12.
- Watching a DVD is considered, by most teens, their number one leisure activity.
- About half of all teens have a TV set in their bedroom.
- Teens spend an average of 20 minutes each weekday on a home computer and the Internet.

LESSON 52 • Analyzing Media Messages **557**

Lesson Resource Manager

- **Unit 9 Fast File Resources**
  Reading Strategy, p. 31
  Vocabulary Practice, p. 32
  Transparency Master and Worksheet, p. 33
  Real-Life Health, p. 35
  Real-Life Health, p. 37
  5-Minute Check, p. 39
  Lesson 52 Quiz, p. 40
- **Unit 9 Transparency**
- **Lesson 52 Transparency**

- **Reading Essentials**
- **Technology**
  TeacherWorks™ CD-ROM
  StudentWorks™ CD-ROM
  Reading Essentials CD-ROM
  Exam*View*® Assessment Suite
  Vocabulary Puzzlemaker

Class Discussion

Adults' Concerns Have students discuss why they think some adults are concerned about the amount of time students spend using media entertainment. **L2**

Extension

Evaluate Prime-Time Shows With their parents' or guardian's permission, have each student watch his or her favorite prime-time television show. Ask students to make note of the use of profanity, sexual content, violence, smoking, alcohol, and drug use. Have students record the messages they think the show sends to its audience. Ask students to present their findings to the class. **L3**

INTERACTIVE CHALKBOARD with Image Bank

PowerPoint® Presentations

This CD-ROM is an editable Microsoft® PowerPoint® presentation that includes:
- Lesson presentations
- Lesson checks
- Interactive graphics
- 5-Minute Checks
- Image Bank
- All transparencies

Journaling Use the Pre- and Post-Reading Responses Strategy on page 17T to determine students' understanding of the possible effects of media messages, both before and after reading the lesson.

National Health Education Standards
Pages 556–557: 2.5, 2.6, 4.2, 4.3, 7.2

557

Evaluating Entertainment

Quick Demo

Video Clip Show a 2–3 minute clip of popular commercials or a content-appropriate music video. Discuss with students what message is being delivered, how it is being delivered, and how it has influenced popular culture. For example, a heavily advertised brand of tennis shoes might set the standard for fashionable teens.

Teacher FYI

TV Guidelines The Educational Resources Information Center (ERIC) suggests the following guidelines for family television viewing. Set time limits for viewing. Plan viewing by using a TV guide or newspaper. Turn the TV on for a specific program, and then turn it off when the program is over. Watch TV as a family and talk about the programs.

INTERACTIVE CHALKBOARD
with Image Bank

Teaching Transparency

Page 33, **Unit 9 Fast File Resources**

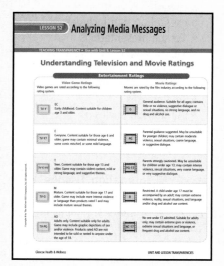

LESSON 52 | Analyzing Media Messages

TEACHING TRANSPARENCY • Use with Unit 9, Lesson 52

Understanding Television and Movie Ratings

Y̶ou should be selective when making decisions about the television programs, movies, music, and other forms of entertainment you choose. There are many quality entertainment choices. However, there is a lot of entertainment that does not contribute to optimal health and well-being.

What to Know About Evaluating Entertainment

Make the Connection

Advertisements For more information on evaluating advertisements, see page 37 in Lesson 4.

The entertainment you choose should meet your family guidelines. Entertainment also should meet your guidelines for personal behavior. It should contain content appropriate for your age group. Entertainment containing violence, sex, or profanity may promote inappropriate behaviors. Smoking, alcohol and drug use should not be portrayed as acceptable behavior. In general, entertainment should contribute to good character. It should lift spirits and encourage positive feelings.

▲ Your guidelines for personal behavior help you choose entertainment.

Questions for Evaluating Entertainment Media

The following questions will help you make good entertainment choices.

- Who paid for the media? Why?
- What message does the media convey?
- Does the media portray risky behaviors, such as smoking or drug use, in an appealing way?
- What values are expressed?
- Does the media contain inappropriate content, such as violence, sex, or profanity?
- What does the media attempt to persuade you to do?

- In what ways is the media presenting a healthy or unhealthy message?
- How did the media make you feel? What impression did it leave you with?
- Does the media live up to your guidelines for personal behavior? Does it follow your family guidelines?
- Does the media have a rating that is appropriate for your age and values?

558 UNIT 9 • Consumer and Community Health

Sensitive Issues

Media Entertainment Teens often may be responsible for making choices about their own entertainment media. Because some parents or guardians have jobs that require them to be at work at night or on weekends, some teens may spend time alone during those times. Have the class discuss how teens can evaluate entertainment media for themselves. Ask the class to develop a set of guidelines for choosing entertainment media that they feel is appropriate for teens. Encourage students to follow these guidelines when they are home alone and responsible for their own entertainment media choices. **L2**

TABLE 52.1 Entertainment Ratings

Video Game Ratings	Movie Ratings
Video games are rated according to the following rating system.	Movies are rated by the film industry according to the following rating system.

	Video Game		Movie	
TV-Y	**EC** Early childhood. Content suitable for children age 3 and older.	**G**	General audience. Suitable for all ages; contains little or no violence, suggestive dialogue or sexual situations, no strong language, and no drug and alcohol use.
TV-Y7	**E** Everyone. Content suitable for those age 6 and older; game may contain minimal violence, some comic mischief, or some mild language.	**PG**	Parental guidance suggested. May be unsuitable for younger children; may contain moderate violence, sexual situations, coarse language, or suggestive dialogue.
TV-Y7-FV	**T** Teen. Content suitable for those age 13 and older. Game may contain violent content, mild or strong language, and suggestive themes.	**PG-13**	Parents strongly cautioned. May be unsuitable for children under age 13; may contain intense violence, sexual situations, very coarse language, or very suggestive dialogue.
TV-G	**M** Mature. Content suitable for those age 17 and older. Game may include more intense violence or language than products rated T and may include mature sexual themes.	**R**	Restricted. A child under age 17 must be accompanied by an adult; may contain extreme violence, nudity, sexual situations, and language and/or drug and alcohol use content.
TV-PG	**AO** Adults only. Content suitable only for adults. Game may include graphic depictions of sex and/or violence. Products rated AO are not intended to be sold or rented to anyone under the age of 18.	**NC-17**	No one under age 17 admitted. Suitable for adults only; may contain extreme gore or violence, extreme sexual situations and language, or frequent drug and alcohol use content.

Ratings systems For decades, movies have used a ratings system. Today, TV programs, music, and video and computer games also are given ratings. The ratings give information about the amount of violence, sex, nudity, strong language, and drug or alcohol use contained in the media. TV and movie ratings in use today are explained in the table above.

Music labels Individual record companies voluntarily provide labeling. The labeling says "Parental Advisory: Explicit Content" for their CDs and DVDs. These labels disclose that the recording may contain strong language or expressions of violence. There may also be references to sex or to alcohol or drug abuse.

Using the Table
Viewing Log For one week, have students keep a log of all television shows and movies they watch, along with the rating for each. If the show has not been given a rating, have them rate each program or movie they watch based on the criteria provided in the chart. At the end of the week, divide students into groups for discussion. Ask students to determine if they think the ratings assigned to the programs or movies they watched were appropriate. Have students discuss the reasoning behind their decisions. **L2** **ELL**

Extension
Create a Graph Using the television portion of their log from Using the Table, above, have students create a graph illustrating the number of hours per day of television they watched of each television rating. Have them evaluate their viewing patterns. Ask students to determine if their television viewing is appropriate. Ask students to compare the number of hours they spent watching television each day with the average time per day teens spend watching television. Average time can be found on page 557. **L3** **ELL**

NHES Assessment/SCASS
Selected Response A television program that is considered to be suitable for all ages would be rated:
A. TV-PG
B. TV-MA
C. *TV-G*
D. TV-14

Cross-Curricular Connections
Music Have students bring in several songs that they feel promote positive messages about self-image, a drug- and violence-free lifestyle, and abstinence. Review the songs. You may want to have students have their parents or guardian sign a permission slip for this activity. Then ask students to share the songs with their classmates. Ask each student to lead a short discussion about the lyrics of the songs he or she has chosen. Have students discuss the messages of the songs. Ask students to discuss how the songs advocate for positive self-image, abstinence, and a drug- and violence-free lifestyle. **L2**

National Health Education Standards
Pages 558–559: 2.5, 2.6, 2.10, 6.1

Class Activity

Have the class list ways people with entertainment addiction may act. Ask students to choose one of these actions and write a short report about how a person can change this action and work toward ending his or her addiction. Have each student lead a short discussion about the action he or she chose. **L3**

3 Assess

Vocabulary Practice

Page 32, **Unit 9 Fast File Resources**

Did You Know?

Violence By age 18, a typical child has witnessed 200,000 acts of violence on television, including 16,000 murders.

Entertainment can be a healthy outlet for stress and pressure but too much use can negatively impact ▼ health status.

A person may develop entertainment addiction. The compelling need to watch television and other entertainment media is called ***entertainment addiction.*** People with entertainment addiction watch many hours of TV each day or are engaged in other forms of entertainment, such as going to movies, listening to music, playing computer games, or "surfing" the Internet. They center their lives around their favorite TV shows or other forms of entertainment. They spend so much time being entertained that there is not much time to be involved in healthful activities. Relationships with family and friends suffer. They may put off doing homework and chores. They have little time to participate in physical activities and are at increased risk of being overweight. Entertainment addiction might be used as a way to cope with feelings like loneliness, shyness, depression, and anxiety.

A person may use entertainment as a way to avoid, or as a substitute for relationships. Some people might find it easier to talk to others through a computer than to have relationships with people in person. E-mail and chat room acquaintances should never be a substitute for healthful relationships with family and friends.

A person may become persuaded to become sexually promiscuous. People portrayed in television shows and movies often engage in promiscuous behavior. To engage in ***promiscuous behavior*** is to engage in casual sexual activities with many people. Consider the impact on a person who watches many television shows and movies in which the actors or actresses engage in promiscuous behavior. This can cause a person to have unrealistic views about life. Being promiscuous is not a satisfying lifestyle. Behaving in this way can lead to an unplanned pregnancy or infection with sexually transmitted diseases.

A person may become persuaded to use alcohol, tobacco, or other drugs. Actors and actresses in movies and television programs smoke and drink. They "light up" or pour a drink during times of stress or suspense. People who see this behavior frequently may begin to believe that a cigarette or alcohol is the answer when life gets difficult. Television programs and movies usually do not show the misery that accompanies years of cigarette smoking or the adverse consequences of alcohol and other drug use.

562   UNIT 9 • Consumer and Community Health

(DI) Differentiated Instruction

Behavioral Disorders So that a student with a behavioral disorder can contribute to the class activity on this page, ask the student to draw upon his or her own attempts at changing behaviors. Then ask the student how these same efforts might apply to people who are trying to overcome entertainment addiction. Praise the student for good behavior during the activity if it is deserved. Depending on the sensitivity of the student, you might opt to have this discussion privately between the two of you. **L2**

National Health Education Standards

Pages 562–563: 1.1, 1.2, 2.1, 2.3, 2.5, 2.6, 6.1, 6.3

desensitization
entertainment
entertainment
  addiction
promiscuous
  behavior
V-Chip

Key Terms Review

Complete these fill-in-the-blank statements with the lesson Key Terms on the left. Do not write in this book.

1. Parents or guardians can block TV programs by using a _____.

2. Exposure to a lot of media violence may result in _____.

3. _____ can include a variety of activities.

4. _____ can lead to an unplanned pregnancy or a sexually transmitted disease.

5. People with _____ center their lives around their favorite TV show.

Recalling the Facts

6. What is considered by most teens their number one leisure activity?

7. List forms of media entertainment.

8. What does the movie rating PG-13 mean?

9. List questions that can be used for evaluating entertainment media.

10. List four guidelines to follow when choosing entertainment.

11. What does the television rating TV-Y7-FV mean?

12. List seven ways health can be harmed by inappropriate entertainment choices.

13. Describe the negative health effects as a result of becoming a couch potato.

14. Explain the television rating TV-MA.

15. Discuss the effects of desensitization.

16. What does the movie rating NC-17 mean?

17. Describe promiscuous behavior.

18. How can a person's problem-solving ability be affected by entertainment?

Critical Thinking

19. Explain the impact media technology has on health.

20. Discuss how to use television ratings and V-chips.

21. Explain why computer addiction can be a health risk.

22. Explain why adults are concerned with the amount of time teens spend on entertainment.

Real-Life Applications

23. Do you think there is a link between media violence and violent behavior? Why or why not?

24. How does the entertainment you choose meet your family's guidelines?

25. Has your behavior been influenced by entertainment you have chosen? How?

26. How can you avoid becoming a couch potato?

Activities

Responsible Decision Making

27. **Role-Play** Suppose your friend admires teen idols who dress in expensive clothes. She complains that she has nothing to wear because she thinks her clothes are outdated and ugly. Have a classmate play your friend. Tell her how media images can influence our attitudes and actions. Discuss unrealistic expectations and responsible decision-making. Refer to the Responsible Decision-Making Model on page 61 for help.

Sharpen Your Life Skills

28. **Analyze Influences on Health** Make a chart that analyzes all of the media you hear or see for three days. In the first column, record when and where you watch or listen to any form of media. In the second column, record the form of media. In the third column, record any unhealthy behaviors you see or hear. Write a short paper on what you learned from doing this exercise.

Visit **www.glencoe.com** for more *Health & Wellness* quizzes.

Key Terms Review

1. V-chip
2. desensitization
3. Entertainment
4. Promiscuous behavior
5. entertainment addiction

Recalling the Facts

6. watching a video or DVD

7. television, movies, music, the Internet, and video and computer games

8. may be unsuitable for children under age 13.

9. See list on page 558.

10. It should: meet family guidelines, meet your guidelines for personal behavior, contain content appropriate for your age, and should contribute to good character.

11. directed toward older children; same as TV-Y7, but with more intense fantasy violence

12. See pages 561–562 for information on technology and health status.

13. See page 561 for information on why being a "couch potato" is not healthful.

14. mature audiences only; may be unsuitable for children under age 17

15. See page 561 for information on desensitization.

16. No one under age 17 admitted.

17. to engage in casual sexual activities with many people

18. See page 561 for information on solutions to life's problems modeled in unrealistic ways.

Critical Thinking

19. Answers will vary, but should include information from pages 561–562.

20. See pages 559–560.

21. See page 562 for information on entertainment addiction.

22. See page 557 for information on adult concerns about media entertainment.

Real-Life Applications

23. Answers will vary, but should mention desensitization.

24. Answers will vary.

25. Answers will vary.

26. Answers will vary, but should include information on engaging in physical activities.

Activities

Responsible Decision Making

27. Answers will vary but should include that having expensive clothes is unnecessary and an unrealistic expectation for most teens.

Sharpen Your Life Skills

28. Answers will vary.

Accessing Reliable Health Care

 Out of Time?

If time does not permit an in-depth study of this topic, use the following activities in this Teacher Wraparound Edition:
• Class Activity, p. 565
• Class Discussion, p. 569
• Explain the Concept, p. 570
• Class Activity, p. 571

1 Focus

HEALTH GOALS **Choosing Wisely** Have students respond to the Health Goals for this lesson by explaining why they should choose wisely when it comes to health-care and insurance providers. *Reasons might include that they, like everyone else, want to get the most coverage for the least amount of money.* **L2**

Write ABOUT IT!

Health Fraud Have students discuss the possible consequences of withholding or lying about their medical history. Ask students to discuss what might happen if the insurance company found out that your classmate was lying. *If the insurance company found out, it could drop the policy and bring a lawsuit against your classmate.* **L2**

Accessing Reliable Health Care

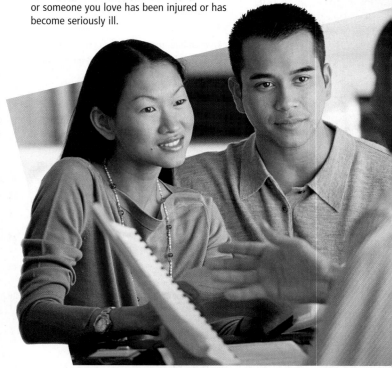

HEALTH GOALS
• I will make responsible choices about health-care providers and facilities.
• I will evaluate ways to pay for health care.

Health care is something we seldom think about until we need it. You have probably never considered what doctor, hospital, or clinic to go to or how you would pay for medical treatment unless you or someone you love has been injured or has become seriously ill.

What You'll Learn

1. List questions that can be used to evaluate a health-care provider. *(p. 566)*
2. Discuss the credentials of various health-care providers. *(p. 565)*
3. List two types of managed-care programs and discuss Medicare and Medicaid. *(p. 567)*
4. Explain five actions you can take to make yourself insurable. *(p. 568)*
5. List 10 questions that can be used to evaluate health insurance coverage. *(p. 568)*
6. Discuss various health-care facilities. *(p. 571)*

Why It's Important

When you are sick or injured, you may need immediate help. Knowing where to get medical help and how to pay for it can save you time, hassle, stress, and money.

Key Terms

• primary care
• specialist
• health insurance
• managed care
• Health Maintenance Organization (HMO)
• Preferred Provider Organization (PPO)
• Medicare
• Medicaid
• inpatient care
• urgent-care center

Write ABOUT IT!

Writing About Health Insurance Suppose a classmate tells you that he or she would not tell an insurance provider about a preexisting condition. He or she says that not telling is one way to ensure that the insurance provider will provide coverage. After you read the information about health insurance on page 567, write a response to this classmate in your health journal.

National Health Education Standards—Guide for Lesson 53		
1.6	Analyze the relationship between access to health care and health status.	pp. 564, 566, 568, 569, 570, 573
3.1	Evaluate the validity of health information, products, and services.	pp. 564, 566, 568, 569, 573
3.2	Utilize resources from home, school, and community that provide valid health information.	pp. 564, 565, 566, 567, 568, 569, 570, 571–572, 573
3.3	Determine the accessibility of products and services that enhance health.	pp. 564, 565–566, 567, 568, 596, 570, 571–572, 573

Health-Care Providers

A trained professional who provides people with medical care is a *health-care provider.* Physicians, health-care practitioners, and allied health professionals are health-care providers.

What to Know About Health-Care Practitioners and Providers

Physicians An independent health-care provider who is licensed to practice medicine is a *physician.* Physicians obtain medical histories, perform physical examinations, give diagnoses, and are licensed to prescribe medications. Some physicians are licensed to perform surgery.

There are two main types of physicians. A *medical doctor (MD)* is a physician who is trained in a medical school and has a medical doctor degree. A *Doctor of Osteopathy (D.O.)* is a physician who is trained in a school of osteopathy and has a doctor of osteopathy degree. Osteopathy uses common medical procedures, but also places a greater emphasis on the relationship between body systems than traditional medicine does. Osteopaths are trained that body systems are all connected and that disturbances in one body system can affect other systems.

Medical doctors and osteopaths can choose to work in primary care or become specialists. *Primary care* is general health care. Physicians who provide primary care often are the first health-care providers that a patient consults. Family practice physicians provide general care. Primary-care physicians can refer patients to specialists. A *specialist* is a professional who has specialized training in a particular area. Almost two-thirds of physicians are specialists.

Health-care practitioners An independent health-care provider who is licensed to provide general or specialized care for a specific area of the body is a *health-care practitioner.* Podiatrists, optometrists, and dentists are health-care practitioners. A *podiatrist* is a doctor of podiatric medicine (DPM) who specializes in the care and treatment of the feet. An *optometrist* is an eye care professional who is specially trained in a school of optometry. An optometrist examines eyes for vision problems, and can prescribe corrective lenses or exercises. A *dentist* is a Doctor of Dental Surgery (DDS) or a Doctor of Medical Dentistry (DMD) who specializes in the care and treatment of the teeth and mouth.

An *allied health professional* is a trained health-care provider who practices under the supervision of a physician or health-care practitioner. Audiologists, dental hygienists, pharmacists, physical therapists and radiologists are allied health professionals.

> **Make the Connection**
>
> **Health-Care Providers** For more information on health-care providers, see page 17 of Lesson 2.

Health-Care Providers

2 Teach

Class Activity
Medical Specialists Have students match a list of specific health problems or procedures to the appropriate type of specialist described in the text.
L2 ELL

PowerPoint® Presentations
This CD-ROM is an editable Microsoft® PowerPoint® presentation that includes:
- Lesson presentations
- Lesson checks
- Interactive graphics
- 5-Minute Checks
- Image Bank
- All transparencies

Note-Taking Refer to the Selective Underlining/Highlighting Strategy on page 16T to assist students in organizing information about the details of health care.

Lesson Resource Manager

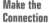

- **Unit 9 Fast File Resources**
  Reading Strategy, p. 43
  Vocabulary Practice, p. 44
  Transparency Master and Worksheet, p. 45
  Real-Life Health, p. 47
  Real-Life Health, p. 49
  5-Minute Check, p. 51
  Lesson 53 Quiz, p. 53
- **Unit 9 Transparency**
- **Lesson 53 Transparency**

- **Reading Essentials**
- **Technology**
  TeacherWorks™ CD-ROM
  StudentWorks™ CD-ROM
  Reading Essentials CD-ROM
  ExamView® Assessment Suite
  Vocabulary Puzzlemaker

> **National Health Education Standards**
> Pages 564–565: 1.6, 3.1, 3.2, 3.3, 3.5, 8.2

Choosing Health-Care Providers

Did You Know?

Insurance Coverage Many health insurance plans cover the services of a select group of health-care providers. Confirm that a doctor is covered before you schedule an appointment with him or her.

Some people pose as health-care providers and treat people without reliable credentials. It is important to carefully choose reliable health-care providers to protect your health status. Health-care providers are listed in the yellow pages of the telephone directory. Local chapters of the American Medical Association (AMA) and the American Dental Association (ADA) also keep lists of their members. Hospitals often have lists of physicians they will recommend, and a trusted physician or other health-care provider may offer recommendations.

Primary-care physician It is important to choose a primary-care physician who will provide basic medical care and help prevent illness. Primary-care physicians are most often family practitioners, pediatricians, or internists. The primary-care physician should be familiar with the patient's medical history and health care needs. They may refer a patient to a specialist if further diagnosis or treatment is needed.

Medical specialists Cardiologists treat the heart and blood vessels. Dermatologists treat the skin. Gastroenterologists treat digestive tract disorders. Geriatricians provide care and treatment of older adults. Gynecologists provide care and treatment of female reproductive health. Internists provide nonsurgical treatment of internal organs. Neurologists treat nervous system disorders. Obstetricians provide care and treatment of pregnant women and their unborn babies. Oncologists treat tumors and cancer. Ophthalmologists provide medical and surgical care and treatment of the eyes. Orthopedists treat muscles, bones, and joints. Otolaryngologists (ENT) treat disorders of the ears, nose, and throat. Pathologists conduct lab studies of body tissues and fluids. Pediatricians provide care and treatment of children and adolescents. Plastic surgeons perform surgery to correct, repair, or improve body features. Psychiatrists treat mental disorders. Radiologists use radiation to diagnose and treat disease. Urologists treat the male and female urinary system and the male reproductive system.

Get to Know Your Health-Care Provider

After you visit a health-care provider for the first time, ask yourself the following questions. Based on your responses, determine whether you are satisfied with your health-care provider or if you want to find a different one.

- Do I feel comfortable sharing my needs and concerns with the health-care provider?
- Did the health-care provider answer my questions?
- Did the health-care provider help me make a plan for my health?
- What are the credentials of the health-care provider?

- What hospital affiliations does the health-care provider have?
- What arrangements can be made for care after hours?
- Who will care for me if the health-care provider is unavailable?
- Does the health-care provider emphasize prevention of illness and injury?

- What does an office visit cost?
- What is the normal billing procedure?
- Is this health-care provider eligible for payment by my health care plan?
- How long do I have to wait to get an appointment with the health-care provider?

566 UNIT 9 • Consumer and Community Health

 Healthy People 2010

Objective 1-1 *Increase proportion of persons with health insurance.*

In the 1997 National Health Interview Survey (NHIS), 83 percent of persons under age 65 and 89.2 percent of persons under age 18 were covered by health insurance. The Healthy People 2010 target is 100 percent. Ask students to assume that 89.2 percent of students in their school are covered by health insurance. Have students figure out the number of students in their school who are not covered. Ask students to make a list of specific and realistic actions that can be taken to meet the 100 percent target. **L3**

Health Insurance

F inancial protection that provides benefits for sickness or injury is *health insurance*. When a person buys insurance, the provider agrees to pay or reimburse the costs of care. The insurance provider predicts that over time it will collect more money in premiums than it will pay out in claims. A *premium* is the amount paid for the insurance coverage. A *claim* is a bill from a health-care provider.

What to Know About Health Insurance

An *insurance policy* is the legal document that outlines the terms of the insurance coverage. Premiums for private insurance policies are paid by the individual, by the employer of the individual, or by a combination of both.

Some insurance policies pay the entire cost of medical care while others pay a portion. A *deductible* is the amount that must be paid by the individual before the insurance company will pay any claims. A *co-payment* is the portion of the medical fee the individual must pay whether or not there is a deductible.

Managed care A system of health-care services designed to control costs is *managed care.* Managed care plans control the types of health care individuals receive and the amount paid for care. Health Maintenance Organizations and Preferred Provider Organizations are two kinds of managed care.

Health Maintenance Organization A business that organizes health-care services for its members is a *Health Maintenance Organization (HMO).* HMOs try to provide care at the lowest possible cost. Except for emergency care or with approval, HMOs cover only services received from the HMO. HMOs encourage preventative health care.

Preferred Provider Organization A business that has a contract with a group of health-care providers who agree to provide services at a reduced rate is a *Preferred Provider Organization (PPO).* A *preferred provider* is a health-care provider who has a contract with the health insurance provider. Individuals must select preferred providers or pay a higher cost for health services.

Government insurance The government offers health-care payment for some people. The major sources of federal insurance coverage include Medicare, Medicaid, coverage for veterans, and coverage for government employees. *Medicare* is for people 65 years of age and older and for people who have received Social Security disability benefits for two or more years. *Medicare* is for people with low incomes.

Did You Know?

Health-Care Costs In the United States, 12 cents out of every dollar is spent on health care.

Reading Review

1. Explain managed care and name two kinds.
2. List examples of government insurance.

LESSON 53 • Accessing Reliable Health Care   **567**

567

Evaluating Health Insurance

Class Discussion

Preexisting Conditions Have students discuss why some insurance companies may not cover problems or conditions that the policyholder had before he or she became covered by the policy. **L2**

Class Activity

Excluded Expenses Divide the class into groups. Have students draft a list of health-related expenses an insurance company should not cover. Ask students to include reasons why they feel that way. Have students discuss these with the class. **L2**

INTERACTIVE CHALKBOARD
with Image Bank

5-Minute Check

Page 51, **Unit 9 Fast File Resources**

1. Which type of doctor is trained that body systems all are connected and that a disturbance in one body system can affect other systems? *Doctor of Osteopathy (D.O.)*

2. What types of health-care providers are considered allied health professionals? *health-care providers who practice under the supervision of a physician or health-care practitioner, including audiologists, dental hygienists, pharmacists, physical therapists, and radiologists*

3. Why is it important to have a primary care physician? *He or she can provide basic medical care and help prevent illness.*

4. What is a co-payment? *it is the portion of the medical fee the individual must pay.*

5. When choosing a health insurance plan, what should a consumer look for? *a plan that gives the most comprehensive coverage at the most affordable price*

Evaluating Health Insurance

Health insurance should cover standard risks of illness and injury for family members. It also should cover special conditions that family members might have that require ongoing medical attention. There are two kinds of expenses: covered and excluded expenses.

How to Evaluate Health Insurance

A ***covered expense*** is a medical expense that is paid for under the terms of a health insurance plan. An ***excluded expense*** is a medical expense that a health insurance plan will not pay. Health insurance plans must be studied carefully in order to know exactly which services are covered and which are excluded.

Health insurance plans are not all the same. Some cost more than others, and some cover more than others. People must evaluate a copy of the health insurance plan, ask company representatives questions about the plan, shop around for health insurance plans, and choose the plan that gives the most comprehensive coverage at the most affordable price.

Some insurance providers will not sell insurance to people they consider high risks, such as people with disabilities or preexisting conditions. A ***preexisting condition*** is a health problem that a person had before being covered by the insurance. According to law, people must disclose all health information to the insurer. If they do not, the insurance provider may cancel the contract.

Make yourself insurable. To increase your chance of being insurable, get routine checkups and immunizations. Learn to do breast or testicular self-exams. Get plenty of rest, sleep, and physical activity. Eat appropriate amounts of healthful foods. Control stress.

Avoid the use of tobacco, alcohol, and other drugs. Limit the amount of fat, sugar, and sodium in your diet. Drive safely and wear your safety belt. Wear a helmet when riding a bicycle. If you have a health condition, make efforts to improve or maintain your condition.

Questions to Ask to Evaluate Health Insurance Coverage

Use these questions to evaluate insurance:

- Is the entire family covered?
- How much are the deductibles?
- Are there financial limits for coverage in a year?
- Are there time limits for extended treatment?
- Are the services I need covered?
- What is not covered?

- Is there a waiting period before coverage begins?
- How many days in the hospital are covered?
- Are there limitations on choices of health-care providers or facilities?
- Is the insurance renewable or can the company cancel it in certain situations?

568 UNIT 9 • Consumer and Community Health

 Sensitive Issues

Health-Care Coverage Be mindful that some students and students' families might not be covered by a health-insurance plan. Not having health insurance might not be a matter of choice for these students' families. The advantages of having health-insurance coverage and the disadvantages of not having health-insurance coverage should be discussed so that students can make prudent choices in their lives, but sensitivity needs to be exercised in this area.

Options for the Uninsured

According to the U.S. Census Bureau, more than 40 million people in the United States do not have health insurance. People without health insurance coverage may neglect preventative health services, such as cancer screenings and immunizations. They often delay getting health care until situations get desperate. During a health crisis they seek treatment in hospital emergency rooms and trauma centers, which is very expensive.

What to Know About Living Without Health Insurance

Health insurance in the United States is largely provided through employment. However, providing health insurance is voluntary for employers, and purchasing insurance is voluntary for employees. Life transitions, such as a new job, unemployment, self-employment, marriage, divorce, and graduation from college, affect health insurance coverage.

Being uninsured may not be a matter of choice. Most people do not choose to be without health insurance. Health insurance premiums are expensive, and for people who do not have the option of employer-provided insurance, the premium may be too expensive. In addition to being able to afford health insurance, people also have to be eligible for health insurance coverage.

The Census Bureau predicts that the number of Americans without health insurance will continue to increase in the future. One reason for this is unemployment. When individuals are unemployed, they do not have the option of employer-provided health insurance. Another reason is rising health-care costs. Because health-care costs have risen so high, it is difficult for many employers to continue to offer the same amount of health insurance coverage. Also, many employers are passing the increasing costs directly to their employees, and many of these employees are unable to afford the health insurance.

People who have chronic health conditions often have difficulty obtaining adequate health insurance coverage. Some insurance plans may place them in a high-risk category that requires them to pay more for their coverage, or an insurance plan may exclude them from coverage altogether. People with chronic health conditions may not be able to keep their job if they are not well enough to work, causing them to lose their employer-provided health insurance coverage. Also, people with health conditions may not be eligible for coverage because of a preexisting condition.

Reading Review

1. What circumstances may lead to being uninsured?

2. How many people in the United States do not have health insurance?

Options for the Uninsured

Class Discussion

Insurance Coverage Have students discuss why life transitions—getting a new job, a change in marital status, unemployment, or self-employment—can affect health coverage. **L2**

Extension

PSA Have students do further research on government health programs such as CHIP (see Health News on page 570). Then ask students to create a public service announcement (PSA) that would increase the public's awareness of government health programs. It should be formatted for a 30-second TV or radio broadcast or podcast. Ask your school's principal if the students can play their PSA over the school's public address system. **L3**

Reading Review

1. *new job; unemployment; self-employment; marriage; divorce; graduation from college; lack of employer-provided insurance; expensive premiums; and chronic health conditions that preclude coverage*
2. *more than 45 million*

Family Involvement

Family Health Coverage Have students discuss health-insurance coverage with their parents or guardian. Have students whose families do not have health-insurance coverage also discuss options for the uninsured with their parents or guardian. The students should share with their families what they've learned in class about government programs, deductibles, co-payments, premiums, covered expenses, excluded expenses, and preexisting conditions. **L3**

National Health Education Standards
Pages 568–569: 1.1, 1.6, 3.1, 3.3

569

Analyzing Graphs

1. 18–24
2. Medicare covers people age 65 and older.

Project

Group Plans Divide students into groups and ask them to investigate what types of group health insurance plans are available in their area. Ask them to compile a directory of the plans. **L2**

Explain the Concept

Government Insurance Students may not understand the difference between Medicaid and Medicare. Explain that Medicaid is a joint federal and state program that helps with medical costs for some people with low incomes and limited resources. Medicaid programs vary from state to state, but most health care costs are covered for those who qualify. Medicare is for people age 65 and older and for people who have received Social Security disability benefits for two or more years.

NHES Assessment/SCASS

Constructed Response Have students write a short response to this question: Why do healthy people usually have the best chance of being insured? **L2**

What to Know About Options for the Uninsured

Did You Know?

Uninsured Over 45 million Americans were without health insurance in 2004.

People who do not have adequate health insurance should investigate all options available for obtaining health insurance. The best way to obtain health insurance is to get a job where insurance is offered and premiums are affordable. However, this is not a realistic option for everyone. Another option is to purchase insurance on your own if you qualify and can afford the premiums. Some people will qualify for Medicaid coverage.

Group health insurance People who are self-employed can contact trade groups, labor unions, associations, chambers of commerce, or other groups that offer group health insurance programs. In some states, health insurance pools exist for people with certain chronic diseases, agricultural workers, asbestos removal workers, and scuba divers.

Short-term health insurance policies For people who are temporarily out of work and looking for employment where health benefits will be offered, short-term health policies may provide the coverage they need. These policies provide coverage usually for a maximum of six months and are usually only renewable one time.

If you plan to leave a job with health insurance coverage, research your policy's conversion options. Sometimes you can convert a group plan to an individual plan. However, you will have to pay the full premiums. The *Consolidated Omnibus Budget Reconciliation Act (COBRA)* gives workers the right to continue their employer's group health benefits for limited periods of time under certain circumstances, including job loss, reduction in hours worked, death, divorce, and other life events.

HEALTH NEWS

The Evolution of Health Insurance

Forms of health insurance existed soon after the United States was founded. In 1789, Congress founded the first hospital for servicemen. Private insurance companies offered hospital plans, and sickness, travel, and accident insurance. By the 1870s, railroad, mining, and other industries employed company doctors. Other businesses began to offer group insurance plans to their employees. In 1965, Medicare and Medicaid were introduced. In 1997, the Children's Health Insurance Program (CHIP) was created.

570 UNIT 9 • Consumer and Community Health

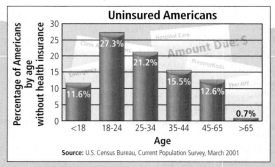

Uninsured Americans

Percentage of Americans by age without health insurance

- <18: 11.6%
- 18-24: 27.3%
- 25-34: 21.2%
- 35-44: 15.5%
- 45-65: 12.6%
- >65: 0.7%

Age

Source: U.S. Census Bureau, Current Population Survey, March 2001

Analyzing Graphs

Study the graph above and answer these questions:

1. Which age group is most uninsured?

2. Why are fewer members of the "over 65" group uninsured?

Health Online Visit www.glencoe.com for more information on forms of health insurance.

⚖ Legal Issues

COBRA In 1986 the Consolidated Omnibus Budget Reconciliation Act (COBRA) was passed. Individuals who experience a qualifying event are able to buy coverage identical to coverage received before the qualifying event, for a limited time. Beneficiaries pay as much as 102 percent of the cost of the plan. Qualifying events for employees include: termination for any reasons other than "gross misconduct" or reduction in hours worked. Qualifying events for spouses and dependent children include: termination of the covered employee for any reason other than "gross misconduct"; reduction in hours worked by the covered employee; covered employee's becoming entitled to Medicare; divorce or legal separation; death of the covered employee; or loss of "dependent child" status under the plan rules.

Health-Care Facilities

People should be aware of the types and locations of health-care facilities in their community. They also should know the hours the facilities are open, the services they provide, and the fees they charge.

What to Know About Health-Care Facilities

Hospital A *hospital* is a health-care facility where people can receive medical care, diagnosis, and treatment on an inpatient or outpatient basis. **Inpatient care** is treatment that requires a person to stay overnight at a facility. **Outpatient care** is treatment that does not require a person to stay overnight at a facility.

Ambulatory surgery center A facility where surgery is performed on an outpatient basis is an *ambulatory surgery center.* The cost of outpatient surgery averages less than one-third the cost of inpatient fees. Many health insurance companies encourage or require patients who need certain types of surgery to choose outpatient surgery in ambulatory surgery centers. However, certain types of surgery require inpatient care.

Urgent-care centers Non-hospital facilities that provide emergency care are **urgent-care centers.** Urgent-care centers do not require an appoinment. Fees at urgent-care centers are less than those at a hospital emergency room, but more than those at a physician's office.

Physician's office A facility that provides routine health care, such as diagnosis, simple testing, treatments, examinations, or minor surgery is a *physician's office.*

Types of Hospitals

There are several different kinds of hospitals. The following are some of them:

- **Private hospital** Owned by private individuals and operates as a profit-making business.
- **Voluntary hospital** Owned by a community or organization and does not operate for profit.
- **Government hospital** Run by the federal, state, or local government for the benefit of a specific population. For example, the Veterans Administration operates hospitals for military veterans.
- **Teaching hospital** Associated with a medical school and/or school of nursing. Teaching hospitals provide training for health professionals in addition to the regular services of most hospitals.

LESSON 53 • Accessing Reliable Health Care **571**

Health-Care Facilities

Class Activity

Urgent Care Have each student locate the urgent-care facility nearest his or her own house. Students should find out the hours of operation, what services are provided, and the cost of the services. **L2**

Teacher FYI

Hospice Many hospice care facilities have a speaker's bureau that will send a hospice nurse out to schools to discuss grief and loss. They also will educate students about hospice and the types of services it provides.

5-Minute Check

Page 52, **Unit 9 Fast File Resources**

1. What are two reasons the number of uninsured Americans might increase? *rising unemployment and rising health-care costs*
2. List two options for people who are uninsured. *group health insurance plans, short-term health insurance policies, individual health insurance plans, and COBRA*
3. Name two types of health-care facilities that provide emergency care. *hospital emergency room and urgent-care center*
4. Why do some health insurance companies encourage patients who need certain types of surgery to choose outpatient surgery and ambulatory surgery centers? *because it costs, on average, one-third less than inpatient surgery for the exact same procedure*
5. What is a teaching hospital? *it provides training for health professionals in addition to the regular services of most hospitals*

National Health Education Standards

Pages 570–571: 1.6, 3.3, 3.5

Selected Response People who need assistance with daily living would be best served by a(n):

A. *extended care facility*
B. hospice
C. health center
D. urgent-care center

3 Assess

Vocabulary Practice

Page 44, **Unit 9 Fast File Resources**

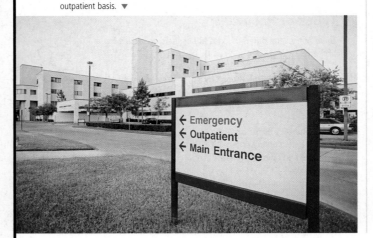

National Health Education Standards

Pages 572–573: 1.1, 1.6, 3.3, 3.5, 6.3

572

Nurse practitioners and physicians' assistants provide some of the services in a physician's office. Some physicians treat a variety of conditions and age groups while others specialize.

Dental offices A facility that provides care of teeth, gums, and mouth is a ***dental office.*** Dentists can specialize in areas of care, such as pediatric dentistry and periodontal disease.

Health center A facility that provides routine health care to a special population is a ***health center.*** For example, there are health centers that provide health care to low-income families. A health department clinic is a facility in most state and local health departments that keeps records and performs services, such as giving immunizations. A mental-health clinic is a facility that provides services for people who have mental disorders. Many mental-health clinics are open 24 hours a day, seven days a week to help people in crisis situations.

In addition to emergency care, hospitals provide medical care on an inpatient or outpatient basis. ▼

← Emergency
← Outpatient
← Main Entrance

Laboratories Medical laboratories perform diagnostic tests, such as blood or urine tests. Dental laboratories make crowns or bridges used to repair teeth. Laboratories can be a part of other facilities, such as hospitals or health centers, but they can also be operated as a separate service.

Extended-care facility A facility that provides nursing, personal, and residential care is an ***extended-care facility.*** Extended-care facilities also provide care for people who need assistance with daily living. Nursing homes and convalescent centers are examples of extended-care facilities. Home health care may be more convenient and affordable than staying in an extended-care facility. Home health care is care provided within a patient's home. Home health-care organizations offer a variety of services, including nursing care, medical treatment, and therapy in the home.

Home health care Agencies provide care in patient's homes that is known as ***home health care.*** Services offered may include nursing, rehabilitation therapy, bathing, housekeeping, and food preparation. Health departments, hospitals, private agencies, and volunteer groups can offer home health-care services.

Hospice Many patients receive hospice care in their home or in the home of a loved one, while others receive hospice care in hospices. ***Hospice*** is care for the terminally ill and their families. Hospice services usually provide care 24 hours a day. Contact and support from hospice staff continues for at least a year after a family member dies.

ⓓⓘ Differentiated Instruction

Learning Disabilities Have students write each type of health-care facility on one side of an index card. On the other side of the index cards, have students write the description of each type of facility. The descriptions of each health-care facility should include the services that are provided and what makes each facility different from the rest. Divide the class into groups of two. Ask students to quiz each other using the cards as prompts. **L2 ELL**

LESSON 53

Key Terms Review

Complete these fill-in-the-blank statements with the lesson Key Terms on the left. Do not write in this book.

co-payment
health insurance
Health Maintenance
  Organization
  (HMO)
inpatient care
managed care
Medicaid
Medicare
preexisting condition
Preferred Provider
  Organization
  (PPO)
primary care
specialist
urgent-care center

1. ———— is treatment that requires an overnight stay at a facility.

2. A(n) ———— is a facility that is not part of a hospital, but provides emergency care.

3. ———— is an organized system of health-care services designed to control health-care costs.

4. A(n) ———— is a medical professional who has training in a particular area.

5. ———— is financial protection that provides benefits for sickness or injury.

6. ———— is general health care.

7. A(n) ———— organizes health-care services for its members.

8. A(n) ———— has a contract with a group of health-care providers who agree to provide health-care services at a reduced rate.

9. ———— is for people with low incomes.

10. ———— is for people 65 years of age and older and for people who receive Social Security disability benefits for two years.

Recalling the Facts

11. Identify why you would see each of the following physicians: dermatologist, orthopedist, and pediatrician.

12. Define co-payment, premium, and deductible.

13. Explain the difference between an HMO and a PPO.

14. List and explain the different types of hospitals.

15. Discuss different health-care facilities.

16. Describe an allied health professional.

17. What is COBRA and who is eligible?

18. Explain how to determine if you are satisfied with a health-care provider.

Critical Thinking

19. Analyze the cost, availability, and accessibility of health services for people of all ages.

20. Discuss reasons why some people do not have health insurance.

21. What actions could be taken to try and keep health-care costs down?

22. Compare an MD and a DO.

Real-Life Applications

23. Analyze why you and your family use the health-care providers you use.

24. What can you do to make yourself eligible for health insurance?

25. Would you prefer an MD or a DO? Why?

26. Would you prefer an HMO or a PPO? Why?

Activities

Responsible Decision Making

27. **Role-Play** Your cousin and his wife are planning on having children in a few years. They are planning on buying insurance and have been comparing insurance policies. They are on a tight budget. One policy costs less, but it does not have maternity coverage. Write a response to this situation. Refer to the Responsible Decision-Making Model on page 61 for help.

Sharpen Your Life Skills

28. **Access Health Services** Write a script in which a person who is interested in purchasing insurance meets with a representative from an insurance company. Be sure to include the family and financial status of the person. Refer to Questions to Ask to Evaluate Health Insurance Coverage on page 568.

Visit **www.glencoe.com** for more *Health & Wellness* quizzes.

LESSON 53 • Study Guide **573**

LESSON 53
STUDY GUIDE

Key Terms Review

1. Inpatient care
2. urgent-care center
3. Managed care
4. specialist
5. Health insurance
6. Primary care
7. HMO
8. PPO
9. Medicaid
10. Medicare

Recalling the Facts

11. See page 566 for information about medical specialists.

12. See page 567 for information about health insurance.

13. HMOs try to provide care at the lowest possible cost. Except for emergency care or with prior approval, HMOs cover only services received from the HMO. PPOs have contracts with a group of health-care providers who agree to provide service at a reduced rate.

14. See the list on page 571 for information on types of hospitals.

15. See pages 571–572 for information about health-care facilities.

16. An allied health professional is a trained health-care provider who practices under the supervision of a physician or health-care practitioner.

17. See page 570 for information about COBRA.

18. See the list on page 566 for questions to help you evaluate a health-care provider.

Critical Thinking

19. Answers will vary, but should include information on managed care, government insurance, group insurance, COBRA, and short-term insurance.

20. See page 569 for information about why some people do not have health insurance.

21. Answers will vary.

22. See page 565 for information about types of physicians.

Real-Life Applications

23. Answers will vary.
24. Answers will vary, but should include information about making yourself insurable.
25. Answers will vary. Students should explain their choices.
26. Answers will vary. Students should explain their choices.

Activities

Responsible Decision Making

27. Answers will vary, but should include information about evaluating health insurance.

Sharpen Your Life Skills

28. Answers will vary.

573

Investigating Health Careers

Out of Time?

If time does not permit an in-depth study of this topic, use the following activities in this Teacher Wraparound Edition:
• Explain the Concept, p. 575
• Class Discussion, p. 576
• Achieving Health Literacy, p. 580

1 Focus

HEALTH GOAL **Health Careers** Have students respond to the Health Goal for this lesson by listing in their health journals as many careers in the health-care field as they can think of in 3 minutes. Have the class discuss what people in these careers do. **L2**

Write ABOUT IT!

Journaling Encourage students to write in their health journals about their dream job. Ask students to describe the kind of work they would like to do. Have students estimate the amount of pay and the benefits they would likely earn on this career path. **L2**

Investigating Health Careers

HEALTH GOAL • I will investigate health careers.

Think about what you will be doing ten years from today. Will you still be in school? Will you have a career that you enjoy and that pays a salary that meets your living needs? There are many career possibilities and opportunities in the health field. This lesson focuses on various career options, qualifications required for each career, and steps you can take to gain firsthand experience in each field. By exploring these options now, you can better prepare for your future.

What You'll Learn

1. List and discuss seven ways to investigate health careers. (p. 575)
2. Explain what it means to be licensed and have certification for a health career. (p. 575)

Why It's Important

Investigating health careers can help you decide what kind of work you would like to do for a living. It also can help you know who you can turn to when you or those you love need health care.

Key Terms

• health career
• credentials
• license for a health career
• certification
• shadowing
• mentor
• volunteering
• certified health education specialist (CHES)

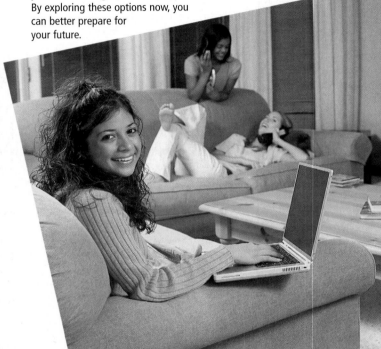

Write ABOUT IT!

Writing About Career Options Suppose your friends decide that they are not going to college. They talk about having fun after graduation. You, on the other hand, want to go to college and are considering a health career. After reading the information about health careers on page 576, write an e-mail in your health journal, telling your friends about your plans for after graduation, and why you have made these plans.

National Health Education Standards—Guide for Lesson 54		
3.2	Utilize resources from home, school, and community that provide valid health information.	p. 575
3.5	Access valid and reliable health products and services.	pp. 574, 575–579, 581

Researching Health Careers

A profession or an occupation in the medical field for which one trains is a *health career*. A health career may be of interest to you. There are steps to take to investigate a health career.

What to Know About Health Careers

Assess Review a listing of health careers that includes information about responsibilities and credentials. A Guide to Health Careers on page 576 in this lesson provides information about many health careers.

Complement Match your interests and abilities with the responsibilities of a health career. For example, a career as a certified athletic trainer may be of interest to you if you enjoy athletics. If you are interested in nutrition, you might enjoy a career as a dietitian.

Investigate Examine the credentials of people in a health career. *Credentials* are the qualifications a person must have. To be qualified for certain health careers, specific education, training, licensing, and certification may be needed.

A *license for a health career* is a document that grants a person the right to practice or use a certain title. A government agency awards a license. *Certification* is the process a person completes to meet specific standards of professional competence. A non-governmental agency grants certification.

Consider Think about opportunities available for obtaining the credentials, including college, career and technical school, or another instructional facility.

Evaluate Estimate the resources needed to obtain the credentials. Consider the time and money needed for training. If you do not have the money, it may be possible to obtain financial support, such as a scholarship or a loan.

Explore Look into employment opportunities and salaries. Choose a health career for which there are employment opportunities and a satisfactory salary.

Participate Become involved in activities, such as shadowing and volunteering, to get firsthand experience in what a health career is like. *Shadowing* is spending time with a mentor as he or she performs work activities. A *mentor* is a responsible person who guides another person. You can shadow various professionals while you are in high school to learn more about a health career. *Volunteering* is providing a service without pay. A good way to try out a health career is to volunteer at a hospital, nursing home, clinic, or public health agency.

Reading Review

1. How can you get firsthand experience in what a health career is like?

2. What credentials might a person in a health career need?

LESSON 54 • Investigating Health Careers **575**

Lesson Resource Manager

- **Unit 9 Fast File Resources**
  Reading Strategy, p. 57
  Vocabulary Practice, p. 58
  Transparency Master and Worksheet, p. 59
  Real-Life Health, p. 61
  Real-Life Health, p. 63
  5-Minute Check, p. 65
  Lesson 54 Quiz, p. 66
- **Unit 9 Transparency**
- **Lesson 54 Transparency**

- **Reading Essentials**
- **Technology**
  TeacherWorks™ CD-ROM
  StudentWorks™ CD-ROM
  Reading Essentials CD-ROM
  Exam*View*® Assessment Suite
  Vocabulary Puzzlemaker

---

2 Teach

Explain the Concept

Getting Involved Students may not understand the difference between shadowing and volunteering. Explain that shadowing is spending time observing a person as he or she performs his or her work duties. Volunteering is performing work duties without pay; sometimes this is done to "try out" a particular career.

PowerPoint® Presentations

This CD-ROM is an editable Microsoft® PowerPoint® presentation that includes:
- Lesson presentations
- Lesson checks
- Interactive graphics
- 5-Minute Checks
- Image Bank
- All transparencies

 Note Taking Refer to the Two-Column Notes: Main Idea-Details Strategy on page 16T. Have students list interesting health careers in the left-hand column and credentials needed for each career in the right-hand column.

Reading Review

1. *shadowing and volunteering*
2. *specific education, training, licensing, or certification*

National Health Education Standards
Pages 574–575: 3.1, 3.2, 3.5, 8.1, 8.3

Class Discussion

Qualifications Have students discuss what characteristics or qualities a person should possess in order to be well-matched with each of the health careers listed. For example, a community health organizer should be a people person, a good speaker, and a caring individual. **L2**

Extension

Investigating Colleges Have students research which colleges and universities in your region offer programs for the health careers listed. Ask students to rank the colleges based on the quality of their health education program for each of the careers listed. **L3**

Class Discussion

Income versus Enjoyment Have students debate which element is more important to them: salary or job satisfaction. They must give concrete reasons for their arguments. **L2**

A Guide to
Health Careers

F or people who enjoy helping others, and would like to work in a professional and respected field where their knowledge and services will always be in demand, a health career can provide that opportunity.

What to Know About
A Guide to Health Careers

Make the Connection

Hearing Problems For more information on hearing problems, see page 346 in Lesson 30.

Audiologists Professionals who diagnose and treat hearing and speech problems are *audiologists.* They test for hearing problems, prescribe hearing aids and devices, and teach speech or lip reading. They hold a master's degree in audiology and need a state license.

▲ Dentists treat injuries of the jaw and mouth as well as diseases of the teeth.

Certified athletic trainers Professionals who work with athletes to help them maintain fitness and prevent and treat injuries are *certified athletic trainers.* They treat athletic injuries, assist with rehabilitation, educate athletes about injury prevention, and refer athletes for further medical treatment. They hold a bachelor's degree and may hold a master's degree. They need certification by the National Athletic Trainers Associ-ation and need a state license.

Clinical psychologists Professionals who study, diagnose, and treat psycho-

logical disorders are *clinical psychologists.* They help people deal with mental disorders, stressors, and life crises; provide individual, group, and family psychotherapy; and plan behavioral modification programs. They hold a doctoral degree in clinical psychology. They need a state license.

Community health educators Professionals who educate people in a community are *community health educators.* They identify community health problems and needs, and plan health promotion programs in the community. They hold a bachelor's degree in health education or a related area. They may need to be a certified health education specialist.

A *certified health education specialist (CHES)* is a person who has completed the certification process recommended for health educators.

Dental hygienists Professionals who work under the direction of a dentist to provide dental care are *dental hygienists.* They provide preventive dental care, teach people how to practice good oral hygiene, clean and examine patients' teeth and gums,

🏛 Community Involvement

Shadowing Have students choose the health career listed on pages 576–579 in which they are the most interested. Ask students to get permission from their parents or guardian to shadow a professional in that field. Have students prepare a list of questions to ask the professional. Questions can include: What are your job responsibilities? What is the average salary in your field? What education is necessary for a career in your profession? What personal characteristics are important to have in your field? Have students write a reaction paper about their experience. **L3**

(t)Photodisc/Getty Images, (b)SuperStock

and take and develop dental X rays. They hold an associate's or bachelor's degree. They need certification from an accredited school of dental hygiene and a state license.

Dentists Professionals who prevent, diagnose, and treat problems of the teeth and mouth, examine X rays, remove decay from and fill cavities, repair broken teeth, remove teeth, and place protective sealants on teeth are *dentists.* They hold a Doctor of Dental Surgery (DDS) or Doctor of Medical Dentistry (DMD) degree. They need a state license.

Dietitians and nutritionists Professionals who counsel people about diet and nutrition, plan nutritional programs, supervise the preparation of foods, and develop menus for people with health problems, are *dietitians* and *nutritionists.* They hold a bachelor's degree in dietetics, foods and nutrition, food systems management, or a related field. They may need certification as a Registered Dietitian (RD), and they need a state license.

Emergency medical technicians (EMTs) Professionals who provide health care to people in emergency situations before they reach the hospital are *emergency medical technicians.*

- *EMT-basics* must be 18 years old, have a valid driver's license, have a high school diploma or equivalent, complete basic EMT training, and have a state certification.
- *EMT-intermediates* administer intravenous fluids, use defibrillators to give life-saving shocks to a person with a stopped heart, and perform other intensive care procedures. They must be 18 years old, have a valid driver's license,

have a high school diploma or equivalent, complete intermediate EMT training, and have a state certification.

- *EMT-paramedics* administer intravenous fluids, use defibrillators, perform other intensive care procedures, administer oral and intravenous drugs, read EKGs, and use monitors and other equipment. They must be 18 years old, have a valid driver's license, have a high school diploma or equivalent, complete EMT-paramedic training, and have a state certification.

Guidance counselors Professionals who assist students with personal, family, education, and career decisions and concerns, and help students develop life skills needed to prevent and deal with problems are *guidance counselors.* They hold a master's degree in counseling. They need state school counseling certification and may need a teaching certificate.

Health education teachers Professionals who teach health education, promote the development of health knowledge, life skills, and positive attitudes toward health and well-being in students are *health education teachers.* They hold a bachelor's degree in health education. They need a teaching certificate with specialization in health education, and may hold the title of Certified Health Education Specialist (CHES).

▲ Emergency medical technicians provide health care in emergency situations.

 Legal Issues

Dietitians Of the 41 states with laws governing dietitians, 27 require licensure, 13 require certification, and one requires registration. The Registered Dietitian credential is awarded by the American Dietetic Association (ADA) to those who pass an exam after completing academic coursework and supervised experience. Practice requirements vary by state; therefore, interested candidates should determine the requirements of the state in which they want to work before taking an exam. Students interested in research, advanced clinical positions, or public health may need an advanced degree.

Class Activity

Job Interview Have students write two questions that might be asked at a job interview for each of the health careers listed. Have students exchange lists and write appropriate answers to the interview questions. **L2**

5-Minute Check

Page 65, **Unit 9 Fast File Resources**

1. What should you consider before choosing a career? *your personal interests and abilities*

2. What are credentials? *the qualifications a person must have to be eligible for a specific job*

3. Why should you explore employment opportunities and salary before choosing a career? *to make sure there is a need for people in that field and that the field will provide a satisfactory salary*

4. What is a mentor? *a responsible person who guides another person*

5. What is a good way to "try out" a career? *by volunteering*

NHES Assessment/SCASS

Selected Response Which of the following health-related careers does not require a state license?
A. physician
B. school psychologist
C. physical therapist
D. pharmacologist

Make the Connection

Healthful Behaviors For more information on practicing healthful behaviors, see page 27 in Lesson 3.

Did You Know?

Registered nurses As the largest health-care career, registered nurses held about 2.2 million jobs in 2000.

Health services managers and administrators Professionals who manage a health services organization are *health services managers and administrators.* They plan, organize, coordinate, and supervise a health services organization. They hold a bachelor's or master's degree in health services administration, business administration, public health, public administration, or another related field. They usually do not need special training or a state license. A nursing home administrator, however, must have special training and a state license.

Licensed practical nurses (LPNs), or licensed vocational nurses (LVNs) Professionals who provide nursing care under the direction of registered nurses or physicians are *licensed practical nurses, or licensed vocational nurses.* They care for people who are sick or injured. They need a high school diploma or equivalent, training as a practical nurse, and a state license.

Medical writers Professionals who write about topics in the areas of medicine and health are *medical writers.* They may write for the media—a newspaper column on medicine or an article for a medical journal; brochures, newsletters, and information sheets for hospitals, medical schools, health organizations, and medical companies; or for on-line medical services. They hold a bachelor's degree with courses in technical writing, English, journalism, communications, and the biological sciences.

Occupational therapists (OTs) Professionals who help people who have disabilities make adjustments are *occupational therapists.* They help people develop, recover, and maintain daily living and working skills. They hold a bachelor's degree in occupational therapy and may need a state license.

Pharmacists Professionals who dispense medications that are prescribed by certain licensed health-care professionals are *pharmacists.* They prepare and dispense drugs, provide information to patients about drugs, and consult with health-care professionals about drugs. They hold a bachelor's degree or a graduate degree in pharmacy. They need a state license, and must complete an internship under a licensed pharmacist.

Pharmacologists Professionals who study composition of drugs and their effects are *pharmacologists.* They study the effects of drugs on the body and mind, research the safety and effectiveness of drugs, and develop new drugs. They hold a bachelor's degree or master's degree in pharmacy, chemistry, medicine, or a related field.

Physical therapists (PTs) Professionals who help people rehabilitate physical disabilities and injuries are *physical therapists.* They help improve mobility, relieve pain, and limit permanent physical disability, teach exercises to speed recovery, and test strength and range of motion to evaluate recovery. They need a certification from an accredited program in physical therapy and a state license.

Physicians Professionals who are licensed to practice medicine are *physicians.* They obtain medical histories, perform physical examinations, give diagnoses, prescribe medications,

578 UNIT 9 • Consumer and Community Health

 Differentiated Instruction

Gifted and Talented Ask students to research the listed health-care careers. Have students find out the job responsibilities, the working conditions, the training and education needed, the earnings, and the expected career prospects in that field. Have students evaluate the careers and determine the one they would most like to have. Ask students to describe the career they would most like to have, and explain why they chose the career to the class. **L2**

and may perform surgery. A Medical Doctor (MD) is a physician who is trained in a medical school and has a doctor of medicine degree. A Doctor of Osteopathy (DO) is a physician who is trained in a school of osteopathy and has a doctor of osteopathy degree. Physicians need a state license.

Radiologic technologists Professionals who work under the direction of a radiologist are *radiologic technologists.* They prepare patients for X-ray examination, take and develop X rays, assist with other imaging procedures—ultrasound, scanning and MRIs, and prepare radiation therapy for patients who have cancer. They hold an associate's or bachelor's degree in radiologic technology and need a state license.

Recreational therapists Professionals who plan and direct medically approved recreational activities are *recreational therapists.* They help patients maintain physical, emotional, and mental well-being and instruct patients in relaxation techniques to reduce stress. They hold an associate's or bachelor's degree in recreational therapy. They may need a state license or other certification.

Registered nurses (RNs) Professionals who provide nursing care in general practice or in one or more of several nurse specialties are *registered nurses.* They monitor patients and record symptoms, assist physicians during examinations and treatments, administer medications, assist in the recovery and rehabilitation of patients, and provide emotional care for patients and their families. They hold a degree from an accredited nursing school. They need state licenses. Nurses who want to special-

ize as clinical nurse specialists, nurse practitioners, or nurse anesthetists must have additional training.

School psychologists Professionals who work with students, parents, school personnel, and teachers to solve learning and behavioral problems are *school psychologists.* They test students' intellectual, emotional, and behavioral skills; work with students who have disabilities or are gifted and talented; and teach students conflict resolution skills. They hold a graduate degree in psychology. They need a state license and must complete a one-year internship with a school psychologist.

Social workers Professionals who help people with social problems are *social workers.* They investigate, treat, and give aid to people who have social problems—mental illness, lack of job skills, serious health conditions, financial difficulties, disability, substance abuse problems, child or domestic abuse, and unplanned pregnancy. They hold a master's degree in Social Work (MSW) and need a state license.

Speech pathologists Professionals who help people overcome speech disorders are *speech pathologists.* They work with people who have speech and language disorders, and people who have oral motor problems that cause eating and swallowing difficulties, as well as counsel parents or guardians and family members. They hold a master's degree in speech pathology and need a state license.

▲ Radiologic technologists assist with X rays and other imaging procedures.

Reading Review

1. What does a medical writer do?

2. Compare a pharmacist and pharmacologist.

SPEAKING OUT
Teens Talk About Health

Analyzing the Feature

Use the following questions to help students uncover the main points of this feature.

1. What experience gave Amanda the desire to become a nurse? *working at a medical mission in Mexico*

2. What were the responsibilities of the nurse Amanda shadowed? *washing babies and performing tests on them*

3. How did shadowing help Amanda with her career choice? *It gave her a direction in which to head.*

Journaling Activity

Ask students to share what they wrote in their health journals about shadowing a career. Have them talk about the things they want to know about the career and the questions they would ask a person whom they were shadowing. **L2**

3 Assess

Vocabulary Practice

Page 58, **Unit 9 Fast File Resources**

National Health Education Standards

Pages 580–581: 3.3, 3.5, 6.3, 8.1, 8.3

Amanda Nauman
Shadowing a Health Career

> **66** . . . shadowing a maternity-care nurse really pointed me in the direction I wanted to go. **99**

Amanda knew she wanted to become a nurse. She had spent some time the previous summer working at a medical mission in Mexico and thought nursing would be a good way to help people. But after spending eight hours shadowing a maternity-care nurse at a local hospital, she gained a much better idea of what she wanted to do. "Following a maternity-care nurse really helped me find my niche in nursing," she explains.

A critical time The nurse Amanda shadowed was responsible for looking after newborn babies and their mothers. During the first 24 hours after the birth, a maternity-care nurse washes babies and does different tests on the newborns. Among the tests are blood tests for different conditions and the Apgar test. This test, performed immediately after the birth, helps doctors and nurses determine a baby's overall health condition. A baby's Apgar score alerts medical personnel to possible problems the newborn might be having adapting to conditions outside the mother.

Helpful advice "One of the new mothers was a nurse herself," Amanda says. "It was neat because she gave me advice too." Amanda was also struck by the diversity of mothers and babies on the ward the day she job-shadowed. "There were really young mothers and some older ones too. One of the women was Arabic-speaking. It was interesting to see how the staff interacted with her, since she didn't speak any English." Amanda's work in Mexico made her aware of the importance of communication in a medical setting. "I had studied Spanish for three years," she notes, "and it really helped when I was in Mexico."

Identifying options Maybe the best thing about job-shadowing is the way it lets young people see what possibilities are available. "Job shadowing helped me see my options," explains Amanda. "I had job-shadowed some other people before. But shadowing a maternity-care nurse really pointed me in the direction I wanted to go."

Making plans That direction now points toward nursing school. Amanda plans to get a two-year associate degree in nursing, followed by some actual working experience before getting her Bachelor of Science in Nursing (BSN). "I want to get into the field as soon as I can," she says. "Then I'll go back to school for another two years to get a BSN, which you need to work in management."

Journaling Activity

Think of a health-care (or any other) career you would like to know more about. Find out what education or training you would need if you chose this career. In your health journal, make a list of five things you would like to learn by shadowing a person in this profession. Also make a list of questions to ask the person you will be shadowing.

580   UNIT 9 • Consumer and Community Health

⚡ Achieving Health Literacy

Effective Communicator Divide the class into groups of two. Have students role-play a phone conversation with a professional whom they would like to shadow. Have students choose a health career that interests them. Ask each student to write a clear list of goals he or she would hope to accomplish through shadowing. Once students have practiced the hypothetical conversations, they can use them as a guide for when they actually contact a person whom they would like to shadow for the Community Involvement activity on page 576. **L2**

STUDY GUIDE

Key Terms Review

Complete these fill-in-the-blank statements with the lesson Key Terms on the left. Do not write in this book.

certification
certified health
education
specialist (CHES)
community health
educator
credentials
health career
license for a health
career
mentor
physician
shadowing
volunteering

1. A _____ is a profession or occupation in the medical field for which one trains.

2. _____ are the qualifications a person must have to be eligible for a job.

3. A _____ for a health career is a document that grants a person the right to practice or use a certain title.

4. _____ is the process a person completes to meet specific standards of professional competence.

5. A _____ is a person who has completed the certification process recommended for health educators.

6. _____ is spending time with a mentor as he or she performs work activities.

7. A _____ is a responsible person who guides another person.

8. _____ is providing a service without pay.

Recalling the Facts

9. What is the difference between being licensed and being certified in a health career?

10. Compare a clinical psychologist with a school psychologist.

11. Explain the difference between an audiologist and a speech pathologist.

12. What credentials do athletic trainers need?

13. What do guidance counselors do?

14. Explain the difference between an RN and an LPN.

15. What do recreational therapists do?

16. What credentials do dentists need?

17. What is the difference between a physical therapist and an occupational therapist?

18. What do dietitians do?

Critical Thinking

19. Compare shadowing, mentoring and volunteering.

20. Explain the process of researching a health career.

21. Compare basic, intermediate, and paramedic EMTs.

22. Consider five health careers and identify personality characteristics people would need to be happy working in each of those careers.

Real-Life Applications

23. Which health careers would you like to shadow? Why?

24. Why is volunteering a good way for you to try out a health career?

25. Would you make a good doctor in terms of personality? Why?

26. If you are in a serious accident, which type of emergency medical technician would you hope came to your aid and why?

Activities

Responsible Decision Making

27. **Write** Suppose your friend tells you that she paid her neighbor to set her up on a diet plan. You know that dietitians in your state must be licensed. Write a response to this situation. Refer to the Responsible Decision-Making Model on page 61 for help.

Sharpen Your Life Skills

28. **Use Communication Skills** Contact a person who works in a health career that interests you. Ask about the training they received and what they like and dislike about their work. Prepare a speech on the career, including creative opening and closing statements.

Visit www.glencoe.com for more *Health & Wellness* quizzes.

LESSON 54

STUDY GUIDE

Key Terms Review

1. health career
2. Credentials
3. license for a health career
4. Certification
5. certified health education specialist (CHES)
6. Shadowing
7. mentor
8. Volunteering

Recalling the Facts

9. A government agency awards a license. A nongovernment agency awards a certification.

10. See page 576 for information on clinical psychologists and page 579 for information on school psychologists.

11. See page 576 for information on audiologists and page 579 for information on speech pathologists.

12. See page 576 for information on athletic trainers.

13. See page 577 for information on guidance counselors.

14. See page 578 for information on LPNs and page 579 for information on RNs.

15. See page 579 for information on recreational therapists.

16. See page 577 for information on dentists.

17. See page 578 for information on physical and occupational therapists.

18. See page 577 for information on dietitians.

Critical Thinking

19. Shadowing is spending time with a mentor as he or she performs work activities, while mentoring is guiding a person and volunteering is providing a service without pay.

20. See page 575 for information on researching health careers. The basic steps are assess, complement, investigate, consider, evaluate, explore, and participate.

21. See page 577 for information on EMTs.

22. Answers will vary.

Real-Life Applications

23. Answers will vary.

24. You can get firsthand experience of what a health career is like.

25. Answers will vary.

26. An EMT-paramedic, because they have the most training.

Activities

Responsible Decision Making

27. Answers will vary but should ask whether the neighbor is licensed dietitian.

Sharpen Your Life Skills

28. Answers will vary. Encourage students to develop strong public-speaking skills.

LESSON
Learning About Public Health

 Out of Time?

If time does not permit an in-depth study of this topic, use the following activities in this Teacher Wraparound Edition:
- Class Discussion, p. 583
- Class Activity, p. 585
- Community Involvement, p. 587

1 Focus

HEALTH GOAL **Public and International Health** Have students respond to the Health Goal for this lesson by watching the national evening news for several nights and listing in their health journals all public health issues addressed. *Issues may include infectious disease, environmental threats, drunk driving, or tobacco.* **L2**

Write ABOUT IT!

Journaling Ask students to write several paragraphs in their health journals about which government officials they would contact if they were concerned about a reduction or an increase in funding for public health services. Also ask them to write what arguments they would make for continuing funding for public health services at the existing level, reducing funding, or increasing funding. **L2**

What You'll Learn

1. Describe why public health is a wise investment. *(p. 583)*
2. List public health agencies. *(p. 584)*
3. Explain why the United States's public health has improved during the past century. *(p. 585)*
4. List five important threats to today's public health. *(p. 586)*
5. Explain bioterrorism. *(p. 586)*
6. Explain the health risks that developing nations face, including undernutrition, unsafe water, and iron deficiency. *(p. 587)*

Why It's Important

People in our nation are enjoying better health and living longer than at any time in the past. You owe most of this to public health.

Key Terms

- public health
- local public health department
- bioterrorism
- undernutrition
- protein-energy malnutrition (PEM)
- micronutrients
- iodine deficiency
- cretinism
- goiter
- vitamin A deficiency

Learning About Public Health

HEALTH GOAL • **I will investigate public and international health needs.**

What comes to mind when you think of public health? Do you think about protection against infectious diseases, investigation of emerging epidemics, immunization programs for children and adults, protection against environmental hazards and threats, and health campaigns against tobacco use and drunk driving? Public health includes all of these efforts and much more.

Write ABOUT IT!

Writing About Public Health Suppose officials propose cutting the health department's budget, including immunizations for children and teens. After reviewing the information about public health agencies on page 584, write a hypothetical letter in your health journal explaining the importance of public health to your community and how reducing funding threatens the health and well-being of community members.

National Health Education Standards—Guide for Lesson 55		
1.6	Analyze the relationship between access to health care and health status.	pp. 582, 583–584, 586, 587–588, 589
2.2	Analyze how culture supports and challenges health beliefs, practices, and behaviors.	pp. 582, 587, 588–591

U.S. Public Health Agencies

O rganized community efforts to prevent disease and injury and promote health is called *public health*. Planned community activities that are carried out by public health departments are *public health programs*. The public health approach is quite different from the health-care approach. Public health emphasizes prevention of disease and injury and promotion of healthy behaviors, rather than treatment of sick and injured people. Many public health activities are invisible to the public, but they quickly become apparent when there are wide-scale health threats, such as a communicable disease outbreak, bioterrorist threat, contamination in the air, food, water, or escalating chronic disease.

What to Know About U.S. Public Health Agencies

Public health is a wise investment for communities, states, and nations because it helps people live longer, enjoy good health, and it saves money. Public health focuses on prevention and can help save our nation billions of dollars. Public health is carried out through a system of local public health departments, state health departments, and federal public health agencies.

Local One of the most important public health agencies is the local public health department. A local government agency that offers programs and services aimed at protecting and promoting the health of a specific community, such as a city or county (or counties), is a *local public health department*

State A state government agency that offers programs and services aimed at protecting and promoting the health of the state and provides support to local health departments is a *state health department.* State health departments often provide funding for training and technical expertise to local health departments to aid them in carrying out their public health programs and enforcing state health laws.

Federal public health agencies are responsible for safe and healthful
▼ environments.

U.S. Public Health Agencies

2 Teach

Class Discussion

An Ounce of Prevention Have students discuss why public health is a wise investment. Ask students how public health saves money. Discuss the phrase "an ounce of prevention is worth a pound of cure." **L2**

PowerPoint® Presentations

This CD-ROM is an editable Microsoft® PowerPoint® presentation that includes:

- Lesson presentations
- Lesson checks
- Interactive graphics
- 5-Minute Checks
- Image Bank
- All transparencies

Discussion Refer to the Read-and-Say-Something Strategy on page 17T as a means for the students to thoroughly cover each of the Key Terms in Lesson 55.

National Health Education Standards
Pages 582–583: 1.6, 2.2, 2.10, 8.1, 8.4

FDA-Regulated Products The products that the FDA regulates represent 25 cents out of every dollar in our nation that people spend.

Federal The ***Centers for Disease Control and Prevention (CDC)*** is the leading federal public health agency for protecting the health and safety of people in the United States at home and abroad.

The CDC works with state and local health departments as well as other agencies in communities, states, the nation, and other countries. It monitors health, detects and investigates health problems, conducts research to enhance prevention, develops and advocates sound public health policies, implements prevention strategies, promotes healthy behaviors, fosters safe and healthful environments, and provides leadership and training.

The CDC is comprised of many offices including the following: the National Center for Chronic Disease Prevention and Health Promotion (NCCDPHP), the National Center for Environmental Health (NCEH), the National Center for Health Statistics (NCHS), the National Center for Infectious Diseases (NCID), the National Immunization Program (NIP), and the National Institute for Occupational Safety and Health (NIOSH).

The CDC is a large organization with headquarters in Atlanta, Georgia. CDC employees work in several other states, and some employees work in other countries. The CDC is an agency of the United States Department of Health and Human Services (USDHHS). The Department of Health and Human Services includes other important federal public health agencies.

The CDC has outlined several challenges that it is working to overcome, including preventing violence and unintentional injury, battling bioterrorism, and working with partners to improve global health.

Federal Public Health Agencies

These agencies are part of the U.S. Department of Health and Human Services.

- **Centers for Medicare and Medicaid Services (CMS)** manages the Medicare and Medicaid programs and the Children's Health Insurance Program. Medicare provides health insurance for millions of older adults and disabled individuals. Medicaid provides health coverage for millions of low-income persons, including children and older adults.

- **Food and Drug Administration (FDA)** ensures the safety of foods and cosmetics, and the safety and efficacy of pharmaceuticals, biological products, medical devices, feed and drugs for pets and farm animals, and some consumer products.

- **Health Resources and Services Administration (HRSA)** provides access to essential health services for low-income and uninsured people, and in rural and urban neighborhoods where health care is scarce. The HRSA ensures the health of mothers and children, increases the number and diversity of health-care professionals in underserved communities, and provides supportive services for people with HIV infection.

- **Indian Health Services (IHS)** operates hospitals, health centers, school health centers, and health stations that assist Native Americans and Alaska natives.

- **National Institutes of Health (NIH)** supports research projects on diseases, such as cancer, Alzheimer's disease, diabetes, arthritis, heart ailments, and AIDS; includes 19 separate health institutes, seven separate health centers and the National Library of Medicine.

- **Substance Abuse and Mental Health Services Administration (SAMHSA)** works to improve the quality and availability of substance abuse prevention, addiction treatment, and mental-health services; provides federal grant money to states to support and maintain substance abuse and mental-health services.

584 UNIT 9 • Consumer and Community Health

Differentiated Instruction

Gifted and Talented Ask students to explore the history of public health and the people who have significantly contributed to its advancement. Have students choose one person who made a notable impact in this field and write a biography of or create a multimedia presentation on that person's life, outlining his or her specific contribution and the impact it has had on public health. People who made a notable impact in public health include Dorothea Dix, Joseph Goldberger, Florence Nightingale, Hildrus A. Poindexter, and Benjamin Waterhouse. **L3**

Public Health

Public health departments have done an extraordinary job of meeting public health needs in the past 100 years. There has been remarkable improvement in the health and life expectancy of our nation's population during the past century. Since 1900, the average life span of persons in the United States has increased by more than 30 years. Advances in public health are responsible for 25 years of this gain.

What to Know About Public Health

Today, Americans live in healthier conditions, know more about taking care of their health, and live longer than in the past. These trends are largely the result of public health services. The CDC identified ten great public health achievements of the twentieth century.

Vaccination Eradication of smallpox; elimination of poliomyelitis in the Americas; and control of measles, rubella, tetanus, diphtheria, and other infectious diseases, are due to vaccinations.

Motor-vehicle safety Both vehicles and highways are safer due to engineering efforts. Personal behaviors have been affected by education and have contributed to reductions in motor-vehicle-related deaths.

Safer workplaces Work-related health problems, severe injuries, and deaths have been reduced.

Control of infectious diseases Infections from contaminated water have been reduced due to improved sanitation. Other infectious diseases are controlled by using antibiotics.

Decline in deaths from heart disease and stroke Risk-factor modification, access to early detection, and better treatments have resulted in fewer deaths from heart disease and stroke.

Safer and healthier foods Better nutrition and less contamination resulted in safer foods. Food fortification has almost eliminated micronutrient malnutrition in the U.S.

Decline in infant and maternal mortality Better hygiene and nutrition, antibiotics, greater access to health care, and medical advances resulted in healthier babies and mothers.

Family planning Fewer STD transmissions, smaller family size, and fewer unplanned pregnancies resulted from family planning services.

Fluoridation of drinking water Tooth decay is reduced due to fluoridation of drinking water.

Recognition of tobacco use as a health hazard Antismoking campaigns lowered the prevalence of smoking and prevented smoking-related deaths.

> **Make the Connection**
>
> **Accessing Information** For more information on accessing health information, products, and services, see page 17 in Lesson 2.

Work-related injuries have been reduced due to public health laws. ▼

Class Activity

Life Without Public Health Have students write a report about what life would be like without each of the public health advances made in the past century. Have students answer this question: Would the average life-span of U.S. citizens have increased by more than 30 years if it weren't for advances in public health? **L2**

Quick Demo

Fortified Food Show the class some examples of fortified foods, such as calcium-fortified orange juice and iron-fortified cereal. The examples can be containers, advertisements in magazines, or store advertisements. **ELL**

Explain the Concept

Public Health versus Medical Care Explain the difference between public health and medical care. Public health emphasizes prevention of disease and promotion of health for all people. The medical or health-care approach treats one person at a time to prevent and treat illness and disease.

⟨⟩ Cross-Curricular Connections

Social Studies Ask students to research the history of public health in the United States. Ask the class to identify five leading public health figures and write a short play incorporating the leading public health figures as the main characters. Have the class put the production on for other classes in your school. Students can participate in this project in a variety of ways: as researchers, writers, or actors. **L2**

> **National Health Education Standards**
> Pages 584–585: 1.6, 2.10

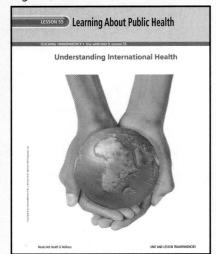
Public Health Problems

Although public health has made great improvements in the health of our population, many public health problems remain. Public health problems that need attention include injuries, teen pregnancy, high blood pressure, tobacco use, and substance abuse. Growing threats from the resurgence of infectious diseases, increases in violence, and escalating costs of health care are other examples of immediate and challenging concerns. As our population grows in terms of the number of older adults, health problems such as Alzheimer's disease and arthritis, and the need for long-term care and home health care will also become widespread. There also are growing threats to our environment that concern public health officials.

Newly recognized infectious diseases
Although public health has had major successes in fighting infectious diseases, such as smallpox, measles, and polio, today's public health professionals are dealing with an ever-expanding group of newly recognized infectious diseases, such as E coli, cyclospora, cryptosporidium, Hanta virus, West Nile virus, Ebola, HIV, and severe acute respiratory syndrome (SARS). While the number of new infectious diseases rises, the illnesses once controlled through the use of antibiotics are reemerging as public health threats by becoming resistant to the antibiotics used to fight them.

Bioterrorism There also is the threat of bioterrorism. ***Bioterrorism*** is the use or threatened use of bacteria, viruses, or toxins as weapons. Although there are a number of infectious agents that could potentially be used as weapons, those of most concern are smallpox, anthrax, botulism, and plague. Other agents that could be used include salmonella, E coli, and tuberculosis. Public health officials are working hard to protect our nation from the threat of bioterrorism.

New problems There will also always be new problems that present themselves. In today's world, there is an increase in international travel. This heightens the possibility that infectious disease agents can rapidly be spread from one area of the world to another. Overcrowding in cities with poor sanitation increases the risk of certain infectious diseases. Increases in the distribution of food from one area of the world to other areas of the world raise the likelihood that foodborne illness will be spread.

Reading Review

1. Name some newly recognized infectious diseases.
2. Which infectious agents that can be used as weapons are of most concern?

▲ When infectious agents or toxins are suspected, trained personnel follow special procedures when handling the material.

Health Project

Public Health Threats Have students create a multimedia presentation about problems and issues that continue to be a threat to public health. Ask students to include statistical information on the scope of the problems, who in particular is affected by the problems, and what, if anything, is being done to alleviate these problems. Ask students to focus on problems that affect teens and to describe how they would alleviate the problems. **L3**

International Health Needs

I n many ways, the world is a healthier and safer place today than it was in the past. Progress has been made in reducing the impact of many infectious diseases. Smallpox has been eradicated from the world, and efforts toward eliminating polio are proving successful. Throughout the world, more people now than ever before have access to clean water and food, so there are fewer waterborne and food-related illnesses. In more educated parts of the world, cigarette smoking rates are decreasing, and so are death rates from motor vehicle accidents. However, the World Health Organization points out that in many other ways the world is becoming more dangerous.

What to Know About International Health

Lifestyles of populations are changing around the world to be more in line with wealthy societies. These changes bring new risks to the health of these populations such as tobacco use, excessive alcohol use, obesity, physical inactivity, high blood pressure, and high blood cholesterol. Poverty also continues to cause an enormous amount of disease and poor health conditions throughout the world.

Poverty The major cause of health conditions resulting from undernutrition, unsafe water, poor sanitation and hygiene, and iron deficiency is poverty. In developing countries today, there are 170 million underweight children due to lack of food. On the other hand, there are more than one billion adults worldwide who are overweight and at least 300 million who are obese.

Undernutrition A deficiency in calories, protein, vitamins, or minerals as a result of inadequate diet and frequent infection results in *undernutrition.* It is a huge problem in developing countries. The most serious and deadly form of undernutrition is protein-energy malnutrition (PEM). *Protein-energy malnutrition (PEM)* is undernutrition that is the result of inadequate calorie intake to satisfy the body's nutritional needs. Infants and young children with protein-energy malnutrition are likely to have stunted growth and are vulnerable to infections and death.

Micronutrient deficiencies A threat to the health and development of the world's population, particularly preschool children and pregnant women in low-income countries, is micronutrient deficiency. Vitamins

> **Make the Connection**
>
> **Vitamins and Minerals** For more information on vitamins and minerals, see page 286 in Lesson 25.

International Health Needs

Class Activity

Feeding the Needy Divide the class into groups. Have each group research an international organization that is involved in feeding the needy. Ask students to determine how much money each organization raises each year, how they raise the money, what percentage of the money is used to actually feed the needy and what percentage is used for administration costs, and how many people they help each year. Ask the groups to present their findings to the class. **L2**

5-Minute Check

Page 77, **Unit 9 Fast File Resources**

1. Besides smallpox, anthrax, botulism, and plague, which infectious agents could be used as weapons of bioterrorism? *salmonella, E.coli, and tuberculosis*
2. How many children in developing countries are underweight due to lack of food? *170 million*
3. What is the world's most prevalent cause of brain damage? *iodine deficiency*
4. What is most common nutritional disorder in the world? *iron deficiency*
5. What is malaria? *a serious, life-threatening disease that is transmitted by the bite of a female Anopheles mosquito*

Community Involvement

International Health Organizations Have students choose five international health organizations about which they would like to learn more. Ask students to research the international health organizations they chose. Students should research the goals of each organization and determine what volunteer activities are available. Ask each student to create a public service announcement describing his or her international health organizations. Have each student share his or her public service announcement with the class. **L3**

> **National Health Education Standards**
> Pages 586–587: 2.2, 2.10

Breastfeeding Have students research the health benefits of breastfeeding and what women can do to keep themselves and their babies healthy while breast-feeding. Students should recount their findings in a written report. **L3**

Reading Review

1. anemia, premature birth, low birth weight, slow physical and intellectual growth, infections, elevated risk of death
2. vitamins and minerals needed by the body in minuscule amounts to produce enzymes, hormones, and other substances that are essential for proper growth and development

3 Assess

Vocabulary Practice

Name_____ Date_____ Class_____
LESSON 55 Learning About Public Health
Vocabulary Practice
Use the terms to fill in the blanks below. Some terms may be used more than once.

bioterrorism   local public health department   public health
cretinism   micronutrients   undernutrition
goiter   protein-energy malnutrition (PEM) vitamin A deficiency
iodine deficiency

1. _____ is the result of an inadequate diet and frequent infections.
2. _____ are vitamins and minerals that are needed by the body to produce substances necessary for proper growth and development.
3. _____ is the unnatural enlargement of the thyroid gland.
4. _____ is the use of infectious agents as weapons.
5. A serious and irreversible form of mental disability that is a result of not getting enough iodine is _____.
6. In pregnant women, _____ causes night blindness.
7. Infants and young children with _____ are likely to have stunted growth.
8. The organized efforts of _____ programs are apparent when there are widespread health threats.
9. _____ emphasizes the prevention of disease and the promotion of healthy behaviors.
10. Smallpox, anthrax, and botulism are three potential agents of _____.
11. A(n) _____ is a government agency that offers programs and services to a specific community, such as a city or county.
12. _____ is the most prevalent cause of brain damage.

70 LESSON 55 • Learning About Public Health   UNIT 9

Page 70, Unit 9 Fast File Resources

National Health Education Standards

Pages 588–589: 1.6, 2.2, 2.10, 6.3, 8.1, 8.4

588

---

and minerals that are needed by the body, in only minuscule amounts, to produce enzymes, hormones, and other substances essential for proper growth and development are **micronutrients.**

The most important micronutrient deficiencies are iodine, vitamin A, and iron. *Iodine deficiency* is the world's most prevalent cause of brain damage. Serious iodine deficiency during pregnancy may result in stillbirths, miscarriages, and birth defects such as cretinism. *Cretinism* is a serious and irreversible form of mental disability. One of the world's greatest public health achievements is the progress that has been made against cretinism and iodine deficiency. This was accomplished by placing iodine in salt. Iodized salt also is responsible for lowering the rate of goiter. *Goiter* is an unnatural enlargement of the thyroid gland.

Vitamin A deficiency is the leading cause of preventable blindness in children and raises the risk of disease and death from severe infections. In pregnant women, vitamin A deficiency causes night blindness and may increase the risk of death. Vitamin A deficiency can be reduced through a combination of breastfeeding and increased intake of vitamin A through diet and supplements.

Iron deficiency is the most common nutritional disorder in the world. Iron deficiency is the main cause of anemia. The health consequences for children are premature birth, low birth weight, slowed physical and intellectual growth, infections, and elevated risk of death. For pregnant women, anemia is often a cause of maternal death. Treating and preventing iron deficiency requires increasing

Reading Review

1. What are the consequences of iron deficiency?
2. Define micronutrients.

intake of iron-rich foods, taking supplements, and treating infections, such as hookworm, malaria, and schistosomiasis.

Poor feeding practices Lack of access to food is not the only cause of undernutrition. Poor feeding practices, including inadequate breastfeeding, offering the wrong foods to children, and giving too little food to children, all contribute to undernutrition. Public health workers counsel parents on the correct foods for each age group and help them overcome various feeding problems. They teach mothers about the health benefits of breastfeeding.

Lack of water and sanitation Water is important for many aspects of life, and access to clean water is very important to good health. Millions of people worldwide, mostly in developing countries, lack access to safe drinking water and adequate sanitation. The lack of clean water and sanitation is one of the world's most pressing crises.

Malaria A serious, life-threatening disease that is transmitted by the bite of a female *Anopheles* mosquito is called ***malaria.*** Four out of ten people in the world are at risk for contracting malaria. Those who survive an episode of malaria are at risk for brain damage. Unfortunately, there is no effective vaccine for malaria. Mosquito nets treated with insecticide can help to reduce malaria transmission. Prompt access to treatment and medicines can help save lives.

HIV Infection with HIV is a global epidemic that will continue to expand unless there are increased efforts to protect the world's population from it.

Achieving Health Literacy

Problem Solver Tobacco use is the fastest-growing cause of death in the world—it kills almost 5 million people each year. Although tobacco use has been decreasing in many industrialized countries, there have been large increases in smoking prevalence in developing countries, especially among males. Have students research tobacco use in industrialized and developing countries. Have students create a multimedia presentation, including at least two graphs. Ask students to present their findings to the class. **L3**

LESSON 55 STUDY GUIDE

bioterrorism
cretinism
goiter
iodine deficiency
local public health department
malaria
micronutrients
protein-energy malnutrition (PEM)
public health
state health department
undernutrition
vitamin A deficiency

National Health Information Center

Key Terms Review

Use what you know about the Key Terms on the left to answer the following questions.

1. What is the cause of undernutrition?
2. What groups of people are most affected by micronutrient deficiencies?
3. What is the job of the local public health department?
4. What is the world's most prevalent cause of brain damage?
5. Protein-energy malnutrition is a result of what?
6. Define bioterrorism.
7. How can vitamin A deficiency be reduced?
8. What is cretinism?
9. Define public health.
10. What causes goiter?

Recalling the Facts

11. What kinds of bioterrorism threats are our government concerned about?
12. Who is at risk for undernutrition?
13. What does it mean to have protein-energy malnutrition, and who is at risk?
14. Why are micronutrients important?
15. Why is iron deficiency a concern?
16. What causes cretinism?
17. Explain how local, state, and federal health departments work together.
18. What problems does vitamin A deficiency cause?

Critical Thinking

19. How are public health departments responsible for Americans living longer today than 100 years ago?
20. Analyze the impact of the availability of health services in U.S. communities and the world.
21. Assess the impact of population and economy on community and world health.
22. What are some public health problems that still need attention? At the local level? At the national level? How are local and national officials responding to these problems?

Real-Life Applications

23. Which of the services provided by your local public health department do you think is the most important? The most used?
24. Rank the list of public health services found on page 584 according to what you think is most important, with number one being the most important.
25. List in order what you think will be our nation's top three public health problems in the next ten years. Why do you think so?
26. If you were a billionaire and wanted to help a developing country, what could you purchase that would help the people the most?

Activities

Responsible Decision Making

27. **Discuss** Suppose you and a friend are hiking on public land near your home. You spot a man dumping unmarked metal barrels off the back of his truck into a secluded ravine. Discuss with a classmate what you would do. Refer to the Responsible Decision-Making Model on page 61 for help.

Sharpen Your Life Skills

28. **Advocate for Health** Most people take public health services for granted and do not understand how critical they are for us to enjoy our current lives. In a small group, design and produce a pamphlet identifying several public health services and why they are important.

Visit **www.glencoe.com** for more *Health & Wellness* quizzes.

LESSON 55 • Study Guide **589**

Key Terms Review

1. inadequate diet and frequent infection
2. enzymes, hormones, and other substances essential to growth and development
3. It offers programs and services aimed at protecting and promoting the health of a specific community.
4. iodine deficiency
5. inadequate caloric intake to satisfy the body's nutritional needs
6. the use or threatened use of bacteria, viruses, or toxins as weapons
7. through a combination of breast-feeding and intake of vitamin A through diet and supplements
8. a serious and irreversible form of mental disability
9. organized community efforts to prevent disease and injury and promote health
10. iodine deficiency

Recalling the Facts

11. smallpox, anthrax, botulism, and plague
12. mostly people who live in developing countries, although it can affect people who live in more developed countries as well
13. It is undernutrition that is the result of inadequate caloric intake to satisfy the body's nutritional needs; infants and young children
14. Deficiencies of micronutrients, such as iodine, vitamin A, and iron, can have serious health consequences.
15. It is the most common nutritional disorder in the world.
16. severe iodine deficiency
17. See pages 583 for information on public health agencies.
18. See page 588 for information on vitamin A deficiency.

Critical Thinking

19. See page 585 for information on public health achievements.
20. See pages 583 and 587–588.
21. See pages 587–588.

22. See page 586 for information on public health problems.

Real-Life Applications

23. Answers will vary. Students should explain their choices.
24. Answers will vary. Students should explain their choices.
25. Answers will vary. Students should explain their choices.
26. Answers will vary. Students should explain their choices.

Activities

Responsible Decision Making

27. Answers will vary, but should include telling authorities.

Sharpen Your Life Skills

28. Answers will vary.

589

Key Terms Review

1. a
2. e
3. i
4. f
5. b
6. g
7. h
8. k
9. d
10. c

Recalling the Facts

11. Federal laws apply to every state in the country. State laws apply to everyone within a state and cannot violate federal laws. Ordinances apply to everyone in a county or municipality and cannot violate state or federal laws.

12. compare quality and price; check the company's reputation; get a written estimate; never accept verbal guarantees; understand contracts before signing; never sign incomplete contracts; keep contracts, warranties, guarantees, and receipts; use caution when giving out bank account numbers; and never pay in order to collect a "prize"

13. to choose; to be heard; to safety; to be informed; to satisfaction of basic needs; to redress or remedy; to consumer education; to environmental health

14. Record your weekly income and expenses; subtract your total expenses from your total income; determine whether your budget is balanced, i.e. income is greater than or equal to expenses; if not, reduce expenses or increase income to avoid debt.

15. See page 558.

16. Health Maintenance Organizations (HMOs) and Preferred Provider Organizations (PPOs)

17. See page 568.

18. A license grants a person the right to practice or use a certain title and is awarded by a government agency. Certification is granted by a nongovernmental agency to a person who meets specific standards of professional competence.

19. Local public health departments, state health departments, the CDC, the NHIS. See page 584 for more examples and descriptions.

20. poverty, undernutrition, micronutrient deficiencies, poor feeding practices, lack of water and sanitation, HIV

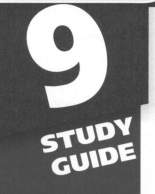

Key Terms Review

Match the following definitions with the correct Key Terms. Do not write in this book.

a. bioterrorism (p. 586)
b. consumer rights (p. 544)
c. credentials (p. 575)
d. debt (p. 553)
e. desensitization (p. 561)
f. Health Maintenance Organization (HMO) (p. 567)
g. interest (p. 553)
h. Medicare (p. 567)
i. micronutrients (p. 588)
j. recall (p. 547)
k. urgent-care center (p. 571)
l. V-chip (p. 560)

1. the use or threatened use of bacteria, viruses, or toxins as weapons
2. the effect of reacting less and less to the exposure of something
3. vitamins and minerals that are needed by the body in only miniscule amounts
4. a business that organizes health-care services for its members
5. the privileges that a consumer is guaranteed
6. additional money that is paid for the use of a larger sum of money
7. a government health insurance plan for people 65 years of age and older
8. a facility that is not part of a hospital that provides emergency care
9. the condition of owing
10. the qualifications a person must have

Recalling the Facts

11. Explain the hierarchy of health laws. (Lesson 50)
12. List the steps you can take to be a more successful consumer. (Lesson 50)
13. List the eight rights included in the Consumer Bill of Rights. (Lesson 50)
14. Explain how to make a budget. (Lesson 51)
15. Identify four guidelines to use when choosing entertainment. (Lesson 52)
16. Identify two kinds of managed-care programs to cover health-care costs. (Lesson 53)
17. List five actions you can take to make yourself insurable. (Lesson 53)
18. Explain the difference between being licensed and being certified. (Lesson 54)
19. Identify four public health agencies, and explain what each does. (Lesson 55)
20. Identify five important threats to today's public health. (Lesson 55)

Critical Thinking

21. Explain why health fraud is often targeted at teens and older adults. (Lesson 50)
22. Discuss how you can have time for the important activities in your life. (Lesson 51)
23. Discuss reasons a person must be careful when using credit cards. (Lesson 51)
24. Explain how health can be harmed by inappropriate entertainment choices. (Lesson 52)
25. Describe how technology has affected entertainment. (Lesson 52)
26. Discuss various health-care facilities. (Lesson 53)
27. Explain how to evaluate health insurance coverage. (Lesson 53)
28. Explain using volunteering and shadowing to investigate health careers. (Lesson 54)
29. Why has the United States' public health improved during the past century? (Lesson 55)
30. Identify the health risks that people in developing nations face. (Lesson 55)

Use **Interactive Tutor** at **www.glencoe.com** for additional help.

Critical Thinking

21. Teens are often overly concerned about their looks. Older adults with health problems may be vulnerable to claims of quick cures or recaptured youth.

22. Set goals, set priorities, make a schedule, make a to-do list, be organized, learn to say "no" to unimportant activities if you do not have time.

23. Interest will be charged on unpaid balances. Serious debt problems may arise if charging more than can be paid each month becomes a habit.

24. A person may become inactive, out of shape and overweight; become desensitized to violence; see solutions to life's problems modeled in unrealistic ways; develop entertainment addiction; withdraw from relationships; become persuaded to engage in promiscuous behavior; become persuaded to use alcohol, tobacco, or other drugs.

Health Literacy Activities

What Do You Know?
Responsible Citizenship Write factual questions and answers about health insurance. Form two teams with classmates. Compete by giving the opposing teams the answers for which they must supply the correct questions. Tabulate the correct number of questions to determine a winner.

Connection to Social Studies
Self-Directed Learning Create a world map using poster paper and markers or computer graphics. Research the life span of people in ten countries. Illustrate this information on your world map. Which factors influence the life spans of the people living in the ten countries you selected?

Family Involvement
Problem Solving Have a family meeting to evaluate your use of entertainment media. Discuss your family guidelines with your parents or guardian. Refer to the criteria for evaluating entertainment and entertainment ratings in Lesson 52.

Investigating Health Careers
Effective Communication Choose one of the medical specialties that interests you from the list on p. 566. Conduct research on the specialty. Write a one-paragraph description of the specialty. Would you enjoy a career in this medical specialty? Why or why not?

Group Project
Critical Thinking Some people are resistant to the idea of community water fluoridation. Investigate the pros and cons of having a water supply fluoridated. List these on a sheet of paper. After looking at both sides of the issue, what is your stand? Do you support community water fluoridation? Why or why not? Visit **www.glencoe.com** for more information.

Standardized Test Practice

Read the following selection and answer the questions that follow.

In 2002, drug companies spent $2.7 billion on ads aimed at consumers. At least 8.5 million Americans each year request a drug they have seen an ad for from their doctors. Advertising drugs directly to consumers is a debated topic in the health-care industry. On one side of the argument, consumer groups and some government agencies claim drug companies sometimes do not explain risks and side effects associated with drugs. On the other side of the argument, drug companies respond that their ads help make consumers better informed about the drugs they take. With spending for consumer ads rising, consumers will probably see many more of these ads in the future.

Multiple Choice

1 According to this paragraph, which statement is true?
  A 8.5 million doctors write prescriptions for advertised drugs.
  B Consumers spent $2.7 billion for advertised drugs.
  C Drug companies never explain side effects in their ads.
  D Spending for consumer ads is rising each year.

2 Which statement best expresses the author's attitude?
  A The advertising of drugs to consumers is wrong.
  B Drug companies have a right to mislead consumers.
  C The advertising of drugs to consumers is here to stay.
  D Consumer groups interfere with the health-care system.

Open-Ended

3 Write a paragraph explaining how consumers can use drug ads to become better informed about health-care issues.

 www.glencoe.com

---

25. Technology has made entertainment more accessible, abundant, and influential.
26. See pages 571–572.
27. Evaluate a copy of the health insurance plan; ask company representatives about the plan; shop around for various plans; choose the plans that give the most comprehensive coverage at the most affordable price. Use the questions on page 568.
28. Volunteering and shadowing a mentor allow teens to get firsthand experience in what a health career is like.
29. achievements in vaccinations, sanitation, antibiotics, medical advancements, better nutrition, motor-vehicle safety, workplace safety, family planning, fluoridation of drinking water, and recognition of tobacco use as a health hazard
30. undernutrition, micronutrient deficiencies, lack of water or sanitation, poor feeding practices, malaria, and HIV

Health Literacy Activities

 What Do You Know?
The questions and answers that students create will vary. Listen carefully to make sure students answer correctly.

Connection to Social Studies
Students' world maps will vary, but should include average life spans for people in ten different countries and factors that influence life span. Ask students to list sources and discuss the reliability of those sources.

Family Involvement
Ask student volunteers to share their family guidelines with the class.

Investigating Health Careers
Students may choose to interview a person who works in the field, in addition to doing research in the library. Students should document their sources. Ask students to share their findings in class.

Group Project
Students should provide well-reasoned arguments for their stands on fluoridation. Conduct a class debate.

Standardized Test Practice

Multiple Choice
1. D   2. C

Open-Ended
3. Answers will vary, but should include ways to evaluate the information provided in drug ads. Paragraphs should contain correct spelling, capitalization, punctuation, grammar, usage, and sentence structure.

Environmental Health

STANDARDS AND FEATURES

Lesson	National Standards	State/Local Standards	Activities and Features
Lesson 56 *(2 sessions, 1 block)* Learning About Environmental Issues	1.3, 1.5, 2.10, 8.3		
Lesson 57 *(2 sessions, 1 block)* Preventing Air and Water Pollution	1.3, 2.10		**Health News:** HEVs and FCVs, p. 605
Lesson 58 *(1 session, 1 block)* Preventing Noise and Visual Pollution	1.3, 7.2, 8.3		**Using Life Skills:** Practicing Healthful Behaviors: Avoiding Noise Pollution, p. 614
Lesson 59 *(2 sessions, 1 block)* Practicing Recycling and Conservation	7.2		**Just the Facts:** Energy Conservation, p. 621 **Speaking Out:** Working on a Recycling Program, p. 623
Lesson 60 *(1 session, 1 block)* Protecting the Environment	1.3, 7.1, 7.2		**Using Life Skills:** Advocating for Health: Creating a Plan to Protect Your Community's Environment, p. 629 **Facts About:** Indoor Air Quality, p. 630

Key to Differentiated Instruction

L1 Level 1 activities should be appropriate for students with learning difficulties.

L2 Level 2 activities should be within the ability range of all students.

L3 Level 3 activities are designed for above-average students.

ELL ELL activities should be within the ability range of English language learners.

FAST FILE RESOURCES

INTRODUCING THE UNIT

Parent and Family Letter	p. 1	Health Behavior Contract	p. 3
Spanish Parent and Family Letter	p. 2	Unit Focus Transparency Master and Worksheet	p. 4

TEACHING THE UNIT LESSONS

Reproducible Student Pages	Lesson 56	Lesson 57	Lesson 58	Lesson 59	Lesson 60
Reading Strategy	p. 7	p. 19	p. 31	p. 43	p. 55
Vocabulary Practice	p. 8	p. 20	p. 32	p. 44	p. 56
Transparency Master and Worksheet	p. 9	p. 21	p. 33	p. 45	p. 57
Real-Life Health	p. 11	p. 23	p. 35	p. 47	p. 59
5-Minute Check	p. 15	p. 27	p. 39	p. 51	p. 63
Lesson Quiz	p. 16	p. 28	p. 40	p. 52	p. 65

CLOSING THE UNIT

Family Involvement Activity	p. 69	Health in the News	p. 79
Community Involvement Activity	p. 71	Health Career Research Activity	p. 81
Health Lab	p. 73	Unit Test A	p. 83
Activity: Strengthening Health Skills	p. 77	Unit Test B	p. 87

Technology

- **Interactive Chalkboard CD-ROM**
- **TeacherWorks™ CD-ROM**
- **StudentWorks™ CD-ROM**
- **Reading Essentials CD-ROM**
- **Exam*View*® Assessment Suite**

Glencoe Exclusive!

TeacherWorks™
All-In-One Planner and Resource Center

www.glencoe.com
- **Vocabulary Puzzlemaker**
- **Interactive Tutor**
- **Your Health Checklist**
- **Web Links**
- **Student Web Activities**

UNIT 10

Environmental Health

TEST YOUR ENVIRONMENTAL IQ

Use the three statements on the student page to initiate a class discussion about environmental health. *Additional True/False statements are:*

4. **Solid waste is a problem that affects many parts of the environment, and precycling and recycling can help reduce waste.**
   TRUE: Precycling is a process of reducing waste, and recycling is the process of breaking down or re-forming a waste product so it can be used again.

5. **Air pollution is a contamination of the air that causes negative effects on life and health.**
   TRUE: People cause the most air pollution, and, with the human population growing, air pollution is increasing, which can increase the likelihood of respiratory disease and infection.

6. **People may always remove things from the natural environment when they are hiking, camping, or fishing.**
   FALSE: In protected areas, removing or damaging parts of the natural environment often is illegal. Leaving everything in its place helps protect the natural habitat.

 Outdoor Recreation Activities

Environmentalism Ask students what they think the proverb means and whether they agree or disagree with the quote. **L1**

UNIT 10 Environmental Health

TEST YOUR ENVIRONMENTAL IQ
True or False?

1. **You cannot live more than one day without clean drinking water.**
   FALSE: The human body cannot go more than a few days without drinking water, but it can handle one day without drinking anything even though it is not recommended.

2. **Most paper is recyclable.**
   TRUE: Paper fills over 40 percent of landfill space even though most of it is completely recyclable.

3. **Each person can make an impact on protecting the environment.**
   TRUE: Every time a person recycles or reuses an item, the environment benefits. Each act by itself is small, but many people doing small environmentally friendly acts makes a big difference.

> "We don't inherit the Earth from our parents . . . we borrow it from our children."
>
> —Proverb

 Outdoor Recreation Activities

Discuss Many outdoor recreation activities, such as camping and using off-road vehicles, can damage the environment if not done responsibly. Research recreation activities in national parks that pose a threat to the environment. Create a graphic computer presentation with your results. Include what steps can be taken to minimize the impact of these recreation activities.

LESSON 56	**LESSON 57**	**LESSON 58**
Learning About Environmental Issues	Preventing Air and Water Pollution	Preventing Noise and Visual Pollution

592   UNIT 10 • Environmental Health

Two-Minute Unit Launcher

Discussion Pollution involves many aspects of the environment, from visual pollution, such as graffiti on a wall, to air pollution, such as smog in a city. Divide students into groups and ask each group to choose an environmental concern they have and three reasons their environmental concern is important to their community. Have each group present its concern to the class and ask the rest of the class to brainstorm ideas of how to improve this environmental issue in their community. Use the students' ideas to introduce the concepts covered in the unit. **L2**

EVALUATING MEDIA MESSAGES

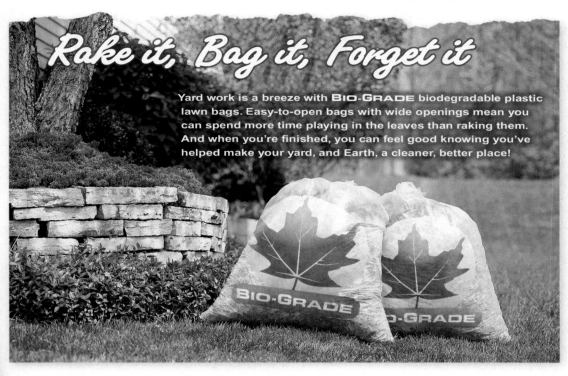

Rake it, Bag it, Forget it

Yard work is a breeze with **BIO-GRADE** biodegradable plastic lawn bags. Easy-to-open bags with wide openings mean you can spend more time playing in the leaves than raking them. And when you're finished, you can feel good knowing you've helped make your yard, and Earth, a cleaner, better place!

 WHAT'S YOUR VERDICT?

To evaluate this advertisement, use the criteria for analyzing and evaluating health messages delivered through media and technology that you learned in Unit 1.

Visit www.glencoe.com to find regularly updated statistics about noise pollution. Using the information provided, determine the answer to this question: What noise regulations are in effect in your area?

Visit www.glencoe.com to use *Your Health Checklist* ✔, an interactive tool that helps you determine your health status.

| **LESSON 59** | **LESSON 60** |
| Practicing Recycling and Conservation | Protecting the Environment |

Health Online

Answer Many communities have laws that define acceptable noise levels in decibels. These levels may vary in commercial and residential areas, and they may vary for day and evening hours. Lawmakers put these rules into effect to protect citizens from having to live, work, and attend school in noisy environments. Students should be aware that fines may be imposed on a person or a business not abiding by local noise ordinances. **L2**

 What's Your Verdict?

Ads Some companies market their products as environmentally friendly to encourage consumers to purchase them. Have students bring in examples of advertising for both recycled and biodegradable products. Working in groups, the students can compare the products and analyze the ads to determine how the product can affect the environment in a positive way. **L2**

Health Journal

Write an Essay Have students write in their health journals actions they do on a daily basis that could be stopped or altered to help protect the environment. Then, ask them to write a list of activities or new habits they can work on that would improve the environment. Have them list ways they can track their progress as they change their habits. **L2**

INTERACTIVE CHALKBOARD
with Image Bank

Unit Focus Transparency

Page 4, **Unit 10 Fast File Resources**

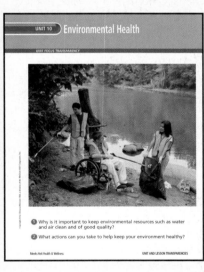

UNIT 10 Environmental Health

① Why is it important to keep environmental resources such as water and air clean and of good quality?

② What actions can you take to help keep your environment healthy?

National Health Education Standards

Pages 592–593: 1.3, 2.5, 2.10, 3.1

593

LESSON 56

Learning About Environmental Issues

Out of Time?

If time does not permit an in-depth study of this topic, use the following activities in this Teacher Wraparound Edition:

- Health Goals, p. 594
- Healthy People 2010, p. 596
- Family Involvement, p. 598

1 Focus

HEALTH GOALS **Environmental Awareness** Have students respond to the first Health Goal for this lesson by recording in their health journals a list of current environmental issues. They should include both local issues and global concerns. They should also list as many organizations and laws that protect the environment as they know. *Lists might include water pollution, air pollution, global warming as well as Environmental Protection Agency, various nonprofit environmental organizations, Clean Air Act, Safe Drinking Water Act.* **L2**

Write ABOUT IT!

Role-Play Have students role-play the scenarios they wrote in their health journals. Then discuss which response would be most effective to encourage the person who littered to change his or her behavior. **L2**

LESSON 56

What You'll Learn

1. List global environmental issues. *(p. 595)*
2. Identify the connection between population and the environment. *(p. 595)*
3. Discuss facts related to families and children who are homeless. *(p. 596)*
4. Explain why maintaining the ozone layer is important to health. *(p. 597)*
5. Describe the greenhouse effect and global warming. *(p. 598)*
6. Identify ways to stay informed about environmental issues. *(p. 599)*

Why It's Important

Many factors affect the quality of life on Earth, which, in turn, affects your life and health. You can learn how to contribute to a better environment for Earth.

Key Terms

- environment
- malnutrition
- homelessness
- ozone layer
- biodiversity
- deforestation
- greenhouse effect
- global warming
- extinction
- habitat

594 UNIT 10 • Environmental Health

Learning About Environmental Issues

 HEALTH GOALS
- I will stay informed about environmental issues.
- I will be aware of organizations that protect the environment.

Scientifically, the ***environment*** includes all of the living and non-living factors that you interact with each day. It includes resources, such as the air you breathe, the water you drink, the food you eat, other organisms, soil, and the climate in which you live. This lesson will help you to become aware of how some environmental factors could affect your health.

 Write ABOUT IT!

Writing About Environmental Issues The ocean and trees help make this environment beautiful. Suppose you noticed someone throw a candy wrapper on the ground. What would you do to help keep this environment clean? Would you say anything to the person who littered? Write your response in your health journal.

National Health Education Standards—Guide for Lesson 56		
1.3	Analyze how environment and personal health are interrelated.	pp. 594, 595–598, 601
1.5	Propose ways to reduce or prevent injuries and health problems.	p. 599
2.10	Analyze how public health policies and government regulations can influence health promotion and disease prevention.	pp. 599, 600, 601
8.3	Work cooperatively as an advocate for improving personal, family, and community health.	p. 597

Environmental Issues

P eople's use of resources can affect the environment. When the quality of the environment deteriorates, the quality of people's health is affected. Changes in environmental quality may be community issues or they may be global, impacting the health of everyone on Earth. Some important global environmental issues are population growth rate, global warming, the thinning of the ozone layer, and the reduction in the amount of existing rain forests.

What to Know About Environmental Issues

Population growth rate Population growth rates are an important environmental issue. The growth in human population can affect the environment. As of the end of the year 2003, more than 6.3 billion people lived on Earth. According to the World Bank Group, the world's population is growing by 200,000 people each day.

Several factors contribute to the rise in population. Food resources and available health services have improved worldwide. People also are living longer, and infant mortality rates have declined.

As population grows, it consumes more of Earth's resources. Some nations with high population growth rates are not always able to feed all of their people. There may be increased stress on resources.

Some governments work to make sure their citizens have food, clean water, shelter, and adequate health care. Therefore, as the number of

people increases, the demand for health services and other public services increases. If a country has limited economic resources, it may be difficult to meet the needs of its people. As a result, many people suffer from poverty, hunger, and homelessness and the health problems that go along with these issues. Some of the world's fastest growing populations live in countries with limited economic resources, so the problem is increasing for these governments.

Poverty and hunger exist in all parts of the world. **Poverty** is a condition in which a person does not have sufficient resources to eat and live healthfully. People who are poor and hungry often are more at risk for disease. Some people who live in poverty suffer from malnutrition. **Malnutrition** is a condition in which the body does not receive either the energy nutrients or the balance of nutrients required for optimal health.

Make the Connection

Volunteering For more information about volunteering, see page 66 in Lesson 7.

LESSON 56 • Learning About Environmental Issues **595**

Class Activity

Brainstorm Save some of the trash from your home over one day, such as packages, newspapers, and unwanted mail. Bring the trash to class and ask students to imagine this amount of trash for everyone in the community, the state, and the nation. Have them brainstorm ways to reduce the amount of trash in your life and to dispose of the trash that is generated in an environmentally friendly way. **L1**

PowerPoint® Presentations

This CD-ROM is an editable Microsoft® PowerPoint® presentation that includes:
- Lesson presentations
- Lesson checks
- Interactive graphics
- 5-Minute Checks
- Image Bank
- All transparencies

Discussion Refer to the KWL Strategy on page 17T. Ask students to brainstorm a list of what they already know about environmental issues before reading the lesson and list what they would like to learn from the lesson. After reading, go back to the chart and discuss what the class has learned.

Lesson Resource Manager

- **Unit 10 Fast File Resources**
  Reading Strategy, p. 7
  Vocabulary Practice, p. 8
  Transparency Master and Worksheet, p. 9
  Real-Life Health, p. 11
  Real-Life Health, p. 13
  5-Minute Check, p. 15
  Lesson 56 Quiz, p. 16
- **Unit 10 Transparency**
- **Lesson 56 Transparency**

- **Reading Essentials**
- **Technology**
  TeacherWorks™ CD-ROM
  StudentWorks™ CD-ROM
  Reading Essentials CD-ROM
  ExamView® Assessment Suite
  Vocabulary Puzzlemaker

National Health Education Standards
Pages 594–595: 1.3, 8.1

Children and Homelessness

According to the National Center on Family Homelessness, homeless children have twice as many ear infections, five times more diarrhea and stomach problems, and six times as many speech problems as other children. Homeless children are four times more likely to develop asthma. They suffer physical and sexual abuse at two to three times the rate of other children. They experience going hungry at more than two times the rate of other children.

Explain the Concept

Homelessness and Disease In some cases, the conditions of being homeless increase the risk of contracting certain diseases, including tuberculosis. Tuberculosis is a contagious disease caused by the bacterium *Mycobacterium tuberculosis.* In a person with a compromised immune system—such as someone suffering from malnutrition or the stress of living in overcrowded, unsanitary conditions—an infection is more likely to result upon exposure to the bacteria. Left untreated, the bacteria ultimately destroy lung tissue and can result in death.

NHES Assessment/SCASS

Selected Response Lack of affordable housing, unemployment, or illness may lead to which of the following:

A. homelessness
B. poverty
C. malnutrition
D. all of the above

> **Make the Connection**
>
> **Mental Health** For more information about mental health, see page 89 in Lesson 9.

Homelessness Poverty and hunger also have been associated with homelessness, a major health concern in the United States. ***Homelessness*** means having no permanent residence. When many people think about homelessness, they often think about adults. However, homelessness affects many families every year. As many as 3.5 million Americans experience homelessness at some point during an average year. About 1.35 million of them are children. Below are facts you may not know about homelessness in the United States:

- Families are the fastest growing segment, accounting for more than 40 percent of the nation's homeless people.
- Most children who are homeless find themselves in this situation because their parents are unable to find affordable housing. Unemployment, illness, or domestic violence further interfere with a family finding housing.
- Children who are homeless have an increased risk of being homeless when they become adults.

Some organizations ▶ combine volunteer labor, donated money and materials, no-interest loans, and homeowner labor to build or rehabilitate affordable homes.

The health-related problems of children caused by homelessness are significant. Children who are homeless between the ages of 6 and 17 have high rates of mental-health problems, primarily anxiety and depression. About one-third of children who are homeless have a mental-health problem that affects their daily activities. Almost half of all children who are homeless suffer anxiety and depression. In addition, children who are homeless suffer from hunger and may be in poor health.

A lack of affordable housing is a major contributor to homelessness. In many cities, housing costs have risen and are not affordable for many people. Since they cannot afford to pay rent, they often resort to living with other family members, in hotels, or on the streets. Nonprofit agencies in some cities provide financial assistance to help people who are homeless find affordable housing. There are other agencies that help people who are homeless obtain needed furnishings and access to medical care.

People who are healthy function better. When people do not have to spend all of their time and energy fighting illnesses, they have more resources to address other problems. This helps them to find jobs, which enables them to afford housing. Other programs offer help with education, such as college classes and job training so that people can find employment and have an income.

There are many things that people can do to help homeless persons. They can volunteer at shelters for the homeless. They can help by making

---

👫 Healthy People 2010

Objective 8-29 *Reduce the global burden of disease due to poor water quality, sanitation, and personal and domestic hygiene.*

According to the World Health Organization, 2,668,200 deaths worldwide were attributable to these factors in 1990. The target for Healthy People 2010 is to reduce this number by 20 percent (2,131,560). Better water supplies and sanitation may increase the average life expectancy in developing countries by 15 years. Have students consider the connection between poor water quality and lack of adequate sanitation and illness. Ask students: How are these related? What actions can be taken to reduce the number of deaths from illnesses caused by these factors? **L2** people aware how to donate clothing and personal care items, furniture, and food to homeless shelters. Volunteers also can tutor homeless children in after-school programs so that the children increase their chances of succeeding in school.

Other ways to help the homeless are to advocate within communities for jobs, health services, and housing.

Thinning of the ozone layer The air that you breathe is a little more than 21 percent oxygen. Each molecule of oxygen in the air is made up of two atoms of the element oxygen. However, there is another form of oxygen that you depend upon: ozone. *Ozone* is a molecule that is made up of three atoms of oxygen. Ozone is found in a layer of Earth's atmosphere starting about ten miles above Earth.

The *ozone layer* is a protective layer of the upper atmosphere that prevents most of the ultraviolet (UV) radiation from the Sun from reaching Earth's surface. Too much UV radiation is harmful to living tissue. It has been associated with skin cancer, cataracts (KA tuh raks), and other health conditions.

▲ Rain forests cover about 7 percent of the land on Earth.

▲ Reusing and recycling materials decreases the need for new materials to be processed.

A seasonal ozone reduction over the Antarctic is thought to be caused by human-produced chemicals, such as chlorofluorocarbons, or CFCs. Smaller seasonal reductions also have been observed over the Arctic and there also is a small downward trend in global ozone concentrations. Concerns over these effects have caused nations worldwide to phase out the use of CFCs.

Reduction of rain forests Rain forests are located near the equator around the globe in Latin America, Africa, and Asia. A *tropical rain forest* is a hot, wet, forested area that contains many species of trees, plants, and animals.

Rain forests cover about 7 percent of the land on Earth. The vegetation in rain forests produces oxygen and removes carbon dioxide from the atmosphere.

Biodiversity Many of the world's plant and animal species live in tropical rain forests, which means they have a high biodiversity. *Biodiversity* refers to the variety of species in an area. This variety gives humans food, vegetation, and medicine. About 25 percent of modern drugs, including aspirin, originated in the rain forests.

Did You Know?

CFCs Chlorofluorocarbons (CFCs) are a group of gases that are used as a propellant in aerosol sprays and as coolants in air conditioners, insulation, and refrigerators. They are thought to be a leading cause of the thinning of the ozone layer. Companies have been gradually phasing out the use of these chemicals.

⚖ Legal Issues

Clean Air and CFCs As part of the Clean Air Act, the United States Environmental Protection Agency ruled that the production and use of CFCs, chemicals that are known to deplete the ozone layer, would be limited. The ruling required that producers of CFCs gradually reduce the production of CFCs until the chemicals were completely phased out by January 1, 2000. This was later amended by an international accord in which 24 countries agreed to end the production of CFCs by December 31, 1995. As a result of these efforts, the rate of accumulation of CFCs in the atmosphere is no longer accelerating.

1. **How does population growth rate affect the environment?** *More people use more resources from the environment.*

2. **What is poverty?** *a condition in which a person does not have sufficient resources to eat and live healthfully*

3. **Why is the thinning of the ozone layer a health concern?** *More UV radiation from the sun will reach Earth's surface. Too much UV radiation is harmful to living tissue. Overexposure is associated with skin cancer, cataracts, and other health conditions.*

4. **Why are tropical rain forests important to the environment?** *The vegetation in rain forests produces oxygen and removes carbon dioxide from the atmosphere.*

5. **Explain how you can help improve the environment.** *conserve electricity, plant trees, recycle, buy recycled products, buy products that help the environment*

Reading Review

1. *Answers can include population growth rate, homelessness, poverty and health, thinning of the ozone layer, reduction of rain forests, biodiversity, deforestation, and greenhouse effect and global warming.*

2. *a protective layer of the upper atmosphere that traps UV radiation from the Sun and prevents it from reaching Earth's surface*

Make the Connection

Accessing Health Information For more information about how to access valid health information, see page 20 in Lesson 2.

Reading Review

1. Name four environmental issues.

2. What is the ozone layer?

Painkillers, medicines for heart ailments and arthritis, and drugs used to treat leukemia come from rain forest plants. If these species become extinct, these valuable sources will no longer be available.

Deforestation Some rain forests face reduction by deforestation. Cutting down the trees for the timber or using the land for growing crops can result in *deforestation.* Approximately 12 million hectares are cleared each year. It takes 80–100 years for deforested land to fully regrow.

In some countries, the forests slowly are being cleared for agricultural land. The soil that remains is suitable for agriculture, sometimes only for a short time. Once cleared, the soil may have little agricultural value after the first few years. More land is cleared, and the cycle continues.

Trees absorb carbon dioxide during photosynthesis and release oxygen during respiration. As a result of deforestation, less oxygen is released and less carbon dioxide is absorbed.

Ways Some People Try to Help the Environment

The following are ways individuals help their community's health.

- Save electricity: Using electricity puts gases from fossil fuels into the air.
- Plant trees: Trees absorb carbon dioxide, a greenhouse gas.
- Recycle: Recycling saves natural resources. Using recycled paper means that fewer trees need to be cut down.

- Buy recycled products: Some recycled products are made with less energy than products made from new materials each time.
- Buy products that help the environment: Certain household appliances are built to use less electricity than conventional appliances.

598   UNIT 10 • Environmental Health

Greenhouse effect and global warming On any day, cloudy or rainy, the Sun's radiant energy strikes Earth's surface, warming it up. Some of this energy is emitted back into space, but certain gases in Earth's atmosphere, primarily water vapor, absorb some of this energy, and radiate it back toward Earth's surface.

This emission of radiant energy by gases in Earth's atmosphere is called the *greenhouse effect.* The greenhouse effect helps make Earth warm enough to sustain life. Other gases involved in the greenhouse effect are carbon dioxide and methane.

Data indicate that Earth's average surface temperature has increased by about 1°F over the past 100 years. This increase in Earth's average global temperature is called *global warming.* At the same time Earth's average temperature has increased, the concentration of carbon dioxide in Earth's atmosphere also has increased.

This increase in carbon dioxide is due primarily to the use of fossil fuels as an energy source. Some evidence indicates that global warming might be due to the increase in carbon dioxide in Earth's atmosphere.

Because environmental issues are large issues, it may seem that there is little an individual person can do to contribute to global environmental health. However, small steps taken by many people can have a positive impact on the environment. The list on the left shows ways that some people attempt to improve the environment, including saving electricity, planting trees, recycling, buying recycled products, and buying products that help the environment.

 Family Involvement

Caring for the Environment Conserving energy, recycling, and buying recycled products are activities that can be done as a family to be more effective in helping keep the environment healthy. Have students talk to their families about what they can do to help reduce threats to the health of our environment. Then, with their family members, they can create a list of environmentally friendly actions they currently practice and a list of environmentally friendly actions they would like to practice. The family can set a specific health goal to begin a new habit that is environmentally friendly. To set a health goal, they can use the steps from How to Set Health Goals on page 57 of Lesson 6. **L2**

Staying Informed

There are many ways to stay informed about environmental issues. The media can be a source of environmental information. Environmental agencies and organizations have home pages on the Internet. Radio and TV newscasts and other programs often deal with or focus on environmental issues. Many magazines and journals report on environmental issues.

How to Stay Informed About Environmental Issues

Environmental agencies and organizations Government and some nongovernmental agencies and organizations are reliable sources of information about environmental issues. A number of regulatory agencies have been established to protect the environment and the general public. A *regulatory agency* is an agency that enforces laws to protect the general public. There are international environmental laws and national, state, and local environmental regulatory agencies.

State and local agencies Each state has its own Environmental Protection Agency, which is required to carry out the national environmental regulations within the state. Like the federal EPA, state agencies can fine individuals, companies, or organizations who pollute the environment.

Local environmental agencies On the local level, a public health department is the environmental regulatory agency. County and community public health departments enforce environmental standards and regulations and provide information on the environment.

Federal Agencies that Protect the Environment Some of the federal agencies that monitor and protect the environment in the United States and their functions are explained here. Visit your school or community library for help on researching other agencies that protect the environment.

The Environmental Protection Agency (EPA) reduces and controls environmental pollution. The EPA publishes information on environmental issues and regulations. **The Occupational Safety and Health Administration (OSHA)** oversees safety in the workplace environment, and it sets and enforces standards for a safe and healthy workplace. **The National Institute for Occupational Safety and Health (NIOSH)** conducts research on health hazards in the workplace.

◀ The EPA was created in 1970 to work to protect the environment throughout the United States.

LESSON 56 • Learning About Environmental Issues **599**

Community Involvement

Environmental Advocates Ask students to create a list of questions to ask a member of the community to find out what the local environmental issues are. They can speak with local companies and industries to learn what positive steps businesses have taken to protect the environment and any environmental projects they have planned currently. Or, they can talk to an environmental advocacy group to find out what environmental issues are important in their community and how students can help if they are interested. Have students write the findings of their interviews and share them with the class. **L2**

Class Activity

Environmental Awareness Have students compare the lists they made at the beginning of the lesson about environmental issues, organizations, and laws that protect the environment to those laws outlined in the text. Ask students to evaluate how accurate they were, their level of awareness, and what steps they can take to improve their level of awareness. **L2**

Reading Review

1. an agency that enforces laws to protect the general public
2. a federal act that protects animal and plant species threatened by extinction

3 Assess

Vocabulary Practice

Page 8, **Unit 10 Fast File Resources**

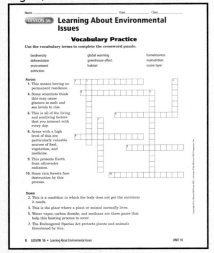

TABLE 56.1   **Federal Acts to Regulate the Environment**

Act	Functions
Clean Air Act	Allows the EPA to set standards for major air pollutants. A ***pollutant*** is any harmful substance released into the environment.
Comprehensive Environmental Response, Compensation, and Liability Act	Provides federal funding to clean up uncontrolled or hazardous waste sites and oil and chemical spills.
Clean Water Act	Sets regulations on wastes going into water and on the operation of waste treatment plants; makes it illegal to release pollutants in rivers, streams, lakes, etc.
Safe Drinking Water Act	Protects the quality of drinking water; sets standards for owners and operators of public water systems.
Endangered Species Act	Protects animal and plant species threatened by extinction; makes it illegal to remove an endangered species from its natural habitat. ***Extinction*** is the death of all members of a species of plant or animal. A ***habitat*** is the place where an animal or plant normally lives.
National Environmental Policy Act	Requires all government agencies to consider and assess the impact on the environment before taking any action that might affect the environment.
Toxic Substances Control Act	Authorizes the EPA to set standards for the manufacture, use, transportation, and disposal of toxic substances.
Occupational Safety and Health Act	Sets a series of minimum safety and health standards that all employers must meet.

Nongovernmental advocates There also are nongovernmental environmental organizations that advocate for the environment, educate the public on environmental issues, and organize projects to improve the environment. Some nongovernmental advocates work to help specific parts of the environment, like local water sources or local air quality. Other groups work to improve the overall environment. Many companies also work to lessen their impact on the environment.

Congress has passed many laws that affect the water you drink, the air you breathe, and the environment you live in. Table 56.1 lists important federal acts that have made the U.S. a healthier place to live.

▲ The timber wolf is one of hundreds of plants and animals protected by the Endangered Species Act.

Reading Review

1. What is a regulatory agency?
2. What is the Endangered Species Act?

ⓓⓘ Differentiated Instruction

Gifted and Talented Have students investigate whether any endangered species, plants, or animals live in the local area. If so, have them choose one and research information about its biology and habitat. Ask students to research these questions: What is the history of the organism in the local area, and what events led to its being endangered? What local laws or regulations are in place to protect the organism? Students can share the results of their research with the class in the form of a multimedia presentation. **L3**

biodiversity
deforestation
environment
extinction
greenhouse effect
global warming
habitat
homelessness
malnutrition
ozone layer
poverty
tropical rain forest

Key Terms Review

Complete these fill-in-the-blank statements with the lesson Key Terms on the left. Do not write in this book.

1. The protective layer of the upper atmosphere is the _____.
2. An animal or plant normally lives in a(n) _____.
3. Cutting down trees to grow crops is _____.
4. Gases in the atmosphere can trap heat, causing the _____.
5. Everything around a person is called the _____.
6. The death of all members of a species of plant or animal is called _____.
7. When people do not get the nutrients they need, they are said to suffer from _____.
8. The increase in the average global temperature is _____.
9. Not having affordable housing can result in _____.
10. The variety of species in an area is _____.

Recalling the Facts

11. What is ozone and how is it different from the oxygen that you breathe?
12. How do chlorofluorocarbons affect the ozone layer?
13. What is the fastest growing group of people who are homeless?
14. What is the environment made up of?
15. What are three federal agencies that regulate the environment?
16. Why is maintaining biodiversity important to human beings?
17. Name three sources of information about the quality of the environment.
18. Describe the greenhouse effect.

Critical Thinking

19. Why can homelessness cause health problems for an individual? For a family?
20. How might the health of an individual be affected by a change in the quality of the environment?
21. Why is the ozone layer important for health?
22. Why can poverty cause health problems for an individual? For a family?

Real-Life Applications

23. Name two things you could do to help the environment?
24. Name three ways you can stay informed about the environment.
25. How is regulation of the environment helpful to your health?
26. What is the importance of the Clean Water Act to your community's health?

Activities

Responsible Decision Making

27. **Write** Your classmate just changed the oil in his car and does not know where to dispose of the old oil. He considers dumping it in the grass. Another classmate suggests throwing it down the sewer drain in the street. You know that doing so would harm the environment. Write a response to this situation. Refer to the Responsible Decision-Making Model on page 61 for help.

Sharpen Your Life Skills

28. **Analyze Influences on Health** Different countries and different parts of the world may have different environmental issues. What are five important environmental issues in the U.S.? Research another country on another continent. What are five important environmental issues in that country? What are five global environmental issues? In each case, state the possible reason(s) for the problems.

Visit **www.glencoe.com** for more *Health & Wellness* quizzes.

LESSON 56 • Study Guide **601**

LESSON 56
STUDY GUIDE

Key Terms Review

1. ozone layer
2. habitat
3. deforestation
4. greenhouse effect
5. environment
6. extinction
7. malnutrition
8. global warming
9. homelessness
10. biodiversity

Recalling the Facts

11. Ozone is made up of three atoms of oxygen; the oxygen we breathe is made up of two atoms.
12. A seasonal ozone reduction over the Antarctic is caused by human-produced chemicals such as CFCs.
13. families
14. everything around you
15. Answers can include the Environmental Protection Agency, Occupational Safety and Health Administration, National Institute for Occupational Safety and Health.
16. Many species of plants and animals provide humans with food, vegetation, and medicine. Loss of these sources could occur if these species become extinct.
17. Web sites from regulatory agencies, radio and TV newscasts, magazines, journals
18. the emission of radiant energy by gases in Earth's atmosphere

Critical Thinking

19. Answers can include malnutrition, poor health care, domestic violence, anxiety, depression.
20. Answers will vary.
21. It protects us from harmful UV rays.
22. See page 595.

Real-Life Applications

23. Answers will vary.
24. See page 599.

---

25. Regulations make sure toxic substances are not put into the air and water to the extent that they would affect health.
26. See page 600.

Activities

Responsible Decision Making

27. Answers should include the fact that the friends choose not to dump the oil into the sewer because it will negatively impact the environment. The oil can be taken to a place that disposes of it safely, such as a gas station.

Sharpen Your Life Skills

28. Answers will vary depending on the countries involved.

601

Out of Time?

If time does not permit an in-depth study of this topic, use the following activities in this Teacher Wraparound Edition:
- Health Goals, p. 602
- Quick Demo, p. 603
- Health Project, p. 605
- Community Involvement, p. 607

1 Focus

HEALTH GOALS **Journaling** Have students respond to the Health Goals for this lesson by brainstorming ways they can help reduce air and water pollution in their local area. Students should record their ideas in their health journals. *Ideas can include walking, taking public transportation, or carpooling, choosing not to smoke, choosing not to dispose of toxic chemicals in waterways.* **L2**

Write ABOUT IT!

Discuss Have students discuss the recreational activities that they listed in their health journals. **L2**

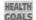 **LESSON**

Preventing Air and Water Pollution

HEALTH GOALS
- **I will help keep the air clean.**
- **I will help keep the water safe.**

Clean air and clean water are important for your health. Clean air helps keep your lungs healthy, and you need to drink clean water every day to stay healthy. This lesson discusses the effects of polluted air and water and what you can do to keep air and water safe.

What You'll Learn
1. Discuss how air pollution affects health. *(p. 603)*
2. Identify sources of air pollution. *(p. 604)*
3. Discuss the effects of indoor air pollution on health. *(p. 605)*
4. Discuss ways to keep the air clean. *(p. 606)*
5. Identify sources of water pollution. *(p. 607)*
6. Discuss how water pollution affects health. *(p. 607)*
7. Outline ways the government works to keep water clean. *(p. 609)*
8. Outline ways to help keep water safe. *(p. 610)*

Why It's Important
Your good health depends on the quality of your environment. Learn what you can do to help keep your environment healthy and thus protect your health.

Key Terms
- atmosphere
- particulates
- fossil fuels
- acid rain
- smog
- runoff
- PCBs
- dioxins
- giardiasis
- dysentery

 Write ABOUT IT!

Writing About Water Pollution Suppose you wanted to use this water for recreational purposes. After you read the information on page 610 about keeping water clean, answer these questions: What recreational activities can you think of that would not pollute this water? What are some recreational activities that would pollute this water? Write a list of each type of activity in your health journal.

602 UNIT 10 • Environmental Health

National Health Education Standards—Guide for Lesson 57		
1.3	Analyze how environment and personal health are interrelated.	pp. 602, 603–605, 607, 608, 610, 611
2.10	Analyze how public health policies and government regulations can influence health promotion and disease prevention.	pp. 602, 603, 606, 609

Air Pollution and Health Status

M any factors contribute to air pollution, which can have many different effects on people's health status. In one area affected by air pollution, some people might experience effects, others might experience no effects, and still others might develop lung ailments that can be deadly years later.

How Air Pollution Affects Health Status

Air quality The quality of the air that people breathe changes depending on the materials that are in Earth's atmosphere. The *atmosphere* is the layer of gases that surrounds Earth. Many kinds of substances are found in air. Natural substances that result from such events as dust storms, forest fires, or erupting volcanoes contribute materials to the atmosphere. Human activity also releases materials into the atmosphere. Burning fuels to provide heat, electric power, and transportation release gases and solid particles. Materials released into the environment that can damage health are pollutants. Air pollution occurs when pollutants are released into the atmosphere.

Air Quality Index The Environmental Protection Agency (EPA) measures air quality in all major cities in the United States daily. The table on this page shows Air Quality Index (AQI) information that is available for ground-level ozone, particulate matter, carbon monoxide, and nitrogen and sulfur dioxides. Some cities have

ozone alerts warning people with respiratory problems to stay indoors when the ozone level is high.

Effect of air quality on health status Air pollution in the form of fine liquid or fine solid particles, called *particulates,* harms health status in different ways. For example, particulates can damage, destroy, or interfere with the action of *cilia,* hairlike structures in the respiratory system that remove dust, pollen, and other particles from the air. This increases the likelihood of respiratory diseases and infections, such as asthma, emphysema, bronchitis, pneumonia and lung cancer.

Air pollution also contributes to heart disease, eye and throat irritation, and a weakened immune system. Even healthy people who exercise and stay fit can become ill in areas where air pollution is concentrated.

The EPA uses the Air Quality Index to indicate how clean the air is and if it will affect people's health ▼ status.

Air Quality Index

Index Values	Descriptors	Colors
0-50	Good	Green
51-100	Moderate	Yellow
101-150	Unhealthy for sensitive groups	Orange
151-200	Unhealthy	Red
201-300	Very unhealthy	Purple
301-500	Hazardous	Maroon

LESSON 57 • Preventing Air and Water Pollution **603**

Quick Demo
Particulate Matter Prior to class, place a coffee filter over the end of a vacuum cleaner attachment. Secure it using a rubber band. Go outside and turn on the vacuum cleaner, allowing the coffee filter to collect particulate matter as air passes through it. Bring the filter into class and allow students to examine it using a magnifying glass to see particulates in the air they breathe. Provide students with a clean coffee filter as a comparison. **ELL**

INTERACTIVE CHALKBOARD
with Image Bank

PowerPoint® Presentations

This CD-ROM is an editable Microsoft® PowerPoint® presentation that includes:
- Lesson presentations
- Lesson checks
- Interactive graphics
- 5-Minute Checks
- Image Bank
- All transparencies

Summarizing Refer to the Read-Recall-Check-Summarize Strategy on page 16T. Have the class read each section on air and water pollution and then brainstorm as a class to see what they recall about each topic. Finally, have students check to see if they were correct before using those notes to write summaries.

National Health Education Standards
Pages 602–603: 1.3, 1.5, 2.10, 6.1, 7.2

Explain the Concept

Environmental Tobacco Smoke (ETS)
In June 2006, the U.S. Surgeon General issued a scientific report concluding that there is no risk-free level of exposure to secondhand smoke. Even brief exposure to ETS can cause immediate harm. Nonsmoking adults exposed to ETS at work or home increase their risk of developing heart disease by 25 to 30 percent and lung cancer by 20 to 30 percent. The health effects of ETS on children can also be deadly. Exposure to ETS is associated with sudden infant death syndrome (SIDS), asthma, bronchitis, pneumonia, and ear infections. Exposure to ETS is responsible for between 150,000 and 300,000 lower respiratory tract infections in children under 18 months and up to 15,000 hospitalizations for respiratory tract infections per year.

NHES Assessment/SCASS

Selected Response According to the Air Quality Index, at what index value of air quality should people with respiratory problems consider staying indoors?

A. yellow and above
B. orange and above
C. red and above
D. maroon

◄ Sunlight, water vapor, and pollution combine to form a brown haze, which is known as smog.

Major Sources of Air Pollution

Fossil fuels Nonrenewable energy sources that formed from plant or animal remains over many millions of years are *fossil fuels.* Coal, oil, and natural gas are fossil fuels. Burning fossil fuels releases carbon monoxide, carbon dioxide, nitrogen oxides, sulfur oxides, and particulates into the atmosphere and is a major source of air pollution.

Carbon monoxide is an odorless, tasteless gas. It is poisonous and reduces the ability of blood to carry oxygen to body cells. *Sulfur oxides* are sulfur-containing chemicals that irritate the nose, throat, and eyes. *Nitrogen oxides* are nitrogen-containing chemicals that appear as a yellow-brown haze in the atmosphere and irritate the respiratory system. When sulfur oxides and nitrogen oxides combine with water vapor, *acid rain* is the result. Some scientists think that acid rain can destroy plants and crops, may change the acidity of water in lakes, can cause fish in these lakes to die, and can damage buildings. Other scientists disagree.

Particulates Soot, ash, dirt, dust, and pollen are particulates. Some particulates travel deep into the lungs.

Did You Know?

Air Pollution Six out of ten people in the United States live in areas with excessive levels of air pollution, according to the Environmental Protection Agency.

This can cause coughing, wheezing, asthma attacks, respiratory infections, bronchitis, and lung cancer.

Smog A combination of smoke and fog is **smog.** In the presence of sunlight, water vapor in the air, motor vehicle emissions, smoke, and particles from factories can combine to form smog.

Smog contains low-level ozone, which forms close to Earth's surface. Low-level ozone is a health hazard. It can irritate the eyes, lungs, and throat and produce headaches, coughing, and shortness of breath. Hot, humid days can result in an ozone alert; people with asthma or other respiratory problems are advised to stay indoors.

Motor vehicle emissions Substances released into the atmosphere by motor vehicles with gasoline or diesel engines are *motor vehicle emissions.* These emissions include carbon monoxide, airborne lead, sulfur oxides, and nitrogen oxides. Inhaling motor vehicle emissions increases the risk of respiratory diseases, including lung cancer, asthma, and bronchitis. Low levels of carbon monoxide can increase chest pain in persons with chronic heart disease.

Indoor air pollution The concentration of pollutants may be even higher indoors because pollutants are trapped. Secondhand smoke, also called environmental tobacco smoke, is exhaled smoke and sidestream smoke. Secondhand smoke has been declared a Group A carcinogen by the EPA because it can cause cancer in humans. Breathing secondhand smoke also increases the risk of respiratory infections and asthma.

🚶 Healthy People 2010

Objective 8-1 *Reduce the proportion of persons exposed to air that does not meet the U.S. Environmental Protection Agency's health-based standards for harmful air pollutants including ozone, particulate matter, carbon monoxide, sulfur dioxide, and lead.*

The 1997 baseline percentages of people exposed to higher than acceptable levels of these pollutants ranged from 43 percent for ozone to less than 1 percent for exposure to lead. In 1997, the number of people in the United States living in areas with unhealthy air was estimated at 120 million. The target for 2010 is to reduce the percentage of people overexposed to each of the pollutants listed above to zero. Have students brainstorm ways to improve the air quality in your community. List their suggestions on the chalkboard. **L2**

Poorly vented wood-burning stoves, gas appliances, kerosene heaters, furnaces, or stoves can emit carbon monoxide and sulfur dioxide. Some of these also emit particulates. This can cause carbon monoxide poisoning, which can be fatal. Symptoms include headaches, nausea, vomiting, fatigue, dizziness, and unconsciousness.

Building materials Building materials can be sources of indoor air pollution. *Formaldehyde,* a colorless gas with a strong odor, traditionally is used as a disinfectant and preservative. Formaldehyde is used in the manufacture of particleboard, plywood, furniture, and other wood products. It also is found in insulation, cosmetics, upholstery, carpets, household appliances, and cigarette smoke. Breathing formaldehyde can cause shortness of breath, coughing, dizziness, throat and eye irritation, headaches, nausea, asthma attacks, and cancer.

Asbestos is a heat-resistant group of minerals that was used as fireproof insulation in many older buildings and homes. Breathing loose asbestos fibers is very dangerous. Asbestos has been linked to lung and gastrointestinal cancer. Its use is now severely restricted.

Radon A naturally occurring odorless, colorless radioactive gas that is released from rocks and soil is *radon.* Radon can enter homes through cracks in the floors and basement walls and through drains and sump pumps. Inhaling radon increases the risk of lung cancer. Radon detectors can detect the presence of radon in a building.

www.glencoe.com

HEALTH NEWS

HEVs and FCVs

Hybrid electric vehicles and fuel cell vehicles, which use sources of energy other than gasoline, are in the news.

A hybrid electric vehicle (HEV) combines a traditional internal combustion engine with an electric motor, allowing for a significant increase in fuel economy. Emissions are reduced by one-third to one-half in HEVs. A fuel cell vehicle (FCV) runs on an electric motor. An FCV creates its own electricity using hydrogen gas and oxygen from the air. When hydrogen and oxygen combine, electricity is generated with only heat and water as byproducts.

Although these vehicles are environmentally beneficial, challenges must be overcome in order for them to become common on our roads. Some of these challenges include the production and storage of hydrogen in the FCVs, the cost of the vehicles, and a method for obtaining alternative fuels.

 For more information on alternative-energy vehicles, visit www.glencoe.com.

Energy Efficiency of Vehicles

FCV
Range: 100 miles
Fuel Economy
100 mpg (equiv.)
Refueling
Plug-in
Environmental friendliness (includes emissions)
Zero emissions
* not including production of hydrogen

Conventional
Range: 350 miles
Fuel Economy
27.5 mpg
Refueling
Fill up
Environmental friendliness (includes emissions)
Base

HEV
Range: 450-500 miles
Fuel Economy
50-70 mpg
Refueling
Fill up less often
Environmental friendliness (includes emissions)
95% cleaner than today's standards

Analyzing the Illustration
Study the graph above and answer these questions:

1. Which car has the largest total range?

2. How is each vehicle powered?

HEALTH NEWS

Analyzing the Illustration
1. Hybrid electric vehicle
2. FCV, electricity; conventional, gasoline; HEV, gasoline and electricity

Project

Class Discussion Ask students what they think vehicles will be like in the future. Do they think one of the three fuel forms presented will be used by everyone or will all three be available in 25 years? **L3**

Explain the Concept

Sick Building Syndrome Sick Building Syndrome (SBS) is a term used to describe occurrences of people reporting acute health effects that seem to be linked to time spent in a building, but no specific illness or cause can be identified. Symptoms may include headache, dizziness, fatigue, throat irritation, and a dry cough. Possible causes of SBS include indoor pollution from chemical contaminants, such as cleaning agents, that emit volatile organic compounds (VOCs); biological contaminants, such as mold; and chemical contaminants from outdoor sources, such as motor vehicle exhaust, which can enter a building through intake vents and windows. A poorly ventilated building only increases the problem.

Health Project

Alternate Vehicles Have students research the availability of hybrid electric vehicles and fuel cell vehicles in your area and answer the following questions: How much do they cost? Is that price more or less expensive than a gasoline-powered vehicle of a similar size? What obstacles exist to keep the cars from being practical for everyday use? What kind of work is necessary to maintain the vehicles properly? If a student knows someone who owns an HEV or FCV, the student can interview this person to get his or her opinion of the car. Have students report their findings to the class. **L2**

National Health Education Standards
Pages 604–605: 1.3, 7.2

Keeping the Air Clean

Everyone on Earth has a responsibility to help keep the air free from pollutants and to protect the atmosphere. There are actions that individuals can take to make a difference. Everyone can do something to improve air quality.

Actions You Can Take to Keep Air Clean

Smoking Don't smoke. If you do smoke, then take steps to quit. Carbon monoxide and other chemicals from cigarette smoke pollute the air.

Driving Avoid driving at high speeds, which uses fuel less efficiently and releases more pollutants into the atmosphere. Drive a motor vehicle that gets good gas mileage. Service your motor vehicle regularly to keep the engine running efficiently. Consider carpooling, using public transportation, walking, or riding a bicycle.

Cleaning up at home You can take steps to reduce indoor air pollution, which is sometimes far greater than outdoor pollution. See Table 57.1 for things that can be done at home.

TABLE 57.1 Ways to Clean the Air at Home

Polluting Agent	Steps to Take
Asbestos	Have your home checked for asbestos dust if your home was built before 1977. If it is in good condition, you can have it sealed. Removal creates more dust.
Radon	Follow directions in a home test kit from a hardware store to check for presence of radon, install a fan to circulate air, seal cracks in the basement floor and walls.
Carbon monoxide (CO)	Install a CO detector. Check all space heaters, furnaces, water heaters, and wood-burning stoves to make sure they are properly vented. Change furnace filters frequently.
Formaldehyde	Seal all wood products.
Cleaning agents and hobby supplies	Limit use of cleaners, paints, wood stains, and glues with strong solvents. Open windows, when possible, to ventilate your home. Use nontoxic glues and paints. Buy only the amounts that you need.
Yard	Do not burn trash or yard waste. Plant trees.

Water Pollution and Health Status

W ater is necessary for life. You would die within a few days if you did not have some source of water. *Water pollution* is contamination of water that causes negative effects on life and health. Water can become contaminated in many ways. Sewage, chemicals, radioactive wastes, and other substances dumped or accidentally spilled directly into or near sources of fresh water can cause contamination.

NO ADMITTANCE. DO NOT ENTER THE WATER. NO SWIMMING, FISHING, WADING THE WATER & LAKE SEDIMENT CONTAIN HAZARDOUS SUBSTANCES.

What to Know About Water Pollution and Health Status

Runoff and groundwater When pollutants, such as chemicals or sewage, are dumped near water sources, they can enter the water source as runoff. *Runoff* is water that runs downslope along Earth's surface. It may run into a body of water, evaporate, or accumulate in puddles. When snow melts, when it rains, or when people water grass or crops, some of the water seeps into the ground and becomes *groundwater.* As the runoff flows, it picks up pollutants from the environment and carries them into water sources.

Toxic chemicals Toxic chemicals are poisonous substances. Many substances that we use daily fall into this category. Waste materials from manufacturing, cleaning agents, paints, and oil are examples of toxic substances that can enter the water source. Sometimes they are illegally dumped into bodies of water and frequently they are carried by runoff. Fish living in polluted water may take in the toxic chemicals and either die or pass them along to other animals. Eating contaminated fish can cause illness or death for both animals and human beings.

PCBs Chemicals called polychlorinated biphenyls, or *PCBs,* were used in many applications, such as electrical equipment, pigments, and carbonless copy paper. Manufacture of PCBs stopped in the late 1970s when it was found that they had substantial health risks. PCBs build up in the environment and can be released as a result of improper disposal of industrial wastes. They can get into the food chain and be consumed by humans.

In the body, PCBs collect in fatty tissues and in the liver. The most common results of excessive PCB exposure are skin rashes and acne-like conditions. People who consume PCBs are at risk for having children with birth defects, reproductive disorders, and liver and kidney damage.

Did You Know?

Bottle vs. Tap Consumers may not know that the FDA standards for bottled water are almost identical to the standards for tap water.

Water Pollution and Health Status

Class Discussion

Local Water Life Ask students what life can be found in local bodies of water. List their answers on the chalkboard, then lead a discussion about how water pollution might affect these species. **L2**

Teacher FYI

Contaminated Fish Certain chemicals that enter water can be accumulated by bottom-dwelling animals and passed up the food chain to fish. In some areas, toxins including mercury, PCBs, dioxins, and DDT can be found at higher than safe levels in top predators such as largemouth bass and walleye. The National Listing of Fish and Wildlife Advisories (NLFWA) contains information about fish consumption advisories that are issued by local governments. The advisories warn the public when contaminant levels are unsafe and of the health risks involved in eating contaminated fish.

Community Involvement

Water Quality Have students contact the local public utilities or water department and obtain a report on the water quality of the drinking water provided to the area. The report should explain what each measurement means and show that it meets a minimum standard set by a regulatory agency. Ask students to research these questions: Where is the water source for the area? What treatment does drinking water receive before reaching consumers? How long does the process take to go from wastewater to drinkable water? **L3**

National Health Education Standards

Pages 606–607: 1.3, 1.5, 2.10, 6.1, 7.1

Make the Connection

Water You can learn how important water is to your daily diet by reviewing page 289 in Lesson 25.

Reading Review

1. What is the Air Quality Index?
2. What substances make up motor vehicle emissions?
3. Name three ways to keep air clean.
4. What are PCBs?

Eating contaminated fish can ▶ cause illness or death.

Dioxins A group of chemicals used in insecticides are *dioxins.* Forest fires and volcanic eruptions produce small amounts of dioxins naturally. Paper mills also produce dioxins as a result of bleaching pulp and paper. Dioxins often are found in fish that live downstream from paper mills. People who eat these fish can become ill.

Lead Lead can enter a home in several ways. Old lead pipes can put it into the water supply, and older car emissions can put lead into the air. A major source of lead poisoning in the United States is house paint. Even though lead is no longer used in house paint, old lead paint is still on the walls in millions of homes. Lead can affect most body systems. Lead damages nerve cells, the kidneys, and the immune system.

Fertilizers When fertilizers enter natural waterways, they deposit nutrients in the water. The build-up of nutrients causes an overgrowth of algae and other plant life. The plants use up oxygen in the water as they decompose. As a result, some of the animal life in natural bodies of water dies.

Trihalomethanes Throughout the world, small amounts of chlorine are added to water supplies to prevent the growth of organisms that cause cholera, typhoid, and dysentery. The addition of chlorine kills these organisms and has saved the lives of millions of people. However, when water that contains natural organic substances is disinfected with chlorine, byproducts, such as chloroform, are produced. Trihalomethanes are four harmful chemicals that are produced when chlorine attacks pollutants in water. Trihalomethanes are linked to an increased risk of bladder and colorectal cancers, birth defects, and disorders of the central nervous system.

Microorganisms Microorganisms, such as parasites and bacteria, enter water supplies where sewage is not properly treated. The improper operation of a septic tank or the failure of a waste treatment plant to properly treat sewage can be the source of microorganism contamination. Microorganism contamination can cause illness.

A microorganism that occasionally gets into water systems is *Giardia lamblia,* which is a parasite that lives in the intestines and causes *giardiasis* (jee ahr DI uh suhs), which is a stomach and intestinal infection that causes abdominal cramps, nausea, gas, and diarrhea. There are several organisms that can cause *dysentery.* This is a severe infection of the intestines that causes diarrhea and abdominal pain.

Millions of people in countries without clean water supplies become sick each year from microorganisms. In many industrialized countries, the public is alerted at once if the water supply is found to contain microorganisms. Beaches may be closed and people may be advised to boil water to eliminate microorganisms before they drink it.

608   UNIT 10 • Environmental Health

 Health Project

Water Usage Ask students to record water usage in their homes for two weeks. Have each student create a chart comparing their family's water usage to the national averages from the U.S. Department of the Interior listed below. Ask students how much less water they think would be used if they implemented water conservation strategies in their homes. **L2** **ELL**

Bath: 50 gallons
Shower: 2 gallons per minute
Brushing teeth: 1 gallon
Washing hands/face: 1 gallon
Shaving face/legs: 1 gallon

Dishwasher: 20 gallons/load
Washing dishes by hand: 5 gallons/load
Washing clothes (machine): 10 gallons/load
Flushing toilet : 3 gallons
Drinking water: 8 oz per glass (one-sixteenth of a gallon)

Keeping the Water Clean

M any organizations—from local agencies to international agreements—work to keep the water clean. Some groups monitor wastewater treatment plants; others make sure laws are followed. You, too, can help keep the water in your home and in your community safe, which is an important factor for maintaining a good health status.

What to Know About Keeping the Water Clean

EPA regulations Steps have been taken to reduce water pollution. The Environmental Protection Agency (EPA) requires public suppliers to notify people if water does not meet safety standards.

The *Clean Water Act* (CWA) is a law that regulates wastewater and operation of wastewater treatment plants. This act makes it illegal to release pollutants into the water.

The *Safe Drinking Water Act* (SDWA) is a law that protects the quality of drinking water. This law sets standards for owners and operators of public water systems.

Monitoring water quality at home Water from a faucet might be contaminated if it has an unusual odor or an orange, red, or brown appearance. Contact the local public health department or water company to have it tested. Until you are assured it is safe, drink bottled water. Water treatment systems, such as water filters, are available. Research the various systems to see which works best before purchasing one.

Outdoor water safety hazards Water from streams or ponds might look, smell, and taste clean. However, this water might be contaminated. Do not drink water of unknown safety. Carry your own bottled water or boil water for 10 minutes before using it for drinking or cooking.

Lakes and reservoirs supply 70 percent of the drinking water consumed in the United States, according to the Environmental
▼ Protection Agency.

Explain the Concept

Preventing Water Pollution The EPA recommends taking the following actions to help reduce the amount of pollution reaching water:

- Use fertilizers sparingly.
- Have septic tanks pumped and inspected regularly.
- Reuse or mulch disturbed soil.
- Do not dump waste materials or chemicals down storm drains.
- Clean up chemical spills properly.
- Minimize pesticide use.
- Direct roof drains away from paved surfaces and bare soil.
- Wash your car at a carwash rather than in the driveway.
- Check your car for leaks and recycle motor oil.
- Pick up after your pet.

Class Activity

Water Testing Simple, inexpensive water quality test kits with test strips can be ordered from a biological supply company. Most kits test for chlorine, water hardness, alkalinity, and pH. Have students bring in samples of tap water, well water, or rain water to test. **L2**

DI Differentiated Instruction

Visual Impairment Arrange for a telephone interview between a student with visual impairment and the director of the local water-treatment plant. Have the student find out the source of the local water supply, the major pollutants encountered, how the water is treated, and any other questions the student would like answered. The student with visual impairment may wish to conduct the interview on a speaker phone so that an unimpaired student can take notes that will help in formulating a final oral report. **L2**

National Health Education Standards
Pages 608–609: 1.3, 2.10, 7.2

609

Actions You Can Take to Keep the Water Clean

You might think that personal habits and activities have little effect on the quality of the water. However, each person has a great influence on the quality of the water that is available where he or she lives. The following are ways to help keep the water safe and to keep yourself and others healthy.

Detergents Consider using phosphate-free detergents and biodegradable soaps and shampoos. A *biodegradable product* is a product that can be broken down by living organisms into harmless and reusable materials.

Get the lead out. Let water run until it is cold (30 seconds to two minutes) when getting water to cook with or drink. Drink and cook with water from the cold water tap only, because hot water is likely to contain higher levels of lead than cold water.

Actions That Contaminate Water

The following are ways to avoid contaminating water:

- Do not pour toxic chemicals, such as paints and solvents, down the drain or in the toilet. Dispose of them at a hazardous waste collection center.
- Do not pour toxic chemicals on the ground. These substances can contaminate groundwater supplies in water runoff.
- Do not dump garbage or toxic chemicals into lakes, streams, rivers, ponds, storm sewers, or ditches.
- Do not dispose of plastics, such as plastic cups and bags, in waterways. Many birds tend to eat plastic, which fills their stomachs. These birds won't eat nutritious food if they feel full.

610 UNIT 10 • Environmental Health

Septic tanks If you have a septic system, have the septic tank serviced and pumped out once a year.

Landscape to conserve water. Plant trees and shrubs to discourage water runoff and soil erosion. Choose plants that are best suited for the geographic area you live in. Select yard plants that need little or no fertilizer.

Compost Practice conservation of resources. Consider converting yard trimmings into compost. As plant materials decay, they can be used as a soil conditioner, releasing nutrients gradually into the soil. Composting will decrease the need for fertilizer.

When water problems occur If the water looks discolored or smells strange, call your local health department or water company to report a possible problem. Then follow their recommendations in regards to its safety and what you may need to do to treat it.

Support actions for clean water. Support community efforts to clean rivers, lakes, and streams and to preserve wetlands.

Test if you suspect contamination. Test drinking water for lead contamination if the presence of lead is suspected. Leaving lead in the system has too many negative health implications for you and for the health of others.

Be prepared. You may want to keep several gallons of bottled water on hand in case water in your area becomes contaminated. That way, you can have enough water to drink, cook, and wash dishes with until the problem is corrected.

LESSON 57 STUDY GUIDE

Key Terms Review

Complete these fill-in-the-blank statements with the lesson Key Terms on the left. Do not write in this book.

acid rain
atmosphere
dioxins
dysentery
fossil fuels
giardiasis
groundwater
particulates
PCBs
radon
runoff
smog

1. _____ were used to manufacture pigments.
2. An infection of the intestines that causes nausea and diarrhea is called _____.
3. Fuels that are formed by animal remains are called _____.
4. Smoke plus fog is _____.
5. Chemicals that are used in insecticides are called _____.
6. The _____ is the layer of gases that surrounds the Earth.
7. A gas emitted by rocks is called _____.
8. A severe infection causing abdominal pain is _____.
9. Rain that has a high acid content is called _____.
10. Tiny particles in the air are called _____.

Recalling the Facts

11. Name three ways people can improve to air quality.
12. Discuss how air pollution affects your health.
13. List sources of air pollution.
14. Name two alternatives to gas-powered cars and explain how they affect the air quality.
15. What habits can drivers change to benefit the environment?
16. How do waste materials get into our lakes and rivers?
17. What is the relationship between household chores and air pollution?
18. Identify sources of water pollution.

Critical Thinking

19. What is the relationship between damaged cilia and getting sick?
20. Why should people think twice about exercising in polluted air?
21. Why might a person not know if he or she is inhaling carbon monoxide?
22. Why should cracked walls in a basement be repaired?

Real-Life Applications

23. How does the Air Quality Index help protect you?
24. How does keeping your motor vehicles well-maintained affect air quality?
25. If you heard a smog alert on the news, what would you do?
26. Why do you think people dump hazardous materials into streams and lakes?

Activities

Responsible Decision Making

27. **Role-Play** You are mountain biking with a friend and you both become very thirsty. You stop for water. Your friend dips his or her canteen in a stream that looks clear and clean and takes a drink. Your friend offers you a drink from the canteen. Should you drink the water? Refer to the Responsible Decision-Making Model on page 61 for help. Then, with a classmate, role-play how you would respond to your friend's offer.

Sharpen Your Life Skills

28. **Access Health Services** Research health agencies that help keep air and water clean. You can obtain assistance with your research at your school or community library. Make a directory of the agencies. Identify the name of the agency, its address, phone number, and Web site, and what this agency does to help keep the environment clean. Contact several of the agencies and ask them to send you information about their services and activities. Share the information with your classmates.

Visit **www.glencoe.com** for more *Health & Wellness* quizzes.

LESSON 57 STUDY GUIDE

Key Terms Review

1. PCBs
2. giardiasis
3. fossil fuels
4. smog
5. dioxins
6. atmosphere
7. radon
8. dysentery
9. acid rain
10. particulates

Recalling the Facts

11. Answers might include: do not smoke, carpool, limit use of cleaners.
12. Answers can include eye and throat irritation, lung ailments, and heart disease.
13. fossil fuels, particulates, smog, motor vehicle emissions, indoor air pollution, building materials, and radon
14. Hybrid electric and fuel cell vehicles. The hybrid electric vehicle gets better gas mileage than a fuel-powered car. The fuel cell vehicle emits no air pollutants.
15. Answers can include carpooling, keeping cars well maintained.
16. intentional or accidental dumping of waste; contaminates, runoff, and groundwater
17. Some household cleaners can contribute to air pollution.
18. See pages 607–608.

Critical Thinking

19. Damaged cilia can allow harmful substances to get into the lungs and cause illness.
20. Polluted air can make them ill.
21. It is odorless and colorless.
22. Radon can enter the home through cracks in basement walls.

Real-Life Applications

23. The AQI can help people decide whether to stay indoors or go outside.
24. It will put fewer pollutants into the air, and it will get better gas mileage.
25. People with respiratory problems or allergies should stay indoors; avoid exercising outdoors.

26. Answers can include to avoid paying to have them disposed of properly or to hide the fact that they create or use the materials.

Activities

Responsible Decision Making

27. Do not drink the water since you do not know if the water is contaminated.

Sharpen Your Life Skills

28. Check that student includes the name of the agency, their address, phone number, and Web site, and what this agency does to help keep the environment clean.

Preventing Noise and Visual Pollution

 Out of Time?

If time does not permit an in-depth study of this topic, use the following activities in this Teacher Wraparound Edition:

- Teacher FYI, p. 613
- Quick Demo, p. 614
- Community Involvement, p. 615

1 Focus

HEALTH GOALS **Journaling** Have students respond to the first Health Goal for this lesson by making a list of instances of noise and visual pollution they encounter in a day. Ask students how these types of pollution can adversely affect a person's health. *Lists may include noise from construction, radios, jet planes, or automobiles; graffiti, litter, and billboards or other signs. Exposure to loud noises can lead to hearing loss, visual pollution may affect a person's emotional health.* **L2**

Discuss Ask students why they think people paint graffiti onto buildings and if they have ideas on how to discourage them from doing this. **L2**

Preventing Noise and Visual Pollution

HEALTH GOALS
- **I will help keep noise at a safe level.**
- **I will help improve the visual environment.**

Sound can be a source of relaxation, but it also can be a source of discomfort and annoyance. *Noise* is sound that produces discomfort or annoyance. Noise can cause health problems and is an environmental pollutant. Another sense, sight, also can be made pleasant or annoying. As with noise, environments also can be visually polluted. This lesson will help you evaluate your surroundings as they relate to noise and visual pollution.

What You'll Learn

1. Explain how sound affects health status. *(p. 613)*
2. Discuss ways to keep noise at a safe level. *(p. 614)*
3. Evaluate ways negative and positive visual environments might influence health status. *(p. 615)*
4. Evaluate ways to improve the visual environment. *(p. 616)*

Why It's Important

You will learn how sound and visual factors in your environment affect health. You also will learn how a healthful environment can help you maintain good health.

Key Terms

- noise
- sound waves
- pitch
- loudness
- decibel
- noise pollution
- tinnitus
- visual environment
- graffiti
- visual pollution

Writing About Visual Pollution These teens are helping to keep their environment visually appealing. Suppose you noticed someone scrawling graffiti on a school wall. What could you do? After reading the information about improving the visual environment on page 616, write your ideas in your health journal.

National Health Education Standards—Guide for Lesson 58		
1.3	Analyze how environment and personal health are interrelated.	pp. 612, 613–615, 617
7.2	Demonstrate a variety of healthy practices and behaviors that will maintain or improve the health of self and others.	pp. 612, 614, 615, 617
8.3	Work cooperatively as an advocate for improving personal, family, and community health.	p. 616

Sound and Health Status

T hink about a time you heard an unexpected, loud, or frightening sound. Maybe your heart started to beat faster. Did you feel frozen in your tracks? Maybe you wanted to be able to shout for help and found you couldn't make a sound. These sounds can be unnerving. Other sounds, like ocean waves or quiet music, can make you feel relaxed and peaceful. Sounds sometimes are taken for granted, but they can affect health.

How Sound Affects Health Status

Sound waves The sounds people hear, whether they are the coos of a baby or the roar of machinery, are the result of sound waves. **Sound waves** are regular vibrations of air. When a drum is struck, the drum head vibrates, or moves up and down. The vibrations create sound waves that move away from their source, eventually reaching and vibrating people's eardrums.

Pitch and loudness Vibrations can produce sound waves that have different frequencies, or pitches. **Pitch** is how high or low a sound is.

Humans can hear sounds with frequencies between about 20–20,000 cycles per second. Some animals can hear sounds with higher or lower frequencies. Dogs, for example, can hear high-pitched sounds with frequencies as high as 45,000 cycles per second, while elephants and cows can hear sounds with frequencies as low as 16 cycles per second.

Sounds have different intensities. This means that they carry different amounts of energy. **Loudness** is related to the intensity of sound.

Decibels A unit used to measure the loudness or intensity of specific sounds is a *decibel* (dB). The chart on this page shows the average loudness of sounds that you may be exposed to. Sounds that measure more than 70 dBs are considered noise pollution.

Did You Know?

Double Duty In addition to helping with air pollution, trees can help with noise pollution, too. The branches and leaves absorb sound waves.

Noises That Can Cause Permanent Hearing Loss After Eight Hours		Noises That Can Cause Immediate and Permanent Hearing Loss	
Sound	**dBs**	**Sound**	**dBs**
Vacuum cleaner	85	Jackhammer (3 ft away)	120
Power lawn mower	85	Earphones on loud	125
City traffic	90	Concert	130
Motorcycle	90	Rivet gun	130
Garbage truck	100	Jet engine (100 ft away)	135
Chain saw	100	Air-raid siren	140
Car horn	110	Gunshot	140
Stereo bass in car	115	Rocket launch site	180

Source: Adapted from Association of Hearing Aid Audiologists

---

2 Teach

Teacher FYI

Hearing Loss Approximately 30 million Americans have impaired hearing. Hearing loss due to acoustic trauma is a form of sensory hearing loss in which damage to the mechanisms of hearing in the inner ear occurs. At first, patients may experience tinnitus or begin to notice they have trouble hearing people talk in crowded, noisy places. There is no treatment that can completely restore hearing that has been damaged as a result of acoustic trauma.

INTERACTIVE CHALKBOARD with Image Bank

PowerPoint® Presentations

This CD-ROM is an editable Microsoft® PowerPoint® presentation that includes:
- Lesson presentations
- Lesson checks
- Interactive graphics
- 5-Minute Checks
- Image Bank
- All transparencies

Discussion Refer to the Think-Pair-Share Strategy on page 17T. After students have read the lesson, ask them to think about what they have read about noise and visual pollution, pair up to share that information, and then get involved in whole-class discussion.

Lesson Resource Manager

- **Unit 10 Fast File Resources**
  Reading Strategy, p. 31
  Vocabulary Practice, p. 32
  Transparency Master and Worksheet, p. 33
  Real-Life Health, p. 35
  Real-Life Health, p. 37
  5-Minute Check, p. 39
  Lesson 58 Quiz, p. 40
- **Unit 10 Transparency**
- **Lesson 58 Transparency**

- **Reading Essentials**
- **Technology**
  TeacherWorks™ CD-ROM
  StudentWorks™ CD-ROM
  Reading Essentials CD-ROM
  Exam*View*® Assessment Suite
  Vocabulary Puzzlemaker

National Health Education Standards
Pages 612–613: 1.3, 6.1, 7.2

613

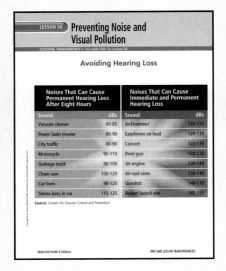
Activity: Using Life Skills

Practicing Healthful Behaviors: Avoiding Noise Pollution

To practice healthful behaviors to reduce health risks, you can make a health behavior contract: 1) Write your name and the date. 2) Write the healthful behavior you want to practice as a health goal. 3) Write specific statements that describe how this healthful behavior reduces health risks. 4) Make a specific plan for recording your progress. 5) Complete an evaluation of how the plan helped you accomplish the health goal.

1 Listen to the radio, television, CD player, and video games at safe levels. If you can't have a normal conversation with these devices on, they are too loud.

2 Keep the volume in your headphones at a safe level. If other people can hear the sounds from your headphones when you are wearing them, the volume is turned up to the point that it can damage your hearing.

3 Wear protective earplugs when you go to concerts and movies. Earplugs are inexpensive and small. People won't notice them.

4 Wear ear protection when outside with snow blowers, leaf blowers, or lawn mowers, or when riding a motorcycle, a jet ski, or a snowmobile.

5 If someone is causing noise pollution and you feel safe doing so, politely ask him or her to stop. If someone asks you to turn down the volume, be respectful of the request.

▲ Noise levels above 120 dBs can cause immediate and permanent hearing damage.

Noise Pollution

Noise Sound that is loud or constant and causes hearing loss, stress, fatigue, irritability, and tension is noise. ***Noise pollution*** is annoying or harmful noise. Noise is a pollutant because it can adversely affect health status. The body responds to noise as a threat and goes through the general adaptation syndrome (GAS).

Prolonged noise pollution can cause ulcers, headaches, high blood pressure, and hearing loss.

Noise pollution also can cause accidents by interfering with concentration.

Acoustic trauma According to the Occupational Safety and Health Administration (OSHA), daily exposure of eight hours or more to noise levels averaging over 85 dBs will result in hearing loss. Noise below 85 dBs also can damage hearing, but it will take longer. Noise above 120 dBs can cause immediate and permanent hearing damage. An ***acoustic trauma*** is an immediate and permanent loss of hearing caused by a short, intense sound.

Exposure to loud noises may cause a threshold shift. ***Temporary threshold shift (TTS)*** is a protective measure that goes into effect in the ear when exposed to loud noises for limited periods of time. Noise-induced ***permanent threshold shift*** is a permanent loss of ability to hear certain ranges. People's hearing becomes muffled, and tinnitus may develop.

Tinnitus (TI nuh tuhs) is a ringing or buzzing sensation in the ears. Tinnitus can affect concentration and ability to sleep, and it can be a source of frustration.

Make the Connection

GAS For more information about general adaptation syndrome, see page 100 in Lesson 10.

614 UNIT 10 • Environmental Health

⚖️ **Legal Issues**

Hearing Protection and the Workplace The Occupational Safety and Health Administration (OSHA) requires that noisy workplaces have hearing conservation programs. This includes having a yearly hearing test for employees exposed to an average of 85 decibels or more of noise during an eight-hour workday. Nearly 5 million employees fall into this category. Individual hearing protectors are required when noise levels are higher than 90 decibels during an eight-hour workday. These hearing protectors, either earplugs or earmuffs, must be provided by the employer at no cost to employees.

The Visual Environment

Are you ever affected by the sights around you? Your *visual environment,* which is everything that you can see, can play an important role in how you feel and function. If your surroundings are pleasant and clean, you can generally feel happy and are more productive. If your surroundings are cluttered, dirty, or disorganized, you can feel stressed and distracted.

What to Know About the Visual Environment

Positive visual environment Do you live in a positive visual environment? A positive visual environment exists when the environment is visually appealing to you. Suppose you are outdoors. You look around and see buildings that are well cared for and a community park with flowers. This is a positive visual environment.

Negative visual environment What if you look around and see graffiti and litter collecting along the curb? *Graffiti* is writing or drawings that deface public surfaces, without permission of the owner. Although public works of art can be very pleasing, most graffiti and trash make up a negative visual environment. A negative visual environment contains visual pollution. *Visual pollution* for many communities includes uncut weeds, litter, graffiti, and badly cared-for buildings. It also can include unregulated placement of billboards, lighted signs, telephone and utility poles, and abandoned buildings.

Your visual environment includes your indoor surroundings as well. A positive indoor visual environment might be a room that is clean, neat, attractive, and free of clutter. Visual pollution in an indoor environment might include an overflowing trash can and dirty laundry scattered around the floor.

Effects on health A positive visual environment can greatly improve your health. It can improve your mood, motivate you, relieve stress, and improve your social health.

For example, the sight of an attractive painting or a sunrise can be energizing. The sight of a clean desk and a neat room can help people feel motivated. People are better able to focus and concentrate when they are not distracted by visual pollution.

Did you know that you are part of the visual environment, too? Making sure that you are well-groomed and have a clean and healthful appearance can improve social health. It shows others that you care for yourself and have self-respect.

Overall, a positive visual environment contributes to quality of life.

Did You Know?

Color Scientists who study color found that it even affects the way you think something tastes.

Reading Review

1. What is a sound wave?
2. How can someone avoid noise pollution?
3. How does the visual environment affect health?

LESSON 58 • Preventing Noise and Visual Pollution **615**

The Visual Environment

5-Minute Check

Page 39, **Unit 10 Fast File Resources**
1. What is noise pollution? List three examples of noise pollution. *Noise pollution is any harmful or annoying noise. Examples include loud noise from televisions, radios, video games, or headphones.*
2. What is acoustic trauma? *an immediate and permanent loss of hearing caused by a short, intense sound*
3. Why is it important to avoid noise pollution? *Noise pollution can cause ulcers, headaches, high blood pressure, accidents and hearing loss.*
4. List three examples of visual pollution. *weeds, litter, graffiti; see page 615 for more examples*
5. How can visual pollution adversely affect your health status? *If your surroundings are cluttered, dirty, or disorganized, you can feel stressed or distracted.*

Reading Review

1. *regular vibrations of air*
2. *See steps in Activity: Using Life Skills on page 614.*
3. *A positive visual environment can improve mood, motivate, relieve stress, or improve social health. A negative visual environment can cause stress.*

Community Involvement

Organize a Cleanup Have students evaluate their community for visual pollution. Have students categorize the types of visual pollution into groups such as weeds, litter, billboards and signs, graffiti, and abandoned buildings. Ask students: Does the community need a cleanup? How could they organize a cleanup? What can be done to remove weeds and litter from an area? What can be done to remove graffiti from an area? What organizations could they contact to have billboards or neon signs removed? Have students brainstorm solutions to rid their communities of visual pollution. **L2**

National Health Education Standards

Pages 614–615: 1.1, 1.2, 1.3, 4.4, 7.2

NHES Assessment/SCASS

Performance Event Have students identify and record in their health journals areas around the school that could be improved visually. Ask students how, specifically, these areas could be improved and what actions can be taken to make this happen. *Students may write a letter to or meet with administration officials, they may want to form a group to oversee a project, or they may want to have a fundraiser to support any costs involved in a cleanup.*
L2

3 Assess

Vocabulary Practice
Page 32, **Unit 10 Fast File Resources**

Look around your visual environment. It is likely that you will see things that could be improved. Improving your visual environment could be as simple as cleaning your room, or it could involve picking up litter in a park.

How to Improve the Visual Environment

> **E** **Make the Connection**
>
> **Advocate** For more information about the importance of being an advocate for your community, see page 65 in Lesson 7.

You may not think you have much control over your visual environment, but you do—especially in your room, around your house, and in your neighborhood. If you have bad habits, such as littering, start by making the effort to find a trash can instead of throwing your trash on the ground. Then, work on developing good habits to keep your visual environment pleasant. This table presents a list of some things you can do to improve your surroundings. Not only will you appreciate the results of your effort, so will other people in your community who notice what you are doing. Your actions may encourage them to join you in keeping your community clean.

TABLE 58.1 Ways to Improve the Visual Environment

The Problem	The Action
Clutter and litter	Organize belongings so that they are stored neatly. Keep an area free of clutter in which to work on projects. Throw litter into a trash container wherever you are.
Atmosphere and color	Add a plant or an aquarium to your room or home. Plants add color and can improve the air you breathe. Consider painting the walls in your room. (Bright red, yellow, and orange have an energizing effect. Blues and greens have a relaxing effect.) Hang photographs or prints to break up large, bare wall areas or areas where a wall might be damaged.
The view outside	Hang a plant or a bird feeder outside your window. Plant a garden. Keep the yard, no matter how small, uncluttered and mowed.
Community or neighborhood cleanup	Organize a clean-up campaign. Many groups sponsor community clean-up campaigns in which teens can participate. Plant trees and flowers. Do yard work that older citizens might not be able to handle anymore.

(DI) Differentiated Instruction

Gifted and Talented Have students who need an additional challenge research problems associated with light pollution. Light pollution is considered by some people to be a growing problem. Bright lights from stores, parking lots, and street lamps that stay on all night can interfere with seeing a starry sky at night. They may also be costly and inefficiently use energy, depending on the type of light. Have students share the results of their research, as well as some solutions, with the class.   **L3**

acoustic trauma
decibel
graffiti
loudness
noise
noise pollution
permanent
  threshold shift
pitch
sound waves
tinnitus
visual environment
visual pollution

Key Terms Review

Complete these fill-in-the-blank statements with the lesson Key Terms on the left. Do not write in this book.

1. Drawings on a public surface are called _____.

2. A sound that causes tension is _____.

3. The loudness or intensity of sound is measured per _____.

4. Unattractive sights are called _____.

5. A ringing sensation in the ear is called _____.

6. Everything that you can regularly see is your _____.

7. The highness or lowness of a sound is its _____.

8. Annoying or harmful noise that can adversely affect health status is called _____.

9. Regular vibrations of air are called _____.

10. _____ is related to the intensity of sound.

Recalling the Facts

11. Why should people avoid sitting in the front row of a rock concert?

12. How does sound travel from an object or a person to one's ears?

13. Daily exposure of eight hours or more to noise at what level (in dB) will result in hearing loss?

14. What is the relationship between noise and health? What kinds of health problems can noise pollution cause?

15. What is the relationship between visual environment and health?

16. What protective measure goes into effect in the ears when exposed to loud noise for a limited period of time?

17. What is a health-conscious rule of thumb to follow when listening to the radio, television, CD players, and video games?

18. At what decibel level does sound become noise pollution?

Critical Thinking

19. Why do you think some students like to listen to loud music?

20. Why would a person who has tinnitus have difficulty studying?

21. What is the relationship between color and how you feel?

22. How can a neighborhood with high visual pollution change?

Real-Life Applications

23. What can you do to your house to improve your visual environment?

24. How has visual pollution affected you?

25. How can you limit noise pollution in your life?

26. If a friend showed you graffiti that he or she made, what would you do?

Activities

Responsible Decision Making

27. **Write** Your friends invite you to join them at a concert. Your parents or guardian insist that you wear earplugs. You take the earplugs with you to the concert. However, you are nervous about using them because you think your friends will make fun of you. Write a response to this situation. Use the Responsible Decision-Making Model on p. 61 for help.

Sharpen Your Life Skills

28. **Practice Healthful Behaviors**
Identify a visual pollution problem in your community. Write a plan to improve or correct the situation. Obtain permission from a parent or guardian, from your teacher, and if necessary, from the local government to present the plan to the appropriate people. Ask classmates to help. Take before and after photographs of the project.

Visit www.glencoe.com for more *Health & Wellness* quizzes.

LESSON 58 • Study Guide 617

Key Terms Review

1. graffiti
2. noise
3. decibel
4. visual pollution
5. tinnitus
6. visual environment
7. pitch
8. noise pollution
9. sound waves
10. Loudness

Recalling the Facts

11. The speakers are loud enough to damage the ear quickly.
12. sound waves
13. over 90 decibels
14. Noise can cause tension, hearing loss, headaches, ulcers, and high blood pressure.
15. Positive visual environments can decrease stress, motivate people, and improve moods. Negative visual environments can cause stress and negatively affect moods.
16. temporary threshold shift
17. It is too loud if you cannot hold a conversation with the device on.
18. more than 70 decibels

Critical Thinking

19. Answers will vary.
20. Tinnitus can affect a person's ability to concentrate, which would affect studying.
21. Certain colors can elevate your mood.
22. Neighbors can work to clean up the area to improve the visual environment.

Real-Life Applications

23. Answers will vary, but can include planting flowers, cleaning, decorating.

24. Answers will vary, but can include affected the student's mood or encouraged them to litter.
25. Answers will vary, but can include listening to headphones at a safe level.
26. Students can use the Responsible Decision-Making Model to help them decide to report the problem to an adult.

Activities

Responsible Decision Making

27. Role-play responses will vary but should include the effects of not wearing earplugs at the concert.

Sharpen Your Life Skills

28. Plans can include cleaning up litter or painting over graffiti.

LESSON 59

Practicing Recycling and Conservation

Out of Time?

If time does not permit an in-depth study of this topic, use the following activities in this Teacher Wraparound Edition:

• Class Activity, p. 620
• Quick Demo, p. 622
• Health Project, p. 623

1 Focus

HEALTH GOALS **Conserve Energy and Natural Resources** Have students respond to the first Health Goal for this lesson by listing reasons why it is a good idea to conserve energy and natural resources. *Reasons might include save money, save natural resources, and preserve the environment.* **L2**

Write ABOUT IT!

Answers Students' responses might include: Tell your friend that he should not throw trash into the recycling bin since it is not a recyclable material. Instead, your friend should find a trash can to dispose of the waste properly. **L1**

LESSON 59

Practicing Recycling and Conservation

HEALTH GOALS
• I will conserve energy and natural resources.
• I will help reduce and dispose of waste.

For each person in the United States, about five pounds of solid waste are thrown away each day. Discarded materials such as paper, metals, or plastic are *solid waste*. Most solid waste is dumped in layers and buried in *landfills*. The saving of resources including natural resources is *conservation*. Anything obtained from the natural environment to meet people's needs is a *natural resource*.

What You'll Learn

1. Evaluate sources of energy. *(p. 619)*
2. Practice ways to conserve energy. *(p. 620)*
3. Practice ways to conserve water. *(p. 621)*
4. Describe ways to recycle. *(p. 622)*
5. Describe ways to dispose of waste. *(p. 624)*

Why It's Important

The Earth needs to be protected. You can play a role in helping to make the environment a better place in which to live. This lesson provides you with ways to protect and preserve the environment.

Key Terms

• landfills
• conservation
• nuclear reactor
• solar energy
• geothermal energy
• hydrogen power
• precycling
• leachate
• incinerator
• composting

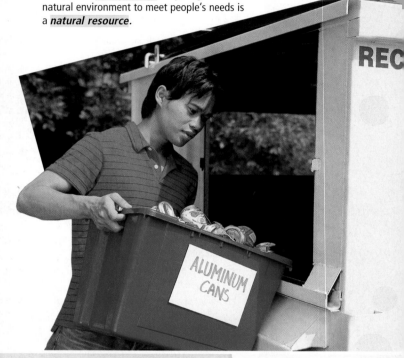

Write ABOUT IT!

Writing About Recycling Suppose that you are walking by a recycling bin in your neighborhood with some friends. One of your friends is eating a bag of potato chips. He decides he is done with the chips and says he is going to throw them in the recycling bin. After you read the information about recycling on page 622, write an entry in your health journal about why you would tell your friend not to throw the chips in the bin.

National Health Education Standards—Guide for Lesson 59		
7.2	Demonstrate a variety of healthy practices and behaviors that will maintain or improve the health of self and others.	pp. 618, 620–622, 625

Energy and Natural Resources

The ability to do work is *energy*. A scientific law that says that energy cannot be created or destroyed but can change in form is the *law of conservation of energy*. There are a variety of sources of energy.

What to Know About Energy and Natural Resources

Fossil fuels A fossil fuel is a fuel that is formed from plant or animal remains as a result of pressure over many years. A black or brown solid that contains stored energy formed from pressurized decayed plants is *coal.* It is the most abundant fossil fuel in the United States.

The black liquid mineral, formed from pressurized microscopic marine organisms that are trapped in rock beneath Earth's surface is *petroleum,* or *crude oil.* It is removed through wells and processed to produce gasoline, heating oil, diesel oil, or asphalt.

An energy source that is found underground above deposits of oil and is the cleanest burning fossil fuel is *natural gas.* Methane, propane, and butane are types of natural gas.

Other sources of energy There are other sources of energy besides fossil fuels. A more expensive source of energy, *nuclear energy,* is produced by splitting atoms of uranium into smaller parts. A radioactive substance that is mined and used to power nuclear reactors and produces

a large amount of electrical power is *uranium.* A *nuclear reactor* is a device that splits atoms to produce steam that generates electricity.

Electricity generated from flowing or falling water is *hydroelectric power.* Dams are built to store water and direct its flow through *turbines,* which are rotating engines.

The energy of the sun is *solar energy,* which can be converted into electrical energy or heat.

Organic plant matter produced by solar energy is *biomass.* Burning of wood, sewage, agricultural wastes, and algae can be used as sources of energy.

Heat transferred from underground sources of steam or hot water is *geothermal energy.* It can be used to heat homes, produce electricity, and power industrial plants.

Energy from wind is *wind energy.* Wind turbines change wind energy into electricity.

Energy that is produced by passing electrical current through water to burn hydrogen, which yields a high amount of energy, is *hydrogen power.*

Make the Connection

Automobiles For more information about hydrogen power and automobiles, see page 605 in Lesson 57.

Reading Review

1. Name the three types of fossil fuels.
2. Describe hydroelectric power.
3. What is the most abundant fossil fuel in the United States?

Lesson Resource Manager

- **Unit 10 Fast File Resources**
  Reading Strategy, p. 43
  Vocabulary Practice, p. 44
  Transparency Master and Worksheet, p. 45
  Real-Life Health, p. 47
  Real-Life Health, p. 49
  5-Minute Check, p. 51
  Lesson 59 Quiz, p. 52
- **Unit 10 Transparency**
- **Lesson 59 Transparency**

- **Reading Essentials**
- **Technology**
  TeacherWorks™ CD-ROM
  StudentWorks™ CD-ROM
  Reading Essentials CD-ROM
  ExamView® Assessment Suite
  Vocabulary Puzzlemaker

Energy and Natural Resources

2 Teach

Extension

Sources of Energy Have groups of students research the advantages and disadvantages of each type of energy source described in the text. Students can create 30-second infomercials about the sources of energy. **L3**

Reading Review

1. *coal, petroleum, natural gas*
2. *Dams are built to store water and direct flow through a rotating engine called a turbine. This produces electric energy.*
3. *coal*

PowerPoint® Presentations

This CD-ROM is an editable Microsoft® PowerPoint® presentation that includes:
- Lesson presentations
- Lesson checks
- Interactive graphics
- 5-Minute Checks
- Image Bank
- All transparencies

CRISS **Vocabulary** Refer to the Sentence Synthesis Strategy on page 16T, and ask students to brainstorm sentences using the list of key terms as well as other words in bold print in the lesson.

```
National Health
Education Standards
Pages 618–619: 7.2
```

Conservation

Household Energy Use Divide the class into groups and assign each group a room of the house (kitchen, bathroom, laundry, garage, home office, bedroom, etc.). Then ask them to make a list of all the electronic and electric items they might use in that room. Ask students to research if there are alternatives to the electronic and electric items that could be used. For example, ask students if all kitchen stoves are electric. Have students research the energy-efficiency of the electronic, electric, and alternative items. Have the class create a floor plan of a house. In each of the rooms, students should list or draw and label the electronic or electric items as well as the alternative forms of the items. **L3** **ELL**

NHES Assessment/SCASS

Performance Task Many companies have begun to develop automobiles that are energy-efficient. For example, automobiles exist that use gasoline and electricity together. Have students research energy-efficient and hybrid automobiles. Have students design a poster illustrating the automobile. The poster should include information about the car, and about the car's energy efficiency. **L3**

Conservation

Many people take energy for granted. They do not always realize how much energy they use. They do not always know how much energy and money they waste. They can conserve energy by developing habits that use less energy and by using energy-saving devices.

How to Conserve Energy and Natural Resources

> **Make the Connection**
>
> **Health Advocacy** For more information on being a health advocate, see page 65 in Lesson 7.

Drying clothing on a clothesline can save your family money that would otherwise be spent on electricity ▼ to run a clothes dryer.

Lights Use lamps instead of overhead lights when reading. Use fluorescent bulbs, or use lower wattage bulbs. When you leave a room, turn off all lights.

Household items When using batteries, use rechargeable batteries. If possible, use manual appliances instead of electrical appliances. For example, use a manual can opener instead of an electric can opener. Turn off appliances when not in use. In warm weather, dry clothing on a clothesline instead of in a dryer. When purchasing products for the home, choose those that are more energy efficient and include energy-saving features. Many new appliances now have energy ratings listed as part of the description of the appliance.

Heating and cooling In warm weather, use fans instead of air conditioners. Also, plant fast-growing trees to shade your home and to help keep your home cooler.

In cold weather, wear an additional layer of warm clothing instead of turning up the heat. Installing weather-stripping around windows and doors helps prevent heat loss. Turn the thermostat down at night or when you are away from home. A furnace should be serviced once per year, and filters should be replaced frequently for the furnace to work efficiently.

Traveling Try alternative methods to driving a motor vehicle, such as biking or walking. Carpooling and public transportation are other cost-effective ways to travel. Many cities are trying to encourage carpooling by adding restricted lanes for travel. To be permitted in these lanes, vehicles must have at least two passengers.

620 UNIT 10 • Environmental Health

DI Differentiated Instruction

Gifted and Talented Have students research alternative types of mass transportation (examples: electrical cars, buses, and trains) and write a paper on innovative ideas in transportation. Ask them to address the pros and cons of each alternative. Have students create a bulletin board illustrating their results. Ask students which method(s) they think would be most likely to be adopted by a state or federal government. **L3**

Just the FACTS: ENERGY CONSERVATION

> **Should you set your thermostat lower at night to save energy?**

the FACTS Turning down the temperature at night by 8 to 10 degrees may save 8 to 16 percent of your heating costs, depending on the temperature you are heating and cooling to and how much you are charged for electricity or gas. The fuel used to reheat your home is saved when the temperature drops to the lower level. The longer the temperature stays at the lower level, the more energy you save. Many homes have a thermostat that sets the temperature back automatically every night and returns it to the daytime level in the morning.

> **Do lights, computers, and other appliances use less energy and last longer if you leave them on rather than turning them off when they are not in use?**

the FACTS The amount of power needed to turn on an appliance is much smaller than the amount of energy it uses while it is running. An incandescent light bulb has to be turned off for only a very short time to save the amount of power needed to turn it back on again. If you are not going to need a fluorescent light bulb for 30 seconds, it pays to turn it off. If you are not going to use a computer for an hour or more, turn it off. Screen savers do not save energy, but many computers have a "sleep" feature that does. Turning appliances off and on used to limit their lifetimes, but this is not true of today's appliances.

> **Are fluorescent lights bad for your health?**

the FACTS Today's fluorescent lights no longer have the hum and obvious flicker that used to cause annoyance, headaches, and other problems. They also provide a better color than the old lights. Fluorescent lights use less energy and are three to four times more efficient than incandescent lights. A fluorescent light bulb also lasts about ten times longer than an incandescent one. Using modern fluorescent lights can save energy.

Ways to Conserve Water

Bathing and showering Filling a bathtub requires a lot of water. Showering typically uses less water. To help reduce the amount of water used during a shower, install a low-flow shower head, and take shorter showers. Fix leaks in faucets and pipes quickly.

Washing dishes and clothing When manually cleaning dishes, do not allow water to run. If you are using a dishwasher, run it only when it is full. When using a washing machine for clothes, run it only for a full load of clothes.

Washing vehicles When washing a vehicle, pull it into the yard. This way, the water that falls off the car also can be used to water the lawn. Use soaps that are safe for plants and flowers.

Outdoors Water the lawn and gardens only at the coolest time of the day. Planting trees in the yard also will help conserve water because they store water and release it into the ground. When mowing the lawn, keep grass height higher and use a mulching lawn mower. This will help the ground retain water. Using mulch around flowers, trees, and shrubs also will help the ground retain more water.

Other uses of water When brushing your teeth, do not let the water run. Keep water in the refrigerator instead of allowing tap water to run until it is cool enough to drink.

Toilets Buy a toilet that has a smaller tank and requires less water to fill the bowl. Do not use the toilet as a trash can. Only flush after use.

Did You Know?

Water Usage The average American uses roughly 150–250 gallons of water per day through methods of flushing, drinking, washing, etc.

Reading Review

1. Name two ways to conserve energy.
2. Name two ways to conserve water.
3. Does a shower or a bath require more water?

LESSON 59 • Practicing Recycling and Conservation **621**

621

Precycling and Recycling

Selected Response Which of the following potentially recyclable materials makes up the greatest percentage of the nation's trash?

A. glass
B. plastics
C. *paper products*
D. metals

Class Activity

Precycling Have students choose three ideas from the list of nine precycling tips, and ask them to write a list of several ways they can change their habits with regard to each precycling idea. Have students present their ideas to the class. *Students might list that they could use cloth bags for groceries. They would have to be prepared and have several cloth bags with them when they go to the store.* **L2**

Quick Demo

Recycling Refer to the fact in the Did You Know? box on this page. Explain to the class how much energy could be saved if people participated in recycling. Show this kind of computation on the chalkboard: If each student in the class recycled 4 bottles, that would save energy equivalent to burning a 100-watt lightbulb for 16 hours per student. With 20 students in the class, that is 320 hours. If each student in a school of 1200 students recycled 4 bottles, that would be 19,200 hours. **ELL**

Precycling and Recycling

Solid waste is a problem that affects many parts of the environment. It pollutes the air, water, and soil. The landfills where solid wastes are dumped take up space and can contaminate water supplies and pollute the air.

Did You Know?

Recycling Recycling one glass bottle saves enough energy to light a 100-watt bulb for four hours.

What to Know About Precycling and Recycling

How to recycle Solid wastes come in two forms: nonbiodegradable and biodegradable. Nonbiodegradable waste, such as plastics, aluminum cans, and glass cannot be broken down by natural processes and can last for hundreds of years. Waste that is biodegradable, such as foods and certain paper products, can be broken down by living organisms. The process of re-forming or breaking down a waste product so that it can be used again is ***recycling***.

Recycling can help reduce the amount of solid waste in landfills and can help conserve natural resources. Recycling involves collecting reusable material and reusing it for a new product. Many communities have recycling programs or centers.

Some commonly recycled materials are: paper, glass, plastics, aluminum, and other metals. According to the Environmental Protection Agency's Office of Solid Waste Management, the nation's trash consists of: 35.7 percent paper products, 16.1 percent other materials, such as leather, wood, and rubber, 12.2 percent yard waste, 11.4 percent food waste, 11.1 percent plastics, 7.9 percent metals, 5.5 percent glass.

Guidelines for precycling Some solid wastes can be precycled. A process of reducing waste is ***precycling***. It includes purchasing products in packages or containers that have been or can be broken down and used again, purchasing products that have little packaging, and repairing existing products rather than throwing them out and buying new ones.

Nine Tips for Precycling

You can help reduce waste by following these guidelines.

- Purchase paper items made from recycled paper.
- Purchase beverages in returnable or refillable containers or containers made of materials that can be broken down and used more than once.
- Use diapers made of cloth that can be cleaned and re-used.
- Use both sides of a sheet of paper.

- Use cloth bags instead of plastic or paper bags.
- Use cloth napkins and towels to dry hands.
- Use reusable plastic containers to store leftover food.
- Purchase food items in multi-serving containers that have a small amount of packaging.
- Purchase biodegradable products.

622 UNIT 10 • Environmental Health

 Community Involvement

Recycling Have students visit local businesses and interview managers about their current precycling and recycling practices. After the interview, students could identify the strengths and weaknesses of the companies' programs. Have students research the options for precycling and recycling different types of waste products in your community. Ask students to create a brochure encouraging precycling and recycling. Students' brochures also should include a list of the places where students and other members of your community can recycle their waste products. Have students ask local organizations if they may place the brochures in their establishments. Have students share their brochures and their experience with local organizations. **L2**

SPEAKING OUT

Kyle Knox
Working on a Recycling Program

> **"We really had to make it just as easy for them to recycle as to throw their paper away."**

People were skeptical that the recycling program at Kyle Knox's school would work. "We took a lot from the custodial staff," he explained. "They said stuff like, 'We give it three months and then you'll quit.' They thought that students wouldn't have the commitment to continue a project like this and that we'd get frustrated and give it up. But we didn't."

Don't throw it all away. The project Kyle helped start was for paper recycling. "We put bins in classrooms. The idea was that when people had a piece of paper, they'd toss it in our recycling bin instead of into the trash can. We started out with 50 bins. We put them in the classrooms where students use a lot of paper, like English, history, and foreign languages."

Wanted: people and money Getting the ball rolling wasn't easy. Kyle described the challenges his group faced. "The first thing we needed was people who were interested. At the beginning we had about ten people, with about seven of them regulars. Then we needed money. We made a proposal to student council. We told them we wanted to start this recycling program at school, and that we would keep it going. They had some extra money and bought us the stuff we needed to begin: about 50 bins, barrels, and a big cart. We're like a transfer station. We empty all the bins and take the paper to the big recycling dumpsters behind the school."

Making it easy Another challenge Kyle's group faced was getting students to use the bins. "We tried to make people aware of the recycling program," he said. "We made signs and put up announcements. We also put information sheets next to the bins so people would understand what we were doing." Support from other students was mediocre to begin with, Kyle reported. "But when exam time came around and the end of the quarter, people started throwing away stuff in their notebooks. Then things started to pick up."

The key to getting students to use the bins was making it simple. "You can't force people to do something like this," Kyle said. "We really had to make it just as easy for them to recycle as to throw their paper away."

Was it all worth it? "Definitely," Kyle said. "The first six months were hard. But we recycled 16,000 pounds of paper over those first six months. At 117 pounds a tree, you can do the math. We saved a lot of trees."

As for the future, the recycling program is expanding. "We've gotten bins for all the rooms," he said.

Save on All Athletic Slides

Journaling Activity

Some people at Kyle's school thought that teens wouldn't have the commitment to carry out a long-term project. What about your school? Does your school have a recycling program? If it does not, write a plan of action that could be implemented to develop a recycling program in your school. Describe some barriers to implementing a recycling program. How would you overcome those barriers?

LESSON 59 • Practicing Recycling and Conservation **623**

SPEAKING OUT

Analyzing the Feature

Use the following questions to help students uncover the main points of this feature.

1. What were some challenges Kyle faced when starting his recycling project? *lack of support, lack of interest, need for money and supplies*
2. How did Kyle's group spread the word about the program? *signs, announcements, information sheets*
3. What characteristics does Kyle show? *determination, creativity, work ethic, desire to improve the environment*

Journaling Activity

Ask students to share their thoughts about the lack of support Kyle received in the beginning. Have students write in their health journals about barriers Kyle had to overcome. Ask students to explain why they think Kyle was successful. **L2**

Health Project

Recycling Group Encourage the class to plan a recycling program for your school. Have students create a plan of action to implement an ideal recycling plan (budget, timeline, personnel needed). Ask a few students to find out what your school does to recycle. Assign others to talk to the council or the administration about funding. Have students present their recycling plan to the class. Student presentations should include information gathered from the discussion with the administration, the project budget, and timeline. **L3**

National Health Education Standards
Pages 622–623: 1.3, 5.6

Reading Review

1. *A sanitary landfill is where solid waste is spread in thin layers, compacted, and covered with a fresh layer of dirt. A secure landfill has protective liners to reduce or prevent leachate from escaping through water run-off.*
2. *biohazardous or medical waste*
3. *Recycling is the process of re-forming or breaking down a waste product so it can be used again. Precycling is a process of reducing waste.*

3 Assess

Vocabulary Practice

Page 44, Unit 10 Fast File Resources

Name _____ Date _____ Class _____

LESSON 59 Practicing Recycling and Conservation

Vocabulary Practice

Use the terms to fill in the blanks below. Some terms may be used more than once.

composting · conservation · geothermal energy · hydrogen power · incinerator · landfills · leachate · nuclear reactor · precycling · solar energy

1. Produced with an electrical current and water, _____ yields a high amount of energy.
2. Reducing waste by _____ includes actions such as buying items with less packaging.
3. _____ are places where solid waste is layered and buried.
4. The _____ of natural resources will help to ensure that there are enough of them for the future.
5. Biomass is organic plant matter that is produced by _____
6. A(n) _____ is powered by uranium.
7. Showering instead of taking a bath, fixing leaky faucets, and watering in the coolest parts of the day are three ways to help with water _____
8. A(n) _____ can reduce the volume of solid waste, but it also can release pollutants into the air.
9. To prevent _____ from escaping through water runoff, a secure landfill has liners.
10. _____ is a way to recycle yard and kitchen waste into a soil conditioner.
11. Heat from underground steam or hot water called _____ is used to heat homes.
12. Hazardous waste can leach out of _____ and get into the surrounding environment.

44 LESSON 59 · Practicing Recycling and Conservation   UNIT 10

Waste Disposal

Individuals, families, industries, businesses, and farms all produce large amounts of waste. Though much of this waste ends up in landfills, some of it must be disposed of in other ways to protect our health. There are several different ways to dispose of this waste; however, controversy exists as to which is the best method.

Ways to Dispose of Waste

Landfills There are two types of landfills. A *sanitary landfill* is a waste disposal land site where solid waste is spread in thin layers, compacted, and covered with a fresh layer of dirt daily. The dirt contains bacteria to help break down the organic material in the garbage. A *secure landfill* is a landfill that has protective liners to reduce or prevent leachate from escaping through water runoff. Liquid that drains from a landfill is called *leachate* (LEE chayt). Hazardous wastes and nonbiodegradable materials should not be sent to a landfill.

Incineration A furnace in which solid waste is burned and energy is recovered in the process is an *incinerator.* Incinerators reduce the volume of solid waste, but can release pollutants into the atmosphere. Some incinerators use the heat produced by burning to create steam that provides electricity. Most biohazardous waste, or medical waste, is incinerated. Infectious waste from medical facilities is *biohazardous waste,* or *medical waste.* It includes syringes, needles, tubes, blood vials, and other items that can contain tissues and body fluids from a person or animal.

Composting A mixture of decayed organic material generally used to fertilize and condition the soil is *compost* (KAHM pohst). The breakdown by bacteria of plant remains to *humus* (HYEW muhs), which is a soil conditioner, is *composting.* In some communities, yard waste is separated from other kinds of waste and transported to compost landfills. Many individuals have their own compost piles in which they place yard waste and plant scraps from the kitchen. Food wastes, such as meat and eggs, should not be composted because they will attract flies and rodents. The use of mulching mowers helps reduce yard waste and serves as a natural fertilizer. A *mulching mower* is a lawn mower that cuts the grass into small pieces that can be left on a lawn to decompose naturally.

Deep-injection wells A well that pumps waste into porous rock far below the level of groundwater is a *deep-injection well.* Hazardous wastes may be disposed of in deep-injection wells. Any solid, liquid, or gas in a container that is harmful to humans or animal life is *hazardous waste.* Hazardous waste includes paints, solvents, cleaners, acids, alkalis, pesticides, petroleum products, such as gasoline and motor oil, and other toxic chemicals. Hazardous waste can leach out of landfills and escape into the environment. Hazardous waste cannot be incinerated because it might cause an explosion.

Reading Review

1. What is the difference between a sanitary landfill and a secure landfull?

2. What types of solid waste are incinerated?

3. What is the difference between recycling and precycling?

624 UNIT 10 · Environmental Health

⚖ Legal Issues

Waste Disposal Every state has laws which govern how certain types of waste can be discarded. For example, it is illegal to place hazardous waste such as paints, pesticides, or other toxic chemicals in your regular trash can. Some communities have designated drop-off sites for hazardous waste. Another example is banned incineration. People in cities are not allowed to burn their trash, but some rural areas allow it. Have students research regulations in their communities and present their findings to class. **L3**

Key Terms Review

Complete these fill-in-the-blank statements with the lesson Key Terms on the left. Do not write in this book.

composting
conservation
geothermal energy
hazardous waste
hydrogen power
incinerator
landfill
leachate
natural resource
nuclear reactor
precycling
solar energy

1. Energy from the sun is called _____.
2. Energy produced by passing electrical current through water is _____.
3. Waste is dumped in a(n) _____.
4. Liquid that drains from a landfill is called _____.
5. Heat transferred from underground sources is called _____.
6. The saving of resources is called _____.
7. A furnace that burns solid waste is a(n) _____.
8. Breaking down plant remains to humus is known as _____.
9. Atoms are split to produce steam in a(n) _____.
10. When you purchase containers or other packages that can be broken down, you practice _____.

Recalling the Facts

11. What are some ways that people can effectively precycle?
12. Why might you use a cloth towel instead of paper napkins for drying your hands?
13. Why is it more environmentally friendly to dispose of a paper cup rather than a plastic cup?
14. How can the sun play a role in energy production?
15. What are types of fossil fuels?
16. What are other sources of energy besides fossil fuels?
17. What are some ways to conserve energy?
18. How can recycling help the environment?

Critical Thinking

19. Why is it easier to grow plants in soil that comes from composting piles?
20. Why are plants considered a natural resource?
21. Why would an automobile engine using natural gas be better for the environment than one that uses gasoline from a refinery?
22. If someone wanted to recycle, what might prevent him or her from doing so?

Real-Life Applications

23. Why do you think hydroelectric power is not the number one source of power for most cities?
24. How can your family help protect the environment?
25. If you were asked to do laundry at home, why should you do a full load?
26. Why do you think it is suggested that you not water the lawn during the afternoon?

Activities

Responsible Decision Making

27. **Determine** Suppose you drive to school alone. Two of your neighbors also have cars and suggest you ride to school together. They say you can take turns driving. Write what decision you would make, and explain your decision. Refer to the Responsible Decision-Making Model on page 61 for help.

Sharpen Your Life Skills

28. **Analyze Influences on Health** Suppose you had to live without electricity, petroleum, and natural gas. How would your life be different than it is right now? How might this situation affect your health? Do some research and write a one-page paper on this topic. Share your paper with your classmates.

Visit **www.glencoe.com** for more *Health & Wellness* quizzes.

LESSON 59 • Study Guide   **625**

Key Terms Review

1. solar energy
2. hydrogen power
3. landfill
4. leachate
5. geothermal energy
6. conservation
7. incinerator
8. composting
9. nuclear reactor
10. precycling

Recalling the Facts

11. by purchasing products in packaging that has been or can be recycled; that have little or no packaging, and by repairing products rather than buying new ones
12. A towel can be washed and re-used, while a paper napkin is thrown away.
13. A plastic cup cannot be broken down, while a paper cup can be broken down and is therefore better for the environment.
14. The sun produces solar energy, which can be converted into electrical energy or heat.
15. coal, petroleum, natural gas
16. nuclear energy, hydroelectric power, solar energy, biomass, geothermal energy, wind energy, and hydrogen power
17. See page 620.
18. It reduces solid waste in landfills and can help conserve natural resources.

Critical Thinking

19. Composted soil has more nutrients in it.
20. Plants are natural parts of the environment and therefore are natural resources.
21. Natural gas is a cleaner-burning fossil fuel.
22. lack of recycling facilities, lack of cooperation from school or business to start a program

Real-Life Applications

23. Many cities do not have large bodies of water that they can use for power.
24. You can conserve energy and practice recycling or precycling.
25. A full load uses less water and energy than several small loads.
26. During the hottest part of the day, some of the water may evaporate instead of soaking into the soil.

Activities

Responsible Decision Making

27. This is a good idea, as it would reduce the number of cars on the road, which would help reduce the use of gasoline.

Sharpen Your Life Skills

28. Answers will vary.

LESSON 60

Protecting the Environment

 Out of Time?

If time does not permit an in-depth study of this topic, use the following activities in this Teacher Wraparound Edition:

- Class Discussion, p. 627
- Class Activity, p. 628
- Family Involvement, p. 630
- Class Activity, p. 632

1 Focus

HEALTH GOALS **Protect the Environment** Ask students to respond to the first Health Goal for this lesson by listing ways they can help protect the environment. *Answers include recycle household trash, conserve water, use recycled material.* **L2**

Write ABOUT IT!

Answers Students' journal entries should discuss taking responsibility for preserving and protecting the natural environment. Students should decide to pick up the trash left by the campers and leave no trace of their own visit so that others also can enjoy the natural environment. **L2**

LESSON 60

Protecting the Environment

HEALTH GOALS
- I will protect the natural environment.
- I will be a health advocate for the environment.

Plants, animals, insects, mountains, oceans, and the sky make up the *natural environment*. The natural environment influences quality of life. The degree to which a person lives life to the fullest is *quality of life*. To help improve quality of life and the natural environment, you can participate in health advocacy. Taking responsibility to improve the quality of life and encouraging others to do the same is *health advocacy*.

What You'll Learn

1. Explain how the natural environment protects health status. *(p. 627)*
2. Describe ways to protect the natural environment. *(p. 628)*
3. Discuss actions health advocates can take for the environment. *(p. 631)*
4. Describe ways to be a health advocate for the environment. *(p. 632)*

Why It's Important

When you help improve the environment, you also help improve your health and the health of others. You can learn skills that can help you achieve this.

Key Terms

- natural environment
- quality of life
- health advocacy
- nature preserve
- wildlife sanctuary
- national parks
- community park
- nature trail
- beach
- conservatory

Write ABOUT IT!

Writing About Health Advocacy Suppose that you are camping in a state or national forest. When you are packing up your camping gear, you notice the campers beside you have left without picking up their trash. After reading the information about protecting the natural environment on page 628, explain in your health journal what action you would take and why. What other actions could you take for health advocacy?

National Health Education Standards—Guide for Lesson 60		
1.3	Analyze how environment and personal health are interrelated.	pp. 626, 627, 630, 634
7.1	Analyze the role of individual responsibility for enhancing health.	pp. 626, 632
7.2	Demonstrate a variety of healthy practices and behaviors that will maintain or improve the health of self and others.	pp. 626, 628–630, 632–635

The Natural Environment

P icture a forest, an ocean, a mountain, the sky, a park, a field. Just thinking about nature and the natural environment can give one a sense of awe and appreciation. These places provide people with the opportunity to enjoy the natural environment and improve their quality of life.

Places Created to Help You Appreciate the Natural Environment

An area restricted for the protection of the natural environment is a *nature preserve.* A place reserved for the protection of plants and animals is a *wildlife sanctuary.* Government-maintained areas of land open to the public are *national parks* and *state parks.* An area of land set aside to preserve natural scenery and recreation is a *community park.*

A path through a natural environment is a *nature trail.* A path designed for recreational activities, such as walking, jogging, biking, and hiking, is a *recreational trail.*

The shore of a body of water, covered by sand, gravel, or rock, is a *beach.* A park in which animals are cared for and shown to the public is a *zoo.*

A greenhouse in which plants are grown and displayed to the public is a *conservatory.* An area where trees, flowers, and other plants are grown and landscaping is maintained is a *garden.*

Did You Know?

National Parks
Yellowstone National Park was the world's first national park.

How the Natural Environment Improves Health Status

The natural environment provides:

- a quiet place to spend time by yourself. This can contribute to your well-being. It gives you time to collect your thoughts.
- a place in which you can participate in physical activities. You might enjoy outdoor physical activities, such as hiking, in-line skating, swimming, and playing basketball.

- a place such as the zoo, a park, the beach, where you spend time with family members and friends.
- a place in which you can enjoy leisure time. *Leisure time* is time free from work or duties. During their leisure time, some teens collect leaves, observe the stars, watch birds, and participate in physical activities.

- a place in which you can relieve stress. Most people feel more relaxed after walking through a park, spending time at a zoo or at a nature preserve, or visiting a conservatory.
- a place where you can observe wildlife. In large national parks, you may see bears, wolves, bison, or elk.

LESSON 60 • Protecting the Environment **627**

Lesson Resource Manager

- **Unit 10 Fast File Resources**
  Reading Strategy, p. 55
  Vocabulary Practice, p. 56
  Transparency Master and Worksheet, p. 57
  Real-Life Health, p. 59
  Real-Life Health, p. 61
  5-Minute Check, p. 63
  Lesson 60 Quiz, p. 65
- **Unit 10 Transparency**
- **Lesson 60 Transparency**

- **Reading Essentials**
- **Technology**
  TeacherWorks™ CD-ROM
  StudentWorks™ CD-ROM
  Reading Essentials CD-ROM
  Exam*View*® Assessment Suite
  Vocabulary Puzzlemaker

The Natural Environment

2 Teach

Class Discussion

Enjoying the Environment Ask students to give reasons why having national parks, forest preserves, wildlife sanctuaries, etc. is beneficial to people. *Answers might include: protects the environment and provides places for people to enjoy nature and improve their quality of life.* Ask the class to name as many parks, trails, preserves, gardens, etc. as they can in the area. Write the names on a poster as they list them. Hang the poster in your room as a reference for this and other classes. **L2**

INTERACTIVE CHALKBOARD with Image Bank

PowerPoint® Presentations
This CD-ROM is an editable Microsoft® PowerPoint® presentation that includes:
- Lesson presentations
- Lesson checks
- Interactive graphics
- 5-Minute Checks
- Image Bank
- All transparencies

CRISS
Project

Discussion Refer to the Authentic Questions Strategy on page 17T, and ask students to write down questions that arise as they read the lesson for later class discussion.

National Health Education Standards
Pages 626–627: 1.3, 7.1, 7.2, 8.2, 8.3

Protecting the Natural Environment

Explain the Concept

Habitats Explain to the class why it is important not to disturb a natural habitat. Use an example of one small change—or many small changes—caused by people that can result in a big change for a plant or animal that lives in a very delicate habitat. For example, use of a certain chemical might kill birds. Other animals might feed on the birds and become ill.

NHES Assessment/SCASS

Performance Event Ask students to write a short paper about a time they did not act in a way that would protect the environment, such as when they were on a trip to the beach, when they took a walk in a park, or when they were camping. Ask them whether they would change their actions if they could. Ask what they should have done differently. **L2**

Class Activity

Clean Up Have the class go outside and clean up an area around your school or in the surrounding community. Make sure to have them take notice of how the area looks before they clean it and then after, so that they can see a difference. Have students develop a map of their school community. Specify locations that were particularly high in litter. Ask students what could be done to prevent the litter. **L2 ELL**

Protecting the Natural Environment

YOU CAN HELP SAVE THE BEACH
PLEASE USE WALKOVERS
FOOT TRAFFIC WILL KILL VEGETATION

People can take responsibility for preserving and protecting the natural environment. Follow rules and obey the laws to protect the earth. The following are actions you can take to help protect the natural environment.

How to Protect the Natural Environment

Follow all rules. Many places created to help people enjoy the natural environment post rules to follow. Rules might involve staying in certain areas, keeping pets on a leash, and following safety guidelines. If there are signs in the natural environment asking visitors to refrain from bringing dogs or other animals into that environment, respect the rules.

Do not leave belongings behind. Whatever you take into a natural area should go with you when you leave the area.

When you are at a park, resist the temptation to pick wildflowers so that others may enjoy them as well. ▼

Do not litter or leave other objects. Bring garbage bags to collect trash and other wastes.

Do not destroy the environment. Leave as little trace as possible of having been in a natural environment. Do not damage trees or plants. Do not carve initials in trees. Do not write graffiti on rocks, trees, bridges, trail signs, or buildings.

Do not take things out of the natural environment. Leave everything in its place so that you do not harm the natural habitat. A *habitat* is a place where an animal or plant normally lives. Do not pick flowers. Do not break branches off of trees. Do not take animals or other objects from the natural environment.

Do not feed wild animals. If you feed wild animals, you make them dependent on humans for food and they will not learn to feed themselves. Some animals starve to death after people leave the area.

Stay on trails. Trails are designed to protect people from possible dangers

628

DI Differentiated Instruction

Hearing Impairment Team up a hearing impaired student with a non–hearing impaired student. Instruct the non-impaired student to face his or her partner throughout the activity to enable lip reading. Have students select a state or national park. Encourage students to obtain pictures of the state or national park. Have students create a poster with a picture of their chosen park and some general information about the selected park. Have students share their experiences with the natural environment (such as visiting a state park). **L2**

(tl)Photodisc/Getty Images; (b)Freeman Patterson/Masterfile

Activity: Using Life Skills

Advocating for Health: Creating a Plan to Protect Your Community's Environment

You can do many things, both large and small, to help protect the environment. You also can influence others with your Earth-friendly behavior. Using the ideas below along with your own ideas, make a checklist of ten things you can do every week to help keep your planet healthy.

1 **Select a health-related concern.** You can choose from the following environmental health concerns.

2 Conserve energy. Using electricity puts greenhouse gases into the air. When you're finished with the television, the computer, and the lights, turn them off. Instead of driving everywhere you go, try walking, taking the bus or subway, or riding your bike. If you must drive, try carpooling with other people. You will help save your family money that would otherwise have been spent on utilities and transportation.

3 Plant trees and bushes and volunteer. Plants absorb some of the carbon dioxide that contributes to global warming. Plus, trees become homes for insects, birds, and squirrels. Volunteer to help clean up litter or help wildlife organizations.

4 Recycle and buy smart. Many towns have drop-off bins for aluminum cans, plastic, and paper. Instead of throwing these things away, place them in a separate container and take them to the drop-off site every week. When you purchase products, check the labels to see if they are recyclable. Also, consider choosing products that don't have a lot of wasteful packaging.

5 Reduce the amount you use. Do you really need a bag to carry that one item you bought at the store? Do you need a new notebook when you have one from last year? Also, give your old clothes to a charity that will resell them, or sell them yourself at a thrift store. Buy a reusable water bottle instead of drinking bottled water and throwing the bottle away.

6 Gather reliable information. The more you know about the environmental issues in your community, the more you can work to make a difference.

7 Identify your purpose and target audience, and develop a convincing and appropriate message. Deliver your message to your target audience.

and to protect the natural environment. Walk in single file rather than side-by-side when hiking with two or more people to make sure everyone stays on the trail.

Keep fires small and make sure they are extinguished before leaving. Follow park rules for building fires. Make sure that fires are completely out before leaving the area. Forest fires can be started by fires that are still smoldering.

Be considerate of others when in the natural environment. Do not make loud noises, such as screaming or playing loud music. Do not "hog"

equipment and facilities. Walk or ride on the appropriate side of trails. Do not ride bikes or skateboards or use rollerblades if the signs in the natural environment ask visitors to refrain from those activities.

Do not drink out of lakes and streams or consume wild plants. The water in many lakes and streams may look clean, but it may be polluted with microorganisms and other pollutants that harm health. Do not consume wild berries or mushrooms that you find in natural environments. Many wild plants are poisonous and can cause illness or death.

Reading Review

1. Name three places you can visit to appreciate the natural environment.

2. What can you do to protect the natural environment?

LESSON 60 • Protecting the Environment **629**

FACTSABOUT
INDOOR AIR QUALITY

Extension

Detection Have students visit a local hardware store with their parent or guardian. Students should locate the alarms and detectors that signal a problem with gases or other pollutants. Ask students to list the type of detector, what problem it detects, and the cost of the device. **L3**

Investigating the Issue

- *Radon: make sure house is well-ventilated; Carbon monoxide: use an exhaust fan over a gas stove, keep central heating system clean and in good condition, and install a carbon monoxide alarm; Biological pollutants: make sure house is well-ventilated, or replace water-damaged building materials; Secondhand smoke: do not smoke in the home; VOCs: use products in well-ventilated areas according to instructions on label.*
- *Exposure to asbestos can lead to the development of lung cancer and other lung diseases. Exposure to lead at an early age can adversely affect both mental and physical development.*
- *Some plants, such as spider plants and peace lilies, remove certain VOCs from indoor air through leaves, roots, and bacteria in soil.*

National Health Education Standards
Pages 630–631: 1.3, 2.5, 7.2, 8.2, 8.3, 8.4

FACTSABOUT
INDOOR AIR QUALITY

▲ Many stores provide equipment to detect harmful gases such as carbon monoxide.

You probably are familiar with most outdoor air pollutants, such as ozone, carbon monoxide, and sulfur dioxide, but did you know that indoor air can be as contaminated, if not more so, as outdoor air? According to the U.S. Environmental Protection Agency (EPA), indoor levels of air pollutants may be 2–5 times higher and can be more than 100 times higher than outdoor levels of air pollutants. Indoor air pollutants can cause allergies, asthma, and lung cancer.

Radon Exposure to high concentrations of radon gas is the second leading cause of lung cancer in the United States. Radon is a colorless, tasteless gas that is released naturally during the decaying process of uranium, a radioactive element found in many rocks and soils. Radon seeps into a building through breaks in the foundation. When radon is released into the open air, the concentration is so low it is harmless. However, in a poorly-ventilated house, indoor radon concentrations can build up to between 20 and 15,000 times outdoor levels, exposing the occupants to health risks.

Carbon monoxide (CO) A colorless, odorless, tasteless gas released from kerosene and gas space heaters and other home heating sources, carbon monoxide is deadly in high concentrations. Carbon monoxide binds to hemoglobin in the blood in place of oxygen. Symptoms of carbon monoxide poisoning include fatigue, dizziness, nausea, confusion, and impaired vision and coordination. Carbon monoxide alarms can be used to indicate when levels of CO become dangerous.

Biological pollutants Exposure to biological pollutants in a home, such as molds, mildews, cockroaches, and dust mites, can lead to allergies or asthma. More than 20 million Americans have asthma, and it is the leading cause of childhood hospitalizations and school absenteeism. Some molds and mildews release disease-causing toxins that can lead to respiratory illness and memory loss.

Environmental tobacco smoke (ETS) Environmental tobacco smoke (ETS), or secondhand smoke, from tobacco products is another source of indoor air pollution. ETS is a known cause of lung cancer and heart disease in nonsmoking adults. Children exposed to ETS are at an increased risk of developing asthma, bronchitis, pneumonia, and other respiratory illnesses.

Volatile organic compounds Household products, such as paints, varnishes, stored fuels, and cleaners, release volatile organic compounds (VOCs) both during use and while being stored. Effects from exposure to organic pollutants can range from irritation of the eyes, nose, and throat to headaches to damage to the liver, kidneys, and central nervous system. Reading the labels on household products, using them in well-ventilated areas, and taking precautions, such as wearing protective gear during use, can help reduce exposure to VOCs and protect people from the adverse effects of VOCs.

Investigating the Issue

Visit www.glencoe.com to research more information about indoor air quality.

- What precautions can be taken against the indoor air pollutants listed above?
- How does exposure to other pollutants, such as asbestos and lead, affect human health?
- How can plants improve indoor air quality?

Choose one source of indoor air pollution. Write a script for a public service announcement, warning people about this pollutant.

 Family Involvement

Survey Have students survey their parents or guardian regarding the kinds of indoor pollutants they may have in their homes. Ask them to find out about protective devices such as carbon monoxide alarms, and hazards such as radon, cleaners, chemicals, etc. Have them investigate how the house is ventilated, and share the information they have learned in this lesson with their parents. Have students create a family pledge containing activities that the family will do to improve indoor air quality, such as installing smoke and carbon monoxide detectors, eliminating environmental tobacco smoke, or getting houseplants. **L2**

Environmental Health Advocacy

A person who promotes health is a ***health advocate.*** A person who promotes a healthful environment is a ***health advocate for the environment.*** Health advocates for the environment take actions to improve the quality of the environment. They avoid actions that may threaten the environment. Health advocates for the environment work together with other people to promote environmental health. They encourage others to join them in taking responsibility for the environment. They have successfully influenced the passage of laws that protect the environment.

What to Know About Health Advocacy for the Environment

The National Community Service Trust Act There are many different things that people do to play a role in helping the environment. When the National Community Service Trust Act was passed in 1993, a strong push to help the environment began. This act is a national service initiative. People who want to help the environment receive financial aid to help them pay for college.

Summer opportunities For students in high school who are between ages 16 and 18, there are summer programs in which they can work for a month at a time in outdoor settings on public lands. Experience is not needed. Participants can learn about careers in conservation. It's a productive way to spend the summer and also learn about the environment.

Your community People can participate in various community-service programs. They can work on special projects, such as taking steps to beautify the community. You may see people picking up trash along the side of the road or planting flowers in a local park.

Americorps The federal government started a program called Americorps. Americorps is similar to the Peace Corps, but instead of working in another country, Americorps participants work in the United States. When people work for Americorps, they perform a number of tasks to help the community. In turn, the participants receive a small stipend and/or funds to help pay for a college education or to repay a student loan.

There are many environmental activities that people in Americorps undertake, such as beautifying communities and creating vegetable gardens in previously unusable land. These actions help the environment and the community.

> **Make the Connection**
>
> **Health Advocacy** For more information on health advocacy, see page 65 in Lesson 7.

Environmental Health Advocacy

Extension

Volunteer Discuss the importance of volunteer service. Explain that 2 hours of volunteer work may not seem like much, but if 1000 students gave 2 hours each, you would have 2000 hours of service to a cause. Ask students to calculate the total hours that would be donated if each person in their town or city gave 2 hours. Have students contact a non-profit organization that focuses on the environment and learn about volunteer opportunities. **L2**

INTERACTIVE CHALKBOARD with Image Bank

5-Minute Check

Page 64, **Unit 10 Fast File Resources**

1. What is the National Community Service Trust Act? *a national service initiative that provides financial aid to people for working to help the environment*
2. What are some of the ways Americorps works to help the environment? *beautifying communities and creating gardens in previously unusable land*
3. How can you get involved in a program dedicated to the environment? *Volunteer your time.*
4. Why might indoor pollutant levels be higher than outdoor levels? *Having a house closed up contains the pollutants.*
5. How can children be at risk due to tobacco smoke? *Breathing in secondhand smoke increases risk of respiratory illnesses.*

🏛 Community Involvement

Health Advocate Ask someone who works full-time in a position of environmental health advocacy to come in and talk to the class about his or her job and the career or volunteer opportunities in their field. Instruct students to prepare questions ahead of time for the guest speaker. Questions might include: What specific environmental issues does your organization address? Have you worked on passing laws to protect the environment? Do you work with other types of health advocates? Have students take notes on the information presented by the speaker. Ask students to identify the main job requirements of the speaker's position, as well as the benefits and drawbacks of the position. **L2**

Environmental Health Advocates

Environmental Health Advocates

You can be a health advocate for the environment. You also can be a role model to others when you take responsibility for the environment. There are a variety of ways to become an effective health advocate for the environment.

How to Be a Health Advocate for the Environment

Take responsibility for your own actions regarding the environment. Do not allow circumstances or peer pressure to cause you to forget or avoid your responsibility for a healthy environment. For example, do not throw trash out the window of a motor vehicle because the other people in the car want to get rid of it. Instead, take advantage of the opportunity to be both a health advocate for the environment and a role model for your friends.

Stay informed about environmental issues that affect your community, the nation, and the world. New discoveries are made every day. New technology constantly brings about change rapidly. Read about environmental issues in newspapers and magazines, and learn about factors that may harm the quality of your environment, and the positive things individuals and companies are doing to preserve and protect the environment. Make sure information you read or hear is accurate. Check the source for reliability.

Take actions to promote the environment. Look for ways you can protect and improve the environment, such as conserving water and energy, recycling, building a compost pile, planting trees, and maintaining an environment free of litter.

Encourage others to protect the environment. Share the information you have learned in this unit with family members and friends. Invite others to join your efforts to protect the environment.

Volunteer to work on environmental improvement projects in your community. Identify environmental organizations or groups involved in improving your community, and obtain permission from a parent or guardian to volunteer in these organizations or groups.

Organize environmental improvement projects. Being a health advocate for the environment involves taking responsibility. Suppose you see a need for improvement in an area of the environment, such as air or water pollution. Don't wait for someone else to organize an environmental improvement project. Choose a way to improve your environment and, with permission from your parents or guardian, take action.

LESSON 60 STUDY GUIDE

Key Terms Review

Complete these fill-in-the-blank statements with the lesson Key Terms on the left. Do not write in this book.

1. Plants and animals are protected in a special place reserved for them called a(n) _____.
2. Government maintained areas of land open to the public are _____.
3. The degree to which a person can live life to its fullest is called _____.
4. Plants are grown in a building and displayed to the public in a(n) _____.
5. The shore of a body of water, covered by sand, gravel, or rock, is a(n) _____.
6. Everything around a person not made by people is a(n) _____.
7. Taking responsibility to improve the quality of life is known as _____.
8. An area of land kept for natural scenery and recreation is _____.
9. A path through a natural environment is called a(n) _____.
10. A restricted area for the protection of the natural environment is a(n) _____.

beach
community park
conservatory
health advocacy
national parks
natural environment
nature preserve
nature trail
quality of life
recreational trail
wildlife sanctuary
zoo

Recalling the Facts

11. How can the environment play a role in one's physical fitness?
12. How can the natural environment serve to provide family enjoyment?
13. Why should people avoid drinking water from a lake?
14. How can people learn about environmental protection programs throughout the world?
15. What does a health advocate for the environment do?
16. How can the natural environment improve health status?
17. Why is feeding wild animals detrimental to their health?
18. What actions can people take in their communities to protect the natural environment?

Critical Thinking

19. Why is it important to avoid taking things out of a natural environment?
20. How does a nature preserve protect the environment?
21. How does the natural environment affect quality of life?
22. Why is following rules important in protecting the natural environment?

Real-Life Applications

23. What can you do to protect a habitat?
24. What can you do to beautify an inner city community?
25. How can you appreciate the natural environment?
26. How can you be an environmental health advocate?

Activities

Responsible Decision Making

27. **Decide** You are visiting a park with a friend. You see some wildflowers. Your friend wants to pick some and take them home. There is a sign that says not to pick the flowers. Your friend says no one will know if you pick flowers. What is the responsible action to take? Refer to the Responsible Decision-Making Model on page 61 to see the steps involved in making responsible decisions.

Sharpen Your Life Skills

28. **Advocate for Health** Select from Places Created to Help You Appreciate the Natural Environment a place that you have in your community. Write a list of ten actions you can take to help protect and improve this place. With several of your classmates, obtain permission from your parents or guardians to complete one of the actions on your list.

Visit **www.glencoe.com** for more *Health & Wellness* quizzes.

LESSON 60 • Study Guide **633**

Key Terms Review

1. wildlife sanctuary
2. national parks
3. quality of life
4. conservatory
5. beach
6. natural environment
7. health advocacy
8. community park
9. nature trail
10. nature preserve

Recalling the Facts

11. Beaches, parks, recreational trails and hiking trails provide places for people to exercise.
12. Families can visit parks, zoos, beaches, or nature preserves.
13. Lakes may be polluted with microorganisms and other pollutants that harm health.
14. reading newspapers and magazines, watching the news
15. He or she takes actions to protect the environment and encourages others to do the same.
16. The natural environment can improve quality of life, which can improve health.
17. Feeding wild animals may make them dependent on humans for food, and they may lose their natural hunting instincts.
18. See page 628.

Critical Thinking

19. so you do not harm the natural habitat
20. It restricts the activities of humans to preserve the natural environment.
21. See page 627.
22. Rules are designed to protect the environment. If one person does not follow the rules, then the person may harm the environment.

Real-Life Applications

23. See page 628.
24. Trees or gardens can be planted in vacant lots.
25. Take time to relax and enjoy nature; go for a hike; use a nature trail to observe plants and animals.
26. By encouraging family and friends to help protect the environment.

Activities

Responsible Decision Making

27. Do not pick the flowers as it can disturb the natural environment. Suggest to your friend that you try growing the flowers at home.

Sharpen Your Life Skills

28. Answers will vary.

Key Terms Review

1. k	6. b
2. e	7. h
3. i	8. d
4. c	9. j
5. l	10. g

Recalling the Facts

11. Answers should include two of the following: food resources and health services have improved, people are living longer, and infant mortality has declined.
12. Answers should include two of the following: the EPA, OSHA, and NIOSH.
13. See pages 604–605 for complete list.
14. carbon monoxide, carbon dioxide, nitrogen oxides, sulfur oxides, and particulates
15. A decibel (dB) is a unit used to measure the loudness or intensity of specific sounds.
16. Effects include frustration, loss of sleep, loss of concentration, and inability to hold a conversation and learn.
17. paper, glass, plastics, and aluminum and other metals
18. coal, petroleum, and natural gas
19. See page 627 for complete list.
20. See page 632 for complete list.

Critical Thinking

21. Some gases in the atmosphere trap and reflect the sun's rays, which warm the earth's surface.
22. If they drive every class day to school, approximately 180 days of 20 minutes of driving to and from school, that would be 3600 minutes less pollution per year.
23. Carbon monoxide reduces the ability of the blood to carry oxygen to body cells and thus causes a lack of energy and, if taken in long enough, causes death.
24. Some scientists think that acid rain can kill crops, resulting in a shortage of some kinds of food.
25. Tinnitus can cause a lack of sleep and thus affect concentration and learning.

UNIT 10 STUDY GUIDE

Key Terms Review

Match the following definitions with the correct Key Terms. Do not write in this book.

a. conservation *(p. 618)*
b. dioxins *(p. 608)*
c. geothermal energy *(p. 619)*
d. graffiti *(p. 615)*
e. habitat *(p. 600)*
f. health advocacy *(p. 626)*
g. landfill *(p. 618)*
h. natural environment *(p. 626)*
i. particulates *(p. 603)*
j. smog *(p. 604)*
k. tinnitus *(p. 614)*
l. wildlife sanctuary *(p. 627)*

1. a ringing in the ears
2. a place where a plant normally grows
3. air pollution that is in the form of fine liquid or solid particles
4. what water that is heated underground produces
5. a place reserved to protect animals
6. chemicals used in insecticides
7. plants, animals, insects, mountains, oceans, and the sky
8. unauthorized writing or drawings on buildings
9. a mixture of gases in the air that cause air pollution
10. trash that is buried in layers of dirt

Recalling the Facts

11. What are two factors that have increased world population? *(Lesson 56)*
12. What are two federal agencies that help protect the environment? *(Lesson 56)*
13. Name three kinds of waste substances that can pollute the air. *(Lesson 57)*
14. What is released into the air after fossil fuels burn? *(Lesson 57)*
15. What is the relationship between loudness and decibels? *(Lesson 58)*
16. What are two effects of tinnitus on health? *(Lesson 58)*
17. What are some commonly recycled materials? *(Lesson 59)*
18. Name three types of fossil fuels. *(Lesson 59)*
19. Name five places that can help you enjoy the natural environment. *(Lesson 60)*
20. Name two ways to be a health advocate. *(Lesson 60)*

Critical Thinking

21. Why can the greenhouse effect cause the temperature to rise? *(Lesson 56)*
22. How could one person have an impact on pollution if he or she decides to bicycle ten minutes to school instead of drive? Use a numerical example. *(Lesson 57)*
23. Why can inhaling carbon monoxide cause you to feel tired? *(Lesson 57)*
24. How can acid rain affect the food you eat? *(Lesson 57)*
25. Why might a person who has tinnitus suffer from poor grades? *(Lesson 58)*
26. Why would a teen need to worry about acoustic trauma? *(Lesson 58)*
27. Why should plastics not be placed in a compost pile? *(Lesson 59)*
28. How can the sun heat a home? *(Lesson 59)*
29. How can the natural environment affect a person's quality of life and susceptibility to disease? *(Lesson 60)*
30. How can being a health advocate serve to help your community? *(Lesson 60)*

Use **Interactive Tutor** at **www.glencoe.com** for additional help.

---

26. Damage to teens' hearing can be temporary, but it also can be permanent. As people age, their hearing may naturally decline. If a teen starts with a lessened ability to hear, he or she may suffer great hearing loss as he or she ages.
27. Plastics are not biodegradable.
28. The sun can be used to produce solar energy, which can, in turn, be used to heat a home.

29. The natural environment can provide a place to relax, exercise, or watch animals. All of these things can help reduce stress. Stress can put a person at risk for certain diseases. Also, a polluted environment can put a person's health at risk.
30. A health advocate can take actions to improve the community, such as taking the initiative to organize a community clean-up campaign.

Health Literacy Activities

What Do You Know?
Critical Thinking Some people think that a single person cannot have an impact on a community. In 5 minutes, make a list of ways one person can improve his or her community. Share your list with your classmates, crossing out items that other classmates had listed. The person with the most unique answers wins.

Connection to Art
Responsible Citizenship Select a natural environment in which to spend a few hours. You might spend time in a community park or a nature preserve. Describe your visit in a creative manner. You might write a poem or story or draw a picture that describes your experience.

Family Involvement
Problem Solving Evaluate your family's precycling and recycling habits and how you dispose of waste. What are your precycling and recycling habits? How do you dispose of solid waste? What changes might you make to precycle, recycle, and dispose of waste more efficiently? Discuss your ideas with a parent or guardian.

Investigating Health Careers
Self-Directed Learning There are many different kinds of careers to help the environment. Using the library, select one career and identify the job tasks, education needed, and rewards of pursuing this career. You also could interview a person who has an environmental career to help you identify job tasks, etc. Create a brochure promoting the chosen career. Give a 5-minute presentation to your classmates regarding the career you chose.

Group Project
Effective Communication In a group of four students, research a type of power plant. You might research an oil refinery, a hydroelectric power plant, or a geothermal power plant. Make a diagram describing the power plant, including the flow of energy and the working parts, and share it with your classmates. Discuss which type of power plant is safer, least expensive to maintain, efficient, etc. Visit **www.glencoe.com** for more information.

Standardized Test Practice

Read the following selection and answer the questions that follow.

Since 1992, consumers have had a way to easily choose household appliances that use less water and energy. Energy Star is a program of the federal government's Environmental Protection Agency. Energy Star-rated appliances feature advanced technology, which allows them to use from 10 percent to 50 percent less energy than other appliances. For example, an Energy Star refrigerator on the market today uses 40 percent less energy than a refrigerator sold just two years ago. A family that trades in a ten-year-old refrigerator for a new Energy Star model would save enough electricity to light their home for three months! A new Energy Star washing machine saves up to 22 gallons of water every load.

 www.glencoe.com

Multiple Choice

1 Which statement best describes the author's attitude?
  A Energy Star is a way to choose energy-efficient appliances.
  B Energy Star places labels on selected appliances.
  C People who don't use Energy Star are irresponsible.
  D Appliances made before 1992 are not energy-efficient.

2 In this paragraph, the word *feature* means
  A characteristic   C invented
  B buy   D have

Open-Ended

3 Energy Star appliances often cost more than non-Energy Star models. Write a paragraph explaining why you feel the extra cost is either justified or not justified. Support your explanation with reasons.

Health Literacy Activities

What Do You Know?
Answers will vary, but might include picking up trash along the road, planting flowers and trees, organizing a recycling program, etc.

Connection to Art
Answers will vary. Provide students with a list of parks, nature preserves, conservatories, or zoos and botanical gardens they could visit in your area. If there are none within a reasonable distance, students could complete the activity in their own backyards.

Family Involvement
Answers will vary. Ask students to find out about recycling services that are available in your community. Discuss ways to encourage more people to make use of them.

Investigating Health Careers
Student presentations will vary. Before students begin their research, ask them what careers have been chosen, and, if necessary, suggest alternate careers to ensure that student presentations cover a variety of options.

Group Project
Check groups' diagrams for detail and correctness.

Standardized Test Practice

Multiple Choice
1. A   2. D

Open-Ended
3. Students' paragraphs should offer support for their position. For example, those who feel that the extra cost is justified may cite the beneficial effect of saving energy and water on the environment. Those who feel the extra cost is not justified may claim that the difference that one household can make is negligible, or that many families cannot spend more on appliances. Paragraphs should contain correct spelling, capitalization, punctuation, grammar, usage, and sentence structure.

Injury Prevention and Personal Safety

STANDARDS AND FEATURES

Lesson	National Standards	State/Local Standards	Activities and Features
Lesson 61 *(2 sessions, 1 block)* Reducing Unintentional Injuries	1.1, 1.5, 4.1, 4.2, 6.3, 7.1, 7.3		**Using Life Skills:** Using Goal-Setting and Decision-Making Skills: Creating a Contract for Motor Vehicle Safety, p. 648
Lesson 62 *(1 session, 1 block)* Staying Safe During Severe Weather and Natural Disasters	2.5, 2.10, 4.1, 6.3, 7.1, 7.3, 8.2		
Lesson 63 *(2 sessions, 1 block)* Reducing the Risk of Violence	1.1, 1.3, 1.5, 2.1, 2.3, 2.5, 2.10, 4.1, 4.3, 6.3, 7.1, 7.2		**Using Life Skills:** Setting Health Goals and Using Decision-Making Skills: Patterns of Behavior Test, p. 662
Lesson 64 *(1 session, 1 block)* Respecting Authority and Obeying Laws	1.5, 1.8, 1.9, 2.1, 2.3, 4.1, 4.2, 5.7, 6.3		
Lesson 65 *(3 sessions, 1 block)* Protecting Yourself From Physical Violence	1.1, 1.5, 1.8, 1.9, 2.1, 2.3, 2.10, 4.1, 5.7, 6.3, 7.1, 7.2, 7.3		**Health News:** Violence Against Women Act, p. 681
Lesson 66 *(4 sessions, 2 blocks)* Protecting Yourself From Sexual Violence	1.5, 2.10, 3.4, 3.5, 4.1. 4.2, 4.3, 4.4, 5.3, 5.5, 6.3, 7.1, 7.3, 8.2		**Using Life Skills:** Resistance Skills: Reducing the Risk of Date Rape, p. 689 **Facts About:** Date-Rape Drugs, p. 690 **Just the Facts:** Rape, p. 693
Lesson 67 *(2 sessions, 1 block)* Staying Away From Gangs	1.5, 1.8, 1.9, 2.1, 2.3, 4.1, 4.4, 7.2, 7.3, 8.2, 8.3, 8.4		
Lesson 68 *(1 session, 1 block)* Reducing Weapon Injuries	1.1, 1.5, 1.9, 2.10		
Lesson 69 *(5 sessions, 2 blocks)* Performing Common First Aid Procedures	1.1, 1.5, 3.4, 4.1, 5.3, 5.5, 6.3, 7.1, 7.2		**Speaking Out:** Getting First Aid Training, p. 713
Lesson 70 *(4 sessions, 1 block)* Performing Emergency First Aid Procedures	1.3, 1.5, 2.1, 2.3, 2.5, 3.2, 4.1, 4.4, 6.3, 7.2, 7.3, 8.3		

Key to Differentiated Instruction

L1 Level 1 activities should be appropriate for students with learning difficulties.

L2 Level 2 activities should be within the ability range of all students.

L3 Level 3 activities are designed for above-average students.

ELL ELL activities should be within the ability range of English language learners.

FAST FILE RESOURCES

INTRODUCING THE UNIT

Parent and Family Letter	p. 1	Health Behavior Contract	p. 3
Spanish Parent and Family Letter	p. 2	Unit Focus Transparency Master and Worksheet	p. 4

TEACHING THE UNIT LESSONS

Reproducible Student Pages	Lesson 61	Lesson 62	Lesson 63	Lesson 64	Lesson 65	Lesson 66	Lesson 67	Lesson 68	Lesson 69	Lesson 70
Reading Strategy	p. 7	p. 19	p. 31	p. 43	p. 55	p. 69	p. 83	p. 95	p. 107	p. 119
Vocabulary Practice	p. 8	p. 20	p. 32	p. 44	p. 56	p. 70	p. 84	p. 96	p. 108	p. 120
Transparency Master and Worksheet	p. 9	p. 21	p. 33	p. 45	p. 57	p. 71	p. 85	p. 97	p. 109	p. 121
Real-Life Health	p. 11	p. 23	p. 35	p. 47	p. 59	p. 73	p. 87	p. 99	p. 111	p. 123
5-Minute Check	p. 15	p. 27	p. 39	p. 51	p. 63	p. 77	p. 91	p. 103	p. 115	p. 127
Lesson Quiz	p. 16	p. 28	p. 40	p. 52	p. 65	p. 79	p. 92	p. 104	p. 116	p. 131

CLOSING THE UNIT

Family Involvement Activity	p. 135	Health in the News	p. 145
Community Involvement Activity	p. 137	Health Career Research Activity	p. 147
Health Lab	p. 139	Unit Test A	p. 149
Activity: Strengthening Health Skills	p. 143	Unit Test B	p. 153

Technology

Glencoe Exclusive!

TeacherWorks™
All-In-One Planner and Resource Center

- **Interactive Chalkboard CD-ROM**
- **TeacherWorks™ CD-ROM**
- **StudentWorks™ CD-ROM**
- **Reading Essentials CD-ROM**
- **Exam*View*® Assessment Suite**

www.glencoe.com
- **Vocabulary Puzzlemaker**
- **Interactive Tutor**
- **Your Health Checklist**
- **Web Links**
- **Student Web Activities**

Injury Prevention and Personal Safety

TEST YOUR INJURY IQ

Use the three statements on the student page to initiate a class discussion about injury prevention and personal safety. *Additional True/False statements are:*

4. **Most homicides are committed by someone whom the victim knows.**
   TRUE: Most homicides follow arguments and fights between people who know each other.

5. **Unintentional injuries are the leading cause of death in the United States in the age group 1–34.**
   TRUE: In 2002, more than 90,000 people died as a result of unintentional injuries.

6. **In an emergency situation no one will be able to provide assistance before the EMTs arrive.**
   FALSE: In 2002, nearly 12 million people learned lifesaving skills such as water safety, first aid, and CPR.

in the news Predator Database

Discuss Have students discuss the advantages and disadvantages of having a public database that lists individuals convicted of abusing children. Some issues to address are the rights of the criminal who has served his or her sentence and the rights of the community in which the criminal resides. **L2**

Injury Prevention and Personal Safety

> "In the long run, we shape our lives, and we shape ourselves. The process never ends until we die. And the choices we make are ultimately our own responsibility."
>
> —Eleanor Roosevelt, First Lady and U.S. delegate to the United Nations

TEST YOUR INJURY IQ
True or False?

1. **Lightning is the leading cause of weather-related deaths in the United States.**
   FALSE: Floods are the leading cause. Lightning is second. Lightning is, however, the most dangerous and most frequently encountered weather hazard that people experience.

2. **Fifty-two percent of motor vehicle accidents occur less than five miles from home.**
   TRUE: Car accidents are more likely to occur during short trips than long trips. Always wear your safety belt, regardless of how far you are going.

3. **Everyone who stays in an abusive relationship doesn't want to get out.**
   FALSE: Since a major component of abuse is isolation, the victim lacks a support system, and therefore, is dependent on the abuser.

in the news Predator Database

Discuss Over the past few years, public databases have been established that list individuals convicted of abusing children. Research how these databases work. Discuss with your class the arguments for and against having these databases. Write a report on the results of your research.

LESSON 61	LESSON 62	LESSON 63	LESSON 64	LESSON 65
Reducing Unintentional Injuries	Staying Safe During Severe Weather and Natural Disasters	Reducing the Risk of Violence	Respecting Authority and Obeying Laws	Protecting Yourself from Physical Violence

636   UNIT 11 • Injury Prevention and Personal Safety

Two-Minute Unit Launcher

Discussion Tornado safety procedures vary depending on a person's location. On the chalkboard or overhead, draw a floor plan of a house without a basement, a house with a basement, a mobile home, and a motor vehicle. Have students discuss the safest place to be for each floor plan if a tornado is in the vicinity. Ask students where they should go if a tornado is in the vicinity while school is in session. Ask students to give reasons for their choices. Tell students that they should compare their answers to what they learn as they study Lesson 62. **L2**

EVALUATING MEDIA MESSAGES

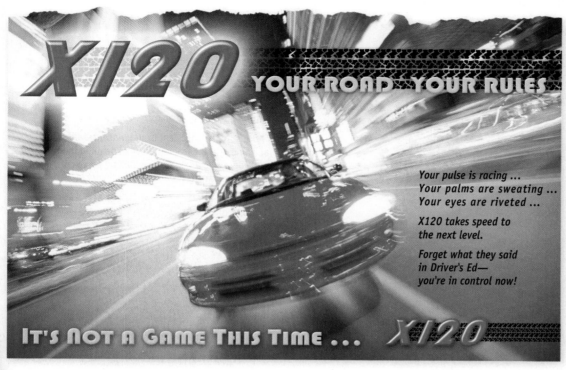

X120
YOUR ROAD · YOUR RULES

Your pulse is racing ...
Your palms are sweating ...
Your eyes are riveted ...

X120 takes speed to the next level.

Forget what they said in Driver's Ed— you're in control now!

IT'S NOT A GAME THIS TIME ... X120

 WHAT'S YOUR VERDICT?
To evaluate this advertisement, use the criteria for analyzing and evaluating health messages delivered through media and technology that you learned in Unit 1.

Visit www.glencoe.com to find regularly updated statistics about U.S. natural disasters. Using the information provided, determine the answer to this question: What U.S. natural disasters occurred last year?

Visit www.glencoe.com to use *Your Health Checklist* ✔, an interactive tool that helps you determine your health status.

LESSON 66	LESSON 67	LESSON 68	LESSON 69	LESSON 70
Protecting Yourself From Sexual Violence	Staying Away from Gangs	Reducing the Risk of Weapon Injuries	Performing Common First Aid Procedures	Performing Emergency First Aid Procedures

UNIT 11 • Injury Prevention and Personal Safety **637**

Health Online

Answers Flooding, wild fires, hurricanes, and tornadoes all caused damage to homes, businesses, and nature last year. It is an individual's responsibility to know the meanings of different tones of sirens, and the safety procedures for different natural disasters. Students can check healthmh.com or contact local agencies to find out how their area is alerted to natural disasters, what they should do to prepare their family and home for a natural disaster, and how they can be sure that they would be aware of a natural disaster warning (i.e., where is the nearest siren?).

 What's Your Verdict?

Evaluating Ads Discuss the advertisement with the class. Ask students the following questions: What advertising strategies are being used to sell the product? Who is the target audience? Does the advertisement encourage responsible and safe behavior? Ask students to identify advertisements they have seen that encourage safe behavior and advertisements they have seen that encourage unsafe behavior. **L2**

Health Journal

Write an Essay Ask students to write an essay in their health journals about how they have kept themselves safe during the past week. Encourage students to write about decisions that they had to make; for example, whether or not they should pass a slower moving vehicle while driving. **L2**

INTERACTIVE CHALKBOARD with Image Bank

Unit Focus Transparency
Page 4, **Unit 11 Fast Files Resources**

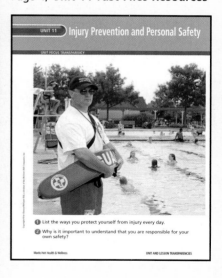

National Health Education Standards
Pages 636–637: 1.1, 1.3, 2.6, 2.10, 6.3, 7.2, 8.2, 8.3

Reducing Unintentional Injuries

LESSON 61

Out of Time?

Reducing Unintentional Injuries

If time does not permit an in-depth study of this topic, use the following activities in this Teacher Wraparound Edition:

- Class Activity, p. 640
- Class Discussion, p. 642
- 5-Minute Check, p. 644
- Explain the Concept, p. 646

1 Focus

HEALTH GOALS **Motor Vehicle Safety** Have students respond to the second Health Goal for this lesson by listing ways to reduce the possibility of motor vehicle-related injuries. *Answers might include wearing safety belts, not riding with someone who is under the influence of drugs or alcohol, maintaining vehicle safety, using child restraints, and obeying traffic laws.* **L2**

Write ABOUT IT!

Discuss Have students discuss their responses to this situation. On the chalkboard or overhead transparency, list ideas that the class thinks are safe solutions. *Safe solutions might include, asking a parent or guardian to supervise the pool or spa area while they swim, or waiting until the lifeguard is on duty to swim.* **L2**

What You'll Learn

1. Analyze ways to reduce the risk of unintentional injuries in the community. *(p. 639)*
2. Analyze ways to reduce the risk of unintentional injuries in the home. *(p. 640)*
3. Analyze ways to reduce the risk of unintentional injuries in the workplace. *(p. 642)*
4. Analyze ways to reduce the risk of unintentional injuries in motor vehicles. *(p. 644)*
5. Analyze ways a person can reduce the risk of injury from road rage. *(p. 647)*

Why It's Important

Unintended injuries may be prevented by living a healthy lifestyle, ensuring a safe environment, and avoiding unnecessary risks.

Key Terms

- heat detector
- smoke detector
- suffocation
- repetitive strain injury (RSI)
- Occupational Safety and Health Act (OSH Act)
- graduated license
- high-risk driving
- child safety restraint
- Lower Anchors and Tethers for Children (LATCH)
- road rage

Reducing Unintentional Injuries

HEALTH GOALS
- I will follow safety guidelines to reduce the risk of unintentional injuries.
- I will follow guidelines for motor vehicle safety.

An injury that results from an accident is an *unintentional* injury. Unintentional injuries are the leading cause of death in the United States for people ages 1 to 34. More than 90,000 people die, and about 31 million people go to emergency rooms as a result of unintentional injuries.

Write ABOUT IT!

Writing About Reducing Risk Suppose your family is on vacation. You and your brother want to swim in the hotel pool, but there is a sign that says "No lifeguard on duty before 10:00 A.M. and after 8:00 P.M. Swim at your own risk." Your brother says, "Come on, we both know how to swim." After you read the information about ways to reduce the risk of drowning on page 639, write a response to this situation in your health journal.

National Health Education Standards—Guide for Lesson 61					
1.1	Predict how healthy behaviors can impact health status.	p. 639	6.3	Implement strategies and monitor progress in achieving a personal health goal.	p. 649
1.5	Propose ways to reduce or prevent injuries and health problems.	pp. 638, 639, 642, 647, 648, 649,	7.1	Analyze the role of individual responsibility for enhancing health.	pp. 639-642, 644, 645, 646, 647, 649
4.1	Utilize skills for communicating effectively with family, peers, and others to enhance health.	pp. 638, 649			
4.2	Demonstrate refusal, negotiation, and collaboration skills to enhance health and avoid or reduce health risks.	p. 638	7.3	Demonstrate a variety of behaviors to avoid or reduce health risks to self and others.	pp. 638, 639-642, 644, 645, 646, 647, 649

Injuries in the Community

Injuries in the Community

Teens often are injured in the community. They may be injured because they disregard safety guidelines, because peers may influence them to be daring, or because they are stressed or overtired and careless or less alert.

What to Know About Unintentional Injuries in the Community

Bicycling Almost 600,000 people are treated in emergency rooms for bicycle-related injuries each year. Most deaths and serious injuries due to bicycling involve head injuries. The most serious injuries occur when bikes collide with motor vehicles.

Drowning Many drownings occur in swimming pools and hot tubs. Young children also drown in bathtubs, toilets, and sinks. People who are strong swimmers can become tired or be pulled under by the current and drown. Drowning also can result from boating accidents. Alcohol is a major factor in teen-related drownings and most boating accidents.

Ways to Reduce the Risk of Injuries from Bicycling Accidents

- Wear a bicycle helmet and shoes.
- Obey traffic rules followed by motor vehicle drivers.
- Ride on the right, with the flow of traffic.
- Check that the bicycle and all safety equipment are in good condition.
- Wear clothing that will not get caught in the chain of the bicycle. Wear reflective clothing at night.
- Watch for the sudden opening of motor vehicle doors.
- Walk the bicycle across busy streets.
- Do not ride with another person on the bicycle.
- Beware of unsafe road conditions, such as ice and potholes.

Ways to Reduce the Risk of Drowning

- Learn to swim and have training before participating in water sports.
- Never swim or use a hot tub alone and do not leave children alone near water.
- Swim only in well-lit designated areas and in sight of a lifeguard.
- Stay out of the water in threatening weather.
- Leave the water if you have cramps or are tired.
- Enforce an alcohol-free policy around water.
- Wear a life jacket when participating in water sports.
- Never boat with others who speed or do not follow safety guidelines.
- Do not overload a boat or personal watercraft.
- Check the depth of water before entering.
- Install a childproof fence around pools.
- Do not walk on untested ice.

LESSON 61 • Reducing Unintentional Injuries **639**

Lesson Resource Manager

- **Unit 11 Fast File Resources**
  Reading Strategy, p. 7
  Vocabulary Practice, p. 8
  Transparency Master and Worksheet, p. 9
  Real-Life Health, p. 11
  Real-Life Health, p. 13
  5-Minute Check, p. 15
  Lesson 61 Quiz, p. 16
- **Unit 11 Transparency**
- **Lesson 61 Transparency**

- **Reading Essentials**
- **Technology**
  TeacherWorks™ CD-ROM
  StudentWorks™ CD-ROM
  Reading Essentials CD-ROM
  ExamView® Assessment Suite
  Vocabulary Puzzlemaker

Injuries in the Community

2 Teach

Explain the Concept

Alcohol Effects Explain to students why alcohol is a major factor in drownings and boating accidents. Explain that judgment, memory, and sensory perception are impaired by alcohol. One drink will make the average person feel relaxed. Two-and-a-half drinks in one hour can affect the average person's judgment and lower his or her inhibitions. After five drinks, the average person will experience blurred vision, slurred speech, poor muscle coordination, and a lack of rational judgment.

PowerPoint® Presentations
This CD-ROM is an editable Microsoft® PowerPoint® presentation that includes:
- Lesson presentations
- Lesson checks
- Interactive graphics
- 5-Minute Checks
- Image Bank
- All transparencies

Discussion Refer to the Seed Discussion Strategy on page 17T in order to stimulate discussion on unintentional injuries and injuries from car wrecks.

National Health Education Standards
Pages 638–639: 1.1, 1.5, 4.1, 4.2, 7.1, 7.3

639

Injuries in the Home

Class Activity

Home Injury After reading Injuries in the Home, ask students to survey their homes. Have them make a list of possible hazards. Ask students to write how to reduce the risk of injury that might be caused by these hazards. **L2**

Extension

Graphs Divide the class into groups. Ask each group to research the types of unintentional injuries commonly treated at a local emergency room. Have students make a multimedia presentation including charts or graphs of the results. Ask each group to share their presentation with the class. **L3**

Teacher FYI

Poisonous Houseplants Ingestion of household plants by children under age five is the leading reason for inquiries reported to poison control centers nationwide. Houseplants can refresh indoor air by replacing the carbon dioxide we exhale with oxygen and absorbing pollutants. However, many popular houseplants can be poisonous to children and pets.

Injuries in the Home

Many accidents that result in injury and death occur in the home. A few easy and inexpensive steps can be taken to make the home a safe environment.

What to Know About Unintentional Injuries in the Home

Make the Connection

Poisoning For more information about first aid for poisoning, see page 745 in Lesson 70.

Poisoning A harmful chemical reaction from a substance that enters the body is called *poisoning.* Most poisonings in the home result from children swallowing household products and OTC drugs. Taking very high doses of vitamin and mineral supplements also may result in poisoning.

Some substances cause poisoning when inhaled, such as glue, gasoline, and carbon monoxide. *Carbon monoxide* is an odorless, tasteless gas emitted from motor vehicles, gas stoves, heaters, lawn mowers, and chimneys.

Falls Falls can be caused by hazards, such as poor lighting, loose carpets, trailing wires, and unsteady stair rails. Falls can result in spinal cord injuries. Young children are at particular risk because their sense of balance is not fully developed. Teens injured due to falls often have taken unnecessary risks and may have ignored safety precautions or been showing off.

Ways to Reduce the Risk of Poisoning

- Use childproof containers for potential poisons and keep them out of the reach of children.
- Place warning stickers on any potential poisons.
- Place childproof latches on the doors of all cabinets in which harmful substances are kept.
- Do not keep a motor vehicle or lawn mower running in a closed garage.
- Do not use outdoor grills indoors.
- Check chimneys for blockage, and have them cleaned regularly.

Ways to Reduce the Risk of Falls

- Do not take risks in high places.
- Use a sturdy ladder when climbing. Keep your body in the center of the step and face the ladder when climbing down.
- Place an infant or young child in a playpen, crib, or safety seat when out of your sight.
- Use appropriate child safety devices to block stairways and windows.
- Be cautious if wearing shoes with slippery bottoms or high heels.

 Sensitive Issues

Injuries and Death Students may know someone who has suffered a serious injury, or they may have known someone who died. Grieving takes time. Students should acknowledge and accept all feelings, both positive and negative. Crying offers a release. Encourage students to discuss their feelings openly and honestly with friends, family, teachers, or other trusted adults. Suggest using a journal to express their thoughts and feelings. Encourage students to get involved in activities again. Suggest that students join a support group that can provide an opportunity to share with others who have experienced similar loss. If the healing process becomes too overwhelming, encourage students to seek professional help. Have a list of support groups, counselors, and resources available for students.

Fires Most deaths and injuries related to fire occur in the home. Home fires are often caused by improper use and disposal of candles, cigarettes, lighters, and matches. All homes should be equipped with a fire extinguisher, a heat detector, and at least one smoke detector on each floor.

A *heat detector* is an alarm that sounds when the room temperature rises above a certain level. A *smoke detector* is an alarm that sounds when smoke is detected. A fire escape plan should be set up in advance that includes two different ways to escape from each room and a meeting place outside the home. Take the following actions if your home is on fire: Cover your mouth and nose with cloth to filter the air. Crawl out of the home to stay below the smoke. Do not open doors that feel warm or hot and open cool doors slowly. Call 911 or the fire department after you have escaped. Meet family members at the designated meeting place. Do not go back into a burning building. Tell fire officials if people or animals are inside the building. If a door is hot and cannot be opened, stuff rugs, blankets, or clothes around door cracks to stop smoke from entering. Call out a window for help.

Airway obstruction An obstruction of the airway by an external object that blocks the mouth and nose, such as plastic bags, pillows, or blankets, is *suffocation.* The result of an obstruction of the airway by an internal object, such as food or small toys, is *choking.* The result of external compression of the airway when an object, such as a cord, string, jewelry, or crib slats compresses the neck, is *strangulation.*

Top Ten Injuries for Ages 14–18 in the U.S. in 2000

Cause of Death	Number of Deaths	Percentage of Deaths
MV traffic	4,062	77.7%
Drowning	340	6.5%
Poisoning	226	4.3%
Other land transport	134	2.6%
Firearm	100	1.9%
Fire, burn	82	1.6%
Pedestrian, other	81	1.6%
Other transport	68	1.3%
Suffocation	67	1.3%
Fall	64	1.2%
Total Deaths	5,224	

Source: Produced by: Office of Statistics and Programming, National Center for Injury Prevention and Control, CDC. Data Source: National Center for Health Statistics' (NCHS) Vital Statistics System for numbers of deaths.

Ways to Reduce the Risk of Fires

- Have a no smoking policy in the home to reduce the risk of fires.
- Keep all matches, cigarette lighters, and flames out of children's reach.
- Do not overload electrical outlets or run cords under rugs.
- Do not leave items, such as irons or electric hair styling products, plugged in for long periods of time.
- Do not leave food cooking on the stove unattended; check food cooking in the oven often.

Ways to Reduce the Risk of Suffocation

- Keep small objects out of the reach of children.
- Do not allow children to play with plastic bags or toys that are not appropriate for their age.
- Check sleeping infants and children to be sure their breathing is not blocked by a pillow, blanket, or stuffed toy.
- Cut food into small pieces that are easy to swallow.
- Do not tie a rope or cord around the neck, even as a joke.

LESSON 61 • Reducing Unintentional Injuries **641**

Family Involvement

Smoke Detectors Have students discuss ways to reduce the risk of fires with their families. Ask students, with their families, to test the smoke detectors in their home. Heat and carbon monoxide detectors also can be tested if they are present. Have students replace batteries if needed. Ask students, with their families, to set up a fire escape plan for their house. Remind students that their fire escape plan should include two different ways to escape from each room and a designated meeting place outside the home. Ask students to present their fire escape plans to the class. **L2**

NHES Assessment/SCASS

Constructed Response Ask students to list possible fire hazards in the kitchen. Have students write possible ways to reduce the risk of a fire in the kitchen. *Ways to reduce risk may include: Never leave food that is cooking unattended. Always set a kitchen timer. Keep stove surfaces free of clutter. Do not hang curtains or towel racks close to the stove. Keep flammable liquids away from the stove. Do not overload outlets. Have a fire extinguisher in the kitchen. Keep all of the vents on microwave ovens cleared of obstructions.* **L2**

Extension

Contact Fire Department Have students contact the local fire department to determine common causes of fires in the community during the past year. Ask students to prepare a poster or graph illustrating their findings, and then make a presentation to the class. **L3**

Quick Demo

Smoke Detector Bring in a battery-powered home smoke detector. Show students how to test the battery of the smoke detector. Also, demonstrate how to change the battery when it dies. **ELL**

National Health Education Standards

Pages 640–641: 7.1, 7.3

Class Discussion

Teen Jobs Ask students if they have part-time jobs. List the types of jobs that they have. Ask students to identify any aspects of their job that might be dangerous. Ask if they know of anyone who has been injured at their workplace and if so, what types of injuries occurred. Ask for suggestions to reduce these workplace injuries. **L2**

Class Activity

Newspaper Bring the Help Wanted section of a local newspaper to class. Ask students to locate at least five different types of jobs in the employment section of the classified ads. For each of the jobs, have students hypothesize whether the jobs have possible health hazards, such as repetitive strain injury affecting computer operators. Ask students to brainstorm ideas of ways to prevent the injuries mentioned. **L2**

Injuries in the Workplace

A work-related injury is any injury acquired while working. The injury does not have to be the result of one specific event. Repetitive strain injuries, such as back strain and carpal tunnel syndrome, are legitimate workers compensation claims. Teens are more likely to be hurt on the job than adults.

How to Reduce the Risk of Injury in the Workplace

Did You Know?

Workplace Injury
Each year, over 200,000 teens are injured on the job, around 100,000 of those seriously enough to need emergency room treatment. About 70 of those injuries are fatal.

Are there any rules about minors who work? The Fair Labor Standards Act (FLSA) contains child labor laws to protect the health and safety of minors. The act limits the hours minors under age 16 can work, and prohibits employing minors under age 18 for certain occupations.

What types of injuries occur in the workplace? Common workplace injuries to teens involve lacerations, contusions, abrasions, sprains and strains, bruises, burns, fractures, and dislocations. Most teen work injuries occur where the most teen workers are employed—retail shops, restaurants, and grocery stores. More teen workers are injured than adult workers, even though teens are prohibited from working at dangerous jobs.

What is repetitive strain injury? An increasingly common workplace injury is *repetitive strain injury (RSI)*, which is an injury that occurs from repeated physical movements.

RSI damages tendons, nerves, muscles, and other soft body tissues. Symptoms include tingling; tightness; pain and stiffness in hands, wrists, fingers, arms, and elbows; and weakness in hands. To prevent RSI when typing, sit straight and relax hands and wrists. Keep the computer screen at eye level and position the keyboard so hands and wrists are straight. Take regular breaks when using a computer.

What should my employer do to protect my health and safety? Your employer must meet safety guidelines for healthful working conditions. The *Occupational Safety and Health Act (OSH Act)* is a series of health and safety standards that all employers must meet. Recognized health hazards must be eliminated. Employees must regularly review safety regulations. New employees must be trained on equipment and made aware of hazards. Also, minors are prohibited from working dangerous jobs by the FLSA.

⚖ Legal Issues

Rights and Responsibilities of Teen Workers Occupational Safety and Health Administration (OSHA) laws help keep teens healthy and safe while on the job. Have students research the rights and responsibilities of teen workers. Ask them to write a report on their findings. *Rights should include: a safe and healthful workplace; refusal to work if you feel unsafe; report safety hazards; work only the hours and types of jobs permitted; use protective equipment when necessary; health and safety training; paid at least minimum wage; payment of medical care if injured or sick due to the job; work without racial or sexual harassment. Responsibilities should include: follow safety and health rules; use required equipment; follow safe work practices; ask questions; tell a supervisor if you feel threatened, or endangered, unsafe or uncomfortable; be aware of your environment; be involved in improving worksite safety and health.* **L3**

TABLE 61.1 FLSA Bans for All Minors Under the Age of 18

Hazardous Occupations	Examples and Exemptions
1. Manufacturing or storing explosives	Bans working where explosives are manufactured or stored, but permits work in retail stores selling ammunition, gun shops, trap and skeet ranges, and police stations.
2. Driving or working as an outside helper on motor vehicles	Bans operating motor vehicles and working as outside helpers on motor vehicles (17-year-olds may drive during daylight hours for limited times and under limited circumstances).
3. Coal mining	Bans most jobs in coal mines.
4. Logging and sawmilling	Bans most jobs in logging and timbering (including cutting firewood) and in sawmills.
5. Power-driven woodworking machines	Bans the operation of power-driven woodworking machines, including chain saws, nailing machines, and sanders.
6. Exposure to radiation	Bans exposure to radioactive substances and ionizing radiation.
7. Power-driven hoisting apparatuses	Bans the operation of power-driven hoisting apparatuses, such as forklifts and non-automatic elevators, but does not apply to chairlifts or to lifts used to raise cars in garages.
8. Power-driven, metal-forming, punching, and shearing machines	Bans the operation of power-driven metal-working machines, but permits the use of most machine tools.
9. Mining other than coal	Bans most jobs at metal mines, quarries, aggregate mines, and other mining sites, including underground mines, open-cut mines, quarries, and sand and gravel operations.
10. Power-driven meat-processing machines, slaughtering, and meat packing plants	Bans the operation of power-driven meat-processing machines, such as meat slicers, saws, and meat choppers, wherever used, including use on items other than meat, such as cheese and vegetables.
11. Power-driven bakery machines	Bans the operation of power-driven bakery machines, such as vertical mixers (including most countertop models), dough rollers, and dough sheeters.
12. Power-driven paper products machines	Bans the operation of power-driven paper products machines, such as paper balers, box compactors, and printing presses. (16- and 17-year-olds may load, but not operate or unload, certain paper binders and box compactors under specific guidelines.)
13. Manufacturing of brick, tile, and related products	Bans most jobs in the manufacture of brick, tile, and similar products.
14. Power-driven circular saws, band saws, and guillotine shears	Bans the operation of power-driven band and circular saws and guillotine shears.
15. Wrecking, demolition, and ship-breaking	Bans most jobs in wrecking, demolition, and ship-breaking operations, but does not apply to remodeling or repair work that is not extensive.
16. Roofing	Bans most jobs in roofing operations, including ground work and removal of old roofs.
17. Trenching and excavation	Bans most jobs in trenching and excavating work, including trenches over four feet deep.

LESSON 61 • Reducing Unintentional Injuries **643**

Using the Table

Occupations Banned for All Minors Under the Age of 18 Ask students to study Table 61.1. Have students think about reasons minors are banned from these occupations. Have students create a table illustrating the dangers each occupation poses. L2

Extension

Child Labor Laws Ask students to research the need for and the development of child labor laws in the United States. Have students create a multimedia presentation, including a timeline of the development. Ask students to share their presentations with the class. L3

Teacher FYI

Fair Labor Standards Act Approximately 100,000 adolescents are injured in the workplace every year and more than 100 are killed on the job. The Fair Labor Standards Act was enacted in 1938 to protect children in the workplace. It is still enforced today.

Health Project

Child Workers Divide the class into groups. Assign each group one of the following roles: child worker, parents of child worker, farm owner, teacher of child worker, doctor of child worker, government official, and grocery store owner. Ask each group to research children working in agriculture from their character's point of view. Ask each group to present their character's point of view to the class. Allow for class discussion after the presentations. Ask students to write in their health journals why they agreed or disagreed with each point of view. L2

National Health Education Standards
Pages 642–643: 1.5, 2.10, 7.1, 7.3

Motor Vehicle Accidents

INTERACTIVE CHALKBOARD
with Image Bank

5-Minute Check

Page 15, **Unit 11 Fast File Resources**

1. Why are motor vehicle accidents one of the leading causes of teen injury and death? *driver behavior, poor roadway maintenance, roadway design, and equipment failures.*

2. What is carbon monoxide? *an odorless, tasteless gas emitted from motor vehicles, gas-stoves, heaters, lawn-mowers, and chimneys*

3. Why should houses have smoke, heat, and carbon monoxide detectors? *A smoke detector sounds when smoke is detected. A heat detector sounds when room temperature rises above a certain level. A carbon monoxide detector sounds when carbon monoxide is detected.*

4. Why are teens often injured in the community? *disregard safety guidelines, peers influence them to be daring, they are stressed or overtired and careless or less alert*

5. What is the leading cause of death for teenagers? *motor vehicle accidents*

Motor Vehicle Accidents

Motor vehicle accidents are the leading cause of death for teenagers. According to the National Highway Traffic Safety Administration, teenagers are involved in three times as many fatal crashes as other drivers. In the year 2000, over 2500 drivers under the age of 19 died in motor vehicle crashes. Four factors that contribute to many motor vehicle accidents are driver behavior, poor roadway maintenance, roadway design, and equipment failure. Many motor vehicle crashes are caused by excessive speed or aggressive driver behavior.

Did You Know?

Driving Risks Two out of five deaths among U.S. teens are the result of a motor vehicle crash.

Safety Guidelines to Reduce the Risk of Motor Vehicle Accidents

How can I obtain a valid driver's license? You must pass a written and a driving test. Many teens take a driver education course to gain knowledge and skills needed to pass these tests. The courses are required in some states and are offered by schools, organizations, and private companies. Check your state laws and opportunities to learn driving skills. You may have to get a learner's permit or a graduated license first.

A *learner's permit* is an authorization to drive when supervised by a licensed driver of a certain age with no other passengers in the motor vehicle. A *graduated license* is a conditional license given to new drivers that restricts driving privileges, such as being allowed to drive only during the day.

The likelihood of accidents during the first year of driving is high. One in five 16-year-old male drivers and one in ten 16-year-old female drivers has an accident during the first year of driving.

What does it mean to be a defensive driver? A defensive driver is a driver who guards against the unsafe actions of other drivers. Defensive driving is one way to reduce the risk of accidents.

Defensive driving includes taking the following actions: Obey traffic laws, including speed limits. Make sure the intersection is clear when the light turns green. Anticipate what other drivers might do and be prepared to act quickly. Never tailgate. Stay alert.

Other tips for defensive driving include: avoid distractions, such as loud music or talking on a cellular phone while driving. Listen to traffic reports and adjust plans accordingly. Check that all parts of a motor vehicle are working properly.

⚖ Legal Issues

Getting a Driver's License Graduated driver licensing (GDL) introduces drivers to the experience of driving in stages. A comprehensive GDL system consists of a learner's stage, an intermediate stage, and an unrestricted driving stage. GDL optimal provisions include: teens, in the learner's stage, must be 16 years old, must be supervised by an adult when driving, must complete 30–50 hours of supervised driving, and must remain in this stage for six months. Teens in the intermediate stage must have no unsupervised driving at night, must not have more than one teenage passenger, and must remain in this stage until they are 18 years old. People, in the unrestricted driving stage, must be at least 18 years old. Ask students to research the requirements to get a driver's license in your state.
 L2

Driving safely Dangerous driving that can result in crashes is called ***high-risk driving.*** It includes behaviors, such as speeding, trying to beat red lights or a train, racing other drivers, jumping hills, drinking and driving, doing "donuts" or "fishtails," and hanging out of motor vehicles.

Do not ride in a motor vehicle with a driver who chooses high-risk driving. If you are already in the vehicle, ask the driver to stop driving dangerously. If the driver continues to drive recklessly, ask him or her to stop and let you out, and then call another person for a ride.

Are there ways to avoid hitting deer? Motorists most often hit animals at dusk and at dawn. Be a defensive driver. Stay alert and control your speed so you can stop suddenly if needed. If you see an animal in the road, honk your horn with one long blast, but do not flash your lights. Brake firmly, but do not swerve, which can confuse the animal. You also could lose control, and possibly hit another car.

Look for other deer, because deer seldom travel alone. If your vehicle strikes a deer, do not touch it. The frightened deer could hurt you or itself. Move your car off the road and call the police or local game warden.

Do I need to wear a safety belt if my vehicle has an air bag? Yes. An air bag is a cushion in motor vehicles that inflates upon impact. Air bags cushion people from being thrown into the wheel, dashboard, and windshield. A ***safety belt*** is a seat belt and shoulder strap.

Air bags are not a substitute for safety belts. Front air bags often are effective in protecting people involved in frontal crashes, but offer little or no protection in side, rear, and rollover crashes. Some cars have side curtain air bags to protect people involved in side and rollover crashes.

Safety belts should be worn by the driver and passengers at all times. The lap belt should be snug and low across the hips and pelvis, and the shoulder belt should be snug and across the chest and collarbone.

Is it ever safe to drink and drive? No. Drinking alcohol is the leading cause of motor vehicle accidents for teens. Teens involved in motor vehicle accidents that involved drinking may have thought they were safe drivers. Alcohol impairs judgment, reaction time, and motor skills. Drinking is a leading cause of high-risk driving.

What should I do if I suspect that someone who is driving has been drinking? Even if an adult who has been drinking insists he or she is OK, call your parents, guardian, other responsible adult, or a taxi for a ride.

Watch for animals crossing the road, especially at dawn ▼ and at dusk.

LESSON 61 • Reducing Unintentional Injuries **645**

Family Involvement

Black Box New tools are being used to encourage teens to drive safely. The family car can be equipped with a black box that records everything done behind the wheel. It records the car's speed; it also gives a warning when the driver is going too fast, turning too hard, or aggressively accelerating or braking. If the action does not cease within 10 seconds, it is recorded. The trip data can then be downloaded onto a personal computer and reviewed. A bumper sticker can be placed on the family car that asks other drivers to report the driver's behavior on a toll-free telephone line. Ask students to discuss, with their parents or guardian, their opinion of these and similar tools. Have students determine the opinions of their parents or guardian. Have students write a paragraph in their health journals discussing their opinions. **L2**

Teacher FYI

Safety Belts An Insurance Institute for Highway Safety survey concluded that high school students use safety belts less often than occupants of motor vehicles in other age groups. Even when adults are driving and using safety belts, many teens riding with them do not buckle up. The National Highway Traffic Safety Administration reports that, in 2001, two-thirds of teens killed in motor vehicle crashes were not wearing their safety belts at the time of the crash.

NHES Assessment/SCASS

Selected Response Which of the following actions is not recommended if you see an animal on the road?
A. control your speed
B. honk your horn
C. swerve
D. brake firmly

Class Discussion

Owning a Car Using the chalkboard or an overhead transparency, write *small, medium, full-size,* and *SUV.* Ask students to list the advantages and disadvantages of owning a vehicle of each size. *Answers should include: insurance, price of the vehicle, gas mileage, maintenance costs, and crash safety.* **L2**

National Health Education Standards
Pages 644–645: 7.1, 7.3

Crash Impact Bring in scale models or toy cars (economy, mid-sized, family and luxury), trucks, vans and SUVs. Demonstrate where the bumpers of each would impact the other vehicles in an accident. **ELL**

Explain the Concept

Traffic Violations Explain to students that all traffic violations have consequences. They can become part of a person's criminal record. A person's license can be suspended as a result of several minor tickets or, in some cases, one serious ticket. A conviction of a traffic offense, such as reckless driving, speeding, or driving with a suspended license, can result in fines and possibly impact a person's driving record. In addition, a person's insurance company may increase his or her rates.

Reading Review

1. *obey traffic laws, make sure intersections are clear, anticipate actions of other drivers and be prepared to act quickly, never tailgate, stay alert, avoid distractions, check that the motor vehicle is working properly*

2. *speeding, trying to beat red lights or trains, racing, jumping hills, drinking and driving, doing "donuts" or "fishtails," hanging out of a motor vehicle*

3. *a restraint system designed to work independently of the vehicle safety belt system to simplify child safety seat installation*

4. *revoked license, increased insurance rates, fines, and imprisonment*

▲ Child safety seats for older infants face the front.

I will be driving my younger siblings to day care. What actions should I take to ensure their safety? The National Highway Traffic Safety Administration (NHTSA) recommends that all children under the age of 12 should ride in the back seat of a motor vehicle. This protects them from injury due to air bags and puts them farthest away from most impacts.

All infants and small children must be placed in a child safety restraint. A **child safety restraint** is a child safety seat designed for a small child that is secured in the back seat of a motor vehicle. Child safety seats for infants under 20 pounds face the rear. Child safety seats for older infants face the front. Older children who weigh up to 60 pounds may need booster seats. Always read the child safety restraint's directions for proper use.

As of September 1, 2002, the Department of Transportation's National Highway Traffic Safety Administration requires new child safety seats to have a simpler, specialized way of attaching to a vehicle seat. **Lower Anchors and Tethers for Children (LATCH)** is a restraint system designed to work independently of the vehicle seat belt system to simplify child safety seat installation and reduce misuse. The National

Reading Review

1. What actions can be taken when driving defensively?

2. What behaviors are associated with high-risk driving?

3. What is LATCH?

4. What are the consequences of a traffic violation?

Highway Traffic Safety Administration stresses that the proper use of this system will save up to 50 lives per year and prevent nearly 3000 injuries in crashes.

Consequences of a traffic violation Any violation of the current traffic laws is a **traffic violation.** After a certain number of traffic violations, a driver's license can be revoked for a period of time. Motor vehicle insurance rates will increase. A person may have to attend additional driver education classes. Serious violations, such as driving without a license and/or driving under the influence, may result in imprisonment or fines. Committing traffic violations also increases the risk of injuring or killing oneself and others.

How safe are sport utility vehicles (SUVs)? Generally, the lightest vehicles in each class have higher crash rates than heavier vehicles. In an accident involving a heavy and a light vehicle, rates of death are higher among occupants of the light vehicle. Because SUVs and large trucks are high-riding vehicles, in a crash they can override the bumpers on a small motor vehicle and strike occupants in the chest or head.

However, SUVs are more likely than cars to flip over if the driver loses control. The National Highway Traffic Safety Administration reports that SUVs, pickup trucks, and vans are more likely to roll over in a single vehicle crash than passenger cars. Single vehicle crashes do not involve another vehicle and typically are caused by a driver losing control, leaving the road, and hitting an object. Rollover crashes, both single and multi-vehicle, cause roughly 10,000 deaths each year.

DI Differentiated Instruction

Gifted and Talented Ask students to contact the National Commission Against Drunk Driving (NCADD) for pamphlets and other materials. Invite a speaker from NCADD to talk to the class, if possible. Ask students to research similar organizations, such as Recording Artists, Actors and Athletes Against Drunk Driving (RADD) and Students Against Destructive Decisions (SADD). Have students create a pamphlet for each organization. Then have students compare and contrast the information from each organization, and share their observations with the class. **L3**

Motor Vehicle Violence

Teens need to protect themselves from violence while they are driving or riding in motor vehicles. Some people pretend to be helpful and then assault people who have motor vehicle trouble. Others hitchhike and then rob or injure people who stop to give them a ride. Some motorists become violent toward other motorists.

Make the Connection

Conflict Resolution For more information on conflict-resolution skills, see page 51 in Lesson 5.

What to Know About Motor Vehicle Violence

Road rage Any display of aggression by an angry or impatient driver or passenger of a motor vehicle is *road rage.* Examples include verbal abuse, hand gestures, intimidating stares, driving in an intimidating manner, throwing objects at or bumping other vehicles, and threatening another driver.

Events cited as provoking road rage include slow driving, loud music, refusing to allow another motorist to pass or cutting him or her off, taking a parking space, tailgating, and failing to signal. The American Automobile Association (AAA) Foundation for Traffic Safety recommends that to prevent provoking other drivers and passengers, you should avoid eye contact with an aggressive driver, stay calm, do not react to a person trying to provoke you, keep a safe distance from people driving unpredictably, and report incidents of road rage to the police or call 911.

Carjacking Motor vehicle theft that occurs by force, or threat of force, while the driver and/or passengers are still in the motor vehicle is called *carjacking.* Protect yourself by following the strategies listed below.

Ways to Prevent Motor Vehicle Violence

- Have a cell phone to use in case of emergency.
- Keep the fuel tank full and your vehicle in good condition to prevent breakdowns.
- Carry a flashlight, road flares, and a "send help" sign in case your vehicle breaks down.
- Stay in your vehicle and keep your doors locked and your windows rolled up if someone other than a police officer stops to offer help.
- Never leave children in an unattended vehicle.
- Never leave keys in the ignition or the engine running.
- Lock your vehicle at all times and keep your keys with you.
- Keep valuables out of sight.
- Check the seats and the floor before getting into a vehicle.
- Try to drive and park in safe, well-lighted areas.
- If you think you are being followed, go to a public place and call the police.
- Keep your vehicle in gear when at a stoplight.
- Be cautious of anyone approaching your vehicle when it is stopped.
- Drive to a nearby phone and call 911 if someone needs help.
- Never hitchhike or pick up a hitchhiker.
- Do not resist if an armed person demands your vehicle.
- Get a latch for the inside of your trunk so that you can escape if forced inside.

LESSON 61 • Reducing Unintentional Injuries **647**

Using Life Skills

Using Goal-Setting and Decision-Making Skills Divide the class into pairs of students. Have students look at the contract on the student page about motor vehicle safety. Ask students to discuss the contract and any problems that they might face in following it. Have them make modifications to the contract based on personal circumstances. Suggest that students take contracts home to sign with their parents or guardian. **L2**

3 Assess

Vocabulary Practice

Page 8, **Unit 11 Fast File Resources**

Name _____ Date _____ Class _____

LESSON 61 **Reducing Unintentional Injuries**

Vocabulary Practice

Use each vocabulary term given below in a sentence that clearly demonstrates the meaning of the term.

child safety restraint | Occupational Safety and Health Act (OSH Act)
graduated license | road rage
heat detector | repetitive strain injury (RSI)
high-risk driving | smoke detector
Lower Anchors and Tethers for Children (LATCH) | suffocation

1. heat detector _____

2. smoke detector _____

3. suffocation _____

4. repetitive strain injury (RSI) _____

5. Occupational Safety and Health Act (OSH Act) _____

6. graduated license _____

7. high-risk driving _____

8. child safety restraint _____

9. Lower Anchors and Tethers for Children (LATCH) _____

10. road rage _____

8   LESSON 61 • Reducing Unintentional Injuries   UNIT 11

National Health Education Standards

Pages 648–649: 1.5, 2.10, 4.1, 6.2, 6.3, 7.1, 7.3

Activity: Using Life Skills

Using Goal-Setting and Decision-Making Skills: Creating a Contract for Motor Vehicle Safety

Your family and friends count on you to be a safe driver and to think about safety when you ride with others. Thinking responsibly will help you avoid injury to yourself and others. It will also protect your family's property and keep your insurance costs from rising. Setting goals for safety using a contract will help you make responsible decisions when you use a motor vehicle.

1 Describe the situation that requires a decision. List possible decisions that you might make (or have made). With a partner, list several decisions you made recently as a driver or passenger in a motor vehicle.

2 Share the list of possible decisions with a parent, guardian, or other responsible adult. Show your teacher the list you have made.

3 Use the six questions in the Responsible Decision-Making Model (on page 61) to evaluate the consequences of each decision. Do they show respect for yourself and others? Do they follow the guidelines of responsible adults? Do they demonstrate good character?

4 Decide which decision is the most responsible and appropriate. Talk with your partner about whether decisions you made met the guidelines in the Responsible Decision-Making Model.

5 Act on your decision and evaluate the results. Even if all your decisions meet the guidelines of the Responsible Decision-Making Model, you will benefit from signing a contract for Motor Vehicle Safety. Review the contract at the right, then copy it, add additional guidelines that are important to you, and sign and date it. Ask your parents to sign and date the contract too.

Contract for Motor Vehicle Safety

I recognize that driving a motor vehicle is a privilege that has been granted to me. I understand that I must obey all traffic laws and drive in a safe manner. I will follow each of the safety guidelines in this contract. I understand that my driving privileges will be taken away if I break this contract.

1. I will obtain permission from my parents or guardian before driving any motor vehicle.
2. I will obey all traffic laws, including speed limits.
3. I will wear a safety belt when I am in a motor vehicle.
4. I will follow curfews and community guidelines.
5. I will not allow more passengers in my motor vehicle than there are safety belts.
6. I will not allow passengers in my motor vehicle who do not demonstrate good character.
7. I will not drink alcohol or use drugs.
8. I will not drive if I have taken OTC or prescription drugs that warn against operating a motor vehicle.
9. I will not be a passenger in a motor vehicle with anyone I know or suspect has been drinking or using drugs.
10. I will not be a passenger in a motor vehicle whose driver does not have a valid driver's license.
11. I will not allow peers to pressure me to practice unsafe driving habits.
12. I will avoid driving in severe weather, such as snowstorms and thunderstorms.
13. I will not drive in situations in which I do not feel safe, such as in heavy traffic.
14. I will not drive if I am tired, upset, or angry.
15. I will recognize that other drivers may not be operating a motor vehicle safely and will drive defensively.
16. I will not participate in behavior that may be distracting when driving.
17. I will keep music and voices at a reasonable volume so I can hear sirens and other traffic sounds.
18. I will not allow another person to drive my motor vehicle without permission of my parent or guardian.
19. I will carry my license and registration with me when I am driving a motor vehicle.
20. I will keep a copy of my insurance coverage in the glove box of my motor vehicle.
21. I will _____
_____

Signed,

(teen) _____ (date) _____

(parent or guardian) _____ (date) _____

Community Involvement

Motor Vehicle Safety As a class, ask students to create a brochure about motor vehicle safety. The brochure should describe defensive driving, the need for safety belt use, the consequences of traffic violations, and ways to prevent motor vehicle violence. It also should include a contract for motor vehicle safety that teens and their parents or guardian can sign. Word processing and computer graphics programs can be used to make the brochure. With the administration's permission, distribute the brochures to students who drive. **L2**

choking
child safety restraint
graduated license
heat detector
high-risk driving
Lower Anchors and
    Tethers for
    Children (LATCH)
Occupational Safety
    and Health Act
    (OSH Act)
poisoning
repetitive strain
    injury (RSI)
road rage
smoke detector
suffocation

Key Terms Review

Complete these fill-in-the-blank statements with the lesson Key Terms on the left. Do not write in this book.

1. A(n) _____ is an alarm that sounds when smoke is detected.

2. A(n) _____ is a device that sounds an alarm when the room temperature rises above a certain level.

3. _____ is the obstruction of the airway by an external object that blocks the mouth and nose.

4. A(n) _____ is a conditional license given to new drivers that restricts driving privileges.

5. _____ includes behaviors such as speeding, trying to beat red lights, drinking and driving, and attempting driving stunts.

6. A(n) _____ is a seat designed for a small child that is secured in the back seat of a motor vehicle.

7. _____ is aggressive actions of drivers and passengers of motor vehicles.

8. The _____ is a series of minimum safety and health standards that all employers must meet.

9. The _____ is a restraint system designed to work independently of the vehicle seat belt system to simplify child safety seat installation and reduce misuse.

10. _____ is an injury that occurs from repeated physical movements.

Recalling the Facts

11. Identify ways to reduce the risk of poisoning.

12. What are common injuries of working teens?

13. Identify ways to reduce the risk of fires.

14. List the steps that can be taken to obtain a valid driver's license.

15. Identify ways to reduce the risk of drowning.

16. Identify ways to reduce the risk of injury due to bicycle accidents.

17. List five occupations banned for all minors under age 18.

18. Identify ways to prevent vehicle violence.

Critical Thinking

19. Discuss how the OSH Act protects people in the workplace.

20. Describe what it means to be a defensive driver.

21. Explain why a safety belt should be worn even if your motor vehicle has air bags.

22. Analyze events that provoke drivers and passengers to participate in road rage and how road rage can be prevented.

Real-Life Applications

23. Describe what you should do if a stranger approaches your vehicle.

24. How would you handle offers of a ride from a high-risk driver?

25. Explain how you can reduce your risk of falls.

26. Your boss asks you to perform a hazardous job. How would you handle the situation?

Activities

Responsible Decision Making

27. **Write** Your classmate has a new vehicle. He or she asks if you want to go for a ride and see how fast it can go. Write a response to this situation. Refer to the Responsible Decision-Making Model on page 61 for help.

Sharpen Your Life Skills

28. **Access Health Information** Obtain permission from a parent or guardian. Call the Poison Control Center. Obtain a list of items that are potential poisons. Place a warning label on any of these items you may have in your home.

Visit www.glencoe.com for more *Health & Wellness* quizzes.

LESSON 61 • Study Guide **649**

LESSON 61
STUDY GUIDE

Key Terms Review

1. smoke detector
2. heat detector
3. suffocation
4. graduated license
5. high-risk driving
6. child safety restraint
7. road rage
8. OSH Act
9. LATCH
10. repetitive strain injury

Recalling the Facts

11. See page 640.
12. lacerations, contusions, abrasions, sprains, strains, bruises, burns, fractures, dislocations
13. See page 641.
14. See page 644.
15. See page 639.
16. See page 639.
17. See page 643.
18. See page 647.

Critical Thinking

19. Recognized health hazards must be eliminated, safety regulations must be reviewed regularly, and new employees must be trained on equipment and made aware of hazards.
20. A defensive driver guards against unsafe actions of other drivers.
21. Front air bags offer little protection in side, rear, and rollover crashes.
22. slow driving, loud music, not allowing a driver to pass, cutting a driver off, taking a parking place, tailgating, failing to signal; avoid eye contact, stay calm, keep a safe distance, report incidents to police

Real-Life Applications

23. Answers will vary, but may include being cautious, calmly driving to a well-lighted, public place and calling the police.

---

24. Answers will vary, but should include politely refusing then calling a parent, guardian, other responsible adult, or a taxi for a ride.
25. See page 640.
26. Answers will vary, but should include refusing to do the job, or telling a parent or legal guardian.

Activities

Responsible Decision Making

27. Answers will vary, but students should include that they would politely refuse.

Sharpen Your Life Skills

28. Answers will vary.

Staying Safe During Severe Weather and Natural Disasters

 Out of Time?

If time does not permit an in-depth study of this topic, use the following activities in this Teacher Wraparound Edition:
- Class Discussion, p. 651
- Cross-Curricular Connections, p. 652
- 5-Minute Check, p. 653

1 Focus

HEALTH GOAL **Natural Disasters** Have students respond to the Health Goal for this lesson by listing ways to be safe during natural disasters. *Answers might include keeping a flashlight and extra batteries, a first aid kit, candles, matches, water, and blankets ready for use in an emergency.* **L2**

 ABOUT IT!

Journaling Have students research the weather conditions during which a tornado is likely to develop. Ask students to write a paragraph in their health journals about how they would know to listen to the radio for possible tornado warnings. **L2**

LESSON 62

Staying Safe During Severe Weather and Natural Disasters

HEALTH GOAL • I will follow safety guidelines for severe weather, natural disasters, and national alerts.

An event caused by nature that results in damage or loss is a *natural disaster*. You may live in or travel to a high-risk area for severe weather or natural disasters so you need to be prepared.

What You'll Learn

1. List five ways to prepare for severe weather and natural disasters. *(p. 651)*
2. Discuss ways to stay safe during a landslide, flood, earthquake, tornado, hurricane, wildland fire, electrical storm, winter storm, and terrorist attack. *(p. 651)*

Why It's Important

Severe weather, natural disasters, and national alerts can happen with little to no warning. It is important to know what to do if you must deal with any of these situations, so you can be ready and safe.

Key Terms

- natural disaster
- landslide
- flash flood
- hurricane
- tornado watch
- tornado warning
- wildland fire
- severe thunderstorm watch
- severe thunderstorm warning
- Homeland Security Advisory System

 ABOUT IT!

Writing About Tornado Safety Suppose that while babysitting young children at a neighbor's house, you hear on the radio that a tornado warning has just been issued by the National Weather Service. You are concerned about the safety of the children under your care. Review the information about tornado safety on page 652 and write an entry in your health journal about what you would do in this situation.

National Health Education Standards—Guide for Lesson 62		
2.5	Evaluate the effect of media on personal and family health.	pp. 651, 655
2.10	Analyze how public health policies and government regulations can influence health promotion and disease prevention.	pp. 651, 654, 655
4.1	Utilize skills for communicating effectively with family, peers, and others to enhance health.	pp. 650, 655
6.3	Implement strategies and monitor progress in achieving a personal health goal.	p. 650
7.1	Analyze the role of individual responsibility for enhancing health.	pp. 651–654
7.3	Demonstrate a variety of behaviors to avoid or reduce health risks to self and others.	pp. 650, 651–654, 655
8.2	Demonstrate how to influence and support others to make positive health choices.	p. 655

Safety Guidelines

P repare yourself and your family for severe weather, natural disasters, or national alerts by taking the following actions: Contact your local emergency management office or chapter of the American Red Cross for a copy of their emergency plans. Know which emergencies could occur in your area. Know the warning signals for your community, such as sirens or announcements. Know your city's evacuation routes. Develop a family emergency plan. Include an escape plan, two meeting places (one near your home in case of fire, and one outside your neighborhood in case of evacuation). Identify emergency contact numbers (one in your area and one out of town). Make sure all family members know the name and phone number of these two people. Teach all family members how and when to turn off gas, electricity, and water. Prepare an emergency kit.

What to Know About Safety Guidelines

The following items should be in your emergency kit at all times: a flashlight with extra batteries; a radio with extra batteries; a first-aid kit; important papers, including family records, a list of emergency contact numbers, and a copy of your family's emergency plan; waterproof bags for valuables and mementos; rubber gloves; and rain gear and sturdy shoes.

The following items should be put into your emergency kit when severe weather, natural disasters, or national alerts are predicted: a supply of medication; candles and waterproof matches; a supply of water (one gallon per person per day); nonperishable food and a nonelectric can opener; any special requirements for babies, older adults, or disabled individuals; cash and credit cards; and blankets or sleeping bags.

During all of the following severe weather situations, listen to the radio or watch TV for the latest emergency information, and keep your emergency kit close by. Evacuate immediately if instructed to do so.

Landslides A movement of a mass of earth or rock is a *landslide.* Water from rain and melting snow is absorbed into the ground at the top of a slope and seeps through cracks in the underlying sandstone. When it comes to a layer of shale or clay that is on the slope, the water collects along the upper surface of this layer, and softens it. If the support is weak, a mass of earth and rock slides down the slope.

Lesson Resource Manager

- **Unit 11 Fast File Resources**
  Reading Strategy, p. 19
  Vocabulary Practice, p. 20
  Transparency Master and Worksheet, p. 21
  Real-Life Health, p. 23
  Real-Life Health, p. 25
  5-Minute Check, p. 27
  Lesson 62 Quiz, p. 28
- **Unit 11 Transparency**
- **Lesson 62 Transparency**

- **Reading Essentials**
- **Technology**
  TeacherWorks™ CD-ROM
  StudentWorks™ CD-ROM
  Reading Essentials CD-ROM
  Exam*View*® Assessment Suite
  Vocabulary Puzzlemaker

Safety Guidelines

2 Teach

Class Discussion

Emergency Supplies Review with the class the items that should be included in an emergency kit. Ask students why these items would be useful in an emergency. Have them discuss other items that they feel should be included. **L2**

PowerPoint® Presentations

This CD-ROM is an editable Microsoft® PowerPoint® presentation that includes:
- Lesson presentations
- Lesson checks
- Interactive graphics
- 5-Minute Checks
- Image Bank
- All transparencies

Note-Taking Refer to the Two-Column Notes: Main Idea-Detail Strategy on page 16T. Have students list the crises discussed in the lesson in the left column and the corresponding safety guidelines in the right column.

National Health Education Standards
Pages 650–651: 1.5, 2.5, 2.10, 4.1, 6.3, 7.1, 7.3

651

Class Discussion

Severe Weather On the chalkboard or an overhead transparency write these terms: *landslides, earthquakes, floods, hurricanes,* and *tornadoes.* Ask the students to indicate what they should do if they are exposed to each of these situations. Record students' answers under each of the topics. Compare the answers. Ask students if there are any actions that they can take that are common to each situation. Some students might state that they do not live where any of these events might occur. Counter this by explaining that they might move to or be on vacation in an area where they do occur. **L2** **ELL**

Extension

Research Tornadoes Ask students to research one of the following topics concerning tornadoes: the states where tornadoes most commonly occur and why tornadoes occur there, or when and where the most damaging tornado touched down and the amount of damage it caused. Have students make a map or graph illustrating their findings. Ask students to present the information to the class. **L3**

NHES Assessment/SCASS

Performance Event Assign each student an emergency situation. Ask students to write an essay describing how they should react in the situation. For example, the student is in a hotel in a large city when an earthquake occurs. What should he or she do? Have students present their plans to the class. Discussion can follow. **L2**

▲ A hurricane is a tropical storm with winds in excess of 73 miles per hour.

Did You Know?

Hurricane Rotation Hurricanes rotate counterclockwise around their centers in the northern hemisphere and clockwise in the southern hemisphere.

If you are indoors, look for landslide warning signs such as doors or windows cracking; new cracks in walls or foundations; cracks widening on the ground or pavement; water breaking through ground surface in new locations; fences, utility poles, or trees tilting or moving; and a faint rumbling sound increasing in volume. Stay inside. Move to the second story, if possible. Stay out of the path of the landslide.

If you are outdoors, try to get out of the path of the landslide. Run to the nearest high ground in a direction away from the path. Run to the nearest shelter, such as a building or group of trees, if debris is approaching. Curl into a tight ball and protect your head if escape is not possible.

Floods A temporary condition of partial or complete deluge of normally dry land by an overflow of inland or tidal waters, or the rapid accumulation of surface waters from any source is a *flood.* A flood that occurs suddenly is a *flash flood.* Flash floods are the number one weather-related cause of death in the United States.

If you are indoors and if time permits, bring outdoor belongings indoors. Move valuable possessions to the second story, if possible. Turn off utilities at the main switch and turn off the main gas valve if instructed to do so.

If you are outdoors, climb to higher ground and stay there. Avoid walking through flood waters of more than a few inches.

If you are in a motor vehicle, do not drive through flood waters. Abandon the vehicle if it stalls and climb to higher ground. Do not attempt to move a stalled vehicle.

Hurricanes A tropical storm with heavy rains and winds in excess of 73 miles per hour is a *hurricane.* If there is a risk of a hurricane, take the following actions: Secure buildings by boarding up windows and checking tiedowns. Turn the refrigerator and freezer to the coolest settings and open them only when necessary. If you are in a mobile home, evacuate immediately.

If you are indoors, stay inside, away from windows. Avoid using open flames, such as candles, as a source of light or heat. Open flames can easily become a fire hazard.

If you are outdoors, seek shelter indoors.

Tornadoes A tornado is a violent, rapidly spinning windstorm that has a funnel-shaped cloud. A *tornado watch* is an emergency alert that is issued when the weather conditions are such that a tornado is likely to develop. A *tornado warning* is an alert issued when a tornado has been sighted or indicated by radar.

If you are indoors, go to the basement, storm cellar, or an inner hallway or small inner room on the lowest level of the building away from windows and corners. Get under a piece of sturdy furniture and hold on to it. Protect your head and neck. If in a mobile home, evacuate immediately.

 Cross-Curricular Connections

Geography Have students research areas in the United States where landslides, hurricanes, earthquakes, and floods frequently occur. Students also should research why these areas are conducive to severe weather. Ask students to create a map of the United States, indicating these areas. The maps should include oceans, mountain ranges, large lakes, and large rivers. Have students use a key (colors or symbols) to represent the severe weather conditions. Ask students to present their maps to the class. Have students discuss how oceans, mountain ranges, large lakes and large rivers affect weather. **L3**

If you are outdoors, seek shelter indoors. Lie in a ditch or low-lying area or crouch near a building, if you cannot get indoors. Use your arms to protect your head and neck.

If you are in a motor vehicle, do not try to out-drive a tornado. Get out of the vehicle immediately. Seek shelter indoors. Lie in a ditch or low-lying area or crouch near a building if you cannot get indoors. Use your arms to protect your head and neck.

Earthquakes A violent shaking of Earth's surface caused by the shifting of plates that make up Earth's crusts is an **earthquake.**

If you are indoors, take cover under a piece of heavy furniture or against an inside wall and hold on tightly. Stay inside. Do not try to leave a building. Be prepared for aftershocks.

If you are outdoors, move into the open, away from buildings, street lights, and utility wires. If you are on a bridge, get off of it as soon as possible. Be prepared for aftershocks.

Wildland fires A fire that occurs in the wilderness is a **wildland fire.**

If you are indoors, close windows, doors, and vents. Take down flammable window coverings and close all nonflammable window coverings. Close gas valves and turn off pilot lights. Open fireplace damper and close fireplace screen. Move flammable furniture to the center of the room. Turn on a light in each room for visibility in heavy smoke. Place valuables that would not be damaged by water in a pool or pond. Aim sprinklers on roofs and on anything that might be damaged if adequate water is available.

If you are outdoors, do not attempt to outrun the fire if you are trapped.

Crouch in a body of water if possible. Cover your head and upper body with wet clothing. Seek shelter in a cleared area of rocks if water is not available. Breathe the air close to the ground through a wet cloth.

Electrical storms A storm that has lightning and thunder is an **electrical storm.** An emergency alert that is issued when the weather conditions are such that a severe thunderstorm is likely to develop is a **severe thunderstorm watch** An alert that is issued when a severe thunderstorm has been sighted or indicated by radar is a **severe thunderstorm warning.** If there is a risk of electrical storms, review the safety guidelines for tornadoes and flash floods, which may accompany thunderstorms.

Secure outdoor objects, such as lawn furniture, that could blow away or cause damage or injury. Take light objects inside. If you are indoors, close windows and outside doors. Unplug electrical items and disconnect cable and telephone lines because lightning could follow wires. Avoid bathtubs, water faucets, and sinks because metal pipes can transmit electricity.

If you are outdoors, seek shelter inside a building or car. If no structure is available, go to an open space and squat low to the ground as quickly as possible. If you are in the woods, find an area protected by a low clump of trees—never stand underneath a single large tree.

▲ Earthquakes can cause severe damage to buildings.

Wildland Fires More than four out of every five wildland fires are started by people.

LESSON 62 • Staying Safe During Severe Weather and Natural Disasters **653**

⊘ Health Project

Severe Weather and Natural Disasters Have students determine the severe weather and natural disasters that are likely to occur in your area. Ask students to create a public service announcement about one type of severe weather or natural disaster that is likely to occur. The PSA should include the following information: a detailed description of the severe weather or natural disaster, the time of year it is most likely to occur in the area, the dangers to health status that are associated with it, and strategies to protect oneself against those dangers. Any outstanding statistics that are available also could be included. Have each student present his or her PSA to the class. **L2**

Reading Review

1. *Seek shelter inside a building or car, or go to an open space and squat low to the ground.*
2. *Take cover under a piece of heavy furniture or against an inside wall and hold on tightly. Do not try to leave the building.*

3 Assess

Vocabulary Practice
Page 20, **Unit 11 Fast File Resources**

National Health Education Standards
Pages 654–655: 1.5, 2.5, 2.10, 4.1, 7.1, 7.3, 8.3

Crouch with hands on knees. Avoid tall structures, such as towers, tall trees, fences, telephone lines, and power lines. Stay away from natural lightning rods, such as golf clubs, tractors, fishing rods, bicycles, and camping equipment. Stay away from rivers, lakes, and other bodies of water. Be aware of the potential for flooding in low-lying areas.

If you are isolated in a level field or prairie and you feel your hair stand on end, which indicates that lightning is about to strike, bend forward, and put your hands on your knees. A position with feet together and crouching while removing all metal objects is recommended. Do not lie flat on the ground.

If you are in a motor vehicle, pull safely to the shoulder of the road away from any trees. Stay in the car and turn on the emergency flashers until the rain subsides. Avoid flooded roadways.

Winter storms A storm in the form of freezing rain, sleet, ice, heavy snow, or blizzards is a ***winter storm.***

If you are indoors, remain indoors until the storm has passed. Close all windows and doors.

If you are outdoors, seek shelter immediately.

If you are in a motor vehicle, travel only if necessary. Keep winter storm supplies in your motor vehicle—sand, shovel, rope, scraper, flares, heavy blanket, warm clothing, nonperishable food items—in case you become stranded. Do not leave your vehicle.

Reading Review

1. What should you do if you are outdoors during a thunderstorm?
2. What should you do if you are indoors during an earthquake?

The Homeland Security Advisory System

The world changed on September 11, 2001 when our nation was attacked by terrorists. Our nation is at risk for terrorist acts now and, most likely, in the future. Individuals and organizations must be watchful, prepared, and ready to respond to terrorist acts. The ***Homeland Security Advisory System*** is a system of the United States federal government to inform federal, state, and local authorities and the American people of the risk of terrorist acts. Risk includes both the likelihood of a terrorist attack occuring and the possible severity of the attack. This national alert system has five warnings, known as threat conditions. Each threat condition has a description and a corresponding color.

This system helps people to make rational decisions about how to react to the threat. A specific threat condition means that organizations need to take specific actions to reduce being vulnerable to terrorist attacks. When the threat condition increases to a higher level, organizations need to be ready to respond in the event of a terrorist act. Threat conditions can apply to the entire nation, a geographic region, or an industrial area.

(DI) Differentiated Instruction

Learning Disabilities Review with students the safety guidelines to follow if a person is in a motor vehicle during a winter storm, including the winter storm supplies which people should keep in their motor vehicles. Ask each student to prepare a winter storm supplies kit for his or her family's motor vehicle. Ask students to present their kits to the class. Have the class discuss the reasons each item is needed in a winter storm supplies kit. **L1**

62 STUDY GUIDE

earthquake
electrical storm
flash flood
Homeland Security
  Advisory System
hurricane
landslide
natural disaster
severe thunderstorm
  warning
severe thunderstorm
  watch
tornado warning
tornado watch
wildland fire

Key Terms Review

Complete these fill-in-the-blank statements with the lesson Key Terms on the left. Do not write in this book.

1. An event caused by nature that results in damage or loss is a(n) _____.

2. A(n) _____ is issued when weather conditions are such that a severe thunderstorm is likely to develop.

3. A(n) _____ is issued when a tornado has been sighted or indicated by radar.

4. An emergency alert issued when weather conditions are such that tornadoes are likely to develop is a(n) _____.

5. A tropical storm with heavy rains and winds in excess of 73 mph is a(n) _____.

6. A fire that occurs in the wilderness is a(n) _____.

7. A(n) _____ is given when a severe thunderstorm has been sighted or indicated by radar.

8. A(n) _____ occurs suddenly and is the number one cause of weather-related deaths in the U.S.

9. The _____ is a system used to warn of the risk of terrorist acts.

10. Movement of a mass of earth or rock is a(n) _____.

Recalling the Facts

11. List items to include in your emergency kit.

12. Explain what to do if you are in a motor vehicle during a tornado.

13. What should you do if you are outdoors during a landslide?

14. Describe what to do if you are indoors during a tornado.

15. Explain what to do if you are in a motor vehicle during a winter storm.

16. Describe what to do during wildland fires.

17. Explain what to do if you are indoors during an earthquake.

18. What should you do if you are outdoors during an electrical storm?

Critical Thinking

19. Discuss the Homeland Security Advisory System. Describe the coding of the threat conditions.

20. Describe how severe weather conditions could possibly lead to a natural disaster.

21. Explain how to prepare for severe weather, natural disasters, or national alerts.

22. Discuss why you should not evacuate a building during a tornado or an earthquake.

Real-Life Applications

23. What would you do if you were driving and there was a flash flood?

24. While vacationing in a coastal town, a hurricane approaches. Describe what your family should do.

25. Why should you review the safety guidelines for tornadoes and flash floods during an electrical storm?

26. What would you do if you were in a mobile home during a tornado?

Activities

Responsible Decision Making

27. **Write** Your younger brother is watching TV when a severe thunderstorm warning is issued. He wants to finish watching his show. Write a response to this situation. Refer to the Responsible Decision-Making Model on page 61 for help.

Sharpen Your Life Skills

28. **Advocate for Health** Write a public service announcement (PSA) identifying the safety guidelines for severe weather that might affect your community. Obtain permission from your principal to read your PSA over the school PA system.

Visit **www.glencoe.com** for more *Health & Wellness* quizzes.

LESSON 62 • Study Guide 655

STUDY GUIDE

Key Terms Review

1. natural disaster
2. severe thunderstorm watch
3. tornado warning
4. tornado watch
5. hurricane
6. wildland fire
7. severe thunderstorm warning
8. flash flood
9. Homeland Security Advisory System
10. landslide

Recalling the Facts

11. See page 651.
12. get out of the vehicle, seek shelter or lie in a ditch, and use your arms to protect your head and neck
13. See page 652.
14. See page 652 for information on tornadoes.
15. See page 654.
16. See page 653.
17. See page 653.
18. See page 653.

Critical Thinking

19. See page 654.
20. Answers could include a landslide, flood, or wildland fire resulting from an electrical storm.
21. See page 651.
22. It is safer to be in the shelter of a building during an earthquake or a tornado (except a mobile home in the case of a tornado).

Real-Life Applications

23. Do not drive through flood water, abandon the vehicle and climb to higher ground if the vehicle stalls, and do not move the stalled vehicle.
24. Evacuate if instructed to do so.

25. Answers will vary, but may include electrical storms can lead to flooding and weather conditions may become favorable for tornadoes.

26. Evacuate immediately. Seek shelter indoors, lie in a ditch or low-lying area or crouch near a building. Use your arms to protect your head.

Activities

Responsible Decision Making

27. Answers will vary, but should include explaining the danger and unplugging the electric and cable.

Sharpen Your Life Skills

28. Answers will vary.

655

Reducing the Risk of Violence

LESSON 63

Out of Time?

If time does not permit an in-depth study of this topic, use the following activities in this Teacher Wraparound Edition:
- Class Discussion, p. 657
- Class Activity, p. 659
- Class Discussion, p. 661

1 Focus

HEALTH GOAL **Reducing Risk** Have students respond to the Health Goal for this lesson by listing protective factors in their lives that will reduce the risk of violence for them. *Answers will vary, but should include the protective factors listed on page 660.* **L2**

Write ABOUT IT!

Behavior Ask students to consider their own behavior and decide which type of behavior they most often exhibit (aggressive, passive, or assertive). Have students determine if their behavior could be healthier and if so, what changes could be made. Have students write an entry in their health journals describing their self-analysis. **L2**

Reducing the Risk of Violence

HEALTH GOAL • I will practice protective factors to reduce the risk of violence.

Acts of violence are often seen on television and in movies, and described in music lyrics. If teens are exposed to violence repeatedly, they may become desensitized to it, and therefore, may be unable to recognize what is and what is not violent.

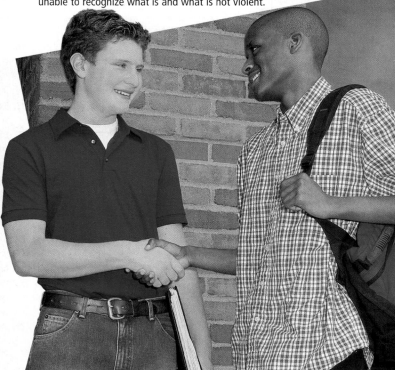

What You'll Learn

1. List and discuss nine types of violence. *(p. 657)*
2. Identify 20 risk factors that increase the likelihood that a person will become a perpetrator or a victim of violence. *(p. 659)*
3. Identify 20 protective factors that reduce the likelihood that a person will become a perpetrator or a victim of violence. *(p. 660)*
4. Explain how passive, aggressive, and assertive behavior influence the risk of being a perpetrator or a victim of violence. *(p. 661)*

Why It's Important

If you act violently, you could permanently harm your health, go to prison, or die. You also might hurt or kill other people.

Key Terms

- violence
- perpetrator of violence
- victim of violence
- assault
- homicide
- child abuse
- domestic violence
- elder abuse
- aggressive behavior
- passive behavior

Write ABOUT IT!

Writing About Assertive Behavior Suppose that someone tells you that another student in your school has been spreading an untrue rumor about you. You are angry about this and concerned about your reputation. Review the information on assertive behavior on page 661. Write an entry in your health journal about how you could resolve this conflict in an assertive—rather than an aggressive or passive—way.

National Health Education Standards—Guide for Lesson 63					
1.1	Predict how healthy behaviors can impact health status.	pp. 659–662, 663	2.10	Analyze how public health policies and government regulations can influence health promotion and disease prevention.	p. 658
1.3	Analyze how environment and personal health are interrelated.	p. 659	4.1	Utilize skills for communicating effectively with family, peers, and others to enhance health.	pp. 656, 663
1.5	Propose ways to reduce or prevent injuries and health problems.	pp. 656, 660–663			
2.1	Analyze how family influences the health of individuals.	p. 659	4.3	Demonstrate strategies to prevent, manage or resolve interpersonal conflicts without harming self or others.	p. 656
2.3	Analyze how peers influence healthy and unhealthy behaviors.	pp. 659–660			
2.5	Evaluate the effect of media on personal and family health.	p. 656		NHES Standards for Lesson 63 continued at www.glencoe.com.	

Key Terms Review

Complete these fill-in-the-blank statements with the lesson Key Terms on the left. Do not write in this book.

authority
conscience
delinquent behavior
diversion
juvenile detention
juvenile offender
mentor
moral code
probation
role conformity
social reciprocity
status offenses

1. A _____ is a set of rules a person uses to control behavior.

2. A _____ is a sense of right or wrong that prompts responsible behavior and causes feelings of guilt following wrong behavior.

3. _____ is the desire to behave in ways that other people approve of.

4. _____ is the act of people treating others as they themselves wish to be treated.

5. _____ is an illegal action committed by a juvenile.

6. _____ is the power and right to apply laws and rules.

7. _____ is a sentence in which an offender remains in the community under the supervision of a probation officer for a specific period of time.

8. _____ are types of behavior for which an adult would not be arrested, such as truancy, alcohol use, running away, defying parents or guardians, and breaking curfew.

9. _____ is the temporary physical restriction of juveniles in special facilities until the outcome of their legal case is decided.

10. _____ is an approach to rehabilitation that involves sending juvenile offenders somewhere to learn how to obey laws.

Recalling the Facts

11. List examples of status offenses for which juvenile offenders can be arrested.

12. When do people begin to develop a conscience?

13. Name correctional facilities where juvenile offenders might be sent.

14. List the consequences juvenile offenders may face.

15. Why does the first stage of moral development occur in early childhood?

16. When do people reach the stage of role conformity?

17. Identify ways that teens who have been juvenile offenders can change their behavior.

18. Describe the purpose of a boot camp.

Critical Thinking

19. Describe the stages a person goes through to develop a moral code.

20. Explain why some teens may challenge authority and break laws.

21. Describe the diversion approach to rehabilitation.

22. Discuss possible short- and long-range consequences of being a juvenile offender.

Activities

Responsible Decision Making

27. **Write** You are with two friends at a bowling alley. Your friends suggest that you all steal a pair of bowling shoes. Write a response to this situation. Refer to the Responsible Decision-Making Model on page 61 for help.

Real-Life Applications

23. How do you feel when you do something wrong? Why?

24. Do you feel you have reached Stage 3 in your moral development?

25. How do you exhibit social reciprocity?

26. Discuss how consistent rewards and punishments influence your behavior.

Sharpen Your Life Skills

28. **Analyze Influences on Health** Locate an article about a person who has committed a violent crime. Do they show remorse for their actions? What form of restitution would be appropriate? Write a response to the article in your journal.

Visit www.glencoe.com for more *Health & Wellness* quizzes.

LESSON 64 • Study Guide 669

Key Terms Review

1. moral code
2. conscience
3. Role conformity
4. Social reciprocity
5. Delinquent behavior
6. Authority
7. Probation
8. Status offenses
9. Juvenile detention
10. Diversion

Recalling the Facts

11. truancy, alcohol use, defying parents or guardian, breaking curfew
12. between ages 5 and 7
13. detention centers, training schools, ranches, camps, farms, halfway houses, and group homes
14. probation, make restitution, spend time in a correctional facility, or a diversion program
15. During childhood people learn right from wrong.
16. between ages of 10 and 13
17. See page 668.
18. uses rigorous drills, hard physical training, and structure to teach discipline and obedience

Critical Thinking

19. See page 665.
20. Some teens were raised with unclear expectations, some are influenced by peers, and some teens have no principles to guide their behavior.
21. an approach to rehabilitation that involves sending a juvenile somewhere to learn how to obey laws
22. See page 667.

Real-Life Applications

23. Answers will vary, but should include a discussion about morals, a conscience and/or social reciprocity.

24. Answers will vary.
25. treat others as you wish to be treated
26. Answers will vary but should include: rewards for good behavior encourage good behavior, punishments for bad behavior discourage bad behavior.

Activities

Responsible Decision Making

27. Answers will vary but should include deciding not to steal the shoes.

Sharpen Your Life Skills

28. Answers will vary.

LESSON 65

Protecting Yourself From Physical Violence

 Out of Time?

If time does not permit an in-depth study of this topic, use the following activities in this Teacher Wraparound Edition:
- Family Involvement, p. 672
- Community Involvement, p. 675
- Class Discussion, p. 676

1 Focus

HEALTH GOAL **Self-Defense** Have students respond to the Health Goal for this lesson by listing some self-defense strategies. *Answers might include: listen to your intuition, have keys ready when you get to your car, keep doors locked at your house, keep a list of emergency phone numbers, walk in lighted areas, and hang up on harassing phone calls.* **L2**

Write ABOUT IT!

Self-Defense Classes Have students research self-defense classes that are offered in your area. Have students ask: What martial arts form, if any, are the self-defense classes based on? Ask students to observe one of the classes. Have students write an entry in their health journals describing self-defense classes in your area. **L2**

LESSON 65

What You'll Learn

1. Discuss strategies of self-defense. *(p. 671)*
2. Explain hazing. *(p. 675)*
3. Discuss bullying. *(p. 676)*
4. Identify signs of child abuse and describe laws about mandatory reporting. *(p. 678)*
5. List six categories of mental and emotional abuse. *(p. 679)*
6. List the phases of a violent relationship and things that victims need to know. *(p. 680)*
7. Identify warning signs of dating violence and discuss defensive measures. *(p. 682)*
8. Identify how victims and perpetrators can facilitate recovery. *(p. 683)*

Why It's Important

You want to live happily and free from harm. Learning self-defense strategies can help protect you from violence, emotional trauma, and death.

Key Terms

- unnecessary risk
- self-defense strategies
- random violence
- awareness
- hazing
- bullying
- teasing
- battering
- protective order
- victim recovery

Protecting Yourself from Physical Violence

HEALTH GOAL • **I will practice strategies to help protect myself from physical violence and abuse.**

A chance that is not worth taking is an ***unnecessary risk***. You can avoid unnecessary risks that jeopardize your safety. Strategies that can protect people from violence are called *self-defense strategies*.

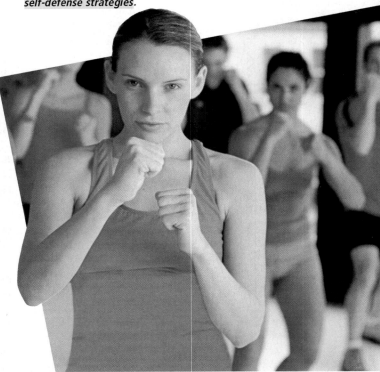

Write ABOUT IT!

Writing About Self-Defense News reports about assaults in your community have made a friend of yours feel concerned about her personal safety. She is considering taking a self-defense class, but she is too shy to sign up. Read the information about self-defense on page 671 and then write a hypothetical e-mail to your friend in your health journal, telling her why it is important to learn self-defense strategies.

National Health Education Standards—Guide for Lesson 65					
1.1	Predict how healthy behaviors can impact health status.	pp. 671–674, 677, 679, 680, 682, 684, 685	2.1	Analyze how family influences the health of individuals.	p. 675
			2.3	Analyze how peers influence healthy and unhealthy behaviors.	pp. 674, 675, 676–677, 682
1.5	Propose ways to reduce or prevent injuries and health problems.	pp. 670, 672–674, 685			
1.8	Analyze personal susceptibility to injury, illness, or death if engaging in unhealthy behaviors.	p. 677	2.10	Analyze how public health policies and government regulations can influence health promotion and disease prevention.	pp. 675, 678, 681
1.9	Analyze the potential severity of injury or illness if engaging in unhealthy behaviors.	p. 677		NHES Standards for Lesson 65 continued at www.glencoe.com.	

Self-Defense

V iolence over which a person has no control is *random violence*. A person may be a cashier in a store and be injured during a robbery. This person is a victim of random violence. Random violence is unsettling, because there is nothing victims can do to avoid their fate. But being aware of danger can prevent many acts of violence. This does not mean that you need to live in a state of fear, but you do need to be cautious.

What to Know About Self-Defense

Awareness The first line of self-defense is to be aware of the people and situations around you. ***Awareness*** is your ability to "read" the people and situations around you. By being aware of your surroundings, many acts of random violence can be avoided.

Awareness is not being afraid or suspicious. Your degree of awareness should be determined by the situation you are in. You should be more aware when you are walking alone at night than when shopping in a mall with your friends.

The sooner you become aware of a threat, the more options you have to respond to it. If you see or sense that a situation may be dangerous, change your route and prepare to run or defend yourself.

Defend yourself Successful self-defense is not winning a fight; it is about avoiding it. If it is not possible to avoid a fight, try to defuse it. If you can't defuse it, try to escape from it. If you can't escape, you may have to fight your way out of the situation.

There is only one rule if you are attacked: you must survive. You need to do everything you can: scream, scratch, hit, kick, and/or attack with a common object. Do everything you can to end the threat or to have enough time to escape.

Tell an adult A trusted adult needs to know if you suspect a person or situation is dangerous. He or she can talk with you about self-defense.

Self-defense strategies There are strategies you can use to reduce your risk of random violence. Trust yourself if you have a gut feeling that a person or situation may be dangerous. Avoid the person or situation whenever possible. It's better to be safe and risk embarrassment, than to be in a situation that may be unsafe. Give up personal belongings rather than risk being harmed. If you are in danger and want help, yell "Call 911!" or say "Walk me to the store on the corner, I'm being followed."

Know where you are going. Do not walk too close to buildings. Carry yourself with confidence. Have your keys ready when you approach your car or building. Do not label key chains with your name or address. Vary your routine. Drive or walk different routes every day. Do not talk about your plans where strangers can overhear you. Always carry a cell phone or enough change for a telephone call.

Make the Connection

Reduce Risk For more information on protective factors for reducing the risk of violence, see page 659 in Lesson 63.

Class Activity

Dangerous Situations Divide the class into groups of three or four students. Ask each group to think of a dangerous situation, such as a stranger asking for a ride or for directions, and develop a safe solution to the situation. Ask each group to role-play their situation for the class. Have the class critique the solution. **L2**

INTERACTIVE CHALKBOARD with Image Bank

PowerPoint® Presentations

This CD-ROM is an editable Microsoft® PowerPoint® presentation that includes:
- Lesson presentations
- Lesson checks
- Interactive graphics
- 5-Minute Checks
- Image Bank
- All transparencies

Journals Use the Teacher-Student Journal Strategy as described on page 17T to provide a confidential means for the students to express themselves about bullies and bullying.

Lesson Resource Manager

- **Unit 11 Fast File Resources**
  Reading Strategy, p. 55
  Vocabulary Practice, p. 56
  Transparency Master and Worksheet, p. 57
  Real-Life Health, p. 59
  Real-Life Health, p. 61
  5-Minute Check, p. 63
  Lesson 65 Quiz, p. 65
- **Unit 11 Transparency**
- **Lesson 65 Transparency**

- **Reading Essentials**
- **Technology**
  TeacherWorks™ CD-ROM
  StudentWorks™ CD-ROM
  Reading Essentials CD-ROM
  Exam*View*® Assessment Suite
  Vocabulary Puzzlemaker

National Health Education Standards

Pages 670–671: 1.1, 1.5, 4.1, 7.1, 7.3, 8.3

Self-Defense at Home

Class Activity

Improving Safety at Home After reading the information about self-defense strategies for the home, ask students to list three of these strategies that are used in their homes. Have students explain to the class how each of these strategies reduces the risk of random violence in their homes. **L2**

Extension

Alarm Systems Have students contact two alarm system companies to get information. Ask students to compare the two alarm systems. They should include cost, service, features, and potential problems of each alarm system. Ask students to make a chart illustrating their comparisons. Have students indicate which company they would select. **L3**

Teaching Transparency

Page 57, **Unit 11 Fast File Resources**

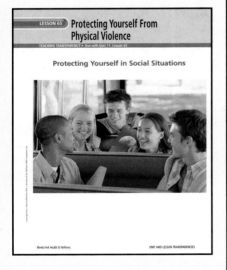

LESSON 65 **Protecting Yourself From Physical Violence**

TEACHING TRANSPARENCY • Use with Unit 11, Lesson 65

Protecting Yourself in Social Situations

Meeks Heit Health & Wellness   UNIT AND LESSON TRANSPARENCIES

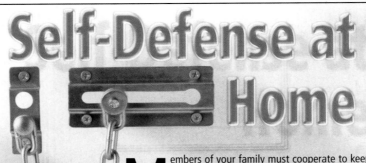

Self-Defense at Home

Members of your family must cooperate to keep your home safe from perpetrators. A *perpetrator of violence* is a person who commits a violent act. A perpetrator may enter your home intending to take possessions without intent to cause harm, be surprised, and respond by harming someone in your family. You can reduce the risk of being harmed in your home by practicing self-defense strategies.

Self-Defense Strategies for the Home

There are strategies you can use to reduce your risk of random violence in your home.

Doors and windows Have your keys ready before going to your door. Have good locks on doors and windows and keep them locked when you are home alone. Use wooden or metal rods to secure sliding doors and windows. Consider having a one-way viewer in your door. Do not hide, or give your house key to anyone other than a trusted friend. If you lose a set of keys, have your locks changed as soon as possible. If your garage door opener is lost or stolen, have your opener code changed.

Security Consider having a home security alarm system installed. Have lights at all entrances. At night, leave one or more lights on. Keep hedges and bushes trimmed so that doors are visible to neighbors and passers-by.

When away Have your mail, newspaper delivery, and other services suspended when you leave for an extended period of time. Ask a trusted neighbor to check your home and vary the position of the drapes while you are away.

The phone If you receive bothersome phone calls, do not talk. Hang up and report them to the telephone company and police. Keep a list of emergency phone numbers by the phone.

Strangers If you find a stranger or vehicle in your driveway, or if there are signs that someone has entered your home go to a safe place and call the police. Never let a stranger into your home. If someone asks to make an emergency phone call, offer to make the call while they wait outside if you want to do so. Ask to see photo-identification before allowing a repair person to enter your home. When speaking on the phone or answering the door, always give the impression someone else is in the home with you. Report any stranger who does not have identification to the police. Be cautious about giving out information about where you live.

🏠 Family Involvement

Self-Defense Strategies Ask students to discuss self-defense strategies for the home with their families. Have students with their families determine which self-defense strategies their families use. Have students ask the following questions: Do you have the mail, newspaper delivery, and other services suspended when you leave for an extended period of time? Do you have a trusted neighbor or friend check on your home while you are away? Do you keep a list of emergency phone numbers by the phone? Ask students to write a report on their findings. **L2**

Self-Defense in Public

You come from and go to many different places. You walk through the streets in your community. When you finish work, you may walk home or to a car. You may stop at an automated teller machine (ATM) to get some money from the bank. Whenever you are in public places, other people might harm you. You can reduce the risk of being harmed in public places by practicing self-defense strategies.

Self-Defense Strategies for Public Places

The basics Tell someone where you will be and what time you expect to be home, especially if you will be with someone you don't know well.

Be aware of your surroundings. Be cautious when using ATMs and do so during the day whenever possible. Use pay telephones only when they are in well-lighted places where there are many other people. Do not turn your back toward a street or a lobby when you are using a public telephone; turn your back toward the telephone.

When walking Wear comfortable shoes that allow you to run from trouble. When on the street, walk facing oncoming traffic; it will be harder for someone to abduct you. Vary your route if you routinely walk to and from school or work. Walk briskly with your head up and move in a confident manner. Carry your purse tucked under your elbow and hold it firmly with one hand.

Speed up, cross the street, turn around, run, or do whatever you feel is necessary if you suspect a person may be following you. Seek help in a nearby store or public place. Do not talk to strangers who approach you. Keep your distance if someone in a car stops to ask you for directions. Ignore the person or call out directions to them.

At night Avoid walking alone at night or in high-risk areas. Stay on well-lighted streets and avoid deserted areas, alleys, and staircases. Carry a flashlight and use it to light up potentially dangerous areas. It also could be used as a weapon in an emergency. Wait only in safe and well-lighted areas for public transportation.

Transportation After boarding public transportation, stay with a group of people or sit near the driver, if possible. Know your bus schedule so that you do not have to wait any longer than necessary. When dropping someone off, be sure they are safely inside before driving away. Have them do the same for you. Never accept a ride from a stranger or someone you do not trust. Never pick up a hitchhiker.

Defending yourself Carry a loud whistle or buzzer to get attention if you need it. Yell, scream, or shout loudly for help if someone is bothering you in a public place. Consider carrying pepper spray.

Reading Review

1. Why is it important to walk facing oncoming traffic?

2. When using a bus for transportation, why should you know the schedule?

LESSON 65 • Protecting Yourself from Physical Violence **673**

Self-Defense in Social Situations

You are probably often in many social situations. Sometimes you meet new people. Other times, you socialize with friends and other people you already know. When you socialize, you do not expect to be harmed, especially when you socialize with people you know, but you can still be at risk. Whenever you socialize, other people are in a position to harm you. You can reduce the risk of being harmed in social situations by practicing self-protection strategies.

Self-Defense Strategies for Social Situations

The basics Trust your intuition. Signals of intuition include gut feelings, anxiety, doubt, hesitation, fear, and suspicion. Choose to be with other people when you socialize with someone for the first time. Stay away from places where you will be alone with someone you do not know well or do not trust. Do not go anywhere with a stranger, even if you are supposed to meet other people. Do not use alcohol or other drugs.

When socializing with someone for the first time, choose to be ▼ with other people.

Expressing affection Set limits for expressing affection and clearly communicate these limits to others. Do not pressure another person to drink alcohol or to express affection beyond their limits. A person who has been drinking is accountable for his or her sexual behavior. Be aware that some people consider sexual teasing or a seductive manner an invitation for sexual activity, even when it is not.

Ask the other person to tell you clearly what his or her limits are when you are confused or feel you are getting mixed messages. Do not assume you and another person want to express affection in the same ways or have the same limits. Use physical force to get away if someone continues sexual behavior after you have set clear limits.

Pay attention to the warning signs that indicate a person might try to harm you, such as a disrespectful attitude toward you, a dominating attitude, extreme jealousy, unnecessary physical roughness, and/or a history of violent and/or abusive behaviors.

674 UNIT 11 • Injury Prevention and Personal Safety

🎓 Differentiated Instruction

Physical Challenges Individuals who have physical challenges are often more vulnerable to becoming victims of violence. Enlist the help of a physical education teacher, police officer, and/or a self-defense instructor to personalize methods of self-protection for students who have physical challenges. Have the student practice the methods until he or she is certain that they have been mastered. Ask the student to repeat the methods periodically in order to remember them. **L1**

Hazing

Most teens want to be a part of a group. Being a part of a group helps form a sense of identity and fulfills needs for belonging and friendship. Some groups require an initiation to become a member or to stay a part of a group. When groups use humiliation, ridicule, embarrassment, mental or physical discomfort, or dangerous activities to initiate a person into a group it is called hazing. *Hazing* is the physical and/or emotional abuse a person endures while trying to become or stay part of a group, regardless of that person's willingness to participate.

What to Know About Hazing

Hazing is more than pranks; it is about power and control over others, which sets up the climate for abuse to occur. Hazing is dangerous and can easily get out of hand because some teens may be willing to do just about anything in order to belong to a group—even dangerous or illegal behavior. Some groups may force teens to steal, take drugs, or break other laws in order to belong to the group. Other groups verbally and/or emotionally abuse teens during hazing.

Teens have died or been injured during hazing incidents—in motor vehicle accidents or from falling, drowning, or being beaten. Some teens have died of alcohol poisoning after being forced to drink large quantities of alcohol during initiation ceremonies.

If you are being threatened by hazing, tell your parents or guardian, a coach, a counselor, a school administrator, or a law enforcement official what you have experienced.

If you are a member of a group, create ways to form bonds within your group that are not in any way humiliating, demeaning, or hurtful. Your group can institute community-building initiation activities, such as playing recreational games together, participating in a ropes course, taking on a fundraising activity or a service project, or being a mentor for younger youth.

Anti-hazing rules Many schools have strict anti-hazing rules and written policies. Many schools take strong disciplinary action against members of a group in the case of hazing. Hazing is against the law in most states. Find out what your state law says about hazing and what the legal penalties are for violating antihazing laws.

Did You Know?

Hazing A national survey of 1500 high school juniors and seniors, conducted by Alfred University in the year 2000, showed that almost half (48 percent) of the students had been subjected to some form of hazing.

◀ Group members should work to find ways to bond that do not involve hazing.

LESSON 65 • Protecting Yourself from Physical Violence **675**

Hazing

Class Discussion

Hazing Have students review the definition of hazing. Have the class discuss how initiations can be conducted without hazing. Ask students to describe initiations to clubs and organizations they may have experienced. If a situation surfaces that is inappropriate, remind students that hazing is physical and emotional abuse—regardless of the person's willingness to participate—and redirect the discussion to non-hazing strategies for initiation. Be aware that some students might belong to a gang, and gangs have initiation rites. **L2**

Extension

Fraternity and Sorority Hazing Ask students to research college fraternity and sorority hazing of the past and present. Have students investigate the following questions: What other college organizations engage in hazing? What kind of hazing goes on in these organizations? How many students have been injured or killed during hazing episodes? What do colleges do to discourage hazing? Have students research laws against hazing. Ask the class to create a pamphlet of their findings. With permission, post copies of the pamphlet in seniors' classrooms. **L3**

🏛 Community Involvement

Initiation Ceremonies Ask students to research initiation ceremonies of community organizations. Have students write a report about one of the initiation ceremonies. Students should include a description of the ceremony and whether they feel it is a positive or a negative initiation strategy. For example, some communities have a ropes course which groups may visit to build trust within their organization. Ask students to explain why they would or would not participate in the initiation activities they have researched. Students might include a list of the potential benefits and hazards of each strategy. **L2**

National Health Education Standards
Pages 674–675: 1.1, 1.5, 2.1, 2.3, 2.10, 7.1, 7.3

Bullying

Class Discussion

Bullying Ask students to review the definition of bullying. Have the class discuss the results of bullying. Have them identify ways someone can resolve a bullying situation. Record the students' answers on the chalkboard or overhead transparency. **L1**

Explain the Concept

Bullying versus Teasing Explain the difference between bullying and teasing. Bullying is someone repeatedly doing or saying something in order to intimidate or dominate another person. Teasing is someone a person knows well, making fun of the person in a good-humored way. Explain that teasing can become bullying if it becomes cruel, causes distress, or becomes one-sided.

Quick Demo

Verbal Bullying Demonstrate to the class how a bully can verbally abuse someone. For example a bully can taunt someone, call someone names, isolate someone, spread rumors about someone and/or lie about someone. Use an imaginary person in the demonstration to ensure students are not embarrassed or injured. **ELL**

Bullying

Most teens have experienced what it feels like to be bullied. Three out of every four teens will be bullied during their school years. About one-third of teens say that they have been bullied three or more times in the past year. According to the National Crime Prevention Council, 60 percent of teens witness bullying at least once a day.

What to Know About Bullying

Repeatedly doing or saying things to intimidate or dominate another person is called ***bullying.*** A bully is a person who hurts or frightens people who are perceived to be smaller or weaker. Bullying someone is violent behavior and it is wrong. No one has the right to hurt or intimidate others.

Bullying can be physical or verbal. Bullying may include: taunting, making fun of or isolating someone; name-calling; pushing, hitting, poking, pinching, hair-pulling, kicking, or other physical abuse; spreading rumors, telling lies, or setting someone up to get in trouble; taking money or things from someone; making faces or obscene gestures at someone; excluding someone; pressuring someone to do something he or she doesn't want to do; and sexually harassing someone in any way.

Teasing Bullying is much different than teasing. ***Teasing*** is making fun of someone in a good-humored way. Teasing is usually done by someone who knows you well and cares about you. Teasing can turn into bullying if it becomes cruel, causes someone distress, or becomes one-sided and repeated.

Characteristics of Bullies

Teens who bully others:

- need to feel powerful and in control. They enjoy the power that aggression brings. They feel entitled to recognition, privilege and special treatment.
- may have an inflated self-image. Those who bully often believe that they are superior to others and brag about it.
- receive satisfaction from inflicting injury and suffering on others. Bullies find pleasure in taunting or dominating another person, even if it is obvious that the victim is distressed.

- lack empathy or feeling of concern for their victims.
- often lie about their actions, saying that their victims provoked them in some way. Bullies often blame the victim for the abuse.
- often believe it is OK to bully others. It is common for them to rationalize their actions by thinking that the victim did something to deserve this treatment.
- often come from a home in which physical punishment is used. Some bullies have been abused at home or were bullied themselves.

- often are defiant toward adults and are likely to break school rules.
- can be boys or girls. Girls are more likely to bully with words while boys are more likely to resort to physical attacks. For this reason, bullying by girls is often ignored or not taken as seriously as bullying by boys. Both types of bullying are harmful and serious.
- are often popular and well-liked by their peers and teachers.

676 UNIT 11 • Injury Prevention and Personal Safety

 Achieving Health Literacy

Problem Solver Have students read current articles and/or books that discuss teen bullying. Ask students to determine the most common forms of bullying in which teen boys and teen girls participate. Have students come up with a possible solution for the problem of teen bullying for both genders. Have each student present each possible solution to the class. Ask the class to discuss the possible solutions including the pros and cons of each solution. After the discussion, have each student write in his or her health journal how he or she might resolve a bullying situation. **L2**

Why bullying is harmful It is obvious that victims of bullying can receive physical injury from their abuse. Victims of bullying also are fearful of being in places where they are subjected to bullying. The stress that results from this fear can lead to school absences, trouble sleeping at night, difficulty concentrating on schoolwork, depression, and other stress-related symptoms. Continually facing intimidation is tough on a person's self-esteem. Feeling helpless to stop harassment from bullies, victims may also see themselves as helpless in other areas of their lives. Some victims of bullying retaliate for the abuse in violent ways, including suicide and murder.

Teens who bully are at risk of criminal behavior. They often lack social skills needed to be successful in life. If they do not learn to improve their social skills, they will continue to have problems relating to others throughout their lives. Bullies are more likely to drop out of school, and may have difficulty keeping a job.

Peers of victims who are bullied are also affected by bullying. Students may not associate with a victim out of fear of also being bullied. They may fear reporting bullying out of fear of retaliation from bullies. Some who witness bullying experience feelings of guilt because they did not stand up to the bully or offer to help stop the abuse. Because of group pressure, students who witness bullying are sometimes drawn into the bullying behavior.

Who is bullied? Teens who are bullied tend to be quiet and shy, and they do not make assertive responses when someone bullies them. They may lack friends and social support at school. They may not be confident in their physical abilities and strength. They tend to be smaller and physically weaker than peers.

Teens who are perceived as different are sometimes victims of bullying. Someone who is overweight or who has a speech impediment, a physical disability, or a learning disability, is at an increased risk of being bullied. Sometimes being a member of a different religious faith or race incites incidents of bullying.

Teens who are bullied are usually younger than the bullies. They feel that nobody will help them or be able to stop the bullying, and they do not tell because they fear the bullying may become worse as a result.

How to handle bullying Sometimes bullying stops when a person takes actions to stop it. Bullies continue as long as it works, because it makes them feel powerful. Many bullies will stop if they know they do not threaten their victim.

Strategies to avoid becoming a victim of bullying include having confidence that you can deal with the bully in a peaceful way. Violence may put you at further risk of injury. Humor can often be used to defuse a tense situation. Be assertive. Stand up for your feelings and needs. Say "no" to a bully's demands. Look the bully in the eye. Tell the bully to stop threatening you. Walk away and ignore any further taunting. If you fear physical harm, find a teacher or move toward friends who can provide support. When bullying is persistent, get help from an adult. Telling an adult rarely makes the situation worse and may help both you and the bully.

> **Make the Connection**
>
> **Appropriate Action** For more information about being self-confident and assertive, see page 48 in Lesson 5.

National Health Education Standards
Pages 676–677: 1.1, 1.8, 1.9, 2.3, 5.7, 7.1

Class Discussion

Bullied After students have read the section, "Who is Bullied?" discuss how these characteristics may lead someone to be bullied. Ask the following questions: Which characteristics cannot be changed by the individual? *Answers might include: physical disabilities, learning disability, religion, and age.* Which characteristics can be changed? *Answers might include: being more assertive, developing friendships and social supports.* Discuss how a person can handle being bullied. *Answers might include: have confidence, be assertive, ignore further taunting, and get help from an adult.* **L2**

5-Minute Check

Page 64, **Unit 11 Fast File Resources**

1. What is teasing? *making fun of someone in a good-humored way*
2. How are peers of bullying victims harmed? *They may fear being bullied, they may feel guilty for not intervening, or they may be drawn into the bullying.*
3. When are initiation ceremonies considered hazing? *when they are humiliating, ridiculing, embarrassing, cause mental or physical discomfort, or are dangerous*
4. Define *bullying*. *repeatedly doing or saying things to intimidate or dominate someone*
5. How can teasing turn into bullying? *if it becomes cruel, causes someone distress, or becomes one-sided and repeated.*

---

① **Differentiated Instruction**

Learning Disabilities Students who have learning disablities are sometimes bullied (rejected or isolated) by peer groups. Teachers can highlight specific interests, hobbies or strengths of the students who are learning disabled. Encourage the student to demonstrate to the class an interest or hobby that will be interesting to peers. Being an expert at something "cool" can increase status and acceptance among peers. Students who are learning disabled can also be given leadership positions in the classroom. Leadership also can increase status and acceptance among peers. Leadership may be an unfamiliar role and may require some guidance in order to ensure success. **L1**

Child Abuse

Class Discussion

Child Abuse Ask students to review the types of child abuse. Write "physical abuse," "neglect," and "sexual abuse" on the chalkboard or overhead transparency. Have students define each type of abuse. Ask students to list signs of each type of abuse. **L2**

Class Activity

Child Abuse Laws Ask students to contact local authorities to identify who is required by law in your area to report suspected cases of child abuse. Have students ask what signs would compel these people to report the abuse. Ask students to write a report about why they think these people are required to report suspected instances of abuse. **L2**

NHES Assessment/SCASS

Selected Response What is the most common type of child abuse?
A. physical abuse
B. sexual abuse
C. emotional abuse
D. neglect

The harmful treatment of a minor that can cause injury or psychological damage is called *child abuse*. Child abuse may involve physical abuse, emotional abuse, sexual abuse, or neglect. As a result of investigations conducted by child protective services (CPS) agencies, approximately 872,000 children were found to have been victims of abuse or neglect in the year 2004.

What to Know About Child Abuse

Did You Know?

Child Abuse An average of three children die each day in the U.S. as a result of child abuse or neglect. Children under the age of one make up almost one-half of child abuse and neglect deaths.

It is important for you to keep in mind that most cases of child abuse occur behind closed doors and are not reported. The most common type of child abuse is neglect, which is followed by physical abuse and emotional abuse.

Physical abuse Maltreatment that harms the body is *physical abuse.* A student who is unusually bruised or burned might be suffering from physical abuse. Other signs that a child has been physically abused include bites, internal injuries, fractures, and abrasions on different body parts.

Neglect Maltreatment that involves the lack of proper care and guidance is *neglect.* A parent or guardian might not provide adequate supervision, food, shelter, clothing or medical care.

Emotional abuse Maltreatment that involves nonphysical assault, such as constant criticism, threats, rejection, and withholding love or guidance is *emotional abuse.* You will learn more about emotional abuse later in this lesson on page 679.

Sexual abuse Maltreatment that involves an adult, an adolescent, or an older child using power to involve a minor in inappropriate sexual activity is *sexual abuse.* There are no age limits for victims of sexual abuse. Even infants can be abused. Sexual abuse includes activities such as fondling, intercourse, exhibitionism, and commercial exploitation through prostitution or the production of pornographic materials.

Child abuse laws There are laws in every state (and the District of Columbia) that identify mandatory reporters. A *mandatory reporter* is a person who is required by law to report suspected child abuse. Any person, however, may report incidents of child abuse or neglect. Mandatory reporters usually include professionals who work with children, such as health-care workers, mental-health professionals, teachers and other school personnel, law enforcement officials, and child care providers. In some states, any person who suspects child abuse is required to report it.

In most cases the identity of the person making the report of suspected child abuse remains confidential. Reports of child abuse are often made to child welfare agencies or to the police, and are usually investigated rapidly. If an investigation shows that a child is in danger, that child will likely be placed in protective custody or in a foster home.

678 UNIT 11 • Injury Prevention and Personal Safety

 Sensitive Issues

Victims of Abuse Some students may have been or may now be victims of abuse. Encourage students to seek help if they are a victim of abuse. The students need to know that there are agencies available to assist victims of abuse. Have a list of resources available for students to use. Lists can include police, pediatricians, children's hospitals, child psychologists, mentoring organizations, child abuse hotlines, and the Department of Human Services.

Mental and Emotional Abuse

Maltreatment that involves nonphysical assault is called *mental and emotional abuse.* This type of abuse is the most difficult to identify because the effects are not as obvious as those of physical abuse.

What to Know About Mental and Emotional Abuse

Mental and emotional abuse is dangerous to victims. A victim might have low self-esteem. Children who are emotionally abused are more likely to attempt suicide.

Mental and emotional abuse is about power and control. It can be found in any type of relationship, including parent-child, dating, marriage, employer-employee, peers, and teacher-student. Mental and emotional abuse includes the following abusive behaviors.

Rejection Refusing to acknowledge a person's presence, making a person feel inferior, or devaluing a person's thoughts and feelings is rejection.

Degradation Insulting, ridiculing, imitating, or diminishing the identity, dignity and self-worth of a person is degradation.

Terrorization Inducing fear or threatening or placing a person in an dangerous environment is terrorization.

Isolation Restricting social contact, contact with family members, or limiting freedom within a person's environment is isolation.

Corruption and exploitation Training a person to accept illegal ideas or behaviors, using a person for advantage or profit, or training a person to serve the interests of the abuser is corruption and exploitation.

Denying emotional responsiveness Failing to provide care in a sensitive and responsive manner, being detached and uninvolved, or ignoring a person's mental health is denying a person emotional responsiveness.

Signs of Mental and Emotional Abuse

A child who is being mentally or emotionally abused:

- is depressed or apathetic.
- experiences behavioral difficulties.
- withdraws from peers.

- is developmentally and/or mentally delayed.
- exhibits behaviors such as facial tics or rocking motions.

- reacts fearfully to authority.
- verbally reports that she or he is being emotionally abused.

LESSON 65 • Protecting Yourself from Physical Violence   **679**

Cross-Curricular Connections

Literature Ask students to read a work of literary fiction involving an abusive situation. Have students summarize the abusive situation in their health journals. Then, ask students to analyze the abusive situation using the following questions: What was the relationship between the abuser(s) and the victim(s)? How did the victim(s) deal with the abusive situation? Would you deal with a similar situation differently? If so, how would you deal with it differently? Have students write their analyses in their health journals. **L3**

Mental and Emotional Abuse

Class Discussion

Mental and Emotional Abuse Write rejecting, degrading, terrorizing, isolating, corrupting/exploiting, and denying emotional responsiveness on the chalkboard or overhead transparency. Ask students to discuss characteristics of each, so they can identify the types of mental and emotional abuse. **L2**

Class Activity

Dealing with Abusive Situations Divide the class into groups. Ask students to imagine that they have noticed a neighborhood child who exhibits the signs of mental and emotional abuse that are identified in the lesson. Ask each group to devise a way to deal with the situation. Have each group present their solution to the class. **L2**

National Health Education Standards
Pages 678–679: 1.1, 2.10

Domestic Violence

Class Discussion

Three Phases Write on the chalkboard or overhead transparency the three phases of domestic violence. Ask the class to describe each phase. Have the class give examples of behavior for both the offender and the abused in each phase. **L2**

Class Activity

Victim of Domestic Violence Divide the class into groups containing three or four students each. Ask one student in each group to record the group's answers. Ask students what a person should do if he or she is a victim of domestic abuse. Have students talk about the reasons some people remain in abusive relationships. Ask each group to present and explain their answers. The goal is for students to identify ways to get out of domestic violence situations and to understand that people who stay in domestic violence situations are not weak—that there are many reasons people feel they have to stay. **L2**

Reading Review

1. *buildup or escalation phase, acute battering phase, and honeymoon phase*
2. *physical abuse, isolation from family or friends, emotional abuse, economic abuse, intimidation, stalking, or sexual abuse*

Domestic Violence

Abuse used by one person in a relationship to control the other is ***domestic violence.*** Domestic violence takes many forms and can happen frequently or once in a while. Domestic violence occurs at all levels of society and in all communities.

What to Know About Domestic Violence

Domestic violence is about power and control. Domestic violence can include: physical abuse, isolation from family or friends, emotional abuse, economic abuse by withholding money, intimidation, stalking, and/or sexual assault.

Victims of domestic violence become fearful, angry, and confused about what is happening. Escape may seem impossible.

Victims of domestic violence live in difficult circumstances. Since they usually live in the same home as the offender, they often face repeated and prolonged attacks. Relationships that exhibit signs of domestic violence go through the following three phases.

Buildup or escalation phase Frustration, anger, and tension build up inside the domestic violence offender. The offender becomes increasingly controlling and/or cruel. He or she sometimes uses alcohol and/or other drugs to deal with feelings. The victim often becomes submissive in an attempt to keep the offender calm.

The acute battering (explosion) phase This is the phase when abuse and battering occur. ***Battering*** is intentional, harmful touching of another person without their consent. Battering "unloads" the tension that has built up. If the victim resists or fights back, the offender may become even more violent. Following abuse, victims usually feel fearful, trapped, depressed, and helpless.

Honeymoon phase In this phase the offender has unloaded his or her tension and feels physical relief. The offender is usually ashamed of the violence and may express remorse. There is often apologizing, gift-giving, and/or pleading for forgiveness. The offender may even threaten to commit suicide if the victim leaves and/or promise to enter a treatment program. The victim often succumbs to these promises, believing that the offender will change. After a while, something triggers the cycle again.

What victims of domestic violence need to know The abuse is not the victim's fault and the victim does not deserve it. Alcohol and/or drugs may be involved in the abuse, but they do not cause it. Waiting for offenders to change and trying harder to please them will not work. Abuse will get worse, not better. Victims should talk about the abuse with someone they trust. Victims should be aware of the emergency services available, and they should be prepared to use them when necessary. Children who learn violence at home are at risk of having violent relationships.

Reading Review

1. What are the three phases of relationships that exhibit domestic violence?
2. What types of abuse can be included in domestic violence?

 Sensitive Issues

Domestic Violence Be aware that some students might be living in a home where domestic violence occurs. Students need to know that there are agencies in the community available to assist victims of domestic violence. Have a list of resources available for students to use. Lists can include police, doctors, hospitals, psychologists, domestic violence hotline, women's shelters, lawyers and the Department of Human Services.

Domestic violence laws Most domestic violence cases are handled by state and local authorities. State domestic violence laws prohibit physical abuse and threatened or attempted physical abuse. Most state laws also prohibit sexual abuse, emotional abuse, and even financial exploitation.

All states have laws that allow victims of domestic violence to obtain protective orders. A ***protective order*** is an order of the court issued by a judge to prohibit a domestic violence offender from committing further acts of violence, harassing or threatening the victim, and going near the victim's home or place of work.

Sometimes protective orders also require a domestic violence offender to pay for child support, spousal support, alternative housing of a victim, or compensation for damages caused by the violence. Sometimes a domestic violence offender is required by the protective order to attend counseling.

Protective orders are enforced by the police. Violation of a protective order is a criminal offense.

More states are strengthening laws that deal with domestic violence. Some states prohibit domestic violence offenders from owning or possessing guns. Some states require domestic violence training for law enforcement personnel, prosecutors, and judges, and medical and mental-health professionals. Some states order electronic monitoring of domestic violence offenders when they are released from custody. Some states are increasing funding for services and counseling for victims.

 www.glencoe.com

HEALTH NEWS

Violence Against Women Act

In 1994, the United States Congress passed the Violence Against Women Act (VAWA). This act recognizes domestic violence by making certain actions federal offenses. For example, it became a federal crime for a person to cross state lines in an effort to continue to injure, harass, or intimidate an intimate partner. An *intimate partner* is defined by law as a spouse, a former spouse, people who share a child in common, or who cohabitate or have cohabitated. Under this law, if a violent crime is committed against an intimate partner that results in bodily harm, the penalty could result in a prison sentence of anywhere from 5 to 20 years, or a life sentence if the victim is killed. Another law in the act bans anyone facing a restraining order for domestic violence or who has already been convicted of a misdemeanor crime of domestic violence from possessing a firearm.

The law also allowed grants to be awarded to nonprofit organizations and local law enforcement agencies in order to strengthen the effectiveness of domestic violence prevention. Such grants included money for the establishment of the National Domestic Violence Hotline. Money was also given to local governments to increase community support and service programs for victims of domestic violence, including shelters for battered women.

The Violence Against Women Act was reauthorized in 2000 and 2005 in an effort to strengthen and update domestic violence laws.

 Visit **www.glencoe.com** for more information about the prevention of domestic violence.

Violence Against Women by Intimate Partner

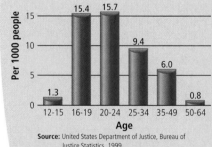

Source: United States Department of Justice, Bureau of Justice Statistics, 1999.

Analyzing Graphs
Study the graph above and answer these questions:

1. Which age group is most likely to experience abuse?

2. Which age group is least likely to experience abuse?

Analyzing Graphs
1. 20–24
2. 50–64

Project
Violence Against Women Act Ask students to research the VAWA of 1994 and 2000. Have students research the number of violations of the act. Ask students to present their findings to the class. **L3**

NHES Assessment/SCASS
Constructed Response Ask students if they feel that current laws are effective in protecting people from domestic violence. Have students give reasons to support their answers. **L2**

 ## Community Involvement

Community Aid Ask students to research the agencies that are available to assist victims of domestic abuse in the community. Students might use the phone book or begin by talking with the school nurse or the local health department. Have the class compile the information and make posters or pamphlets that identify these agencies, including their phone numbers. Post them, with permission, in public buildings in your community, including your school. Shelters usually don't give out addresses for safety reasons. **L2**

> **National Health Education Standards**
> Pages 680–681: 1.1, 2.10

Dating Violence

Class Discussion

Dating Violence After the class has read the warning signs of potential dating violence, ask students to consider if they or anyone they know has ever dated someone that had one or more of the characteristics that are identified. Advise students to not give names of offenders or victims. Have the class discuss why these are warning signs. **L2**

Class Activity

Journaling The National Domestic Violence Hotline lists several concerns that might indicate that someone you are dating has a potential for dating violence. Have students assume that their best friend is dating someone with several of these characteristics. Ask them to write what they would do to help their friend in their health journals. **L2**

Dating Violence

When one person in a dating relationship uses physical, emotional, or sexual abuse to control the other person, it is called *dating violence*. Dating violence is more than just arguing and fighting.

What to Know About Dating Violence

Make the Connection

Media For more information about violence in the media, see page 558 in Lesson 52.

Dating violence occurs when one or both partners have not learned positive ways of solving problems and dealing with intense emotions.

Warning signs Dating violence can happen to males or females. There are signs that might indicate that a person is prone to dating violence. Teens should be aware of partners who are jealous and possessive and who try to control them by giving orders, not taking their opinions seriously, or making all decisions.

Partners who tell you where you can or cannot go or with whom you can or cannot talk may be prone to dating violence. Those who try to keep you away from your friends and family and who make your family and friends concerned about your well-being and safety may be prone to dating violence. Partners who use alcohol or other drugs or try to get you to use alcohol or other drugs are prone to dating violence. Also, those who are cruel to animals are prone to dating violence.

Men or women who abuse dating partners usually were abused as children, quickly lose their temper, may find great enjoyment watching violent movies and/or playing violent video or computer games, and have very strict ideas about the roles of men and women in relationships.

If your partner seems to act differently around others than around you, has unpredictable mood swings, and frightens and threatens you, be aware that these are signs of dating violence. If your partner calls you names or tries to lower your self-esteem, says that you wouldn't be anything without him or her, says that no one else would ever go out with you, and puts you down, makes fun of, or embarrasses you in front of others, he or she is commiting dating violence.

If your partner is physically abusive toward you, pressures you or is forceful for sex, thinks that physical abuse is romantic or sexy, has abused former dating partners, and blames his or her abusive behavior on you or others, your partner is committing dating violence.

If dating violence occurs, or you suspect that it could occur If you are a victim of dating violence, you might think that it is your fault, and you may feel as if you deserve the violence. This is not true. Dating violence is not your fault. No one deserves to be in a violent dating relationship. Do not ignore it and hope that it will go away. You need to get out of the relationship. Tell someone you trust and who can help. Do not spend time alone with the abuser.

 Community Involvement

Community Resources Ask each student to locate one resource within the community where teens can go for assistance if they are experiencing dating violence. Ask students to contact the resource to determine the services that are offered. Have the class compile the information and make posters or pamphlets that identify these resources, including their addresses, phone numbers, and services offered. Post them, with permission, in public buildings in your community, including your school. **L2**

Recovery from Violence

A person who has been harmed by violence is a ***victim of violence***. The emotional pain that follows violence often is deeper and lasts longer than the physical injuries. Victims of violence may need help to recover from violence, and perpetrators of violence need to change violent behavior.

What to Know About Recovering from Violence

Victims of violence may experience different reactions after being harmed. Victims' responses may be influenced by the way they usually act or by the kind of violence they experienced. They may be highly emotional, depressed, and cry often. They may avoid others. They may neglect everyday tasks and have difficulty concentrating. They may have difficulty sleeping or have nightmares and flashbacks. They usually are very angry and afraid. They may try to numb their feelings with alcohol or drugs.

Post-traumatic stress disorder Some victims are able to recover without help. However, most do not recover quickly or easily. ***Post-traumatic stress disorder (PTSD)*** is a condition in which a person mentally relives a stressful experience again and again. PTSD is common in people who have experienced violence. The signs of PTSD include sleep problems, irritability, and trouble concentrating. When something reminds them of the experience, they respond with much emotion.

Secondary victimization Victims often experience additional pain after the violence. ***Secondary victimization*** is hurtful treatment experienced by victims after they experience violence. For example, many victims must attend the trial of the perpetrator and may have to answer painful questions. Also, people may try to find fault with the victim's behavior. If they can find fault, they can convince themselves that this type of violence will never happen to them. Secondary victimization usually is not intentional.

Victim recovery A person's return to physical and emotional health after experiencing violence is ***victim recovery.*** Victim recovery may include treatment for physical injuries, treatment for emotional pain, support from family and friends, repayment for money or property losses, and/or education in self-protection skills. The purpose of recovery programs is to help victims survive the pain, heal, and move forward with self-confidence. Survivors of violence are resilient.

(DI) Differentiated Instruction

Gifted and Talented Ask students to research local agencies that aid victims of violence. Have students choose one agency that they are interested in. Ask students, with permission from their parents or guardian, to visit the agency to learn more about the services it offers. Offer credit or extra credit if they decide to volunteer at one of these agencies. Many school systems require community service as part of their graduation requirements. **L3**

Recovery from Violence

Extension

Postraumatic Stress Disorder Ask students to research cases of postraumatic stress disorder. Ask students to write a report describing the violent situation that caused the condition, as well as the signs, symptoms, effects and possible treatments of postraumatic stress disorder. Have students present their findings to the class. **L3**

Class Discussion

Victim Recovery Ask students to discuss why it is important that victims participate in a victim recovery program. Ask students to consider what might occur if a person does not participate in a program. Write the responses on the chalkboard or overhead transparency. **L2**

National Health Education Standards
Pages 682–683: 1.1, 3.4, 7.1, 7.2

683

Class Activity

Recovery and Intervention Have students choose five of the bulleted points from the student page and give a hypothetical situation for each. Have students share their hypothetical situations with the class. **L2**

Reading Review

1. *Without help, they may continue to allow others to treat them with disrespect, they may need medical treatment, or they may act out in violent ways.*

2. *no longer blames others for his or her actions, does not do or say things that frighten others, respects others' feelings, people feel comfortable around him or her, does not attempt to control others, has received treatment for alcohol or drug problems*

3 Assess

Vocabulary Practice

Page 56, **Unit 11 Fast File Resources**

Name _____ Date _____ Class ____

LESSON 65 **Protecting Yourself From Physical Violence**

Vocabulary Practice

Use the terms to fill in the blanks below. Some terms may be used more than once.

awareness	protective order	teasing
battering	random violence	unnecessary risk
bullying	self-defense strategies	victim recovery
hazing		

1. _____ is making fun of someone in a good-natured way.

2. _____ is a chance that is not worth taking.

3. A person who is injured during a mugging is a victim of an act of _____

4. Walking alone at night is a time to sharpen your _____ of your surroundings.

5. _____ may include treatment for physical injuries, treatment for emotional pain, and support from family and friends.

6. Repeatedly doing or saying things to intimidate or dominate another person is called _____

7. A victim of domestic violence can obtain a(n) _____ to keep a domestic violence offender from going near the victim's home or workplace.

8. When groups use dangerous activities to initiate a person into a group, it is called _____

9. The steps that people can take to protect themselves from violence are called _____

10. _____ is a form of abuse that involves the intentional and harmful touching of another person without their consent.

11. The violation of a(n) _____ is a criminal offense.

12. _____ is your ability to "read" the people and situations around you.

56 LESSON 65 • Protecting Yourself From Physical Violence   UNIT 11

Reasons for victim recovery Victims may need a medical examination if they have experienced physical injuries. They may need blood tests to determine if they have become infected with any STDs. Victims also may need help with trust issues. To have close relationships, people must feel safe. Victims also may lack self-respect and allow others to harm them. Without help, they may continue to allow others to treat them with disrespect. Victims also may need to learn better ways to protect themselves. Victims who do not fully recover are at risk for behaving in violent ways. This is especially true if violence occurred in the family. Victims who were abused by parents or a guardian may grow up and be abusive parents themselves someday.

Perpetrator recovery People who behave in violent ways usually want to stop. Many believe they can't help it. They are wrong. A person can stop behaving in violent ways, but changing violent behavior is not easy. Violence is usually learned as a child, and it becomes ingrained when a person repeatedly uses it to deal with problems. But it also can be unlearned. It is very important for children who are abused to receive treatment and counseling so they do not become abusive themselves.

Perpetrators of violence must want to change. Perpetrators must expect that change may only occur after a long period of time. Perpetrators need education and counseling in order to change. Being arrested, being barred by protective orders from seeing their victim(s), spending time in jail or prison, being placed on probation or a sexual offender list, and receiving clear messages from family, friends, and authorities help deter a person from using violence in the future.

There are signs that a perpetrator's behavior is changing. The person no longer blames others for his or her behaviors. The person does not do or say things that frighten others. The person respects others' feelings. The person's family and friends feel comfortable during time spent together. People feel safe around the person. The person does not attempt to control others. The person has received treatment for any alcohol or other drug use problems.

Reading Review

1. Why is victim recovery important?

2. What are signs that a perpetrator is changing his or her behavior?

Recovery and Intervention Programs

Recovery programs and intervention programs can be expected to be successful only if they help perpetrators:

- understand what is violent and abusive,
- understand why they are violent,
- learn to control their behavior,
- take responsibility for their behavior without blaming others or minimizing it,
- deal with their anger in non-threatening ways,
- recognize how tension and anger build up and learn how to appropriately deal with those emotions,
- deal with another person's anger,
- appropriately express their emotions,
- learn negotiation, conflict resolution, and listening skills so that they can build respectful relationships,
- learn about the cycle of violence,
- improve their self-esteem,
- improve their support systems,
- understand how alcohol and other drug use increases the chances of acting violently,
- learn appropriate alternatives to violence.

684   UNIT 11 • Injury Prevention and Personal Safety

⚖ Legal Issues

Domestic Violence Laws Give students a list of local attorneys or local law enforcement agencies that they can contact to ask for information about the penalties for violence against a spouse or a date, and the penalty for violating a restraining order. Ask students to contact one of the authorities from the list. Students also should ask about programs that help the offenders change their behavior. Have students write a report on their findings. Ask students to share their reports with the class. **L2**

awareness
battering
bullying
hazing
neglect
protective order
random violence
self-defense
  strategies
teasing
unnecessary risk
victim recovery

Key Terms Review

Explain the relationship between the pairs of lesson Key Terms below. Do not write in this book.

1. random violence—self-defense strategies
2. awareness—unnecessary risk
3. battering—protective order
4. teasing—bullying
5. battering—hazing
6. random violence—unnecessary risk
7. victim recovery—self-defense strategies
8. bullying—hazing

Recalling the Facts

9. Describe the types of child abuse.
10. What self-defense strategies should you use in social situations?
11. What "home" self-defense strategies should you use when you will be away?
12. Who is a mandatory reporter of child abuse?
13. What "home" self-defense strategies should you use with strangers?
14. Describe the causes and symptoms of post-traumatic stress disorder.
15. What are the characteristics of a bully?
16. What self-defense strategies should you use when walking in public?
17. What are the signs of mental and emotional abuse in children?
18. Describe a person who is more likely than others to be bullied.

Critical Thinking

19. Analyze ways to show disapproval of inconsiderate and disrespectful behavior, such as the behavior of bullies.
20. Examine the legal ramifications of hazing, bullying, and dating violence.
21. Discuss the categories of mental and emotional abuse.
22. Describe the phases of domestic violence. Explain why victims of domestic violence often stay with their abusers.

Real-Life Applications

23. Discuss how the family and friends of victims of violence can help them recover.
24. In what setting do you think you are at highest risk for harm, and what defensive strategies can you use to protect yourself?
25. Discuss what actions you can take to help prevent and stop hazing and bullying in your social groups and at school.
26. Describe what you would do if you were a victim of dating violence.

Activities

Responsible Decision Making

27. **Write** A female friend has a part-time job as a childsitter for a family you know. She tells you that the father of the children for whom she childsits teases her in a sexual way. She says she is very uncomfortable with his teasing and that she feels unsafe around him, but she does not know what to do. Write a response to this situation. Refer to the Responsible Decision-Making Model on page 61 for help.

Sharpen Your Life Skills

28. **Use Communication Skills**
Interview a police officer about crime in your community. Before the interview, prepare ten questions, including questions about the type and frequency of violent or abusive acts. Ask questions about how young people can protect themselves and how they can report illegal actions they observe. Take notes on the police officer's responses.

Visit **www.glencoe.com** for more *Health & Wellness* quizzes.

Key Terms Review

1. Self-defense strategies can be used to protect oneself from random violence.
2. Awareness reduces unnecessary risk.
3. A protective order prohibits an offender from committing future acts of battery.
4. Teasing can turn into bullying if it becomes cruel, causes distress, or becomes one-sided.
5. Hazing can include battery.
6. Unnecessary risk increases your chance of being a victim of random violence.
7. Learning self-defense strategies can be a part of victim recovery.
8. Bullying and hazing are acts of physical and/or emotional abuse.

Recalling the Facts

9. See page 678.
10. See page 674.
11. See page 672.
12. a person who is required by law to report suspected child abuse
13. See page 672.
14. a violent act; sleep problems, irritability, trouble concentrating, emotional responses to memories of the event
15. See page 676.
16. See page 673.
17. See page 679.
18. See page 677.

Critical Thinking

19. See page 677.
20. Answers will vary.
21. See page 679.
22. See page 680.

Real-Life Applications

23. See page 683.
24. Answers will vary but should include a risk situation and appropriate self-defense strategies.
25. Answers will vary.

26. Answers will vary, but should include ending the relationship, and telling someone.

Activities

Responsible Decision Making

27. Answers will vary, but should include telling a responsible adult and avoiding the man.

Sharpen Your Life Skills

28. Answers will vary, but should include information about self-defense strategies and about how to report illegal actions.

LESSON 66

Protecting Yourself From Sexual Violence

Out of Time?

If time does not permit an in-depth study of this topic, use the following activities in this Teacher Wraparound Edition:

• Class Discussion, p. 688
• 5-Minute Check, p. 691
• Class Discussion, p. 692
• Differentiated Instruction, p. 695

1 Focus

HEALTH GOAL **Alcohol and Date Rape** Have students respond to the Health Goal for this lesson by listing reasons why they should avoid alcohol and other drugs in a dating situation. *Answers might include: against family guidelines, legal issues, STDs, unplanned pregnancy, risk of date rape.* Record student answers on the chalkboard or on an overhead transparency. **L2**

Write **ABOUT IT!**

Writing a Letter Students' letters should contain information regarding the physical and mental effects of rape. The letters also should include information on the legal issues regarding rape. Have a volunteer read his or her letter to the class. Ask the class if they have other ideas to add to the letter. **L2**

LESSON 66

What You'll Learn

1. Explain the relationship between alcohol and other drugs and date rape. *(p. 688)*
2. Identify guidelines to follow to reduce the risk of date rape. *(p. 689)*
3. Discuss sexual abuse. *(p. 691)*
4. List steps to take if you are sexually harassed or stalked. *(p. 692)*
5. Discuss the legal and ethical consequences of sexual assault, harassment, abuse, and rape. *(p. 688, 691, 693)*
6. Identify steps victims can take to better recover from sexual violence or abuse. *(p. 694)*

Why It's Important

To avoid sexual violence and abuse, you have to be alert to possible problems and warning signs. Your awareness helps protect you as well as those around you.

Key Terms

• sexual assault
• rape
• date-rape drugs
• sexual abuse
• incest
• sexual harassment
• stalking
• restraining order
• rape survivor
• rape trauma syndrome

Protecting Yourself from Sexual Violence

HEALTH GOAL • **I will practice strategies to help protect myself from sexual violence.**

Images of sexual violence are all too common in television shows and movies. Some music lyrics make references to sexual violence. These images and references can lead to mistaken ideas about rape, sexual abuse, sexual harassment, and stalking, which can put teens at risk. Sexual violence and abuse is always wrong. It is never the victim's fault if sexual violence or abuse occurs. This lesson will teach you how to better protect yourself against sexual violence and abuse.

Write **ABOUT IT!**

Writing About Sexual Violence Suppose that a friend tells you that she was recently raped and asks you not to tell anyone. How would you respond? After you read the information about recovering from violence on page 694, write a letter to your friend in your health journal explaining why it is important to report the rape and to have a physical examination.

National Health Education Standards—Guide for Lesson 66

1.5	Propose ways to reduce or prevent injuries and health problems.	pp. 686, 689, 692, 697	4.1	Utilize skills for communicating effectively with family, peers, and others to enhance health.	pp. 689, 690, 692, 694, 696
2.10	Analyze how public health policies and government regulations can influence health promotion and disease prevention.	pp. 691, 693, 697	4.2	Demonstrate refusal, negotiation, and collaboration skills to enhance health and avoid or reduce health risks.	pp. 687, 689
3.4	Determine when professional health services may be required.	pp. 686, 692, 694, 695	4.3	Demonstrate strategies to prevent, manage or resolve inter-personal conflicts without harming self or others.	pp. 692, 693, 697
3.5	Access valid and reliable health products and services.	p. 686		NHES Standards for Lesson 66 continued at www.glencoe.com.	

Rape

A ny type of unwanted sexual contact is **sexual assault**. Rape is a form of sexual assault. **Rape** is the threatened or actual use of physical force to get someone to have sex without giving consent. Though many people may believe that sexual assault is the same thing as rape, rape is only one form of sexual assault. Verbal threats, grabbing, or fondling are some other forms of sexual assault.

What to Know About Rape

Rape Though anyone can be a victim of rape, the majority of victims are women. And, although anyone can be a perpetrator of rape, the majority of perpetrators are male. A perpetrator of rape can be a stranger to a victim, though most perpetrators know the victim in some way. In all forms of sexual assault and rape, anger and a need for power usually are the motivating factors. All forms of sexual assault and rape are forms of violence, and all are unethical and illegal.

Acquaintance rape The majority of rape cases involve a form of rape called acquaintance rape. **Acquaintance rape** is when a person who is raped knows the rapist. **Date rape** is when rape occurs in a dating situation.

Facts about date rape Teens sometimes are confused about date rape. They may believe that sex without consent is acceptable in some situations. Sex without consent is never acceptable—it is rape. Rape is never the victim's fault. Circumstances do not change this definition of unlawful behavior.

Some males may believe that the male role is to be the aggressor and the female role is to be the resister. Some males might believe that when a female say "no," she really means "maybe" or "yes." As a result, these males might ignore messages of non-consent and force a female to have sex. They have committed rape. Some males might misinterpret signs of affection. They might believe that cuddling or kissing indicate a desire to have sex. They might believe females say "no" because they think that is what females are supposed to say, but that they don't really mean "no." These males might ignore female resistance and force sex. But males must stop when a female says "no." Forcing a person to have sex is rape.

At all times, people must be consistent, say "no" clearly, and not encourage sexual advances. People should keep their limits clear when they express affection. If a male becomes more forceful, a female should resist more forcefully. Say "no" firmly and yell, scream, or run away, if necessary. Males must stop when a female says "no." Forcing a person to have sex is rape.

If a female puts herself in a risk situation—perhaps by accompanying a male to his home or by being alone with a male she doesn't know very well—do her actions indicate consent to have sex even if she says "no"? No, they do not. If a male forces a female to have sex, even when she is in a risk situation, he has committed rape. Females should avoid putting themselves in risk situations. If they do put

Extension

Without Consent Have students interview a lawyer or a judge to find out what the legal meaning of the phrase "without consent" is in regard to rape. Have students present their findings to the class. **L3**

Class Discussion

Date Rape and Drugs Ask students why many instances of date rape involve alcohol and other drugs. *Reasons should include: increased likelihood of being in a risk situation, impaired judgment, intensification of feelings, and need for control.* **L2**

Class Activity

High-Risk Situations Have students create scenarios that would increase someone's risk for becoming a victim of date rape. For example, going on a first date alone, or leaving your drink on a table while you go to the bathroom. Have students create flash cards that describe the scenario on the front. On the back of the flash cards, have students write solutions to the scenarios. For example, go on a group date, bring your drink with you when you leave the room. Students can use the flash cards to increase their knowledge of date safety and to review for quizzes or tests. **L2**

Make the Connection

Resisting Sexual Violence For more information on resistance skills, see page 47 in Lesson 5.

themselves in a risk situation, it can be difficult to defend themselves or to get help if sexual advances occur. Males must always stop when a female says "no." If a females wears clothes that a male considers to be revealing, do her clothes indicate consent to have sex even if she says "no"? No, they do not. If a male assumes that a female wants to have sex and forces her to do so, he has committed rape. While people have the right to wear what they want without the threat of harm, females should realize that others might not respect that right. Males must realize that the clothing a female wears does not equal consent for sex. Forced sex is always rape. Both males and females must understand that rape is never the victim's fault. The perpetrator is always the one at fault.

Laws concerning rape As mentioned earlier, rape is the threatened or actual use of physical force to get someone to have sex without giving consent. An important part of this definition are the words "without consent." There are laws to interpret what "without consent" means. If a person does not willingly agree to

When teens are in a social setting, they should never leave their water or soda unattended because someone might slip a date-rape drug into ▼ their drink.

have sex, there is no consent, and sex in this case is considered rape. The law states that people under a certain age and people who do not have certain mental abilities are considered unable to give consent, even if they agree to have sex. A person who has sex with someone described as not able to give consent is guilty of committing rape.

Anyone under the influence of alcohol or other drugs cannot give legal consent to have sex. In other words, having sex with someone who has been drinking or using drugs can be considered rape in a court of law, even if the person did not say "no." Drunkenness or being high on drugs is not considered a legal defense against rape.

Alcohol and Other Drug Use

The use of alcohol and other drugs greatly increases the possibility that date rape might occur because of the following reasons.

Increased likelihood that you might be in a risk situation If females use alcohol and/or drugs, they might make wrong decisions concerning their personal safety. They might not be able to think clearly and, thus, not be able to follow their gut instincts about a person's character. Females must be careful about whom they spend time with, especially if they are going to be alone with a person. If a female is in a risk situation, it may be difficult for her to defend herself from sexual advances or rape.

Impaired judgment If males use alcohol and/or drugs, they also might make wrong decisions. They might not

⚖ Legal Issues

Penalties Have students research federal and state laws and legal consequences for committing rape, attempted rape, sexual assault, and sexual battery. In groups, have students research the incidence of rape in an assigned state and in the United States. Students' reports should include a description of their state's laws, the incidence of rape in their state and in the United States, the incidence of conviction for rape charges, and the associated penalties for each. Each group should organize a multimedia presentation for the class. After the presentations, have the class discuss the similarities and differences among state's laws. **L3**

Activity: Using Life Skills

Resistance Skills: Reducing the Risk of Date Rape

Rape is always the perpetrator's fault. However, there are several steps that you can take to help reduce your risk of becoming a victim of date rape. If you are raped, contact the police and seek medical treatment.

1 Say "no" with self-confidence, and give reasons for saying "no." Set clear limits for sexual behavior, and communicate these limits to people whom you date. Firmly tell a person to stop when you experience unwanted sexual advances.

2 Repeat your "no" response several times, and use nonverbal behavior to match verbal behavior. Respond by yelling, screaming, or running away if the person does not stop.

3 Influence others to make responsible decisions. Spend time with friends and family that you trust.

4 Avoid situations in which there will be pressure to make wrong decisions, avoid people who make wrong decisions, and resist pressure to engage in illegal behavior. Avoid dating or being in the company of someone who is very controlling or demanding, and avoid drinking alcohol and using other drugs that interfere with your judgment and ability to respond. Also, avoid being in isolated places.

▲ It is important for teens to date people who share their commitment to set limits on sexual behavior.

be able to think clearly, and so they might ignore messages of non-consent from females and force sex because their judgement is impaired. But drunkenness or being high on drugs is not a legal defense against rape.

Intensified feelings and the need for control Rape is an act of violence. A person who is a rapist often has an increased need to control a companion. The rapist may try to get the victim in an isolated location and then use threats or intimidation to control and assault the victim. He or she also is more likely to act upon that need after using alcohol or other drugs. Indeed, many rapes have reportedly happened after alcohol or other drug use has occurred.

Date-Rape Drugs

Some drugs are used to sedate and depress a person's central nervous system, leaving him or her vulnerable to sexual assault. These types of drugs are called ***date-rape drugs*** and are dangerous because they can be slipped into a person's beverage without his or her knowledge. A person might not be able to see, smell, or taste the drug. People have died after these drugs have been slipped into their drinks. Be careful in any type of social setting because a date-rape drug could be slipped into your drink without your knowledge. Avoid setting your drink down, and never leave it alone if you plan to continue drinking it.

Flunitrazepam (also known as roofies), GHB, and ketamine are drugs that have been used as date-rape drugs. See Facts About on the next page for more information on date-rape drugs.

Reading Review

1. What does "without consent" mean?
2. Why are date-rape drugs dangerous?

LESSON 66 • Protecting Yourself from Sexual Violence **689**

Achieving Health Literacy

Critical Thinker Ask students to imagine that they are volunteers at a rape crisis hotline. How would they respond to the following calls?

1. My boyfriend forced me to have sex with him. Is that rape?
2. There have been two rapes in my neighborhood lately. What can I do to protect myself?
3. One of my co-workers pushed me into an empty room and forcibly kissed and touched me, even though I told him "no." Is that sexual assault? **L1**

(adapted from *Violence Prevention: Totally Awesome Teaching Strategies for Safe and Drug-Free Schools,* by Linda Meeks, Philip Heit, and Randy Page)

689

FACTSABOUT

DATE-RAPE DRUGS

NHES Assessment/SCASS

Performance Task Have students research the Hillory J. Farias and Samantha Reid Date-Rape Drug Prohibition Act of 2000. Students should write reports on their findings, including the two teens' stories, the drugs used in each case, and the legal consequences for the people who gave the teens the drugs. Students should evaluate how effective this law has been in reducing or preventing crimes involving date-rape drugs. **L2**

Investigating the Issue

- *The drink testing strips or coasters change color when exposed to a liquid that contains a date-rape drug.*
- *Precautions include not accepting open drinks from anyone you do not know and trust; not leaving your drink unattended; accepting drinks only in unopened containers, such as bottles or cans; not drinking from punch bowls, pitchers, or tubs; staying alert and aware; and leaving if you suspect date-rape drugs may be at the club or party.*

FACTSABOUT
DATE-RAPE
DRUGS

What are date-rape drugs? Reports of the use of drugs, such as flunitrazepam (more commonly known as roofies), Gamma-Hydroxybutyrate (GHB), and ketamine, to facilitate a rape have been increasing since the early 1990s. Many times, these drugs are dropped into a person's drink at a bar or party without his or her knowledge.

▲ Roofies (the pills), GHB (the liquid), and ketamine (the powder) can easily be slipped into a drink.

Rohypnol

Rohypnol, a pill sometimes referred to as roofies, R2, roaches, Mexican valium, or the forget-me-pill, is a prescription sedative/depressant that is used as a treatment for insomnia or as a pre-anesthetic in other countries. Roofies are not manufactured or sold legally in North America. When dissolved in liquid, including water, the drug is often undetectable. It is tasteless and odorless.

Effects The effects of roofies include impaired judgment, motor skills, and memory loss, including amnesia. Dizziness, drowsiness, confusion, and a state of semiconsciousness also can result from its use. All of these effects increase in intensity and duration if roofies are taken in combination with alcohol or other drugs. Noticeable effects occur within 15–20 minutes of administration. The effects can last 12 hours. The drug is detectable in urine for up to 72 hours after administration.

GHB

GHB, sometimes called liquid ecstasy, Clear X, Liquid X, liquid dream, and Chemical X, is a colorless, odorless liquid that is a depressant/anesthetic. Although GHB used to be marketed as a body-building supplement, the manufacture, distribution, and possession of GHB has been illegal in the United States since 2000. The effects of GHB include dizziness, nausea, drowsiness, amnesia, hallucinations, and coma. The effects can be felt within 15–30 minutes after administration and can last from 3–6 hours.

Ketamine

Ketamine, also called Special K, Super K, KO, and Ket Kat, is a legal drug used as a veterinary sedative or as an anesthetic on humans. Effects include delirium, hallucinations, amnesia, and coma. If ingested, the effects can be felt in about 10–20 minutes and are short-lived compared to those of roofies and GHB, lasting only 3 hours.

Dangers of date-rape drugs The effects of all of these drugs leave the user vulnerable to sexual attack. These drugs remain detectable in the body for only a limited time after use. In many instances, if an assault is not reported immediately, there might be no physical evidence that these drugs were used in a sexual attack.

Investigating the Issue

Visit **www.glencoe.com** to research more information about date-rape drugs.

- Find out more information about the test strips and coasters that can be used to determine the presence of a date-rape drug in a drink. How do these work?
- What precautions can you take at clubs and parties to avoid ingesting a date-rape drug?

Create a pamphlet that contains facts about date-rape drugs and what precautions can be taken against becoming a victim.

Health Project

Posters Working in groups or individually, have students make posters about date-rape drugs. Assign each group or individual a date-rape drug to research. Students should create an informational poster regarding the assigned drug. Posters should include information about the effects of the drugs and the potential consequences of use. They should also point out ways that teens can protect themselves. Have students share their posters with their classmates. Have students ask questions about drugs described on the posters to create discussion. **L2 ELL**

Sexual Abuse

Maltreatment that involves any sexual contact that is forced on a person without his or her consent is *sexual abuse*. Sexual abuse can take many different forms. It can consist of a single incident of sexual contact, or it can consist of repeated incidents of sexual contact.

What to Know About Sexual Abuse

Sexual abuse Sexual abuse behaviors can include rape, incest, or any type of sexual contact. Exploitation of children under the age of 18 can consist of promoting minors to engage in sex acts, using minors to produce pornography, or encouraging and promoting prostitution. All forms of sexual abuse are wrong, and the perpetrator is always the one at fault. Victims of sexual abuse are never the ones at fault.

Incest Sexual abuse in which the abuser is a close relative of the victim is called *incest.* Incest is the most common form of sexual abuse. Children often do not recognize incest as abuse. It might be considered as favoritism by a child. Incest is always wrong, and the perpetrator is always the one at fault. Although victims might feel that they did something to cause the abuse, they need to understand that they are not to blame. Incest is never the fault of the victim.

A child or teen who is sexually abused might have difficulty sharing information about the abuse. The young person might fear that his or her parent will be penalized by law enforcement authorities. The young person might worry that the family will break up. As a result, he or she is reluctant to report the abuse. The

young person needs to realize that these things might occur, but that he or she needs to report the abuse to make it stop. The abuser needs to get help to stop the abuse. The young person also needs to get help to recover from the abuse.

A young person also might feel unjustly ashamed and guilty. A young person might disclose sexual abuse immediately after an incident, or it may take several months, or even years, before he or she discloses the abuse or it is discovered by someone else. Often a young person does not disclose sexual abuse out of fear that a perpetrator will harm him or her further. He or she also is likely to feel shame and embarrassment, which hinder disclosure. The young person should remember that the abuse is not his or her fault and that seeking help can stop it from occurring.

Laws All states have laws that prohibit sexual abuse and require teachers and health professionals to report suspected cases of abuse. The identity of the person who is reporting the suspected abuse remains confidential when an abuse case is filed with child welfare agencies or the police. If an investigation reveals that a child is in danger, that child will be placed in protective custody or in a foster home.

Did You Know?

Sexual Abuse In 2000, 93 percent of juvenile sexual assault victims knew their attacker: 34.2 percent were family members and 58.7 percent were acquaintances. Only 7 percent of the perpetrators were strangers to the victim.

LESSON 66 • Protecting Yourself from Sexual Violence   **691**

Sexual Harassment and Stalking

Class Discussion

Sexual Harassment Have students read the definitions of sexual harassment and stalking. Write the definitions on the chalkboard or on a transparency for an overhead projector. Ask the class to give examples of behaviors that illustrate stalking and sexual harassment and discuss how they fit the definitions. Ask students to discuss appropriate responses to these behaviors. **L2**

Class Activity

Solutions Ask students to research a real-life sexual harassment or stalking case. Students can receive help with their research at the school or community library. Instructors may want to specify that the cases the students choose be outside the community, so that no one the students know is involved. Students should summarize the cases and include what was done to resolve the problem. After sharing the information with the rest of the class, have students brainstorm other ways of solving the problem. **L2**

Explain the Concept

Stalking Television and movies often portray stalking in a narrow way—implying that it's stalking only if the stalker actually follows the person everywhere he or she goes. Explain to students that stalking behavior can also involve telephone harassment, mail and e-mail, and various means of intimidation. Often a stalker will express affection for a victim even while engaging in threatening behavior. If a student suspects he or she is being stalked, he or she should tell a trusted adult.

Sexual Harassment and Stalking

Unwanted sexual behavior that ranges from making sexual comments to forcing another person into unwanted sexual acts is ***sexual harassment***. Examples of sexual harassment include telling sexual jokes, making inappropriate gestures, staring at someone in a sexual manner, and touching someone in sexual ways. ***Stalking*** is repeatedly engaging in harassing or threatening behavior, such as following or making harassing phone calls to a person.

What to Do If You Are Sexually Harassed or Stalked

Did You Know?

Stalking It is estimated that one out of every 12 U.S. women (8.2 million) has been stalked at some time in her life, and one out of every 45 U.S. men (2 million) has been stalked at some time in his life.

Sexual Harassment

Ask the person who is harassing you to stop. Be direct about what behavior is bothering you. The person might interpret a lack of response as encouragement.

Keep a record of what happened. Write down the date and time, describe the situation and behavior, and explain how you handled the situation. Save any notes, letters, or pictures.

Check to see if there are guidelines to follow for the specific situation. For example, if the harassment occurred at school, check school guidelines. If the harassment occurred at work, check work guidelines.

Report the harassment to the appropriate person in charge. This person may be a boss, teacher, or school counselor.

Determine if you want to take legal action. Sexual harassment is against all companies' policies. It also is a violation of the Civil Rights Act of 1964.

Stalking

Tell a trusted adult. Tell your parents or guardian and school officials what is happening. As much as possible, avoid being alone.

Keep a record of each case of stalking. Write down the date, time, what was said, and what happened.

Save evidence. Evidence would include notes and letters that might have been written to you, and answering machine tapes with messages left on them.

Try to obtain a restraining order. A ***restraining order*** is an order by a court that forbids a person from coming within a certain distance of the victim.

Contact the police department to report the stalking. Consider pressing charges against the person who is stalking you.

Seek counseling. Seek appropriate counseling or join a support group for victims of stalking.

🏛 Community Involvement

Sexual Violence Have a police officer, a psychiatrist, or a psychologist who specializes in recovery from sexual violence come to class. Have the guest speaker talk about his or her profession and what he or she does on a typical day. Have students create a list of questions to ask the guest speaker. Have students write a short paper about their feelings and experiences about the guest speaker. Tell students to answer these questions in their papers: Do they believe they would like the job? What skills would the professional need to deal with the emotional stress of the job? What are some other issues related to the job? **L2**

❝If a woman wears skimpy clothing or puts herself in risky situations, is she asking to be raped?❞

the FACTS No one asks to be raped and no one deserves it. If you force a person to have sex, you have committed rape. Rape victims range from infants to the elderly. Three out of every 20 rape victims are under the age of 12. More than 13,000 people are raped at work every year. No victim asks for or deserves to be raped.

❝If a rapist is overcome with the desire to have sex, then is rape a crime of passion?❞

the FACTS Rape is an act of violence—a way of humiliating and controlling another human being. About 70 percent of rapes are planned in advance. Many convicted rapists are married or have sexual partners at the time of the rape. The victims of this crime feel the violence both physically and emotionally. Many suffer from rape trauma syndrome.

❝When a woman says 'no,' she means 'yes.' Then she falsely reports a rape.❞

the FACTS Some men believe that they are supposed to be the aggressor in a relationship. They think that a woman who refuses to have sex is just playing "hard to get." These men cannot imagine that a woman actually does not want to have sex with them, so they rape her. According to the FBI, approximately 8 percent of reported rapes are found to be unfounded. On the other hand, over half of rape victims do not even report the crime.

Rape Rape is the threatened or actual use of physical force to get someone to have sex without giving consent. Have students read the statements in Just the Facts. Ask students whether they agree or disagree with the answers to the questions and statements. This discussion may uncover misconceptions students have about rape. **L2**

Extension

Laws Have students research laws that protect against stalking. Have students create a multimedia presentation for the class. **L2**

Sexual Harassment and Stalking Laws

Sexual harassment Sexual harassment is illegal. The federal law, Title VII of the Civil Rights Act of 1964, strictly prohibits sexual harassment in the workplace. Title IX, also a federal law, makes it clear that sexual harassment should never occur in a school. People have a right to be free from sexual harassment, and these laws help to protect their rights. Many states also have laws that protect against sexual harassment. In addition, most schools have developed policies to deal with sexual harassment. Many schools and places of employment train employees on how to prevent and deal with sexual harassment.

Stalking Some people who stalk others are trying to form a relationship or extend a relationship with the person they are stalking. In some cases, a stalker takes further action, and stalking leads to injury or murder. Before anti-stalking laws began to be passed in the 1990s, victims of stalking had few opportunities for protection. Many were victimized by prolonged intimidation and physical harm because there were no laws available to protect victims from stalking crimes. In 1992, the United States Congress passed an anti-stalking law to serve as a model for states. This law encouraged states to pass similar laws, making stalking a felony offense with stiff penalties.

In 1994, the Violence Against Women Act (VAWA) made it a federal crime for a person to cross a state line with the intent to injure, harass, or intimidate his or her spouse or intimate partner. Since California became the first state to pass an anti-stalking law, every state and the District of Columbia have passed anti-stalking laws. These laws give law enforcement agencies more power to arrest and prosecute stalkers, and they give more protection to stalking victims. Victims of stalking need to become familiar with the current anti-stalking laws in the state and community in which they live. Support groups also offer information.

Reading Review

1. What is the definition of sexual harassment?

2. What are two things to do if you are sexually harassed?

3. What are two things to do if someone is stalking you?

Reading Review

1. *unwanted sexual behavior that ranges from making sexual comments to forcing another person into unwanted sexual acts*

2. *Ask the person to stop, keep a record of events, check to see if there are guidelines to follow for the specific situation, report the harassment to an appropriate person, decide if you want to take legal action.*

3. *contact the police department, keep a record of events, save evidence, try to obtain a restraining order, tell a trusted adult, seek counseling*

NHES Assessment/SCASS

Selected Response Which state was the first to pass an anti-stalking law?

A. New York
B. Ohio
C. *California*
D. Texas

🖊 Achieving Health Literacy

Critical Thinker Have students create a scenario in which a person is sexually harassed. Students should describe the situation and why this instance is sexual harassment. Students should write a one-page summary of how the person might feel. Choose the best examples and lead a class discussion regarding the scenarios. Have students get into groups and discuss the scenario read to them. Have the students discuss actions they would take in a similar situation. **L2**

National Health Education Standards

Pages 692–693: 1.5, 2.10, 3.4, 4.1, 7.1, 7.3

Recovery from Violence

Extension

Resources Ask students to research community agencies that are available to assist victims of sexual violence. Students can create a list of agency names, addresses, phone numbers, and what services the agencies provide. Interested students can create a pamphlet that includes the information and obtain permission to make the pamphlets available to other students in the school. **L3** **ELL**

Class Activity

Posters Have students create posters that include drawings, photos, or collages that visually describe the steps people can take to help them recover from rape. Students also can choose to make a poster about another topic that pertains to rape. There should be little text on the posters. **L2** **ELL**

Class Activity

Circle of Support Have students take out a blank sheet of paper. On the paper have students draw four circles that resemble a bull's-eye. In the center of the center circle (A) have students write the names of people with whom they have the closest relationships. In the next circle (B) have students write the names of people with whom they are friends but who are not part of their inner circle. In the next circle (C) have students write the names of people in the school (i.e. teachers) with whom they feel close. In the outermost circle have students identify resources in their community where they could go for help. Do not ask students to share their circles of support with the class; rather, tell them that the circles are for their own reference. **L2** **ELL**

Recovery from Violence

Survivors of sexual violence and abuse often experience feelings of anger, fear, shock, confusion, and depression. In many instances, they blame themselves for what happened. The world that they may have felt was safe and predictable is suddenly unsafe and unpredictable. The survivor may ask, "Why me?"

What to Know About Recovery for Survivors

Make the Connection

Survivor Recovery For more information on recovery for survivors, see page 683 in Lesson 65.

The purpose of recovery programs is to help victims survive the pain, heal, and move forward with self-confidence. This may be difficult for survivors. Recovery does not mean that they forget what happened. Instead, recovery is being able to understand and believe that being a victim was not their fault. A survivor will never forget what has happened, but with time and effort, a survivor can accept the reality of what has happened and work through his or her feelings. Survivors of rape or sexual abuse can and do recover. Recovery can be a powerful and positive step in the survivor's life. There are several steps survivors can take to fully recover.

Talk about what happened. It is important to share feelings, thoughts, and experiences. Survivors need a support network of family members and trusted friends who can help them through the recovery process.

Get a complete medical examination. Survivors of sexual violence and abuse need to get a complete examination. They need to have physical injuries treated. They might need blood tests to determine if they have become infected with a sexually transmitted disease and need to be tested for pregnancy.

Seek counseling. Survivors may need counseling and support services for emotional trauma. School counselors and physicians can tell them about the counseling and support services offered in the community.

Join a support group. There are support groups for survivors of sexual violence and abuse. Survivors might ask school counselors or look in the local phone directory or newspaper to find support groups.

Practice self-defense strategies. Survivors can gain confidence so that they can protect themselves from further harm. They can learn about risk

694 UNIT 11 • Injury Prevention and Personal Safety

 Family Involvement

Family-Based Board Game Have students create an activity that can involve their parents and siblings. Have students brainstorm ideas with their family. For example, the student can create a quiz show or a board game that relates to drugs, alcohol, and sexual violence. Possible topics could be myths surrounding rape and sexual assault, social norms and peer pressure of teenagers, or knowledge-based information on drugs and alcohol. Have students write a short paper about their experience creating a family board game or quiz show. Ask students to brainstorm other family-based activities that could be created. **L1**

situations and how to avoid them. They can learn and practice self-defense strategies.

Try to remain hopeful and optimistic about the future. Survivors might not believe it right away, but the world is a wonderful place, and recovery and happiness are possible.

Recovery Efforts for Rape Survivors

A *rape survivor* is a person who has been raped. Rape survivors often need treatment for both physical injuries and emotional damage. A rape survivor should not take a shower after a rape until a medical exam has been performed so health status can be determined and evicence collected. Rape survivors may become infected with HIV or other STDs. Female rape survivors may become pregnant.

Rape trauma syndrome After the rape, survivors might be in shock or feel frightened or guilty. They might feel responsible for the rape. They might wonder why they were chosen to be the rapist's victim. They might not want other people to know what happened to them. Some rape survivors experience rape trauma syndrome. *Rape trauma syndrome* is a condition in which a rape survivor experiences emotional responses and physical symptoms over a period of time. After a rape, survivors might feel ashamed, angry, afraid, guilty, and powerless.

Physical symptoms include nausea, headaches, and sleeplessness. Emotional responses may last from several weeks to several years. Rape survivors might experience problems when

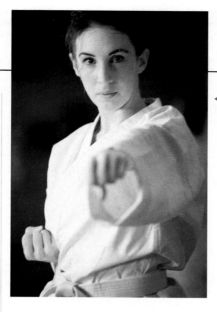

◄ Rape survivors sometimes gain confidence by learning and practicing self-defense strategies.

becoming intimate with someone. They may experience new problems in existing relationships with family members and friends. Many survivors fear retaliation from the rapist. They often change their living habits by changing their telephone numbers, moving, or moving in with others.

To recover and to avoid the lasting effects of rape trauma syndrome, survivors need treatment for both physical injuries and emotional damage. Sometimes victims are examined by sexual assault nurse examiners (SANEs), who are trained to deal with emotional damage caused by rape, as well as physical injuries.

Resources Many resources are available to help rape survivors in their recovery. Rape crisis centers are available in many communities. Hospitals and women's centers also offer counseling and support groups. Rape victims can call the National Sexual Assault Hotline at 1-800-656-HOPE (4673) for information on local support groups and resources.

LESSON 66 • Protecting Yourself from Sexual Violence **695**

5-Minute Check

Page 78, **Unit 11 Fast File Resources**

1. What is the most common form of child sexual abuse? *incest*
2. What federal law prohibits sexual harassment in the workplace? *Title VII of the Civil Rights Act of 1964*
3. When were the first anti-stalking laws passed? *1990s*
4. Why is it important for a person who has been a victim of sexual violence to get a medical examination? *They need to have physical injuries treated, and they need to be tested for STDs, HIV, and pregnancy.*
5. What can survivors of rape or sexual abuse do to help their own recovery? *Talk about it with a friend, seek counseling, get a medical exam, join a support group, learn self-defense strategies, and remain hopeful.*

Teaching Transparency

Page 71, **Unit 11 Fast File Resources**

LESSON 66	Protecting Yourself From Sexual Violence

TEACHING TRANSPARENCY • Use with Unit 11, Lesson 66

Helping Victims of Sexual Violence

National Resources for Victims of Sexual Violence	
Name of Organization	What the Organization Does
Office for Victims of Crime	Assists in victim recovery; provides information, statistics, and updates on victim issues
Violence Against Women Office	Provides information about violence against women; handles policy and legal issues regarding violence against women
Sexual Assault Resource Service (SARS)	Offers information for nursing professionals who provide sexual assault evaluations
Rape, Abuse, and Incest National Network (RAINN)	Provides statistics, prevention tips, and counseling information

Meeks Heit Health & Wellness

UNIT AND LESSON TRANSPARENCIES

Differentiated Instruction

Hearing Impairment To help ensure that a student with hearing impairment understands class discussions, provide the student with key vocabulary words, such as stalking, incest, sexual harassment, and STDs, several days before the discussion. Make sure the student is seated in a spot that is visually accessible to the entire group. Rephrase or restate what other students contribute, while you point to the speaker. Face the student to enable speech reading. Remember not to stand with your back to a window while speaking, as that puts your mouth in shadow rather than light. **L2**

National Health Education Standards

Pages 694–695: 1.2, 3.4, 4.1, 4.4

695

National Resources for Victims

Divide the class into four groups, and assign each group to research one of the organizations in Table 66.1 (National Resources for Victims of Sexual Violence). Have students contact the organizations for information. Students can use the information they gather to make a half-page informational advertisement for the organization. **L2**

Reading Review

1. *A condition in which a rape survivor experiences emotional responses and physical symptoms over a period of time.*
2. *Family and friends may experience feelings of anger, inadequacy, and guilt.*

3 Assess

Vocabulary Practice

Page 70, **Unit 11 Fast File Resources**

National Health Education Standards

Pages 696–697: 1.5, 2.10, 4.1, 4.4, 7.1, 8.2

696

TABLE 66.1 National Resources for Victims of Sexual Violence

Name of Organization	What the Organization Does
Office for Victims of Crime	Assists in victim recovery; provides information, statistics, and updates on victim issues.
Violence Against Women Office	Provides information about violence against women; handles policy and legal issues regarding violence against women.
Sexual Assault Resource Service (SARS)	Offers information for nursing professionals who provide sexual assault evaluations.
Rape, Abuse, and Incest National Network (RAINN)	Provides statistics, prevention tips, and counseling information.

Providing support for a rape victim If you know someone who has been raped, there are ways that you can provide support. Be sure never to blame the victim for the rape.

Give the victim time to feel comfortable with discussing the rape, but encourage the victim to share feelings and thoughts when he or she feels ready. When the victim does share their experiences, thoughts, or feelings with you, believe what the victim says about the experience and the feelings that are shared.

Try to be supportive, but not overly protective. Realize that it might take weeks, months, or years for the victim to begin working through the recovery process. As the person feels more comfortable, encourage the victim to get help from a rape crisis center, a counselor, or mental-health professional.

Advice for family members and friends Friends, family members, spouses, boyfriends, or girlfriends of people who are victims of sexual assault also are victims. This is because the crime has affected their lives, too. Husbands, wives, boyfriends, or girlfriends of sexual assault victims might feel angry, inadequate, and guilty. They might worry that their partner is pregnant or infected with a sexually transmitted disease, including HIV. Family members might have similar worries and fears. Family members might want to seek counseling to help them work through this difficult time.

Recovery for Perpetrators

If you have committed an act of sexual violence, you don't have to continue being violent. You can get help and change your behavior. Research shows that teenagers who have committed acts of sexual violence may be able to change their behavior so that they do not commit such acts in the future.

Changing this behavior requires entering and completing a treatment program that offers help from mental health professionals. Treatment programs include relapse prevention, which helps individuals develop skills so that they do not return to a previous pattern of inappropriate behavior.

Relapse prevention should teach offenders to understand any thoughts, feelings, or situations that trigger acts of sexual violence. It also helps individuals in treatment to identify thinking patterns that contribute to committing acts of sexual violence.

Reading Review

1. What is rape trauma syndrome?
2. Why might family members of rape victims need counseling?

696 UNIT 11 • Injury Prevention and Personal Safety

🛡 Sensitive Issues

Sexual Violence While it is important to point out ways to avoid sexual violence, it also is important to emphasize that rape, sexual assault, sexual abuse, sexual harassment, and stalking are never the victim's fault. Students in the class may be affected by sexual violence, and they may be experiencing a form of trauma syndrome. They may wrongly feel they are to blame for the violence. Emphasize to students that victims of sexual violence never ask to be assaulted, and that it is never their fault. Ask students to discuss issues and attitudes around sexual assault and how they feel in regards to these issues. **L2**

Key Terms Review

Match the definitions below with the lesson Key Terms on the left. Do not write in this book.

1. obsessing about a person with the intent to threaten or harm that person

2. having sexual contact with a family member

3. any sexual contact forced on a person without his or her consent.

4. any type of unwanted sexual contact

5. an order by a court that forbids a person from coming within a certain distance of the victim

6. a person who has been raped

7. roofies, GHB, ketamine

8. condition in which a rape survivor experiences emotional responses and physical symptoms over a period of time

9. unwanted sexual behavior that ranges from making sexual comments to forcing another person into unwanted sexual acts

10. the threatened or actual use of physical force to get someone to have sex without giving consent

Recalling the Facts

11. What is date rape, and is there ever a situation in which it is acceptable?

12. Describe what "without consent" means in regards to date rape.

13. How does alcohol and other drug use increase the risk of date rape?

14. What actions can you take to decrease your risk of becoming a victim of rape?

15. Why are date-rape drugs dangerous?

16. What are the laws and ethical issues regarding sexual abuse, rape, and sexual harassment?

17. What is the difference between sexual abuse and incest?

18. How can a person recover from sexual violence?

Critical Thinking

19. Analyze the steps that you can take to protect yourself from rape and date rape.

20. Why is any form of sexual assault, rape, or sexual abuse never the victim's fault?

21. Why would there be different interpretations about what "without consent" means?

22. Why is it important for victims of harassment or stalking to keep detailed records?

Real-Life Applications

23. What should you do if you think someone you know is being sexually abused?

24. What would you do if someone was stalking you?

25. What can you do to protect yourself from sexual harassment?

26. How can you help someone who is recovering from sexual violence?

Activities

Responsible Decision Making

27. **Write** Suppose a neighbor who is a friend of your family makes you feel uneasy. He or she stares at you and makes sexual comments and gestures to you. What should you do? Write a response to this situation in your health journal. Refer to the Responsible Decision-Making Model on page 61.

Sharpen Your Life Skills

28. **Access Health Information** Examine the laws and legal consequences in your state, community, job, and school regarding sexual harassment, date rape, and sexual abuse. Gather information and write a one-page journal entry about the ethical and legal consequences of these behaviors.

Visit **www.glencoe.com** for more *Health & Wellness* quizzes.

LESSON 66 • Study Guide **697**

Sidebar (left column)

LESSON
66
STUDY
GUIDE

acquaintance rape
date-rape drugs
date rape
incest
rape
rape survivor
rape trauma
   syndrome
restraining order
sexual abuse
sexual assault
sexual harassment
stalking

LESSON 66
STUDY GUIDE

Key Terms Review

1. stalking
2. incest
3. sexual abuse
4. sexual assault
5. restraining order
6. rape survivor
7. date-rape drugs
8. rape trauma syndrome
9. sexual harassment
10. rape

Recalling the Facts

11. Date rape is when rape occurs in a dating situation. There is never a situation in which date rape is acceptable.

12. If a person does not willingly agree to have sex, then it is "without consent." People under a certain age, and people who do not have certain mental abilities also are considered not able to give consent.

13. increased likelihood of being in a risk situation, interferes with judgment, intensifies feelings and the need for control

14. Set and communicate clear limits for sexual behavior to those you date; firmly say no to unwanted sexual advances.

15. They impair judgment, induce memory loss, and can cause death.

16. All states have laws that prohibit sexual abuse and require teachers and health professionals to report suspected cases of abuse.

17. Incest is a type of sexual abuse in which the abuser is a close relative of the victim.

18. talk about what happened, get a complete medical examination, seek counseling

Critical Thinking

19. See steps on page 689.

20. There is never a situation where it is OK. Any forced sexual contact is sexual assault or rape.

21. People under a certain age and those with mental disabilities are not considered able to give legal consent, even if they agree to have sex.

---

22. They provide evidence for law authorities.

Real-Life Applications

23. Encourage victim to share feelings and thoughts when ready, encourage victim to get help, talk to an adult.

24. See page 692.

25. See page 692.

26. encourage victims to share feelings and thoughts when ready, believe victim

Activities

Responsible Decision Making

27. Answers will vary.

Sharpen Your Life Skills

28. Answers will vary.

697

Out of Time?

If time does not permit an in-depth study of this topic, use the following activities in this Teacher Wraparound Edition:
- Quick Demo, p. 700
- Legal Issues, p. 700
- Community Involvement, p. 702

1 Focus

HEALTH GOAL **Health Risks** Have students respond to the Health Goal for this lesson by listing reasons why it is risky to belong to a gang. *Reasons might include drugs, unplanned pregnancy, jail, injury, and death.* **L2**

Write ABOUT IT!

NHES Assessment/SCASS

Constructed Response Students should write one to two paragraphs evaluating each "offer" and the pros and cons of each decision. When they are finished writing, have students pair off and debate the pros and cons of each decision. **L2**

LESSON

67

What You'll Learn

1. Discuss characteristics of gang members. *(p. 699)*
2. Identify different roles of gang members. *(p. 699)*
3. Discuss reasons why it is risky to belong to a gang. *(p. 700)*
4. Explain how a gang can cause conflict in schools, families, and communities. *(p. 700)*
5. Analyze why teens join gangs. *(p. 701)*
6. Analyze strategies to avoid gangs. *(p. 702)*
7. Explain how a teen who belongs to a gang can leave the gang. *(p. 702)*
8. Discuss reasons why some teens have become anti-gang gang members. *(p. 702)*

Why It's Important

Gang involvement can lead to drug abuse, jail, unplanned pregnancy, violence, injury, and death. Knowing how to recognize gang members and how to stay away from them will help you avoid dangerous situations.

Key Terms

- gang
- hard-core gang member
- regular gang member
- wanna-be
- could-be
- prestige crime
- jumping-in
- anti-gang gang

Staying Away from Gangs

HEALTH GOAL • **I will stay away from gangs.**

A group of people involved in violent and illegal activities is a *gang*. Some gangs consist of a few neighborhood teens. Others have thousands of members who cooperate in highly organized illegal activities. Gang violence is an increasing problem. Gangs exist in big cities as well as smaller cities, suburbs, and rural areas. This lesson will give you facts about gangs. You will learn how to recognize gang members. You will learn why it is risky to belong to a gang and how you can protect yourself from gangs.

Write ABOUT IT!

Writing About Gangs Suppose one classmate is pressuring you to join a gang and another classmate is asking you to join an anti-gang group. Both classmates tell you that their group will give you a sense of belonging and that you can leave if you do not like their group. After you read the information about gangs on page 699, write your responses to your classmates in your health journal.

National Health Education Standards—Guide for Lesson 67

1.5	Propose ways to reduce or prevent injuries and health problems.	pp. 698, 702, 703	4.1	Utilize skills for communicating effectively with family, peers, and others to enhance health.	pp. 698, 703
1.8	Analyze personal susceptibility to injury, illness, or death if engaging in unhealthy behaviors.	pp. 698, 703	4.4	Demonstrate how to ask for and offer assistance to enhance the health of self and others.	p. 703
1.9	Analyze the potential severity of injury or illness if engaging in unhealthy behaviors.	pp. 698, 703	7.2	Demonstrate a variety of healthy practices and behaviors that will maintain or improve the health of self and others.	p. 702
2.1	Analyze how family influences the health of individuals.	pp. 700, 701			
2.3	Analyze how peers influence healthy and unhealthy behaviors.	pp. 700, 701, 703		NHES Standards for Lesson 67 continued at www.glencoe.com.	

698

Recognizing Gangs

You may have an idea of what gang members are like. For example, you may think that gang members only live in large cities and are from low income areas. This is not necessarily true. Gang members live in big cities, small cities, suburban, and rural areas, and come from families who have different income levels. However, most gang members have some common characteristics of which you should be aware.

How to Recognize Gangs

Gang members band together as a group. Gang members hang out only with other gang members.

Gang members play specific roles. Gangs have clear structures. A *hard-core gang member* is a senior gang member who has the most influence. There usually are several hard-core gang members who are leaders and tell others what to do. A *regular gang member* is a gang member who belongs to the gang and obeys the hard-core gang members. A *wanna-be* is a child or teen who is not a gang member, but may wear gang clothing and engage in violent or criminal behavior because he or she wants to be a gang member. A *could-be* is a child or teen who is interested in belonging to a gang. A could-be often is a younger friend or family member of gang members.

Gang members follow specific rules. Gangs have strict rules for the behavior of gang members. These rules are set by the hard-core gang members. There are harsh consequences for gang members who break the rules.

Gang members operate within a territory and refer to this territory as their "turf." They may draw graffiti on buildings to let others know it is their turf. Gang members may injure and kill people, including members of other gangs, who trespass on their turf.

Gang members identify themselves with certain colors, types of clothing or tattoos. They may choose one specific color to wear or one particular item of clothing to wear, such as colored shoelaces. Gang members may get tattoos to identify themselves as members of the gang for life.

Gang members have their own vocabulary, logos, and signals. Gang members invent code words and ways to identify themselves as members of the gang, such as hand signals and handshakes, and graffiti, also called "tagging."

Gang members identify themselves by nicknames. When people join gangs they are given a nickname, or street name, to disguise the gang member when he or she is involved in illegal activity.

Did You Know?

Gangs in the U.S. Researchers estimate that in the year 2002 there were more than 21,500 active gangs and 731,500 gang members in the U.S..

Recognizing Gangs

2 Teach

Class Discussion

Gangs in the Media Have students identify television shows, music, or movies that refer to gangs or are about gangs. Have students discuss how gangs are portrayed in the media. Ask students if they think gangs are portrayed realistically or are glorified in the media. Evaluate the media's portrayal of gangs. **L2**

INTERACTIVE CHALKBOARD
with Image Bank

PowerPoint® Presentations

This CD-ROM is an editable Microsoft® PowerPoint® presentation that includes:
- Lesson presentations
- Lesson checks
- Interactive graphics
- 5-Minute Checks
- Image Bank
- All transparencies

CRISS Project

Discussion Refer to the Think-Pair-Share Strategy on page 17T and ask students to *think* about gangs and gang activities, *pair* up to discuss what they know, and finally, *share* with the class during discussion.

Lesson Resource Manager

- **Unit 11 Fast File Resources**
  Reading Strategy, p. 83
  Vocabulary Practice, p. 84
  Transparency Master and Worksheet, p. 85
  Real-Life Health, p. 87
  Real-Life Health, p. 89
  5-Minute Check, p. 91
  Lesson 67 Quiz, p. 92
- **Unit 11 Transparency**
- **Lesson 67 Transparency**

- **Reading Essentials**
- **Technology**
  TeacherWorks™ CD-ROM
  StudentWorks™ CD-ROM
  Reading Essentials CD-ROM
  Exam*View*® Assessment Suite
  Vocabulary Puzzlemaker

National Health Education Standards

Pages 698–699: 1.5, 1.8, 1.9, 2.3, 4.1, 4.4, 7.2, 7.3, 8.2, 8.3, 8.4

Why Gangs Are Risky

Why Gangs Are Risky

Why Gangs Are Risky

NHES Assessment/SCASS

Performance Task Divide students into groups and ask each group to create a Public Service Announcement (PSA) about the risks of joining a gang. If possible, encourage students to film their PSAs or to read them over the school's PA system. After groups share their PSAs, have students write responses to the following questions in their health journals. Do they think such PSAs are effective? Why or why not? **L2**

Quick Demo

Lifelines Have students braid together four or five pieces of string or yarn. Each piece of string or yarn should be a different color, and each should represent an aspect of a student's life such as family, friends, teachers, coaches, etc. Tell students that the strings represent "lifelines"—the things that keep teens from joining gangs. Ask students to imagine what could happen if a person chose to turn away from family, friends, and school. Snip the strings in a braid and show how the "lifelines" no longer hold. Explain to students that if they are involved with their families, friends, and school, they are much less likely to think about joining a gang. **ELL**

Reading Review

1. *teens who wish to be initiated often perform the most serious crimes; teens who wish to join may be beaten; females may be raped by several members*

2. *A hard-core member is a senior gang member who has the most influence. A regular gang member obeys hard-core gang members. A wanna-be is a child or teen who wears gang clothing or engages in violent crimes because he or she wants to be a gang member. A could-be is someone who is interested in becoming a gang member.*

Belonging to a gang is risky. Belonging to a gang often means that a gang member will have enemies. Rivalry exists among gangs. Gang rivalry results in fighting, homicide, and other acts of violence. Gang members have sought revenge against rival gang members for insults, "trespassing" on gang turf, and personal disputes.

Why It Is Risky to Belong to a Gang

Make the Connection

Injuries For more information on reducing weapon injuries, see page 705 in Lesson 68.

Revenge If gang members feel they have been insulted or cheated they may seek revenge. Revenge might include an assault or a drive-by shooting. Family members of gang members are at risk as well, since gang members often retaliate against the family members of rival gang members. Gang members often carry weapons to protect themselves from rival gangs. Gang members can be involved in illegal weapon sales as well as drug trafficking and drug use. These activities can lead to violence.

Crimes Gang members might commit crimes to gain respect from other gang members. A ***prestige crime*** is a crime committed to gain status from other gang members in the gang. A gang member might assault another gang member, participate in a drive-by shooting, or steal in an effort to establish a tough reputation.

Violence Gang members also participate in violence against their own gang members. Gang members who do not follow orders are beaten.

Initiation Teens who want to join a gang must participate in violent behaviors before they are admitted. These teens must go through an initiation period to prove they are "worthy" of gang membership. During the initiation period, they are subject to any gang member's demand at any time. Teens who are going through initiation often commit the most serious crimes so that the gang members do not have to do the "dirty work" themselves. These crimes can include murder, drug trafficking, weapons dealing, robbery, beating up other people, drive-by shootings, or beating up or killing rival gang members.

Initiation also may involve jumping-in. ***Jumping-in*** is an initiation rite in which a potential gang member is beaten by gang members. The potential gang member might have to fight all of the gang members either one by one or all at once, and this can continue for hours or even days. Teens have been severely injured and even died from jumping-in. Initiation for females might involve being "sexed-in." This means they are raped by one or more male gang members. This puts them at risk for unplanned pregnancy, infection with HIV and other STDs, and emotional trauma.

Sometimes teens might believe they are being initiated into a gang when they are actually just being used by gang members. Gang members demand that the teen participate in criminal or sexual activities, but then they refuse the teen membership into the gang.

Reading Review

1. Why is initiation into a gang risky?
2. What roles do gang members play?

Legal Issues

Penalties Assign students to research the legal penalties for gang activities. Students might research laws regarding gangs and schools, gangs and crime, or gangs and associated costs to society. Have students create "anti-gang" posters. Hang these posters in the classroom. Ask students to choose three posters, and have them write a one- to two-page response to the three chosen posters. They should explain why they chose each poster and describe them. Ask the students to include in their responses whether the posters relay the information effectively. **L2**

Why Teens Join Gangs

There are many reasons teens give for joining gangs. Teens might think gangs will provide something that they are lacking in their lives, or that gangs will provide a way to escape other problems. It is important to know the truth about these misconceptions.

Myths About Gangs

I feel left out and the gang will help me feel like I belong. Gangs may appear to be close-knit groups that offer a teen security and excitement. Teens who are gang members are considered property of the gang. Gang leaders believe they own their members and can use them to do whatever they want. Gang members who break a rule might be injured or killed.

I can escape family problems by being in a gang. Many gang members have been raised in homes with unstable families. They have been raised in families in which there is physical abuse, sexual abuse, drug abuse, and neglect. Teens who think about joining a gang believe they will be escaping the abuse. They believe that unlike their family members, gang members will care for them and pay attention to them. However, these same abusive behaviors exist among gang members. Gang leaders abuse gang members. Fighting, drug abuse, and rape are common among gang members.

I can get money for the things I want by being involved in gang activities. Teens may be attracted to gangs by the opportunity to earn money to help their families, but gang members make their money from drug trafficking, stealing, and other illegal activities. Gang members are more likely to get a criminal record from these activities than to make money. A person who has a criminal record often has more difficulty finding a job. Gang members also are at high risk of dropping out of school.

I get protection from gang members. Gang members might offer to protect a member from others. However, once a teen is a member of a gang, the risk of harm and threats from others is greatly increased. Teens are often harmed when they are initiated into gangs. Gang members frequently assault the new member. Gang members are constantly at risk of being harmed by rival gangs. Involvement in drug trafficking and criminal activity also increases the risk of being harmed.

Teens who join gangs often feel that they don't "fit in" with their peers.

LESSON 67 • Staying Away from Gangs **701**

Why Teens Join Gangs

NHES Assessment/SCASS

Performance Event Place students in small groups of two to four students. Tell them to brainstorm reasons why teens join gangs. Have one student in each group record the reasons. After all the reasons for joining a gang are recorded, groups should evaluate the validity of each reason, using their critical-thinking skills. **L2** **ELL**

INTERACTIVE CHALKBOARD with Image Bank

5-Minute Check

Page 91, **Unit 11 Fast File Resources**

1. How can teens recognize gang members? *Gang members wear certain colors and types of clothing and may have tattoos.*
2. List three reasons why being in a gang is risky. *STDs, jail, injury, unplanned pregnancy, drug use, and death*
3. List three misinformed reasons why teens join gangs. *Teens may think a gang will make them feel like they belong, that they can escape family problems by being in a gang, or that they can get money or protection by being in a gang.*
4. What is "jumping-in?" *an initiation rite in which a potential gang member is beaten by other gang members*
5. What is a prestige crime? *a crime committed to gain status from other members of a gang*

🔥 Health Project

Alternative Solution Have students research organizations in the community that offer activities for teenagers such as recreational centers, skating rinks, movie theaters, etc. Have students contact these organizations about opportunities for teenagers. Ask students if they find these activities interesting. Ask them if there are sufficient resources for teens in your community and if not, what types of resources students would like to have. Ask students to create a proposal, including an action plan, to establish safe, alternative resources for teens in your community. Examples might include a teen-friendly coffee house, or drug- and alcohol-free parties and outdoor movie nights. Encourage students to present their proposals to community leaders for consideration. **L2**

National Health Education Standards
Pages 700–701: 2.1, 2.3

NHES Assessment/SCASS

Selected Response What do anti-gang gangs do to protect themselves from gangs?

A. hang around gang members
B. wear gang colors
C. *walk to school together*
D. participate in gang activities

3 Assess

Vocabulary Practice

Page 84, **Unit 11 Fast File Resources**

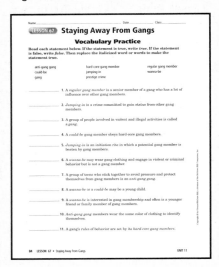

National Health Education Standards

Pages 702–703: 1.5, 1.8, 1.9, 2.3, 4.1, 4.4, 7.2, 7.3, 8.2, 8.3, 8.4

702

Protecting Yourself

I t is risky to belong to a gang. Tell a parent, guardian, or responsible adult if you are pressured to join a gang. If a teen is involved in a gang, they may think there is no way out. However, teens who are involved in gangs can leave.

How a Gang Member Can Leave a Gang

Young teens who join gangs often are not aware of what being in a gang involves. Being in a gang is often not what they had hoped. It can be risky, stressful, and, at times, boring. Leaving a gang isn't easy. Gang members might harm the teens or their family members. Some gangs allow members to leave if they survive a severe beating, or "jumping-out," but many do not survive. Other gangs do not allow gang members to leave under any circumstances.

Many teens have successfully left gangs and started lives without gangs, violence, and fear. Law enforcement officers have helped protect many gang members who wanted to leave their gangs. Many communities have gang counselors who help gang members leave gangs. Teens who want to leave a gang might move to another neighborhood, community, or state to be safe. The best way to avoid having to leave a gang is not to join one in the first place.

Safety in numbers Some teens who live in communities in which there are gangs have formed anti-gang gangs. An ***anti-gang gang*** is a group of teens who stick together to avoid pressure and to protect themselves from gang members. The goal of anti-gang gangs is for teens to continue with daily activities without being pressured or threatened by gang members. Anti-gang gangs walk together as a group to and from school and after-school activities. An adult might accompany them for additional protection.

These teens recognize that gang members are less likely to pressure them to join a gang when they are in a group. They do not hang around gang members, participate in gang activities, or wear clothing or take other actions to identify themselves as a group. Anti-gang gangs are informal, and any teen who wants to avoid gangs can become involved.

> **Make the Connection**
>
> **Resisting Gangs** For more information on resistance skills, see page 47 in Lesson 5.

How to Protect Yourself from Gangs

Avoiding gangs and gang members will help protect you from violence.

- Stay away from gang members.
- Avoid gang turf and places where gang activity takes place as much as possible.
- Be aware of gang colors in your community and in nearby communities.
- Do not stay out late at night.

- Do not listen to music that supports gang activities.
- Do not write graffiti.
- Spend time with family members and mentors.
- Obey laws and respect authority.
- Avoid alcohol and other drugs.

 Community Involvement

Gang Activity Have students interview law enforcement officers in your community about gang-related activity. Have students ask these questions during the interviews: Are gangs a problem in this community? Does the local law enforcement agency keep statistics on gang-related crime? If so, what do they track? Has the rate of gang-related crime changed over time? What are the most common gang-related crimes? Have students present their findings to the class using charts and graphs to illustrate different types of gang-related crimes such as vandalism, drug offenses, and violent crime. They should explain what local law enforcement is doing to combat gang-related crime. **L2**

67 STUDY GUIDE

anti-gang gang
could-be
gang
hard-core gang
   member
jumping-in
prestige crime
regular gang
   member
wanna-be

Key Terms Review

Explain the relationship between the pairs of lesson Key Terms below. Do not write in this book.

1. anti-gang gang—gang

2. hard-core gang member—regular gang member

3. could-be—wanna-be

4. jumping-in—prestige crime

Recalling the Facts

5. What roles do members play in a gang?

6. Why is it risky to belong to a gang?

7. How can a gang cause conflict in schools, families, and communities?

8. How does initiation into a gang increase a teen's risk for injury or death?

9. Describe one myth about gangs. Why is the myth false?

10. How might a teen who belongs to a gang leave the gang?

11. Why do some teens become anti-gang gang members?

12. How can you recognize a gang member?

13. Why do gang members commit prestige crimes?

14. Why does the risk of violence increase when a teen joins a gang?

15. Why might teens think they will be safe when they join a gang?

16. What is the best way to avoid having to leave a gang?

17. How are family members at risk if a teen joins a gang?

18. How does joining a gang increase the risk of unplanned pregnancy and STD infection for females?

Critical Thinking

19. Why is it dangerous to be friends with a member of a gang even if you are not a member?

20. Why is it dangerous to "try out" or associate with a gang by becoming a wanna-be or could-be?

21. How can joining a gang increase a person's risk for poverty?

22. Why is it important to know gang colors and symbols in your community?

Real-Life Applications

23. Why do you think gangs exist in cities, suburbs, and rural areas?

24. Analyze strategies for avoiding gangs.

25. Why do you think teens who are being initiated into gangs often commit the most serious crimes?

26. Why do you think gangs require teens who want to join to participate in "jumping-in" or being "sexed-in?"

Activities

Responsible Decision Making

27. **Write** Your younger brother tells you he made money after school. A gang member paid him to keep an eye out for police in your neighborhood. What should you do? Write a response to this situation. Refer to the Responsible Decision-Making Model on page 61 to review the steps involved in making responsible decisions.

Sharpen Your Life Skills

28. **Advocate for Health** Work with other students to design a poster titled "50 Things to Do Besides Joining a Gang." Target the poster toward children. Obtain permission from a parent or guardian and ask a principal of a middle school or elementary school for permission to hang the poster where children will see it.

Visit www.glencoe.com for more *Health & Wellness* quizzes.

LESSON 67 • Study Guide   **703**

STUDY GUIDE

Key Terms Review

1. An anti-gang gang is a group of teens who stay together in a group to avoid gang pressure, while a gang is a group of people who cooperate in violent and illegal activities.

2. A hard-core gang member has the most influence, while a gang member who obeys the hard-cores is a regular gang member.

3. A could-be is a child or teen who is interested in joining a gang, while a wanna-be may engage in illegal activity because he or she wants to be a gang member.

4. Jumping-in is an initiation rite of being beaten by gang members, while a crime committed to establish a tough reputation is a prestige crime.

Recalling the Facts

5. See page 699.
6. See page 700.
7. Gangs can encourage members not to attend school, to disobey parents, to leave home, and to disobey the law and law officials.
8. New members may be beaten, raped, or become involved in violent crime.
9. See page 701.
10. See page 702.
11. to ensure they can continue daily activities without harassment or pressure to join a gang
12. See page 699.
13. to gain status in the gang
14. rivalry disputes; prestige crimes; see page 700
15. gangs may protect their members against other people and rival gangs
16. never join a gang
17. gang members often retaliate against the family members of rival gang members
18. females often are required to have sex with members of the gang

Critical Thinking

19. You could end up in a dangerous situation.

---

20. Rival gang members could think you are in the gang and commit violence against you.
21. See page 701.
22. so you can avoid gangs

Real-Life Applications

23. Gangs may provide a sense of belonging.
24. Answers will vary. See page 702.

25. so the hard-core gang members do not get into trouble with the law
26. so new members know who is in charge

Activities

Responsible Decision Making

27. Answers will vary.

Sharpen Your Life Skills

28. Answers will vary.

Out of Time?

If time does not permit an in-depth study of this topic, use the following activities in this Teacher Wraparound Edition:

- Health Goal, p. 704
- What Would You Do?, p. 704
- 5-Minute Check, p. 706

1 Focus

HEALTH GOAL **Gun Safety** Have students respond to the Health Goal for this lesson by identifying what they should do if they encounter a gun that is not safely stored. *Answers might include: stay away from it, leave the area at once, and tell a responsible adult.* **L2** **ELL**

NHES Assessment/SCASS

Constructed Response Ask students to write one to two paragraphs about the possible consequences of sneaking a weapon into school. Have students create a list of consequences on the chalkboard, and rate which one is most likely. Ask students how they would respond to the situation. **L2**

LESSON 68

Reducing Weapon Injuries

HEALTH GOAL • **I will follow guidelines to help reduce the risk of weapon injuries.**

Devices used for fighting, or **weapons**, are widely available in society. In the past few years, almost one in five high school students reported carrying a gun, a knife, or a club to school or elsewhere. Teens are more likely to use weapons to solve disagreements today than they were in the past. This lesson includes ways to reduce the risk of being injured by a weapon. This lesson also emphasizes the risks associated with being unsafe around guns.

What You'll Learn

1. Discuss laws regarding the sale of handguns and rifles to teens. *(p. 705)*
2. Analyze strategies for avoiding injury from weapons. *(p. 706)*
3. Discuss laws regarding carrying a concealed weapon. *(p. 705)*
4. Analyze how not carrying a weapon can help prevent accidental and deliberate injuries. *(p. 706)*
5. Discuss how a gun should be safely stored in a home. *(p. 706)*
6. Discuss safety actions you should take if you see a gun that is not safely locked up. *(p. 706)*

Why It's Important

It is important that teens know the laws pertaining to weapons in their state in order to be safe around weapons. It also is important that teens know actions they can take to be safe around weapons.

Key Terms

- weapons
- concealed weapons

Writing About Weapons Suppose you overhear two teens from your school talking about slipping a hunting knife into school through an open window. They say they just want to scare someone with it. After you read the information on weapons and safety on page 705, brainstorm the possible consequences of their actions in your health journal.

National Health Education Standards—Guide for Lesson 68		
1.1	Predict how healthy behaviors can impact health status.	p. 705
1.5	Propose ways to reduce or prevent injuries and health problems.	pp. 704, 706, 707
1.9	Analyze the potential severity of injury or illness if engaging in unhealthy behaviors.	pp. 705, 707
2.10	Analyze how public health policies and government regulations can influence health promotion and disease prevention.	pp. 705, 707

Weapons and Safety

Guns, knives, razor blades, pipe bombs, brass knuckles, clubs, and stun guns are examples of weapons. Guns are the type of weapon most likely to be used to harm teens.

What to Know About Weapons

Gun laws The Youth Handgun Safety Act, part of the Omnibus Violent Crime Control and Law Enforcement Act of 1994, federally prohibits the possession of a handgun or ammunition by a person under the age of 18, or the private transfer of a handgun or ammunition to a juvenile. The law includes a number of exceptions, such as possessing a firearm for farming, hunting, and other specific uses. Some states have established different age limits. There is no federal minimum age for possession of a long gun (rifle or shotgun).

Laws on carrying **concealed weapons,** or weapons partially or fully hidden from view, specify the conditions under which individuals may carry weapons in public. These laws include weapons such as guns, knives, and clubs, and vary widely from state to state. Some states prohibit carrying concealed weapons. In most states, a concealed weapons permit is required to carry a weapon.

The Gun-Free Schools Act requires school districts to have policies that require any student who brings a firearm to school to be expelled from school. This act also requires that these students be referred to the criminal justice or juvenile delinquency system.

Carrying a weapon can increase the risk of injury. Teens sometimes carry guns or other weapons (with parental permission) to hunt animals or to go target shooting. However, there are many situations in which it is unsafe for a teen to carry a weapon.

Carrying a gun increases the risk of injury due to accidental discharge. In 2000, nearly 14 percent of the deaths due to accidental discharge of firearms occurred to teens ages 15–19.

Carrying a weapon also increases the risk that it will be used to settle a disagreement or fight. Teens who carry a weapon might use the weapon if they get into a fight. If they had not had the weapon, they might have settled their disagreement in a more rational way.

Carrying a weapon also increases the risk of it being used in a crime. A person who is carrying a weapon might have it stolen from them and used in a crime, or a teen might use it in a crime.

Did You Know?

Unintentional Injuries Of firearm-related unintentional fatalities, over 70 percent involve handguns.

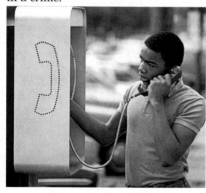

◀ Reporting a firearm at school to the police and to school authorities may prevent a dangerous incident.

Reading Review

1. What are the laws concerning guns?
2. How does carrying a weapon increase the risk of injury?

LESSON 68 • Reducing Weapon Injuries **705**

2 Teach

Reading Review

1. *The Youth Handgun Safety Act federally prohibits the possession of a handgun or ammunition by a person under the age of 18. The Gun-Free School Act requires that school districts require any student who brings a firearm to school to be expelled.*
2. *Accidents may happen or a gun may be used to settle an argument.*

PowerPoint® Presentations

This CD-ROM is an editable Microsoft® PowerPoint® presentation that includes:
- Lesson presentations
- Lesson checks
- Interactive graphics
- 5-Minute Checks
- Image Bank
- All transparencies

 Journals Refer to the Pre- and Post-Reading Response Strategy on page 17T and ask students to use their health journals to write about what they know about guns and gun safety before reading the lesson and then again after reading.

National Health Education Standards
Pages 704–705: 1.1, 1.8, 1.9, 2.10, 4.1, 5.7, 7.3

1. What is the definition of a weapon? *a device used for fighting*

2. What is a concealed weapon? *a weapon that is partially or fully hidden from view*

3. What are laws related to concealed weapons? *Some states prohibit carrying a concealed weapon. In other states, a concealed weapon permit is required to carry a weapon.*

4. What is the safe way to store a gun in your home? *unloaded in a locked container; away from ammunition*

5. What are some legal uses of guns? *target shooting, in occupations where guns are necessary, or for hunting*

3 Assess

Vocabulary Practice

Page 96, **Unit 11 Fast File Resources**

Gun Safety

Some people, such as police officers, use guns for their occupation, while others use them for hunting or target shooting. Many of these people use and store their guns safely. However, it is important for everyone to know general gun safety guidelines to help reduce the risk of injury.

What to Know About Gun Safety

Make the Connection

Making Responsible Decisions For more information on making responsible decisions, see page 61 in Lesson 6.

At home If you have guns in your home, be sure they are stored unloaded in a secured, locked container, such as a gun safe or a strongbox, with the key in a secure place out of the reach of children. Guns that cannot be locked up should be stored unloaded with a durable trigger lock. Ammunition should be stored in a secure container away from a gun. All guns should be out of the sight and reach of children.

Away from home If you happen to see a gun that is not safely locked up at a neighbor's house, at school, or on the street, there are some guidelines to follow. First, do not touch the gun. The gun may be loaded, and it is a serious risk to you and those around you if not handled properly. A gun you see at school or on the street may have been used in a crime. Second, leave the area at once. If the gun is loaded and someone decides to pick it up or play with it, everyone in the area is in immediate danger. Last, immediately tell a responsible adult, such as a parent, guardian, teacher, or law enforcement officer, where the gun is located.

Additional actions Along with knowing what to do if you see a gun, it is also important to know additional actions you can take to reduce the risk of being injured by a gun.

Suppose you want to purchase a gun for hunting. Ask your parents or guardian for permission. Learn how to use the gun. Make sure it is stored unloaded in a locked container.

Avoid being in situations that are unsupervised by parents or guardians where there will be access to guns. You cannot be certain what will happen if another person has a gun and does not know how to use it correctly.

Always follow laws because they protect you and others. Do not carry a gun to school or have one in your car. Remember, it is illegal to carry a weapon to school. Do not pretend you are going to use a gun. Pretending can be misinterpreted, and this may lead to violence. If you know that someone at your school is keeping a gun or other weapon there, immediately tell a teacher or your principal. Also inform school authorities if you know that someone is planning to bring a gun or other weapon to school. You will help to keep yourself and others safe by keeping weapons out of your school.

Do not provoke or argue with someone who has a gun. Keep your distance. Remember, guns often are used to inflict injury when someone becomes emotional. Remain calm.

Differentiated Instruction

Gifted and Talented Give students the following scenario: Imagine that you have been appointed to the position of chief safety officer of your school. In this position, you are responsible for implementing safety rules that would help keep the students in your school safe both in and around the school building. Describe five rules you would have and then present these to your class. You classmates can then share how they would feel about these rules. For example, you may have rules about carrying identification cards that must be shown every day to enter the building, passing through security detectors each morning, or unannounced locker searches. **L2**

Key Terms Review

Complete these fill-in-the-blank statements with the lesson Key Terms on the left. Do not write in this book.

1. Devices used for fighting, such as guns, knives, and clubs, are known as _____.

2. Weapons that are partially or completely hidden from view are considered to be _____.

Recalling the Facts

3. What is the penalty for students who take firearms to school?

4. What is the federal minimum age for possession of a long gun?

5. Why does carrying a weapon increase the risk of injury due to accidents?

6. Why does carrying a weapon increase the risk that it will be used in a fight?

7. How does carrying a weapon increase the risk that it will be used in a crime?

8. What are the federal laws regarding the sale and possession of handguns and rifles to teens?

9. What are some recreational uses for guns?

10. Name an occupation in which a firearm might be carried.

11. Explain the different types of laws that states have regarding carrying a concealed weapon.

12. Name several examples of weapons.

13. What are the guidelines for safely storing a gun at home?

14. Why is it important that you not touch a weapon that you find on the street?

Critical Thinking

15. How does the Gun-Free Schools Act help prevent injuries?

16. Why is it dangerous to pretend to have a gun?

17. Why are emotional situations and guns a bad combination?

18. How can deciding not to carry a weapon help prevent accidental and deliberate injuries?

19. Why is it important that guns be kept out of reach of children?

20. Analyze strategies for avoiding weapons.

21. Why is it recommended to store guns unloaded and away from ammunition?

Real-Life Applications

22. What should you do if someone offers to give you a handgun?

23. What should you do if you are at a friend's house and he wants to show you his dad's guns but his parents are not home?

24. Why do you think laws were passed to limit gun sales and possession of certain types of guns by teens?

25. How would you react if you saw a weapon at school?

26. Why do you think the Gun-Free Schools Act requires such a strict punishment?

Activities

Responsible Decision Making

27. Role-Play You and a friend see a man putting a gun into the trash bin behind a restaurant. Your friend says, "Let's get out of here and pretend we didn't see anything." Role-play your response to the situation. Refer to the Responsible Decision-Making Model on page 61 for help.

Sharpen Your Life Skills

28. Advocate for Health Research the laws in your state regarding the sale of handguns, rifles, and ammunition. Make a poster to illustrate the laws. Ask one of your school's administrators for permission to display the poster in a prominent place in your school.

Visit **www.glencoe.com** for more *Health & Wellness* quizzes.

LESSON 68 • Study Guide **707**

Key Terms Review

1. weapons
2. concealed weapons

Recalling the Facts

3. expulsion from school and referral to the criminal justice or juvenile delinquency system
4. no minimum age
5. A gun could misfire or be dropped and go off accidentally.
6. It might be used in the heat of the moment. If it was not available, the disagreement might have been settled differently.
7. It could be stolen by a criminal.
8. Federal law prohibits the sale and possession of handguns to teens. Minors may possess rifles.
9. hunting, target shooting
10. police officer
11. Each state is different, but in most states a concealed weapon permit is required.
12. gun, knife, club
13. Keep guns locked up, unloaded, and out of sight and reach of children. Ammunition should be locked up in a separate location.
14. It may be loaded. It may have been used in a crime.

Critical Thinking

15. It discourages teenagers from carrying guns.
16. Pretending can be misinterpreted and lead to violence.
17. Guns are more likely to be used when someone becomes emotional.
18. If you do not have a weapon, it cannot be used accidentally or in anger.
19. Children may not understand the danger of guns and could injure themselves or others.
20. Answers will vary but should include strategies from p. 706.
21. Children cannot access them. An angry person may calm down in the time it takes to access and load the weapon.

Real-Life Applications

22. Do not take it. Inform authorities.
23. Tell him you would rather wait until his parents are home. If he persists, leave.
24. Handguns are not used for hunting. There is no "good" reason for teens to have handguns.
25. Do not provoke the person with the weapon. Immediately tell a teacher or your principal.
26. to emphasize the importance of the law and to prevent tragedies

Activities

Responsible Decision Making

27. Answers will vary; should inform authorities

Sharpen Your Life Skills

28. Answers will vary.

Performing Common First Aid Procedures

Out of Time?

If time does not permit an in-depth study of this topic, use the following activities in this Teacher Wraparound Edition:
- Health Goal, p. 708
- Quick Demo, p. 716
- Health Project, p. 719
- Class Activity, p. 719

1 Focus

HEALTH GOAL **Common Injuries** Have students respond to the Health Goal for this lesson by listing basic injuries and common first aid procedures used to treat the injuries. *Possible answers include: a bruise and applying ice to it to help minimize the swelling.* **L2**

Role-Play Have students write what they would do in this situation. After reading page 716, have two students role-play the situation and discuss the correct procedure for administering first aid in this situation. **L2**

LESSON 69

What You'll Learn

1. Describe the contents of first aid kits and where they should be kept. *(p. 709)*
2. Distinguish between actual and implied consent. *(p. 710)*
3. Explain how to follow universal precautions. *(p. 711)*
4. Explain first aid procedures for sudden illnesses and burns. *(pp. 712–715)*
5. Explain first aid procedures for injuries to muscles, bones, and joints. *(p. 716)*
6. Describe first aid procedures for cold temperature-related and heat-related illnesses. *(p. 718)*

Why It's Important

When you know first aid procedures, you can respond quickly to a situation that calls for first aid. You will not panic if someone is injured or ill.

Key Terms

- first aid
- actual consent
- implied consent
- universal precautions
- burn
- splint
- fracture
- dislocation
- hypothermia
- heatstroke

Performing Common First Aid Procedures

HEALTH GOAL • **I will be skilled in common first aid procedures.**

An emergency exists whenever a person is injured or experiences sudden illness. The person needs immediate care. *First aid* is the immediate and temporary care given to a person who has been injured or suddenly becomes ill. This lesson explains how to respond to common situations that call for first aid.

Writing About First Aid Suppose you and a friend are hiking at a state park. Your friend suddenly falls and hits her knee against a rock. She is unable to move and complains of having terrible pain. After reading the information about first aid in this lesson, write a short paragraph in your health journal explaining how you would respond to this situation.

National Health Education Standards—Guide for Lesson 69				
1.1	Predict how healthy behaviors can impact health status.	pp. 710, 721	5.3	Justify when individual or collaborative decision making is appropriate.	p. 708
1.5	Propose ways to reduce or prevent injuries and health problems.	pp. 708, 712, 717, 721	5.5	Predict the potential short and long-term impact of each alternative on self and others.	p. 721
3.4	Determine when professional health services may be required.	pp. 712, 714–721	6.3	Implement strategies and monitor progress in achieving a personal health goal.	pp. 708, 710, 712, 713, 721, 722
4.1	Utilize skills for communicating effectively with family, peers, and others to enhance health.	pp. 708, 713			
				NHES Standards for Lesson 69 continued at www.glencoe.com.	

First Aid Kits ✚

I t is important to keep first aid kits at home and in the family car. Carry a first aid kit when you participate in outdoor activities, such as camping and hiking. When you are away from home, ask where first aid kits are kept. You can purchase a first aid kit from a drugstore or the local chapter of the American Red Cross.

What to Know About First Aid Kits

Purchasing kits You also can purchase items and assemble a first aid kit yourself. In the kit, keep items needed to follow universal precautions, which are discussed on page 711. Add any special medicines you or family members need. Check the first aid kit often for items with expiration dates that have expired. Be certain that flashlight batteries work.

Kit items Many items are essential in a first aid kit. A cold pack is necessary to aid in reducing swelling of an injured body part. Activated charcoal is used to absorb toxins in case of ingestion of a poisonous substance. Keep antiseptic ointment and antiseptic hand cleaner on hand to kill germs on the skin. Wounds should be covered with adhesive bandages. Gauze pads and a roller bandage or adhesive tape also are used for covering open wounds. Scissors are used to cut the gauze. Triangular bandages are used for wrapping covered wounds as well as giving support to or immobilizing an arm.

Other useful items in a first aid kit include plastic bags and disposable gloves to protect against infection when exposed to bodily fluids from a victim. A small flashlight and extra batteries are necessary to provide light in case you are working to assist a victim in the dark. Also included in the first aid kit should be tweezers, which are used to remove splinters or other foreign objects from the skin. A blanket is included to help keep the body warm and prevent loss of body temperature.

> **Make the Connection**
>
> **Health Information** For more information on accessing valid health information, products, and services, see page 17 in Lesson 2.

◄ A first aid kit contains many essential items.

First Aid Kits

2 Teach

Class Activity

First Aid Kit Checklist Have the students create a list of equipment, dressings, and medications they have or would have in their first aid kits. Be sure they include any medication or equipment for any special needs. The students should have their parents go over the list with them to be sure everything they need is listed and available in their family first aid kits. **L2**

INTERACTIVE CHALKBOARD with Image Bank

PowerPoint® Presentations

This CD-ROM is an editable Microsoft® PowerPoint® presentation that includes:
- Lesson presentations
- Lesson checks
- Interactive graphics
- 5-Minute Checks
- Image Bank
- All transparencies

Note Taking Refer to the Two-Column Main Idea-Detail Strategy on page 16T. Students are to list sudden illnesses and injuries in the left-hand column and first aid procedures for the illnesses and injuries in the right-hand column.

Lesson Resource Manager

- **Unit 11 Fast File Resources**
  Reading Strategy, p. 107
  Vocabulary Practice, p. 108
  Transparency Master and Worksheet, p. 109
  Real-Life Health, p. 111
  Real-Life Health, p. 113
  5-Minute Check, p. 115
  Lesson 69 Quiz, p. 116
- **Unit 11 Transparency**
- **Lesson 69 Transparency**

- **Reading Essentials**
- **Technology**
  TeacherWorks™ CD-ROM
  StudentWorks™ CD-ROM
  Reading Essentials CD-ROM
  ExamView® Assessment Suite
  Vocabulary Puzzlemaker

> **National Health Education Standards**
> Pages 708–709: 1.5, 4.1, 5.3, 6.3, 7.1, 7.2

Consent to
Give First Aid

Consent to Give First Aid

Y ou must have consent to give first aid. Consent means permission. There are two types of consent: actual and implied. There also are laws that protect people who give first aid in good faith.

What to Know About Consent to Give First Aid

Actual consent Oral or written permission from a mentally competent adult to give first aid is called ***actual consent.*** Tell the victim who you are, what you plan to do, and the first aid training that you have had. If the person gives you permission, this is actual consent.

A parent or guardian must give actual consent if the victim is a child or is not mentally competent. A supervising adult with legal permission from parents to care for the child also can give actual consent. Do not give first aid if the victim is a child or is not mentally competent when a parent or guardian or supervising adult with legal permission to care for the child says "no."

Implied consent Assuming the victim would grant permission to give first aid if he or she was capable is ***implied consent.*** Implied consent is given when the victim is a mentally competent adult who is unconscious; or a child or an adult who is not mentally competent, when no adult who can grant actual consent is present.

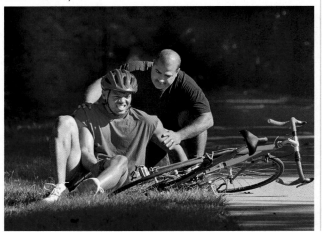

Knowing first aid can assist you in helping someone who is injured. ▼

Good Samaritan Laws

Many states have ***Good Samaritan laws*** which are laws that protect people who give first aid in good faith and without gross negligence or misconduct. Good Samaritan laws cannot provide complete legal protection. Anyone giving first aid should be properly trained and should apply the correct procedures and skills.

Universal Precautions

Y ou must protect your health when giving first aid to another person. A victim's bodily fluids might contain harmful pathogens. For example, blood and certain other bodily fluids might contain HIV or HBV. HIV is found in blood, semen, vaginal secretions, and urine. A person who is infected with HIV might develop AIDS. HBV also is found in blood. A person who is infected with HBV might develop hepatitis B. You still can help a victim without putting yourself at risk of infection with these pathogens.

What to Know About Universal Precautions

Universal precautions Follow universal precautions in any situation in which you might have contact with blood and other bodily fluids. *Universal precautions* are steps taken to prevent the spread of disease by treating all human blood and bodily fluids as if they contained HIV, HBV, and other pathogens when providing first aid or health care.

TABLE 69.1   Universal Precautions
Precaution and Explanation
Wear disposable latex gloves. Your hands and fingers may have tiny cuts or openings you cannot see. Pathogens in a victim's blood or other bodily fluids may enter your bloodstream through these tiny cuts or openings. Latex gloves are made of a special rubber through which many pathogens cannot pass under normal conditions. Do not wear the same gloves more than once. Cover any cuts, scrapes, or rashes on your body with a plastic wrap or sterile dressing. Avoid touching objects that have had contact with the victim's blood.
Wash your hands. Use waterless, antiseptic hand cleanser after removing gloves. This provides extra protection. Do not eat or drink anything while giving first aid. Wash hands after giving first aid and before eating or drinking. This will prevent pathogens from entering your body. Do not touch your mouth, eyes, or nose while caring for a victim.
Use a face mask. Use a face mask or a shield with a one-way valve when performing first aid for breathing emergencies. You may have tiny cuts or openings in your lips or mouth. There may be blood in the saliva or vomit in the victim's mouth. The victim may be bleeding from the mouth or nose. The face mask protects you from the victim's blood. Follow the instructions provided with the face mask. Do not use the face mask to give first aid to more than one victim without sterilizing it.

LESSON 69 • Performing Common First Aid Procedures **711**

Achieving Health Literacy

Effective Communicator Have students prepare a mural illustrating how to follow universal precautions when giving first aid, as well as the importance of universal precautions. Be sure they include all universal precautions and an explanation as to why these need to be followed. Encourage your students who draw well to provide the illustrations for following universal precautions. Students who are good writers can provide an explanation for each precaution. Get all students involved in the final product and display the mural on a wall in the classroom or in the hallway. **L3** **ELL**

711

Sudden Illness

An illness that occurs without warning signals is called a ***sudden illness***. Signs of sudden illness may include dizziness and confusion, weakness, changes in skin color, nausea, vomiting, and diarrhea. Seizures, paralysis, slurred speech, difficulty seeing, and severe pain also may indicate sudden illness.

First Aid for Sudden Illness

What to do for sudden illness Call the local emergency number and obtain medical care immediately. Give first aid if the illness poses a threat to the victim's life. Try to keep the victim calm. Help the victim rest comfortably. Cover the victim with a blanket if he or she is chilled. Prevent the victim from getting overheated. Monitor the victim for changes in consciousness. Do not give an unconscious victim anything to eat or drink.

What to do for fainting Put the victim on his or her back and elevate the victim's legs 8–12 inches above the level of the heart. Do not elevate the legs if you suspect a head, neck or back injury. Loosen tight clothing. Do not splash water on the victim, slap the victim's face, or use smelling salts.

What to do for vomiting Turn the victim on his or her side. Allow the victim to complete the vomiting process. The victim may be given small sips of clear liquids, such as water or broth. Increase the amount of fluids if they can be tolerated without vomiting. Have the victim relax until strength is regained. If vomiting continues, seek medical care.

What to do for seizures Place something under the victim's head to cushion the head from injury. Remove any nearby objects that might injure the victim. Loosen the clothing around the victim's neck. Do not restrain the victim. Do not place anything in the victim's mouth or between the teeth. Look for a medic alert tag that would indicate a chronic illness. If you think the victim may have been poisoned, try to identify the source and call the poison control center. If the seizure is related to a high fever, lower the body temperature with cool compresses. Observe the victim until he or she is fully awake.

▲ One way to assist the victim of a sudden illness is to keep the person as comfortable as possible.

Reading Review

1. What is first aid?
2. What is actual consent?

SPEAKING OUT

Teens Talk About Health

Nathan Washatka
Getting First Aid Training

> 66 Knowing you'd be able to help save someone's life is the greatest feeling in the world. 99

When people ask Nathan Washatka, "Why take a first aid course?" he's got an answer for them. "I think the question should be 'why not?'" he explained. Before he took the course, Nathan said he knew what he called the "common sense" stuff to do, "like putting a bandage on a cut." But after completing the course, he felt confident he'd be ready for most kinds of emergencies. He would soon find out.

Into the pool The first aid course Nathan took was aimed at lifeguards, his summer job. It included general first aid techniques, as well as cardiopulmonary resuscitation (CPR). The class, sponsored by the local Red Cross, met for four hours a day, on Saturdays and Sundays, for one month. The class included both class time and time practicing techniques in the pool. Class learning featured the use of artificial "victims," life-size mechanical dolls who need CPR and other emergency first aid. "I was one of the younger people in the course," Nathan said. "Some were college kids, while others were adults taking refresher courses to maintain their certification."

Crunch time As it turned out, within a few weeks of completing the course, Nathan got the chance to put his first aid skills to the test. "This little girl fell and bumped her head in the wading pool. She got this enormous bruise on her forehead—the largest bruise I've ever seen." Nathan knew from his course that applying ice to the bruise was the right treatment. Later that same summer, Nathan's class training allowed him to help another child in need.

"This little boy cut his head open against a jagged brick wall," he explained. "It was scary because there was blood everywhere. He came up to me crying." Again, Nathan knew what to do—apply pressure to the wound, bandage it, and apply ice. Nathan also kept a cool head himself. "The hardest part," he said, "was dealing with all the people around, trying to tell me what to do. But I was confident from my class that I was doing the right thing."

The greatest feeling In the future, Nathan would like to attend medical school. "Saving people, fixing broken bodies, sounds like a cool profession," he said. Does Nathan recommend taking a first aid course? "Definitely!" he answered. "A lot of high schoolers complain that they can't see the application of the classes they take. But this is something you walk away from knowing you've definitely learned something practical. Knowing you'd be able to help save someone's life is the greatest feeling in the world."

Journaling Activity

Nathan described a time when he had to put what he knew about first aid to the test. Describe a situation when you were under pressure to perform in a serious situation. How did you handle it?

LESSON 69 • Performing Common First Aid Procedures **713**

SPEAKING OUT

Analyzing the Feature

Use the following questions to help students uncover the main points of this feature.

1. How did Nathan feel after taking the first aid training? *He felt more confident that he would be ready for most kinds of emergencies.*
2. What did the first aid course include? *It included general first aid techniques as well as CPR.*
3. Why does Nathan recommend that everyone take a first aid course? *Because it is something practical that you learn, and you can use it to save a life.* **L2**

Class Activity

First Aid Course Promotion
Have students find out where first aid courses are offered. Then, in pairs, have them create a poster or pamphlet promoting the courses and encouraging other students at school to take them. Tell students to be sure the posters and pamphlets promote how taking the courses can help save lives. **L2** **ELL**

Journaling Activity

Refer students to the Journaling Activity on the student page. Ask students to share stories about times they were under pressure to perform in a serious situation. Perhaps it was a sports event, an academic challenge, or an event that occurred at home or on vacation. Ask students if they felt that the pressure affected their performance either positively or negatively. **L2**

Health Project

Taking Part in a First Aid Course Encourage students to find out where first aid courses are offered and sign up for one. Have them keep a journal of where they took the class, what they learned, and the types of equipment they used. After they have finished the course, have them reflect on what they enjoyed most about the course and their feelings about taking it. Ask them to answer these questions in a short paper: Do they feel more confident now about facing an emergency situation? Do they understand why people need refresher courses on first aid? Was there anything they wish they had spent more time on in the course? Would they like to take the course again in the future? Is this something they would encourage others to participate in? **L3**

National Health Education Standards
Pages 712–713: 1.5, 3.4, 4.1, 5.6, 6.3, 7.2, 7.3

Burns

BURNS

An injury caused by heat, electricity, chemicals, or radiation is a **_burn_**. The seriousness of a burn depends on the cause of the burn, the length of time the victim was exposed to the source of the burn, the location of the burn on the body, the depth of the burn, the size of the burn, and the victim's age and health condition.

What to Know About First Aid for Burns

Make the Connection

Sunburn For more information about how repeated sunburns can increase the risk for skin cancer, see page 535 in Lesson 49.

Burns are usually described as first-degree burns, second-degree burns, or third-degree burns. These descriptions help explain the seriousness of the burn.

What to do for first-degree burns A burn that affects the top layer of skin is a **_first-degree burn._** Most sunburns are first-degree burns. The skin becomes red and dry. The area may swell and be painful to touch. First-degree burns usually heal in six days without permanent scarring.

First aid for a first-degree burn

1. Stop the burning. Get the victim out of the sun. Remove the victim from the source of the burn.

2. Cool the burned area with cool, running tap water or water from a garden hose, or have the victim get into the bath or shower.

3. Use sheets or towels soaked in cold water to cool a burn on the face or other areas that cannot be soaked. Keep adding cool water.

4. Wear latex gloves. Loosely cover the area with dry, sterile bandages.

What to do for second-degree burns A burn that involves the top layers of skin is a **_second-degree burn._** The skin becomes red. Blisters form and may open and discharge clear fluid. The skin appears wet and blotchy. Second-degree burns usually heal in two to four weeks. Slight scarring may occur.

First aid for a second-degree burn

1. Call the local emergency number and obtain medical care immediately if the burns are larger than 2–3 inches, or on the face or hands.

2. Stop the burning. Remove the victim from the source of the burn.

3. Cool the burned area with cool water or cool cloths.

4. Do not break blisters or remove tissue.

5. Loosely cover the area with dry, sterile bandages.

6. Elevate the burned area above heart level.

7. Loosely cover the victim with clean, dry sheets if burns cover large parts of the body. This helps prevent infection and reduces pain. Treat the victim for shock (explained in Lesson 70).

 Community Involvement

Help for Burn Victims Have students interview physicians on how they have treated burn victims. Questions they can ask include: What are the most common burns you have treated? What age group do you most often deal with when it comes to burns? How do you believe most of the burns could have been prevented? What procedures must serious burn victims go through? How long are the treatments? What types of physical and mental difficulties do burn victims encounter? What type of medical, financial, and mental-health assistance is available to victims of serious burns? Have the students use the information to write a community newspaper article. **L3**

What to do for third-degree burns A burn that involves all layers of skin and some underlying tissues is a *third-degree burn.* A third-degree burn may affect fat tissue, muscle tissue, bones, and nerves. The skin becomes darker and appears charred. The underlying tissues may appear white. A third-degree burn is painless if nerve endings are destroyed. It also can be very painful. Third-degree burns may take months or years to treat. Permanent scarring often occurs. Some victims require skin grafting and plastic surgery.

First aid for a third-degree burn

1. Remove the victim from the source of the burn and obtain medical care immediately.

2. Treat the victim for shock.

3. Determine if the victim is breathing. Give rescue breathing if necessary.

4. Do not remove clothing stuck to the burn. Do not break blisters or remove tissue.

5. Do not apply anything cold to the burn.

6. Loosely cover the area with dry, sterile bandages or clean cloth.

What to do for electrical burns A burn that occurs when electricity travels through the body is an *electrical burn.* The cause may be lightning or contact with faulty electrical equipment or a power line. The seriousness of an electrical burn depends on the strength of the electrical current and the path the current takes through the body. There may be wounds where the electrical current enters and leaves the body.

First aid for an electrical burn

1. Call the local emergency number and obtain medical care immediately. All electrical burns must be examined by a doctor. They may appear minor, but may be very deep.

2. Do not go near the victim until the source of electricity is turned off.

3. Treat the victim for shock.

4. Do not move the victim.

5. Loosely cover the area with dry, sterile bandages.

6. Do not use cool water or compresses, as the victim may be in shock.

What to do for chemical burns A burn that occurs when chemicals in a laboratory or in products get on the skin or into the eyes or body is a *chemical burn.* The burn continues as long as there is contact with the chemical.

First aid for a chemical burn

1. Remove the victim from the chemical causing the burn. If the chemical is dry or solid, brush it off the skin with a cloth. Have the victim remove any clothing with the chemical on it.

2. If the exposure is serious, call the local emergency number and obtain medical care immediately.

3. Flush the skin or eyes with cool, low-pressure running water for 15–30 minutes. Take special precautions if only one eye is involved. Have the victim turn the head and run the water from the nose away from the eye. This keeps water with the chemical in it from running into the other eye.

4. Loosely cover the area with dry, sterile bandages.

Did You Know?

Burns You should not remove clothing or anything else that is sticking to a severe burn.

Class Activity

Identifying the Burns Have the students write down the signs for each type of burn. Then have them read the signs to each other, attempt to identify each type of burn, and explain to each other how they would treat that type of burn. **L2**

Explain the Concept

Getting the Third Degree Ask if anyone has ever seen a third-degree burn. Emphasize that many of them look like deep wounds and are white and charred-looking. Also, most are painless at first, due to the fact that nerve endings are completely burned and unable to send messages to the brain. Unlike first- and second-degree burns, one must avoid applying anything cold to third-degree burns, since doing so may cause shock. Also, to prevent swelling, do not remove any clothing or materials stuck to the burned areas.

Extension

Support for Burn Victims Have students research organizations that offer support and assistance to burn victims. You might want to invite a representative from one of these organizations to speak to the class about the organization's services. **L3**

DI Differentiated Instruction

Visual Impairment Plan ahead to provide for students who are visually impaired. You might check with other health personnel at your school or within the community to borrow 3-dimensional models of the three degrees of burns which will enable your students who are visually impaired to "feel" the differences among the three degrees of burns. Describe burns in terms of duration of exposure and temperature as well as appearance. Visually impaired students can compose questions for the victim or witnesses to assess the severity of a burn even though they can't see it. **L1**

National Health Education Standards
Pages 714–715: 3.4, 7.2, 7.3

Muscle, Bone, and Joint Injuries

Quick Demo

Making a Triangular Sling Bring in a towel or small blanket and a couple of safety pins. Have a student volunteer as a victim. The base of the sling should be about 55 in long and the sides about 40 in long. You can fold the blanket or towel into those dimensions. Be sure to support the injured arm. Slide the sling under the arm on the victim's injured side. The long side should be lined up with the uninjured side with the injured arm right down the middle. Pull the bottom corner over the victim's injured side shoulder. Leave the fingers showing. Tie the sling around the victim's neck, but be sure the knot is not pressed into the back of the neck. Fold over the extra cloth at the victim's elbow and secure it with the safety pins. Check for snugness and loosen if necessary. **ELL**

Class Activity

Improvised Slings Have students bring in a small blanket, towel, or sweater. Then have them work with a partner to try to create a triangular sling. Encourage them to be creative. Check to see if the injured parts have been properly immobilized. If not, point out what they did correctly and what needs to be improved in order to achieve the immobilization of the injured arm. Emphasize that the slings need to be snug, but loose enough for blood to flow. Let both partners try to create a sling for each other. **L2 ELL**

Muscle, Bone, and Joint Injuries

There are 206 bones in the body and more than 600 muscles. A *joint* is the point where two bones meet. *Ligaments* are the fibers that connect bones together. *Tendons* are tough tissue fibers that connect muscles to bones. Injuries involving muscles, bones, and joints are common in teens. The most common injuries are fractures, dislocations, sprains, and strains.

Did You Know?

First Aid Perform only the first aid skills you have been trained to give. Do not perform skills beyond your knowledge, such as those you may have seen on a television show.

What to Know About First Aid for Muscle, Bone, and Joint Injuries

How to use splints Material or a device used to protect and immobilize a body part is a *splint.* A splint should only be used when you need to move a victim without emergency help and need to keep an injured body part immobile, and only if it does not hurt the victim. A folded blanket, towel, sheet, or bandage might be used as a soft splint. Rolled-up newspapers, sticks, or boards may be used as a rigid splint.

► A splint is used to immobilize a body part.

Emergency medical personnel may use a board as a splint.

First aid when using a splint

1. Call the local emergency number for a life-threatening injury.

2. Attempt to splint the injury in the position you find it to immobilize the injured part. A splint for an injured bone must include the joints above and below the injured bone. A splint for an injured joint must include the bones above and below the injured joint.

3. Check circulation to ensure that the splint is not too tight.

What to do for fractures A break or a crack in a bone is a *fracture.* A fracture in which there is a break in the skin is an *open fracture.* A fracture in which there is no break in the skin is a *closed fracture.* A fracture can be very serious if a break in a bone damages an artery or interferes with breathing. The

716   UNIT 11 • Injury Prevention and Personal Safety

🟦 Family Involvement

Household Items to the Rescue With their parents, have students make a list of objects and materials they could use as splints and slings. Encourage students to show their families how to make a triangular and an improvised sling and have them practice on each other with different types of objects and materials. Have the students, with the help of their parents, create a poster illustrating how to create an improvised sling. Encourage them to be creative and try to come up with as many ideas as they can. **L2 ELL**

signs of a fracture include pain, swelling, loss of movement, and deformity. Signs of a fracture of the skull include bleeding from the head or ears, drowsiness, and headache.

First aid for fractures

1. Call the local emergency number and obtain medical care immediately.
2. Treat for bleeding and shock.
3. Keep the injured part from moving. Use a splint when appropriate.
4. Keep a victim with a head injury immobile.
5. Apply ice to the injured area to prevent swelling.
6. Follow universal precautions while controlling bleeding.

What to do for dislocations The movement of a bone from its joint is a *dislocation.* Dislocations often are accompanied by stretched ligaments. The signs of a dislocation are pain, swelling upon movement, loss of movement, and deformity.

First aid for a dislocation

1. Call the local emergency number and obtain medical care immediately.
2. Splint above and below the dislocated joint in the position it was found. Apply cold compresses.

What to do for sprains An injury to the ligaments, tendons, and soft tissue around a joint caused by undue stretching is a *sprain.* The most common sprain occurs to the ankle. Sprains also may affect the knee, wrist, finger, shoulder, or spine. The signs of a sprain include pain that increases with movement or weight bearing, tenderness, and swelling.

First aid for sprains

1. Follow the PRICE treatment.
2. The victim should not be allowed to walk if there is a leg injury.
3. Immobilize the area and get prompt medical help if a fracture is suspected.

What to do for strains An overstretching of muscles and/or tendons is a *strain.* A strain is commonly referred to as a pulled muscle. A strain is usually not as serious as a sprain. One of the most common strains involves the muscles of the back. Signs of strain include pain, swelling, stiffness, and firmness to the area.

First aid for strains

1. Follow the PRICE treatment.
2. Get prompt medical help for a severe strain.

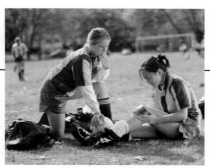

▲ One step in the PRICE treatment is to apply an ice pack to an injury as soon as possible after the injury occurs.

The PRICE Treatment

The PRICE treatment is described below.

- **Protect:** Protect the injured part by keeping it still.
- **Rest:** Rest the injured part for 24 to 72 hours. More rest is required for severe injuries. Do not exercise the injured area until healing is complete.
- **Ice:** Apply cold water, a cold compress, or an ice pack for 20 minutes as soon as possible after the injury occurs.
- **Compression:** Wrap the injury with a bandage to limit swelling. The bandage should not be compressed so tight that it restricts blood flow.
- **Elevation:** Raise the injured body part above heart level to reduce swelling and to help drain blood and fluid from the area.

LESSON 69 • Performing Common First Aid Procedures **717**

Cold Temperature-Related Illnesses

Class Discussion

Burns and Frostbite Ask students how burns and frostbite are similar, in both the ways they affect the body and the ways in which they are treated. *Burns and frostbite are similar in the sense that in both, the body tissue has been damaged. First aid for both injuries involves helping the affected body areas return to their normal temperature and state.* Ask students if they have experienced frostbite and how it felt. *Some will say the affected area felt numb, and if any have had serious frostbite, they may say it felt as if the area was burning.* Ask students who have had frostbite what parts of the body were affected. *Most will say the fingers, toes, ears, and nose.* Ask students how frostbite can be prevented. *Skin needs to be covered well with dry, warm clothing. Students also can limit their time outdoors during extremely cold conditions.* **L2**

Cold Temperature-Related Illnesses

C old temperature-related illnesses are conditions that result from exposure to low temperatures. The most common cold temperature-related emergencies are frostbite and hypothermia.

First Aid for Cold Temperature-Related Illnesses

What to do for frostbite The freezing of body parts, often the tissues of the extremities, is called *frostbite.* Frostbite may involve the fingers, toes, ears, and nose. People exposed to subfreezing temperatures or snow are at risk for developing frostbite.

Signs of frostbite include numbness in the affected area, a waxy, discolored appearance to the skin, and skin that is cold to the touch.

First aid for frostbite For mild frostbite, rewarm the affected area in lukewarm water. For severe frostbite, call the local emergency number and obtain medical care immediately.

Do not attempt rewarming if a medical facility is near. Take the following steps if medical help is not available.

1. Remove any clothing or jewelry that interferes with circulation. Handle the affected area gently.

2. Soak the affected body part in water that has a temperature between 100°F and 105°F. Test the water by having someone who has not been exposed to the cold, place his or her hand in the water. Water that is too warm for that person's hand is too warm to use on the victim. Warming usually takes 25 to 40 minutes, until the tissues are soft.

3. Apply warm, moist cloths to warm the ears, nose, or face.

4. Do not rub the affected body part.

5. Do not allow a victim to walk on frostbitten toes or feet, even after rewarming the area.

6. Place dry, sterile gauze between the toes and fingers to absorb moisture and avoid having them stick together.

◄ Avoid frostbite by dressing appropriately in cold weather.

Cross-Curricular Connections

Science Have a group of students research how frostbite affects the integumentary system in the extremities of the body (fingers, ears, and toes). Ask students to answer these questions: How does frostbite actually cause numbness and discoloration of the skin? Why are the extremities affected more easily than other parts of the body? What is the temperature at which frostbite starts to occur in the extremities? What can occur if a frostbitten appendage is placed in hot water? How does drinking alcohol and smoking increase your chances of obtaining frostbite? Have the group create a multimedia presentation and share its findings with the class. **L3**

What to do for hypothermia A reduction of the body temperature so that it is lower than normal is called *hypothermia.* Hypothermia results from overexposure to cool temperatures, cold water, moisture, and wind. The outside temperature can be as high as 50°F, and a person can still suffer from hypothermia. Those most likely to suffer from hypothermia when exposed to extreme cold are older adults, people who are ill, children, people who are hungry or tired, and people who consume alcohol in excess.

Most cases of hypothermia are mild. The victim will shiver and feel cold. The pulse rate slows down and becomes irregular as the body temperature drops. A drop in body temperature affects the brain and spinal cord causing the victim to experience symptoms such as loss of coordination, slurred speech, and confusion. Eventually, a victim can become unconscious. A victim can die if hypothermia is not treated.

First aid for hypothermia

1. Call the local emergency number and obtain medical care immediately.
2. Try to raise the body temperature by getting the victim into a warm environment.
3. Handle the victim gently.
4. Remove any wet clothing, and replace it with dry clothing.
5. Place something warm above and below the victim, such as blankets.
6. Cover the victim's head.
7. Give the victim warm, sweet liquids to drink. Never give alcohol to a victim of hypothermia.

▲ A victim of hypothermia needs to quickly get to a warm environment.

First aid for moderate hypothermia (body temperature from 84°F to 94°F)

1. Warm the victim. Use an electric blanket, a sleeping bag, or several blankets to wrap the victim. A person with normal body temperature can lay next to the victim to lend body heat.
2. Place the victim in a tub of water with a temperature no greater than 105°F if available.
3. Place hot packs around the victim's head, neck, chest, back, and groin. Be careful not to burn the victim.

First aid for severe hypothermia (body temperature below 84°F)

1. Do not rewarm a victim who can be transported to a medical facility within 12 hours.
2. Calm the victim.
3. Avoid unnecessary movement of the victim.
4. Maintain an airway.
5. Keep the victim lying down.
6. Do not give CPR to the victim unless he or she is not breathing normally. Continue CPR until the victim is transported to a medical facility.

Did You Know?

Frostbite You should not rub toes or hands to try to warm them up if you think there is frostbite.

Reading Review

1. What is a fracture?
2. What is frostbite?

Heat-Related Illnesses

Heat-Related Illnesses

Conditions that result from exposure to temperatures that are higher than normal are called *heat-related illnesses.* Heat cramps, heat exhaustion, and heat stroke are the most common heat-related illnesses.

First Aid for Heat-Related Illnesses

What to do for heat cramps Painful muscle spasms in the legs and arms due to excessive fluid loss through sweating are called *heat cramps.*

First aid for heat cramps

1. Have the victim rest in a cool, shaded area and give him or her cool water to drink.
2. Stretch the muscle gently.

First aid for heat cramps includes resting and drinking ▼ cool water.

What to do for heat exhaustion Extreme tiredness due to the body's inability to regulate its temperature is called *heat exhaustion.* Heat exhaustion can be life-threatening. A victim of heat exhaustion will have a body temperature that is below normal. Other signs of heat exhaustion include cool, moist, pale, or red skin; nausea; headache; dizziness; fast pulse; and weakness.

First aid for heat exhaustion

1. Have the victim lie down in a cool place, elevate the feet, and drink cool water.

2. Observe the victim for signs of heatstroke.
3. If the victim does not recover in half an hour, or gets worse, call the local emergency number and obtain medical care.

What to do for heatstroke (sunstroke) An overheating of the body that is life-threatening is *heatstroke.* Sweating ceases so that the body cannot regulate its temperature. The victim has a high body temperature and rapid pulse and respiration rate. The skin becomes hot and dry. A victim feels weak, dizzy, and has a headache. A victim may be unconscious.

First aid for heatstroke

1. Call the local emergency number and obtain medical care.
2. Remove the victim's heavy clothing; wrap the victim in cool, wet towels or sheets; place ice packs near the neck, armpits, and groin; and have victim rest in a cool place. Give sips of water only if the victim is conscious and can swallow.
3. Continue cooling the victim until a body temperature of 102°F is reached.

720   UNIT 11 • Injury Prevention and Personal Safety

actual consent
burn
dislocation
first aid
fracture
Good Samaritan laws
heat cramps
heatstroke
hypothermia
implied consent
splint
universal precautions

Key Terms Review

Complete the fill-in-the-blank statements with the lesson Key Terms on the left. Do not write in this book.

1. _____ is oral or written permission from a mentally competent adult to give first aid.

2. _____ is assuming the victim would grant permission to give first aid if capable.

3. _____ are steps taken to prevent the spread of disease by treating all human blood and body fluids as if they contained HIV, HBV, and other pathogens.

4. A(n) _____ is a break or crack in a bone.

5. A(n) _____ is the movement of a bone from its joint.

6. A(n) _____ is a material or device used to protect and immobilize a body part.

7. A(n) _____ is an injury caused by heat, electricity, chemicals, or radiation.

8. _____ is immediate and temporary care given to a person who has been injured or suddenly becomes ill.

9. An overheating of the body that is life-threatening is _____.

10. A reduction of body temperature so that it is lower than normal is _____.

Recalling the Facts

11. What is frostbite?

12. Identify first aid situations that require professional health services.

13. Describe treatment for a first degree burn.

14. What first aid should you give for a sprain?

15. What is a third-degree burn?

16. Explain the RICE treatment for injuries.

17. What causes hypothermia?

18. Explain the difference between actual and implied consent.

Critical Thinking

19. Why is it important to obtain consent from a conscious victim before giving first aid?

20. Explain the importance of using universal precautions when giving first aid.

21. What injury would you suspect if there is pain, swelling upon movement, and deformity of the injured body part?

22. What would you do if you were on a river-rafting trip with someone who has deep blue lips and is shivering uncontrollably?

Real-Life Applications

23. What would you do if your friend fainted?

24. Explain what you would need to do before moving a victim with a broken leg.

25. Explain if you will need actual or implied consent to give first aid to a conscious child when there is no adult around.

26. Explain how you may prevent harm to yourself when you encounter a person who has received an electrical burn.

Activities

Responsible Decision Making

27. **Analyze** A friend suggests making a prank call to 911, saying that you could report that your neighbor's house is on fire. Then you could hide and watch the fire trucks arrive. Write a response to this situation. Analyze how your behavior would affect your health or the health of others. Refer to the Responsible Decision-Making Model on page 61 for help.

Sharpen Your Life Skills

28. **Advocate for Health** Make a list of emergency telephone numbers, such as the Poison Control Center, your physician, the fire department, the police department, and any other important emergency telephone numbers. Place these numbers by the telephones in your home. Make wallet-sized copies of these numbers so that you and your family can carry them with you at all times.

Visit **www.glencoe.com** for more *Health & Wellness* quizzes.

LESSON 69 • Study Guide **721**

Key Terms Review

1. Actual consent
2. Implied consent
3. Universal precautions
4. fracture
5. dislocation
6. splint
7. burn
8. First aid
9. heatstroke
10. hypothermia

Recalling the Facts

11. The freezing of body parts, often the tissues of the extremities.
12. Answers will vary. See pages 712 and 714–720.
13. See page 714.
14. See page 717.
15. a burn that involves all layers of the skin and some underlying tissues
16. See page 717.
17. Hypothermia results from overexposure to cool temperatures, cold water, moisture, and/or wind.
18. See page 710.

Critical Thinking

19. A conscious victim may know information about his or her condition that you do not know.
20. Universal precautions are designed to protect both you and the victim from pathogens.
21. These are signs of a dislocation.
22. These are signs of hypothermia. Get the victim to dry land and out of wet clothes. Try to warm the victim with a fire or blankets. Obtain medical care immediately.

Real-Life Applications

23. See first aid for sudden illnesses, page 712.
24. You would need to immobilize the injured leg to prevent further injury.
25. implied consent
26. Do not go near the victim until the source of electricity is turned off.

Activities

Responsible Decision Making

27. Responses will vary. Students should analyze the situation to determine that this is not responsible behavior.

Sharpen Your Life Skills

28. Discuss with students the importance of having telephone numbers available in case of an emergency. This will save time and might possibly save a life.

Performing Emergency First Aid Procedures

LESSON 70

Performing Emergency First Aid Procedures

Out of Time?

If time does not permit an in-depth study of this topic, use the following activities in this Teacher Wraparound Edition:
- Health Goal, p. 722
- Quick Demo, p. 725
- Class Activity, p. 730
- Extension, p. 736

1 Focus

HEALTH GOAL **Emergency First Aid Procedures** Have students respond to the Health Goal for this lesson by asking what they know about emergency first aid procedures. *Comments should range from knowing how to perform CPR to how to perform abdominal thrusts, and that these procedures can be used to save lives.* Explain that these procedures can save lives, but that they can also be dangerous if done incorrectly or irresponsibly. **L2**

Write ABOUT IT!

Journaling Have students write a paragraph in their health journals explaining what they would do in this situation. After reading the lesson, have a class discussion. Ask students to share their journal entries with the class. **L2**

What You'll Learn

1. Discuss steps to take when checking a victim. *(p. 723)*
2. Explain first aid procedures for choking. *(p. 725)*
3. Explain first aid procedures for CPR. *(p. 728)*
4. Describe first aid procedures for heart attack. *(p. 738)*
5. Explain first aid procedures for shock. *(p. 739)*
6. Describe first aid procedures for wounds. *(p. 740)*
7. Explain first aid procedures for poisoning and stroke. *(pp. 744, 748)*

Why It's Important

You never know when an emergency will happen. When you know first aid procedures, you will not panic, and you can respond quickly by giving the help that is needed.

Key Terms

- victim assessment
- universal distress signal
- abdominal thrusts
- shock
- cardiopulmonary resuscitation (CPR)
- cardiac arrest
- rescue breaths
- laceration
- tetanus
- nosebleed

Performing Emergency First Aid Procedures

HEALTH GOAL • **I will be skilled in emergency first aid procedures.**

Actions taken when a person is seriously injured or suddenly becomes ill are called *emergency first aid procedures*. These first aid procedures keep the victim as safe as possible until trained medical personnel arrive, which could be a few minutes or a few hours.

Write ABOUT IT!

Writing About Emergencies Suppose you are on your way home from school one day and witness a motor vehicle accident on the street not far from your home. Two victims seem to have serious injuries. After reading the information about emergency first aid in this lesson, write an entry in your health journal explaining how you would respond to this situation.

National Health Education Standards—Guide for Lesson 70

1.3	Analyze how environment and personal health are interrelated.	p. 744	2.3	Analyze how peers influence healthy and unhealthy behaviors.	p. 751
			2.5	Evaluate the effect of media on personal and family health.	p. 751
1.5	Propose ways to reduce or prevent injuries and health problems.	pp. 722, 725–732, 734–737, 738, 739, 742, 743, 744–747, 748, 749, 750	3.2	Utilize resources from home, school, and community that provide valid health information.	p. 751
			4.1	Utilize skills for communicating effectively with family, peers, and others to enhance health.	pp. 722, 739, 751
2.1	Analyze how family influences the health of individuals.	p. 751			
				NHES Standards for Lesson 70 continued at www.glencoe.com.	

Checking a Victim

A check of the injured or medically ill person to determine if certain conditions are present is a *victim assessment*. Performing a victim assessment includes making sure that the victim has an open airway and is breathing normally. Performing a victim assessment also includes checking to see if the victim is severely bleeding or if the victim has other injuries.

What to Know About Checking a Victim

Call the emergency number. If the victim is conscious, ask the victim what happened. If the victim does not respond, call the local emergency number and obtain medical care immediately.

1. If the victim looks unconscious, tap the victim and shout loudly to see if he or she responds, as shown in **Figure A.**

2. Check for breathing if the victim does not respond. Place your ear near his or her mouth and nose and look toward the victim's chest, as shown in **Figure B.** Look for chest movement, listen and feel for air.

3. If the victim is not breathing, support the victim's head and neck and position the victim on his or her back, as shown in **Figure C** on page 724.

> **Make the Connection**
>
> **First Aid** For more information on performing common first aid procedures, see page 716 in Lesson 69.

Checking a Victim

2 Teach

Quick Demo

Checking a Victim Have a student volunteer to be a victim. He or she should pretend to be unconscious. Demonstrate all steps in checking a victim and explain the details of shouting for help, correct ways to check for breathing, and how to give rescue breaths to the victim.
L2 **ELL**

INTERACTIVE CHALKBOARD with Image Bank

PowerPoint® Presentations

This CD-ROM is an editable Microsoft® PowerPoint® presentation that includes:
• Lesson presentations
• Lesson checks
• Interactive graphics
• 5-Minute Checks
• Image Bank
• All transparencies

CRISS Project

Note Taking Use the Selective Underlining/Highlighting Strategy on page 16T as a means for students to organize the steps in administering first aid.

Lesson Resource Manager

• **Unit 11 Fast File Resources**
  Reading Strategy, p. 119
  Vocabulary Practice, p. 120
  Transparency Master and Worksheet, p. 121
  Real-Life Health, p. 123
  Real-Life Health, p. 125
  5-Minute Check, p. 127
  Lesson 70 Quiz, p. 131
• **Unit 11 Transparency**
• **Lesson 70 Transparency**

• **Reading Essentials**
• **Technology**
  TeacherWorks™ CD-ROM
  StudentWorks™ CD-ROM
  Reading Essentials CD-ROM
  Exam*View*® Assessment Suite
  Vocabulary Puzzlemaker

> **National Health Education Standards**
> Pages 722–723: 1.5, 3.4, 4.1, 6.3, 7.2, 7.3

When Not to Help Have students think of emergency situations when a person should not attempt to physically help the victim by himself or herself. *Whenever a person puts himself or herself in immediate danger, he or she should avoid helping the other person. For example: a person is trapped in a building that is on fire, a person has fallen into a frozen lake, or a person has electrocuted himself or herself and water is present around him or her.* Explain that professional help should be obtained, but the rescuer should not place himself or herself in danger. **L2**

4. Tilt the head back and lift the chin of the victim. The victim's mouth should be open, as shown in **Figure D**. Recheck for signs of breathing for 5 seconds. Repeat step 3.

5. If there are still no signs of breathing, wear a face mask, shield, or some other type of barrier for protection, as shown in **Figure E**. Follow the instructions provided with the mask. Blow two rescue breaths of air into the victim's mouth. Give each breath over 1 second. Each breath should make the chest rise.

6. If the victim's chest does not rise when the first rescue breath is given, again tilt the victim's head back and lift the chin (as shown in **Figure D**), and give the second rescue breath.

7. Check the victim's body for severe bleeding, as shown in **Figure F**. Be certain to follow universal precautions to avoid contact with the victim's blood. Check for other injuries. See page 742 for instructions on controlling bleeding.

724   UNIT 11 • Injury Prevention and Personal Safety

🏠 Family Involvement

Emergency Checklist Have students work with their parents to create a home emergency phone list, and a "what to do in case of emergency" list. Included on the list should be the names and numbers of close friends of the students as well as names and numbers of their parents' close friends. Have students include a veterinarian's emergency number for their pets as well as emergency numbers for the entire family. Encourage students to keep the lists in a visible location for everyone and suggest that the lists be placed next to the family first aid kit. **L2 ELL**

Choking

An emergency in which the airway is blocked is called *choking.* A piece of food or other small object may block the airway. A conscious victim will cough to try to dislodge the piece of food or object.

First Aid for Choking

If a victim can talk, the victim is getting enough air. Encourage the victim to continue trying to cough up the object.

Call for help if the victim cannot cough or speak. If the victim cannot get enough air to talk or cough, or the cough is very weak, the airway is completely blocked.

The victim may indicate that he or she is not breathing. The ***universal distress signal*** is a warning that a person is having difficulty breathing and is shown by clutching at the throat with one or both hands.

The airway must be opened quickly when someone is choking. ***Abdominal thrusts*** are a series of thrusts to the abdomen that force air from the lungs to dislodge an object. The method of giving abdominal thrusts is different for adults and children versus infants.

What to do if you are choking

1. If possible, call the local emergency number and obtain medical care immediately. If you cannot speak, do not hang up. The emergency dispatcher can trace your call and send an ambulance to your location. Be aware that an emergency dispatcher cannot trace a call made from a cellular phone. Use a regular telephone if at all possible.

2. Get the attention of someone around you. Use the universal distress signal if you are unable to speak.

3. Give yourself abdominal thrusts if no one can help you. Make a fist with one hand, and grab the fist with your other hand, as shown in **Figure A.** Give yourself five quick abdominal thrusts. Apply pressure inward and push up toward your diaphragm in one smooth movement. Repeat until the object is dislodged.

4. If a sturdy chair is available, push your body against the back of the chair, pushing between the waist and ribs. Hold onto the chair with your hands to push yourself back up. Repeat until the object is dislodged.

LESSON 70 • Performing Emergency First Aid Procedures **725**

Choking

Quick Demo

Choking Demonstrate to the whole class what to do in a choking situation. Demonstrate the universal distress signal for choking, showing the position of the hands. Simulate abdominal thrusts while explaining that this motion should be continued until the object is dislodged or until help arrives. **ELL**

Class Activity

Role-Play Have students reinforce their understanding of what to do for first aid during a choking situation. Have them partner up with a fellow student. One should pretend to be the victim and demonstrate the universal distress signal for choking. The other should simulate the motions involved in performing abdominal thrusts. Have each pair practice a few times, then switch roles. Stress to students that they should not actually perform the abdominal thrusts; they should merely simulate them. Actually performing the thrusts could cause injury. **L2** **ELL**

National Health Education Standards
Pages 724–725: 1.5, 3.4, 6.3, 7.2, 7.3

Class Discussion

Calling the Emergency Number Ask students what kind of information should be given when they speak with an emergency number dispatcher. *They should always provide information on what happened, the victim's noticeable injuries, their location and/or the victim's location, and their phone number. They should also find out anything else they can do to help.* **L2**

Teacher FYI

Heimlich Creator U.S. surgeon Henry J. Heimlich, M.D., is the creator of the Heimlich maneuver, the simple and innovative technique that is referred to in this book as the abdominal thrust. The Heimlich maneuver became popular in the 1960s and is sometimes displayed on posters in public places.

Explain the Concept

Are They Choking or Not? Explain to students that if a person is coughing, crying, or even wheezing, indicating he or she can't breathe, let him or her try to dislodge the object without intervention. A good, solid cough can do more than any abdominal thrust.

What to Do If an Adult or Child Older Than One Year Is Conscious and Choking

Call the emergency number. To obtain medical care immediately, call the local emergency number. Ask the victim if he or she is choking. Do not do anything if the victim can speak or cough easily. Encourage the victim to continue coughing to dislodge the object.

1. If the victim is conscious but cannot speak, breathe, or cough, stand behind the victim and wrap your arms around the victim's waist. Make a fist with one hand. Place the thumb side of the fist into the victim's abdomen above the navel and below the rib cage, as shown in **Figure A.** Grab your fist with the other hand.

2. Give five quick abdominal thrusts. Apply pressure inward and push up toward the victim's diaphragm in one smooth movement, as shown in **Figure B.** Repeat the cycle of five abdominal thrusts until the object is dislodged. The victim may need rescue breaths after the object is dislodged. **Rescue breaths** are delivered by breathing air into an unconscious victim who is not breathing, but has a pulse. Pages 728–732 explain how to perform rescue breathing on adults, older children, younger children, and infants. Stay with the victim and watch for breathing difficulties.

What to Do If an Adult or Child Older Than One Year Is Unconscious and Choking

1. Call the local emergency number and obtain medical care immediately.

2. Roll the victim on to his or her back. Open the victim's airway by lifting the victim's chin while tilting the head back. Find the lower part of the victim's breastbone and measure up the width of two fingers from that point.

3. Place the heel of your other hand directly over the heel of the first hand and interlock your fingers. Do not let your fingers touch the victim's chest.

4. Position your shoulders over your hands and lock your elbows straight. Exert pressure straight down. Compress the chest 30 times at a rate of about 100 compressions per minute.

5. Look for an object in the victim's mouth. If you see one, remove it. Place a face mask or shield over the victim's face. Place your mouth over the mask and give two slow breaths.

6. Repeat the cycle of 30 chest compressions, a check for an object in the victim's mouth, and two breaths until the object is dislodged.

---

① Differentiated Instruction

Learning Disabilities Have a student read each paragraph in this section to the student who has a learning disability. After each paragraph, have the student who has a learning disability read the paragraph and then give a brief description of what needs to be done during that step of first aid for choking. Have the student reader come up with questions to help the student who has a learning disability through each paragraph. Both students should refer to the illustrations throughout this section for a better understanding of what to do for a person who is choking. **L1 ELL**

What to Do If an Infant Is Choking

1. Call the local emergency number and obtain medical care immediately, whether the infant is conscious or unconscious.

2. If the victim is coughing or crying, do not interfere. Coughing can help clear an airway. If the infant has stopped coughing and the object has not come out, place the victim face up on your upper leg. Make certain that the victim's head is lower than the rest of the victim's body. Press two or three fingers in the center of the breastbone, as shown in **Figure A.** Give five quick chest thrusts.

3. If the infant cannot cough, cry, or breathe, place the victim face down on your forearm or upper leg. Support the victim's head by placing your hand around the lower jaw and chest. Use the heel of your other hand, as shown in **Figure B,** and give five quick blows to the victim's back between the shoulder blades.

4. Repeat chest thrusts and back blows until the object is dislodged. After each set of five chest thrusts and back blows, try to breathe into the mouth and nose of the infant. If air goes in, provide rescue breathing. If not, continue giving another set of back blows and thrusts.

5. If the infant is unconscious and choking, use the chest compressions/rescue breaths first aid technique described in "How to Give CPR to Infants" on page 731.

CPR

Cardiopulmonary Resuscitation

A first aid technique that is used to restore heartbeat and breathing is called *cardiopulmonary resuscitation (CPR)*. The first aid procedures for CPR that are presented in this book follow general guidelines of the American Heart Association and the American Red Cross. For training and certification, contact your local chapter of the Red Cross to find out when CPR training classes are held.

Rescue Breaths

A victim will become unconscious if he or she is without oxygen for only a few minutes. If the body is without oxygen, eventually the heart will stop beating and blood will stop circulating to body organs. The different body systems will fail and the victim will die. With rescue breaths, an unconscious victim who is not breathing can receive air. Rescue breaths give a victim the oxygen needed to stay alive.

What to Know About Giving Rescue Breaths

Follow the instructions provided with the face mask or shield. The instructions might include:

Adults and children

1. Apply the rim of the mask between the victim's lower lip and chin, thus pulling back the lower lip to keep the mouth open under the mask.
2. Position the end marked "nose" over the victim's nose. Seal the mask.
3. Open the victim's airway and blow slowly, as shown in **Figure A.**
4. Remove your mouth from the victim's mouth to allow the victim to exhale.
5. If the victim vomits, remove the mask and clear the victim's airway. Reapply the mask.

Infants

Follow the same procedures, except reverse the mask so the end marked "nose" is under the infant's chin.

A face mask or shield should be worn for rescue breaths. Place it between your mouth and nose and the victim's mouth and nose. This helps prevent you from having contact with the victim's bodily fluids.

Ⓐ

⚡ Cross-Curricular Connections

Science Have students research information on how the lack of oxygen to the body affects various body systems. Have students answer these questions: What body systems begin to shut down when deprived of oxygen? How does oxygen normally work throughout these body systems? How long can the body be deprived of oxygen before permanent damage will occur? After students have determined the answers to these questions, have them write a report to present to the class. Students might want to add variety to the presentation by using charts, visuals, or even some type of multimedia presentation. **L3**

How to Give Rescue Breaths to Adults and Older Children

1. Call the local emergency number and obtain medical care immediately.

2. Roll the victim on his or her back. Tilt the victim's head back in the following way: Place one hand under the victim's chin and lift up while pressing down on the victim's forehead with your other hand, as shown in **Figure A.**

3. Use a face mask or shield for protection. Follow the instructions provided with the mask. Apply the mask. Open the victim's airway. Breathe slowly into the victim, as shown in **Figure B**, giving two slow breaths.

4. Give each breath over 1 second long, one after the other. Each breath should make the chest rise.

5. If the victim's chest does not rise after the first rescue breath, tilt the head and lift the chin again as shown in **Figure A**. Then give the second rescue breath.

6. After giving two rescue breaths, immediately begin chest compressions. Continue performing CPR until professional medical help arrives. See page 732 for further instructions on performing CPR.

Using a Face Mask If you have first aid mannequins available for the students, have them pair up with each other and practice the correct use of a face mask on the mannequin. Ask the students to answer these questions: How are your hands placed on the face mask? How do you keep the face mask secure? How is it cleaned after being used? Have one partner observe the other and point out what is being done correctly. Have them practice three times, then switch roles. Stress the safety issue of cleaning the mask between uses. **L2** **ELL**

Explain the Concept

Barrier to Infection Explain to students that the use of a face mask during any first aid procedure is a preventative measure against disease and infection for both themselves and the person who is injured. Knowing that they might encounter an emergency at any time should help them focus on being prepared to protect themselves during an emergency. Several different types of first-aid masks are available for individuals to purchase. Students can contact their local Red Cross or American Heart Association for more information on where to purchase first aid masks. Stress to students that some type of barrier between them and the victim is better than no barrier at all.

Tips for Giving Rescue Breaths

Did You Know?

Breathing Once a person has stopped breathing, permanent brain damage or death may occur in 4 to 6 minutes.

When a person stops breathing, it is a serious emergency. There is the chance that you are the only person in the vicinity who can assist the victim. Here are several things to remember.

A person can stop breathing for many reasons: accidents of all kinds, choking, heart attack, drowning, suffocation, shock, poisonous gas, or other medical problems.

Call for help or send someone for help, if possible, before starting to give rescue breaths.

Before beginning rescue breaths, do not loosen clothing or attempt to warm the victim.

Unless the victim is lying in a dangerous area, do not move the victim. For instance, if a person is overcome by smoke or chemical gas or vapors, he or she should be moved to an area with uncontaminated air. Be sure to get permission before caring for a conscious victim. Unconscious victims need immediate resuscitation.

Breathing barrier Try to always use a barrier between you and the victim to reduce the risk of disease transmission when giving breaths. Again, after delivering rescue breaths, begin chest compressions.

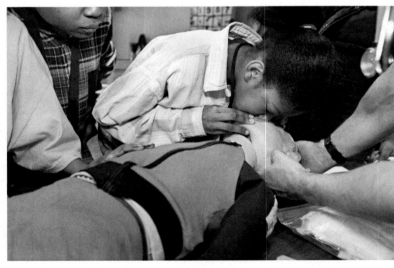

Rescue breaths are ▶ taught as part of a CPR training course.

✛ Cross-Curricular Connections

Art Have students create bookcovers containing pictures of first aid face masks. The bookcovers can contain information on why people should have a face mask, the average cost for one, and where to obtain one. The bookcovers also can point out how to correctly use a face mask. Encourage students to be positive and creative and to consult with the art teacher for illustrative suggestions. Students may use bulletin board paper of different colors, brown paper bags, or other materials for their bookcovers. **L2**

How to Give Rescue Breaths to Infants and Young Children

1. Call the local emergency number and obtain medical care immediately for an unconscious infant or child known to be at risk for heart problems.

2. If you are alone with an unresponsive infant or child, provide about 2 minutes of care, including rescue breaths and chest compressions (about five cycles), before leaving the child to call the emergency number. (For instructions on giving chest compressions to infants and young children, see pages 734–736)

3. Roll the victim onto his or her back.

4. Tilt the victim's head back slightly, as shown in **Figure A.** For an infant, the head should be tilted so the ears are lined up with the shoulders, as shown in **Figure B.**

5. Follow the instructions provided with the mask. Apply the mask.

6. Pinch a child's nose and cover the mouth if the mask permits.

7. For an infant, cover the mouth and nose with your mouth.

8. Give two slow breaths. Each breath should be slow and gentle, lasting about 1 second.

9. Watch to see if the victim's chest slowly rises, as shown in **Figure C.**

10. Remove your mouth to allow the victim to exhale between breaths.

Class Activity

Role-Play Have an infant first aid mannequin available or use a baby doll. Explain this scenario to the students: they were babysitting a neighbor's infant girl one evening. As the student is coming out of the bathroom, he or she sees the child unconscious on the floor, not breathing. Have three students individually demonstrate what each would do in that situation. Tell students what they did correctly, if they placed the face mask on the mannequin correctly, and if they provided enough breaths. Discuss the differences between rescue breaths for adults and rescue breaths for infants. **L2 ELL**

Extension

Rescue Breaths for the Young Have students read the instructions of how to give rescue breaths to infants and young children. Then have them write a 30-second public service announcement that could be used to inform the public on the importance of knowing how to give rescue breaths to infants and young children. **L2**

Teacher to Teacher

Career Search In this activity, students will research types of careers involved in saving the lives of victims during emergency situations (firefighters, police officers, EMTs, school staff, coaches). You may want to have your school guidance counselor do a presentation on these types of careers and/or ask the counselor to help students with their research. This activity brings about lively discussion and helps students focus on health-care and service careers while learning about responding to emergency situations. **L2**
Deborah Kose
Lakeview Junior High School, Pickerington, OH

National Health Education Standards
Pages 730–731: 1.5, 3.2, 3.4, 6.3, 7.2, 7.3

1. What are rescue breaths? *a way of breathing air into an unconscious victim who is not breathing*

2. What is different about using a face mask for giving rescue breaths to an infant? *You must be sure the mask is reversed with the end marked "nose" placed under the chin.*

3. Why should you use a face mask when giving rescue breaths to an unconscious victim? *This helps prevent you from having contact with the victim's bodily fluids.*

4. If the victim's chest does not rise when the first rescue breath is given, what should you do? *Tilt the victim's head back again, lift the chin, and give the second rescue breath.*

5. When should you begin chest compressions? *immediately after giving the second rescue breath*

Class Discussion

ER in the Media Ask students to write in their health journals about how emergency situations are portrayed in the movies and on TV. Ask them to answer these questions: Are face masks used in first aid situations in the media? How realistic are the scenes? **L2**

Chest Compressions

According to the American Heart Association, after delivery of rescue breaths, immediately begin chest compressions. Experts have concluded that the combination of compressions and rescue breaths will most likely give the best outcome for all victims of cardiac arrest. As part of the new recommendations from the American Heart Association, the ratio of compression-to-rescue breath is now 30:2. Please contact your local chapter of the Red Cross to find out more about CPR.

How to Give Chest Compressions to Adults and Older Children

1. You should start chest compressions immediately after you have given the unconscious victim two rescue breaths.

2. Find the lower part of the victim's breastbone and measure up the width of two fingers from that point, as shown in **Figure A**.

3. Place the heel of your other hand directly over the heel of the first hand as shown in **Figure B**. Interlock your fingers. Do not let them touch the victim's chest.

4. Position your shoulders over your hands and lock your elbows straight, as shown in **Figure B**. Exert pressure straight down. Compress the chest 30 times at a rate of about 100 compressions per minute.

5. Push hard and fast. Exert enough pressure to depress the breastbone about 1 to 2 inches.

6. Use a face mask or shield for protection. Follow the instructions provided with the face mask.

7. Allow the chest to reexpand completely as shown in **Figure C**. The time you allow for the chest to reexpand should equal the compression time.

8. After 30 compressions, stop and give two rescue breaths as shown in **Figure D**. Give each breath over 1 second. Each breath should make the chest rise.

🖋 Achieving Health Literacy

Self-Directed Learner Have students form two groups and designate each group as either the illustrators or the writers. When grouping students, take into account the student's language resources and competencies in writing and dexterity. Some students might perform best as illustrators, while others might be more competent as writers. Have the illustrators draw the steps on how to provide rescue breaths, while the writers write the instructions on how to correctly give rescue breaths. Encourage them to use their own words and be creative when drawing the illustrations for each step. **L2 ELL**

9. If the victim's chest does not rise after the first rescue breath, tilt the head and lift the chin again. Then give the second rescue breath. Do not try more than two times to give a rescue breath that makes the chest rise, because it is important to resume chest compressions as soon as possible.

10. After giving two rescue breaths, immediately resume chest compressions.

11. Continue giving sets of 30 chest compressions and two rescue breaths until the victim recovers or professional medical help arrives.

◄ Students can learn the basics of CPR in a class held at their school or in their community.

Explain the Concept

CPR Certified Reinforce the statement that CPR training is available at the American Red Cross. Only qualified instructors can certify people in CPR.

Teacher FYI

CPR Classes Almost every hospital offers some type of CPR classes during the year. The local YMCA, American Red Cross, and American Heart Association offer classes as well. The classes usually are one or two night sessions. Some classes may be free, or as little as $5. Tell students that if they would like to take a class, they can call any of these organizations for specific dates, times, and cost.

Class Discussion

Need CPR Ask students what they should do if they are faced with an emergency situation that requires CPR, but they are not certified in it. *They should call the emergency number immediately.* **L2**

🏛 Community Involvement

CPR Training at School Call the local American Red Cross or the American Heart Association and encourage them to offer a course at your school to certify students and adults in CPR and first aid response. Ask students to obtain parental permission to take the courses and discuss with parents the benefits of all family members taking the courses. Then have the students create promotional posters announcing the time, date, and reasons to take the course. Have them place the posters around the school and the community. **L2**

How to Give CPR to Young Children

1. If you are alone with an unresponsive child, you should perform five cycles (about 2 minutes) of CPR before you call the local emergency number. Start chest compressions immediately after you have given the unconscious victim two rescue breaths. (See "How to Give Rescue Breaths to Infants and Young Children" on page 731.)

2. Find the lower part of the victim's breastbone and measure up the width of two fingers from that point, as shown in **Figure A**.

3. Place the heel of one hand on the center of the victim's breastbone, as shown in **Figure B**. Exert pressure straight down.

4. Exert enough pressure to depress the breastbone about 1/3 to 1/2 the depth of the chest. If the child is large and more force is needed, place the heel of your other hand directly over the heel of the first hand and interlock your fingers. (See "How to Give Chest Compressions to Adults and Older Children" on page 729.)

5. Compress the chest, 30 times at a rate of about 100 compressions per minute. Each compression forces blood from the heart to other parts of the body.

 Achieving Health Literacy

Effective Communicator Have students create a 5-minute advertisement about taking a CPR class. Have them include the answers to these questions in their advertisements: What are the basic origins of CPR? When and how is it to be used? Where can I get certified? How long does certification last? Is there an age requirement to be certified? What is the cost for certification? Students can record or film their advertisement if the school offers the needed technology. **L3**

6. Allow the chest to reexpand completely after each compression. This allows the victim's blood to completely refill the heart. The time you allow for the chest to reexpand should equal the compression time.

7. After 30 compressions, stop and give two rescue breaths, as shown in **Figure C**. Give each breath over 1 second. Each breath should make the chest rise.

8. If the victim's chest does not rise after the first rescue breath, tilt the head and lift the chin again.

Then give the second rescue breath. Do not try more than two times to give a rescue breath that makes the chest rise, because it is important to resume chest compressions as soon as possible.

9. After giving two rescue breaths, immediately resume chest compressions.

10. Continue giving sets of 30 chest compressions and two rescue breaths, as shown in **Figure D**, until the child recovers or professional medical help arrives.

Reading Review

1. Define rescue breaths.

2. How many chest compressions should you administer to an unconscious young child?

Class Discussion

It's in Your Hands Have students write a response to the following hypothetical situation: You are playing one-on-one basketball with a friend in your backyard when suddenly, your friend passes out. He or she is not breathing and has no pulse. Have a class discussion on what you should do and why. *Students should perform CPR and seek emergency medical assistance.* Now pretend that you are certified in CPR. What would you do and why? *Students should call for emergency medical assistance and respond using CPR because they are trained in the procedure.* **L2**

Class Activity

CPR for Children Have your students write in their own words the steps for administering CPR to a child. Then, in their health journals, have them point out the differences between administering CPR to an adult and to a child. **L2**

Extension

CPR Instructor Certification Have students interview a CPR instructor. Have students ask these questions: What did he or she have to do to become certified in CPR? How long was the process? Does certification have to be renewed, and how is it renewed? How many classes and people has he or she taught? Why did he or she want to become a certified CPR instructor? Have students share the results of their interview with the class. **L2**

National Health Education Standards

Pages 734–735: 1.5, 3.4, 3.5, 6.3, 7.2, 7.3

Class Activity

CPR Have the students try to come up with at least ten health words that can be assembled from the letters that spell out "cardiopulmonary resuscitation." Then have them create a word search with the words they found.

Class Discussion

CPR Renewal Ask students why they believe people need to renew their CPR certification after a number of years. Ask students what type of occupations should or do require their employees to be CPR certified. **L2**

1. *Rescue breaths are a way of breathing air into an unconscious victim who is not breathing.*
2. *Compress the chest 30 times per minute.*

How to Give CPR to Infants

1. If you are alone with an unresponsive infant, you should perform five cycles (about 2 minutes) of CPR before you call the local emergency number. Start chest compressions immediately after you have given the unconscious victim two rescue breaths. (See "How to Give Rescue Breaths to Infants and Young Children" on page 731.)

2. Place two fingers on the victim's breastbone just below the nipple line, as shown in **Figure A**. Exert pressure straight down.

3. Compress the chest, 30 times at a rate of about 100 compressions per minute.

4. Exert enough pressure to depress the breastbone about 1/3 to 1/2 the depth of the chest. Each compression forces blood from the heart to other parts of the body.

5. Allow the chest to reexpand completely after each compression. This allows the victim's blood to completely refill the heart. The time you allow for the chest to reexpand should equal the compression time.

6. After 30 compressions, stop and give two rescue breaths, as shown in **Figure B**. Give each breath over 1 second. Each breath should make the chest rise.

7. If the victim's chest does not rise after the first rescue breath, tilt the head and lift the chin again. Then give the second rescue breath. Do not try more than two times to give a rescue breath that makes the chest rise, because it is important to resume chest compressions as soon as possible.

8. After giving two rescue breaths, immediately resume chest compressions.

9. Continue giving sets of 30 chest compressions and two rescue breaths, as shown in **Figure C**, until the infant recovers or professional medical help arrives.

 Health Project

Riding With the EMT Have students get permission from their parents to interview a health provider (such as an EMT), and observe his or her occupation for a few days. Have students ask these questions: What is his or her occupational description? What did the person have to do to become certified in his or her field? What does he or she enjoy about his or her occupation? What are some obstacles that he or she faces in this occupation? Has the person had to use first aid skills? Is the person willing to share any stories he or she has about using his or her first aid skills? Have the students write a paper on their experiences, expressing if they now have a desire to pursue the career they shadowed. **L3**

A ◄ Place two fingers on victim's breastbone just below nipple line. Exert pressure straight down.

After 30 compressions, ► stop and give two rescue breaths.

B

C

Continue giving sets of 30 chest compressions and two rescue breaths until infant recovers or professional ◄ medical help arrives.

Heart Attack

Heart Attack

Extension

Story Time Have students write a fictional scenario involving a heart attack. Be sure they mention the signs the victim exhibited, what steps the rescuer took to provide first aid, and how the situation ended. Emphasize that even with first aid, sometimes lives still can be lost. **L3**

Teacher FYI

Myocardial Infarction According to the American Heart Association, heart disease is the leading cause of death for Americans today. A heart attack also is known as a myocardial infarction. It always results in either permanent heart damage or death. The American Heart Association reported that more than 1 million people suffered a coronary event, such as a heart attack, in 2001.

Class Discussion

Preventing Heart Disease Ask the students the following questions: What do you believe are the leading causes of heart disease? *smoking, high cholesterol, obesity, high blood pressure, and stress* Of these factors, which ones can we control? *all of them* How can we control these factors? *exercise, nutrition, stop smoking, stress management* Even though we know we can control these factors, why do many people still have heart disease today? *It is the choices people make. Also, change is very difficult for some people.* **L2**

The death of cardiac muscle caused by a lack of blood flow to the heart is called a **heart attack**. A blocked blood vessel prevents blood from getting to the heart tissue. Without blood, the heart tissue does not receive oxygen. This usually causes pain in the center of the chest, beneath the breastbone. **Cardiac arrest** occurs when the heart stops beating and blood stops flowing through the body. To prevent cardiac arrest, prompt action must be taken when there are warning signs of a heart attack.

First Aid for Heart Attack

1. Have the victim stop activity and rest in a comfortable position.
2. Ask the victim about his or her condition. Does the victim have a history of heart disease? Is the victim taking any medications?
3. Call the local emergency number and obtain medical care immediately.
4. Comfort the victim until help arrives. Help the person take the prescribed heart medication.
5. Observe the victim for changes in condition.
6. If cardiac arrest occurs, the victim is not breathing and has no pulse, a person should perform CPR.

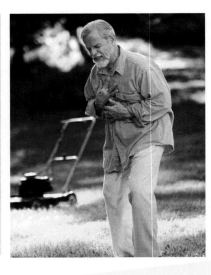

◄ A heart attack may come on suddenly and with no warning.

Heart Attack Warning Signs

The warning signs of a heart attack include:

- persistent pain or pressure in the center of the chest that is not relieved by resting or changing position
- pain that spreads from the center of the chest to the shoulder, arm, neck, jaw, or back

- dizziness
- sweating
- fainting
- difficulty breathing

- shortness of breath
- pale or bluish skin color
- moist face
- irregular pulse

📖 Family Involvement

Heart Disease in the Family Have students discuss with their parents ways in which they can live healthier lives in an effort to decrease their chances of developing heart disease. Have the students develop a contract stating responsible life choices they will make, or continue to follow, throughout their lives. Some items in the contract might include activities that lower blood pressure, cholesterol levels, and stress. Ways they can develop an exercise program, eat nutritious foods, and avoid alcohol and tobacco also may be included in the contract. Have the student and the parents sign the contract, indicating that they will support and reinforce healthy life choices at home. **L2**

Shock

Any serious injury or illness can lead to shock. **Shock** *is a dangerous reduction in blood flow to the body tissues.* The body organs fail to function properly when they do not receive oxygen. Shock can lead to collapse, coma, and death if untreated. Signs of shock include rapid, shallow breathing; cold, clammy skin; rapid, weak pulse; dizziness; weakness; and fainting.

What to Know About First Aid for Shock

1. Call the local emergency number and immediately obtain medical care for the victim.
2. Have the victim lie down.
3. Elevate the victim's legs about 8 to 12 inches above heart level, as shown in **Figure A,** unless you suspect head, neck, or back injuries or broken bones in the hips or legs.
4. Leave the victim lying flat if you are unsure of the victim's injuries.
5. Control external bleeding. Wear protective gloves.
6. Help the victim maintain normal body temperature. Cover the victim with a blanket if he or she is cold. Do not give the victim anything to eat or drink.

Class Discussion

When Seconds Count Have students discuss the following situation: Suppose you walk into the gym locker room one day to find your friend unconscious on the floor. He or she is cold, clammy, and his or her breathing is very shallow. What do you do? *Answers will vary. Students should recognize these as symptoms of shock and they should follow procedures of treatment for shock.* **L2**

NHES Assessment/SCASS

Performance Event Have the students read through the first aid steps to follow for shock. Then have them write about an emergency scene involving a victim going into shock. Have them refer to the steps as they describe what they are doing and how they are handling the situation. **L2**

Explain the Concept

Different Types of Shock Explain to students that there are different types of shock. People can suffer shock from an allergic reaction to insect stings, medication, or food. An allergic reaction to food is known as anaphylactic shock. Shock due to injury is known as traumatic shock. Explain that in any type of shock you should follow the prescribed steps for treating shock.

DI Differentiated Instruction

Hearing Impairment Give visual cues for a student with hearing impairment to reinforce what is being taught in the classroom. Demonstrating techniques for treating people in shock, rather than teaching through lecture, will help a student with hearing impairment better understand the process that the treatment requires. Diagrams illustrating each treatment step also are useful tools. **L2 ELL**

National Health Education Standards
Pages 738–739: 1.5, 3.4, 4.1, 4.4, 6.3, 7.2, 7.3

Wounds

Class Activity

Vocabulary Puzzle Have the students use this lesson's vocabulary words (words that are in **boldface** and *italic*) to create a word puzzle. Have them use the definitions for each word as clues. **L2** **ELL**

NHES Assessment/SCASS

Performance Task Have students research the effects of the different types of wounds on the integumentary system. Have the students answer these questions: Why are some wounds more painful than others? Why do some bleed more than others? Why do some form scars as they heal and others do not? Have the students write a short paper on the results of their research. **L3**

Explain the Concept

Closed Wounds Explain to students that closed wounds can be caused by illness, injury, or certain medications and sometimes can be difficult to detect. If a person breaks a bone or sustains a blunt or penetrating blow to the body, a closed wound can occur, especially in the abdomen.

Wounds

An injury to the body's soft tissues is called a *wound*. A *closed wound* is an injury to the soft tissues under the skin. An *open wound* is an injury in which the skin's surface is broken. There are many types of wounds.

First Aid for Wounds

Did You Know?

Bleeding A person with a severe cut can bleed to death in a matter of minutes if he or she does not receive prompt first aid treatment.

Bruise A wound in which damage to soft tissues and blood vessels causes bleeding under the skin is a *bruise.* The tissues change color and swell. A bruise may appear red and then change to blue or purple. Large bruises may indicate serious damage to deeper body tissues.

Incision A cut caused by a sharp-edged object, such as a knife, razor, scissors, or broken glass is an *incision.* Bleeding from an incision may be heavy. There may be damage to large blood vessels, nerves, and deep soft body tissues if the cut is deep.

An abrasion is often
▼ referred to as a scrape.

Laceration A cut that causes a jagged or irregular tearing of the skin is a *laceration.* Bleeding from a laceration can be heavy. There is a risk of infection because foreign matter is forced through the skin.

Abrasion A wound caused by rubbing or scraping away of the skin is an *abrasion,* or scrape. There is a risk of infection, as dirt and other matter can become ground into the wound. An abrasion may be painful if it exposes nerve endings. Bleeding is usually limited.

Avulsion A wound in which the skin or other body tissue is separated or completely torn away is an *avulsion.* This injury may result in a piece of skin hanging as a flap. It may result in a body part, such as a finger, being completely torn from the body. Bleeding is heavy if deeper tissues are damaged.

Puncture A wound that is produced when a pointed instrument pierces the skin is a *puncture.* A needle, nail, piece of glass, knife, or bullet can cause a puncture wound. Puncture wounds do not usually bleed much unless a major blood vessel is damaged. The risk of infection from a puncture wound is high. A tetanus shot may be given if the victim has not had one recently.

Cross-Curricular Connections

Social Studies Acupuncture was once thought of as quackery, but it has recently gained respect among some in the medical community. Have students do research on acupuncture. Ask them to find the answers to these questions: What is acupuncture? How do the miniature punctures allegedly help the body? What is the history behind it? Where did it originate? In what country is acupuncture practiced the most? What types of studies have been done to show if it is effective and reliable? Have students present their findings to the class as oral reports. Then have students set up a class debate as to whether acupuncture is or is not an effective form of medical treatment for some illnesses. **L3**

How to Prevent Infection

What is infection? A wound must be kept clean to prevent infection. An *infection* is a condition in which pathogens enter the body and multiply.

Wash wounds and abrasions with clean running water for at least 5 minutes. Continue rinsing until the wound shows no sign of foreign matter. If you do not have access to running water, you can use any source of clean water. For superficial wounds or abrasions, apply antibiotic ointment and cover the wound with a sterile bandage to keep it clean.

Signs of infection Watch the wounded area closely for signs of infection. There may be swelling and redness. The wounded area may become warm, throb with pain, or discharge pus.

Medical care Get medical care if the wound is deep and bleeding or if the wound appears to need stitches. Also seek medical care if there is a wound to the face or if the victim has been bitten by an animal or another person. Medical care is needed if you start to run a temperature above 100°F; the area around the wound feels numb or has red streaks; you cannot move comfortably; or the wound is draining thick, creamy, and grayish fluid.

Alcohol and hydrogen peroxide are generally not recommended for open wounds since they are painful and tend to slow healing.

How to prevent tetanus If you have ever stepped on a nail or been bitten by an animal, your physician may have given you a tetanus shot. Some wounds, especially puncture wounds, put you at risk for a tetanus infection.

◀ People are given an immunization against tetanus when they are children, but everyone needs a booster shot every five to ten years.

Tetanus, or *lockjaw,* is a disease caused by a type of bacteria that grows in the body and produces a strong poison that affects the nervous system and muscles.

A DTaP is an immunization given in childhood to protect against tetanus, diphtheria, and pertussis (whooping cough).

A booster shot is needed every five to ten years after the childhood series. A booster shot also is needed when a wound is caused by a dirty object, such as a rusty nail.

How to Treat an Infection

The following are four steps you can use to treat infection.

1. Wash the wound in clean running water for at least 5 minutes.
2. Apply an antibiotic ointment to abrasions or superficial wounds.
3. Elevate the infected area above the level of the heart.
4. Seek medical attention.

LESSON 70 • Performing Emergency First Aid Procedures **741**

Quick Demo

Stop the Bleeding Be sure to have a clean cloth available. Have a student volunteer to play a victim. Explain that the victim has just fallen and cut his or her elbow. Follow the instructions given and explain what you are doing as you complete the process. *Explain that they should apply direct pressure to a wound to stop the bleeding. Tell them to add another clean cloth on top of the first cloth if the blood soaks through, but emphasize that they should not remove the first cloth.* **L2**

Class Activity

Bandages Pair off students. Be sure to have a clean cloth and some type of bandage to secure the cloth for each pair of students. Have each pair of students practice how to control bleeding. Go around the room and place each pair of students in different scenarios. Some could have wounds on the arms, others on the leg, and others head wounds. Vary the types of wounds from group to group and challenge each group to attempt to stop the bleeding of wounds in various places on the body. By the end, each group should have tried to control bleeding at three different wound locations on the body. **L2** **ELL**

How to Control Bleeding

The first priority for any wound is to stop severe bleeding and prevent germs from entering the wound. A person with severe bleeding could bleed to death in a matter of minutes.

1. If the bleeding is severe, call the local emergency number and obtain medical care immediately.
2. Cover the wound with a clean cloth or sterile dressing and apply direct pressure with your hand, as shown in **Figure A.**
3. Add more cloth if the blood soaks through, but do not remove the first piece of cloth.
4. Do not remove any foreign objects that are lodged deep in the wound.
5. If you do not suspect fractures, elevate the wounded body part above heart level, as shown in **Figure B.** This helps reduce blood flow to the area.

6. Secure the cloth or sterile dressing with some type of bandage, as shown in **Figure C.**
7. If the bleeding does not stop, continue to apply direct pressure to the wound.
8. Locate the closest pressure point. The pressure point technique compresses the main artery that supplies blood to the affected body part. This technique stops circulation within the limb.

9. It is important to remember that if the use of the pressure point technique is necessary, it should be used in conjunction with direct pressure and elevation. Using the pressure point technique to stop bleeding is not a substitute for direct pressure.

❤ Health Project

How Much Is Too Much? Have students research the effects of blood loss on the human body and write a report. Ask them to answer the following questions in their reports:
- How much blood is in the human body?
- As blood is lost, what are the cumulative effects on the body?
- How fast can the body lose blood, depending on the wound size?
- How do humans recover lost blood?

Collected information may be presented in a written report, a poster display, or as a multimedia presentation to the class. **L3**

How to Stop a Nosebleed

A **nosebleed** is a loss of blood from the mucous membranes that line the nose. Most nosebleeds are caused by a blow to the nose or cracked mucous membranes in the nose. Nosebleeds also may occur due to blowing, sneezing, or picking the nose. Sometimes they may result from an allergy, infection, or a tumor. Nosebleeds usually are easy to control. If a nosebleed occurs without obvious cause or frequently, a physician should be consulted.

1. Use protective gloves if you are assisting the victim. Have the victim sit with his or her head slightly forward and pinch the nostrils firmly together. Sitting slightly forward helps the blood flow toward the external opening of the nose instead of backward down the throat.

2. The nostrils should be pinched firmly together for about five minutes before releasing. The victim

◀ Try to preserve a knocked-out tooth until you are able to get to a dentist.

should breathe through the mouth and spit out any blood in the mouth.

3. An ice pack may be applied to the bridge of the nose.

4. Repeat this procedure for another ten minutes and get medical help if the bleeding does not stop.

What to Do When a Tooth Is Knocked Out

There are various recommendations on how to deal with a tooth that has been knocked out of its socket.

1. If possible, have the victim gently insert and hold the knocked-out tooth in its socket.

2. Otherwise, place the tooth in cold milk or in water if milk is not available. Do not touch the root of the tooth.

3. The victim should see a dentist immediately. The sooner the tooth is placed back inside the socket, the better the chance it can be saved.

▲ Get medical help if a nosebleed is severe or prolonged.

Reading Review

1. What is a heart attack?
2. What is a puncture?

Quick Demo

Stopping the Nosebleed Ask for a volunteer. Tell the students that you are going to demonstrate how to stop a nosebleed using the steps on the student page. Explain the concepts as you demonstrate. Then have students practice the technique on themselves. **L2**

Teacher FYI

Nasal Septum The cartilage in the middle of the nose is known as the nasal septum. If it is ever dislocated or broken, it will never heal. That is why it is important to wear some type of face shield or protector when involved in any contact sport.

Class Discussion

Losing Your Teeth Ask if anyone has ever lost a tooth. *Everyone should raise their hands since students at this age should have lost their baby teeth.* Ask if anyone has ever had a tooth knocked out. *If anyone has, ask if he or she would like to share his or her experience. If no, explain that when a tooth is knocked out it is very important to stop the bleeding and to save the tooth for possible reinsertion.* **L2**

Reading Review

1. *A heart attack is the death of cardiac muscle caused by a lack of blood flow to the heart.*
2. *A puncture is a wound produced when a pointed instrument pierces the skin.*

ⓓⒾ Differentiated Instruction

Behavioral Disorders Enlist the assistance of the school counselor or a parent of the student who has a behavioral disorder. Set up a telephone interview with the student's dentist, who should be familiar with the student's problems. The counselor or parent should supervise the interview. Have the student ask the dentist about the procedure for inserting a knocked-out tooth back into its socket. He or she should report findings to you or, if possible, to the class. Be generous with praise for good behavior during the exercise. **L2 ELL**

National Health Education Standards
Pages 742–743: 1.5, 3.4, 6.3, 7.2, 7.3

Poisoning

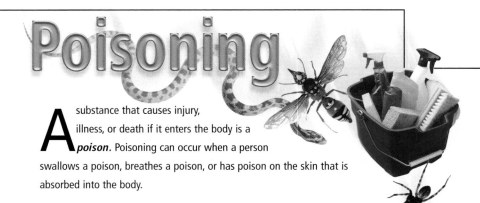

Poisoning

A substance that causes injury, illness, or death if it enters the body is a *poison.* Poisoning can occur when a person swallows a poison, breathes a poison, or has poison on the skin that is absorbed into the body.

First Aid for Poisoning

> **Make the Connection**
>
> **Decisions** Sometimes injuries occur when one does not make responsible decisions. For more information on making responsible decisions, see page 61 in Lesson 6.

Causes of poisoning Most cases of poisoning occur when small children swallow medicines or products, such as cleaning solutions or pesticides. Some people are poisoned by certain foods, such as shellfish or mushrooms. Some substances cause poisoning in larger amounts; for example, a person can be poisoned by taking too many pills or by drinking too much alcohol too quickly. Combinations of drugs, such as alcohol and sleeping pills, can cause poisoning.

Poisoning also can occur from breathing the fumes of household products, such as glue, paints, and cleaners. Certain gases, such as carbon monoxide, cause poisoning. Chlorine that is added to swimming pools is dangerous to breathe. Fumes from certain drugs, such as crack cocaine, also can cause poisoning.

Some poisons get on the skin and are absorbed into the body. Products, such as pesticides and fertilizers, can cause poisoning if they get on the skin. People using these products should wear gloves and protective clothing to prevent poisoning. They also should wear a mask to keep from breathing in fumes from these products. Poisons from plants, such as poison ivy and poison oak, also can get on the skin. These poisons are absorbed into the body and can cause a reaction in some people.

Poisoning can occur when a needle is used to inject drugs into the body. Bites or stings from insects, spiders, bees, snakes, and marine life can cause poisoning.

Warning signs of poisoning The signs of poisoning vary with the poison, but may include difficulty breathing, nausea, vomiting, chest and abdominal pain, sweating, and seizures. Skin rashes and burns on the lips or tongue also may indicate poisoning.

What to do for poisoning The Poison Control Center will tell you whether or not to induce vomiting in the victim. Victims who have swallowed acid substances, bleach, or gasoline

◀ Keep all poisonous household products out of the reach of children.

🔖 Family Involvement

products should not vomit. These substances can burn the esophagus, mouth, and throat if the victim vomits. Never induce vomiting in a victim who is drowsy or unconscious or who is having convulsions. You may be advised to dilute the poison by having the victim drink water or milk.

The victim may be advised to take activated charcoal. It is sometimes used when vomiting is not advised. Activated charcoal is a product used to absorb poisons that have been swallowed. It is sold in both liquid and powder forms at drugstores. It counteracts the effects of the poison.

Never try to give an unconscious victim anything by mouth, and do not try to neutralize the poison with lemon juice, vinegar, or any other substance, unless the Poison Control Center or a doctor tells you to do so.

What to do if you touch a poisonous plant Touching poisonous plants, such as poison ivy, poison sumac, or poison oak, can result in skin redness, swelling, and itching. If you touch a poisonous plant:

1. Wash the affected body parts with soap and water immediately.
2. Remove any clothing that may have some of the poison on it.
3. Use over-the-counter drugs to relieve itching, if needed.
4. Call a physician if the reactions are severe.

What to do for snakebites Poisoning can occur from being bitten by a poisonous snake, such as a coral snake or a pit viper. Examples of pit vipers are rattlesnakes, copperheads, and water moccasins. Symptoms of a bite from a poisonous snake include pain at the site of the wound, rapid pulse, dimmed vision, vomiting, and shortness of breath. The victim may experience shock and become unconscious.

1. Treat for shock.
2. Keep the victim still. This will reduce the speed with which the poison can travel through the body.
3. Keep the bitten area below the level of the heart.
4. Get prompt medical care.

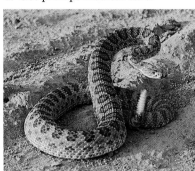

◀ If a person is bitten by a poisonous snake, he or she should receive medical care immediately.

First Aid for Poisoning

Follow these steps if you suspect someone has been poisoned:

- Obtain medical care immediately.
- Be cautious. Protect your health and safety. Do not risk injury.
- Move the victim to a safe location, if possible and if necessary.
- Keep the victim's airway open.
- If you have been trained in CPR, perform CPR if the victim is not breathing normally. Remember to use a face mask or shield when giving rescue breaths to the victim.
- Determine the type of poison. Ask the victim what type of poison it might be. Be on the lookout for empty bottles and containers or needles. Recognize fumes and odors that may be the cause. Are there bees, snakes, or poisonous plants in the area? Try to determine how much poison has been absorbed by the body and the time the poisoning occurred.

Reading Labels Have students bring in labels from household cleanser and insecticide containers that are empty and are being discarded. Have them read the labels. Ask them to answer these questions: What are the active ingredients contained in the product? What are procedures to follow if a person is incorrectly exposed to the product? Should vomiting be induced or should the victim drink a liquid and wait for help to arrive? **L2** **ELL**

Explain the Concept

Venom Explain the difference between venom and poison. Explain that venom is injected, absorbed, or inhaled. Snakebites contain venom composed of neurotoxins that affect the nervous system and hemotoxins that affect the circulatory system. Explain that antivenom is produced when small quantities of venom are injected into animals and the antibodies created by the animals are used as serum.

Teacher FYI

Poison Ivy As the saying goes, "Leaves of three, let them be." An easy way to identify poison ivy is that its leaves are clustered in groups of three. It is a myth that the poison ivy rash on a person exposed to poison ivy can spread the poison. Only the oil, even on dead plants, can spread poison ivy. Almost 90 percent of the population is allergic to poison ivy; however, negative reactions to poison ivy can develop over time in people who previously were not affected by the plant.

🔅 Cross-Curricular Connections

Science Have one group of students consult with a science teacher or do research on the differences among poison ivy, poison oak, and poison sumac. Another group will report on different types of poisonous snakes, or an abstract of varying household cleanser labels. Encourage students to be creative and to design something that exhibits the uniqueness of the poison, as well as its danger. The completed work may be displayed as collages, pictures, photographs, or even watercolors. The two groups may work together to set up a display center in the classroom. Emphasize imagination. **L2**

National Health Education Standards

Pages 744–745: 1.3, 1.5, 3.4, 6.3, 7.2, 7.3

Class Discussion

Harmless Bee Sting? Have students write a reaction to the following situation: You and your friend are walking through the park when suddenly a bee stings your friend on the neck. He shrugs it off because he knows he is not allergic to bees. A few minutes later, the area where your friend was stung swells, he begins to wheeze, and then he falls to the ground. Ask students what they would do in this situation. *This appears to be an allergic reaction. Get medical help immediately.* **L2**

Explain the Concept

Itsy, Bitsy Spider Bring in pictures of the most common types of poisonous spiders: the brown recluse, the black widow, and the tarantula. Explain that in the United States, the brown recluse is found mostly in the southern states, while the black widow can be found everywhere. The tarantula is usually found in New Mexico, Arizona, Texas, and southern California. Emphasize to students that they should shake out their shoes if they have been outside for a long period of time and that they should be careful around dark, damp areas of the house where spiders may hide.

Did You Know?

Immediate Care
Prompt medical attention is needed for a victim who does not know what stung him or her, has had a previous allergic reaction to a sting, has been stung on the face or neck, or has difficulty breathing.

What to do for insect stings Stings from bees are one of the most common insect-related problems. Bee stings can create a serious health problem for people who are allergic. These people should carry medication to prevent a serious allergic reaction. They also should wear a medic alert tag.

Most people do not have an allergic response to bee stings. If the person is known to be allergic to bees, or if the swelling is severe or covers a large area of the body, call the local emergency number and obtain medical care immediately. The bee will leave its stinger in the skin when it stings. Hornets, wasps, and yellow jackets do not leave stingers in the skin.

1. Remove the stinger. Do not try to remove the stinger with a tweezer. The tweezer will force the bee's venom into the body. Flick the stinger away with a nail file, fingernail, credit card, or a similar object.
2. Place something cold over the area to relieve the pain.

Antibiotic ointment helps to prevent infection from a tick bite. ▶

What to do for spider bites Being bitten by a black widow spider can be deadly. A bite from this spider will produce a dull, numbing pain. Headache, muscular weakness, vomiting, and sweating also may occur.

1. Call the local emergency number and obtain medical care for the victim immediately.
2. Wash the bitten area with soap and water.
3. Apply ice to relieve the pain.
4. Get prompt medical help. An antivenin may be given. An antivenin is a medicine that reduces the effects of the poison.

A bite from the brown recluse spider also is dangerous. A bite from this spider produces an open ulcer. Chills, nausea, and vomiting may follow.

1. Wash the affected part with soap and water.
2. Get prompt medical help.

What to do for marine animal stings Stings from marine animals, such as the stingray, sea urchin, spiny fish, jellyfish, sea anemone, or man-of-war can cause serious allergic reactions. Breathing difficulties, heart problems, and paralysis may result. Call the local emergency number and obtain medical care immediately.

Stings from a stingray, sea urchin, or spiny fish:

1. Remove the victim from the water as soon as possible.
2. Remove the stingray, sea urchin, or spiny fish.
3. Flush the injured area with water.
4. Do not move the injured part.
5. Soak the injured area in hot water for 30 minutes to relieve pain.

Cross-Curricular Connections

Computer Science Have students choose a poisonous animal or insect listed on pages 746–747. Have them research information on their scientific names, where they are primarily found, their physical description, behavior, habitat, food hunting skills, and any other interesting facts they can find on the animal or insect. Have students use a computer to create pamphlets containing information on the animal or insect they chose. Encourage the use of visuals on the pamphlets. **L3**

6. Clean the injured area and apply a bandage.

7. Seek medical attention. A tetanus shot may be required.

Stings from a jellyfish, sea anemone, or man-of-war:

1. Remove the victim from the water as soon as possible.

2. Soak the injured area in vinegar as soon as possible. Vinegar offsets the effects of the toxin from the sting. Rubbing alcohol or baking soda can be used if vinegar is not available.

3. Do not rub the wound. Rubbing spreads the toxin and increases pain.

What to do for tick bites A tick is an insect that attaches itself to any warm-blooded animal. It feeds on the blood of the animal. There is great concern about diseases spread by ticks. Two such diseases are Lyme disease and Rocky Mountain spotted fever. *Lyme disease* is a bacterial disease transmitted through a tick. The ticks that spread Lyme disease are those found on field mice and

◀ Ticks can spread Lyme disease and Rocky Mountain spotted fever.

deer. The ticks are very small. The bacteria that cause Lyme disease are transmitted through the bite of an infected tick. A rash starts and spreads to approximately seven inches across. The center of the rash is light red and the outer ridges are darker red and raised. A victim may have fever, headaches, and weakness. Prompt medical attention is needed. Antibiotics are used for treatment.

Rocky Mountain spotted fever is a potentially life-threatening disease carried by a tick. Cases of this disease are not confined to the Rocky Mountain region. Symptoms include high fever, weakness, rash, leg pains, and coma. Prompt medical attention is needed. Antibiotics are used for treatment.

Did You Know?

Tick Bite Do not put nail polish or petroleum jelly on a tick bite. Do not try to kill the tick by burning it with a match. These are not appropriate first aid procedures.

How to Remove a Tick

A tick should always be removed from the body.

- Grasp the tick with tweezers as close to the skin as possible. Use a glove or plastic wrap to protect your fingers if you do not have tweezers.
- Pull the tick slowly away from the skin.
- Wash the area and your hands with soap and water.
- Apply an antibiotic ointment or antiseptic to the area to prevent infection.

- Save the tick in a jar and watch for signs of infection for the next several weeks.
- Obtain medical help if the tick cannot be removed or if part of it remains under the skin. Medical help also is needed if signs of Lyme disease or Rocky Mountain spotted fever develop.

LESSON 70 • Performing Emergency First Aid Procedures **747**

Teacher FYI

Tick Talk Ticks, which have eight legs, are not actually insects; they are arachnids, like spiders and mites. Insects have only six legs. Lyme disease obtained its name from the town of Lyme, Connecticut, where the first outbreak of Lyme disease took place. Fifty percent of the deer ticks in New Jersey are infected with Lyme disease.

5-Minute Check

Page 130, **Unit 11 Fast File Resources**

1. What are some warning signs of a heart attack? *persistent pain or pressure in the chest; pain that spreads from the chest to the shoulders, neck, jaw, or back; fainting; dizziness; sweating*

2. What is an avulsion? *a wound in which the skin or other body tissue is separated or completely torn away*

3. How can you prevent a wound from becoming infected? *Wash a minor wound with clean running water for at least 5 minutes, apply antibiotic ointment, and cover the wound with a sterile bandage.*

4. What are some warning signs of poisoning? *difficulty breathing, vomiting, nausea, chest and abdominal pain, seizures, and skin rashes*

5. What should you do if someone is stung by a bee? *Remove the stinger and place something cold over the affected area to relieve pain.*

National Health Education Standards
Pages 746–747: 1.5, 3.4, 7.2, 7.3

747

Stroke

Extension

Rehab for Stroke Have students do research on the types of treatments available for a person who has had a stroke. Ask them to answer these questions: How is a stroke diagnosed? What type of rehabilitation is available for a person who has had a stroke and what does it involve? How successful are these rehabilitation programs? What types of organizations exist to assist people who have had a stroke? Have students do multimedia presentations on the results of their research. **L3**

Teacher FYI

Stroke Mortality Rate In the year 2000, strokes killed 167,661 people. Stroke is the third leading cause of death and the leading cause of disability in the United States according to the American Heart Association. Strokes are more common in men than in women.

3 Assess

Vocabulary Practice

Page 120, **Unit 11 Fast File Resources**

National Health Education Standards

Pages 748–749: 1.5, 3.4, 4.4, 6.3, 7.2, 7.3, 8.2, 8.3

Stroke

A condition caused by a blocked or broken blood vessel in the brain is called a *stroke*. A stroke can occur when a clot moves through the bloodstream and lodges in the brain. A clot can form inside one of the arteries in the brain, or a blood vessel in the brain can burst. A head injury or tumor may cause an artery to burst. Blood cannot get to all parts of the brain, resulting in the injury or death of some brain tissue.

What to Know About First Aid for Stroke

The damage that occurs during a stroke depends on the part of the brain that is affected. A victim may suffer loss of vision or have slurred speech. Body parts can become paralyzed, often affecting one side of the body, including the face, torso, and one arm or leg. Sometimes blood cannot flow to the parts of the brain that control heart rate or breathing, and death results. Other times a patient may remain conscious, but confused. To prevent disability and death, prompt action must be taken when there are signs of stroke.

◄ A stroke is caused by a blocked or broken blood vessel in the brain.

First aid for stroke involves these steps:

1. Call the local emergency number and obtain medical care for the victim immediately.

2. Keep the victim lying down with his or her head and shoulders raised to relieve the force of blood on the brain.

3. Check the airway. Keep the victim's air passage open.

4. Position the victim on his or her side if there is fluid or vomit in the mouth.

5. Do not give the victim anything to drink.

6. Comfort the victim until help arrives.

Remember: every second counts. The longer a stroke victim goes without treatment, the greater the damage.

Stroke Warning Signs

A stroke victim may be conscious or unconscious. The warning signs of a stroke include:

- weakness or paralysis on one side of the body
- blurred vision
- severe headache
- slow breathing rate

- loss of speech or trouble talking or understanding speech
- unequal size of pupils in the eyes

748   UNIT 11 • Injury Prevention and Personal Safety

 Community Involvement

Warning Signs Have students form groups of three or four. Have some groups create posters listing the most common warning signs and first aid for heart attacks and strokes. Have others research statistics for hearts attacks and strokes and create signs to display this information. Another group might research the leading causes for these two types of diseases and create prevention signs to help inform the community. After the signs are created, have students obtain permission from community businesses and malls to display the signs. **L2** **ELL**

Key Terms Review

Complete these fill-in-the-blank statements with the lesson Key Terms on the left. Do not write in this book.

abdominal thrusts
bruise
cardiac arrest
cardiopulmonary resuscitation (CPR)
heart attack
laceration
nosebleed
rescue breaths
shock
tetanus
universal distress signal
victim assessment

1. First, check for bleeding when doing a(n) _____ because victims may bleed to death.

2. Perform _____ on a victim who is choking and having trouble speaking.

3. Perform _____ after you are certain the victim is not breathing normally.

4. _____ is used to restore heartbeat and breathing.

5. _____ occurs when the heart stops beating.

6. A(n) _____ is loss of blood from the mucous membranes that line the nose.

7. A(n) _____ is a warning that a person has difficulty breathing and is shown by clutching at the throat with one or both hands.

8. A(n) _____ is a cut that causes a jagged tearing of the skin.

9. _____ is a dangerous reduction in blood flow to the body tissues.

10. _____ is caused by bacteria that produce a strong poison that affects the nervous system and muscles.

Recalling the Facts

11. What are emergency first aid procedures?

12. What are some things to look for when giving a victim assessment?

13. What are rescue breaths?

14. How should you perform abdominal thrusts on an unconscious adult victim?

15. How many compressions are given after every two rescue breaths when performing CPR?

16. List seven warning signs that might indicate a heart attack.

17. What is a laceration?

18. Describe first aid for a bee sting.

Critical Thinking

19. Explain why choking is an emergency.

20. Why is it important to allow the chest to reexpand completely after each compression given in CPR?

21. Why is it important to follow universal precautions when administering first aid to a bleeding victim?

22. Why is treating for shock important when an accident victim may appear to have nothing wrong with him or her?

Real-Life Applications

23. What precautions can be taken to protect against poisoning in your home?

24. What would you do if you suspected someone was having a heart attack?

25. How would you determine if a person was in shock due to an illness or injury?

26. Explain why you should wash the affected area if you think you have come in contact with a poisonous plant.

Activities

Responsible Decision Making

27. **Infer** A friend falls down the stairs at your house and is bleeding. Should you wear the gloves in the first aid kit to give first aid? Write a response to this situation. Refer to the Responsible Decision-Making Model on page 61 for help.

Sharpen Your Life Skills

28. **Advocate for Health** Have a family discussion about the importance of having a first aid kit at home. With your parents' or guardians' approval, make or purchase a first aid kit. Place it where your family has decided it should be kept.

Visit www.glencoe.com for more *Health & Wellness* quizzes.

LESSON 70 • Study Guide **749**

LESSON 70
STUDY GUIDE

Key Terms Review

1. victim assessment
2. abdominal thrusts
3. rescue breaths
4. CPR
5. Cardiac arrest
6. nosebleed
7. universal distress signal
8. laceration
9. Shock
10. Tetanus

Recalling the Facts

11. actions taken when a person is seriously injured or suddenly becomes ill

12. Check for an open airway, signs of breathing, circulation, and bleeding.

13. a way of breathing air into an unconscious victim who is not breathing

14. See page 726.

15. 30

16. See page 739.

17. See page 740.

18. See page 746.

Critical Thinking

19. If a person is choking, he or she is not getting air (oxygen) into the body. A person will live only a few minutes without oxygen.

20. It allows the victim's blood to completely refill the heart.

21. Following universal precautions will reduce and/or prevent the risk that you will become infected with or spread pathogens.

22. A victim of a serious injury or illness may experience shock with no apparent visible symptoms. Shock can lead to collapse, coma, and death if untreated.

Real-Life Applications

23. Answers will vary.

24. See page 739.

25. Look for rapid, shallow breathing; cold, clammy skin; rapid, weak pulse; dizziness; weakness; and fainting.

26. Washing the affected area helps to remove the poison and lessens the chance of infection.

Activities

Responsible Decision Making

27. Wearing latex gloves when treating a victim for bleeding is a universal precaution. You are being both safe and responsible, and protecting yourself and the victim from possible infection and/or disease.

Sharpen Your Life Skills

28. Stress the importance of being prepared in case of emergency. Having necessary items on hand could possibly save a life.

749

UNIT 11
STUDY GUIDE

Key Terms Review

1. i	6. j
2. e	7. g
3. b	8. l
4. h	9. d
5. c	10. k

Recalling the Facts

11. This protects them from injury due to air bags and puts them farthest away from most impacts.
12. See page 652.
13. lacking self-respect; being unable to manage anger; using alcohol or other harmful drugs; carrying a weapon; belonging to a gang; see page 659
14. in three stages: will I get into trouble?; what will people think of me if I behave in this way?; is my behavior responsible?
15. Pay attention to people who are around you; do not look lost; do not walk too close to buildings; carry yourself with confidence; have your keys ready when you approach your car or building. See pages 671–674 for more self-defense strategies.
16. to test for possible pregnancy, or exposure to HIV or other STDs
17. myths: to feel like they belong; to escape family problems; to get money; to get protection
18. it's illegal; accidental injury; could be used in heat of moment to settle a fight; increases risk of use in a crime; increases risk of suicide
19. Call for emergency help; get away from source of burn; cool area down with cool water or cold cloths; do not break blisters or remove tissue; elevate burn area above heart level; cover victim with clean dry sheets if large parts of the body are burned; treat for shock. See page 714.
20. Give self-abdominal thrusts.

Critical Thinking

21. Air bags are designed to work with belts to help protect you in front, side, rear, and roll-over crashes.
22. Severe weather can occur without much warning.
23. Some people with passive behavior bottle up anger and then lash out.

11
STUDY GUIDE

Key Terms Review

Match the following definitions with the correct vocabulary words. Do not write in this book.

a. actual consent *(p. 710)*
b. assault *(p. 657)*
c. bullying *(p. 676)*
d. first aid *(p. 708)*
e. flash flood *(p. 652)*
f. heatstroke *(p. 720)*
g. prestige crime *(p. 700)*
h. probation *(p. 667)*
i. repetitive strain injury *(p. 642)*
j. sexual harassment *(p. 692)*
k. tetanus *(p. 741)*
l. weapon *(p. 704)*

1. an injury that occurs from repeated physical movements
2. a flood that occurs suddenly
3. a physical attack or threat of attack
4. a sentence in which an offender remains in the community under the supervision of a probation officer for a specific period of time
5. an attempt to hurt or frighten people who are smaller or perceived to be weaker
6. unwanted sexual behavior, including making sexual comments
7. a crime committed to gain status from other gang members
8. an instrument or device used for fighting
9. the immediate and temporary care given to an injured or ill person
10. caused by a type of bacteria that affects the nervous system and muscles

Recalling the Facts

11. Why should infants sit in a child safety seat in the back seat of a motor vehicle? *(Lesson 61)*
12. What actions should you take if you hear the siren for a tornado warning? *(Lesson 62)*
13. What are five risk behaviors for violence? *(Lesson 63)*
14. How do people develop a moral code? *(Lesson 64)*
15. What are five ways you can be safe in public places? *(Lesson 65)*
16. Why do many victims of violence need a complete medical examination? *(Lesson 66)*
17. What are some reasons teens join gangs? *(Lesson 67)*
18. Why should you not carry a weapon to school? *(Lesson 68)*
19. What should you do to treat a second-degree burn? *(Lesson 69)*
20. What should you do if you are alone and choking? *(Lesson 70)*

Critical Thinking

21. Why should you wear a safety belt even if a motor vehicle has air bags? *(Lesson 61)*
22. Why is it crucial to make preparations before severe weather occurs? *(Lesson 62)*
23. Why might a person with passive behavior become a perpetrator of violence? *(Lesson 63)*
24. Why do some teens rebel? *(Lesson 64)*
25. Why might some people blame victims even when they are not at fault? *(Lesson 65)*
26. What should you do if you are sexually harassed? *(Lesson 66)*
27. Why should you stay away from gangs? *(Lesson 67)*
28. What are the consequences of taking a gun to school? *(Lesson 68)*
29. Why is it important to be aware of Good Samaritan laws? *(Lesson 69)*
30. Why is it important to take universal precautions while performing first aid? *(Lesson 70)*

Use **Interactive Tutor** at **www.glencoe.com** for additional help.

---

24. because of unclear expectations, peer influences, and the lack of principles
25. so they won't feel vulnerable—"If it was their fault and I'm smart, it won't happen to me."
26. Tell an adult. See page 692 for guidelines.
27. to stay safe and out of trouble
28. being prosecuted in a court of law; being expelled from school
29. Laws vary from state to state, but it is best to be trained in first aid in order to be protected under the law.
30. to avoid spreading or being infected by pathogens

Health Literacy Activities

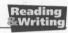

What Do You Know?
Problem Solving Make a "Wheel of Misfortune." Draw a circle on a piece of paper and divide into ten sections. In each section write a "misfortune" related to each lesson in this unit. Exchange wheels with classmates and analyze strategies for responding to each "misfortune."

Connection to Literature
Critical Thinking Identify a literary work (novel, poem, or short story) that deals with injury prevention and personal safety problems. Describe the problem(s) in the literary work, how the characters handled the problem(s), and how you might handle the problem(s) differently.

Family Involvement
Responsible Citizenship Review Lessons 69 and 70 with family members. With which first aid procedures are family members familiar? With which are they not familiar? What ways can your family improve their knowledge of first aid procedures? Write a one-page paper on the answers to these questions.

Investigating Health Careers
Effective Communication Obtain permission from your parent or guardian to interview a professional who works within the injury prevention and safety field (police officer, firefighter, EMT, counselor, etc.). Ask questions about why he or she chose that career, what he or she likes most and least about working in that field, what kinds of problems he or she sees, and what he or she wishes teenagers knew. Write an article about the interview for your school newspaper or a teen magazine. Obtain permission from school officials and/or parents to publish it.

Group Project
Self-Directed Learning Have students form groups to check the library for statistics about injuries or deaths caused by various weapons during the past year. Have the groups come together and chart the information to share with classmates. Visit www.glencoe.com for more information.

Standardized Test Practice

Reading & Writing

Read the following selection and answer the questions that follow.

Scientists have identified personal and social characteristics of both bullies and those who often become their victims. Bullies tend to be hotheaded, lack the ability to understand other people's feelings, frequently dislike rules, and become frustrated easily. Victims are often insecure, cautious, and have a hard time asserting themselves with other students. Bullies tend to be aggressive and have positive attitudes toward violence. Victims, especially boys, are often physically weaker and smaller than average. Bullies' families may lack effective supervision or use overly harsh punishment. Victims may come from families in which parents are overprotective. Finally, bullies' friends are often bullies themselves. Victims, however, can lack close friends and be "loners."

Multiple Choice

1 In this paragraph, the words *asserting themselves* mean
   A understanding the feelings of others
   B making friends
   C standing up for one's rights and opinion
   D keeping up

2 Which organizational framework does the author use in this paragraph?
   A comparing and contrasting bullies' families and victims' families
   B comparing and contrasting bullies and their victims
   C chronological order
   D moving from general ideas to specific examples

Open-Ended

3 Think about a bullying experience you have witnessed. How suitable do you feel the scientists' findings are to the situation you witnessed? Explain your answer.

www.glencoe.com

Standardized Test Practice

Reading & Writing

Multiple Choice
1. C   2. B

Open-Ended
3. Allow students to voice their feelings on this topic. Answers will vary. Students' paragraphs should describe the situation and evaluate the relevance of the findings in the paragraph to the situation. Students will probably find that while some findings do not fit the case, many or most, in fact, do. Paragraphs should contain correct spelling, capitalization, punctuation, grammar, usage, and sentence structure.

What Do You Know?
This can be used as a review of important concepts learned in this unit.

Connection to Literature
Encourage students to talk with their language arts teachers about literary works that include injury and personal safety.

Family Involvement
Have students share their one-page papers with the class.

Investigating Health Careers
If students are unable to interview someone in person, they should make up a list of questions the health professional could answer over the phone or in a letter or e-mail.

Group Project
Use the chart to discuss important statistics on injuries or deaths caused by weapons during the past year.

Health Resources

Mental and Emotional Health

American Psychological Association
750 First Street NE
Washington, DC 20002-4242
800-374-2721

The APA is a scientific and professional organization that represents psychology in the U.S. The APA focuses on research and professional development.

National Institute of Mental Health
National Institutes of Health
Public Information and Communications Branch
6001 Executive Boulevard
Room 8184, MSC 9663
Bethesda, MD 20892-9663
866-615-6464

The Institute conducts research on mental disorders, the brain, and behavior; supports research at universities and hospitals; collects, analyzes, and disseminates information; and supports the training of scientists.

National Clearinghouse on Child Abuse and Neglect Information
Children's Bureau/ACYF
Administration for Children and Families
U.S. Department of Health and Human Services
330 C Street SW
Washington, DC 20447
800-394-3366

The clearinghouse is a national resource for professionals and citizens seeking information on child abuse and neglect and child welfare.

National Mental Health Association
2001 North Beauregard Street
6th Floor
Alexandria, VA 22311
800-969-6642

The National Mental Health Association is a nonprofit organization addressing all aspects of mental health and mental illness. The NMHA has more than 340 affiliates nationwide. The NMHA works to improve the mental health of Americans through advocacy, public education, research, and services.

Family and Social Health

The Children's Defense Fund
25 East Street NW
Washington, DC 20001
800-233-1200

The Children's Defense Fund is a private, nonprofit organization that works to provide children with a successful passage to adulthood with the help of caring families and communities. The CDF focuses on education and advocacy.

The Child Welfare League of America
440 First Street NW
3rd Floor
Washington, DC 20001
202-638-2952

CWLA is an association of almost 1200 public and private nonprofit agencies that assist over 3.5 million abused and neglected children and their families each year with a wide range of services.

National Adoption Center
1500 Walnut Street
Suite 701
Philadelphia, PA 19102
800-862-3678

The National Adoption Center expands adoption opportunities for children throughout the United States, particularly for children with special needs and those from minority cultures.

Growth and Development

The American Academy of Pediatrics
141 Northwest Point Boulevard
Elk Grove Village, IL 60007
847-434-4000

The American Academy of Pediatrics is a not-for-profit corporation with 57,000 member pediatricians in the U.S., Canada, and Latin America. The mission of the AAP is to attain optimal physical, mental, and social health and well-being for all infants, children, adolescents, and young adults. The AAP focuses on professional development, research, and advocacy.

Centers for Disease Control and Prevention

U.S. Department of Health and Human Services
1600 Clifton Road NE
Atlanta, GA 30333
800-311-3435

The Centers for Disease Control and Prevention (CDC) is recognized as the lead federal agency for protecting the health and safety of people at home and abroad, providing credible information to enhance health decisions, and promoting health through strong partnerships.

The National Council on the Aging

300 D Street SW
Suite 801
Washington, DC 20024
202-479-1200

The NCOA is a private, nonprofit association of organizations and professionals dedicated to promoting the dignity, self-determination, well-being, and contributions of older persons through leadership, service, education, and advocacy.

Nutrition

Center for Food Safety and Applied Nutrition

U.S. Food and Drug Administration
5100 Paint Branch Parkway
College Park, MD 20740
888-723-3366

The Center for Food Safety and Applied Nutrition carries out the mission of the Food and Drug Administration (FDA). CFSAN is responsible for ensuring the nation's food supply is safe, sanitary, wholesome, and honestly labeled and that cosmetic products are safe and honestly labeled.

Food and Nutrition Information Center

Agricultural Research Service
U.S. Department of Agriculture
National Agricultural Library
Room 105
10301 Baltimore Avenue
Beltsville, MD 20705-2351
301-504-5719

FNIC's mission, since 1971, has been to collect and disseminate information about food and human nutrition.

U.S. Department of Agriculture

1400 Independence Ave SW
Washington, DC 20250-1380

The USDA supports production of agriculture by ensuring a safe, affordable, nutritious, and accessible food supply; caring for agricultural, forest, and range lands; supporting sound development of rural communities; providing economic opportunities for farm and rural residents; expanding global markets for agricultural and forest products and services; and working to reduce hunger in America and throughout the world.

Personal Health and Physical Activity

American Alliance for Health, Physical Education, Recreation, and Dance

1900 Association Drive
Reston, VA 20191-1598
800-213-7193

A professional organization that promotes healthy lifestyles through high-quality programs in health, physical education, recreation, dance, and sport. AAHPERD focuses on research and professional development.

American College of Sports Medicine

401 West Michigan Street
Indianapolis, IN 46202-3233
317-637-9200

The ACSM promotes and integrates scientific research, education, and practical applications of sports medicine and exercise science to maintain and enhance physical performance, fitness, health, and quality of life. A main ACSM focus is on public awareness and education about the positive aspects of physical activity for people of all ages.

American Dental Association

211 East Chicago Avenue
Chicago, IL 60611-2678
312-440-2500

The ADA is a professional association of dentists committed to the public's oral health; ethics; science; professional advancement; and leading a unified profession through initiatives in advocacy, education, research, and the development of standards.

American Medical Association

515 North State Street
Chicago, IL 60610
800-621-8335

The AMA is the national professional organization for all physicians and an advocate for physicians and their patients. The AMA's main focus is on being an essential force for progress in improving the nation's health through public health initiatives, legislation, and marketplace interventions.

National Health Council

1730 M Street NW
Suite 500
Washington, DC 20036
202-785-3910

The NHC is comprised of 115 member organizations, including voluntary health agencies, professional and membership associations, nonprofits, and business and industry. The NHC focuses on promoting quality health care for all people, promoting the importance of medical research, and promoting the role of voluntary health agencies.

Alcohol, Tobacco, and Other Drugs

Al-Anon/Alateen

1600 Corporate Landing Parkway
Virginia Beach, VA 23454-5617
800-425-2666

To help families and friends of alcoholics recover from the effects of living with the problem drinking of a relative or friend. Similarly, Alateen is a recovery program for young people. Alateen groups are sponsored by Al-Anon members.

Alcoholics Anonymous

P.O. Box 459
New York, NY 10163
212-870-3400

Alcoholics Anonymous is a fellowship of men and women who share their experience, strength, and hope with each other that they may solve their common problem and help others to recover from alcoholism.

National Clearinghouse for Alcohol and Drug Information

Substance Abuse and Mental Health Services
Administration
U.S. Department of Health and Human Services
P.O. Box 2345
Rockville, MD 20847
800-729-6686

The clearinghouse is a one-stop resource for information about substance abuse prevention and addiction treatment.

National Institute on Drug Abuse

National Institutes of Health
6001 Executive Boulevard, Room 5213
Bethesda, MD 20892-9561
301-443-1124

NIDA supports more than 85 percent of the world's research on the health aspects of drug abuse and addiction. NIDA also works to educate policy makers, health professionals, and the public on drug abuse and addiction.

Office on Smoking and Health

Center for Chronic Disease Prevention and Health
Promotion
Centers for Disease Control and Prevention
U.S. Department of Health and Human Services
4770 Buford Highway NE, MS-KSO
Atlanta, GA 30341-3734
800-232-1311

OSH is responsible for leading and coordinating strategic efforts aimed at preventing tobacco use among youth, promoting smoking cessation among youth and adults, protecting nonsmokers from environmental tobacco smoke (ETS), and eliminating tobacco-related health disparities.

Communicable and Chronic Diseases

Alzheimer's Association

225 North Michigan Avenue
Suite 1700
Chicago, IL 60601-7633
800-272-3900

The Alzheimer's Association is the largest national voluntary health organization supporting Alzheimer's research and care.

American Diabetes Association

1701 North Beauregard Street
Alexandria, VA 22311
800-342-2383

The American Diabetes Association is the nation's leading nonprofit health organization providing diabetes research, information, and advocacy.

American Heart Association

National Center
7272 Greenville Avenue
Dallas, TX 75231
800-AHA-USA-1

The American Heart Association is a national voluntary health agency whose mission is to reduce disability and death from cardiovascular diseases and stroke. The AHA has 12 affiliate offices that cover the U.S. It relies on its many volunteers and donors to help spread accurate, reliable health information.

American Lung Association
 61 Broadway
 6th Floor
 New York, NY 10006
 212-315-8700

Founded in 1904 to fight tuberculosis, ALA is a voluntary health organization that now fights lung disease in all its forms, with special emphasis on asthma, tobacco control, and environmental health.

National Alliance for Hispanic Health
 1501 Sixteenth Street NW
 Washington, DC 20036
 202-387-5000
 866-783-2645

The National Alliance for Hispanic Health is a network of health providers that aims to improve the health and well-being of Hispanics.

National Cancer Institute
 National Institutes of Health
 NCI Public Inquiries Office
 Suite 3036A
 6116 Executive Boulevard MSC8322
 Bethesda, MD 20892
 800-4-CANCER

The NCI, established under the National Cancer Act of 1937, is the Federal Government's principal agency for cancer research, training, and health information dissemination.

Consumer and Community Health

Center for Food Safety and Applied Nutrition
 5100 Paint Branch Parkway
 College Park, MD 20740-3835
 888-723-3366

CFSAN is responsible for promoting and protecting the public's health by ensuring that the nation's food supply is safe, sanitary, wholesome, and honestly labeled, and that cosmetic products are safe and properly labeled.

Environmental Health

Indoor Air Quality Information Clearinghouse
 P.O. Box 37133
 Washington, DC 20013-7133
 800-438-4318

The clearinghouse is a service of the U.S. Environmental Protection Agency that provides free educational materials related to indoor air quality.

National Center for Environmental Health
 Centers for Disease Control and Prevention
 Mail Stop F-29
 4770 Buford Hwy., NE
 Atlanta, GA 30341-3724
 888-232-6789

The National Center for Environmental Health, as a part of the Centers for Disease Control and Prevention, strives to promote health and quality of life by preventing or controlling diseases, birth defects, disabilities, or deaths that are caused by interactions between people and their environment.

Injury Prevention and Personal Safety

American Red Cross National Headquarters
 2025 East Street NW
 Washington, DC 20006
 202-303-4498

The American Red Cross provides relief to victims of disasters and helps people prevent, prepare for, and respond to emergencies. The organization gives health and safety training to the public, provides emergency social services to U.S. military members and their families, and is responsible for half the nation's blood supply and blood products.

National Fire Protection Association
 1 Batterymarch Park
 Quincy, MA 02169-7471
 800-344-3555

The NFPA is an international nonprofit membership organization that is a leading advocate of fire prevention and a source on public safety. It provides and advocates scientifically-based consensus codes, standards, research, training, and education.

**National Highway Traffic Safety Administration,
U.S. Department of Transportation**
 400 Seventh Street SW
 NAO-40
 Washington, DC 20590
 888-327-4236

The NHTSA is responsible for reducing deaths, injuries, and economic losses resulting from motor vehicle crashes. The NHTSA sets and enforces safety performance standards for motor vehicles and motor vehicle equipment, gives grants to state and local governments, to enable them to conduct effective local highway safety programs, sets and enforces fuel economy standards, and conducts research on driver behavior and traffic safety, among other responsibilities.

Pronunciation Key
Use the following key to help you sound out words in the glossary.

a	back (BAK)	yoo	pure (PYOOR)
ay	day (DAY)	yew	few (FYEW)
ah	father (FAH thur)	uh	comma (CAH muh)
ow	flower (FLOW ur)	u (+ cons.)	rub (RUB)
ar	car (CAR)	ur	number (NUM bur)
e	less (LES)	sh	shelf (SHELF)
ee	leaf (LEEF)	ch	nature (NAY chur)
ih	trip (TRIHP)	g	gift (GIHFT)
i (i + cons. + e)	idea, (i DEE uh)	j	gem (JEM)
oh	go (GOH)	ing	sing (SING)
aw	soft (SAWFT)	zh	vision (VIH zhun)
or	orbit (OR buht)	k	came (KAYM)
oy	coin (COYN)	s	cent (SENT)
oo	foot (FOOT)	z	zone (ZOHN)
ew	food (FEWD)		

Como usar el glosario en español:
1. Busca el término en inglés que desees encontrar.
2. El término en español, junto con la definición, se encuentran en la columna de la derecha.

A

English   **Español**

abandonment: (p. 142) refusing responsibility, or choosing to give up responsibility, for those in your care.

abdominal thrusts: (p. 725) series of thrusts to dislodge an object from a choking person's airway.

abstinence from sex: (p. 166) choosing not to be sexually active; 100 percent effective in preventing pregnancy and the sexual transmission of STDs, including HIV.

abuser: (p. 181) person who puts down, threatens, or harms others.

acid rain: (p. 604) rain with a high acid content formed when sulfur oxides and nitrogen oxides combine with water vapor.

acne: (p. 353) noncontagious skin disorder in which skin pores become plugged with oil, dead skin cells, and bacteria.

acquired immunodeficiency syndrome (AIDS): (p. 471) illness in which the body is unable to fight infection because of a lack of T cells.

action plan: (p. 267) detailed description of steps, such as identifying obstacles, to take to reach a goal.

active listening: (p. 43) way of responding—by clarifying, restating, summarizing, or affirming—that shows you hear and understand what someone is saying.

abandono: (pág. 142) rehusar responsabilidad o ceder la responsabilidad por personas bajo el cuidado de uno.

empujes abdominales: (pág. 725) serie de empujes para desalojar un objeto de las vías respiratorias de una persona que se está asfixiando.

abstinencia sexual: (pág. 166) tomar la decisión de no tener relaciones sexuales, lo cual es 100 por ciento efectivo en la prevención de un embarazo y en la transmisión sexual de ETS, incluyendo el VIH.

abusador: (pág. 181) persona que humilla, intimida o hace daño a otros.

lluvia ácida: (pág. 604) lluvia con un alto contenido de ácido, la cual se forma cuando los óxidos de sulfuro y de nitrógeno se combinan con el vapor de agua.

acné: (pág. 353) trastorno no contagioso de la piel en que los aceites, las células muertas y las bacterias tapan los poros cutáneos.

síndrome de inmunodeficiencia adquirida (SIDA): (pág. 471) enfermedad en la cual el cuerpo es incapaz de luchar contra las enfermedades porque carece de células T.

plan de acción: (pág. 267) descripción detallada de pasos a tomar, como el identificar obstáculos, para alcanzar una meta.

escuchar activamente: (pág. 43) manera de responder (al clarificar, exponer en forma modificada, resumir o afirmar) lo cual demuestra que prestas atención y entiendes lo que alguien te está diciendo.

actual consent: (p. 710) permission to give first aid to a conscious, mentally competent adult.

addiction: (p. 84) a compelling desire to use a drug or to engage in a certain behavior, continued use despite negative consequences, and loss of control.

advertisement (ad): (p. 35) paid announcement about a product or service designed to influence what you buy.

advertising: (p. 37) a form of selling products or services using tactics such as brand loyalty, humor, and sex appeal.

aerobic exercise: (p. 375) vigorous, rhythmic exercise that improves cardiorespiratory endurance and body composition.

affection: (p. 138) warm or tender feelings toward another person.

afterbirth: (p. 250) placenta that is expelled after delivery.

aggressive behavior: (p. 661) the use of words or actions that are disrespectful toward others.

agility: (p. 382) ability to rapidly change the body's position.

Air Quality Index (AQI): (p. 397) air quality measure based on levels of five different pollutants.

Alateen: (p. 146) recovery program for codependent teens or for teens with addicted friends or family members.

alcoholism: (p. 419) disease in which a person has an alcohol dependency.

allergen: (p. 496) substance, such as pollen or house dust, that produces an allergic response.

allergy: (p. 496) overreaction of the body to a substance that causes no response in most people.

amino acids: (p. 283) building blocks of proteins.

amniocentesis (am nee oh sen TEE suhs): (p. 245) diagnostic procedure in which a needle extracts fluid from the amniotic sac to determine if genetic defects are present in the fetus.

anaerobic exercise: (p. 375) exercise in which demand for oxygen is more than what is available during exertion.

aneurysm: (p. 516) a weakened area of a blood vessel.

anger-management skills: (p. 98) healthful ways to control and express anger, such as journaling, exercising, and keeping a sense of humor.

angina pectoris (an JY nuh • PEK tuh ruhs): (p. 515) chest pain caused by narrowed coronary arteries.

consentimiento efectivo: (pág. 710) permiso para dar primeros auxilios a un adulto mentalmente competente que está consciente.

adicción: (pág. 84) deseo apremiante de usar una droga o de actuar de cierta manera a pesar de las consecuencias negativas de tales acciones y la périda de control.

propaganda: (pág. 35) anuncio pagado sobre un producto o servicio diseñado para influir en lo que compras.

publicidad: (pág. 37) una forma de vender productos o servicios que usa tácticas como la lealtad a una marca, el humor y el sex appeal.

ejercicio aeróbico: (pág. 375) ejercicio rítmico vigoroso que mejora la resistencia cardiorrespiratoria y la composición corporal.

afecto: (págs. 138, 167) sentimientos cálidos o tiernos hacia otra persona.

secundinas: (pág. 250) expulsión de la placenta después del alumbramiento.

comportamiento agresivo: (pág. 661) uso de palabras o acciones con la intención de faltarle al respeto a otra persona.

agilidad: (pág. 382) capacidad de cambiar rápidamente la posición del cuerpo.

Índice de la Calidad del Aire (AQI): (pág. 397) medida de la calidad del aire que se basa en los niveles de cinco contaminantes diferentes.

Alateen: (pág. 146) programa de recuperación para adolescentes codependientes o para adolescentes con amigos o familiares drogadictos.

alcoholismo: (pág. 419) enfermedad en que una persona tiene una dependencia al alcohol.

alérgeno: (pág. 496) sustancia como el polen o el polvo doméstico que produce una respuesta alérgica.

alergia: (pág. 496) reacción exagerada del cuerpo a una sustancia que en la mayoría de las personas no causa respuesta.

aminoácidos: (pág. 283) constituyentes principales de las proteínas.

amniocentesis: (pág. 245) procedimiento de diagnóstico en que se extrae fluido de la bolsa amniótica para determinar la presencia de defectos genéticos en el feto.

ejercicio anaeróbico: (pág. 375) ejercicio en que la demanda de oxígeno es mayor que la cantidad accesible durante el ejercicio.

aneurisma: (pág. 516) área debilitada de un vaso sanguíneo.

destrezas para el control de la ira: (pág. 98) maneras saludables de controlar y expresar la ira, como por ejemplo, escribir un diario, el ejercicio y mantener el sentido del humor.

angina de pecho: (pág. 515) dolor del pecho causado por la construcción de las arterias coronarias.

Glossary/Glosario

anorexia nervosa: (p. 334) eating disorder in which a person starves himself or herself, weighs 15 percent or more below desirable weight, and may exercise to extremes.

antibody: (p. 485) a protein that fights infections.

anticipatory grief: (p. 123) grief felt before a loss.

antidepressant: (p. 113) drug used to relieve depression.

anti-gang gang: (p. 702) informal group for avoiding gang threats and pressures.

antihypertensives (an ty hy pur TEN sihvz): (p. 519) drugs that lower hypertension or high blood pressure.

antioxidant (an tuh AHK suh duhnt): (p. 303) substance that protects cells from being damaged by oxidation and repairs damaged cells.

antiperspirant: (p. 353) product used to reduce the amount of perspiration.

arrythmia: (p. 516) a heart condition in which the heart may beat very slowly or very fast for no obvious reason.

arteriosclerosis (ahr teer ee oh skluh ROH suhs): (p. 515) a type of coronary heart disease in which the arteries become hardened and thickened.

assault: (p. 657) physical attack or threat of attack.

assertive behavior: (p. 48) expressing ideas, feelings, and decisions without feeling threatened by others' reactions.

asthma: (p. 494) noncommunicable chronic disease in which the bronchial tubes become inflamed, narrowed, and blocked, making breathing difficult.

astigmatism: (p. 344) refractive error in which an irregular shape of the cornea causes blurred vision.

atherosclerosis (a thuh roh skluh ROH suhs): (p. 304) disease in which fat is deposited in artery walls, which narrows the arteries and increases blood pressure.

athlete's foot: (p. 354) fungus that grows on feet.

atmosphere: (p. 603) the layer of gases that surrounds Earth.

attention-deficit disorder/hyperactivity (ADHD): (p. 268) learning disability in which a person is restless and easily distracted.

attitude: (p. 83) feeling or emotion toward something or someone.

authority: (p. 664) the power and right to apply laws and rules.

autoimmune disease: (p. 523) chronic health condition, such as rheumatic fever or type I diabetes, in which the immune system's antibodies turn against the body's own cells.

anorexia nervosa: (pág. 334) trastorno alimentario en que la persona rechaza la ingestión de alimentos que resulta en inanición, pesa 15 por ciento o menos del peso deseado y puede hacer ejercicios exageradamente.

anticuerpo: (pág. 485) proteína que lucha contra infecciones.

pena anticipadora: (pág. 123) pena que se siente antes de una pérdida.

antidepresivo: (pág. 113) droga que se usa para aliviar la depresión.

pandilla antipandillas: (pág. 702) grupo informal para evitar las amenazas y la presión de las pandillas.

antihipertensivos: (pág. 519) drogas que reducen la hipertensión o la presión sanguínea alta.

antioxidante: (pág. 303) sustancia que protege las células de los daños causados por la oxidación y que repara las células dañadas.

antisudoral: (pág. 353) producto que se usa para reducir la cantidad de transpiración.

arritmia: (pág. 516) condición en la cual el corazón puede latir muy lenta o muy rápidamente sin ninguna razón obvia.

arteriosclerosis: (pág. 515) tipo de enfermedad cardíaca coronaria caracterizada por el endurecimiento y engrosamiento de las arterias.

asalto: (pág. 657) ataque físico o amenaza de ataque.

comportamiento asertivo: (pág. 48) manera de expresar ideas, sentimientos y decisiones sin sentir intimidación por las reacciones de otros.

asma: (pág. 494) enfermedad crónica no transmisible en la cual los conductos bronquiales se inflaman, se estrechan y se bloquean dificultando la respiración.

astigmatismo: (pág. 344) error refringente en que la forma irregular de la córnea causa visión borrosa.

aterosclerosis: (pág. 304) enfermedad en la cual los depósitos grasos en las paredes arteriales causan su constricción y elevan la presión sanguínea.

pie de atleta: (pág. 354) hongo que crece en los pies.

atmósfera: (pág. 603) la capa de gases que rodea la Tierra.

trastorno de deficiencia de atención: (pág. 268) incapacidad del aprendizaje en que la persona se siente intranquila y se distrae fácilmente.

predisposición: (pág. 83) sentimiento o emoción hacia algo o hacia alguien.

autoridad: (pág. 664) el poder y el derecho de aplicar leyes y reglas.

enfermedad autoinmunológica: (pág. 523) condición de salud crónica, como la fiebre reumática o la diabetes tipo I, en que los anticuerpos del sistema inmunológico atacan las propias células corporales.

Glossary/Glosario

English	Español

B cell: (p. 485) a type of white blood cell that produces antibodies.

bacteria: (p. 487) single-celled, often beneficial micro-organisms, some of which can cause diseases, such as syphilis, by releasing toxins.

balanced budget: (p. 554) plan in which your income is more than your expenses.

balanced friendship: (p. 164) friendship in which two people give and receive acts of kindness with each other.

basal cell carcinoma: (p. 535) the most common form of skin cancer.

basal metabolic rate (BMR) (BAY suhl • me tuh BAH lik • RAYT): (p. 325) number of calories the body uses at rest.

battering: (p. 680) abuse in which one person is purposefully and harmfully touched without his or her consent.

beach: (p. 627) the shore of a body of water, covered by sand, gravel, or rock.

behavior: (p. 27) way of acting in a situation.

behavior modification: (p. 197) disciplinary technique that rewards desirable behavior and provides negative consequences for undesirable behavior.

benign tumor: (p. 531) noncancerous tumor that does not spread to other parts of the body.

beta-endorphins: (p. 67) substances produced in the brain that produce feelings of well-being.

binge drinking: (p. 413) consuming large amounts of alcohol in a short amount of time, which can quickly raise the BAC to dangerous levels.

binge eating disorder: (p. 336) eating disorder in which a person cannot control eating, eats excessive amounts, and turns to food as a substitute for coping.

biodiversity: (p. 597) variety of species that live in an area.

biological age: (p. 270) a measure of how well a person's body systems are working.

bioterrorism: (p. 586) use or threatened use of bacteria, toxins, or viruses as weapons to cause diseases, such as anthrax, smallpox, and plague.

blackout: (p. 417) period in which a person who drinks cannot remember what has happened or what he or she has done.

blood alcohol concentration (BAC): (p. 411) amount of alcohol in a person's blood, which is affected by factors such as the amount of alcohol consumed, body weight, and gender.

célula B: (pág. 485) tipo de glóbulo blanco que produce anticuerpos.

bacteria: (pág. 487) microorganismos unicelulares, a menudo benéficos, de los cuales algunos causan enfermedades como la sífilis, al liberar toxinas.

presupuesto equilibrado: (pág. 554) plan en que tus ingresos son mayores que tus gastos.

amistad equilibrada: (pág. 164) amistad en que dos personas dan y reciben actos de gentileza mutuos.

carcinoma basocelular: (pág. 535) el tipo más común de cáncer de la piel.

índice metabólico basal (IMB): (pág. 325) número de calorías que el cuerpo usa en estado de reposo.

agresión: (pág. 680) abuso que supone tocar a una persona deliberada y perjudicialmente sin su consentimiento.

playa: (pág. 627) la orilla de una masa de agua, cubierta de arena, gravilla o rocas.

comportamiento: (pág. 27) manera de actuar en una situación dada.

modificación del comportamiento: (pág. 197) técnica disciplinaria que recompensa el comportamiento deseado y provee consecuencias negativas para el comportamiento indeseado.

tumor benigno: (pág. 531) tumor no canceroso que no se propaga a otras partes del cuerpo.

betaendorfinas: (pág. 67) sustancias que se producen en el cerebro y las cuales causan sentimientos de bienestar.

tomar en exceso: (pág. 413) el consumo de grandes cantidades de alcohol en un corto período de tiempo, lo cual puede elevar peligrosamente los niveles de CAS.

trastorno de comer en exceso: (pág. 336) trastorno en que una persona no puede controlar el consumo de alimentos y usa la comida como un sustituto para enfrentarse a problemas.

biodiversidad: (pág. 597) variedad de especies que viven en un área.

edad biológica: (pág. 270) una medida del buen funcionamiento de los sistemas corporales de una persona.

bioterrorismo: (pág. 586) uso o amenaza de usar bacterias, toxinas o virus como armas para causar enfermedades como el ántrax, la viruela y la plaga.

laguna: (pág. 417) período en que una persona con un problema de alcoholismo no puede recordar lo que ha hecho o lo que ha sucedido.

concentración de alcohol en la sangre (CAS): (pág. 411) cantidad de alcohol en la sangre de una persona, la cual se ve afectada por factores como la cantidad de alcohol consumido, el peso corporal y el género de la persona.

Glossary/Glosario

blood pressure/presión sanguínea

blood pressure: (p. 369) force of blood against artery walls.

body composition: (p. 325) percentage of fat tissue and lean tissue in the body.

body image: (p. 264) perception you have of your body's appearance.

botulism (BAH chuh lih zuhm): (p. 320) food-borne illness from improperly canned foods contaminated with *Clostridium botulinum* toxin.

brand-name drug: (p. 406) drug with a registered name or trademark.

bulimia: (p. 335) eating disorder in which a person eats large amounts of food over a short time (binges) and then rids the body of foods that were eaten (purges).

bullying: (p. 676) repeated intimidation or domination of a person perceived as smaller or weaker.

burn: (p. 714) injury caused by heat, electricity, radiation, or chemicals.

cardiopulmonary resuscitation (CPR)/ resucitación cardiopulmonar (RCP)

presión sanguínea: (pág. 369) fuerza de la sangre contra las paredes arteriales.

composición corporal: (pág. 325) porcentaje de tejido graso y tejido magro en el cuerpo.

imagen corporal: (pág. 264) percepción propia de la apariencia del cuerpo.

botulismo: (pág. 320) intoxicación producida por la ingestión de alimentos mal enlatados y contaminados por la toxina *Clostridium botulinum.*

medicamento de marca registrada: (pág. 406) droga con un nombre o marca registrada.

bulimia: (pág. 335) trastorno alimentario en que la persona consume grandes cantidades de alimentos en un corto período de tiempo y luego los purga del cuerpo.

amedrentar: (pág. 676) intimidación o dominación repetida de una persona que se percibe como más pequeña o más débil.

quemadura: (pág. 714) lesión causada por calor, electricidad, radiación o sustancias químicas.

English — **Español**

caloric expenditure: (p. 326) number of calories a person uses for BMR, physical activity, and digestion.

caloric intake: (p. 326) number of calories a person consumes from foods and beverages.

calorie: (p. 282) unit of energy produced by food and used by the body.

cancer: (p. 531) group of diseases in which there is uncontrolled cell division.

carbohydrate (kahr boh HY drayt): (p. 284) nutrient that is the body's main energy source; can be simple (sugars) or complex (starches and fibers).

carbohydrate loading: (p. 314) eating strategy in which a few days of very low carbohydrate intake is followed by a few days of very high carbohydrate intake.

carbon monoxide: (p. 426) poisonous odorless, tasteless gas that interferes with the blood's oxygen-carrying ability.

carcinogen: (p. 426) any chemical known to cause cancer.

cardiac arrest: (p. 739) stopping of the heartbeat.

cardiac output: (p. 368) amount of blood the heart pumps each minute.

cardiopulmonary resuscitation (CPR): (p. 728) first aid technique using chest compressions and slow breaths to restore heartbeat and breathing.

gasto calórico: (pág. 326) número de calorías que usa una persona para el IMB, la actividad física y la digestión.

consumo calórico: (pág. 326) número de calorías que una persona consume de los alimentos y bebidas.

caloría: (pág. 282) unidad de energía producida por los alimentos y la cual usa el cuerpo.

cáncer: (pág. 531) grupo de enfermedades en que ocurre la división celular descontrolada.

carbohidrato: (pág. 284) nutriente que es la fuente principal de energía del cuerpo; puede ser simple (azúcares) o complejo (almidones y fibra).

recarga de carbohidratos: (pág. 314) estrategia alimentaria en que a unos cuantos días de bajo consumo de carbohidratos les siguen unos días de alto consumo de carbohidratos.

monóxido de carbono: (pág. 426) gas venenoso inodoro e insaboro que interfiere con la capacidad de la sangre de transportar oxígeno.

carcinógeno: (pág. 426) cualquier sustancia química causante de cáncer.

paro cardíaco: (pág. 739) paro de los latidos del corazón.

rendimiento cardíaco: (pág. 368) cantidad de sangre que el corazón bombea cada minuto.

resucitación cardiopulmonar (RCP): (pág. 728) técnica de primeros auxilios que usa compresiones del pecho y soplos lentos para restaurar los latidos del corazón y la respiración.

cardiovascular disease: (p. 304) disease of the heart and blood vessels, such as congestive heart failure, coronary heart disease, and stroke.

cardiovascular system: (p. 209) system that consists of blood, blood vessels, and the heart and carries nutrients, hormones, gases, and cellular wastes throughout the body.

caregiver: (p. 275) person providing care for a person who needs assistance because of chronic disease or other health conditions.

celiac disease (SEE lee ak): (p. 308) food intolerance caused by intolerance to gluten in wheat, rye, and certain other grains.

center: (p. 180) self-centered person who ignores others' needs.

certification: (p. 575) process a person completes to meet specific professional competence standards.

certified health education specialist (CHES): (p. 576) person who has completed the certification process recommended for health educators.

chemotherapy: (p. 536) treatment of cancer with anti-cancer drugs.

child abuse: (p. 658) harmful treatment of a minor that can cause injury or psychological damage.

child safety restraint: (p. 646) safety seat for a small child secured in a vehicle's back seat.

childsitter: (p. 254) person who provides responsible care for infants and children; also called a babysitter.

chlamydia (kluh MIH dee uh): (p. 499) most common bacterial STD in the United States; often occurs with no symptoms, is caused by *Chlamydia trachomatis,* and is spread by intimate sexual contact.

cholesterol: (p. 299) fat-like substance made by the body and found in certain foods.

chromosome: (p. 243) threadlike structure that carries genes.

chronic health condition: (p. 522) recurring and persistent health condition, such as diabetes or sickle-cell anemia, that affects a person's health.

chronological age: (p. 270) number of years a person has lived.

cirrhosis: (p. 414) liver disease that can lead to liver failure and death and results from damage caused by alcohol abuse.

clinger: (p. 179) needy, dependent person who suffocates others.

club drugs: (p. 441) collective term used to describe party drugs, such as GHB, Ecstasy, and ketamine, which can cause permanent physical and/or mental damage.

enfermedad cardiovascular: (pág. 304) enfermedad del corazón y los vasos sanguíneos, tal como el fallo cardíaco congestivo, la enfermedad cardíaca coronaria y la apoplejía.

sistema cardiovascular: (pág. 209) sistema que consta de la sangre, los vasos sanguíneos y el corazón y el cual transporta nutrientes, hormonas, gases y desechos celulares a través del cuerpo.

cuidador: (pág. 275) persona que provee cuidados a una persona que necesita asistencia debido a enfermedad crónica u otras condiciones de salud.

enfermedad celíaco: (pág. 308) intolerancia alimenticia causada por la intolerancia al gluten del trigo, centeno y ciertos otros cereales.

centro: (pág. 180) persona egoísta que ignora las necesidades de otros.

certificación: (pág. 575) proceso que completa una persona para cumplir estándares de competencia profesional específicos.

especialista certificado en la educación de salud: (pág. 576) persona que completa el proceso de certificación recomendado para los educadores de salud.

quimioterapia: (pág. 536) tratamiento del cáncer con medicamentos anticancerosos.

abuso de menores: (pág. 658) tratamiento a un menor que le puede causar daño físico o psicológico.

restricción de seguridad para niños: (pág. 646) silla de seguridad para niños pequeños, la cual se amarra en el asiento trasero.

niñera: (pág. 254) persona que provee cuidado responsable para lactantes y niños.

clamidia: (pág. 499) la ETS bacteriana más común en Estados Unidos; con frecuencia no presenta síntomas; es causada por *Chlamydia trachomatis* y se propaga mediante el contacto sexual íntimo.

colesterol: (pág. 299) sustancia tipo grasa que produce el cuerpo y que se encuentra en ciertos alimentos.

cromosoma: (pág. 243) estructura fibrosa que contiene los genes.

condición crónica de salud: (pág. 522) condición de salud persistente y recurrente, como la diabetes o la anemia drepanocítica que afecta la salud de una persona.

edad cronológica: (pág. 270) número de años que ha vivido una persona.

cirrosis: (pág. 414) enfermedad del hígado que puede conducir a fallo hepático y muerte y la cual resulta de los daños causados por el abuso del alcohol.

dependiente: (pág. 179) persona dependiente y necesitada que sofoca a los demás.

drogas de club: (pág. 441) término colectivo con el que se describen las drogas de fiesta como el GHB, el éxtasis y la ketamina, las cuales pueden causar daño mental y o físico permanente.

cluster suicides: (p. 114) series of suicides that occur within a short period and involve people who are somehow connected.

cocaine: (p. 444) highly addictive, illegal stimulant; also called coke.

codeine: (p. 446) narcotic painkiller produced from morphine.

codependence: (p. 88) a problem in which people neglect themselves to care for, control, or try to "fix" someone else.

codependency: (p. 88) condition or relationship in which a person, such as the addict's spouse, is being controlled by the addict's behavior.

codependent: (p. 460) person who neglects himself or herself and instead wants to care for, rescue, or control someone else.

cognitive behavior therapy: (p. 113) talk therapy that can help modify behavior.

cold temperature-related illnesses: (p. 396) conditions, such as frostbite or hypothermia, that result from exposures to low temperatures.

coma: (p. 276) state of unconsciousness.

commercial: (p. 35) advertisement on TV or radio.

common cold: (p. 491) communicable respiratory infection caused by more than 100 different viruses.

communication skills: (p. 41) skills, such as active listening, that help you share feelings, thoughts, and information with others.

community parks: (p. 627) an area of land set aside to preserve natural scenery and recreation.

composting: (p. 624) breakdown of plant remains by bacteria to humus.

concealed weapons: (p. 705) weapon partially or totally hidden from view.

conductive hearing loss: (p. 346) hearing loss that occurs when sound is not transported efficiently from the outer to the inner ear.

conflict-resolution skills: (p. 50) steps that can be taken to resolve a disagreement responsibly and solve problems in a healthy way.

conjunctivitis: (p. 345) inflammation of the eye membranes, resulting in discharge, redness, and discomfort; also called pinkeye.

conscience: (p. 665) sense of right or wrong that guides responsible behavior and produces guilty feelings after wrong behavior.

conservation: (p. 618) saving of resources, such as water and fossil fuels.

grupo de suicidios: (pág. 114) serie de suicidios que ocurren dentro de un corto período de tiempo y que involucran personas vinculadas de alguna forma.

cocaína: (pág. 444) estimulante ilegal altamente adictivo; también denominado coca.

codeína: (pág. 446) calmante narcótico derivado de la morfina.

codependencia: (pág. 88) condición en que una persona evita la intimidad al recurrir a extremos, se descuida a sí misma, niega sus sentimientos y comienza a lidiar con problemas de manera dañina.

codependencia: (pág. 88) cuando una persona se descuida a sí misma para cuidar, controlar o tratar de "arreglar" los problemas de alguien más.

codependiente: (pág. 460) persona que busca rescatar y controlar a otra persona quien sufre de una adicción.

terapia cognoscitiva del comportamiento: (pág. 113) terapia hablada que puede ayudar a modificar el comportamiento.

enfermedades relacionadas con temperaturas gélidas: (pág. 396) condiciones, como las quemaduras por frío o la hipotermia, las cuales resultan de la exposición a bajas temperaturas.

coma: (pág. 276) estado de falta de conocimiento.

anuncio comercial: (pág. 35) anuncio en la televisión o en la radio.

resfriado común: (pág. 491) infección respiratoria transmisible causada por más de 100 virus diferentes.

destrezas de comunicación: (pág. 41) destrezas como el escuchar activamente, que te ayudan a compartir tus sentimientos, pensamientos e información con otros.

parques de la comunidad: (pág. 627) porción de terreno reservada para la preservación del paisaje natural y para la recreación.

abono vegetal: (pág. 624) proceso en el cual las bacterias descomponen los residuos vegetales en humus.

armas escondidas: (pág. 705) arma total o parcialmente fuera de vista.

pérdida conductiva de la audición: (pág. 346) pérdida del sentido de la audición que ocurre cuando el sonido no es transportado eficazmente del oído externo al oído interno.

destrezas de resolución de conflictos: (pág. 50) pasos que se pueden tomar para resolver un desacuerdo responsablemente y resolver los problemas de manera saludable.

conjuntivitis: (pág. 345) inflamación de las membranas oculares, la cual causa enrojecimiento e incomodidad de los ojos.

consciencia: (pág. 665) sentimiento del bien y del mal que guía el comportamiento responsable y produce un sentimiento de culpabilidad después del comportamiento equivocado.

conservación: (pág. 618) ahorro de los recursos como el agua y los combustibles fósiles.

conservatory/conservatorio

conservatory: (p. 627) greenhouse that grows plants and displays them to the public.

Consumer Product Safety Commission (CPSC): (p. 547) federal agency that establishes and enforces product safety standards.

consumer rights: (p. 544) a consumer's guaranteed privileges, such as the right to choose, be heard, informed, and the right to redress or remedy.

controller: (p. 180) possessive, domineering, jealous person.

conversation: (p. 159) verbal exchange of thoughts, feelings, opinions, and ideas.

could-be: (p. 699) child or teen, often a younger relative or friend of a gang member, who is interested in joining the gang.

Council of Better Business Bureaus (BBB): (p. 547) agency that monitors and publishes consumer complaints and advertising and selling practices.

Cowper's glands: (p. 237) internal male reproductive organs that secrete a clear, lubricating fluid into the urethra.

credentials: (p. 575) required career qualifications.

credit card: (p. 553) card used to purchase items that you agree to pay for later.

cretinism: (p. 588) irreversible mental deficiency in a baby caused by iodine deficiency during pregnancy.

culture: (p. 35) arts, beliefs, and customs that make up a way of life for a group of people at a certain time.

curfew: (p. 161) established time when you are to be at home, which helps ensure your safety and reduces worry by your parents or guardian.

custodial parent: (p. 150) parent with whom the children live and parent who also has the legal right to make decisions about the children.

cystic fibrosis: (p. 526) chronic health condition in which abnormally thick mucus forms in the lungs and pancreas.

conservatorio: (pág. 627) invernadero en donde se cultivan plantas y se exhiben al público.

Comisión de Protección de Seguridad del Consumidor (CPSC): (pág. 547) organismo federal que establece y hace cumplir los estándares de seguridad.

derechos del consumidor: (pág. 544) los privilegios garantizados del consumidor, tales como el derecho de escoger, de ser informado, de que sus quejas se escuchan y que se solucionan los problemas.

persona controladora: (pág. 180) persona celosa, dominadora y posesiva.

conversación: (pág. 159) intercambio verbal de pensamientos, sentimientos, opiniones e ideas.

aspirante: (pág. 699) niño(a) o adolescente, a menudo un pariente más joven o amigo de un miembro de una pandilla, quien está interesado en unirse a dicha pandilla.

Agencias del Consejo de Mejores Negocios: (pág. 547) organismo que vigila y publica las quejas de los consumidores y las propagandas y prácticas de ventas.

glándulas de Cowper: (pág. 237) órganos reproductores masculinos internos que secretan un fluido lubricante de color claro en la uretra.

credenciales: (pág. 575) calificaciones que se requieren para una carrera.

tarjeta de crédito: (pág. 553) tarjeta que se usa para comprar artículos, los cuales uno acuerda pagar más tarde.

cretinismo: (pág. 588) deficiencia mental irreversible en un bebé causada por la deficiencia de yodo durante el embarazo.

cultura: (pág. 35) artes, creencias y costumbres que componen la forma de vida de un grupo de personas en cierto momento.

toque de queda: (pág. 161) hora establecida cuando debes estar en casa, lo cual ayuda a asegurar tu seguridad y reduce las preocupaciones de tus padres o apoderados.

patria potestad: (pág. 150) padre con el cual viven los niños y padre quien también tiene el derecho legal de tomar decisiones por los niños.

fibrosis quística: (pág. 526) condición crónica de salud caracterizada por la formación de un moco anormalmente grueso en los pulmones y el páncreas.

English

Español

dandruff: (p. 357) condition in which dead skin is shed from the scalp, producing white flakes.

date-rape drugs: (p. 689) drugs, such as GHB or Special K, that can be slipped into a person's drink without his or her knowledge, sedate the nervous system, and leave the person vulnerable to sexual assault.

caspa: (pág. 357) condición en que se descama la piel muerta del cuero cabelludo produciendo unas escamillas blancas.

drogas para la violación durante una cita: (pág. 689) drogas como GHB o Special K, que se pueden verter en la bebida de una persona sin su conocimiento y las cuales aminoran las funciones del sistema nervioso y dejan a la persona vulnerable al asalto sexual.

dating: (p. 160) having social plans with a person in whom you are romantically interested.

dating skills: (p. 162) skills that help when you are dating, such as not basing your self-worth on your ability to get a date and honoring your dating commitments.

debt: (p. 553) the condition of owing.

decibel: (p. 613) unit used to measure a sound's loudness or intensity.

deforestation: (p. 597) loss of trees resulting from cutting for timber, clearing land for farming, and weather pattern changes.

delayed gratification: (p. 75) voluntarily postponing an immediate reward in order to finish a task before enjoying a reward.

delinquent behavior: (p. 667) illegal action, such as burglary, committed by a juvenile.

delirium tremens syndrome: (p. 419) alcohol withdrawal syndrome in which the person has hallucinations and muscle convulsions.

dementia: (p. 273) decline in mental functioning.

denial: (p. 419) refusal to admit there is a problem.

deodorant: (p. 353) fragrance-containing product that reduces body odor.

dermatologist: (p. 353) doctor who treats skin diseases and disorders.

desensitization: (p. 561) reacting less after frequent exposure to something.

detoxification: (p. 478) treatment process in which an addictive substance is withdrawn from the body, often causing withdrawal symptoms.

developmental stages of marriage: (p. 188) five stages of marriage in which tasks need to be mastered to maintain and develop intimacy.

developmental task: (p. 190) achievement needed in order to reach the next level of maturity.

developmental tasks of adolescence: (p. 264) achievements, such as preparing for a career and having a clear set of values, that need to be mastered in order to become an independent, responsible adult.

diabetes: (p. 307) chronic health condition in which the body does not produce insulin (type I diabetes), or in which the body either does not produce enough insulin or cannot properly use the insulin produced (type II diabetes and gestational diabetes), causing a high blood sugar level.

Dietary Guidelines: (p. 294) recommendations for diet choices among healthy Americans two years of age or older.

cita: (pág. 160) planes sociales con una persona en la cual uno está interesado románticamente.

destrezas para citas: (pág. 162) destrezas que te ayudan durante las citas, como por ejemplo, no basar tu autovalor en tu habilidad de tener una cita y cumplir con tus compromisos para citas.

deuda: (pág. 553) la condición de deber.

decibel: (pág. 613) unidad que se usa para medir el volumen o la intensidad del sonido.

deforestación: (pág. 597) pérdida de los árboles que resulta de talarlos para obtener madera, limpiar el terreno para la siembra de cosechas y los cambios en los patrones meteorológicos.

gratificación aplazada: (pág. 75) postergar voluntariamente una recompensa inmediata con el propósito de terminar una tarea antes de gozar de la recompensa.

comportamiento delincuente: (pág. 667) acción ilegal, como por ejemplo, un robo cometido por una persona joven.

síndrome de delirium tremens: (pág. 419) síndrome de abstinencia alcohólica en que la persona tiene alucinaciones y convulsiones musculares.

demencia: (pág. 273) deterioro del funcionamiento mental.

negación: (pág. 419) no querer admitir que existe un problema.

desodorante: (pág. 353) producto fragante que reduce el olor corporal.

dermatólogo: (pág. 353) médico que trata las enfermedades y trastornos de la piel.

insensibilización: (pág. 561) reaccionar menos después de exponerse a algo.

detoxificación: (pág. 478) proceso de tratamiento en que una sustancia adictiva se retira del cuerpo, lo cual causa con frecuencia síntomas de abstinencia.

etapas de desarrollo del matrimonio: (pág. 188) cinco etapas del matrimonio en que se deben dominar las tareas para el mantenimiento y desarrollo de la intimidad.

tarea para el desarrollo: (pág. 190) logro necesario para alcanzar el próximo nivel de madurez.

áreas para el desarrollo durante la adolescencia: (pág. 264) logros como el prepararse para una carrera y tener valores concretos, los cuales debe dominar una persona para convertirse en un adulto responsable.

diabetes: (pág. 307) condición crónica de salud en la cual el cuerpo no produce insulina (diabetes tipo I) o en la cual el cuerpo no produce suficiente insulina o no puede usar apropiadamente la insulina que produce (diabetes tipo II y diabetes gestacional), ocasionando un alto nivel de glucose en la sangre.

guía dietética: (pág. 294) recomendaciones para la dieta de los estadounidenses saludables de dos años de edad y mayores.

digestive system/sistema digestivo

dyslexia/dislexia

digestive system: (p. 220) breaks food down into nutrients that the body can use and includes the mouth, stomach, and large and small intestine.

dioxins: (p. 608) toxic chemicals that are used in insecticides, are produced during paper making, and occur naturally in small amounts.

dislocation: (p. 717) movement of a bone from its joint.

dissolution: (p. 149) way to end a marriage where the marital partners decide the terms for custody, support, and property.

distancer: (p. 180) emotionally unavailable person who pushes others away.

diversion: (p. 668) sending juvenile offenders somewhere, such as a substance abuse clinic, to learn to obey laws.

divorce: (p. 149) way to end a marriage in which a judge or court decides the terms for custody, support, and property

domestic violence: (p. 658) abuse by one person in a relationship to control the other person.

dose: (p. 405) amount of drug taken at one time.

drug: (p. 404) substance other than food, such as tobacco, marijuana, or prescription drugs, that alters the way the body or mind functions.

drug abuse: (p. 405) intentional use of a legal or illegal drug without medical or health reasons.

drug misuse: (p. 405) incorrect use of a prescription or OTC drug.

drug trafficking: (p. 469) illegal production, transportation, sale, or purchase of drugs.

drug-free lifestyle: (p. 466) lifestyle in which drugs are not misused or abused.

drug-free role model: (p. 466) person with a drug-free lifestyle.

dynamic blood pressure: (p. 369) measure of daytime changes in blood pressure.

dysentery: (p. 608) severe intestinal infection that causes diarrhea.

dysfunctional family: (p. 135) family lacking skills and behaviors promoting responsible, loving relationships; may struggle with addictions, violence, and emotional abuse.

dyslexia: (p. 268) common learning disability that occurs in children who have normal intelligence and vision but have difficulty spelling, reading, and writing.

sistema digestivo: (pág. 220) descompone los alimentos en nutrientes que el cuerpo puede utilizar e incluye la boca, el estómago y los intestinos grueso y delgado.

dioxinas: (pág. 608) sustancias químicas tóxicas que se usan en pesticidas, se producen durante la fabricación del papel y ocurren naturalmente en pequeñas cantidades.

dislocación: (pág. 717) movimiento de un hueso fuera de su articulación.

disolución: (pág. 149) manera de terminar un matrimonio en que los cónyuges deciden los términos de custodia, mantenimiento y propiedad.

persona distanciada: (pág. 180) persona emocionalmente inaccesible que se mantiene apartada de los demás.

diversión: (pág. 668) enviar a los delincuentes juveniles a lugares como una clínica para superar el abuso alcohólico, con el propósito de que aprendan y obedezcan las leyes.

divorcio: (pág. 149) manera de terminar un matrimonio en que un juez o la corte decide los términos de custodia, mantenimiento y propiedad.

violencia doméstica: (pág. 658) abuso realizado por una persona en una relación para controlar a la otra persona.

dosis: (pág. 405) cantidad de una droga que se toma a la vez.

droga: (pág. 404) sustancia no alimenticia como el tabaco, la mariguana o las drogas recetadas que altera la manera en que funciona el cuerpo o la mente.

abuso de las drogas: (pág. 405) uso intencional de una droga legal o ilegal sin razones médicas o de salud.

mal uso de las drogas: (pág. 405) uso incorrecto de una droga recetada o de las que se compran sin receta médica.

tráfico de drogas: (pág. 469) producción, transporte, venta o compra de drogas ilegales.

estilo de vida libre de drogas: (pág. 466) estilo de vida en que las drogas ni se usan erróneamente ni se abusan.

modelo de vida libre de drogas: (pág. 466) persona que sigue un estilo de vida libre de drogas.

presión sanguínea dinámica: (pág. 369) medida de los cambios diarios en la presión sanguínea.

disentería: (pág. 608) grave infección intestinal que causa diarrea.

familia disfuncional: (pág. 135) familia que carece de las destrezas y los comportamientos que promueven relaciones responsables y afectuosas; sus miembros pueden luchar con adicciones, violencia y abuso emocional.

dislexia: (pág. 268) incapacidad común del aprendizaje que ocurre en niños de inteligencia y visión normales, pero quienes tienen dificultad en el deletreo de palabras, el aprendizaje y la escritura.

English	Español

E coli: (p. 320) food-borne illness from undercooked meat, especially hamburger, contaminated with a certain strain of the bacterium *Escherichia coli.*

eating disorder: (p. 332) condition in which there is a compelling need to starve (anorexia nervosa), to binge (binge eating disorder), or to binge and purge (bulimia).

Ecstasy: (p. 440) psychoactive club drug that can produce euphoria and leave the user vulnerable to sexual assault.

elder abuse: (p. 658) physical, emotional, or psychological harm done to an older adult.

electrolyte: (p. 314) nutrient, such as sodium or potassium, that becomes electrically charged when in a solution, such as bodily fluid.

embryo: (p. 246) a developing baby through the second month of growth after conception.

emergency: (p. 19) unexpected, serious situation calling for immediate action from the police, an emergency medical team, or the fire department.

emotion: (p. 95) a specific feeling, such as anger, happiness, or anxiety.

empathy: (p. 124) ability to share others' emotions or feelings.

emphysema: (p. 426) a chronic obstructive pulmonary disease in which the alveoli are unable to function properly.

enabler: (p. 179) one who supports the harmful behavior of others.

endocrine system: (p. 218) glands, such as the pituitary, thyroid, and adrenals, that produce hormones and control many body activities.

enmeshment: (p. 143) condition in which a person becomes obsessed with another's needs and no longer can recognize his or her own needs.

entertainment: (p. 557) variety of activities, such as attending a concert or watching a video, designed to hold people's interest and provide relaxation, stimulation, and recreation.

entertainment addiction: (p. 562) centering life around entertainment, such as watching television or surfing the Internet, reducing time left for healthful activities.

environment: (p. 594) complex of living and nonliving factors—such as climate, air, water, organisms, and natural resources—surrounding a person.

E coli: (pág. 320) enfermedad alimentaria que resulta de la carne mal cocida, especialmente la hamburguesa, contaminada con cierta cepa de bacteria *Escherichia coli.*

trastorno alimentario: (pág. 332) condición en que existe una necesidad apremiante de padecer hambre (anorexia nerviosa), de comer en demasía (trastorno de comer en exceso) o de comer en exceso y luego purgarse de la comida (bulimia).

Éxtasis: (pág. 440) droga de club psicoactiva que puede producir euforia y dejar al usuario vulnerable al asalto sexual.

abuso infantil: (pág. 658) daño físico, emocional o psicológico que se le hace a una persona mayor.

electrolito: (pág. 314) nutriente como el sodio que se carga eléctricamente cuando está en solución, tal como un fluido corporal.

embrión: (pág. 246) bebé en desarrollo de dos meses de gestación.

emergencia: (pág. 19) situación seria e inesperada que requiere acción inmediata de la policía, un equipo médico de emergencia o del cuerpo de bomberos.

emoción: (pág. 95) un sentimiento específico como la ira, la felicidad o la ansiedad.

empatía: (pág. 124) capacidad de compartir las emociones o sentimientos de otros.

enfisema: (pág. 426) enfermedad pulmonar crónica obstructiva en que los alvéolos son incapaces de funcionar debidamente.

facilitador: (pág. 179) aquél que apoya el comportamiento dañino de otros.

sistema endocrino: (pág. 218) glándulas como la pituitaria, la tiroides y las adrenales que producen hormonas y controlan muchas de las actividades del cuerpo.

enmarañar: (pág. 143) condición en que una persona se obsesiona con las necesidades de otros y deja de reconocer sus propias necesidades.

entretenimiento: (pág. 557) variedad de actividades, como ir a un concierto o ver un video, diseñadas para mantener la atención de la gente y proveer relajamiento, estimulación y recreación.

adicción al entretenimiento: (pág. 562) centrar el estilo de vida alrededor del entretenimiento, como ver televisión o navegar por Internet, reduciendo así el tiempo para actividades saludables.

ambiente: (pág. 594) complejo de factores vivos e inanimados, que rodean a una persona. Por ejemplo el clima, el aire, el agua, los organismos y los recursos naturales.

epididymis (e puh DIH duh muhs): (p. 236) comma-shaped, internal male reproductive organs along the upper rear surface of the testes where sperm mature.

expenses: (p. 554) money you pay for products and services and contributions to family and savings.

extinction: (p. 600) death of a plant or animal species.

epidídimo: (pág. 236) órganos reproductores masculinos internos en forma de coma a lo largo de la superficie posterior de los testículos donde maduran los espermatozoides.

gastos: (pág. 554) dinero que pagas por productos, servicios y contribuciones a la familia y a los ahorros.

extinción: (pág. 600) muerte de una especie de planta o de animal.

F

English
Español

Fallopian tube: (p. 229) internal female reproductive structure where an ovum usually is fertilized.

family: (p. 135) basic unit of society that can include people related by blood, marriage, or other legal procedures.

family-social health: (p. 5) the condition of a person's relationships with family members and with others.

faulty thinking: (p. 198) dangerous thought process in which factors are ignored or denied or false information is believed.

Federal Trade Commission (FTC): (p. 547) agency that enforces consumer protection laws and monitors food, drug, and cosmetics advertising.

fertilization: (p. 243) union of an ovum and sperm; also called conception.

fetal alcohol syndrome (FAS): (p. 248) occurrence of severe birth defects, including brain damage, behavior problems, and below normal I.Q., in babies born to mothers who drank alcohol while they were pregnant.

fiber: (p. 284) indigestible part of plant and grain foods that helps move food through the digestive system; also called roughage.

first aid: (p. 708) immediate, temporary care given for sudden illness or injury.

FITT formula: (p. 371) formula in which each letter represents a factor for finding out how to gain fitness benefits from physical activity: F—Frequency, I—Intensity, T—Time, and T—Type.

five stages of loss and grief: (p. 124) psychological stages of grieving, including denial, anger, bargaining, depression, and acceptance.

fixer: (p. 180) person who takes on others' problems, avoids his or her own problems, and is quick to give advice.

flash flood: (p. 652) sudden flood; number one cause of weather-related deaths.

trompas de Falopio: (pág. 229) estructura reproductora femenina interna, donde por lo general se fecunda el óvulo.

familia: (pág. 135) unidad básica de la sociedad que puede incluir a personas emparentadas por sangre, matrimonio u otros procedimientos legales.

salud sociofamiliar: (pág. 5) la condición de las relaciones de una persona con los miembros de la familia y con otras personas.

razonamiento defectuoso: (pág. 198) proceso de pensamiento peligroso en que se ignoran o se niegan los hechos o se cree en falsedades.

Comisión de Comercio Federal: (pág. 547) organismo que hace cumplir las leyes de protección del consumidor y que supervisa los anuncios de alimentos, drogas y cosméticos.

fecundación: (pág. 243) unión de un óvulo y un espermatozoide; también denominada concepción.

síndrome alcohólico fetal: (pág. 248) caso de graves defectos congénitos que incluye el daño al cerebro, los problemas de comportamiento y un cociente de inteligencia por debajo de lo normal en bebés de madres que consumen alcohol mientras están embarazadas.

fibra: (pág. 284) parte indigestible de alimentos derivados de cereales y plantas que ayudan a mover los alimentos a través del sistema digestivo.

primeros auxilios: (pág. 708) cuidado temporal inmediato que se presta debido a una enfermedad o lesión repentina.

fórmula FITT: (pág. 371) fórmula en inglés en que cada letra representa un factor para averiguar cómo alcanzar los beneficios de estar en forma haciendo ejercicio físico: F (frecuencia), I (intensidad), T (tiempo) y T (tipo).

cinco etapas de pérdida y pena: (pág. 124) las etapas psicológicas de pena incluyen la negación, la ira, el regateo, la depresión y la aceptación.

componedor de dificultades: (pág. 180) persona que arregla los problemas de otros, evita sus propios problemas y está lista para dar consejos.

inundación repentina: (pág. 652): inundación que ocurre repentinamente; la causa principal de muertes relacionadas con las condiciones meteorológicas.

fluoride: (p. 350) mineral that strengthens tooth enamel and helps repair tooth areas that have begun to dissolve.

food allergy: (p. 308) abnormal response to food, triggered by the immune system, that can result in severe illness or death and most commonly is caused by shellfish, peanuts, fish, and eggs.

Food and Drug Administration (FDA): (p. 543) federal agency that enforces a number of federal laws that govern health, such as the Controlled Substances Act.

food group: (p. 295) category of foods containing similar nutrients—bread, cereal, rice, pasta group; vegetable group; fruit group; milk, yogurt, cheese group; meat, poultry, fish, dry beans, eggs, nuts group; fats, oils, sweets group.

Food Guidance System (MyPyramid): (p. 296) guide for making healthful food choices.

food intolerance: (p. 308) abnormal response to food that is not triggered by the immune system and results in food not being tolerated well.

food-borne illness: (p. 320) illness caused by consuming beverages or foods contaminated with pathogens; also called food poisoning.

formal intervention: (p. 87) an action by people, such as family members or friends, who want an addicted person to get treatment.

fossil fuels: (p. 604) nonrenewable energy resources, such as oil and natural gas, formed over millions of years from plant or animal remains.

foster care: (p. 155) arrangement in which an unrelated adult assumes temporary responsibility for a child.

fracture: (p. 716) break or crack in a bone.

fungi: (p. 487) single- or multi-celled parasitic organisms that feed on organic material and can cause diseases, such as athlete's foot, ringworm, and thrush.

flúor: (pág. 350) mineral que fortalece el esmalte dental y ayuda en la reparación de las áreas dentales que han comenzado a disolverse.

alergia a los alimentos: (pág. 308) respuesta anormal del sistema inmunológico a alimentos y la cual puede resultar en enfermedad o muerte, causada frecuentemente por los mariscos, los cacahuetes, el pescado y los huevos.

Administración de drogas y alimentos: (pág. 543) agencia federal que hace cumplir un número de leyes federal que gobiernan la salud, como la Ley para Sustancias Controladas.

grupo alimenticio: (pág. 295) categoría de alimentos que contiene nutrientes parecidos: el grupo del pan, los cereales y el arroz; el grupo de los vegetales; el grupo de la leche, el yogur y el queso; el grupo de las carnes, el pollo, el pescado, los frijoles secos, los huevos, las nueces; el grupo de los dulces, los aceites y las grasas.

pirámide alimenticia: (pág. 296) guía que indica el número de porciones de cada uno de los seis grupos alimenticios que se recomiendan diariamente.

intolerancia alimenticia: (pág. 308) respuesta anormal a alimentos que no es una respuesta del sistema inmunológico y la cual resulta en la mala tolerancia de los alimentos.

enfermedad de procedencia alimenticia: (pág. 320) enfermedad causada por el consumo de bebidas o alimentos contaminados con patógenos; también denominada envenenamiento por alimentos.

intervención formal: (pág. 87) una acción de personas como miembros de la familia o amigos, quienes quieren que un adicto trate su adicción.

combustibles fósiles: (pág. 604) recursos no renovables, como el petróleo y el gas natural, que se formaron a lo largo de millones de años a partir de los restos de plantas y animales.

crianza de niños ajenos: (pág. 155) arreglo en que un adulto no emparentado asume la responsabilidad temporal de un niño.

fractura: (pág. 716) rotura o grieta en un hueso.

hongos: (pág. 487) organismos unicelulares o multicelulares que se alimentan de material orgánico y que pueden causar enfermedades como el pie de atleta, la tiña y las aftas.

English

Español

gang: (p. 698) group involved in risky, violent, illegal behaviors.

gastroenteritis (gas tro en tuh RI tuhs): (p. 320) common, sometimes food-borne illness that can be caused by viruses or bacteria.

pandilla: (pág. 698) grupo implicado en comportamientos ilegales, violentos y peligrosos.

gastroenteritis: (pág. 320) enfermedad común, a veces de procedencia alimentaria, que puede ser causada por virus o bacterias.

gene: (p. 243) a unit of hereditary material; can be dominant or recessive.

general adaptation syndrome (GAS): (p. 100) series of body changes resulting from stress—the alarm, resistance, and exhaustion stages.

generational cycle of teen pregnancy: (p. 198): occurs when a teen whose mother was a teen parent becomes pregnant.

generic-name drug: (p. 406) drug with the same active ingredients as a brand-name drug, but usually is less costly.

genital warts: (p. 502) STD caused by the human papillomavirus (HPV), which produces wartlike growths on the genitals and can be linked to cervical cancer.

genuine: (p. 466) sincere, true.

geothermal energy: (p. 619) heat transferred from underground.

gerontology: (p. 271) the study of aging, including physical, mental, and social changes.

giardiasis (jee ar DI uh suhs): (p. 608) stomach and intestinal infection caused by the parasite *Giardia lamblia.*

gingivitis (jin juh VY tuhs): (p. 349) condition in which the gums are swollen, tender, red, bleed easily, and may result in teeth loosening and falling out.

glaucoma: (p. 345) condition in which pressure of the fluid in the eye is high and may damage the optic nerve.

global warming: (p. 598) increase in Earth's average global temperature.

glucose: (p. 523) simple sugar that is the body's main energy source.

goal: (p. 267) achievement you work toward.

goiter: (p. 588) thyroid gland enlargement caused by iodine deficiency.

gonorrhea: (p. 501) highly contagious STD caused by the bacterium *Neisseria gonorrhoeae.*

good character: (p. 75) a person who uses self-control to act on responsible values.

graduated license: (p. 644) restricted driving license for new drivers.

graffiti: (p. 615) drawings or writings on a public surface that can contribute to visual pollution.

grandparents' rights: (p. 150) visitation rights with grandchildren that courts have awarded grandparents.

greenhouse effect: (p. 598) natural warming that occurs when water vapor, carbon dioxide, and methane in Earth's atmosphere trap heat.

grief: (p. 123) deep emotional distress caused by a loss.

gene: (pág. 243) una unidad de material hereditario; puede ser dominante o recesivo.

síndrome de adaptación general: (pág. 100) serie de cambios corporales resultantes del estrés: estado de alarma, estado de resistencia y estado de agotamiento.

ciclo de generaciones de embarazos de adolescentes: (pág. 198) ocurre cuando una persona, cuya madre la tuvo en la adolescencia, también se convierte en madre adolescente.

droga genérica: (pág. 406) droga con los mismos ingredientes activos que una droga de marca, pero que por lo general cuesta menos.

verrugas genitales: (pág. 502) ETS causada por el papillomavirus humano que produce unos bultos pequeños en los genitales y que está ligada al cáncer cervical.

genuino: (pág. 466) sincero, verdadero.

energía geotérmica: (pág. 619) calor que se transfiere desde áreas subterráneas.

gerontología: (pág. 271) el estudio del envejecimiento incluyendo los cambios físicos, mentales y sociales.

giardiasis: (pág. 608) infección estomacal e intestinal causada por el parásito *Giardia lamblia.*

gingivitis: (pág. 349) condición en que las encías se hinchan, se vuelven sensibles, rojizas y sangran fácilmente; puede resultar en el aflojamiento y pérdida de los dientes.

glaucoma: (pág. 345) condición en que la presión del fluido dentro del ojo es alta y puede causar daño al nervio óptico.

calentamiento global: (pág. 598) aumento en la temperatura global promedio de la Tierra.

glucosa: (pág. 523) azúcar simple que es la fuente principal de energía del cuerpo.

meta: (pág. 267) logro que uno se esfuerza en alcanzar.

bocio: (pág. 588) agrandamiento de la glándula tiroides causado por la deficiencia de yodo.

gonorrea: (pág. 501) ETS altamente contagiosa causada por la bacteria *Neisseria gonorrhoeae.*

buen carácter: (pág. 75) persona que usa el autocontrol para actuar de manera responsable.

licencia graduada: (pág. 644) licencia de conducir con restricciones para choferes novatos.

inscripciones anónimas: (pág. 615) dibujos o escritos sobre una superficie pública que puede contribuir a la contaminación visual.

derechos de los abuelos: (pág. 150) derechos de visitar a los nietos concedidos a los abuelos.

efecto de invernadero: (pág. 598) calentamiento natural que ocurre cuando el vapor de agua, el dióxido de carbono y el metano en la atmósfera terrestre atrapan el calor.

pena: (pág. 123) angustia emocional profunda causada por una pérdida.

Glossary/Glosario

English

Español

habitat: (pp. 600, 628) place where an organism normally lives.

habits: (p. 27) fixed, automatic behaviors.

halfway house: (p. 478) live-in facility that provides a supportive, drug-free environment and helps drug-dependent people adjust to living independently in the community.

hard-core gang member: (p. 699) senior, most influential gang member.

hay fever: (p. 496) seasonal respiratory allergies often triggered by airborne pollen.

hazing: (p. 675) potentially dangerous physical and/or emotional abuse endured to be part of a group.

hazing activity: (p. 413) dangerous or demeaning activity in which a person is forced to participate to become a group or club member.

health: (p. 5) quality of life including physical, mental-emotional, and family-social health.

health advocacy: (p. 626) working to improve the quality of life and encouraging others to do the same.

health-advocacy skills: (p. 65) skills used to influence others' health decisions and behaviors and to emphasize health-related concerns and beliefs.

health advocate: (p. 65) one who promotes health and influences others' health behaviors and decisions.

health advocate group: (p. 21) educates the public about specific health conditions and raises funds for research.

health-behavior contract: (p. 32) written plan in which you agree to practice a specific health behavior, such as physical fitness.

health-behavior inventory: (p. 27) personal assessment tool to help you learn if you are practicing healthful behaviors.

health-care facility: (p. 17) place, such as a hospital, where health care is provided.

health-care provider: (p. 17) licensed, trained professional, such as a dentist or physician, who helps people maintain or restore health.

health career: (p. 575) medical field profession or occupation, such as physician or pharmacologist, for which one trains.

health concept: (p. 12) idea formed from comprehension of health knowledge.

hábitat: (págs. 600, 628) lugar donde generalmente vive un organismo.

hábitos: (pág. 27) comportamientos automáticos fijos.

casa de paso: (pág. 478) instalación de vivienda que provee un ambiente libre de drogas y ayuda a los drogadictos a ajustarse a una vida independiente en la comunidad.

miembro incondicional de pandilla: (pág. 699) miembro de pandilla más influyente y antiguo.

fiebre de heno: (pág. 496) alergias respiratorias de temporada causadas por el polen en el aire.

novatada: (pág. 675) abuso emocional y físico potencialmente peligroso al que se somete una persona para ser parte de un grupo.

actividad de dar novatadas: (pág. 413) actividad peligrosa o degradante en que se obliga a una persona a participar para convertirse en miembro de un club o grupo.

salud: (pág. 5) calidad de vida que incluye la salud física, mental-emocional y sociofamiliar.

abogar por la salud: (pág. 626) trabajar para mejorar la calidad de vida y animar a otros a hacer lo mismo.

destrezas para abogar por la salud: (pág. 65) destrezas que se usan para influenciar las decisiones y comportamientos de salud de otros y para enfatizar creencias e intereses relacionados con la salud.

abogado de la salud: (pág. 65) aquel que promueve la salud e influye en los comportamientos y decisiones de salud de otros.

grupo de defensa de la salud: (pág. 21) educa al publico sobre condiciones de salud específicas y recauda fondos para la investigación.

contrato de comportamiento saludable: (pág. 32) plan escrito al que te comprometes a practicar un comportamiento de salud específico, como por ejemplo, estar en buena forma física.

inventario de comportamiento de salud: (pág. 27) herramienta de evaluación personal que te ayuda a entender si estás practicando comportamientos saludables.

centro del cuidado de la salud: (pág. 17) lugar, como un hospital, donde se proveen servicios de salud.

proveedor de cuidados de salud: (pág. 17) profesional entrenado y licenciado, como un dentista o un médico, quién ayuda a las personas a mantener o a restaurar la salud.

carrera en salud: (pág. 575) profesión u ocupación en el campo médico, como por ejemplo, un médico o un farmacólogo, para la cual se entrena una persona.

concepto de salud: (pág. 12) idea que se forma a raíz de la comprensión del conocimiento de la salud.

health fraud/fraude contra la salud

**heat-related illnesses/
enfermedad relacionada con el calor**

health fraud: (p. 545) promotion of drugs, devices, cosmetics, or foods that have not been scientifically proven to be safe or effective in diagnosing, curing, or treating a condition.

healthful behavior: (p. 27) health-promoting behavior that can prevent injury and early death or improve the environment.

healthful family: (p. 135) family that practices skills and behaviors, such as self-respect and strong work ethic, that promote responsible, loving relationships.

healthful friendship: (p. 158) balanced, mutually respectful relationship that encourages healthful behaviors and improves the quality of your life.

health goal: (p. 57) healthful behavior you work to achieve and maintain.

health insurance: (p. 567) financial protection that provides benefits for illness or injury.

health knowledge: (p. 6) information and understanding about health.

health-literate person: (p. 14) one who communicates effectively, is a self-directed learner, critical thinker, and responsible citizen.

Health Maintenance Organization (HMO): (p. 567) managed care plan that organizes health-care services for its members.

health product: (p. 17) item, such as dental floss, made to maintain or restore health.

health professionals groups: (p. 20) group that monitors the training and ethics of health professionals and advocates for them.

health-related fitness: (p. 374) ability of the heart, lungs, muscles, and joints to function optimally.

health service: (p. 17) work performed by a health-care provider.

health status: (p. 6) sum of positive and negative influences on health and well-being, including health knowledge, communication skills, heredity, advocacy skills, and risks.

healthy-helper syndrome: (p. 67) state of increased energy, relaxation, and improved mood that results from being a volunteer.

Healthy People 2010: (p. 58) set of national health goals for disease prevention and health-promoting objectives to be reached by the year 2010.

heat detector: (p. 641) alarm that sounds when it detects room temperature above a certain level.

heat-related illnesses: (p. 397) conditions, such as heatstroke or heat exhaustion, that result from exposure to higher than normal temperatures.

fraude contra la salud: (pág. 545) fomento de drogas, dispositivos, cosméticos o alimentos cuya efectividad o seguridad no ha sido probada científicamente para el diagnóstico, curación o tratamiento de una condición.

comportamiento de salud: (pág. 27) comportamiento fomentador de salud que puede prevenir lesiones y una muerte temprana o que puede mejorar el ambiente.

familia saludable: (pág. 135) familia que practica destrezas y comportamientos como el autorrespeto y una fuerte ética de trabajo, la cual promueve relaciones afectuosas responsables.

amistad saludable: (pág. 158) relación respetuosa mutua y equilibrada que fomenta los comportamientos saludables y mejora la calidad de tu vida.

meta de salud: (pág. 57) comportamiento saludable que uno se esfuerza en alcanzar y mantener.

seguro de salud: (pág. 567) protección financiera que provee beneficios en caso de enfermedad o lesión.

conocimiento de salud: (pág. 6) información y entendimiento de la salud.

persona educada en salud: (pág. 14) persona que se comunica eficazmente, se enseña a sí misma, usa el razonamiento crítico y es un ciudadano responsable.

Organización de Mantenimiento de la Salud: (pág. 567) plan de seguro de salud administrado que organiza los servicios de salud para sus miembros.

producto para la salud: (pág. 17) artículo como el hilo dental, el cual se fabrica para mantener o restaurar la salud.

grupos de profesionales de salud: (pág. 20) grupo que vigila el entrenamiento y ética de los profesionales de la salud y que actúa en su defensa.

eficacia relacionada con la salud: (pág. 374) capacidad del corazón, pulmones, músculos y articulaciones de funcionar óptimamente.

servicios de salud: (pág. 17) trabajo que realiza un profesional de la salud.

estado de salud: (pág. 6) suma de las influencias positivas y negativas sobre la salud y el bienestar; incluyen el conocimiento de la salud, las destrezas de comunicación, la herencia, las destrezas de defensa y los riesgos.

síndrome de ayudante saludable: (pág. 67) estado de alta energía, relajamiento y genio mejorado que resulta de servir como voluntario o voluntaria.

Gente Saludable 2010: (pág. 58) conjunto de metas de salud nacional para la prevención de las enfermedades y con objetivos para fomentar la salud a alcanzarse para el año 2010.

sdetector de calor: (pág. 641) alarma que suena cuando detecta una temperatura ambiental superior a cierto nivel.

enfermedad relacionada con el calor: (pág. 397) condiciones, como la insolación y la postración causada por el calor, que resultan de la exposición a temperaturas más altas de lo normal.

Glossary/Glosario

heatstroke: (p. 720) life-threatening overheating of the body; also called sunstroke.

helper T cell: (p. 485) a white blood cell that signals B cells to produce antibodies

hemophilia: (p. 527) an inherited condition in which blood does not clot normally.

herbal supplements: (p. 288) supplements that contain plant extracts or ingredients and do not have to be proven safe by the FDA.

herpes: (p. 502) incurable STD caused by the herpes simplex virus (HSV).

hidden anger: (p. 97) unrecognized, inappropriately expressed anger.

high-density lipoproteins (HDLs): (p. 369) substances in the blood that transport cholesterol to the liver where it is broken down and excreted.

high-risk driving: (p. 645) dangerous driving habits, such as speeding, that can result in accidents.

HIV negative: (p. 512) a person without HIV antibodies in his or her blood.

Homeland Security Advisory System: (p. 654) national system that warns of the risk of terrorist acts.

homelessness: (p. 596) having no home.

homicide: (p. 657) killing of a person through the act, advantage, or mistake of another person.

honest talk: (p. 476) direct sharing of feelings.

hospice: (p. 276) in-home care or care given in a home-like facility for persons with a terminal illness who are expected to die in less than six months.

hostility: (p. 97) a chronic state of anger.

human immunodeficiency virus (HIV): (p. 471) pathogen that destroys infection-fighting T cells in the body.

hurricane: (p. 652) tropical storm with winds over 73 miles per hour and heavy rains.

hydrogen power: (p. 619) energy produced by passing an electric current through water to burn hydrogen.

hyperactive: (p. 268) unable to sit or stand still for long periods of time.

hyperopia: (p. 344) refractive error in which close objects seem blurred and distant objects are clearly seen; also called farsightedness.

hypoglycemia (hy po gly SEE mee uh): (p. 307) condition in which the pancreas produces too much insulin, causing a low blood sugar level.

insolación: (pág. 720) sobrecalentamiento corporal que pone en peligro la vida.

célula T ayudante: (pág. 485) glóbulo blanco que les indica a las células B que produzcan anticuerpos.

hemofilia: (pág. 527) condición heredada en la cual la sangre no se coagula normalmente.

suplementos herbales: (pág. 288) suplementos que contienen extractos o ingredientes vegetales, los cuales no tienen que ser aprobados por la FDA.

herpes: (pág. 502) STS incurable transmitida por el virus del herpes simplex (VHS)

ira oculta: (pág. 97) ira no reconocida que se expresa de una manera inapropiada.

lipoproteínas de alta densidad (LAD): (pág. 369) sustancias en la sangre que transportan el colesterol hasta el hígado, en donde el colesterol se descompone y se libera.

manejo de alto riesgo: (pág. 645) hábitos de manejo peligrosos, como el conducir a exceso de velocidad, los cuales pueden resultar en accidentes.

VIH negativo: (pág. 512) persona cuya sangre no contiene los anticuerpos del VIH.

Sistema de Advertencia de Seguridad Nacional: (pág. 654) sistema nacional que advierte del riesgo de actos terroristas.

desamparado: (pág. 596) sin hogar.

homicidio: (pág. 657) acto de matar a una persona, ya sea personalmente, por error o por intermedio de otra persona.

conversación honesta: (pág. 476) manera de expresar los sentimientos en forma directa.

hospicio: (pág. 276) cuidado que se proporciona en el propio hogar en una instalación parecida a un hogar para personas con enfermedades mortales cuya muerte se espera en menos de seis meses.

síndrome de hostilidad: (pág. 97) estado crónico de ira.

virus de inmunodeficiencia humana (VIH): (pág. 471) patógenos que destruyen las células T corporales que combaten infecciones.

huracán: (pág. 652) tormenta tropical con vientos de más de 73 millas por hora e intensas lluvias.

energía del hidrógeno: (pág. 619) energía que se produce al pasar una corriente eléctrica por el agua para quemar el hidrógeno.

hiperactivo: (pág. 268) persona que es incapaz de sentarse o quedarse quieta durante largos períodos de tiempo.

hiperopía: (pág. 344) la condición óptica en la cual no se pueden enfocar los objetos cercanos y éstos se ven borrosos y los objetos distantes se pueden ver claramente; también denominada hipermetropía y presbicia.

hipoglicemia: (pág. 307) condición en que el páncreas produce demasiada insulina, lo cual ocasiona bajos niveles de azúcar en la sangre.

hypothermia/hipotermia **integumentary system/sistema integumentario**

hypothermia: (p. 719) lower than normal body temperature resulting from overexposure to cold water, wind, and cool temperatures.

hipotermia: (pág. 719) temperaturas corporales más bajas de lo normal debido a la sobreexposición al agua o al viento frío y a bajas temperaturas.

English

Español

I-message: (p. 42) statement that contains a specific behavior or event, its effect on you, and resulting emotions, and expresses your feelings or thoughts on a subject without blaming or shaming others.

immune system: (p. 214) group of organs, including the lymph nodes, thymus, and spleen, that fights off pathogens and removes harmful organisms from the blood.

implied consent: (p. 710) permission to give first aid to an unconscious adult victim or to a mentally incompetent adult.

inactive decision-making style: (p. 60) habit of a person who fails to make choices and has little control over the direction of his or her life.

incest: (p. 691) sexual contact with a family member.

incinerator: (p. 624) furnace that burns solid waste.

income: (p. 554) money you receive from gifts, your allowance, or pay earned at work.

independent: (p. 262) to be able to rely on oneself.

influenza: (p. 491) highly contagious respiratory infection caused by viruses.

inhalants: (p. 437) inhaled chemicals, such as lighter fluid, that affect mood, can impair judgment, and cause heart failure and instant death.

injection drug use: (p. 471) involves taking illegal drugs, such as heroin or steroids, into the body using a needle.

inpatient care: (p. 478) treatment that requires staying overnight at a drug-free, medically supervised facility, most often for a period of 28 days.

insomnia: (p. 363) sleep disorder in which there is a prolonged inability to fall asleep, stay asleep, or return to sleep when awakened.

instant gratification: (p. 454) wanting something immediately, despite potential harmful effects.

insulin: (p. 523) hormone that regulates the blood sugar level.

integumentary system (in te gyuh MEN tuh ree): (p. 222) covers and protects the body and includes skin, hair, and nails.

mensaje yo: (pág. 42) mensaje que contiene un comportamiento o evento específico, su efecto y emociones resultantes, y el cual expresa tus sentimientos o pensamientos sobre un individuo sin culpar a otros.

sistema inmunológico: (pág. 214) grupo de órganos que incluyen los ganglios linfáticos, el timo y el vaso, los cuales luchan contra los patógenos y eliminan organismos perjudiciales de la sangre.

consentimiento implícito: (pág. 710) permiso de prestar primeros auxilios a una víctima adulta que ha perdido el conocimiento o a un adulto mentalmente incompetente.

ciclo de toma de decisiones inactivo: (pág. 60) hábito de una persona que deja de tomar decisiones y tiene poco control sobre su vida.

incesto: (pág. 691) contacto sexual con un miembro de la familia.

incinerador: (pág. 624) horno crematorio en que se queman desechos sólidos.

ingreso: (pág. 554) dinero que recibes de regalos, de la mesada o dinero que ganas de tu trabajo.

independiente: (pág. 262) capacidad de depender de uno mismo.

influenza: (pág. 491) infección respiratoria vírica altamente contagiosa.

inhalantes: (pág. 437) sustancias químicas que se inhalan, como el fluido de encendedores, que afectan la disposición de ánimo, pueden deteriorar el juicio y causar paro cardíaco y muerte instantánea.

uso de drogas inyectadas: (pág. 471) inyección en el cuerpo de drogas ilegales, como la heroína o los esteroides.

cuidado interno: (pág. 478) tratamiento que requiere una estadía día y noche en una instalación médica supervisada y libre de drogas, por lo general por un período de 28 días.

insomnio: (pág. 363) trastorno en que la persona es incapaz de conciliar el sueño, de mantenerse dormida o volverse a dormir después de ser despertada.

gratificación instantánea: (pág. 454) querer algo inmediatamente a pesar de sus efectos dañinos.

insulina: (pág. 523) hormona que regula los niveles de azúcar en la sangre.

sistema integumentario: (pág. 222) cubre y protege el cuerpo e incluye la piel, el cabello y las uñas.

interdependence: (p. 143) healthy condition in which two people depend on one another, yet each maintains a unique identity.

interest: (p. 553) additional money paid for the use of a larger sum of money.

intimacy: (p. 187) deep, meaningful sharing between two people; can be philosophical, psychological, creative, and physical.

invincible: (p. 123) to view yourself as incapable of being harmed.

iodine deficiency: (p. 588) micronutrient deficiency that can result in brain damage and cretinism.

isokinetic exercise: (p. 375) exercise that uses special weight resistance machines.

isometric exercise: (p. 375) muscle-strengthening exercise that involves tightening a muscle for 5–8 seconds with no body movement.

isotonic exercise: (p. 375) exercise in which a muscle or muscles move against a resistance weight and/or gravity 8–15 times.

interdependencia: (pág. 143) condición saludable en la cual dos personas dependen una de la otra, pero sin embargo cada una mantiene su identidad propia.

interés: (pág. 553) dinero adicional que se paga por el uso de una suma mayor de dinero.

intimidad: (pág. 187) participación expresiva y profunda entre dos personas; puede ser filosófica, psicológica, creativa o física.

invencible: (pág. 123) verse a sí mismo(a) como incapaz de sufrir daño.

insuficiencia de yodo: (pág. 588) deficiencia de micronutriente que puede resultar en daño cerebral y cretinismo.

ejercicio isocinético: (pág. 375) ejercicio que usa máquinas de resistencia de pesos especiales.

ejercicio isométrico: (pág. 375) ejercicio fortalecedor de músculos en el cual se tensa un músculo de 5 a 8 segundos sin mover el cuerpo.

ejercicio isotónico: (pág. 375) ejercicio en que un músculo o los músculos se mueven contra un peso o resistencia y/o la gravedad de 8 a 15 veces.

English	Español

joint custody: (p. 150) arrangement in which both parents keep legal custody of a child or children.

jumping-in: (p. 700) initiation rite in which the potential gang member is beaten by the gang.

juvenile detention: (p. 667) temporary physical restriction of juveniles in a special facility until their legal cases are decided.

custodia mancomunada: (pág. 150) arreglo en que ambos padres mantienen la custodia legal de uno o más niños.

paliza de iniciación: (pág. 700) rito de iniciación en que la pandilla le da una paliza al miembro potencial.

detención juvenil: (pág. 667) restricción física temporal de menores en una instalación especial hasta que se decidan sus casos legales.

English	Español

Kaposi's sarcoma (KS): (p. 505) a type of cancer associated with AIDS.

sarcoma de Kaposi (SK): (pág. 505) un tipo de cáncer asociado con el SIDA.

English	Español

labor: (p. 250) process of childbirth.

laceration: (p. 740) torn and ragged skin wound caused by a cut.

alumbramiento: (pág. 250) proceso de dar a luz.

laceración: (pág. 740) herida desgarrada de la piel causada por una cortadura.

lactase deficiency/intolerancia a la lactosa

lactase deficiency (LAK tays • dih FIH shuhn see): (p. 308) common food intolerance in which lactase, an enzyme that breaks down milk sugar, is missing, resulting in the inability to digest lactose.

lacto-vegetarian diet: (p. 300) diet that excludes meat, fish, eggs, and poultry.

landfill: (p. 618) place where waste is dumped in layers and buried.

landslide: (p. 651) downward mass movement of earth or rock.

law: (p. 543) a rule of conduct, established and enforced by a governing body, that is designed to protect rights of people in a community, state, or nation.

leachate (LEE chayt): (p. 624) liquid that drains from a landfill.

leading health indicators: (p. 59) ten national health concerns, including obesity and substance abuse, being evaluated to know if the nation's health improves from 2000 to 2010.

learning style: (p. 262) the way you gain and process knowledge; for example, visual, kinesthetic, and global styles.

legal age of consent: (p. 169) age at which each state considers a person legally able to give permission for sexual contact.

legal death: (p. 276) brain death or the irreversible stopping of respiratory and circulatory functions.

leisure time: (p. 627) time away from work or duties.

leukoplakia: (p. 429) white patches of abnormal cells in the mouth that can develop into cancer.

liar: (p. 181) person who does not tell the truth.

lice: (p. 357) insects that live and lay eggs in human hair.

license for a health career: (p. 575) document that grants the right the practice or to use a title.

life crisis: (p. 109) event or experience that causes a high stress level.

life expectancy: (p. 58) number of years one can expect to live.

living will: (p. 276) document that details what treatment is wanted if a person is unable to make decisions.

local public health department: (p. 583) local government agency offering services and programs to protect and promote a community's health.

intolerancia a la lactosa: (pág. 308) intolerancia alimenticia común en que una persona carece de lactosa, una enzima que descompone el azúcar, lo cual resulta en la incapacidad de digerir la lactosa.

dieta lactovegetariana: (pág. 300) dieta que excluye las carnes rojas, el pescado, los huevos y la carne de aves de corral.

vertedero sanitario: (pág. 618) lugar donde se echan los desechos en capas y se entierran.

derrumbe: (pág. 651) movimiento descendente de masa de tierra o rocas.

ley: (pág. 543) regla de conducta que un gobierno establece y hace cumplir, la cual está diseñada para proteger los derechos de las personas en una comunidad, estado o nación.

lechada: (pág. 624) líquido que se drena de un vertedero controlado.

índices principales de salud: (pág. 59) diez asuntos de interés de la salud nacional; incluyen la obesidad, el abuso de sustancias los cuales se hallan, bajo evaluación para averiguar si la salud de la nación mejora entre 2000 y 2010.

estilo de aprendizaje: (pág. 262) la manera en que uno gana y procesa el conocimiento, como por ejemplo, los estilos visual, cinestético y global.

edad legal de consentimiento: (pág. 169) edad a la que cada estado considera a un individuo legalmente capaz de dar su consentimiento para el contacto sexual.

muerte legal: (pág. 276) muerte del cerebro o el paro irreversible de las funciones respiratorias y circulatorias.

tiempo libre: (pág. 627) tiempo que se pasa fuera del trabajo u obligaciones.

leucoplaquia: (pág. 429) emplasto anormal de células blancas en la boca que pueden convertirse en cáncer.

mentiroso(a): (pág. 181) persona que no dice la verdad.

piojo: (pág. 357) insecto que vive y pone sus huevos en el cabello de los humanos.

licencia para una carrera en salud: (pág. 575) documento que concede el derecho de practicar o usar un titulo.

crisis de vida: (pág. 109) evento o experiencia que causa un alto nivel de estrés.

expectativa de vida: (pág. 58) número de años que uno espera vivir.

poder especial: (pág. 276) documento que detalla el tratamiento que una persona desea en caso de que ésta no pueda tomar decisiones.

departamento de salud pública local: (pág. 583) agencia gubernamental local que ofrece servicios y programas para proteger y fomentar la salud de una comunidad.

logical consequences discipline: (p. 197) disciplinary technique that allows a child to experience results of undesirable behavior so that he or she will want to change that behavior.

loss: (p. 123) feeling that occurs when something changes or ends or someone dies.

loudness: (p. 613) magnitude of sound.

low birth weight: (p. 201) weight at birth less than 5.5 pounds.

low-density lipoproteins (LDLs): (p. 369) substances in the blood that deposit cholesterol in body cells.

Lower Anchors and Tethers for Children (LATCH): (p. 646) specialized restraint system that works independently of the vehicle's safety belt system and simplifies child safety seat installation and prevents misuse.

LSD: (p. 441) hallucinogen; also called acid or yellow sunshine.

lymphocyte: (p. 485) white blood cell, such as a B cell or a helper T cell, that helps fight pathogens.

disciplina de consecuencias lógicas: (pág. 197) técnica disciplinaria que le permite a un niño o niña experimentar los resultados de un comportamiento indeseado, de modo que él o ella quiera cambiar el comportamiento.

pérdida: (pág. 123) sentimiento que ocurre cuando algo cambia o termina o cuando alguien muere.

volumen sonoro: (pág. 613) intensidad o fuerza del sonido.

insuficiencia ponderal: (pág. 201) peso de nacimiento de menos de 5.5 libras (2.5 kilogramos).

lipoproteínas de baja densidad (LBD): (pág. 369) sustancias en la sangre que depositan colesterol en las células corporales.

anclaje inferior y correas para niños: (pág. 646) sistema de restricción especializado que funciona independientemente del sistema de cinturones de seguridad del vehículo, el cual simplifica la instalación de las sillas de seguridad para niños y previene su mal uso.

LSD: (pág. 441) alucinógeno; también llamado ácido.

linfocito: (pág. 485) glóbulo blanco, como por ejemplo una célula B o una célula T ayudante, que ayuda a combatir los patógenos

English | Español

macrophage (MA kruh fahzh): (p. 485) a type of white blood cell that surrounds and destroys pathogens.

major depression: (p. 110) mood disorder with long-lasting feelings of hopelessness, helplessness, or sadness.

malignant melanoma: (p. 534) most dangerous type of skin cancer.

malignant tumor: (p. 531) cancerous tumor that may spread to other parts of the body.

malnutrition: (p. 595) condition in which a person lacks needed nutrients.

managed care: (p. 567) organized system of health-care services, such as an HMO or PPO, designed to control health-care costs.

marijuana: (p. 438) dried leaves and tops of the cannabis plant; contains THC, damages the lungs, can cause antimotivational syndrome, and is the most commonly used illegal drug in the United States.

marital separation: (p. 149) the cessation of cohabitation between a married couple by mutual agreement or judicial decree.

media: (p. 35) forms of mass communication, such as TV, radio, and newspapers.

macrófago: (pág. 485) tipo de glóbulo blanco que rodea y destruye los patógenos.

depresión severa: (pág. 110) trastorno del ánimo en que la persona experimenta sentimientos de desesperación, desamparo y tristeza que duran mucho tiempo.

melanoma maligno: (pág. 534) el tipo más peligroso de cáncer de la piel.

tumor maligno: (pág. 531) tumor canceroso que se puede extender a otras partes del cuerpo.

desnutrición: (pág. 595) condición en la cual una persona carece de los nutrientes necesarios.

cuidado de salud administrado: (pág. 567) sistema organizado de servicios de cuidado de salud, como una HMO o una PPO, diseñado para controlar los costos relacionados con el cuidado de la salud.

marihuana: (pág. 438) hojas y puntas secas de la planta *Cannabis sativa;* contiene THC, causa daños a los pulmones, puede causar el síndrome de falta de motivación y es la droga ilegal de uso más común en los Estados Unidos.

separación marital: (pág. 149) cese de la cohabitación matrimonial de una pareja casada como resultado de un acuerdo mutuo de decreto judicial.

medios de comunicación: (pág. 35) formas de comunicación en masa, como por ejemplo la televisión, la radio y los periódicos.

media literacy: (p. 36) skill in recognizing and evaluating messages in media.

mediation: (p. 53) process in which an outside person helps people in conflict find a healthful, safe, nonviolent solution.

Medicaid: (p. 567) federal health insurance coverage for low income people.

Medicare: (p. 567) federal health insurance plan for people 65 years of age or older and for those receiving Social Security disability benefits for two years.

megadosing: (p. 314) taking vitamins in excessive amounts.

mental disorder: (p. 89) behavioral or psychological syndrome or pattern that occurs in an individual and that is associated with distress or disability or with significantly increased risk of suffering, death, pain, disability, or an important loss of freedom.

mental-emotional health: (p. 5) the condition of a person's mind and the ways to keep the body in good physical health.

mentor: (p. 457) responsible person who helps and guides another person.

metabolism: (p. 312) rate at which food is converted to energy in body cells.

metastasis (muh TAS tuh suhs): (p. 531) spreading of cancer cells to other body parts.

micronutrients: (p. 588) vitamins and minerals needed in minuscule amounts for proper growth.

mind-body connection: (p. 95) relationship between your thoughts and feelings and bodily responses.

mineral: (p. 287) macro or micro inorganic nutrient that regulates many of the body's chemical reactions.

minor depression: (p. 110) mood disorder with mild feelings of hopelessness, helplessness, or sadness that may go away or become chronic.

moles: (p. 354) smooth, raised areas on the skin that can be lighter or darker than surrounding skin and may darken or increase in number with sun exposure.

moral code: (p. 665) personal set of rules to control your own behavior.

multiple sclerosis (MS): (p. 527) chronic health condition in which the protective covering of the nerve fibers in the brain and spinal cord are destroyed.

muscular system: (p. 217) voluntary and involuntary muscles that maintain posture and provide motion.

myopia: (p. 344) refractive error in which distant objects seem blurred and close objects are clearly seen; also called nearsightedness.

educación para los medios de comunicación: (pág. 36) habilidad de reconocer y evaluar los mensajes de los medios de comunicación.

mediación: (pág. 53) proceso en que una tercera persona imparcial ayuda a personas involucradas en un conflicto a que lo resuelvan de manera segura y sin violencia.

Medicaid: (pág. 567) cobertura de seguro de salud federal para personas de bajos ingresos.

Medicare: (pág. 567) plan de seguro de salud federal para personas de 65 años y mayores y para personas que reciben beneficios por incapacidad del Seguro Social por dos años.

megadosis: (pág. 314) tomar vitaminas en cantidades excesivas.

trastorno mental: (pág. 89) síndrome o patrón psicológico o de comportamiento que ocurre en un individuo y el cual está asociado con angustia o discapacidad o con un mayor riesgo de sufrimiento, muerte, dolor, discapacidad o una pérdida importante de libertad.

salud mental-emocional: (pág. 5) la condición de la mente de una persona y las maneras en que se mantiene el cuerpo en buena salud física.

mentor: (pág. 457) persona responsable que ayuda y guía a otra persona.

metabolismo: (pág. 312) velocidad a la cual los alimentos se convierten en energía en las células corporales.

metástasis: (pág. 531) propagación de células cancerosas a otras partes del cuerpo.

micronutrientes: (pág. 588) vitaminas y minerales necesarios en cantidades diminutas para el crecimiento apropiado.

conexión mente-cuerpo: (pág. 95) relación entre tus pensamientos y sentimientos y tus respuestas corporales.

mineral: (pág. 287) macronutriente o micronutriente inorgánico que regula muchas de las reacciones químicas corporales.

depresión leve: (pág. 110) trastorno del ánimo en que la persona siente sentimientos leves de desesperación, desamparo o tristeza, los cuales pueden desaparecer o volverse crónicos.

lunares: (pág. 354) áreas lisas y elevadas en la piel de color más claro o más oscuro que las áreas circundantes y que pueden volverse más oscuras o aumentar en número debido a la exposición al sol.

código moral: (pág. 665) conjunto personal de reglas para controlar tu propio comportamiento.

esclerosis múltiple: (pág. 527) condición crónica de salud que causa la destrucción de la cubierta protectora de las fibras nerviosas en el cerebro y la médula.

sistema muscular: (pág. 217) músculos voluntarios e involuntarios que mantienen la postura y proveen movimiento.

miopía: (pág. 344) error de refracción en que los objetos distantes se ven borrosos y los objetos cercanos se ven claramente; también denominada vista corta.

English | **Español**

Glossary/Glosario

narcolepsy: (p. 364) chronic, disabling sleep disorder in which a person experiences "sleep attacks" at inappropriate times of day.

narcotics: (p. 446) pain-relieving drugs, such as morphine and heroin, that slow the central nervous system.

National Health Information Center (NHIC): (p. 547) federal agency that refers consumers to organizations that can provide health-related information.

national parks: (p. 627) government-maintained areas of land open to the public.

natural disaster: (p. 650) damaging event, such as a tornado or landslide, caused by nature.

natural environment: (p. 626) everything around a person not made by people, such as the sky, mountains, plants, and animals.

nature preserve: (p. 627) restricted area for protection of the natural environment.

nature trail: (p. 627) path through a natural environment.

negative peer pressure: (p. 462) influence from peers to act irresponsibly.

nervous system: (p. 212) carries messages to and from the spinal cord and brain and all other parts of the body; consists of the brain and spinal cord (central nervous system) and nerves (peripheral nervous system).

nicotine: (p. 425) highly addictive stimulant drug in tobacco products, such as cigarettes and snuff, that constricts blood vessels and increases heart rate and blood pressure.

nicotine patch: (p. 433) patch worn on the skin that slowly releases nicotine into the bloodstream.

noise: (p. 612) unpleasant, annoying sound.

noise pollution: (p. 614) annoying or harmful noise that can have negative effects on health.

nonrapid eye movement (NREM) sleep: (p. 361) sleep period during which the eyes are relaxed.

nosebleed: (p. 743) a loss of blood from the mucous membranes that line the nose.

nuclear reactor: (p. 619) device that splits atoms to produce steam.

nutrient: (p. 282) substance in food that helps with body processes; protein, carbohydrate, fat, vitamin, mineral, and water.

narcolepsia: (pág. 364) trastorno crónico que causa discapacidad, a menudo el resultado de daño cerebral, en el cual la persona experimenta "ataques de sueño" a horas inapropiadas del día.

narcóticos: (pág. 446) drogas analgésicas, como por ejemplo la morfina y la heroína, que aminoran el sistema nervioso central.

Centro de Información de Salud Nacional: (pág. 547) organismo federal que refiere a los consumidores a organizaciones que pueden proveer información relacionada con la salud.

parque nacional: (pág. 627) áreas de terreno que mantiene el gobierno y las cuales están abiertas al público.

desastre natural: (pág. 650) evento dañino, como un tornado o un derrumbe, causado por la naturaleza.

ambiente natural: (pág. 626) todo lo que rodea a una persona y que no está hecho por seres humanos, como por ejemplo, el firmamento, las montañas, las plantas y los animales.

reserva natural: (pág. 627) área restringida para la protección del ambiente natural.

trocha natural: (pág. 627) camino a través de un ambiente natural.

presión de compañeros negativa: (pág. 462) influencia de compañeros para actuar irresponsablemente.

sistema nervioso: (pág. 212) transporta mensajes desde y hasta la médula espinal y el encéfalo y todas las otras partes del cuerpo; consta del encéfalo y la médula espinal (sistema nervioso central) y los nervios (sistema nervioso periférico)

nicotina: (pág. 425) droga estimulante muy adictiva derivada del tabaco, se usa en cigarrillos y el rapé, que deprime los vasos sanguíneos y aumenta los latidos del corazón y la presión sanguínea.

parche de nicotina: (pág. 433) parche que se usa en la piel, el cual libera nicotina lentamente en el torrente sanguíneo.

ruido: (pág. 612) sonido molesto y desagradable.

contaminación por ruido: (pág. 614) ruido molesto o dañino que puede tener efectos negativos en la salud.

sueño (NREM) de movimiento no rápido de los ojos: (pág. 361) período del sueño durante el cual los ojos están en estado de relajamiento.

hemorragia nasal: (pág. 743) pérdida de sangre de las membranas mucosas que forran la nariz.

reactor nuclear: (pág. 619) dispositivo que rompe los átomos para producir vapor.

nutriente: (pág. 282) sustancia en los alimentos que ayuda con los proceso corporales; proteínas, carbohidratos, grasas, vitaminas, minerales y agua.

English | Español

obesity: (p. 329) body weight that is 20 percent or more than desirable weight.

Occupational Safety and Health Act (OSH Act): (p. 642) health and safety standards that must be met by all employers.

one-sided friendship: (p. 164) friendship in which one person does most of the giving and one person does most of the receiving.

ordinances: (p. 543) laws enacted by county and municipal governments.

osteoarthritis: (p. 526) chronic health condition in which the moving parts of joints wear down.

osteoporosis: (p. 306) disease characterized by low bone mass and deterioration of bone tissue.

out-of-order death: (p. 123) death that occurs at an unexpected time in a person's life cycle.

outpatient care: (p. 478) health-care treatment that does not require staying overnight at a medically supervised facility, allowing the person to attend school or work.

ovaries: (p. 228) internal female reproductive organs that produce ova.

over-the-counter (OTC) drug: (p. 407) drug purchased without a prescription that can be used to relieve the symptoms of, but not cure, an illness.

overweight: (p. 329) body weight that is 10 percent or more than desirable weight.

ovo-lacto-vegetarian diet: (p. 300) diet that excludes red meat, fish, and poultry.

ozone layer: (p. 597) protective atmospheric layer that traps UV radiation from the sun.

obesidad: (pág. 329) peso corporal que es un 20 por ciento o más por encima del peso deseable.

Ley de Salud y Seguridad Ocupacional (OSH Act): (pág. 642) estándares de seguridad y salud que deben cumplir todos los empleadores.

amistad unilateral: (pág. 164) amistad en que una persona provee la mayor parte del apoyo y la otra persona recibe dicho apoyo.

estatutos: (pág. 543) leyes que los gobiernos municipales y del país ponen en rigor.

osteoartritis: (pág. 526) condición crónica de salud en que las partes movedizas de las articulaciones se desgastan.

osteoporosis: (pág. 306) enfermedad caracterizada por una masa ósea baja y el deterioro del tejido oseo.

muerte a destiempo: (pág. 123) muerte que ocurre inesperadamente en el ciclo de vida de una persona.

atención ambulatoria: (pág. 478) tratamiento de cuidado de salud que no requiere hospitalización en una instalación médica supervisada, lo cual permite que el paciente asista a la escuela o al trabajo.

ovarios: (pág. 228) órganos reproductores femeninos internos que producen los óvulos.

droga sin receta médica: (pág. 407) droga que se compra sin una receta médica y que se puede usar para aliviar, pero no curar, los síntomas de una enfermedad.

sobrepeso: (pág. 329) peso corporal que es un 10 por ciento más del peso deseable.

dieta ovolactovegetariana: (pág. 300) dieta que excluye las carnes rojas, el pescado y la carne de aves de corral.

capa de ozono: (pág. 597) capa atmosférica protectora que atrapa la radiación ultravioleta del Sol.

English | Español

pacemaker: (p. 516) electrical device implanted in the heart to steady or stimulate heart contractions.

panic disorder: (p. 89) a disorder in which feelings of terror strike suddenly and repeatedly with no warning.

Pap smear: (p. 231) screening test to detect cervical cancer.

parasuicide: (p. 114) suicide attempt in which the person does not intend to die.

particulates: (p. 603) tiny particles in the air—soot, ash, dirt, pollen, and dust.

marcapasos: (pág. 516) dispositivo eléctrico que se implanta en el corazón para regular o estimular las contracciones cardíacas.

trastorno de pánico: (pág. 89) trastorno en que una persona se siente aterrorizada súbita y repetidamente sin aviso previo.

papanicolaou: (pág. 231) examen que se usa para detectar el cáncer cervical.

parasuicidio: (pág. 114) intento de suicidio en que la persona no tiene intención de morir.

particulados: (pág. 603) partículas diminutas en el aire: hollín, cenizas, suciedad, polen y polvo.

passive behavior: (p. 661) the holding back of ideas, feelings, and decisions.

pathogen: (p. 487) disease-causing bacterium, fungus, virus, or protozoan.

PCBs: (p. 607) mixtures of chemicals containing chlorine that can contaminate food and water and cause health problems.

pedigree: (p. 22) chart showing genetic diseases or conditions in families and how family members are related.

peer leader: (p. 466) older student who teaches younger students how to resist pressure to use drugs.

peer pressure: (p. 45) positive or negative influence peers consciously or unconsciously place on others to behave in certain ways.

pelvic inflammatory disease (PID): (p. 168) serious infection of the female internal reproductive organs that can result in sterility.

people pleaser: (p. 164) one who constantly seeks others' approval; a "doormat."

perfectionism: (p. 85) compelling need to be flawless.

periodontal disease (pehr ee oh DAHN tuhl): (p. 349) disease of the gums and other tissues supporting the teeth; main cause of tooth loss in adults.

perpetrator of violence: (p. 657) one who commits a violent act.

personal health record: (p. 23) documents an individual's health history and lists the person's health-care providers.

personality: (p. 83) an individual's unique pattern of characteristics—influenced by heredity, behavior, environment, and attitudes—that makes him or her different from others.

physical dependence: (p. 458) physical need for a drug.

physical fitness: (p. 371) ability to perform physical activities and meet the demands of daily living while being energetic and alert.

pitch: (p. 613) highness or lowness of a sound.

placenta: (p. 246) organ that anchors the developing baby to the uterus.

plaque: (p. 515) hardened fatty deposits on the artery walls.

pneumonia: (p. 492) contagious lung infection caused by bacteria, viruses, or other pathogens.

pollen: (p. 496) powder produced by flowers, trees, and grass that can trigger an allergic response.

comportamiento pasivo: (pág. 661) retención de ideas, sentimientos y decisiones.

patógeno: (pág. 487) bacteria, hongo, virus o protozoario causante de enfermedad.

PCB: (pág. 607) mezcla de sustancias químicas que contienen cloro y que pueden contaminar los alimentos y el agua y causar problemas de salud.

pedigrí: (pág. 22) tabla que muestra las enfermedades o condiciones genéticas en familias y el parentesco entre miembros de una familia.

líder de compañeros: (pág. 466) estudiante mayor que les enseña a los estudiantes más jóvenes a resistir la presión a usar drogas.

presión de los compañeros: (pág. 45) influencia positiva o negativa a la que consciente o inconscientemente los compañeros someten a otros para que se comporten de cierta manera.

enfermedad inflamatoria de la pelvis: (pág. 168) infección grave de los órganos reproductores internos femeninos que puede resultar en esterilidad.

persona complaciente: (pág. 164) persona que requiere la aprobación constante de otros; un "aguantador o sufrido".

perfeccionismo: (pág. 85) necesidad apremiante de no tener fallas.

enfermedad periodontal: (pág. 349) enfermedad de las encías y otros tejidos que apoyan los dientes; la causa principal de la pérdida de la dentadura en adultos.

perpetrador de violencia: (pág. 657) persona que comete un acto de violencia.

récord médico personal: (pág. 23) documenta el historial de salud de un individuo y enumera los proveedores de salud de la persona.

personalidad: (pág. 83) patrón único de las características de un individuo, influido por la herencia, el comportamiento, el ambiente y las predisposiciones, que lo diferencia de otras personas.

dependencia física: (pág. 458) necesidad física por una droga.

acondicionamiento físico: (pág. 371) habilidad de realizar actividades físicas y de satisfacer las demandas del diario vivir mientras la persona se siente enérgica y alerta.

tono: (pág. 613) nivel sonoro que puede ser alto o bajo.

placenta: (pág. 246) órgano que ancla al bebé en desarrollo al útero.

placa: (pág. 515) depósitos de grasa endurecida en las paredes arteriales.

pulmonía: (pág. 492) infección pulmonar contagiosa causada por bacterias, virus u otros patógenos.

polen: (pág. 496) polvo producido por las flores, los árboles y el pasto que puede desatar una respuesta alérgica.

positive peer pressure: (p. 462) influence from peers to act responsibly.

positive reinforcement: (p. 466) reward given when actions are taken that help reach a goal.

positive self-esteem: (p. 78) a person's belief that he or she is worthy and deserves respect.

precycling: (p. 622) waste-reduction process that involves buying products in packages that can be broken down.

Preferred Provider Organization (PPO): (p. 567) business that has a contract with health-care providers to provide health-care services at reduced rates.

prehypertension: (p. 519) a blood pressure range that places people at higher risk of heart disease and stroke.

prejudice: (p. 54) an adverse judgment formed without looking at the facts.

premature death: (p. 368) death before a person reaches his or her life expectancy.

prescription: (p. 406) written order by a licensed health professional for a drug dispensed by a pharmacist that can be used to treat or prevent illness.

prestige crime: (p. 700) crime committed to gain status from other gang members.

preventive discipline: (p. 197) training in which the parent explains correct behavior and consequences of wrong behavior.

primary care: (p. 565) general health care.

principle of cooldown: (p. 393) a workout should end with 5–10 minutes of reduced exercise to help heart rate, breathing rate, temperature, and circulation return to normal.

principle of overload: (p. 393) a workout must include exercise beyond what is usually done to gain additional fitness benefits.

principle of progression: (p. 393) amount and intensity of exercise in a workout must be increased gradually.

principle of fitness reversibility: (p. 393) fitness benefits are lost when training stops.

principle of specificity: (p. 393) a workout should include a specific type of exercise to gain the desired fitness benefit.

presión positiva de compañeros: (pág. 462) influencia de los compañeros a actuar responsablemente.

refuerzo positivo: (pág. 466) recompensa que se concede cuando las acciones que se toman ayudan a alcanzar una meta.

autoestima positiva: (pág. 78) la creencia de una persona de su valor propio y de que merece respeto.

prerreciclaje: (pág. 622) proceso de reducción de desechos mediante el cual se compran productos en empaques que se pueden descomponer.

Organización de Proveedores Preferidos: (pág. 567) empresa que tiene un contrato con los proveedores del cuidado de la salud para proveer servicios de cuidado de salud a precios reducidos.

prehipertensión: (pág. 519) rango de presión arterial que aumenta el riesgo de sufrir enfermedades cardíacas y derrame cerebral.

prejuicio: (pág. 54) juicio adverso que se forma sin considerar los hechos.

muerte prematura: (pág. 368) muerte que ocurre antes de que una persona alcance su expectativa de vida.

receta médica: (pág. 406) orden que emite un profesional de la salud licenciado para un medicamento dispensado por un farmacéutico y el cual se puede usar para tratar o prevenir enfermedades.

delito de prestigio: (pág. 700) delito cometido con el propósito de tener un rango más alto que otros miembros de una pandilla.

disciplina preventiva: (pág. 197) entrenamiento en que un padre explica el comportamiento correcto y las consecuencias de un comportamiento erróneo.

cuidado primario: (pág. 565) atención de salud general.

principio de enfriamiento: (pág. 393) una sesión de ejercicios físicos debe terminar con 5 a 10 minutos de ejercicios reducidos para ayudar a que los latidos cardíacos, el índice de respiración y de circulación retornen a su normalidad.

principio de sobrecarga: (pág. 393) una sesión de ejercicios físicos debe incluir ejercicios más allá de los que se hacen para adquirir beneficios de buenas condiciones físicas adicionales.

principio de progresión: (pág. 393) la cantidad y la intensidad de los ejercicios físicos se debe aumentar gradualmente.

principio de reversibilidad de la buena condición física: (pág. 393) los beneficios de buenas condiciones físicas se pierden al parar el entrenamiento.

principio de especificidad: (pág. 393) una sesión de ejercicios debe incluir un tipo específico de ejercicios para alcanzar los beneficios de buena condición física deseados.

principle of warm-up: (p. 393) a workout should start with 5–10 minutes of easy exercise to warm and stretch muscles and increase blood flow.

proactive decision-making style: (p. 60) habit of a responsible person who is empowered by his or her choices.

probation: (p. 667) sentence in which an offender remains in the community under supervision of a probation officer for a specific period.

promiscuous behavior: (p. 562) engaging in sexual behavior with many people, which may result in an unplanned pregnancy or an STD.

promise breaker: (p. 181) unreliable person who does not keep his or her word.

proof: (p. 411) amount of alcohol in a beverage as measured by a percentage—for example, a beverage with 20 percent alcohol is 40 proof.

prostate gland: (p. 237) internal male reproductive organ that produces a fluid to help keep sperm alive.

prostitution: (p. 471) sexual activity for pay.

protective factor: (p. 452) something that increases the chances for a positive outcome.

protective order: (p. 681) court order forbidding an offender from further harassing, being violent toward, or threatening his or her victim.

protein: (p. 283) nutrient made up of amino acids that is needed for growth, to build, repair, and maintain body tissues.

protein-energy malnutrition (PEM): (p. 587) most deadly form of undernutrition.

protein loading: (p. 314) eating strategy in which extra protein is eaten.

protein supplements: (p. 288) a product taken orally that contains one or more ingredients that contain proteins that are intended to supplement one's diet and are not considered food.

protozoa: (p. 487) single-celled, tiny organisms that produce disease-causing toxins and cause diseases such as malaria and dysentery.

psoriasis: (p. 354) noncontagious, life-long immune system disease that often produces areas of inflamed scaly skin.

psychological dependence: (p. 458) strong craving to continue using a drug for emotional reasons.

psychosomatic disease (si koh suh MA tik): (p. 95) physical illness or disorder caused or worsened by emotional states.

principio de calentamiento: (pág. 393) una sesión de ejercicios debe comenzar con 5 a 10 minutos de ejercicio moderado para calentar y estirar los músculos y aumentar el flujo sanguíneo.

ciclo proactivo de toma de decisiones: (pág. 60) hábito de una persona responsable, quien se siente propulsada por sus opciones.

libertad condicional: (pág. 667) sentencia que dura un período específico de tiempo y en la cual un delincuente permanece en la comunidad bajo la supervisión de un funcionario a cargo de libertad condicional.

comportamiento promiscuo: (pág. 562) tener relaciones sexuales con muchas personas, lo cual puede resultar en un embarazo no planificado o una ETS.

persona que rompe promesas: (pág. 181) persona indigna de confianza que no cumple su palabra.

graduación normal: (pág. 411) cantidad de alcohol en una bebida, lo cual se mide con un porcentaje, por ejemplo, una bebida con 20 por ciento de alcohol tiene una graduación normal de 40.

próstata: (pág. 237) órgano reproductor masculino interno que produce un fluido que ayuda a mantener vivos los espermatozoides.

prostitución: (pág. 471) actividad sexual por la que se paga.

factor de protección: (pág. 452) algo que aumenta la posibilidad de un resultado positivo.

decreto protector: (pág. 681) decreto de la corte que prohibe a un infractor de que continúe hostigando, amenazando o usando violencia hacia su víctima.

proteína: (pág. 283) nutriente hecho de aminoácidos y el cual se necesita para el crecimiento, reparación y mantenimiento de los tejidos corporales.

desnutrición proteicoenergética: (pág. 587) la forma más letal de desnutrición.

carga de proteínas: (pág. 314) estrategia alimenticia en que se consume proteínas adicionales.

suplemento proteico: (pág. 288) producto que se toma oralmente y que está compuesto de uno o más ingredientes que contienen proteínas cuyo propósito es suplementar la dieta de una persona y el cual no se considera un alimento.

protozoarios: (pág. 487) diminutos organismos unicelulares que producen toxinas causantes de enfermedades como la malaria y la disentería.

psoriasis: (pág. 354) enfermedad no contagiosa del sistema inmunológico que se padece de por vida y la cual produce por lo general áreas de piel escamosa e inflamada.

dependencia psicológica: (pág. 458) fuerte antojo de continuar usando una droga por razones emocionales.

enfermedad psicosomática: (pág. 95) enfermedad o trastorno físico causado o agravado por el estado emocional.

puberty/pubertad

puberty: (p. 227) growth and development stage when males and females are able to reproduce.

pubic lice: (p. 503) parasitic STD caused by lice that survive by feeding off human blood; also called crabs.

public health: (p. 583) organized community efforts to prevent disease and injury and promote healthy behaviors.

pubertad: (pág. 227) etapa de desarrollo y crecimiento cuando los hombres y las mujeres son capaces de producir progenie.

piojo púbico: (pág. 503) ETS parasítica causada por piojos que sobreviven chupando sangre humana.

salud pública: (pág. 583) esfuerzos comunitarios organizados para prevenir enfermedades y lesiones y fomentar comportamientos saludables.

English	Español

quality of life: (p. 626) degree to which one can live life to the fullest.

calidad de vida: (pág. 626) nivel en el cual una persona puede vivir la vida plenamente.

English	Español

radon: (p. 535) odorless, colorless, radioactive gas, released from rocks and soil, that is associated with lung cancer.

random event: (p. 10) incident over which a person has little or no control.

random violence: (p. 671) violence over which a person has no control.

rape: (p. 687) threatened or actual use of physical force to make a person have sex without his or her consent.

rape survivor: (p. 695) one who has been raped.

rape trauma syndrome: (p. 695) condition of a rape survivor who experiences emotional responses and physical symptoms over time.

rapid eye movement (REM) sleep: (p. 361) sleep period during which most dreaming occurs that is characterized by rapid eye movements behind closed eyelids.

reactive decision-making style: (p. 60) habit of an easily influenced person who allow others to make his or her choices.

recall: (p. 547) taking products off the market because of safety concerns by the CPSC.

recovery program: (p. 143) a group, such as Alateen, that supports its members as they change to more responsible behaviors.

regular gang member: (p. 699) gang member who obeys hard-core gang members.

radón: (pág. 535) gas radiactivo incoloro e inodoro que liberan las rocas y el suelo y el cual se asocia con el cáncer del pulmón.

evento aleatorio: (pág. 10) incidente sobre el cual una persona tiene poco control o no puede controlar del todo.

violencia al azar: (pág. 671) violencia sobre la cual una persona no tiene ningún control.

violación: (pág. 687) uso de fuerza física o amenaza de usar fuerza física para hacer que una persona tenga relaciones sexuales sin su consentimiento.

sobreviviente de violación: (pág. 695) persona que ha sufrido violación.

síndrome del trauma de la violación: (pág. 695) condición del sobreviviente de violación, quien experimenta síntomas de respuestas emocionales y físicas con el tiempo.

sueño de movimiento rápido de los ojos (REM): (pág. 361) período del sueño durante el cual ocurre la mayor parte de los sueños y que se caracteriza por los movimientos rápidos de los ojos detrás de los párpados cerrados.

estilo reactivo de toma de decisiones: (pág. 60) hábito de una persona fácilmente influenciable, quien permite que otros tomen las decisiones por ella.

retiro: (pág. 547) el retiro del mercado de productos debido a asuntos de seguridad pedido por la CPSC.

programa de recuperación: (pág. 143) grupo, como por ejemplo Alateen, que apoya a sus miembros mientras cambian sus comportamientos por otros más saludables.

miembro regular de pandilla: (pág. 699) miembro de pandilla que obedece a los miembros incondicionales de la pandilla.

Glossary/Glosario

rejection: (p. 159) disappointing feeling of being unwelcome or unwanted.

relapse: (p. 87) return to a previous behavior, such as drug misuse or abuse.

repetitive strain injury (RSI): (p. 642) injury, such as carpal tunnel syndrome, that occurs from repeated physical movements.

reputation: (p. 169) one's overall character as judged by others.

rescue breaths: (p. 728) breathing into an unconscious victim who is not breathing normally.

resiliency: (p. 118) ability to adjust, recover, bounce back, and learn from hard times.

resistance exercise: (p. 380) exercise, such as lifting free weights, in which a force acts against muscles.

resistance skills: (p. 47) skills that help you say "no" to an action or leave a bad situation.

respect: (p. 167) special or high esteem for someone or something.

respiratory system: (p. 215) provides the body with oxygen through the lungs, its main organs, and removes carbon dioxide produced as waste.

responsible decision: (p. 168) a choice that leads to actions that: 1) promote health, 2) protect safety, 3) follow laws, 4) show respect for self and others, 5) follow the guidelines of your parents and/or guardian, 6) demonstrate good character.

Responsible Decision-Making Model: (p. 61) series of steps to follow to make good choices.

restitution: (p. 62) making good for any damage, loss, or harm.

restless legs syndrome (RLS): (p. 364) sleep disorder in which unpleasant sensations in the legs and feet, such as tingling and burning, cause the urge to move them for relief.

restraining order: (p. 692) court order forbidding an offender from coming within a certain distance of the victim.

rheumatic fever: (p. 492) autoimmune disease of the heart that can damage heart valves and result if strep throat is not treated promptly.

risk: (p. 10) chance taken without knowledge of the outcome; can be calculated and have positive effects or be unnecessary and have negative effects.

risk behavior: (p. 27) health-threatening behavior that can cause injury or early death or harm the environment.

rechazo: (pág. 159) sentimiento frustrado de no ser acogido o de ser rechazado del todo.

relapso: (pág. 87) retorno a un comportamiento anterior, como el uso erróneo o el abuso de drogas.

lesión por esfuerzo repetido: (pág. 642) lesión, como el síndrome del túnel carpiano, que ocurre debido al movimiento físico repetido.

reputación: (pág. 169) carácter general de una persona a la manera en que otros la juzgan.

respiración de rescate: (pág. 728) respirar por una persona inconsciente que ha dejado de respirar.

resiliencia: (pág. 118) capacidad de ajustarse, recuperarse, sobreponerse y aprender de los malos tiempos.

ejercicio de resistencia: (pág. 380) ejercicio como el levantamiento libre de pesas, en que una fuerza actúa contra los músculos.

destrezas de resistencia: (pág. 47) destrezas que te ayudan a decir "no" a una acción o a abandonar una mala situación.

respeto: (pág. 167) estima especial o alta estima por alguien o algo.

sistema respiratorio: (pág. 215) provee el oxígeno corporal a través de los pulmones, sus principales órganos, y elimina el dióxido de carbono que se produce como desecho.

decisión responsable: (pág. 168) una opción conducente a acciones que: 1) promueven la salud, 2) te mantienen a salvo, 3) cumplen las leyes, 4) muestran respeto por ti mismo(a) y otras personas, 5) siguen las reglas de tus padres o tus apoderados y 6) demuestran buen carácter.

modelo de toma de decisiones responsables: (pág. 61) serie de pasos a seguir para tomar buenas decisiones.

restitución: (pág. 62) reparación por cualquier daño, pérdida o mal.

síndrome de piernas inquietas: (pág. 364) trastorno del sueño en que una mala sensación en las piernas y en los pies (como un hormigueo y una quemazón) que obliga a la persona a moverlas para obtener alivio.

inhibitoria: (pág. 692) orden de la corte que prohibe a un infractor de acercarse a cierta distancia de la víctima.

fiebre reumática: (pág. 492) enfermedad inmunológica del corazón que puede ocasionar daño a las válvulas cardíacas y ser el resultado de la falta de tratamiento a tiempo de la infección de garganta por estreptococos.

riesgo: (pág. 10) tomar chances sin tener un conocimiento de las consecuencias; puede ser calculado y tener efectos positivos o innecesario y tener efectos negativos.

comportamiento de riesgo: (pág. 27) comportamiento que amenaza la salud y que puede causar lesiones, una muerte temprana o daños al ambiente.

risk factor: (p. 452) something that increases the chances for a negative outcome.

road rage: (p. 647) violence and aggression of drivers and passengers in motor vehicles toward other drivers.

role conformity: (p. 665) desire to behave in ways others approve of.

runoff: (p. 607) water that runs downslope along Earth's surface.

factor de riesgo: (pág. 452) algo que aumenta las posibilidades de un resultado negativo.

furia vial: (pág. 647) violencia y agresión de conductores y pasajeros hacia otros conductores.

papel conformista: (pág. 665) deseo de comportarse en maneras que otros aprueban.

escorrentía: (pág. 607) agua que corre cuesta abajo por la superficie terrestre.

S

English

Español

safe and drug-free school zone: (p. 469) defined area around a school where young people are sheltered from drug sales, in which there are stiffer penalties for selling drugs and carrying weapons.

salmonellosis (sal muh neh LOH suhs): (p. 320) food-borne illness from undercooked chicken, eggs, and other meats contaminated with the bacterium *Salmonella.*

saturated fat: (p. 299) fat from meat, poultry, dairy products, and hardened vegetable fat.

savings: (p. 554) money set aside for future use, such as investing in a certificate of deposit.

secondhand smoke: (p. 428) exhaled smoke and sidestream smoke; also called passive smoking and involuntary smoking.

self-control: (p. 75) degree to which one regulates his or her own behavior.

self-defense strategies: (p. 670) strategies to protect oneself from violence.

self-esteem: (p. 78) a person's positive or negative belief about his or her worth.

self-respect: (p. 74) high regard for oneself.

semi-vegetarian diet: (p. 300) diet that excludes red meat.

sensorineural hearing loss (sen suh ree NUR uhl): (p. 346) hearing loss that results from damage to the inner ear or acoustic nerve.

serotonin: (p. 97) chemical involved in controlling states of consciousness and mood.

severe thunderstorm warning: (p. 653) emergency alert issued when a severe thunderstorm is sighted or indicated on radar.

severe thunderstorm watch: (p. 653) emergency alert issued when a severe thunderstorm is likely to develop.

sex role: (p. 264) way a person acts and his or her feelings about being male or female.

zona escolar segura y libre de drogas: (pág. 469) área definida alrededor de una escuela donde los jóvenes encuentran refugio contra la venta de drogas y en las cuales existen penas severas por vender drogas y llevar armas.

salmonelosis: (pág. 320) enfermedad producida por el mal cocimiento del pollo, los huevos y otras carnes contaminadas con la bacteria *Salmonella.*

grasa saturada: (pág. 299) grasa proveniente de carnes, aves de corral, productos lácteos y grasas vegetales duras.

ahorros: (pág. 554) dinero que se separa para uso futuro, como la inversión en un certificado de depósito.

humo secundario: (pág. 428) humo exhalado y humo indirecto; también conocido como fumar pasivo y fumar involuntario.

autocontrol: (pág. 75) nivel al cual uno regula su propio comportamiento.

estrategias de autodefensa: (pág. 670) estrategias para protegerse a uno mismo de la violencia.

autoestima: (pág. 78) creencia positiva o negativa de una persona sobre su valor propio.

autorrespeto: (pág. 74) alto grado de consideración con uno mismo.

dieta semivegetariana: (pág. 300) dieta que excluye las carnes rojas.

pérdida auditiva sensorineural: (pág. 346) perdida de la audición que resulta de daños al oído interno o al nervio acústico.

seratonina: (pág. 97) sustancia química involucrada en el control de los estados de consciencia y de ánimo.

alerta de tormenta eléctrica rigurosa: (pág. 653) alerta de emergencia que se expide cuando se aviene una tormenta eléctrica rigurosa o cuando el radar detecta dichas tormentas.

aviso de tormenta eléctrica rigurosa: (pág. 653) alerta de emergencia que se expide cuando hay posibilidad de que se desarrolle una tormenta eléctrica rigurosa.

papel sexual: (pág. 264) manera en que actúa una persona y sus sentimientos acerca de su virilidad o su feminidad.

sexual abuse: (p. 691) maltreatment that involves any sexual contact that is forced on a person without his or her consent.

sexual assault: (p. 687) any unwanted sexual contact, including verbal threats, fondling, and rape.

sexual feelings: (p. 167) feelings that result from strong emotional and physical attraction to another person.

sexual fidelity: (p. 169) sexual faithfulness; in marriage having sex only with one's marriage partner.

sexual harassment: (p. 692) unwelcome, intimidating verbal or physical behaviors of a sexual nature.

sexually transmitted disease (STD): (p. 498) a disease caused by pathogens that are transmitted from an infected person to an uninfected person during intimate sexual contact.

shadowing: (p. 575) spending time with a mentor as he or she performs work activities.

shock: (p. 739) dangerous reduction in blood flow to body tissues that may lead to coma and death if untreated.

sickle-cell anemia: (p. 528) chronic, inherited health condition in which the red blood cells are fragile, sickle-shaped, carry less oxygen, and are easily destroyed.

side effect: (p. 407) unwanted body change, such as dry mouth or sleeplessness, that is an unintended effect from a drug.

single-custody family: (p. 152) family in which the child or children live with the parent who has legal custody.

skeletal system: (p. 216) support system whose bones protect organs, produce red and white blood cells, and work with muscles to produce movement.

skill-related fitness: (p. 382) capacity to perform well in physical activities and sports.

sleep: (p. 361) state of deep relaxation in which the brain continues to process information, but there is little movement or consciousness.

sleep apnea: (p. 363) sleep disorder in which there are brief interruptions of breathing during sleep, depriving a person of oxygen.

smog: (p. 604) combination of smoke and fog.

smoke detector: (p. 641) alarm that sounds when it detects smoke.

snuff: (p. 429) smokeless tobacco that is made from chopped tobacco leaves and stems, causes nicotine dependence, and contains carcinogens.

social reciprocity: (p. 665) treating others as you wish to be treated.

abuso sexual: (pág. 691) maltrato que involucra cualquier contacto sexual forzado sobre una persona sin su consentimiento.

asalto sexual: (pág. 687) cualquier contacto sexual indeseado, incluye las amenazas verbales, las caricias sexuales y la violación.

sentimientos sexuales: (pág. 167) sentimientos que son el resultado de una fuerte atracción emocional y física hacia otra persona.

fidelidad sexual: (pág. 169) lealtad sexual; en un matrimonio, tener relaciones sexuales sólo con el cónyuge matrimonial.

acoso sexual: (pág. 692) comportamientos verbales o físicos de intimidación indeseados de naturaleza sexual.

enfermedad transmitida sexualmente (STD): (pág. 498) enfermedad causada por patógenos transmitidos por una persona infectada a una persona sana durante el contacto sexual íntimo.

acompañar a un mentor: (pág. 575) pasar tiempo con un mentor mientras él o ella realiza sus actividades laborales.

choque: (pág. 739) reducción peligrosa en el flujo sanguíneo a los tejidos que puede resultar en coma y muerte si no se trata.

anemia drepanocítica: (pág. 528) condición de salud crónica heredada en que los glóbulos rojos son frágiles, tienen forma de hoz, transportan menos oxígeno y pueden ser destruidos fácilmente.

efecto secundario: (pág. 407) cambio corporal indeseado, como por ejemplo, sequedad de la boca o soñolencia, el cual es el resultado no intencional de una droga.

familia de custodia uniparental: (pág. 152) familia en que uno solo de los padres tiene la custodia legal de los niños.

sistema óseo: (pág. 216) sistema de apoyo cuyos huesos protegen los órganos, producen glóbulos blancos y glóbulos rojos y funcionan junto con los músculos para el movimiento.

aptitud física de destrezas: (pág. 382) capacidad de desempeñarse bien en actividades físicas y deportes.

sueño: (pág. 361) estado de relajamiento profundo en que el encéfalo continúa procesando información, pero en el cual hay poco movimiento o estado de consciencia.

apnea del sueño: (pág. 363) trastorno del sueño en que hay interrupciones breves de la respiración durante el sueño, las cuales privan a la persona de oxígeno.

smog: (pág. 604) combinación de humo y neblina.

detector de humo: (pág. 641) alarma que suena cuando detecta humo.

rapé: (pág. 429) tabaco sin humo compuesto de hojas y tallos de tabaco picados, causa dependencia de la nicotina y contiene sustancias carcinógenas.

reciprocidad social: (pág. 665) tratar a los demás de la manera en que te gustaría ser tratado.

social-emotional booster: (p. 79) positive interpersonal contact that helps a person feel encouraged and supported, choose responsible behavior, and recognize options.

social-emotional environment: (p. 79) quality of one's interactions with family, peers, and adults in the community.

social-emotional pollutant: (p. 79) negative interpersonal contact that closes options and can cause a person to feel discouraged, alienated, and to choose wrong behavior.

sodium: (p. 305) a mineral your body needs only in small amounts.

solar energy: (p. 619) energy from the sun, which can be converted to heat or electrical energy.

sound waves: (p. 613) regular vibrations of air.

specialist: (p. 565) professional, such as a gynecologist or a cardiologist, with specialized training in a particular area.

splint: (p. 716) a device used to protect and immobilize a body part.

stalking: (p. 692) obsessing about a person with an intent to harm.

static stretching: (p. 379) safe and effective flexibility technique that involves stretching a muscle until a pull is felt and then holding the stretch for 15–30 seconds.

status offenses: (p. 667) delinquent behaviors, such as truancy, for which an adult would not be arrested.

stepfamily: (p. 153) consists of the marital partners, their children from previous marriages, and children they've had by their marriage together.

steroids: (p. 449) drugs made from hormones.

stimulants: (p. 444) drugs, such as cocaine and methamphetamine, that speed up the central nervous system and cause multiple, sometimes fatal, health problems; also called uppers.

strep throat: (p. 492) contagious bacterial infection of the throat that can lead to rheumatic fever if not treated promptly.

stress: (p. 100) response of the body to daily living demands.

stress-management skills: (p. 104) health-protective techniques used to prevent and deal with stressors.

stroke: (p. 516) condition caused by a blocked or broken blood vessel in the brain that may result in disability, paralysis, or death.

student-assistance program: (p. 478) school-based drug prevention and treatment program.

sudden infant death syndrome (SIDS): (p. 257) sudden, unexplained death of an infant younger than one year of age.

fomentador socioemocional: (pág. 79) contacto interpersonal positivo que anima y apoya a una persona a que escoja comportamientos responsables y a que reconozca sus opciones.

ambiente socioemocional: (pág. 79) calidad de las interacciones de una persona con su familia, sus compañeros y los adultos en la comunidad.

contaminante socioemocional: (pág. 79) contacto interpersonal negativo que cierra las opciones y que desalienta y aísla a una persona y la impulsa a que escoja una mala conducta.

energía solar: (pág. 619) energía proveniente del Sol que puede ser convertida en energía calórica o eléctrica.

ondas sonoras: (pág. 613) vibraciones regulares de aire.

especialista: (pág. 565) profesional, como un ginecólogo o un cardiólogo, con entrenamiento especializado en un área particular.

tablilla: (pág. 716) dispositivo que se usa para inmovilizar una parte del cuerpo.

acecho: (pág. 692) obsesión sobre una persona con intención de hacerle daño.

estiramiento estático: (pág. 379) técnica de flexión efectiva y segura que involucra estirar un músculo hasta que se siente una contracción y luego se sostiene el estiramiento durante 15 a 30 segundos.

infracciones de estatus: (pág. 667) comportamientos delincuentes, como la haraganería, por los que no se apresaría a un adulto.

familia adoptiva: (pág. 153) consta de los cónyuges matrimoniales, sus hijos de matrimonios anteriores y los hijos que tienen en el matrimonio juntos.

esteroides: (pág. 449) drogas hechas de hormonas.

estimulantes: (pág. 444) drogas, como la cocaína y la metanfetamina, que aceleran el sistema nervioso central y causan problemas de salud múltiples y con frecuencia letales.

infección de garganta por estreptocos: (pág. 492) infección bacteriana contagiosa de la garganta que puede conducir a fiebre reumática si no se trata a tiempo.

estrés: (pág. 100) respuesta corporal a las demandas del diario vivir.

destrezas de manejo del estrés: (pág. 104) técnicas protectoras de la salud que se usan en la prevención y tratamiento de estresores.

apoplejía: (pág. 516) condición causada por la obstrucción o el rompimiento de los vasos sanguíneos que van al encéfalo y la cual puede resultar en discapacidad, parálisis o muerte.

programa de asistencia estudiantil: (pág. 478) programa escolar de tratamiento y prevención del uso de drogas.

Síndrome de Muerte Infantil Súbita (SMIS): (pág. 257) muerte repentina e inexplicable de un lactante de menos de un año de edad.

suffocation: (p. 641) an obstruction of the airway by an external object that blocks the mouth and nose, such as plastic bags, pillows, or blankets.

suicide: (p. 114) intentional taking of one's own life.

suicide prevention strategies: (p. 117) techniques, such as active listening, to help prevent someone from thinking about, attempting, and completing suicide.

support group: (p. 88) group of people who help one another recover from a particular disease, an addiction, or a difficult situation.

asfixia: (pág. 641) obstrucción de las vías respiratorias debido a que un objeto externo bloquea la boca y la nariz, como por ejemplo, una bolsa plástica, una almohada o una colcha.

suicidio: (pág. 114) terminar intencionalmente con la vida propia.

estrategias de prevención de suicidio: (pág. 117) técnicas, como el escuchar, para ayudar a prevenir que una persona piense, intente o que cometa el suicidio.

grupo de apoyo: (pág. 88) grupo de personas que se ayudan mutuamente en la recuperación de una enfermedad particular, una adicción o una situación difícil.

T

English   **Español**

tamper-resistant package: (p. 407) package that is sealed, assuring the buyer that it has not been opened.

tar: (p. 426) thick, sticky fluid formed when tobacco burns that irritates respiratory tissues and is a major cause of cancer.

teasing: (p. 676) making fun of someone in a good-natured way.

technology: (p. 35) in media, using high-tech equipment to communicate information in various forms, such as pop-up Internet ads.

terminal illness: (p. 276) illness that will result in the person's death.

testosterone: (p. 235) hormone secreted by the testes that produces male secondary sex characteristics.

tetanus: (p. 741) bacterial disease that affects the nervous system and muscles and can result from a puncture wound; also called lockjaw.

thrush: (p. 504) opportunistic fungal infection of the tongue and mouth.

time management: (p. 551) organizing time to accomplish priorities, which can increase productivity and reduce stress.

time out: (p. 259) calming-down period that might be needed when a child has a tantrum.

tinnitus: (p. 614) ringing, hissing sensation in the ears that may develop from exposure to loud noises.

tobacco: (p. 425) herbal plant that is grown for its leaves and that contains nicotine.

tolerance: (p. 458) condition in which the body becomes used to a substance and needs more of it for an effect.

empaque a prueba de alteraciones: (pág. 407) empaque que se sella de tal manera para asegurar al comprador que no ha sido abierto.

alquitrán: (pág. 426) fluido pegajoso y grueso formado de la quema del tabaco, el cual irrita los tejidos respiratorios y es una de las principales causas del cáncer.

tomar el pelo: (pág. 676) hacerle bromas a alguien sin malas intenciones.

tecnología: (pág. 35) en los medios de comunicación, uso de equipo de alta tecnología para comunicar información de varias formas, como por ejemplo, anuncios de tráfico adecuado de Internet.

enfermedad letal: (pág. 276) enfermedad que da como resultado la muerte de la persona.

testosterona: (pág. 235) hormona secretada por los testículos que produce las características sexuales secundarias en los varones.

tétanus: (pág. 741) enfermedad bacteriana que afecta el sistema nervioso y los músculos y que resulta de una herida punzante.

afta: (pág. 504) infección fúngica oportunística de la lengua y la boca.

manejo del tiempo: (pág. 551) organizar el tiempo para llevar a cabo las prioridades, lo cual puede aumentar la productividad y reducir el estrés.

espacio separado: (pág. 259) período que podría necesitar un niño para calmarse después de un berrinche.

tinnitus: (pág. 614) sensación de tintineo y siseo en los oídos que puede resultar de la exposición a ruidos fuertes.

tabaco: (pág. 425) planta herbácea que se cultiva por sus hojas y

tolerancia: (pág. 458) condición en que el cuerpo se acostumbra a una sustancia y necesita mayor cantidad de ésta para que la sustancia tenga efecto.

tornado warning/advertencia de tornado　　　　　**urinary system/sistema urinario**

tornado warning: (p. 652) emergency alert issued when a tornado is sighted or indicated on radar.

tornado watch: (p. 652) emergency alert issued when a tornado is likely to develop.

toxemia of pregnancy: (p. 202) disorder of pregnancy that can progress to seizures and coma and is characterized by tissue swelling, protein in the urine, and high blood pressure.

toxin: (p. 412) any poisonous substance, such as alcohol.

training zone: (p. 394) range of overload required to gain fitness benefits.

tryptophan: (p. 363) amino acid found in milk that helps produce relaxation.

tumor: (p. 531) abnormal growth of tissue that can be benign or malignant.

type II diabetes: (p. 367) type of diabetes in which the body either does not produce enough insulin or cannot use the insulin that is produced.

advertencia de tornado: (pág. 652) alerta de emergencia que se expide cuando se ha avistado un tornado en el radar.

aviso de tornado: (pág. 652) alerta de emergencia que se expide cuando existe la posibilidad de que se desarrolle un tornado.

toxemia del embarazo: (pág. 202) trastorno del embarazo que puede progresar a convulsiones y coma y se caracteriza por la hinchazón de los tejidos, la presencia de proteína en la orina y la presión sanguínea alta.

toxina: (pág. 412) cualquier sustancia venenosa, como el alcohol.

zona de entrenamiento: (pág. 394) rango de sobrecarga requerido para obtener beneficios de acondicionamiento físico.

triptofán: (pág. 363) aminoácido lácteo que ayuda a producir el relajamiento.

tumor: (pág. 531) crecimiento anormal de tejidos que puede ser benigno o maligno.

diabetes tipo II: (pág. 367) tipo de diabetes en el cual el cuerpo no produce suficiente insulina o no puede usar apropiadamente la insulina que produce.

U

English　　　　　**Español**

ultrasound: (p. 245) diagnostic procedure using high-frequency sound waves to provide an image of the developing baby and monitor its growth.

ultraviolet (UV) radiation: (p. 534) radiation that comes from the sun, is emitted from sunlamps and tanning booths, and can increase skin cancer risk with repeated exposure.

undernutrition: (p. 586) diet and illness related deficiency in calories, protein, vitamins, or minerals.

universal distress signal: (p. 725) clutching at the throat to show difficulty breathing.

universal precautions: (p. 711) steps to prevent disease spread by treating human blood and bodily fluids as if they contain HIV, HBV, and other pathogens.

unnecessary risk: (p. 670) chance not worth taking.

urgent-care centers: (p. 571) non-hospital facilities that provide emergency health care.

urinary system: (p. 224) removes liquid wastes from the body, maintains water balance, and consists of the kidneys, ureters, bladder, and urethra.

ultrasonido: (pág. 245) procedimiento de diagnóstico que usa ondas sonoras de alta frecuencia para proveer una imagen de un bebé en desarrollo y vigilar su crecimiento.

radiación ultravioleta: (pág. 534) radiación solar; la emiten las lámparas solares y las camas bronceadoras y cuya exposición repetida puede aumentar el riesgo de cáncer de la piel.

mala nutrición: (pág. 586) insuficiencia de calorías, proteínas, vitaminas o minerales relacionada con la dieta y las enfermedades.

señal universal de socorro: (pág. 725) sostenerse fuertemente la garganta para mostrar dificultad respiratoria.

precauciones universales: (pág. 711) pasos para prevenir la propagación de enfermedades al tratar la sangre y fluidos humanos como si estuvieran contaminados con VIH, VBH y otros patógenos.

riesgo innecesario: (pág. 670) chance que no vale la pena tomar.

centros de cuidados de urgencia: (pág. 571) instalaciones que no son hospitales y que proveen cuidado de salud de emergencia.

sistema urinario: (pág. 224) elimina los desechos del cuerpo, mantiene el equilibrio del agua y comprende los riñones, los uréteres, la vejiga y la uretra.

Glossary/Glosario

user: (p. 164) a person who does most of the receiving in a relationship.

uterus: (p. 229) muscular female reproductive organ that receives and supports the fertilized ovum.

abusador: (pág. 164) persona quien recibe la mayor parte de los beneficios en una relación.

útero: (pág. 229) órgano reproductor muscular femenino que recibe y da apoyo al óvulo fecundado.

V

English	Español

vaccine: (p. 485) substance containing dead or weakened pathogens that causes the body to make antibodies for a specific disease-causing agent.

value: (p. 75) standard or belief, such as compassion, good citizenship, and respect.

vas deferens: (p. 236) internal male reproductive structures that act as a passageway for sperm.

V-chip: (p. 560) programmable electronic device that parents or guardians can use to block inappropriate television programs.

vegan diet: (p. 300) diet that excludes foods of animal origin.

vegetarian diet: (p. 300) diet that focuses on vegetables and restricts or eliminates foods of animal origin.

victim assessment: (p. 723) checking an injured or sick person to see if certain conditions, such as an open airway, are present.

victim recovery: (p. 683) a person's return to physical and emotional health after experiencing violence.

victim of violence: (p. 657) person harmed by a violent act.

violence: (p. 657) use of destructive physical force against property, oneself, or others.

visitation rights: (p. 150) guidelines set for visitation of children by the parent who does not have custody.

visual environment: (p. 615) outdoor and indoor surroundings.

visual pollution: (p. 615) unattractive sights, such as graffiti and trash.

vitamin: (p. 286) water-soluble or fat-soluble nutrient that helps the body use energy stored in carbohydrates, fats, and proteins.

vitamin A deficiency: (p. 588) leading cause of preventable blindness.

volunteer: (p. 65) person who donates services and improves others' quality of life.

vacuna: (pág. 485) sustancia que contiene patógenos muertos o debilitados y que hace que el cuerpo forme anticuerpos para agente específico causante de enfermedades.

valor: (pág. 75) norma o creencia, como por ejemplo la compasión, la buena conducta y el respeto.

vasos deferentes: (pág. 236) estructuras reproductoras masculinas internas que actúan como un pasadizo para los espermatozoides.

chip V: (pág. 560) dispositivo electrónico programable que los padres o apoderados pueden usar para bloquear programas televisivos inapropiados.

dieta vegana: (pág. 300) dieta que excluye alimentos de origen animal.

dieta vegetariana: (pág. 300) dieta cuyo enfoque son los vegetales y la cual restringe o elimina alimentos de origen animal.

evaluación de la víctima: (pág. 723) chequeo de una persona lesionada o enferma para averiguar si ciertas condiciones, como las vías respiratorias sin obstrucción, están presentes.

recuperación de una víctima: (pág. 683) retorno de la salud física y emocional de una persona que ha experimentado violencia.

víctima de violencia: (pág. 657) persona que ha sufrido daño debido a un acto de violencia.

violencia: (pág. 657) uso de fuerza física destructora contra la propiedad, uno mismo u otros.

derechos de visita: (pág. 150) conjunto de reglas para el padre o la madre que no tiene custodia para visitar a sus hijos.

ambiente visual: (pág. 615) los alrededores exteriores e interiores.

contaminación visual: (pág. 615) vistas desagradables, como las inscripciones anónimas y la basura.

vitamina: (pág. 286) nutriente hidrosoluble o liposoluble que ayuda al cuerpo a usar la energía almacenada en los carbohidratos, las grasas y las proteínas.

insuficiencia vitamínica A: (pág. 588) causa principal de ceguera que puede prevenirse.

voluntario: (pág. 65) persona que dona sus servicios y mejora la calidad de vida de otros.

volunteer burnout/agobia de voluntario

volunteer burnout: (p. 66) loss of enthusiasm about volunteering that results from feeling overwhelmed.

volunteer center: (p. 66) organization that matches a person's skills with volunteer opportunities.

volunteering: (p. 575) donating a service.

agobia de voluntario: (pág. 66) pérdida del entusiasmo para servir de voluntario, lo cual resulta de sentirse abrumado.

centro de voluntarios: (pág. 66) organización que coordina las destrezas de una persona con las oportunidades de servir como voluntario.

voluntarismo: (pág. 575) donar un servicio.

English	Español

wanna-be: (p. 699) child or teen who may dress in gang clothing and perform violent acts or criminal behaviors to prove himself or herself worthy of belonging to the gang.

warts: (p. 354) noncancerous skin growths caused by the human papillomavirus (HPV).

weapons: (p. 704) device, such as a gun or knife, used to inflict harm.

wellness: (p. 11) quality of life resulting from health status.

Western blot: (p. 512) blood test used to confirm an EIA test, which checks for HIV antibodies.

wildland fire: (p. 653) fire in the wilderness.

wildlife sanctuary: (p. 627) area reserved for protection of plants and animals.

withdrawal symptoms: (p. 458) unpleasant reactions, such as chills, vomiting, and cramps, experienced when a person who is physically dependent on a drug stops using it.

work ethic: (p. 139) attitude of discipline, motivation, and commitment toward tasks.

wrong decision: (p. 62) decision that can be harmful, illegal, unsafe, or show disrespect.

"que quiere ser": (pág. 699) niño o adolescente que se viste con ropas de pandilla y realiza actos de violencia o comportamientos criminales para probar que es digno de pertenecer a la pandilla.

verrugas: (pág. 354) crecimientos cutáneos no cancerosos causados por el papilomavirus humano (PVH).

armas: (pág. 704) dispositivo, como un revólver o un cuchillo, que se usa para infligir daño.

bienestar: (pág. 11) calidad de vida que resulta del estado de salud.

prueba de transferencia de Western: (pág. 512) prueba de sangre que se usa para confirmar un ensayo inmunoenzimático de enzimas (EIA), el cual detecta anticuerpos para el VIH.

incendio de tierras salvajes: (pág. 653) incendio que ocurre en tierras que son salvajes.

santuario de vida salvaje: (pág. 627) área reservada para la protección de plantas y animales.

síntomas de abstinencia: (pág. 458) reacciones desagradables, como los temblores, el vómito y los calambres, que experimenta una persona que depende físicamente de una droga, al dejar de usar dicha droga.

ética laboral: (pág. 139) actitud de disciplina, motivación y compromiso hacia las tareas.

decisión equivocada: (pág. 62) decisión que puede ser dañina, ilegal, peligrosa o que muestra falta de respeto.

English	Español

you-message: (p. 42) statement that blames or shames another person.

mensaje "tú": (pág. 42) declaración que acusa o avergüenza a otra persona.

Index

Index Key

Italic numbers = illustration/photo   **Bold numbers** = vocabulary term

act. = activity

911, calling, 19, *19 act.*

Abandonment, 142

Abdominal thrusts, 725

Abrasions, 740

Abstinence from sex, 166–175, 471; limits for physical affection, 166, 167, 235; practicing after sexual activity, 174–175; pregnancy prevention and, 168, 232; reproductive health and, 168, 232, 240; researching reasons for, 132; resisting pressure to have sex, 170–171, *171 act.*, 172–173; *Speaking Out: Teens Talk About Health,* 176; STD and HIV prevention by, 168, 471, 508

Abuse, 141–142; child abuse, 141, 658, 678, 679; elder abuse, 141, 658; emotional abuse, 141, 678, 679; mental and emotional abuse, 678, 679; neglect, 142, 678; parent abuse, 141; physical abuse, 142, 678; sexual abuse, 140, 142, 678, 691, 694–695; spouse abuse, 141

Abusers, 181

Accessing Health Services, emergency telephone calls, *19 act.*

Accessing Valid Health Information, Products, and Services, help hotlines, *120 act.*; making emergency telephone call, *19 act.*; managing asthma, *495 act.*; pregnancy topics, *249 act.*; scheduling a dental or medical exam, *350 act.*

Accidents. *See* Unintentional injuries

Acid rain, 604

Acne, 353, 356

Acoustic nerve, 346

Acoustic trauma, 614

Acquaintance rape, 418, 687

Acquired immunodeficiency syndrome (AIDS), 471, 504–505, 510–511, 535. *See also* Human immunodeficiency virus (HIV)

Action plans, 267

Activated charcoal, 745

Active immunity, 485

Active listening, 43, *44 act.*

Activity: Using Life Skills, active listening, *44 act.*; alcohol advertisements, *417 act.*; asthma, controlling, *495 act.*; breast self-exams, *233 act.*; budgeting, *554 act.*; cardiovascular health and exercise, *517 act.*; cigarette smoking, quitting, *431 act.*; conflict resolution in families, *146 act.*; date rape, reducing risk of, *689 act.*; dental exams, scheduling, *350 act.*; diabetes, decreasing risk of, *524 act.*; drug use, resisting, *465 act.*; egg

baby exercise, *200 act.*; emergency telephone calls, *19 act.*; environmental health, *629 act.*; evaluating advertisements, *38 act.*; family changes, communicating about, *151 act.*; food labels, *292 act.*; health goals, *59 act.*; health-related fitness assessment, *383 act.*; help hotlines, *120 act.*; menu planning, *317 act.*; motor vehicle safety contract, *648 act.*; noise pollution, avoiding, *614 act.*; pathogens, preventing spread of, *488 act.*; patterns of behavior self-test, *662 act.*; physical fitness plan, creating, *372 act.*; pregnancy topics, researching, *249 act.*; responsible decision making, *470 act.*; schedule, creating a, *552 act.*; sex, resisting pressure to have, *171 act.*; skin cancer facts, *13 act.*; sleep journals, *364 act.*; stress management, *103 act.*; testicular self-exam, *239 act.*; volunteering, *67 act.*, *273 act.*; weight management, *327 act.*

Actual consent, 710

Addictions, 82, 84–87, 141; alcohol. *See* Alcoholism (alcohol dependence); codependence and, 88, 140, 141, 143, 146, 460; to computers, 86; to drugs. *See* Drug addiction; to exercise, 84, 85; family relationships and, 140–141; to gambling, 85; health status and, 84; to nicotine, 85, 425; perfectionism and, 85; recognizing, 87; to relationships, 85; to shopping, 86; teens at risk for, 84; to television, 86; thrill-seeking, 86; treatment options for, 87, 92, 146; to work (workaholism), 86

ADHD. *See* Attention-deficit/hyperactivity disorder (ADHD)

Adipose tissue, 326

Adolescence, developmental tasks of, 190–191, **264**–265

Adrenal glands, 219

Adrenaline, 100, 101, 219

Ads. *See* Advertisements (ads)

Adult Children of Alcoholics (ACOA), 420

Adult day care, 275

Adults, nutrition needs of, 298

Adversity, resiliency against, 660

Advertisements (ads), 35, 37–38; for alcoholic beverages, *417 act.*, 421; appeals used in, 38; evaluation of, 3, 37–38, *38 act.*, 73, 133, 207, 281, 341, 403, 483, 541, 593, 637; false and health fraud, 19, 545, 546; for tobacco products, 430–431

Advertising, 37

Advocating for Health, getting someone to quit smoking, *431 act.*; protecting the environment, *629 act.*; reduce noise pollution, *614 act.*; reduce risk of diabetes, *524 act.*; volunteering, *67 act.*; volunteering to help older adults, *273 act.*

Aerobic exercise, 371, 375

Affection, 138, 167; learning how to express, 138–139; setting limits for physical, 166, 167, 174, 674

African hair, 358

African sleeping sickness, 487

Afterbirth, 250

Aftercare, 668

Age, 270

Aggressive behavior, 48, 661; alcohol use and, 417; patterns of behavior self-test and, *662 act.*

Agility, 382

Aging, 270, 271–274, 376

AIDS. *See* Acquired immunodeficiency syndrome (AIDS)

AIDS dementia complex, 505

AIDS Health Fraud Task Force, 511

Air bags, motor vehicle, 645

Airborne fibers, cancer risk and, 535

Air pollution, 397, 535, 602, 603–606, 630; greenhouse effect and global warming, 598; major sources of, 604–605; ozone layer and, 597; preventing, 606

Air Quality Index (AQI), 397, 603

Al-Anon, 146, 420, 754

Alarm stage, general adaptation syndrome (GAS), 100

Alateen, 146, 754

Alcohol, 411; blood alcohol concentration (BAC) and, 411–413; dependence on (alcoholism). *See* Alcoholism (alcohol dependence); effect on body systems, 414; effect on thinking and decision making, 416–417; entry of into bloodstream, 411; hangovers and blackouts from, 417; production of by fermentation, 411; as a toxin, 412. *See also* Alcohol use

Alcohol dependence. *See* Alcoholism (alcohol dependence)

Alcoholic beverages, 411; advertisements for, *417 act.*, 421; minimum age for consuming, 415, 418; one-half ounce as one drink of, 412; outlawing of during Prohibition, 415; production of by fermentation, 411; proof of, **411;** resisting peer pressure to consume, 422; types of, 411

Alcoholic hepatitis, 414

Alcoholics Anonymous (AA), 146, 420, 754

Alcoholism (alcohol dependence), 85, 419; risk factors for, 420; treatment of, 146, 420

Alcohol use, accidents caused by, 470; alcoholism (alcohol dependence) and, 85, 146, 419, 420; cancer from excessive, 535; date rape, risk of and, 688–689; depression and, 111, 112; drinking and driving and, 418, 645;

Index

Index

Index

Index

Nail infections, 355, 487

Nail products, 355

Nails, 223; artificial, 355; infections of, 355, 487; ingrown, 354

Narcolepsy, 364, 528

Narcotics, 446–447

National Academy of Sciences, 303

National Adoption Center, 752

National alerts (Homeland Security Advisory System), 654

National Alliance for Hispanic Health, 755

National Cancer Institute, 303, 755

National Center for Environmental Health, 755

National Clearinghouse for Alcohol and Drug Information, 754

National Clearinghouse on Child Abuse and Neglect, 752

National Community Service Trust Act, 631

National Council Against Health Fraud, *547*

National Council on Aging, 753

National Domestic Violence Hotline, 681

National Environmental Policy Act, *600*

National Fire Prevention Association, 755

National health concerns, Healthy People 2010 and, 58; ten leading health indicators, 59

National Health Council, 754

National health goals (Healthy People 2010), 58

National Health Information Center (NHIC), *547*

National Highway Traffic Safety Administration (NHTSA), 644, 646, 755

National Institute for Occupational Safety and Health (NIOSH), 599

National Institute of Mental Health, 752

National Institute on Drug Abuse, National Institutes of Health, 754

National Institutes of Health (NIH), 20, 584

National Mental Health Association, 752

National parks, **627**

National Sexual Assault Hotline, 695

Natural disasters, **650,** 651–654; earthquakes, 653; electrical storms, 653–654; emergency kit in case of, 651; floods, 652; hurricanes, 652; landslides, 651–652; tornadoes, 652–653; wildland fires, 653

Natural environment, **626,** 627–632; effect on health status, 627; health advocacy for, *629 act.,* 631, 632; places where one can appreciate, 627; protection of, 598, 628–629

Natural gas, 604, **619**

Natural resources, **618;** energy and, 619; conserving, 620–621

Nature preserves, **627**

Nature trails, **627**

Needles, spread of HIV by sharing, 471, 506

Negative belief statements, 76

Negative influences, protection from, 36

Negative peer pressure, **45,** 462; consequences of giving into, 46; facing up to bad decisions, 46; learning to say "no" (resistance skills), 47; peer pressure statements, 45. See also Peer pressure

Negative self-esteem, **78**

Neglect, **678**

Nerve cells. *See* Neurons

Nervous system, **212**–213; aging and, 271; effect of alcohol use on, 414

Neurologists, 566

Neurons, 213

Newborns, Apgar score for, 251, 580; care for, 256–257; characteristics of, 256. *See also* Babies

Niacin, 286

Nicknames, gang activity and, 699

Nicotine, 424, **425.** *See also* Tobacco; tobacco use

Nicotine addiction, **85,** 425

Nicotine chewing gum, *433*

Nicotine dependence, **85,** 425

Nicotine inhaler, *433*

Nicotine nasal spray, *433*

Nicotine patch, *433*

Nicotine withdrawal syndrome, **425**

911 services, 19, *19 act.*

Nitrogen oxides, **604**

Nitroglycerin, **515**

Nitrous oxide, **441**

Noise, **612;** noise pollution and, 346, 614, *614 act.;* as stressor, 103. *See also* Sound

Noise pollution, 346, 614, *614 act.*

"No," learning to say (resistance skills), 47

Nonbiodegradable solid waste, **622**

Noncommunicable diseases, **494**

Nongovernmental environmental advocates, 600

Non-Hodgkin's disease, 532, *533*

Non-insulin-dependent diabetes mellitus (NIDDM; Type II diabetes), **367,** 523, 524. *See also* Diabetes (diabetes mellitus)

Non-nicotine pill, *433*

Nonrapid eye movement (NREM) sleep, **361**

Nonverbal communication, **41,** 47

Nonviolence, **657**

Norepinephrine, **367**

Nosebleeds, **743**

NREM (nonrapid eye movement) sleep, 361

Nuclear energy, **619**

Nuclear reactor, **619**

Nuclear stress test, *520*

Nurse practitioners, 17

Nurses, 17, 578, 579, 580

Nursing homes, 275, 572

Nutrients, **282;** amount needed by people of different ages, 298; carbohydrates, 284; Dietary Guidelines for, 294, 299; fats, 285; information on in food labels, 290; minerals,

287; proteins, 283; vitamins, 286; water, 289

Nutrition, **282;** day's menu, planning of, *317 act.;* Dietary Guidelines for, 294, 299; dining out and, 316–317, 318, 319; health behavior inventory questions on, 29; healthful breakfast and lunch, 312; healthful dinner, 313; health resources on, 753; snack selection and, 313; sports and, 314, 315; stress and, 101–102. *See also* Diet; eating habits

Nutrition facts, food label, **290**

Nutritionists, **577**

Obesity, **329;** binge eating disorder and, 336; treatment of with medication, 331. *See also* Weight; weight loss

Obsessive compulsive disorder (OCD), **89**

Obstetricians, 566

Occupational Safety and Health Act (OSH Act), 543, 600, **642**

Occupational Safety and Health Administration (OSHA), 599

Occupational therapists (OTs), **578**

Occupations, banning of minors from hazardous, 642, *643*

OCD. *See* Obsessive compulsive disorder (OCD)

Office for Victims of Crime, *696*

Office on Smoking and Health, National Center for Chronic Disease, 754

Oil (petroleum), 604, **619**

Older adults, assistance for, 275; benefits of physical activity for, 368; caregivers for, 275; habits that promote healthful aging in, 274; mental changes experienced by, 273; nutritional needs of, 298; physical changes experienced by, 271–272; social changes experienced by, 273; volunteering to help, *273 act.*

Olive oil, 305

Omega-3 fatty acids, 305, 515

Oncologists, 566

One-mile walk test, 378, *383 act.*

One-sided friendships, 164

Open fractures, **716**

Open-mouth kissing, HIV transmission and, 506

Open wounds, **740**

Ophthalmologists, **344,** 566

Opium, 446, *447*

Opportunistic infections, **504**–505

Optic nerve, **345**

Optometrist, **344,** 565

Oral cancer, **532,** *533*

Oral hairy leukoplakia, 504

Ordinances, 543

Organs, **208**

Organ transplants, HIV infection from, 507

Orthopedists, 566

Osteoarthritis, **526**

Osteoporosis, 271, **272,** 306, 368

Otolaryngologists (ENTs), **346,** 566

Index

Magnification Key

Magnifications listed are the magnification at which images were originally photographed.
TEM–Transmission Electron Microscope
SEM–Scanning Electron Microscope

Art Credits

Glencoe would like to acknowledge the artists and agencies who participated in illustrating this program: Precision Graphics.

Photo Credits

Cover (front)Photodisc/Getty Images, (back)CORBIS; **i** Photodisc/Getty Images; **iv** CORBIS; **vi** Photodisc/Getty Images; **iix** John Henley/CORBIS; **ix** David Young Wolff/PhotoEdit; **xii** Photodisc/Getty Images; **xiii** Tim Fuller; **xv** International Stock/Image State; **xvi** AFP/CORBIS; **xvii** Digital Vision/Getty Images; **2** Bettmann/CORBIS; **3** Ron Fehling/Masterfile; **4** John Henley/CORBIS; **5** (tt)Photodisc/Getty Images, Ken Frick, (t)Jim Cummins/Getty Images, (bl)Rob Lewine/CORBIS, (br)Spencer Jones/Getty Images; **6** Doug Martin; **8** Mary Kate Denny/PhotoEdit; **9** Mark Segal/Index Stock; **10** (tt)CORBIS, (b)Marc Romanelli/Getty Images; **11** Photodisc/Getty Images; **13** Aaron Haupt; **14** Photodisc/Getty Images, Aaron Haupt, Bill Varie/CORBIS; **16** Tom Stewart/CORBIS; **17** Photodisc/Getty Images; **18** (t to b)courtesy Food & Drug Administration, courtesy of the Federal Trade Commission, courtesy of the Consumer Product Safety Commision, Doug Martin, Jose Luis Pelaez/CORBIS; **19** Dwayne Newton/PhotoEdit; **20** Photodisc/Getty Images; **23** KS Studios; **26** Matt Meadows; **27** Photodisc/Getty Images; **28** Photodisc/Getty Images, Ken Frick; **29** Tim Fuller; **30** Jonathan Nourok/PhotoEdit; **31** Micheal Newman/PhotoEdit; **32** Tim Courlas; **33** Jonathan Nourok/PhotoEdit; **34** Matthew Roharik; **35** Photodisc/Getty Images; **38** Jack Hollingsworth/CORBIS; **39** Matthew Roharik; **40** ThinkStock/Index Stock; **41** (tt)Photodisc/Getty Images, (b)Dave Robertson/Masterfile; **42** David Young-Wolf/PhotoEdit; **43** Photodisc/Getty Images; **44** David Schmidt/Masterfile; **47 48 49** Photodisc/Getty Images; **50** Joe Feingersh/Masterfile; **51 53 54** Photodisc/Getty Images; **55** Dave Robertson/Masterfile; **56 58** Photodisc/Getty Images; **59** Matt Meadows; **60** Photodisc/Getty Images; **61** (tt)Photodisc/Getty Images, (b)Tim Fuller; **62** (tt)Photodisc/Getty Images, CORBIS, (others)Doug Martin; **64** Matt Meadows; **65** Aaron Haupt; **66** Photodisc/Getty Images; **67** James Shaffer/PhotoEdit; **68** Aaron Haupt; **69** James Shaffer/PhotoEdit; **70** (l)John Henley/CORBIS, (others)Photodisc/Getty Images; **72** Mary Evans Picture Library/Alamy Images; **73** Digital Vision/Getty Images; **74** Yellow Dog Productions/Getty Images; **75** CORBIS; **76 77** Photodisc/Getty Images; **78** (tt)Photodisc/Getty Images, (b)Digital Vision/Getty Images; **79** CORBIS; **80** (tt)Photodisc/Getty Images, (b)Peter Griffith/Masterfile; **81** Photodisc/Getty Images; **82** Matt Meadows; **84** Photodisc/Getty Images; **86** Eric Fowke/PhotoEdit; **87** Laura Sifferlin; **88** Mary Kate Denny/PhotoEdit; **89** Photodisc/Getty Images; **91** Michael Newman/PhotoEdit; **93** Photodisc/Getty Images; **94** Bob Daemmrich/Stock Boston; **95** Image Source/SuperStock; **96** David Young-Wolff/PhotoEdit; **98** (tt)Photodisc/Getty Images, (b)ThinkStock/Index Stock; **99** Kaz Mori/Getty Images; **100** Photodisc/Getty Images; **101** Brand X Pictures/Getty Images; **103** Tim Fuller; **104 105** Photodisc/Getty Images; **106** Aaron Haupt; **107** Bob Daemmrich/Stock Boston; **108** Brent C. Petersen/CORBIS; **110** CORBIS; **111** Paul Thomas/Getty Images; **112** Photodisc/Getty Images; **113** Leonard Lessin/Photo Researchers; **116** WDCN/Univ.College London/Photo Researchers; **117** Photodisc/Getty Images; **118** David Young-Wolff/PhotoEdit; **119** Photodisc/Getty Images; **120** Aaron Haupt; **121** Digital Vision/Getty Images; **122** Matt Meadows; **123 126** Photodisc/Getty Images; **127** John Henley/CORBIS; **128** Digital Vision/Getty Images; **129** Matt Meadows; **130** Photodisc/Getty Images; **131** (l)David Young-Wolff/PhotoEdit, (c)Peter Griffith/Masterfile, (r)Digital Vision/Getty Images; **132** Nancy Kaszerman/Zuma/CORBIS; **133** Vincent Besnault/Getty Images; **134** Peter Barrett/Masterfile; **135 136 137** Photodisc/Getty Images; **138** George Shelley/Masterfile; **140** Ron Chappel/ThinkStock/Getty Images; **142** Tony Freeman/PhotoEdit; **143 144** Photodisc/Getty Images; **146** FotoKIA/Index Stock Imagery; **147** Photodisc/Getty Images; **148** Aaron Haupt; **151** ThinkStock/SuperStock; **152 153** Photodisc/Getty Images; **154** CORBIS; **156** (tt)Photodisc/Getty Images, (b)David Young-Wolff/PhotoEdit; **157** ThinkStock/SuperStock; **158** Ross Anania/Getty Images; **159** Photodisc/Getty Images; **161** (t to b)SW Productions/Getty Images, Ryan McVay/Getty Images, Don Johnson/Getty Images, Getty Images, Lisette Le Bon/SuperStock, Photodisc/Getty Images; **162 164 165** Photodisc/Getty Images; **166** Bob Glusic/ImageState; **167** Chuck Savage/CORBIS; **169** George Emmons/Index Stock; **171** Aaron Haupt; **172** Ed McDonald; **174** Photodisc/Getty Images, CORBIS; **175 176** Aaron Haupt; **177** Ed McDonald; **178** Matthew Roharik; **180** Bob Daemmrich/PhotoEdit; **181 184** Photodisc/Getty Images; **185** Matthew Roharik; **186** Masterfile; **187 188** Photodisc/Getty Images; **189** Ryan McVay/Photodisc/Getty Images; **192** CORBIS; **193** Laura Sifferlin; **194 195 196** Photodisc/Getty Images; **197** Aaron Haupt; **199** John Evans; **200** Aaron Haupt; **203** Ryan McVay/Photodisc/Getty Images; **204** Photodisc/Getty Images; **205** (l)Gio Barto/Getty Images, (r)Photodisc/Getty Images; **206** Christopher Felver/CORBIS; **207** CORBIS; **208** MAK 1; **209** StudiOhio; **211** Mehau Kulyk/Science Photo Library/Photo Researchers; **212** Aaron Haupt; **214** (tt)Photodisc/Getty Images, (b)Aaron Haupt; **215** CORBIS; **216** (tt)Photodisc/Getty Images, (b)Yoav Levy/Phototake; **217** (tt)CORBIS, (b)Lori Adamski Peek/Getty Images; **218 219** Aaron Haupt; **220** Photodisc/Getty Images, Aaron Haupt; **221** (t to b)Tony Freeman/PhotoEdit, David Young-Wolff/Getty Images, Terry Sutherland; **222** Photodisc/Getty Images; **224** (l)Aaron Haupt, (r)Gen Nishino/Photodisc/Getty Images; **225** MAK 1; **226** Tim Fuller; **227** Photodisc/Getty Images; **233** Matt Meadows; **234** Aaron Haupt; **235** Photodisc/Getty Images; **242** Rubberball Productions/Photodisc/Getty Images; **244 245** Mike Bluestone/Photo Researchers; **246** Photodisc/Getty Images; **247** (t c)Lennart Nilsson/Albert Bonnier Forlag AB, (b)Petit Format/Photo Researchers; **248** (tt)Doug Martin, Beaver English Studio, Photodisc/Getty Images, (b)Edwige/Photo Researchers; **249** Laura Sifferlin; **250** CORBIS; **253** Rubberball Productions/Photodisc/Getty Images; **254** Doug Martin; **255** Photodisc/Getty Images; **256** (tt)Photodisc/Getty Images, CORBIS, (b)Jose Luis Pelaez/CORBIS; **257** Tom Prettyman/PhotoEdit; **258** (tt)file photo, (b)Tom Prettyman/PhotoEdit; **259** CORBIS; **260** Aaron Haupt; **261** CORBIS; **262** Aaron Haupt; **263** (tt)Photodisc/Getty Images, CORBIS, (b)Will Hart/PhotoEdit; **264** (tt)Photodisc/Getty Images, (b)Steve Skjold/PhotoEdit; **265** Myrleen Ferguson Cate/PhotoEdit; **266** CORBIS, Photodisc/Getty Images; **268** Rob Gage/Getty Images; **269** Steve Skjold/PhotoEdit; **270** CORBIS; **271** (tt)Photodisc/Getty Images, (b)Ryan McVay/Photodisc/Getty Images; **272** Gerhard Steiner/CORBIS; **273** David Young-Wolff/PhotoEdit; **274** (tt)Ryan McVay/Photodisc/Getty Images, (b)Michael Newman/PhotoEdit; **275**

Photodisc/Getty Images; **276** CORBIS; **277** Photodisc/Getty Images; **278** Jose Luis Pelaez/CORBIS; **279** (c)Mehau Kulyk/Science Photo Library/Photo Researchers, (others)Photodisc/Getty Images; **280** Michael Pimentel/International Sports Images; **281** Michael Alberstat/Masterfile; **282** Tim Fuller; **283** (tt)Photodisc/Getty Images, (b)Alain Altair/Getty Images; **284-289** Photodisc/Getty Images; **290** Aaron Haupt, Mark Steinmetz; **292** (tr)Jules Frazier/Getty Images, (others)Matt Meadows; **293** Photodisc/Getty Images; **294** David Buffington/Getty Images; **295** Photodisc/Getty Images; **297** (t to b)Tony Freeman/PhotoEdit, Photodisc/Getty Images, Mitch Hrdlicka/Getty Images, Anthony Johnson/Getty Images, Benelux Press/Index Stock Imagery; **298** C Squared Studios/Getty Images; **299** (tt)Photodisc/Getty Images, (t to b)Photodisc/Getty Images, Suza Scalora/Getty Images, Eyewire/Getty Images, Digital Vision/Getty Images, Ryan McVay/Getty Images, Jules Frazier/Getty Images; **300 301** Photodisc/Getty Images; **302** Aaron Haupt; **303** (tc)Thomas Del Brase/Getty Images, (others)Photodisc/Getty Images; **304** Photodisc/Getty Images; **306** (tt)Photodisc/Getty Images, (b)D. Lovegrove/Photo Researchers; **308** Photodisc/Getty Images, CORBIS; **309** Photodisc/Getty Images; **310** Aaron Haupt; **311** (tt)Photodisc/Getty Images, (b)John Evans; **312 313 314** Photodisc/Getty Images; **315** Aaron Haupt; **316** (tt)Photodisc/Getty Images, (b)Spencer Grant/PhotoEdit; **317** Ian O'Leary/Getty Images; **318 319** Photodisc/Getty Images; **322** (tt)Photodisc/Getty Image, (t to b)Doug Martin, Matt Meadows, Laura Sifferlin, Doug Martin; **323** Photodisc/Getty Images; **324** Michael Keller/CORBIS; **325** David Madison/Getty Images; **327** David Young-Wolff/PhotoEdit; **328 329** Photodisc/Getty Images; **330** (tt)Photodisc/Getty Images, CORBIS, (b)Bill Aron/PhotoEdit; **331** Tim Fuller; **333** Aaron Haupt; **337 338** Photodisc/Getty Images; **339** (l)Ian O'Leary/Getty Images, (r)Photodisc/Getty Images; **340** Noah K. Murray/Star Ledger/CORBIS; **341** Joaquin Palting/CORBIS; **342** Aaron Haupt; **343 344** Photodisc/Getty Images; **346** file photo, Photodisc/Getty Images; **348** (tt)file photo, Photodisc/Getty Images, (l)Spencer Grant/PhotoEdit, (r)David Young-Wolff/PhotoEdit; **349** (t)Mary Kate Denny/PhotoEdit, (c b)David McCarthy/Science Photo Library/Photo Researchers; **350** Diamar Stock Photography; **351** Photodisc/Getty Images; **352** Matt Meadows; **353** Photodisc/Getty Images; **354** (t)Stephen J. Krasemann/Photo Researchers, (b)Dr. P. Marazzi/Photo Researchers; **355** (l)Dr.P. Marazzi/Photo Researchers, (r)CORBIS; **356** Jonathan Nourok/PhotoEdit; **357** Photodisc/Getty Images; **358** (t)Digital Vision/CORBIS, (c)Ryan McVay/Getty Images, (b)Photodisc/Getty Images; **359** Matt Meadows; **360** Dominic Oldershaw; **362 366 367** Photodisc/Getty Images; **368** Pierre Arsenault/Masterfile; **369** Brand X Pictures/Getty Images; **370** (tt)Photodisc/Getty Images, (t)Daly & Newton/Getty Images, (c)Photodisc/Getty Images, (b)CORBIS; **371** CORBIS, Photodisc/Getty Images; **372** Peter Cade/Getty Images; **373** Photodisc/Getty Images; **374** Arthur Tilley/Getty Images; **375** Photodisc/Getty Images; **376** (tt)Photodisc/Getty Images, (b)David Sacks/Getty Images; **378** (t)Nathan Bilow/Getty Images, (b)Photodisc/Getty Images; **379 380** Photodisc/Getty Images; **381** Jurgen Reisch/Getty Images; **382** (tt)Terje Rakke/Getty Images, (b)Mitch Diamond/Index Stock; **384** (tt)Photodisc/Getty Images, (b)Jim Cummins/Getty Images; **385** David Epperson/Getty Images; **386** (t)Blake Little/Getty Images, (b)Jeff Greenberg/PhotoEdit; **387** Nick Dolding/Getty Images; **388** (tt)Photodisc/Getty Images, (b)Tony Freeman/PhotoEdit; **390 391** Photodisc/Getty Images; **392** MAK-1; **393** Photodisc/Getty Images; **394** CORBIS; **395** Doug Martin; **396** Photodisc/Getty Images; **398** Aaron Haupt; **399** CORBIS; **400** Photodisc/Getty Images; **401** (l)Tony Freeman/PhotoEdit, (cl)Brand X Pictures/Getty Images, (cr)Jim Cummins/Getty Images, (r)David Epperson/Getty Images; **402** All Star Picture Library/Alamy Images; **403** Jon Feingersh/Getty Images; **404** Bruce Ayres/Getty Images; **405** CORBIS, Photodisc/Getty Images; **406** (tt)Photodisc/Getty Images, (b)Aaron Haupt; **407** Mary Lou Uttermohlen, Elaine Comer Shay, Photodisc/Getty Images, Larry Hamill; **408** Aaron Haupt, CORBIS, Photodisc/Getty Images; **409** (tr)Elaine Comer Shay, (cr)Mary Lou Uttermohlen, (others)Photodisc/Getty Images; **410** Lisa Peardon/Getty Images; **412** Photodisc/Getty Images; **413** Kenji Kerins; **414** Digital Vision/Getty Images; **417** Photodisc/Getty Images; **418** CORBIS; **419 423** Photodisc/Getty Images; **424** Stockbyte/SuperStock; **426** (tt)Photodisc/Getty Images, (b)Dr. E. Walker/Photo Researchers; **427** Aaron Haupt; **428** (tt)Photodisc/Getty Images, courtesy of American Lung Association; **429** (tt)Aaron Haupt, Amanita Pictures, (b)CORBIS; **430** CORBIS; **431** file photo; **432** Photodisc/Getty Images; **433** (t)Laurent/Bouras/Photo Researchers, (tc)Micheal Newman/PhotoEdit (bc)Felicia Martinez/PhotoEdit (b)Josh Sher/Photo Researchers; **434** Photodisc/Getty Images; **435** (t)courtesy of American Lung Association, (b)Photodisc/Getty Images; **436** Michael Kevin Daly/CORBIS; **437** Science Photo Library/Photo Researchers; **438** (tt)Custom Medical Stock Photo, (t)Michael Newman/PhotoEdit, (b)James King-Holmes/Science Photo Library/Photo Researchers; **440** (tt)Photodisc/Getty Images, Scott Houston/CORBIS, (b)Aaron Haupt; **441** (l)Bill Varie/CORBIS, (r)Digital Vision/Getty Images; **442** (tt)Sinclair Stammers/Science Photo Library/Photo Researchers, Bonnie Kamin/PhotoEdit, Scott Houston/CORBIS, (t)Sinclair Stammers/Science Photo Library/Photo Researchers (tc bc)Bonnie Kamin/PhotoEdit, (b)Scott Houston/CORBIS; **443** Aaron Haupt; **444** (tt)Photodisc/Getty Images; **445** (t to b)Victor Habbick Visions/Science Photo Library/Photo Researchers, Lester Lefkowitz/CORBIS, Photodisc/Getty Images, Science Photo Library/Photo Researchers, Photodisc/Getty Images, CORBIS, Bill Aron/PhotoEdit; **446** (tt)Garry Watson/Science Photo Library/Photo Researchers, (b)Richard Heinzen/SuperStock; **447** (t)Carolina Biological Supply Co./Visuals Unlimited, (tc)Custom Medical Stock, (bc)Digital Vision/Getty Images, (b)Garry Watson/Science Photo Library/Photo Researchers; **448** (tt)Photodisc/Getty Images, Michael Newman/PhotoEdit, (t)Michael Newman/PhotoEdit, (b)Tony Freeman/PhotoEdit; **449** (tt)Photodisc/Getty Images, (t)Tom Pantages/Phototake, (b)D. Weinstein/Custom Medical Stock Photo; **450** Photodisc/Getty Images; **451** Michael Kevin Daly/CORBIS; **452** Tom Stewart/CORBIS; **453** (t)Photodisc/Getty Images, (tc)CORBIS, (bc)Tek Image/Photo Researchers, (b)John Evans; **454 456** Photodisc/Getty Images; **457** Jim Arbogast/Photodisc/Getty Images; **458** CORBIS; **460 461** Photodisc/Getty Images; **462** MAK 1; **463 464** Photodisc/Getty Images; **465** Tim Fuller; **466** (tt)Photodisc/Getty Images, CORBIS; **467** Tim Fuller; **468** Matt Meadows; **469** Photodisc/Getty Images; **470** ThinkStock/SuperStock; **471** Photodisc/Getty Images; **473 474** Matt Meadows; **475** (tt)Photodisc/Getty Images, (b)Aaron Haupt; **476** (t)Matt Meadows, (b)Aaron Haupt; **478** B. Barnes/Custom Medical Stock Photo; **479** Matt Meadows; **480** Aaron Haupt; **481** (l)Jim Arbogast/Photodisc/Getty Images, (r)Aaron Haupt; **482** Courtesy Amelie G. Ramirez, PhD; **483** Roy Morsch/CORBIS; **484** MAK 1; **485** Science Photo Library/Photo Researchers; **486** Alfred Pasieka/Photo Researchers; **487** (tt)Aaron Haupt, (l)SCIMAT/Photo Researchers, (r)LSHTM/Photo Researchers; **488** Photodisc/Getty Images; **489** MAK 1; **490 491** Photodisc/Getty Images; **492** (l)S. Camazine/Photo Researchers, (r)CNRI/Photo Researchers; **494** Photodisc/Getty Images; **495** Damien Lovegrove/Photo Researchers; **496** Photodisc/Getty Images; **497** Aaron Haupt; **498** Mark Burnett/Stock Boston; **500** CNRI/Photo Researchers; **501** Eye of Science/Photo Researchers; **507** Elena Rooraid/PhotoEdit; **508** Photodisc/Getty Images; **512** Bill Aron/PhotoEdit; **513** Elena Rooraid/PhotoEdit; **514** Michael Keller/CORBIS; **516** (t)ISM/Phototake, (b)Michael Keller/CORBIS; **517** Tim Fuller; **518** Photodisc/Getty